AF538513

POWER

PRIME MOVER OF TECHNOLOGY

POWER

PRIME MOVER OF TECHNOLOGY

JOSEPH W. DUFFY, Ed.D
Director, Division of Technology
Central Connecticut State College
New Britain, Connecticut

McKnight & McKnight Publishing Company
Bloomington, Illinois

SECOND EDITION
Copyright 1972

First Edition
Copyright 1964

by McKnight & McKnight Publishing Company

Lithographed in U.S.A.

Library of Congress Card Catalog Number: 72-80666

SBN: 87345-420-0

McKNIGHT & McKNIGHT PUBLISHING COMPANY

This publication was prepared by the McKnight & McKnight Editorial Staff under the direction of:

Ronald E. Dale
Managing Editor

Donna Faull
Production Editor

Bettye King
Copy Editor

Peoria Typographers
Peoria, Illinois
Compositor

Elizabeth Purcell
Art Editor

John Lee
Cover Design

Mick Netherton
Printing Production
Illinois Graphics, Inc.
Bloomington, Illinois

To my wife, Theresa,
and to Stephen, Susan, Joseph Jr., and Christine

Preface

Today, our lives are increasingly dependent upon great motive power. Prime movers, such as the internal combustion reciprocating engine, the reaction engine, and the steam turbine engine, furnish the power to affect our technological culture. Magazines, newspapers, television, and radio are constantly relating the feats of power in stationary installations and in space, land, and sea travel. It is also apparent that the increasing volume of industrial production is more dependent upon an available source of power than upon the availability of raw materials or production tools. Raw materials and mechanical power are used to fashion production tools, but without tremendous mechanical power, the raw materials and the production tools are almost useless. These concepts serve to develop the importance and relevance of power as an area of study.

The study of power is concerned with introducing concepts of how man converts, transmits, controls, and applies energy to do work. These *energy processing systems* may be thought of as consisting of two major subsystems. The first is concerned with studying the subsystems of energy conversion referred to as *Prime Movers.* The second will cover the systems designed to "accomplish" or "carry out" the functional responsibility of applying energy to do work. These will be referred to as *Trans-Actional Systems* because of their function.

The energy conversion systems are studied first because they provide the required mechanical energy needed by the trans-actional systems. Their study also serves to introduce the principles of energy transmission and control in systems that can be easily categorized by the energy they employ and their method of conversion. Included are the various prime movers and direct mechanical transformers which had their origin when man first learned to use natural energy to do work and, when these became restrictive, those he developed to apply other forms of energy. Using a historical approach, the basic scientific principles as applied in the evolution and development of the various prime movers are presented. This permits logical development and serves to promote a concept that scientific understanding and application are interdependent and are the warp and weft of which the tapestry of man's technological progress is woven.

The mechanical power that is provided by the prime mover is of little value unless it is used to do work satisfying the needs of man. Usually the mechanical power must be transmitted and controlled to the point of application. This leads us to the second unit of study, the *Trans-Actional Systems.* These may be categorized by the media and the fundamental physical principles they employ such as mechanical, fluid, and electrical systems. The components of these systems can be further categorized by the function they provide such as transmission devices, switching devices, modulation devices, directional devices, etc.

The combined study serves to explain the operation of self-contained systems, such as the automobile, airplane, locomotive, etc., as well as subsystems, i.e. generators, motors, engines, and machines. It should be concluded that the study of power should provide more than instruction in assembly and disassembly of any engine or system. It concerns the following more important but less tangible concepts: why an engine functions in a particular way; how it converts one energy form to another; the development of each type of prime mover plus the methods of its utilization; power distribution and control; the transmission, measurement, and application of energy; the categorization of energy transmission and control devices; the basic physical laws concerned with energy transformation, transmission, and control; and the general safety practices related to this field of study.

The subject matter is firmly based on American industry as an evolving area of study. The learner should be encouraged to seek energy transformation, transmission, and control system application in machine tools, numerically controlled tools, as well as in the field of transportation including surface, marine, air, and space vehicles. The text is written to provide the learner with the basis for a broad study of energy processing. It is hoped that this survey will provide enough material to challenge both the theorist and the practitioner in our future technological culture.

Joseph W. Duffy

Acknowledgments

In compiling this book the author had help from a number of sources. Illustrations prepared especially for the text were drawn by Hugh O'Rourke, Washington School, Union City, N.J., and the following industrial arts students at Montclair State College: Jerry Morano, William Borowski, George Taylor, Raymond Wasdyke, and Martin Falk. Their suggestions, patience, and skill are most appreciated and I will always be grateful.

Thanks are also due the students of Butler and Union High School, New Jersey, for drawing some of the original plates, and to Conrad Angebrandt, a teacher at Hillside High School and to Ralph D. Edelbach, a student of Montclair State College, for the reproduction of many industrial pictures.

To Louis Romano, an industrial arts teacher at Memorial High School in West New York, N.J., a particularly large debt of gratitude is owed for proofreading and for providing constructive criticism of the original manuscript; and gratitude is also owed to Mrs. Elizabeth Romano for her invaluable secretarial assistance.

For the second edition I should like to express my appreciation to William W. Davison and Robert H. Thompson. These two gentlemen have assisted me in establishing a format by providing their professional counsel. They have also team-taught the Energy Processing courses at Central Connecticut State College, insuring that the material content is meaningful, relevant, and teachable.

I should also like to express my appreciation to Dr. Carl E. Frankson, Industrial Arts Department Chairman, for permitting me the necessary professional freedom in order to experiment and develop the course content.

Because of the multiplicity of types of power converters and generators, it was necessary to obtain much of the information from libraries, museums, and industry. The author wishes to acknowledge the splendid cooperation of many firms and institutions in supplying information and illustrations. Figure captions carry credit lines to these many contributors.

Table of Contents

Chapter 21 Fluid Power 472

Chapter 22 Electrical Power and Fluidics 529

Epilogue 546

Index 549

An Introduction to Power

In each epoch of history, many factors interact to determine the nature of technology: the materials available, the accumulated skill and experience of the craftsman, the level of scientific knowledge, the economic and social conditions, the religious or ethical tenets, and last but not least, the philosophical doctrine. This modified technology, in turn, makes its influence felt on the social system. In the technology itself, the level of the tools and machines used to transform raw materials into useful products determines each stage of technical development that has passed as well as those that will surely come.

Long ago, when the limitations of *direct actors* such as the chisel, saw, axe, hammer, and club became apparent and began to restrict technological development, man resorted to *machines* (devices that multiply force) and to *prime movers. Prime movers are devices that convert the power of human and animal muscle, running water, wind, heat,* or *electricity, into a more usable form of energy.*

Thus, each level of technological advance has been determined by the availability of machines and prime movers. It is this that limits the size and types of raw materials which the craftsman works. This availability also limits the nature and dimensions of the machines, tools, and other ultimate products that can be made from the raw materials acquired. The evolution of man's technological advance can be thought of as having occurred in *five eras* or stages, as determined by the major prime mover of that stage. These are shown on the accompanying time graph.

The *first era of power* saw man relying solely upon his own muscle and the simple machines as his only sources of power. This

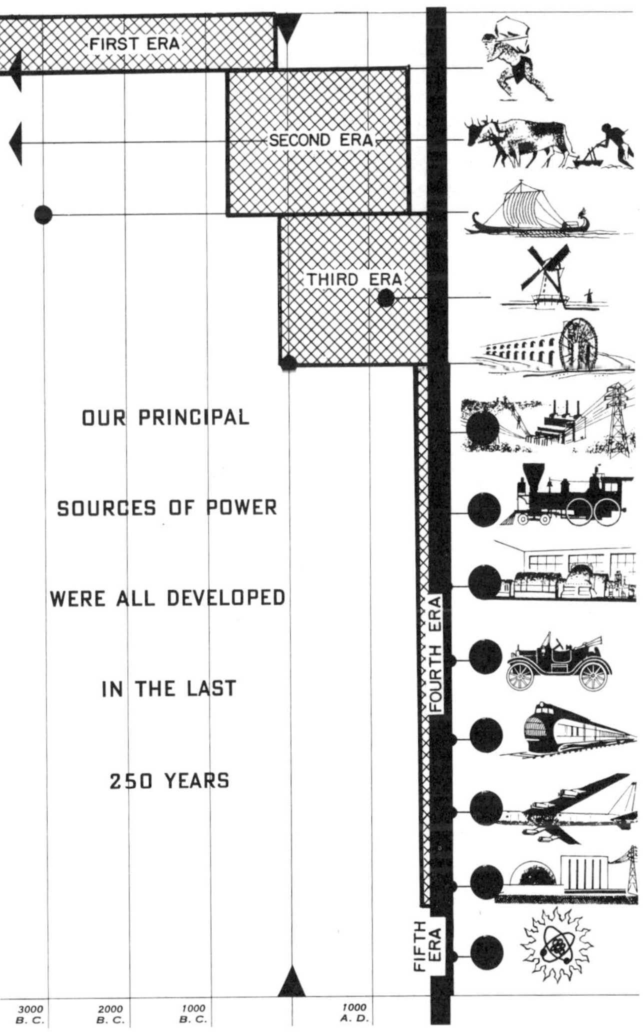

Eras of Power and Major Prime Movers (G.M.)

era covered the period of technological darkness of prehistoric times, to about 600 B.C. Here, man was in his most primitive stage and afforded himself only the satisfaction of his most basic needs, since slavery (the institution that was especially characteristic of the ancient world) afforded luxuries to only a select few.

The *second power era* brought man to the compounding of both human and animal muscle with combinations of simple machines. This initial period of applied mechanics accompanied the emergence of man as he rose above the beast of burden in strength to perform certain work.

The *third era of power* development was an extension of the second, but now man also employed prime movers to convert the forces of wind and water into mechanical energy so that these forces might be utilized to do work for him. This era extended throughout the remainder of the Middle Ages (which ended about 1500), and on through the initial phases of the Industrial Revolution (considered to have occurred between 1750 and 1830). The breakthrough of science which occurs in the latter part of this stage and the re-approachment between the sciences and technology at this time brought together the theoretical and the practical to discover a new source of power—steam.

The *fourth era* of power used steam as energy for whole new concepts in prime movers. This prompted a technological advance that nurtured the ensuing Industrial Revolution, which was due to the ever-widening mercantile system and the new methods of imparting motion. This era began about 1650 and promoted a mechanization of human work. The era lasted throughout the nineteenth century in countries of the Western World and marked the birth of modern machinery and engineering. This period was accompanied by the far-reaching changes and upheavals in the social, economic, and political institutions of the Western World.

The unpredictable *fifth era*, the age of the atom and the electron which are symbolic of the twentieth century, is a stage that has undoubtedly raised man to heights of technological advance that had been considered unthinkable. The introduction of these new forms of power has given us a supply of energy that can be economically transported and reconverted on the spot into the required type of energy. Not only has it affected a change in the types of prime movers that have evolved from their uses, but has had a direct effect in all areas of life.

The technological advance of man has to a major degree determined the past, the present, and will determine the future environs of life. Thus, a study of man's use of prime movers will provide a better understanding of the present industrial society in which we live.

Opposite –
Above: 1662 Mill with Horizontal Water Turbine
(Old Engraving from Science Museum, London)

Below: Modern Hydroelectric Power Plant with 14 Generators Driven by Horizontal Water Turbines at McNary Dam on Columbia River (GE)

PART 

DIRECT MECHANICAL CONVERTERS

Such natural forces
as wind and the weight of water
have potential energy which is harnessed
by the windmill, the water wheel,
or the water turbine,
directly converting energy
to mechanical power.

"Natural Sources of Power,"
A Mural At Kensington Museum, London
(© Science Museum, London)

Natural Power

Muscle as a Source of Power

The principal source of power used by humans during the thousands of years that many persons presume a primitive existence was solely personal muscle. This enabled people to travel, forage for food, make simple tools, hunt, fish, and fight.

Perhaps collective civilizations began during the *New Stone Age* in the lower valleys of the Nile, the Tigris, the Euphrates, and the Indus rivers, as many as 8,000 to 10,000 years ago. These fertile areas allowed the people to turn to agriculture. With this advance from the food *collection* (that was characteristic of early man) to food *production,* these people became skilled in the breeding of domesticated animals. This not only gave them a source of food but the animals also became a source of industrial materials, a means of transportation, protection, and another source of muscle-power.

Simple Machines and Mechanical Advantage

Until man had learned to domesticate and harness animals, the only source of power used by him had been his own muscle. Man soon learned that to extend his arm meant that he could apply greater force, Fig. 1-1. While the use of the *lever* must have been employed by men of this age, great sources of power were available only if the muscles of many men were brought to bear upon a single object.

Subsequently, during the *Bronze* and *Iron* Ages (somewhere between 3,000 and 1,000 B.C., or even earlier), it is believed that the other simple machines were used by man to multiply his muscle power. These simple machines are still used today *because their principle of multiplying force or speed has not changed.* According to the *Law of Conservation of Energy,* more work (output) cannot be obtained from a machine than that applied (input) to it. *Energy* is defined as the *ability to do work;* therefore, energy is the active agent behind any force. Since *work = force × distance,* a machine exerting a larger output force than the applied input force must exert this increased force through a proportionately shorter distance. *Force* may be defined as a *pushing or pulling action* of one object on another, which causes movement. Muscle, wind, water, engines, and machines are all capable of exerting force. *Force* must be thought of as causing motion to change direction and magnitude.

The use of a machine to change the input force to a different output force can be expressed in a ratio called *Mechanical Advan-*

Fig. 1-1. Early Humans Had Only Their Own Muscles for Power (G.M.)

tage (MA). Theoretical Mechanical Advantage (TMA) neglects the power loss due to friction. However, Actual Mechanical Advantage (AMA) considers all factors that influence the difference between the input force and the output force such as the loss of power due to operating friction of a machine. Friction always causes the efficiency of a machine to be below 100%. *Efficiency* of a machinc may be found by dividing work output by work input or Actual Mechanical Advantage by Theoretical Mechanical Advantage.

$$\text{Efficiency} = \frac{\text{Output Work}}{\text{Input Work}}$$

OR

$$\text{Efficiency} = \frac{\text{AMA}}{\text{TMA}}$$

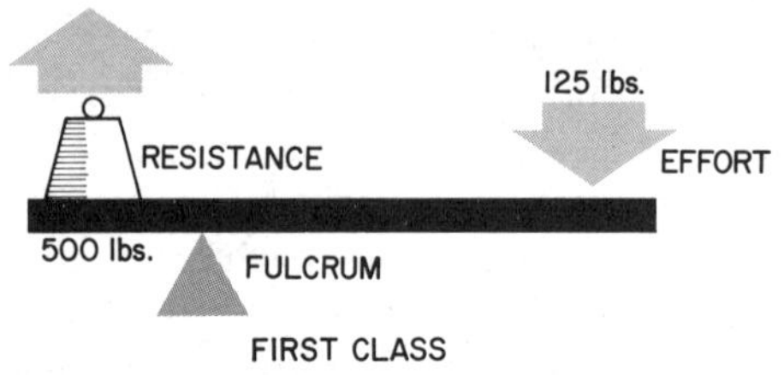

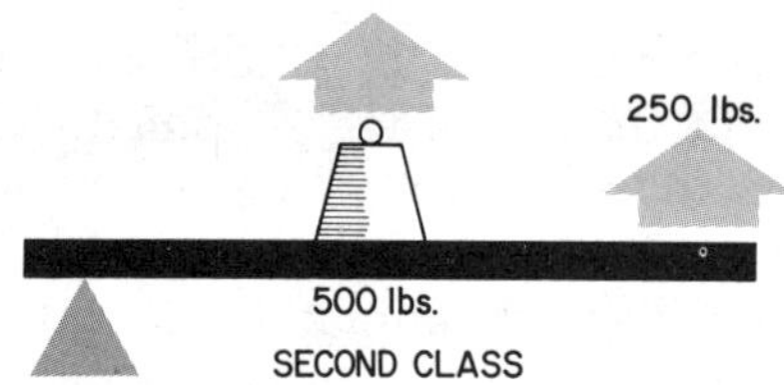

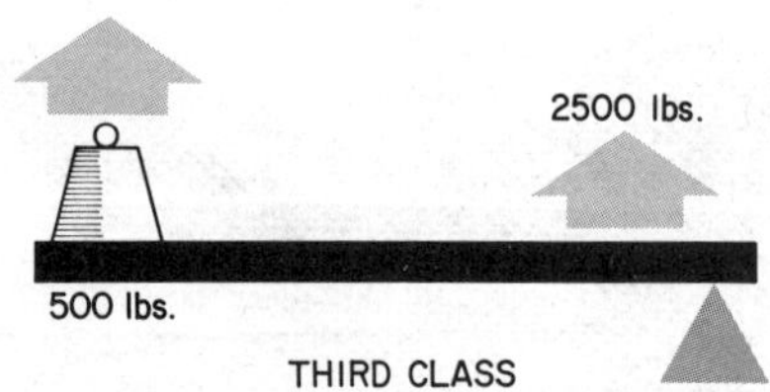

Fig. 1-1A. Types of Levers
A. First Class Lever
B. Second Class Lever
C. Third Class Lever

Levers

All levers are grouped in three classes depending upon the relationships of force to fulcrum to load: (1) first class; (2) second class; and (3) third class. See Fig. 1-1A. The product of the acting force (input) and its distance from the fulcrum is equal to the resistance force (load) times its distance from the fulcrum. Notice that levers always change force direction. Combining levers not only compounds but continually reverses direction of force. Figure 1-2 shows a man using a crank and cogged wheels to increase the MA of the force he applied to do work.

The wheel and axle (gears, pulleys) may be considered as a rotating combination of levers. The TMA of the wheel and axle is the ratio of radius, diameter, circumference, or RPM of the driver to the driven wheel. As with levers, wheels can increase rotational speed, but the output force to do work will decrease. Also, the output force can be increased, but speed of rotation will decrease.

A *pulley* is a wheel that uses a belt, rope, or chain. A *block* is one or more pulleys enclosed in a frame. A pair of blocks threaded with a rope or chain making several loops between them is known as a *block and tackle.* The TMA of a block and tackle is explained by the num-

Fig. 1-2. Lifting Apparatus
(From "De Re Metallica" by Agricola, 1556)
(Science Museum, London)

ber of times the rope passes between the load and the moving block. The TMA of a block and tackle may be found by measuring the distance the load moves *compared* to the distance the effort rope moves. Establishing a ratio of *input distance* to *load distance* in all machines gives their TMA.

The TMA of the inclined plane is determined by the ratio of the length of the plane to the height of the plane above base level. A *screw* may be considered a circular inclined plane. In the jackscrew, the circumference of screw handle travel compared to the pitch of the screw determines TMA. The wedge, screw, and inclined plane all exhibit very low efficiency due to losses from friction. Figure 1-3 shows a man turning a screw to lift water from a well.

Fig. 1-3. Manual Water Pump (From "De Re Metallica" by Agricola, 1556) (Science Museum, London)

In practically all cases where work is done, the *time* that it takes is of major significance. *Power is the rate at which work is done.* Power is determined by dividing the work done by the time it takes.

Torque is a twisting or turning effort around the shaft that tends to cause rotation. Most energy transmission systems generally deal with rotating shafts in engines, motors, couplings, gear reducers, etc. A basic understanding of the function of torque is essential to the application of power transmission. Torque is usually expressed in terms of foot-pounds and therefore is obviously related to horsepower ratings. A mere turning effort is sufficient to have torque present; therfore, it is not necessary to have rotation or motion. Torque is determined by multiplying the applied force by the distance from the point the force is applied to the center of the shaft.

Products of First Era

Some of the accomplishments of man during this *first era* of power development are astounding. In the pyramids of Egypt, built between 2900 B.C. and 1900 B.C., man used limestone cubes weighing 2½ tons apiece as building blocks. See Fig. 1-4. As many as 2,300,000 stones were used covering 13 acres in the Menkaura Temple built about the same time. Also, slabs of stone weighing as much as 200 tons were used to build the Great China Wall begun in 214 B.C. This wall is about 1,500 miles long, 25 feet high, and 12

Fig. 1-4. Building the Pyramids at Guizeh (2900-1900 B.C.) (G.M.)

feet wide. These structures and many more required huge investments of time, human resources, animal resources, and engineering skill. They stand as monuments to man's ability to get things done with only muscle power and simple machines. No doubt the principle of the inclined plane as well as the wheel (in the form of a solid roller) was employed by the Egyptians.

However, even with these machines which then seemed wonderful, man's power output was limited. Muscle—human and animal—was the only force he could apply to any machine, and this was restrictive. He found that muscle power could be obtained only in small amounts and was subject to fatigue. Man could always think of more things to do than he was able to do. This compelled him to look for other sources of energy.

Products of Second Era

The *second era* in the development of power came by *compounding* muscle with a combination of simple machines. This stage emerged a few hundred years before the birth of Christ in the *Hellenistic Civilization* of that time. Compounding had been done earlier for limited uses, as in the combining of muscle power with the wheel to grind corn. See Fig. 1-5. This large wheel was capable of exerting great force on the smaller wheels in relation to that provided by the three men. But it was the "scientists" of the Alexandrian Academy who appeared with the inventions that gave us a knowledge of mechanics that was considered the forerunner of modern engineering. Many of their inventions were designed to develop labor-saving machinery, but actually these machines were never substituted for human labor. There was no concern to conquer nature or to better the conditions of life. No concern was felt for the great mass of slaves whose work provided an elite with the necessities of life. The only real practical application of these early inventions was seen in their war engines and in other mechanisms that were made for show or amusement only.

Archimedes (287-212 B.C.) was the greatest experimenter of the Hellenists. He devoted most of his attention to mechanics and mathematics, working out solutions to problems connected with floating bodies and the simple machines. Archimedes is responsible for laying down the basic laws of mechanics. He is credited with saying, "Give me a place to stand and rest my lever, and I can move the earth."

Coming of Third Era

In the Middle Ages (400 A.D. - 1500 A.D.), however, the use of muscle and machine was

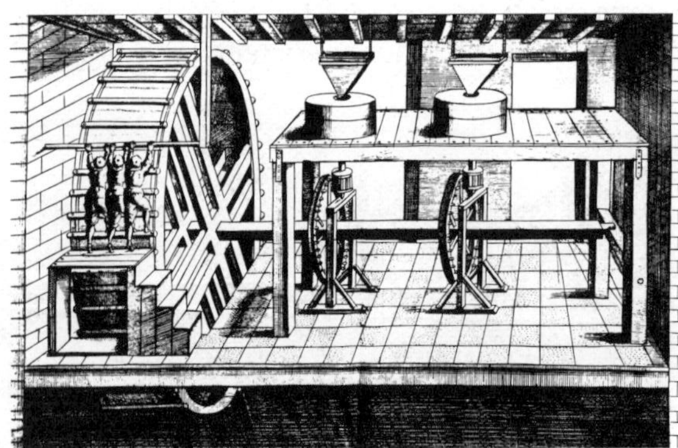

Fig. 1-5. Millstones Driven by Treadwheels (From Veranzio, 1590)
(Science Museum, London)

Fig. 1-6. Millstones and Sharpening Stone (From Veranzio, 1600)
(Science Museum, London)

seen in a perspective different than that held by the Greeks. This was due largely to the opposition to the use of human slave power. A new civilization was being founded which rested less on the backs of slaves and more on new sources of power. One example in this direction is seen in the better use of the draft horse, see Fig. 1-6. The pulling power of draft animals was increased three or four times by an improvement in the harness and by using an iron horseshoe instead of the tied-on shoe. Man also began to replace human muscle power with the energy of water and wind to turn water mills and windmills. Power mills brought in the third era of power and were a major source of power until about 1750.

Water as a Source of Power

Long before the Middle Ages, man had found a use for water. He had learned that water would carry a raft downstream. Later, he put sails or wind gatherers on these watercraft so that he could cross against current or sail upstream, provided the wind blew in the right direction. These first boats went only in the direction the wind blew. It was not until much later, less than 2,000 years ago, that man learned to rig a sail so that he moved at an angle to the wind. Many years later, he learned how to turn the energy of water into work by building an engine. *An engine is a machine for converting energy into mechanical force and motion to do work.*

Waterwheels

The *undershot waterwheel* was one of the first engines designed to do work. See Fig. 1-7, upper left. It appeared at approximately the same time as the engines of the Alexandrian scientists, about 2,200 years ago. Such *impulse* waterwheels were made so that the paddles at the bottom of the wheel merely dipped into a stream or river. These were turned by the action of the water current. The rate of rotation and power were dependent solely on the rate of flow or *kinetic energy* of water. Kinetic energy is that due to motion.

John Smeaton invented the *overshot wheel* in 1750. The flow of water was directed at the top of the wheel on the downward side.

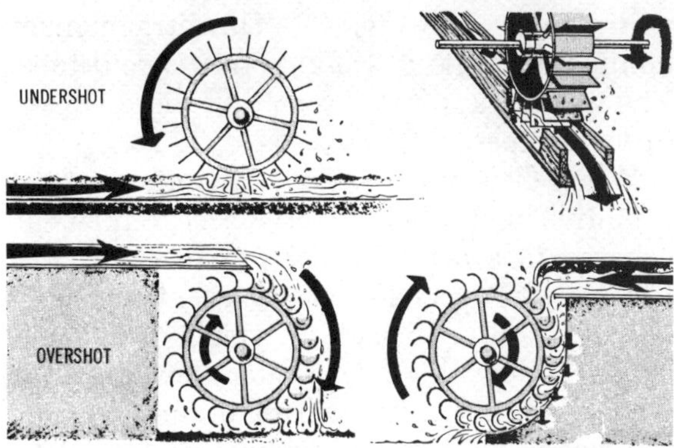

Fig. 1-7. Undershot (top) and Overshot Waterwheels, Improved versions at Right (G.M.)

The kinetic energy (i.e. velocity, and weight of the water) caused the wheel to rotate with moderate speed and power output. See Fig. 1-7, lower left.

An *impulse engine*, then, is one which depends on the kinetic energy of fluids, their weight and force of movement, to produce mechanical energy. Such an engine extracts only part of the potential energy as the fluid still remains in motion and weight remains unchanged.

During the late times of the Roman Empire, these early powered machines were first substituted for animal powered machines with the result that the total energy available to mankind remained at about the same level. Vitruvius, a Roman engineer of the first century B.C., however, converted this primitive mill into a prime mover which had tremendous potential. The *Vitruvian mill* had improved paddles turned by moving water, and a wooden cog gear reduction system to obtain more force. See Fig. 1-8. This mill depended on principles of the lever as applied to wheels, to increase MA as it converted the energy of flowing water to mechanical energy necessary for doing work. During the early Middle Ages, Western Europe realized its importance. Its rapid development and spread then gave man a prime mover capable of yielding 40 to 60 horsepower.

Sometimes these early waterwheels were constructed with a horizontal wheel and a vertical axle. See Fig. 1-9. This arrangement eliminated angle gearing to turn a millstone. The water was often directed to these wheels through pipes.

When General J. V. Poncelet improved the primitive undershot waterwheel in 1824, he ushered in a new class of prime mover. See Fig. 1-10. Poncelet's wheel was fitted with concave, curved blades, which faced upstream below the axle. Water flowed to the wheel beneath a wooden dam, smoothly up the blades, until gravity brought it to rest. The water then ran back across the moving blades exerting additional pressure on the wheel causing rotation as it left the blade. The water left the wheel with little or no forward velocity because it was caused to impart its energy to the wheel. This was the first *reaction* water

Fig. 1-9. Corn Mill Driven by Horizontal Waterwheel (From Ramelli, 1588)
(Science Museum, London)

Fig. 1-8. Corn Mill Driven by Undershot Waterwheel and Gears (From Ramelli, 1588)
(Science Museum, London)

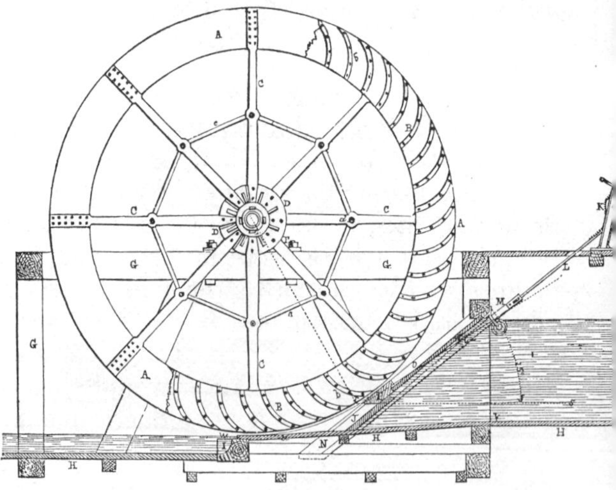

Fig. 1-10. Elevation of Poncelet's Waterwheel (1824) (Smithsonian Institution)

wheel, where the rotational force and speed were not dependent on the rate of the water flow.

A *reaction engine* depends on more than the simple kinetic energy of weight or motion. It utilizes the principle of Newton's third law of interaction which states that every action is accompanied by an equal and opposite reaction. *A reaction engine is one which derives its thrust from the change of momentum of the working fluid.*

The windmill, to be studied later, introduced during the same period was another source of equivalent power. These mills dominated technology until the end of the 18th Century and their capacity determined the range of machinery, processes and products used during that period.

Water Turbines

One of the earliest practical turbines was designed by Benoit Fourneyron in 1823. See Fig. 1-11. This *reaction water turbine* harnessed the power of water (caused by its depth or head) and permitted its escape through a series of blades or vanes. In this turbine, water was directed outward axially over the rotor and permitted to escape outwards after expending its energy to the blades.

The *Barker Mill* had developed this principle 80 years earlier. See Fig. 1-12. It used a vertical tube suspended on two pivots that permitted rotation, and the lower end of the tube was fitted with two tubular arms and an orifice at each end. The *reaction* of the water issuing from these tubes caused rotation.

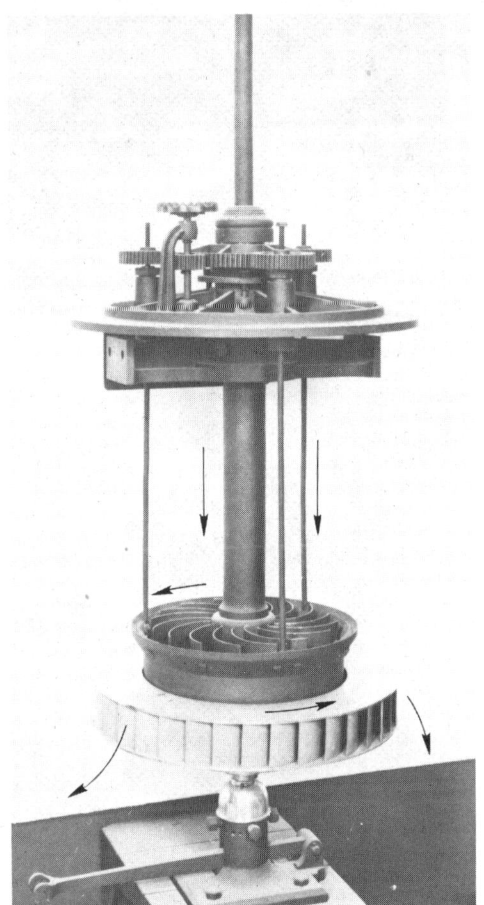

Fig. 1-11. Fourneyron Hydraulic Turbine (1823)
(Smithsonian Institution)

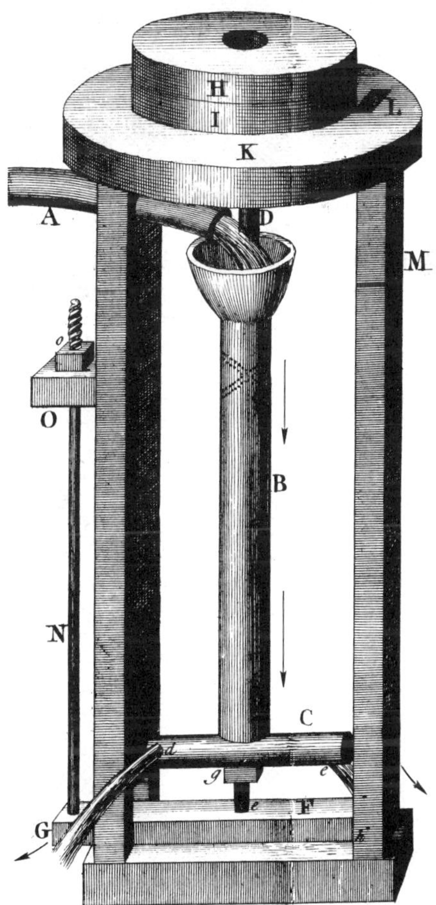

Fig. 1-12. Barker's Mill (1743)
(Science Museum, London)

Modern Water Turbines

Today, we employ more elaborate water turbines, Fig. 1-13. They are much more efficient than the primitive water wheels and built in sizes that will tax one's imagination. Each has a wheel or rotor with a series of blades or vanes to absorb the water's energy. Instead of being placed in an open stream, these rotors are enclosed in a housing with the water directed to them by pipes or *gates*. Usually, a *head* or pressure of water is built up by damming.

There are many kinds of turbines. Fig. 1-14 shows three types. All, however, cause the water to expend its energy on a set of blades

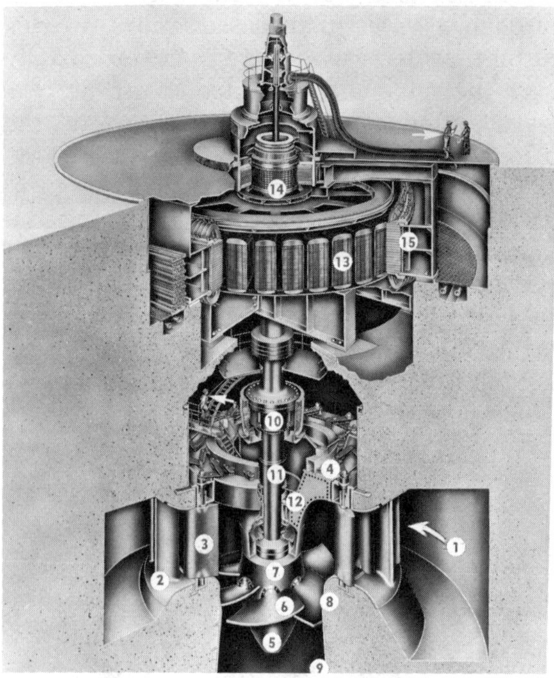

Fig. 1-13. Cross Section of a Kaplan Turbine-Generator—Note Size of Men (Allis-Chalmers)

Water piped from an upper level enters the *spiral casing* (1) which carries it all around the *discharge ring* (8). *Stay vanes* (2) direct the inward flow and *wicket gates* (3) are adjusted by the *gate operating ring* (4) to control the amount of flow. The *runner* turned by this flow of water includes the *runner cone* (5), the *adjustable runner blades* (6), and the *runner hub* (7). The *draft tube* (9) discharges water flow into a lower level lake or stream. A *servo motor* inside the hub at (10) controls the angle of the runner blades. This control and the amount of water admitted by (3) determine the amount of power produced while holding a constant speed.

The main *turbine shaft* (11) sits in a *guide bearing* at (12) and a *thrust bearing* in the supporting beams just below the *generator rotor* (13). Both bearings are well lubricated by an oil system having a pump, an oil cooler, and a reservoir. The *exciter* (14) generates enough current to start the magnetic field. This field is cut by the rotor revolving close to the *stator* (15), thus generating the current carried by the power line, see Chapter 18. The generator is both air and water cooled. Some rotors are about 30 feet in diameter.

Fig. 1-14. Assembling Turbines (Allis-Chalmers)
Three Types of Runners or Impellers are Shown: (1) Francis, (2) Kaplan, (3) Pump-Turbine.

Fig. 1-15. Francis Turbine (1840)
(© Science Museum, London)

that will cause the rotor to turn. In some, the water is directed axially over the rotor. In these, water passes either *outwards* as in the Fourneyron turbine shown in Fig. 1-11, or *inwards* as in the Francis turbine of the 1840's, shown in Fig. 1-15. In others, such as the Pelton turbine shown in Figs. 1-16 and 1-17, the water is directed at high velocity against the bucket-shaped vanes, employing a simple *impulse* principle.

Fig. 1-16. Model of "Hurdy-Gurdy" or Pelton Wheel (1870)
(© Science Museum, London)

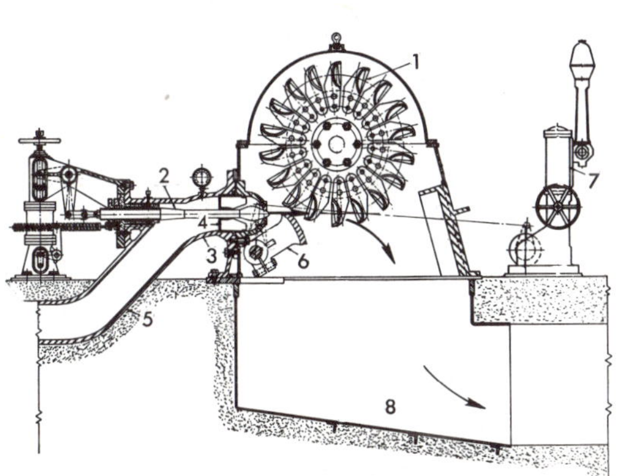

Fig. 1-17. Horizontal-shaft, Overhung, Single-Jet Impulse Turbine (NEMA)

(1) Buckets, (2) Needle Valve, (3) Elbow Nozzle, (4) Vanes, (5) Water Supply, (6) Deflector for Governor, (7) Governor, and (8) Discharge Pit.

Hydroelectric Power

When water turbines turn generators to produce electric current, they are referred to as *hydroelectric power plants.* These turbogenerators must operate at *constant speed* (to produce exactly *60-cycle* current), but with *variable power output*. This variation is due to the customer demand which changes from minute to minute. As more electrical power is demanded, the resistance in the generator increases, and the turbine tends to rotate slower for a given force of water. To compensate for this, a governor automatically opens up the water gates permitting more water to flow to the rotor, increasing the drive force and creating more electrical power. This governor will reduce water flow if the demand for electrical power decreases.

Since their inception less than a century ago, many hundreds of hydroelectric plants have been built. Fig. 1-18 shows a typical installation. Where the head of water is not enough to make the hydroelectric plant practical, man has constructed dams that trap the water to raise its level. Of the three-quarter trillion kilowatt hours of electric power generated in the United States annually, a little less than one-fifth of it is generated from water power.

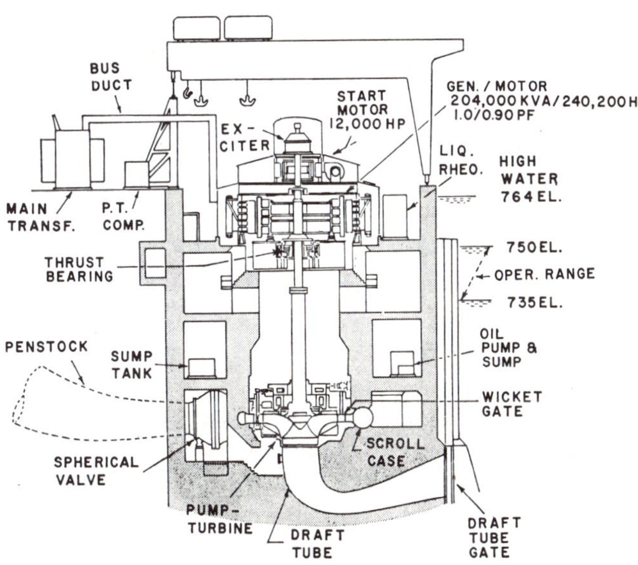

Fig. 1-18. Power Station Equipment Arrangement: Section at a Main Unit (Allis-Chalmers)

Pumped hydro storage now appears to be one way of acquiring economical, reliable, electrical power. There are many such units abroad and in this country. Fig. 1-19 is a drawing of a typical hydro unit. This is the Taum Sauk installation in St. Louis, Missouri. Such a plant employs the pump-turbine, a recent development in the hydraulic field. It is the function of this unit to pump water from a lower level *suction pond* to a higher level *storage lake* during periods of low demand. The pump-turbine can then utilize this potential energy during peak periods by developing power as a hydraulic turbine. Water then flows back through this unit from the storage lake to the lower pool. Rotation is in one direction when operating as a pump and in the opposite direction when acting as a turbine. It is a vertical-shaft unit similar to the Francis turbine, having a conventional spiral case and draft tube. The pump-turbine is directly connected to an electric dynamo which serves as a motor when functioning as a pump and as a generator when the unit operates as a turbine.

Hydro-generating stations, although economical, are not found throughout the world because of the problems in acquiring sufficient quantities of water. Dam building is expensive. Yet, there are countries, such as Canada, Norway, and the U.S.S.R., that are in the process of building huge dams to meet their electrical needs. In fact, engineers have designed some hydroelectric plants that are almost beyond credibility.

Tidal power is being used today in France at the mouth of the Diouris River by a small generating station. Other such plants are being planned for the Rance River, and larger installations are considered for the Bay of Fundy where the United States and Canada touch the Atlantic Ocean.

Wind as a Source of Power

In regions where there is more wind than water, man learned to harness the wind as a form of energy. The windmill is not nearly as ancient as the waterwheel, however.

Types of Windmills

The windmill is said to have had its origin in the deserts of Persia in 643 A.D., where winds blow fiercely much of the time. This Persian style of windmill looked like a revolving door, Fig. 1-20. It had a vertical shaft with door-like vanes.

The idea of a wind machine was introduced into Europe in the 12th Century. See

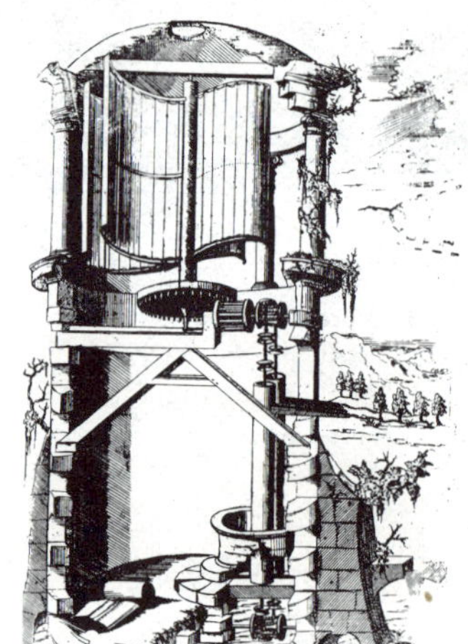

Fig. 1-20. Vertical-Vaned Wind-Driven Water Pump (From Besson, 1560)
(Science Museum, London)

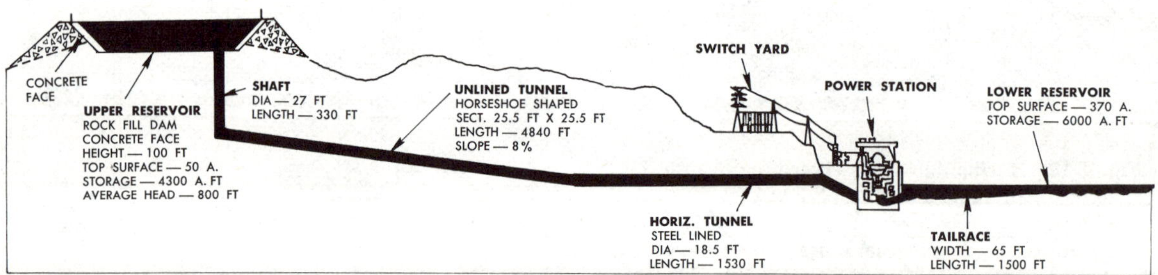

Fig. 1-19. Main Features of the Taum Sauk Pumped-Storage Hydroelectric Plant (Allis-Chalmers)

Fig. 1-21. The earliest type was the *post mill* consisting of a large wooden structure that carried, near the top, a shaft fitted with four arms and a lattice supporting framework to carry the canvas sails. Because of the variety of wind directions, the mill was mounted on a post so that it could be made to face into the wind. Sometimes, the post was surrounded by a circular roofed shed that served as a storehouse.

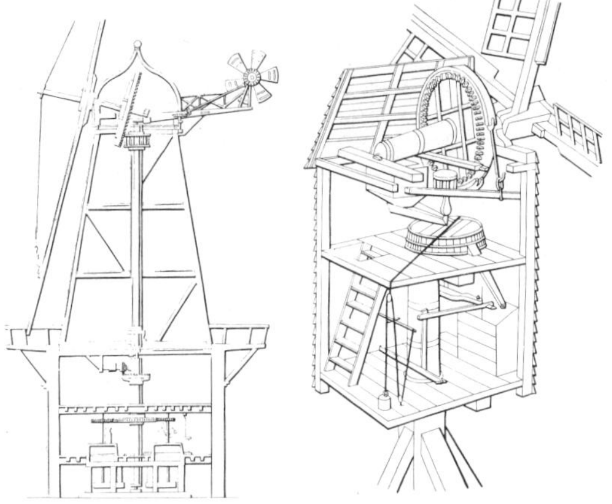

Fig. 1-21. Smock and Post Windmills (1826) (Smithsonian Institution)

The post mill was improved upon by Andrew Maikle in 1784 when he invented the *fantail gear* which automatically rotated the head into the wind. See Fig. 1-22. The small windmill behind the main arms acted as a rudder. When the wind struck at either side of it, it was caused to rotate and turn the head into the wind. These *smock mills,* as they were called, were built as large as 120 feet high with 80 foot sails. Both types of mills had the main shaft connected by gears or belts to grinding stones, water pumps, or other mechanisms.

In the United States, a new type of windmill was introduced, Fig. 1-23. This type consisted of a series of narrow blades arranged like spokes of a wheel. A vane behind the rotor caused it to seek the wind. This mill was a common source of power for pumping water on farms until recently.

Fig. 1-22. Model of Early Nineteenth Century Post Windmill in England (Science Museum, London)

Fig. 1-23. Model of Metal Multi-Vane Windmill in America (Science Museum, London)

Uses of Windmills

The windmill has had somewhat limited usage. It was not as powerful nor as dependable as the waterwheel, so typically was most used in lowlands or other regions which lacked waterfalls. Like the waterwheel, it often was feared by workers who thought it would bring unemployment. A wind-driven sawmill in England was wrecked by a mob in 1768 for this reason.

By 1810, the windmill had become quite efficient and was most often used to pump water for irrigation or drainage. In Europe, it frequently was used to grind corn and grain. The first windmill used to generate electricity was built in Denmark in 1890. By 1910, there were hundreds of these windmill generators dotting the European landscape. They generated about 5 to 25 kilowatts of power and employed a storage battery reserve in case of windless weather.

We do not employ wind turbines today to generate large quantities of electricity because of their variable nature. To use them to charge storage batteries or to store energy in any other form becomes prohibitive because of the cost and problems encountered. There are, however, approximately 3 million windmills in this country, at last report, still being used on farms for pumping, operating small mills, and for generating electrical power.

Terms to Understand

Archimedes
Middle Ages
third stage of power
engine
undershot waterwheel
overshot waterwheel
kinetic energy
impulse engine
Vitruvian mill
prime mover
Smeaton
Poncelet
reaction engine
water turbine
reaction turbine
New Stone Age
Bronze Age
Iron Age
simple machines
work
power
mechanical advantage
first stage of power
second stage of power
Hellenistic civilization
compounding
head
Benoit Fourneyron
axially
rotor
Barker mill
pivot
orifice
Francis turbine
Pelton turbine
turbo-generator
hydroelectric power plant
variable power output
kilowatt
pump-turbine
suction pond
load-factor limitations
off-peak power
on-peak power
tidal power
Persian windmill
post mill
fantail gear
Andrew Maikle
smock mill
Smith-Putnam
wind turbine

Study Questions

1. In each epoch of history, many factors interact to determine the nature of technology: materials available, the accumulated skill and experience of the craftsman, economic and social conditions, religious or ethical tenets, and last but not least, philosophical doctrines. Explain and give possible examples.
2. Differentiate between "direct actors" and "prime movers."
3. Simple machines may multiply force but never work. Explain.
4. Describe the six simple machines with applications of each as they are used today.
5. Describe the difference between work and power.
6. What is meant by mechanical advantage?
7. Explain the "Law of Conservation of Energy."

8. Describe the forms that energy may take and give an application of each.

9. What are the limitations of muscle as a source of power?

10. What is meant by compounding as employed during the second epoch in the development of power?

11. Archimedes was the greatest experimenter of the Hellenists. Explain.

12. The undershot wheel was one of the first engines designed to do work. Explain its principle of operation.

13. Describe why a prime mover can never be 100 percent efficient.

14. What is meant by impulse and reaction engines?

15. Describe the differences between Poncelet's "reaction" waterwheel and the primitive waterwheel.

16. Describe the principle of Smeaton's overshot wheel.

17. What are the differences between waterwheels and water turbines?

18. Describe the differences in the principles of operation of Fourneyron, Francis, Pelton, and Kaplan water turbines.

19. Explain the operation of a pumped hydro storage generating station.

20. Explain some of the unique hydro generating plants that have recently or will be built.

21. Describe the operation of a hydroelectric power plant.

22. Evolve briefly man's use of the windmill as a prime mover.

23. Trace briefly the evolution of the windmill.

24. What are the limitations of wind and water mills?

25. What does the future have in store for these prime movers?

Selected Readings for Part I
Direct Mechanical Converters

A Pictorial History of Science and Engineering, Published by the Editors of *Year & Front* (New York: 1957)

1,000 pictures are used in the presentation of man's technological and scientific progress from the dawn of history to the present.

Asher, Abbott Payson, *A History of Mechanical Inventions,* (New York: Harvard University Press, 1954)

DeCamp, L. Sprague, *Man and Power,* (New York: Golden Press, 1961)

Deery, T. K., and Williams, T. I., *A Short History of Technology From The Earliest Times to 1900* A.D., (New York: Oxford University Press, 1961)

Excellent chapters on early sources of power, the steam engine, and the internal combustion engine, placed in historical perspective to other areas of technology. Contains tables showing the time-relations of selected events in technological history both to each other and to named events in general history.

Epstein, Sam and Beryl, *All About Engines and Power,* (New York: Random Press, 1962)

Forbes, R. J., *Man the Maker,* (New York: Henry Schuman, 1950)

Klemm, Friedrich, *A History of Western Technology,* (New York: Charles Scribners & Sons, 1959)

A history of technology in the form of contemporary writings; it covers the period from Graeco-Roman times to the Atomic Age.

Laver, F. J., *Energy,* (New York: Oxford University Press, 1962)

Marcus, Abraham and Rebecca, *Power Unlimited,* (Englewood Cliffs: Prentice Hall, 1960)

Nevins, Allan, and others, *Energy and Man,* (New York: Appleton-Century, 1960)

Sporn, P., *Energy, Its Production, Conversion, and Its Uses in the Service of Man,* (New York: Pergamon Press, 1963)

Thirring, Hans, *Energy for Man, Windmills to Nuclear Power,* (Bloomington, Indiana: University of Indiana Press, 1958)

On page 18—

1. (top) Early Watt Steam Power Plant (Babcock & Wilcox)

2. Parson Radial-Flow Steam Turbine and Generator, 1891 (© Science Museum, London)

3. 1957 Universal Pressure Boiler Compared with 1882 Boiler in Edison's Pearl Street Power Plant (Babcock & Wilcox)

4. 1960 Nuclear Power Plant, Commonwealth Edison's Dresden Station at Morris, Illinois (GE)
Atomic energy from the reactor (192 foot sphere) is converted to steam energy to turn turbines (building at rear). This drives generators and the electrical power is transmitted to consumers over lines in foreground.

II PART

EXTERNAL COMBUSTION CONVERTERS

The potential energy of a fuel is first released by combustion in a boiler converting water into *steam energy*. This pressure is then piped to an engine where it is converted to *mechanical power* by pistons or by turbines.

Steam Engines

When water is heated to its boiling point it vaporizes as steam and due to increased molecular activity, it expands to at least 1600 times its original volume. If this is done in an enclosed container, tremendous pressure or potential power is formed. This power can be made available by a *heat engine*.

A heat engine is any device that transforms heat energy to mechanical energy. Included by this definition are all steam engines, gasoline or diesel engines, rocket, and airstream engines. Even the body itself may be considered a heat engine because it is capable of doing mechanical work as a result of the energy provided by food which is digested and oxidized.

A heat engine functions by absorbing heat, utilizing part of it to do work, and discharging the remainder at a reduced temperature. Heat loss is thus inherent and causes the low efficiency of heat engines.

Heat Theory

The nature of heat and its effect on various substances in general and gases in particular must be considered to understand the theory underlying the evolution and design of various heat engines. Heat was considered by early scientists as a weightless and invisible fluid which flowed from one body to another in some way. They called this special fluid caloric, and their theory explained rather adequately its peculiar phenomena. This theory persisted until less than 200 years ago when it was noticed by Benjamin Thompson, an American, that during the operation of boring a cannon, huge quantities of heat were produced. He speculated that the energy provided to bore the cannon was converted into heat.

Heat Defined

Heat is generally accepted as that form of energy which results from increased molecular movement. The greater the vibration of molecular movement in a given time, the greater is the heat energy and the higher the temperature of the substance. There is always heat as long as there is molecular movement in a body. Molecular movement is said to stop at minus 273° Centigrade or absolute zero. *Heat energy is released in chemical, physical, or electrical action.* Those substances that have the ability to release high quantities of heat under desired conditions in a chemical reaction may be used as fuels.

Mechanical action generates heat. When substances are physically changed in form by cutting, abrading, twisting, bending, or beating, heat is generated.

When gas is compressed, heat energy is created. The more pressure on the original volume of gas, the greater the heat generated.

When heat is applied to many materials, they are affected in several ways such as expanding, melting, and vaporizing.

Temperature

Temperature may be considered the measurement of the average kinetic energy of molecules at the instant of measurement, or the intensity of heat in a body. It is not the measure of the quantity of heat, for this depends on the nature of the body and its mass as well as its temperature. The temperature scale most familiar to Americans and to the English is the Fahrenheit (F.) scale. In many other countries the Centigrade (C.) scale or the Celsious scale is most common. Temperature may be regarded as analagous (similar) to pressure. In the same way that water will flow from one level to a lower level, heat will flow from one body to another of lower temperature. Temperature may be defined as that property which governs the transference of heat from one body to another. If two bodies are of the same temperature, no transference will occur.

Heat must often be transferred from one place to another to be utilized. It may also be transferred if its accumulation is not to prohibit efficient operation of machinery. The transfer of heat requires a knowledge of methods by which heat moves. The kinetic molecular theory has been employed to explain the movement of heat through matter and space because heat is manifested upon molecular movement.

Coefficient of Expansion

Almost all substances expand when heated. Metals, for instance, expand in all directions. The total increase in the length of a given piece of metal depends on its initial length and the increase in its temperature. The converse is also true; as metal is caused to cool, it will tend to contract. This is an extremely important factor. Engines must use metals of comparable coefficients of linear expansion. It would not do to have the piston expand more rapidly than the cylinder containing it.

Specific Heat

The quantity of heat necessary to raise the temperature of any substance a given amount varies with the *specific heat* of that substance. In general, liquids have a higher specific heat than solids except for mercury. The specific heat of a gas is affected by its pressure.

Temperature of Fusion

When some solids are heated sufficiently they proceed to the next energy level and change to a liquid. This is called *fusion.* The melting temperature is the temperature of fusion. Further addition of heat does not raise the temperature until the substance is entirely liquefied. The additional heat is stored as *latent heat.* The amount of latent heat stored during fusion depends upon the substance and varies with the amount of substance fused.

Latent Heat

Latent heat is the energy stored up in a substance when there is a change of state or phase (solid into liquid or liquid to gas) although the temperature does not change. This latent energy is released *when the state reverts back again.* The more efficient steam engines transform this latent heat energy into mechanical energy.

Vaporization

Changing a substance to a vapor is called *vaporization.* Surface vaporization and boiling are considered *internal vaporization.* When a liquid is heated until it vaporizes at the boiling point, its temperature remains constant and additional heat is absorbed by the vapor as latent heat. When the vaporization is complete, only then will further heat addition cause an increase in temperature.

Steam

Water occurs in three states or energy levels: (1) solid, (2) liquid, and (3) gas. When water is in a vapor or gaseous state, it is called *steam.* The change from one state to another is caused by (or accompanied by changes in) *heat content.* Steam is a carrier or "source" of energy.

Saturated Steam

As the process of evaporation continues, more and more molecules are released to the vapor state. If the vaporization takes place in a confined space, the number of molecules released as vapor begin to strike one another and reenter the liquid. At that point where the amount of molecules leaving the liquid is equal to the amount of molecules reentering the liquid, *saturation occurs.* The space is then said to be saturated with vapor.

Boiling

Evaporation was defined as the escaping of molecules from a liquid to a gaseous state at the surface of the liquid. *Boiling,* however, *is the evaporation of molecules throughout the liquid.* Saturated bubbles of vapor are formed within the liquid and collect more molecules, increase in size, and then escape through the surface. It must be understood that these bubbles would not form if the external pressure of the surrounding liquid and the air pressing on the surface of the liquid were greater than the internal pressure of these bubbles. *Boiling can be easily caused by;* (1) increasing the temperature of the liquid; or (2) reducing the external pressure on the liquid. For this reason, liquids boil at a lower temperature at higher altitudes or in a partial vacuum. The boiling point of a liquid is influenced by the impurities within it. Impurities tend to raise the boiling point; thus, in some heat systems the water is purified to control the boiling point. Impurities sometimes can also react unfavorably with the boiler's metal, causing internal corrosion chemical reaction and premature breakdown.

Superheated Steam

When steam is permitted to leave its source and then is heated further, the steam becomes a vapor with a temperature above its normal vaporization temperature and acquires the qualities of a perfect gas.

Thermodynamics

Thermodynamics is a practical subject concerned with a clearly defined system which is caused directly to interact with its surroundings and to form some useful function. *It is the study of the relationships between heat and other energy forms.* The science of thermodynamics is based on two laws: one deals with energy transformations; and the second deals with the directions in which the transformation will take place.

When heat is applied to a gas at constant pressure, the heat is converted into work by causing the gas to expand. Some of the heat is used to raise the temperature of the gas by increasing the internal energy of the gas. Heat also can only be transmitted from the warmer body to one at a lower temperature. In a heat engine, heat flows from a high temperature boiler to a low temperature exhaust doing work in the process. *The amount of work which can be done depends on the difference in the temperature.* No work could be done if both bodies were at the same temperature. It can be concluded that a definite amount of mechanical energy is equivalent to a given amount of heat. There is a limit to the amount of work which can be obtained, and it is inevitable that some energy will be wasted. When a gas absorbs heat without doing any work, it increases its potential energy. It is said to change its internal energy by the amount equal to the gained heat energy.

Development of Steam Power

Early Experiments

The first heat engine was a *steam turbine* of the *reaction type,* nearly 2,000 years ago. It was described by Hero (or Heron) of Alexandria, a writer, mathematician, and scientist. Hero was referred to as the "Bale of Aeolus," or evil doer of the Greek god of winds. His machine consisted of a cauldron partly filled with water placed over a fire. See Fig. 2-1. The enclosed cauldron had two pipes or trunnions connected to a hollow ball which was permitted to rotate on them.

Fig. 2-1. Aeolipile by Hero of Alexandria, 130 B.C. (Chicago Museum of Science and Industry)

This sphere had two nozzles, bent to face in opposite directions. When the water boiled in the cauldron, the generated steam would surge up into the sphere and out the nozzles resulting in a reaction that caused the sphere to rotate. However, it had no specific use and was considered a scientific oddity. The potential of steam thus remained unknown until the seventeenth century when it was rediscovered as a source of energy.

One of the first to experiment with steam as a basis for new prime movers was Leonardo da Vinci (1452-1519), one of the greatest men of learning that the world has ever seen. Leonardo invented a gun fired by compressed steam in 1495. While this invention remained barren, his notes on steam can be considered as the earliest in the rediscovery of steam.

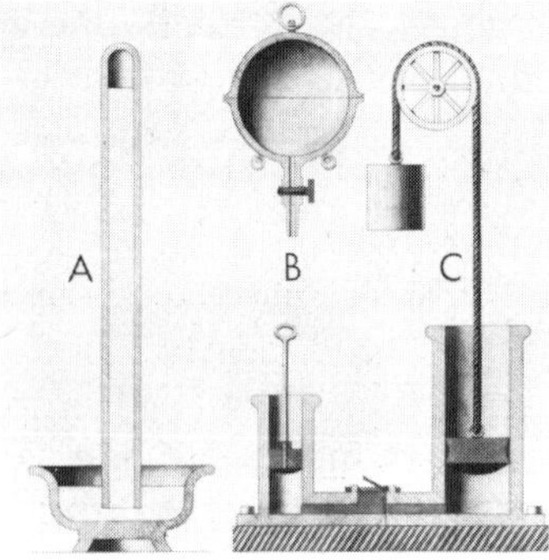

Fig. 2-2. Atmospheric Pressure Apparatus of Torricelli in 1643 (A), and Von Guericke in 1650 (B) and (C) (Science Museum, London)

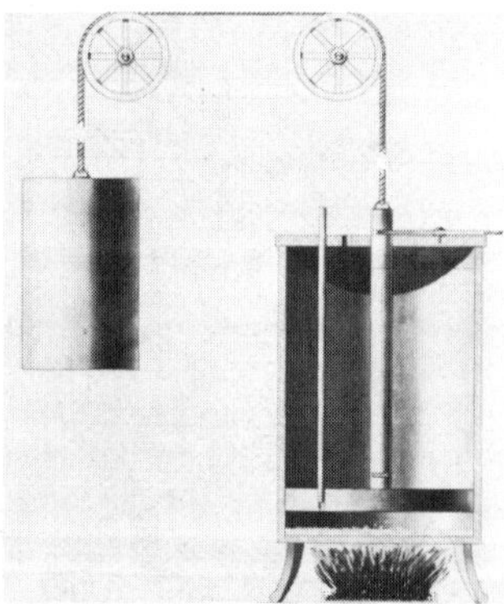

Fig. 2-3. Papin's Steam Cylinder Apparatus (1690) (© Science Museum, London)

The weight pulled up the piston and the valve was closed after the chamber filled with steam. The fire was removed and the condensing steam created a partial vacuum which forced the piston down.

Although mining engineers during the seventeenth century were aware that a suction pump could not draw water above 30 feet, there was no explanation of this limit. Certainly this prompted man to try to explain the nature of atmospheric pressure.

In 1643 Torricelli announced that the pressure of the atmosphere was equal to a column of mercury 30 inches in height. This corresponds to a column of water of about 30 feet in height. His apparatus for determining this is shown at A in Fig. 2-2. He predicted that the pressure of the atmosphere decreased with altitude. This was shown experimentally in 1647 when a barometer was carried to the top of a 4,800 foot mountain and the mercury dropped three inches during the ascent.

Von Guericke, in 1650, gave a spectacular demonstration of the immense force of atmospheric pressure by placing two hemispheres together to form a sphere 20 inches in diameter. The space within was evacuated; that is, a partial vacuum was formed within. Two teams of eight horses could not pull them apart. The atmospheric pressure of 14.7 lbs. per square inch would require a force of several tons to overcome the difference in pressure, or *pressure differential,* imposed by the cross-sectional area of the sphere shown at B in Fig. 2-2. Von Guericke also created a vacuum below a large piston in a cylinder and 50 men could not prevent atmospheric pressure from forcing down the cylinder. See C in Fig. 2-2.

Such experiments suggested that if some simple means could be found for making a vacuum, atmospheric pressure could be employed as a source of power. Steam at this time was not yet considered as a means for creating a vacuum.

Also a part of the search for new prime movers was the work performed by Christian Huygens in 1680, who devised a type of internal-combustion engine by causing a piston to move in a cylinder due to the explosive force of gunpowder. His assistant, Denys Papin, saw the short-comings of using gunpowder. Fig. 2-3 shows his experiment with a cylinder and a piston using steam as the source of energy.

Atmospheric Steam Engines

At this time in England, peat, a semicarbonized form of coal, was being mined. A common difficulty was that of striking water if the mines were dug too deep. Only a very old form of a pump using human and animal muscle power was available, but this means was inefficient. What England needed was a pump that could draw the water out faster than it seeped into the mine.

Denys Papin had failed to put condensing steam and atmospheric pressure to work, but Thomas Savery was successful in 1698. Each cubic foot of boiled water produces at least 1600 cubic feet of steam, and when it is caused to condense, the steam reverts to its original small volume. This shrinkage, using Papin's principle, was employed to draw the water out of the mine. Atmospheric pressure acting on the water at the bottom of the mine forced water up through pipes into the vacuum created in the steam tank by the cooling steam. His patent specification, shown in Fig. 2-4, called the contrivance a *"fire engine."*

Savery's use of steam marked the beginning of an age that used steam as the power for a prime mover that dominated technology until the twentieth century. The *fourth stage* in the development of power had begun.

Steam was admitted to one of two oval vessels (see Fig. 2-4), displacing the water within and driving it out through the check-valves. When the vessel was emptied of water, the steam supply was cut and by introducing cold water, the steam in the vessel was condensed causing a partial vacuum. Water then was drawn up through the sump intake pipe and check-valve. The supplementary boiler preheated the feed water.

In 1712, an English blacksmith named Thomas Newcomen built the first successful

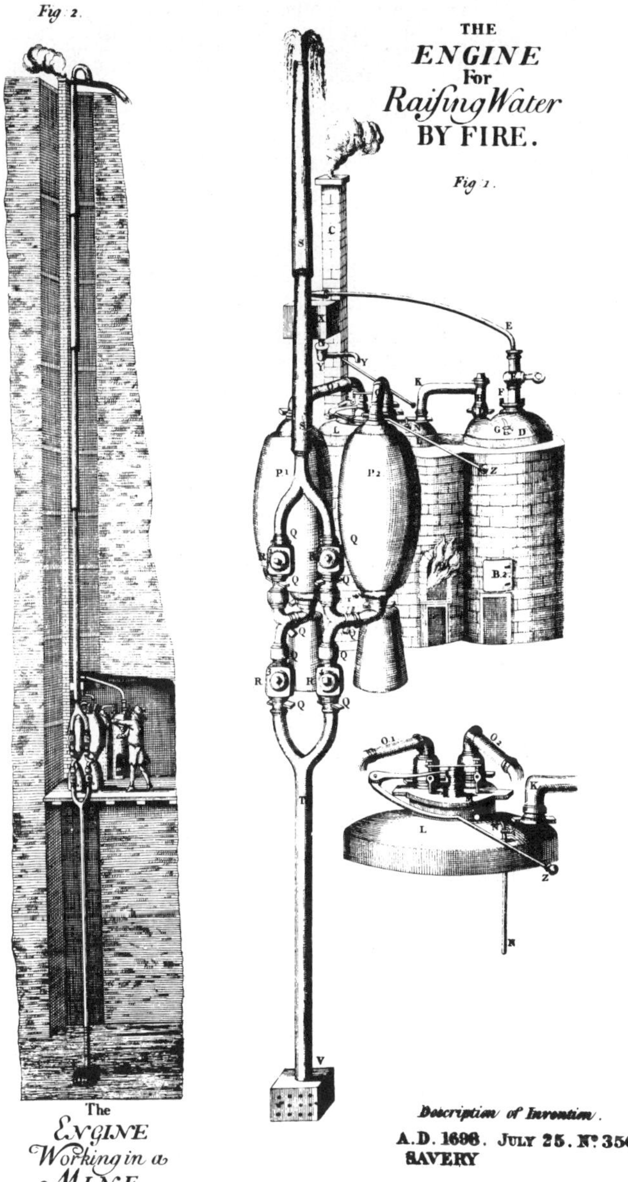

Fig. 2-4. Patent Drawing for Savery's Double Pumping Engine (1698)
(Science Museum, London)

Steam generated in the steam boiler enters vessels P_1 and P_2 alternately. The steam condenses in the operating vessel creating a vacuum. This vessel's lower "Q" valve is opened, and upper "Q" valve is closed. The vacuum draws water from the mine into the vessel. When the vessel is filled, the lower "Q" water valve is then closed and the steam valve is opened. Steam then enters the vessel forcing the water out through the upper water valve. When the steam fills the chamber, the upper "Q" valve and the steam valve are closed and the cycle is ready to be repeated.

steam engine or pump shown in Fig. 2-6. He also employed steam, atmospheric pressure, and the vacuum of the condensing steam as Savery had done. Instead of running the steam and the pumped water in and out of the same chamber, he made a hollow cylinder with a piston sliding up and down as in Papin's experimental engine. Newcomen first raised the piston by steam which was controlled by a manual valve. Then, he opened another valve and sprayed water into the hot cylinder, condensing the steam and creating a partial vacuum. Atmospheric pressure then forced the piston down raising the opposite end of the beam. This pulled up the pump rod and a quantity of water.

This steam engine has been more correctly referred to as an *Atmospheric Beam Engine* because of the principle employed for its operation. The power of the engine was derived from the steam condensing in the cylinder causing a partial vacuum under the piston. This allowed the atmospheric pressure (14.7 pounds per sq. in. at sea level), to push the piston downward. The larger the piston, the greater the engine's power.

Fig. 2-6. Newcomen's Pumping Engine (1712)
(© Science Museum, London)

Reciprocating Steam Engines

Development of Steam Engine

In 1765, James Watt, a Scottish instrument maker, was asked to repair a model of the Newcomen Engine for the University of Glasgow. As he worked on the engine, the imperfections he noticed challenged his curiosity. He read what he could about the principles of its operation, then he began to experiment with druggist's vials for boilers and hollowed canes for pipes. But, he failed to get his models to work properly – at best only a few sputtering strokes.

Separate Condenser Added

Watt continued in his research and stumbled upon the principle of *latent heat* – the secret of unleashing tremendous power. However, there was an obstacle in his path – the need to control and regulate its power once unleashed. He noticed that the steam lost four-fifths of its energy due to the cooling of the cylinder during the action of the engine. This cooling was caused by the spray of cold water injected into the cylinder (after the piston had moved upward) to condense the steam, causing a partial vacuum beneath the piston and returning it.

Ten years passed before Watt solved this tremendous problem of preserving the latent heat energy in steam so that it could be em-

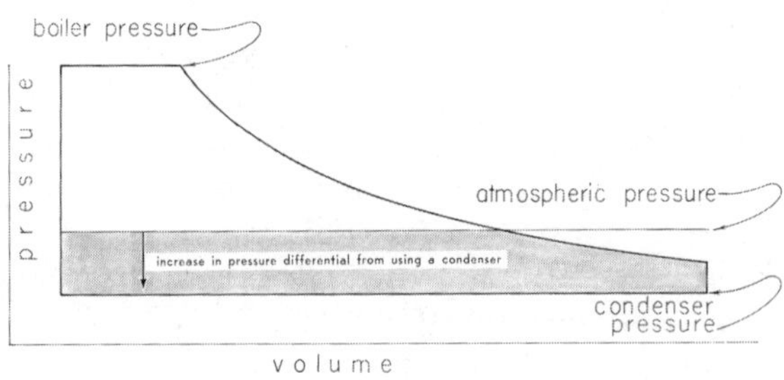

Fig. 2-8. A Condenser Increases Pressure Differential by Reducing Minimum Cylinder Pressure

ployed more fully in the operation of the steam engine. The solution came to him while he was walking one Sunday afternoon. He knew that in order to make a more efficient engine, it was necessary to preserve the heat of the cylinder and the steam entering it. The idea came to him that steam, a fluid, would rush into a vacuum, and if a connection were made between the cylinder and condenser or cold place, the steam would be made to condense outside of the hot cylinder. This is shown graphically in Fig. 2-8. The shaded area shows the gain in pressure differential by using a condenser to reduce minimum pressure in the cylinder. This seemingly simple ideal of a *separate condenser* was to transform the industrial history of mankind. This new engine is shown in Fig. 2-9.

This *condenser* was an empty vessel separate from the cylinder into which the steam was caused to condense. To further preserve the vacuum in the condenser, he employed an air pump to extract from it the condensed steam and water as well as any foreign air caused by leakage. The cylinder now remained hot and could be insulated to preserve its heat. In Newcomen's engine, the top had remained open; Watt covered it by leading the piston through a *stuffing box* in this cover and steam was permitted to enter the top of the cylinder to heat it.

Valves Automated

Watt employed three valves: a steam valve (A), an equilibrium valve (B), and an exhaust valve (C). At the beginning of the downward stroke the exhaust valve was opened to produce a vacuum below the piston, while the steam valve was opened to allow steam to enter above the piston. At the end of the downward stroke, both of these valves were shut and the equilibrium valve was opened. This placed neutral atmospheric pressure on the two sides, and allowed the piston to be pulled back up by the pump rod which was heavy to serve as counterweight.

At first, this engine was manually operated and was used solely for pumping water out of the Cornish mines.

Rotary Motion Added

In 1771, Watt took out a second patent describing five different methods of converting reciprocating motion into rotary motion, including the sun and planetary wheels shown in Fig. 2-10.

Fig. 2-9. Watt's Single-Acting Pumping Engine (1788) (© Science Museum, London)

Fig. 2-10. Model of Sun and Planet Gearing (Science Museum, London)

The crank and connecting rod was already a familiar mechanical device used on the treadle of a lathe, and it would have been a natural means of converting reciprocating motion to rotative motion. However, its application to the steam engine in a particular manner had been patented by James Pickard, whom Watt regarded as a plagiarist of his ideas. Rather than make terms with Pickard, he used the sun and planet gears until the patent expired.

Double Action Added

In 1782, Watt patented the principles of the *double-acting steam engine.* See Fig. 2-11. This used pressure and vacuum alternately on each side of the piston. The idea of permitting the steam expansion to act on the piston forcing it downward (although the admission of steam was cut before the piston completed its stroke), also increased engine efficiency. Both principles, however, were developed by Watt previous to the patent.

Governor Added

Later, in 1788, he invented the *centrifugal governor* by which the speed of the engine was controlled automatically. Two diametrically opposed balls moved outward as their speed increased. Their outward movement caused a downward movement of sleeves on the axle which controlled the steam.

Engine Indicator Added

Watt also invented an *indicator,* see Fig. 2-11, to record a diagram of the relation of the steam pressure to its volume during the operation of the engine because he desired to know what was happening in an engine's cylinder. See Fig. 2-12. The pencil is moved up

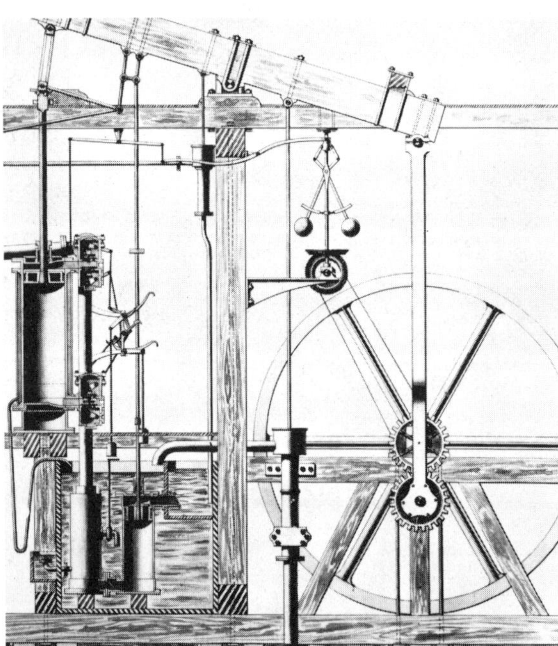

Fig. 2-11. Watt's Double-Acting Rotative Beam Engine with Governor (1788)
(Science Museum, London)
The hot expanding gases pushed the piston up and down. This reciprocating motion was transmitted by the piston rod to the overhead beam, a simple lever, and in turn to the sun and planet gearing.

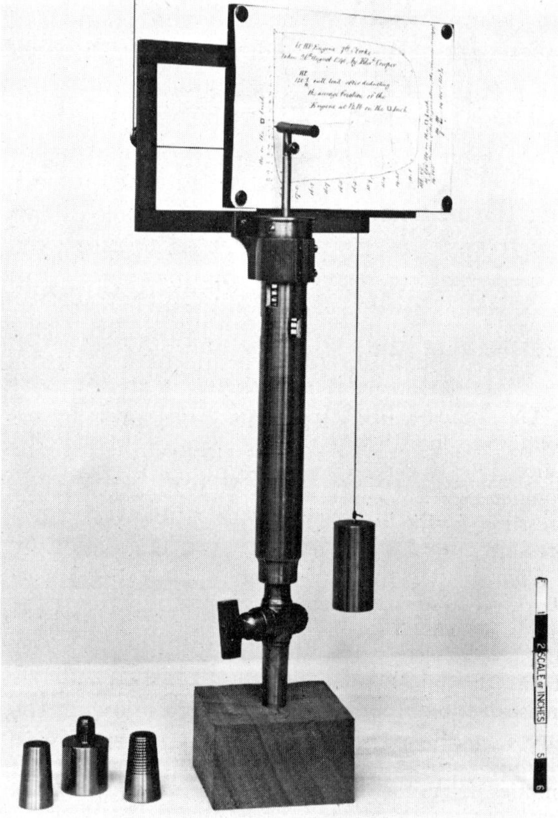

Fig. 2-12. Watt's Steam Engine Indicator (1796)
(Science Museum, London)

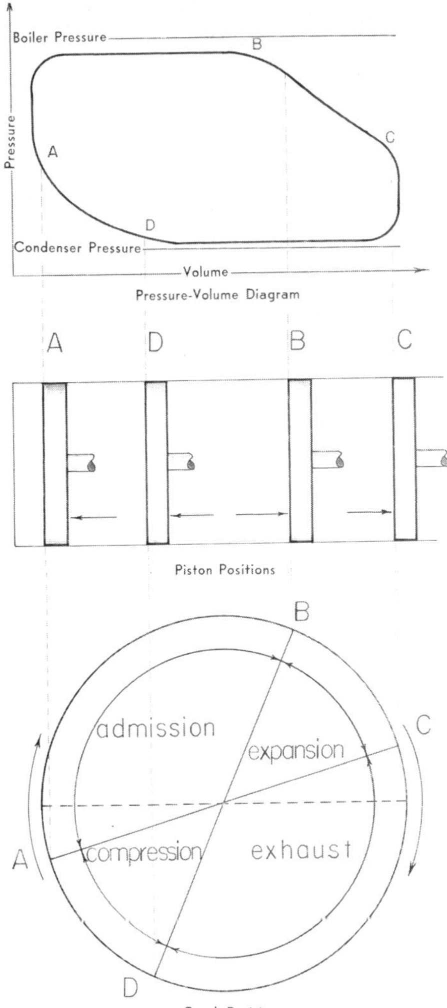

Fig. 2-13. Operation of Watt's Steam Engine Indicator

The indicator diagram (top) is a picture of the conditions inside the cylinder. The horizontal distance notes the position of the piston, therefore the volume; vertical distance indicates pressure. Boiler pressure is the maximum possible and condenser pressure the minimum possible in the cylinder.

Compare the three diagrams. When the piston is at A, the steam admission begins, and pressure builds up almost to the boiler pressure, forcing the piston to move to right until steam cutoff at B. The steam continues to expand and the volume increases as the piston continues to move but the pressure drops to Point C. Spent steam is exhausted as piston returns from C to D. Not all of the steam empties from the cylinder and as the piston continues to return, it compresses the residual steam, showing an increase from D to A. Here new steam is admitted beginning another cycle.

and down by a pressure gauge while the chart moves with the piston. Thus the indicator records both the steam pressure and the position of the piston within the cylinder, diagraming the conditions inside the cylinders. See Fig. 2-13 for an explanation of its operation.

Unit of Power Defined

The commercial success of Watt's engine was rapid. By 1790, most mines replaced the Newcomen engine with a Watt engine which used only a fourth of the fuel of the older engine to do the same work. While this had been a selling point for his engine, Watt also found it necessary to state how many horses his engines would be capable of replacing. He undertook this by experiments to determine the power of an average horse. To be on the safe side, and not overrate his engines, he made his unit of power more than what an average horse is able to exert. He called this unit of measurement, *horsepower.* Watt defined one horsepower as the *ability to do 33,000 ft. lbs. of work per minute or 550 ft. lbs. of work per second.* See Fig. 2-14. This is also the power necessary to raise one ton 16½ feet in one minute, assuming no friction.

Slide Valves Added

Watt also owed much of his success to William Murdock, his assistant, who in 1799 improved the valve system used on the steam engine when he patented the famous *slide*

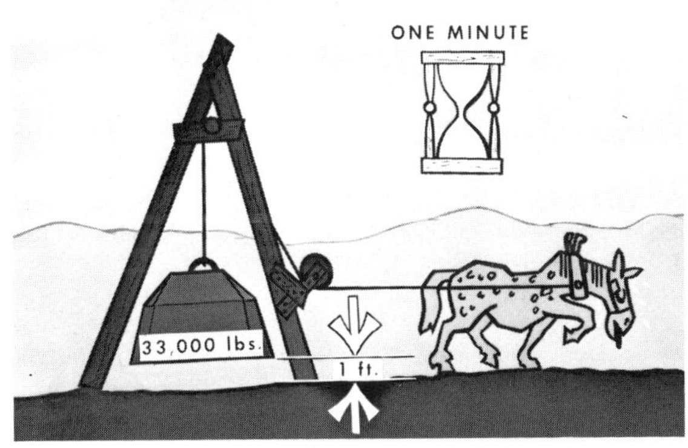

Fig. 2-14. One Horsepower (Ford)

valve, Fig. 2-15. This consisted of a box, provided with openings, or *ports,* which moved inside the steam chest back and forth over the corresponding ports at the ends of the cylinder. He also introduced the idea of an *eccentric* that moved the valve, because of its offcenter collar. In 1801, this valve was improved upon by Murray when he designed the *D valve.* This valve permitted steam to enter each end of the cylinder alternately, cutting the steam supply at the right time and moving to permit the steam to escape through a central port after expending its energy.

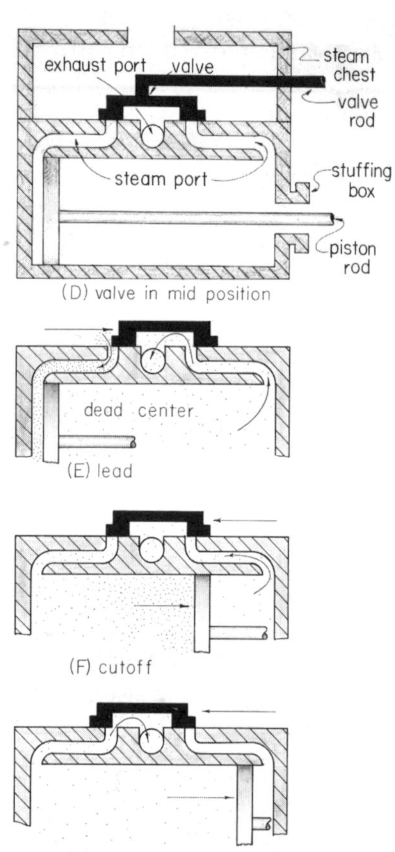

Fig. 2-15. Steam Engine Valve Operation
The valve permits the steam to enter the cylinder alternately, pushing the piston from the top and then the bottom. Position D shows the piston to the left and the valve just prior to admission. Position E shows the valve moving to admit steam which forces the piston to start its stroke. The opposite end of the cylinder is being exhausted of its spent steam. At F, the valve cuts the admission of steam; but expansion continues, forcing the piston to move. Point G shows the valve moving to exhaust the steam just prior to admission at the opposite end of the cylinder.

Compounding Added

Jonathan Hornblower and Arthur Woolf were contemporaries of Watt. Hornblower introduced and Woolf further developed one of the most important improvements of the reciprocating steam engine called *compounding.* In their engine shown in Fig. 2-16, steam was first admitted into a smaller cylinder, allowed to expand somewhat pushing the piston downward. The steam left this cylinder and entered a larger cylinder and further expanded, pushing its piston downward.

Fig. 2-17 shows two ways of doing this. In the *tandom compound* engine (top) both pistons have a common rod and crank, so piston travel is identical. The second cylinder has a larger diameter to receive the greater volume. In the *independent compound,* or

Fig. 2-16. Hornblower's Compound Engine (1781)
(© Science Museum, London)

just compound, engine (bottom) the throws are separate, allowing greater freedom in cylinder design and timing. Note the strokes here are 90° apart, giving smoother power overlap also.

The most important merit of the system came from dividing the whole range of expansion into two cylinders so the fluctuation of temperature in each cylinder was reduced considerably. This helped to limit a source of heat waste caused by the heating and cooling of the metal by the alternating hot and then cooler steam, thus increasing engine efficiency. *When high temperatures are maintained, steam continues to hold its pressure potential (its power to expand) for some time.* It shrinks or condenses only when cooled to less than boiling temperature. Double, triple, and quadruple expansion engines became popular, especially as high pressure steam boilers were developed.

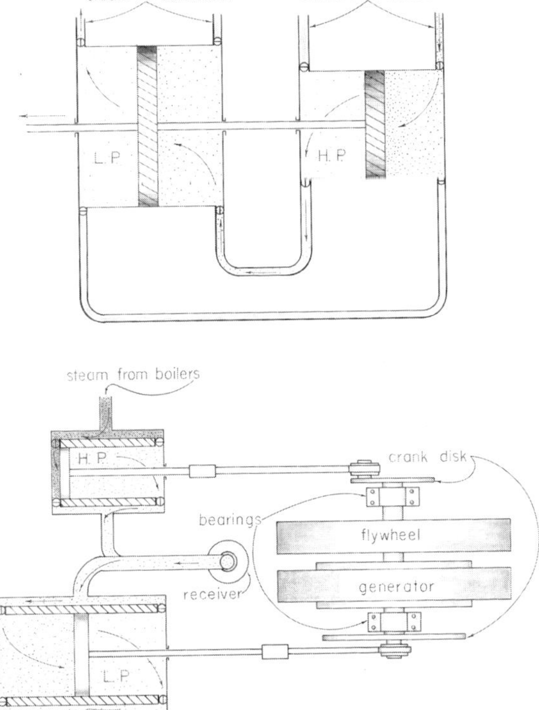

Fig. 2-17. Two Methods of Compounding—Tandem-Compound (top) and Independent-Compound Engines

Steam Engine and Transportation

The problems of applying the steam engine to a means of transport were partly solved by Nicholas Cugnot in 1769, who invented a steam artillery carriage, Fig. 2-18. This gun tractor was a three-wheeler, with the heavy engine and boiler located over the odd front wheel, which pivoted to change direction. The maximum speed was 3 mph, with refueling necessary every 15 miles. The French Ministry was dissatisfied with the engine and exiled the inventor for 20 years. Later, Napoleon recalled him and put him on pension.

In America, Oliver Evans acquired the first patent covering a "self-propelled vehicle" in 1789. He applied steam power to propel the 21-ton Orukter Amphibolis, Fig. 2-19. This was a combination steam wagon and flat boat, the first amphibian on record. He secured more recognition in Europe for his invention than he did in this country.

Steam Locomotive Invented

In England, Richard Trevithick, a British mechanical engineer and inventor, revised the drawings of Evans and designed a *high*

Fig. 2-18. Cugnot's Vehicle
(Smithsonian Institution)

Fig. 2-19. "Orukter Amphibolis," Oliver Evans' Amphibian Driven in Philadelphia, 1805 (G.M.)

pressure non-condensing steam engine. Fig. 2-20 shows how this engine had the cylinders immersed in the boiler steam. On Christmas Eve, 1801, he brought forth a long stroke steam engine directly coupled to the driving wheels, using an American-made boiler for steam generation. The vehicle attained a speed of 5 mph. However, his carriage was considered unsafe because of the difficulty in controlling its direction of travel.

Fig. 2-20. Trevithick High Pressure Engine by Hazledine (1805) (Science Museum, London)

Within a year, Trevithick was back in the public eye with a vehicle that ran on *rails.* The first locomotive traveled on a 100 foot diameter track at 15 to 20 mph earning him a place in recorded history as the designer of the steam locomotive.

By 1804, with the help of Andrew Vivian, he set the steam locomotive to hauling logs. He was the first to realize that another function of the wheels on the track was *increased traction,* so he *coupled the wheels* of a locomotive to provide even greater traction. From almost the beginning, the success of the steam locomotive was evident.

In Philadelphia, John Fitch built several steamboats that were propelled by steam-powered oars and shovel-shaped paddles that kicked like the feet of a swimming duck.

In 1807, Robert Fulton built a steamboat that performed much more smoothly than any water craft of that era, Fig. 2-21. He was the first to establish a steamboat line on the Hudson and make it a profitable adventure. He also invented the steam warship and the double-ended ferryboat.

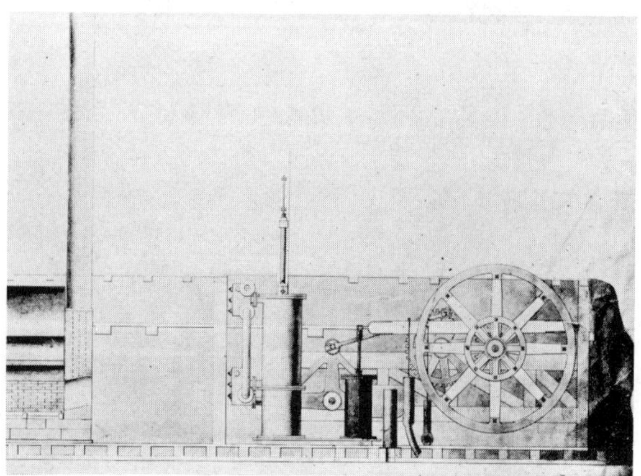

Fig. 2-21. Original Drawing of Robert Fulton's Steamboat Machinery
(New Jersey Historical Society)

Fig. 2-22. Peter Cooper's "Tom Thumb" (Newer Locomotives in Background)

American Railroads Initiated

In the beginning, convinced of the successes of the railroad-systems in England, proponents of such means of locomotion contracted to bring over English locomotives, cars, and rails. These early engines stimulated American designers to develop their own. The Tom Thumb, Fig. 2-22, built by Peter Cooper in 1830 was the first American-made locomotive. Success of the engine caused others to manufacture and improve this prime mover. The locomotive grew in size and proportion to keep pace with the ever-increasing demands for higher capacity and speed.

American Industrial Revolution and the Steam Engine

Prior to the nineteenth century, labor-saving machines had been installed in factories in the United States to compensate for the shortage of labor that existed on the farms and in the cities. American mechanics, toolmakers, and millwrights, were trained to operate them.

Power Transmission Known

By 1830, the average American mechanic knew the principles of *power transmission* by *shaft, chain,* or *belt-drive.* He understood how to transmit power by employing *spiral gears, worm gears, universal joints,* and *friction wheels.* He knew how to use *cams, cranks, pistons, connecting rods, universal rods, couplings,* and *clutches.* The American technician had been forced to evolve these principles when machines were operated by hand-power at slow speed. "Yankee ingenuity" was developed as he learned to adapt and improve his machine for a specific use.

Interchangeability

Also important was the acceptance of the idea of *interchangeable parts.* This idea was pioneered in Gutenberg's movable type for printing in the mid-fifteenth century. Interchangeability in manufacture of musket parts was developed by Eli Whitney in the late eighteenth century. This led to the standardization and duplication of parts which gave a continuous flow of production and made cities conducive to the adaption of the factory system.

Toward a More Efficient Steam Engine

The more popular the steam engine became, the more it became apparent that its efficiency had to be improved. Most of the modifications were made in the valve design and in the action and control of the steam expansion and exhaust. It was realized that these features determined the efficiency of the engine. Most important were the *Corliss Valve Gear* and the *Uniflow Principle.*

Corliss Valve Gear

George Corliss in 1848 began to manufacture a steam engine of greatly improved design. Many honors were bestowed upon him in Europe and America in recognition of his contribution to the advancement of steam engineering. The fact that many Corliss engines are still in operation testifies to the fact that they are still good engines. His famous *Corliss Valve Gear,* shown in Fig. 2-23, employs four separate valves: two *admission valves,* one for the head end and one for the crank end, and two *exhaust valves,* one for the

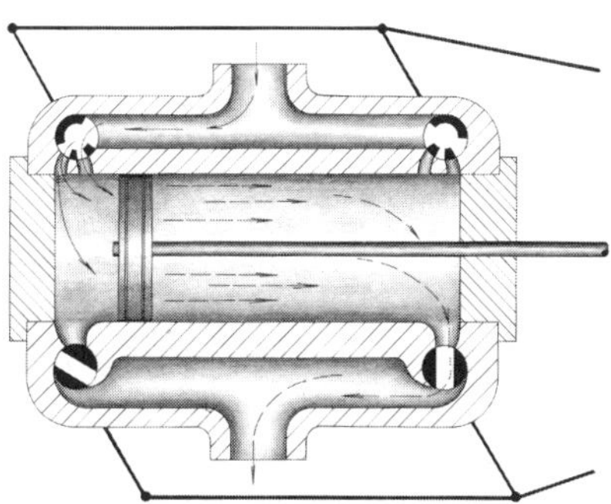

Fig. 2-23. Corliss Valve Gear

head and one for the crank end. Fig. 2-24 shows the rather complicated mechanism in its operation. However, it is very efficient because the live steam enters its own admission port and the spent steam is directed out its own exhaust port. In this way, there is little condensation caused by the exhaust and cooling of the live steam as is the case with the slide valve engine. Also, the pressure of the live steam acting against the top and side of the valve is eliminated. The entire ·alve assembly is surrounded by live steam causing no unbalanced or opposed force. The Corliss engine is usually a low-speed engine.

Fig. 2-24. Horizontal Engine with Corliss Valve Gear (© Science Museum, London)

Uniflow Principle

This is also one of the most efficient valve designs. Engines using this valve principle have *only admission valves;* the exhausting is accomplished through ports in the cylinder wall which are uncovered by the piston as it reaches the end of its power stroke. See Fig. 2-25. The piston must be nearly as long as its stroke and the cylinder twice as long. The steam enters the cylinder at the ends and leaves at the middle, flowing in one direction, not back and forth as in the other engines; hence, the name *uniflow engine* is applied. The spent steam never comes in contact with the live steam and, therefore it is quite an efficient engine. These engines

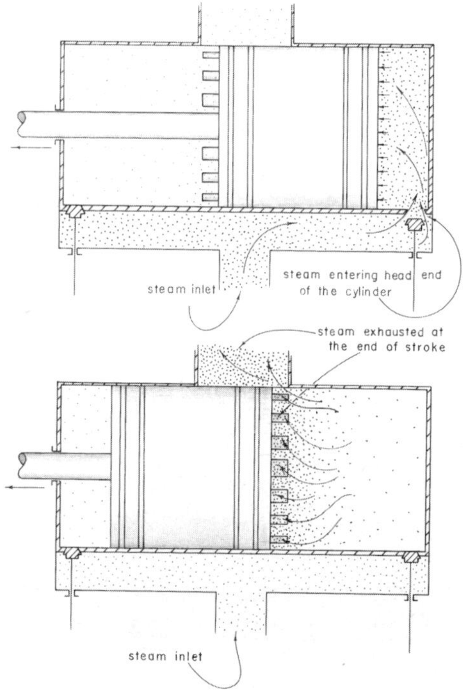

Fig. 2-25. The Principle of the Uniflow Engine—Live Steam Never Contacts Spent Steam

Fig. 2-26. Horizontal Simple Steam Engine (Model by Stuart)

Fig. 2-27. Vertical Independent-Compound Steam Engine (Model by Stuart)

are considered to be in the medium-speed range although they can be operated at high speeds quite easily.

Engines of this type are usually equipped with *poppet valves,* similar to those employed in popular internal combustion engines. It is interesting to note that this port exhaust system is also common in small gasoline engines.

Types of Steam Engines

Steam engines were classified according to the work they performed and also have been divided into the following types of designs: *Simple engines* are those engines where the steam is used in the cylinder once and then exhausted into the atmosphere. See Fig. 2-26. *Compound* and *multi-expansion* engines cause steam to do further work before being exhausted. See Fig. 2-27.

Walking Beam

Newcomen and Watt's *walking beam* engines were the first type and are now extinct. They possessed the unique rocking overhead arm as well as the supporting classical columns and entablatures.

Horizontal

Among the most popular engines were the *horizontal* types of stationary steam engines introduced during the middle of the last century. See Fig. 2-26. They soon became established for general workshop use in textile mills and machine shops. They are almost, if not completely, extinct in this country although they are still used in many other parts of the world.

Reversing

Mill engines, Fig. 2-28, were a simple form as they needed to rotate only in one direction. Later, linkages to reverse valve positions or crank positions allowed an engine to turn in either direction. See Fig. 2-29.

Vertical

Vertical engines became popular in marine installations because they took up less precious space. Their operation was similar to the horizontal engine although reversing mechanisms were most always provided.

Oscillating

Oscillating engines in the 19th Century were considered a triumph of engineering for marine installations and through the efforts of John Penn were perfected to their highest degree. This type of engine had many advantages. It occupied little space, had few working parts, and was easy to service and

Fig. 2-28. Model of Horizontal Tandem-Compound Corliss Mill Engine (Nonreversing) (© Science Museum, London)

Fig. 2-29. Vertical Simple Engine with Crank Reversing Mechanism (Model by Stuart)

maintain. See Fig. 2-30. An interesting feature was the use of the cylinder itself to control the steam entry and exit. It was made to pivot about a fixed point on the valve chest, the motion being derived from the normal movement of the crankshaft, piston, and piston rod. The steam and exhaust ports were covered and uncovered in the proper sequence.

Fig. 2-30. Murdock's Model Oscillating Engine (1785) (© Science Museum, London)

Structure and Operating Principles of the Steam Engine

Pistons and Cylinders

Steam engine *cylinders* are usually made of cast iron with the inside dimension accurately machined so that the *piston* and *rings* will fit properly. Piston rings exert pressure on the walls of the cylinder and naturally cause a certain amount of wear.

Figs. 2-31 and 2-32 show a simple model engine with parts identified. The *cylinder jacket* (I) is a complicated casting because, in addition to being accurately machined on the inside, it must contain *steam passages* for the live steam entering the cylinder and the exhaust steam leaving it. In some engines, the *valves* are also enclosed in the cylinder casting. In this engine, they are located in an adjacent compartment called the *steam chest* (D). A *slide valve* is operated by an *eccentric rod* (G), and a *valve rod* (J) passing through a tight-fitting *stuffing box* (B). The cylinder, steam chest, and passages must be strong enough to withstand the steam pressures at which the engine operates.

The end of the cylinder farthest from the flywheel is closed by a *cylinder head* (K) which is bolted to the *cylinder casting* proper

Fig. 2-31. Vertical Double-Acting Simple Steam Engine (Model by Stuart)
(A) Drain Cocks, (B) Stuffing Box, (C) Crosshead, (D) Steam Chest, (E) Displacement Lubricator, (F) Flywheel, (G) Eccentric Rod, (H) Bed.

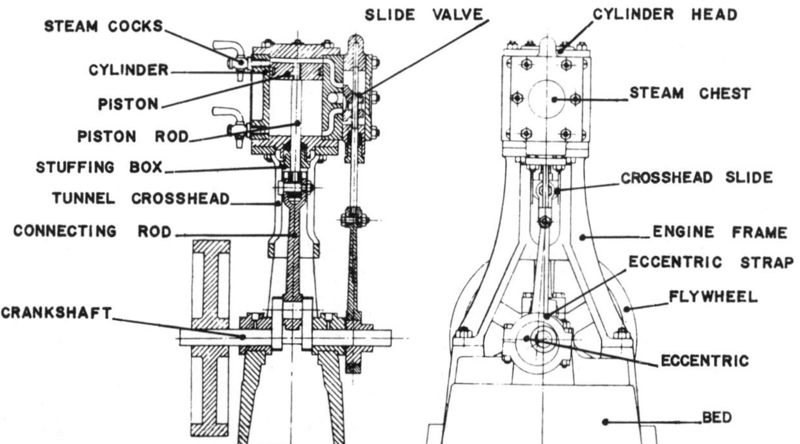

Fig. 2-32. Cross Section and End View of Vertical Double-Acting Simple Steam Engine (Stuart)
(I) Cylinder Jacket, (J) Valve Rod, (K) Cylinder Head, (L) Stuffing Box. Fig. 2-31 shows other parts of this engine.

(I), with the *piston rod* passing through a *stuffing box* (L) in the other end of the cylinder. The lower end of the piston rod is steadied by the *crosshead* (C). The reciprocating motion at this point is changed to rotary motion by the *connecting rod,* and *crankshaft,* to be discussed later. The flywheel (F) keeps the crankshaft turning more smoothly.

Usually, there are two holes in each end of the cylinder. These are tapped and fitted with *cocks* (A), to drain the water when starting up the engine, and to attach the indicator. The *lubricator* (E) keeps internal moving parts oiled.

The piston is cylindrical in shape and is made to fit the cylinder in such a way that a steamtight joint is assured even though it must be permitted to move quite freely back and forth. The only practical way this can be done is to employ *piston rings.* See Fig. 2-33. Other means would not permit the uniform expansion caused by the heat.

In most small engines, pistons are made solid with suitable grooves machined into them. With large pistons, this procedure is not possible. The large heavy piston rings could not be sprung enough to force them onto the piston. For these reasons, large pistons must be made in sections. The hub which fits over the piston rod and supports the other parts is called the *spider* or *piston body.* In some designs, the spider is solid and in others it is hollow. These are divided at the piston-ring grooves so that the rings can be removed. The *bull rings* are supported from

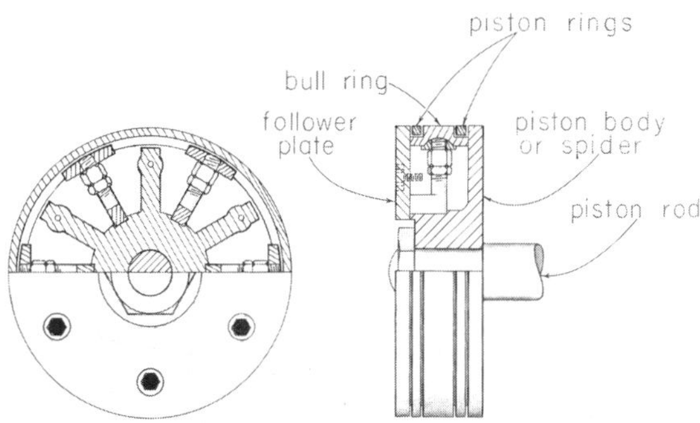

Fig. 2-33. Parts of a Steam Engine Piston

the spider by springs or by adjusting studs. The *end or follower plates* hold the piston and the assembly in place.

The common *snap piston ring* is machined from a ring larger than the diameter of the cylinder into which it is to be used. A slot must be cut in the ring to permit it to be compressed within the cylinder. The tendency of the ring to open holds it firm against the cylinder wall. The ring cuts must be staggered to prevent leakage of steam.

The piston does not travel the entire length of the cylinder. There is linear clearance provided to prevent the piston from striking the cylinder head and damaging the engine. This clearance should be equal at the head and crank ends and is seldom less than one-eighth of an inch.

Steam engine cylinders house steam at higher temperatures and at higher pressures than atmospheric pressure and room temperature. Thus, heat is continually being radiated from the cylinders to the air. This results in a direct loss in efficiency because of the steam condensing in the cylinder. Losses can be reduced by making the cylinder double-walled and filling the space with steam *(steam jacketing),* or by covering the cylinder with heat-insulating material.

Piston Rods, Crossheads, and Connecting Rods

The force of the expanding steam exerted on the piston is transmitted from the cylinder by the *piston rod.* This is shown in Fig. 2-32. One end of the piston rod is attached to the piston head and the other end is connected to the *crosshead.* This rod must be mechanically able to withstand both compression and tension forces since it is subjected to these forces during one cycle.

The piston rod enters through a *stuffing box* to prevent steam leakage. Some boxes, especially on low-pressure saturated steam engines, are filled with *soft braided packing* and covered with a bolted lid. In high pressure, superheated steam engines, *metallic packing* is used. Metallic packing is initially more costly, but lasts longer and hence is more economical.

The *crosshead* is rigidly attached to one end of the piston rod which is connected to the connecting rod by means of a bearing. Because of the crosshead's rigid attachment, it has the same motion as the piston. The purpose of the crosshead is to guide the piston rod and keep it in line with the piston. The crosshead works between *guides* and thus ensures a straight-line movement. The connecting rod end attached to the crosshead must then move in a circular motion with the other end as it moves with the *crankshaft.* The circular motion of the crank puts a thrust on the crosshead guides and causes wear. Therefore, the crosshead is fitted with antifriction metal *slippers* that may be adjusted to compensate for wear. The reciprocating or back and forth motion of the piston and crosshead is changed to circular or rotary motion by means of the *connecting rod.* The force developed in the cylinder is transmitted by the connecting rod from the crosshead to the crank. This requires the connecting rod to have a bearing on each end. These bearings are usually so designed that they may be adjusted for wear.

Crank

The *crank* holds the end of the connecting rod in a rotating motion and transmits the force of the piston through the piston rod and connecting rod to the engine shaft. If the engine shaft has a bearing on each side of the crank, it is called a *center crank engine,* and if there is a bearing on only one side, it is referred to as an *overhung crank engine.* Rather than a crank, some small engines employ a disk which is shrunk on the main engine shaft. The *crankpin* is located in the disk which is *counterweighted* on the side opposite the crank to compensate for the weight of the crankpin and connecting rod. Large engines have cranks made up in sections with the *crankpin arm* extending in one direction and the *counterweight arm* in the other. If the *flywheel* is on the right of the engine when viewed from the cylinder end, it is a *right-handed* engine and vice versa.

The distance from the center of the shaft to the center of the crankpin is referred to as the *radius of throw* of the crank; twice the radius is called the *throw of the crank* or *stroke of the engine.* The piston travels once over its entire path to make one stroke of the engine.

Flywheel

Previous discussion of the operation of the piston in the cylinder has indicated that the force exerted is not uniform throughout the stroke. To cause the engine to run more smoothly, a *flywheel* is attached to the engine shaft. The heavy rim of the flywheel resists any change in the rate of motion. The flywheel takes a certain amount of power to increase its speed. When power is decreased to the shaft, the flywheel power becomes available because of the principle of *inertia,*[1] to prevent a change of speed. During one part of the revolution the flywheel consumes power, and during the other part of the revolution it imparts power to stabilize the rotative effect. The size of the flywheel is determined by the size of the engine, the speed, and the service for which it is designed.

As the flywheel rotates, its rim is always trying to move straight out or to break away from the flywheel. The flywheel must be made to overcome this *centrifugal force* or the flywheel will burst. The general rule is that the *rim speed* of the flywheel should not be more than 6,000 ft. per minute. Engine speeds can be controlled with governors and overspeed tripping devices.

Engines are classified according to the *direction of rotation.* If, when the engine is viewed from the cylinder end, the top of the flywheel rotates away from the viewer, the engine is said to be *running over.* If it rotates toward the viewer, it is said to be *running under.* It is more desirable to have an engine *run over* because the thrust on the crosshead guide will be on the bottom guide during both strokes. The bottom guide is held firm to the engine's foundation.

[1] Principle of Inertia – a body in motion tends to remain in motion; a body at rest tends to remain at rest until acted upon by some external force.

Valves

The reciprocating steam engine needs a valve arrangement which permits steam to enter and leave the cylinder at the beginning and end of the piston's stroke, Fig. 2-34. The exhaust valve must open at the beginning of the return stroke or slightly before to discharge the exhaust steam, and must close at or a little before the piston has completed its return stroke.

Several types of valves have been developed as we have already discussed with most valve systems employing an *eccentric* for their movement. The simple eccentric consists of a circular disk, larger in diameter than the engine shaft, with a hole bored in this disk equal to the shaft diameter, but this hole is not made in the center of the disk. See Fig. 2-35. The distance from the center of this hole to the center of the disk is known as the *eccentricity* or *radius of throw of the eccentric*. The *throw of the eccentric* is twice the eccentricity.

The eccentric revolves with the shaft and has a strap located around it to which the valve rod is attached. When the engine shaft makes one-half of a revolution, the valve moves a distance equal to the throw of the eccentric, or twice the eccentricity. The simple slide-valve engine has but one eccentric. More efficient engines sometimes have two eccentrics, one for the intake and one for the exhaust valves. This makes it possible to control the speed of the engine by adjusting the inlet steam valve which acts as a governor.

Frames and Foundation

The engine requires a solid base and foundation to keep the moving and stationary parts in perfect alignment. The various arrangements of the cylinder, crosshead, bearings and flywheel are numerous. However, with any arrangement, a *solid cast iron bed or base* is most widely used to support the main bearings, crosshead guides, and cylinder.

Governors

Most steam engine applications require the engine to rotate at constant speed, even though the load sometimes varies. The governor adjusts the steam supply as the engine's speed varies with the load.

Though engines can approach, they can never attain a constant speed. The speed of the engine must change to activate the governor and hence the steam supply. A sensitive governor will respond to the slightest variation in engine speed, adjust the steam supply to the new load, and restore the speed to where it was before the load change occurred.

There are several desirable characteristics of a governor; sensitivity, stability, and promptness of response. *Sensitivity* refers to the governor's ability to make adjustments for slight changes in engine speed, but not so sensitive that it is unstable. A *stable* governor has the ability to maintain constant speed

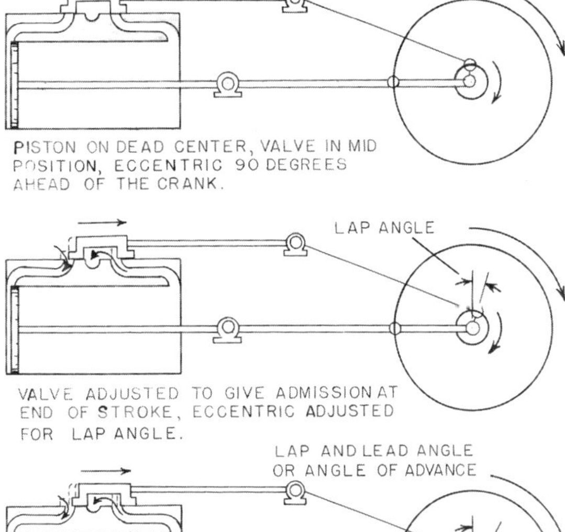

Fig. 2-34. Valve and Eccentric Relationships

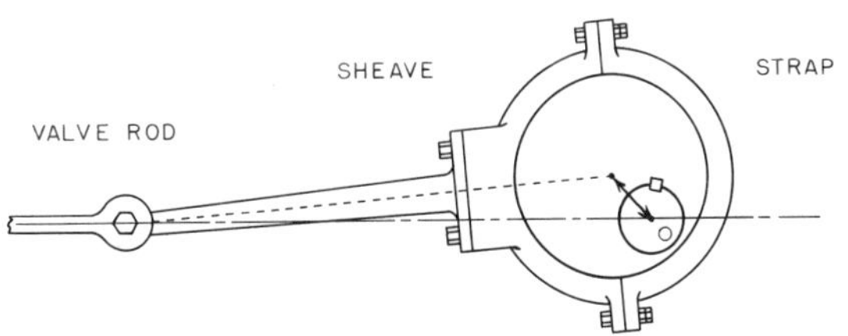

Fig. 2-35. Radius of Throw of the Eccentric

under varying load conditions. The ability of a governor mechanism to quickly restore engine speed determines its *promptness.*

Speed regulation is one measure of a governor's performance and is defined as the change in speed necessary to cause the governor to operate the engine from no load to full load and is expressed in percent of full-load speed.

The *flyball governor,* Fig. 2-36, is the most popular governor mechanism and consists of two or more balls vertically mounted to a shaft which is able to rotate with the engine. The rotating motion of the governor produces centrifugal force which causes the weights (balls) to react against gravity. The force causes them to lift or move away from the shaft in proportion to the engine speed. A decrease in rpm causes the weights to drop proportionately and consequently move in a smaller circle.

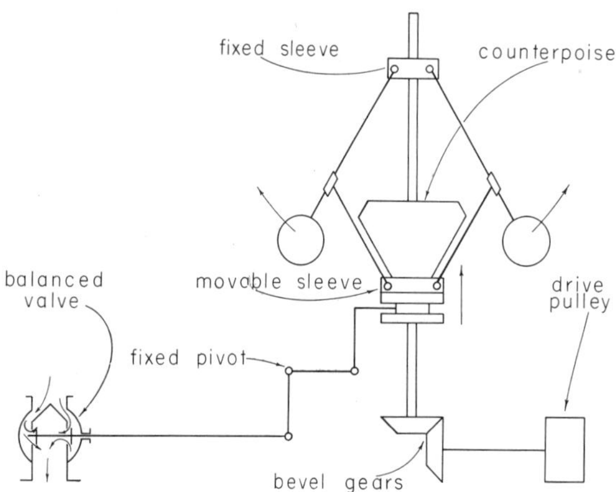

Fig. 2-36. Flyball Governor

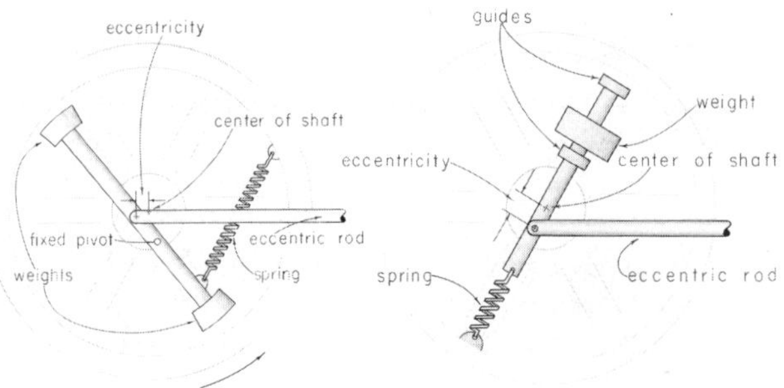

Fig. 2-37. Two Types of Centrifugal Flywheel Governors

Flyball governors are most always driven by belts from the engine shaft. If this belt breaks, the engine behaves as if it were under tremendous load because the governor calls for more steam to be admitted. The engine then would speed up until safe limits were exceeded. To prevent this, a stop valve is installed. The valve is held open by an idler pulley riding on the belt. If the belt were to break the valve would automatically cut the flow of steam to the engine.

The speed of the governor, relative to that of the engine, is determined by the diameter of the pulleys on the engine and governor.

In some engines, *shaft* or *flywheel governors* are employed, Fig. 2-37. These, too, depend on centrifugal force and consist of weights mounted on pivoted arms that rotate with the flywheel as at the left of Fig. 2-37. The centrifugal force created by the rotation of weights pulls against countersprings attached to weighted arms. The weights move in proportion to the flywheel's speed and the tension or pull of the spring. The speed of the engine can be adjusted by changing the tension on the spring. Increasing the tension requires more centrifugal force for a given position of the governor weights, therefore increasing the engine speed. Decreasing the tension slows the engine down.

The weighted arms of the flywheel governors are connected to the eccentrics by linkage which control the valve operating mechanism. This mechanism varies the point of cut off and opening.

Speeds

The speed of an engine usually refers to the revolutions made by the flywheel per minute *(rpm),* while *piston speed* is the number of feet of linear distance the piston travels in one minute *(fpm).*

Many factors determine the *rpm* at which an engine operates, such as steam pressure, valve cut-off, and so on. Engines are normally referred to as *high speed* engines if their flywheel speed is at least 125 rpm. Any lesser speed makes the engine a *low speed* engine. High speed engines usually employ shaft governors, while low speed engines have throttling governors.

Piston speeds usually vary from 300 to 600 fpm for most stationary practice. Some larger engines may have piston speeds from 700 to 800 fpm. Usually, an engine with a long stroke and high piston speed is accompanied by low rotative speed, and a short-stroke engine with low piston speed is accompanied by high rotative speed.

As previously mentioned, the purpose of the flywheel is to carry the engine over dead center. There are two instances during each revolution that the engine is on dead center. This occurs when the piston is momentarily in a stationary position. The heavier the flywheel the more uniform the speed of the engine. However, a point may be reached where too much weight would prove undesirable because it would not improve the operation of the engine, but would increase the wear of the bearings. Therefore, a flywheel should not be made larger than necessary.

Increasing rpm decreases the time during which the engine is on dead center. The size of the flywheel required depends upon the speed at which it is rotating and upon its weight. The higher the speed of rotation, the lighter the necessary weight and the smaller the diameter of the flywheel. This reduction in size then relieves the engine bearing of any unnecessary weight and permits a smaller shaft and lighter foundation to be employed, thereby reducing the cost of the engine.

Small pistons usually travel at high speeds. This is very desirable since their smaller size gives reduced cylinder condensation, and a reduction in weight and cost.

High rotative speed engines are frequently desirable when connected to electric generators and supply a comparatively larger amount of power for a given cylinder size. However, they require more compression and generally are less economical.

The reciprocating steam engine is well adapted for variable speeds, for relatively low rotative speeds, and for situations where great turning power is required. Low-speed steam engines exhibit reliability and low maintenance. In some installations, steam engines are used to operate air compressors, pumps, and other auxiliary equipment. The exhaust steam from these engines is sometimes made available for use in space heating and for industrial processes. When there is need for this exhaust steam, the arrangement can prove to be economical because the power for driving the auxiliaries is a by-product of the normal steam demands.

Low speed engines are more desirable for continuous operation. They require a heavier and larger framework and, therefore, are more expensive than high speed engines.

Engines are referred to as *short stroke* engines when the length of stroke is less than one-half of the diameter of the engine cylinder. A *long stroke* engine has a stroke exceeding one and one-half times the diameter of the engine cylinder.

We must now leave the reciprocating steam engine, having studied its development to the present century. Its potential was nearly exhausted at the turn of the century. At that time reciprocating steam engines ranged in efficiency from 8.5% to 24% depending on the valve systems and the steam pressures used. Engines of 5,000 horsepower were then being built even though the expected vibration, voluminous appetite for fuel, slow speed, tremendous weight, and large size could not be overcome. Industry demanded a new engine to meet the challenge of growth and expansion. It required an engine that would be smoother running, acquire higher speeds, develop greater horsepower, and occupy less space.

Most of all however, industry needed an engine which was more *efficient.* To be 100 percent efficient, it is necessary that all energy be transformed into useful work. This is never possible because of energy lost in overcoming friction, as well as that which is wasted in other forms of energy such as heat, light, and sound, or used to overcome inertia while changing direction of a piston.

A steam engine of totally new design, the *steam turbine,* was to satisfy these demands.

Terms to Understand

steam
heat engines, heat loss
steam turbine
reaction engine
Hero of Alexandria
diametrically
Leonardo da Vinci
vacuum
atmospheric pressure
Torricelli
Von Guericke
pressure differential
Huygens
piston, cylinder
Papin
peat
Savery
"fire engine"
fourth stage of power
Newcomen
atmospheric engine
valve
beam engine
Watt
latent heat
condenser
stuffing box
steam valve
equilibrium valve
exhaust valve
synchronized
sun and planet wheel
crank
connecting rod
plagiarist
patent
double action
centrifugal governor
indicator
horsepower
Murdock
slide valve
ports
steam chest
eccentric
"D" valve
Hornblower
Woolf
compounding
tandem compound
independent compound
engine efficiency
stationary engine
Cugnot
Evans
Orukter Amphibolis
Trevithick
high pressure non-condensing engine
Vivian
Fitch
Fulton
industrial revolution
power transmission
interchangeable parts
Eli Whitney
Corliss valve gear
uniflow principle
poppet valves
simple engines
compound engines
walking beam engine
horizontal engine
vertical engine
oscillating engine
piston rings
steam cocks
spider
steam jacketing
crosshead
stuffing-box packing
flywheel
right-, left-hand engine
inertia
centrifugal force
running over or under
radius of throw
throw of the eccentric
air-pump
frames
governor characteristics
speed regulation
flyball governor
shaft governor
flywheel governor
low or high speed
dead center
short or long stroke

Study Questions

1. What is a heat engine? Explain principles of operation. Why is this energy transformation never 100 percent efficient?

2. The first heat engine was described by Hero of Alexandria. Describe its principles of operation.

3. Torricelli announced the principle of atmospheric pressure as he compared it to a column of mercury 30 inches in height. Explain.

4. Von Guericke demonstrated the force of atmospheric pressure with his hemisphere experiment. Explain.

5. What contribution did Denys Papin make in the story of using steam as a source of power?

6. What was the principle employed in the operation of Savery's fire engine?

7. How did Newcomen improve Savery's engine?

8. Explain how the Newcomen engine operated.

9. James Watt improved Newcomen's engine in several ways. Explain.

10. In a Newcomen engine, the piston was 3 feet in diameter, and the length of stroke 5 feet. During the down-stroke, the pressure within the cylinder was 5 lbs./sq. in. If the atmospheric pressure was 14.7 lbs./sq. in., what was the force on the piston, and what was the work done during one stroke?

11. Explain the function of a flywheel.

12. Explain the principles of operation of the Watt double-acting steam engine.

13. A steam engine has a piston diameter of 15 inches with a 25-inch stroke and operates off a boiler that provides 60 lbs./sq. in. pressure. What is the work done per stroke if the engine is not fitted with a condenser? If the engine were fitted with a condenser in which the pressure was 5 lbs./sq. in., what would be the additional work done per stroke? If the engine operated at 300 strokes per minute, what would be its horsepower rating?

14. What are the main causes of inefficiency in a reciprocating steam engine?

15. Discuss the reasons for a centrifugal governor.

16. Explain the principle of the centrifugal governor.

17. What is an indicator? How does it operate?

18. What is meant by horsepower?

19. Explain the operation of a slide "D" valve, double-acting steam engine.

20. What is the purpose of an eccentric? How is the size of eccentric determined?

21. What are the advantages of high pressure boilers?

22. What is the advantage of a condenser? Why did the locomotive not have a condenser? Why did marine installations need a condenser?

23. What is meant by a compound engine? What is the principle of operation?

24. The valve system of a steam engine is most important. What were the most widely used valve systems and their characteristics?

25. Cugnot's contribution to power development resulted in his exile. Explain.

26. What differences were found in Trevithick's high pressure non-condensing steam engine as compared to the conventional stationary engines of that time?

27. What was Robert Fulton's contribution to the evolution of prime movers?

28. Discuss some of the reasons why the industrial revolution found tremendous support in America.

29. Speculate on how the locomotive played a part in America's history.

30. Explain the principles of operation of the Corliss valve gear.

31. Explain the uniflow principles.

32. How were steam engines classified?

CHAPTER 3

Steam Turbines

The steam turbine has become a prime mover of great importance in our modern technology. Using steam generated by the heat of atomic reaction, turbines provide power for the extended cruises of modern submarines. Similar turbine-equipped atomic power plants are now generating electricity. Various steam-powered generating plants produce 80%[1] of our electricity, the main source of power for industry, business, and the home.

The current growth of industrialization in the Ohio River valley depends on the turbo-generation of economical electric power. This has been made feasible by economical methods of mining coal, and its transportation by river barge. At present consumption rates, the area has a 300-year supply of coal, so turbines should be important for many years to come.

The origin and development of the steam turbine engine is quite interesting, since the steam turbine works in much the same way as does the water turbine. If you recall, the function of the hydraulic or water turbine was to convert the kinetic energy of falling water into mechanical energy. Such power from the water was achieved by permitting water from a high level to pass through the turbine to a lower level. A runner or impeller within the turbine revolved with the falling water. The amount of power and the speed of rotation was dependent on the head of the water, the volume permitted to flow through the blades, and sometimes, the angle of the blades. The steam turbine uses the kinetic and latent energy of a jet of steam.

[1] Water power produces nearly 20%, and internal combustion engines only about ½% of America's supply of electrical power.

Types of Steam Turbines

Impulse Turbines

In the steam turbine, steam at high pressure is piped to nozzles from which it escapes in a jet of extremely high velocity. This speed

Fig. 3-1. Modern Helical-Flow Impulse Turbine (Terry)

The cover has been removed to show working parts. Note the constant-speed governor on the right end of the main shaft, and the over-speed governor at the inlet flange. The view at the right shows how the turbine uses both the speed of the steam and centrifugal force as it rotates at each vane.

may exceed 4,000 feet per second. The jet of steam strikes a series of vanes or blades which are trough-shaped and positioned around the periphery of the rotor in such a way that the rotor is caused to revolve at tremendous speeds. Such engines are called *impulse turbines.*

Fig. 3-2. Branca's Steam Jet Apparatus (1629)
(© Science Museum, London)

Fig. 3-3. DeLaval Turbine (1887)
(Museum of Science and Industry, Chicago)

Fig. 3-4. Parsons' Original Steam Turbine and Dynamo (1884) (Science Museum, London)

Reaction Turbines

In some turbines, the steam is permitted to escape. In others, it is caused to flow through sets of fixed blades. These blades re-direct the flow so that it strikes against a second set of movable blades at such an angle as to give them a stronger push. Every time the steam passes through a row of blades, its pressure is reduced, and therefore its volume increases. Since all the moving blades are on the same shaft and revolve together, the successive stages must have longer blades to pass the increasing volume of steam. These turbines are called *reaction turbines.*

Compound Turbines

In some very large turbines, the *pressure drop* or the increased volume of exhaust steam becomes so great that the steam passages in the last stages would have to be impractically large. To overcome this, the expansion is carried through *two or more separate turbines* (*compound turbines*) in separate casings as in compound or multiple expansion reciprocating engines. Let us now trace the development of the steam turbine.

Development of the Turbine

In 1629, an Italian inventor, Giovanni Branca, published a description of a simple steam turbine engine. See Fig. 3-2. He wanted it to operate a small pounding mill. In this machine, a jet of steam was directed against vanes attached to the rim of a horizontal wheel using the *impulse* principle.

Many inventors have tried to harness steam energy by employing some kind of steam turbine. Kempelen of Prisberg, Hungary, in 1784, and Richard Trevithick in 1815, were two inventors who met some degree of success.

DeLaval Impulse Turbine

However, the break-through in the development of the steam turbine was made by Gustav DeLaval in 1845. See Fig. 3-3. He was seeking a means to separate cream from milk for the dairy industry using a centrifuge. He needed an engine that would develop the necessary high revolutions per minute that the centrifuge required. His studies led him to design an impulse turbine based on the principle of Branca's engine. Some of DeLaval's turbines had *many steam nozzles* located around the periphery of the rotor. These nozzles aimed high pressure steam on the blades of the rotor creating extremely high speeds.

Parson Reaction Turbine

In 1884, Charles Parsons contributed the next major development. His *reaction* turbine, shown in Fig. 3-4, was similar to DeLaval's, but he permitted the steam to expand after the initial impact but while still passing the blades. Fig. 3-5 shows the 15 sets of blades on each side of the steam entrance. This resulted in greater power because of the additional force produced by the expanding steam. Later, Parsons developed this into the *multi-stage turbine*. Each stage was composed of a rotor (a rotating ring of blades) and a stationary ring of blades. Each stage then was progressively larger to allow for the expansion of steam and its ultimate utilization of power. Fig. 3-6 shows a model of a four-stage Parsons turbo-alternator developing 50,000 kilowatts of electricity.

Let us trace the flow of steam through a Parsons turbine from the high pressure inlet. See Fig. 3-7. Steam enters at pressures in excess of 2,000 pounds per square inch. As the steam enters, it strikes the first row of blades. These are tapered with spaces between them. Steam comes from contracting nozzles with tapered, expanding outlets. These tapered outlets permit the steam to expand as it loses some of its pressure, increasing its velocity. This fast moving steam enters the next row of blades at 4,000 feet per second. These blades are attached to the rotor and part of the steam's velocity is converted into kinetic energy causing the rotor to revolve as the direction of the steam is caused to change. This first set of blades operate on the *impulse* principle.

Then the *reaction* principle is utilized in remaining stages as the moving rotor blades cause a decrease in steam pressure and a resulting increase in velocity.

Because of the shape of the stationary and rotor blades, the kinetic energy generated within the blades adds to the force turning the rotor. The steam now passes the second

Fig. 3-5. Blade Details on Parsons' Original Steam Turbine (Science Museum, London)

Fig. 3-6. Model of Parsons' 50,000 kw Turbo-Alternator at Chicago (1924) (Science Museum, London)

Note size of man. Tall tanks at near right are vertical condensers which create an exhaust vacuum.

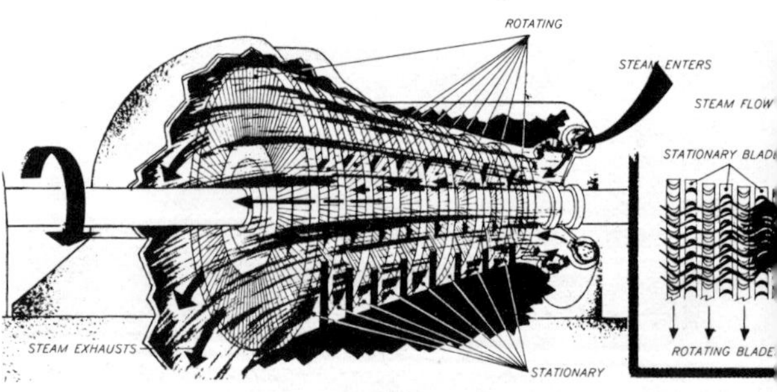

Fig. 3-7. Steam Flow in Modern Reaction Turbine (G.M.)

Fig. 3-8. DeLaval Steam Turbine with Gear Reduction (1895) (© Science Museum, London)

Fig. 3-9. 1500 kw Parsons Turbines at 1907 Power Station (Science Museum, London)

Fig. 3-10. Model of Curtis Steam Turbine (1904) (© Science Museum, London)

row of fixed blades again changing its direction. Flow continues through the succeeding alternate moving and fixed blades. To allow for the increased volume of steam as it expands from the decreased pressure, the blades are made longer and larger with wider spaces between them. The blades then move relatively faster than those nearest the inlet. This process is repeated until the maximum energy of the steam is transformed by the turbine into mechanical energy. This turbine has applications in modern nuclear marine craft and submarines as well as the compression section of the *axial-flow* jet engine.

DeLaval's turbines were usually smaller than Parsons, but attained speeds in excess of 10,000 to 50,000 rpm. Fig. 3-8 shows the reduction gears required to reduce this to usable speeds. Parsons large turbines ran at 5,000 to 10,000 rpm but with greater power. See Fig. 3-9.

Early Applications

Parsons[2] is often given credit for being the first to employ turbines for *marine transportation,* as well as for stationary use in providing *electric dynamos* with a direct source of mechanical power. His first patents in 1884 were for a reaction multi-stage turbine that he used to drive electric generators at 1,000 to 1,500 rpm. In this patent he mentioned the use of this prime mover to propel marine craft. In 1897, the first turbine driven passenger vessel was built. In 1902, the first turbine powered cruiser, the *Amethyst,* was launched.

Curtis Compound Turbine

Charles Curtis patented his first *velocity-compound turbine* in New York, in 1897. See Fig. 3-10. The Curtis turbine worked like the Parson turbine except that the steam was permitted to expand in the nozzles before reaching the vanes of the rotor. The complete expansion from the boiler to the exhaust

[2] Many consider Parsons one of the most creative engineers England has produced. He took out over 320 patents, and in 1927 was knighted and awarded the *Order of Merit* for his contributions to mankind.

occurred in a series of stages each separated by diaphragms. Each stage had a set of nozzles where steam was permitted to impart a portion of its energy to the blades of the rotor. The steam was then directed to another set of nozzles, where it expanded and passed to another rotor. Each stage was progressively larger to compensate for the expansion of the steam. Usually, there were two rows of rotors and one stationary set of blades for each set of nozzles. There was practically no expansion in the stator blades. The object of the several rows of blades was to reduce the velocity for a given speed. The velocity of the steam was reduced per pressure stage in proportion to the rows of rotors. Each pressure stage had as many velocity stages as there were rows of rotors.

Zoelly Turbine

In 1900 Dr. Heinrich Zoelly used a *modified form* of the multi-stage impulse turbine. His design had fewer stages and was very simple. It permitted increasing steam velocities in the blades. In the beginning stage, the nozzles occupied only a proportion of the periphery. Greater area was covered by them in each advancing stage until the last stage where the entire periphery was covered. The blades were shaped with a deeper root on the discharge side. This variation allowed for the loss of velocity in the blades and permitted the steam to flow without producing *eddies*. Eddies are turbulence or back pressure caused by the expansion of steam in the blades.

Turbine Design Problems

Centrifugal Force

One of the most difficult problems that had to be overcome by turbine engineeers was that of centrifugal force. The rotor of a medium-sized modern turbine may weigh in the neighborhood of 15 to 20 tons and have a rotational speed of 3,000 rpm. This makes it imperative that the rotor be correctly balanced. If, for instance, the rotor is out of balance by one pound, assuming the radius to be 4 feet, the force tending to make it vibrate amounts to more than 1½ tons. This is equivalent to the displacement of the center of gravity by 0.001 of an inch. Fortunately, these rotors can be balanced almost perfectly—something which is almost impossible to do in a reciprocating engine.

Also, at these high rotational speeds, it is necessary to form and place the blades in such a way as to prevent centrifugal force from tearing them apart. Accordingly, most rotors are provided with deep grooves—one for each row of blades. In the sides of these grooves, there are grooves that are radially cut. Each blade is given a twist as it is inserted to lock them in place. The fixed blades are similarly secured in grooves inside the top and bottom halves of the casing. Fig. 3-11 shows another method of fastening rotor blades.

Steam Leakage

To prevent steam from leaking past the ends of the rotor blades, a shrouding, shown in Fig. 3-11, is painstakingly fitted. This procedure is known as *end-tightening*. A small

Fig. 3-11. Built-Up Rotor for Steam Turbine — Blades Inset in Foreground (Westinghouse)

Rotors for turbines are either machined from solid chromium-steel forgings, or built up with individual blades, shrunk and keyed to a matching root section. The method used depends on the calculated stresses. Rotors turning faster than 8,000 rpm are usually solid forgings.

Each rotor is precision dynamically balanced after manufacture. Each is also tested at 120 percent of rated speed after it is assembled into its bearings. This results in a complete quality check on its design and manufacture.

clearance is provided between the shrouding and the casing. The stator blades are also end-tightened with a small clearance between their shrouding and the rotor. The edges of the shrouding facing the flow of steam often are sharpened. This causes the steam that does leak past the shrouding ends to become turbulent limiting additional flow. Also, if the sharpened edges were to touch the adjacent surface, they quickly wear away without causing damage.

Another critical point of the turbine concerning steam leakage is along the rotor shaft, where it passes through the casing at the inlet end. No form of packing can be employed because of tremendous rotor speeds. Therefore, what is known as *labyrinth packing* is employed. See Figs. 3-12 and 3-13. This packing has no actual contact between the shaft and the casing. The shaft is provided with a series of grooves into which knife edged rings protrude. The turbulence produced is similar in effect to that just described for end-tightening.

Journal Bearings

The main bearings of a turbine must be made in halves. One half is above and the other half is below the *journals*. The journals are the parts of the shaft which ride within the bearing surfaces. See Fig. 3-14. A bearing consists of a pair of cast iron or bronze shells that rest in a bearing block in the case or bed of the machine. In some instances, these bearings may exceed 20 inches in diameter and support a load in excess of 50 tons at 3,000 rpm.

Thrust bearings absorb end pressure on the shaft. See Fig. 3-15. There must be no metallic contact between the journal and the supporting surface, and the shaft must ride on a film of oil. To insure oil delivery, oil is delivered to the bearings by a pump which is run by the turbine. The oil supply pipeline is interconnected with the governor. In the event of a lubrication failure, the turbine is shut down automatically. In some turbines, the oil is cooled by a cooler consisting of a number of coils through which water is circulated.

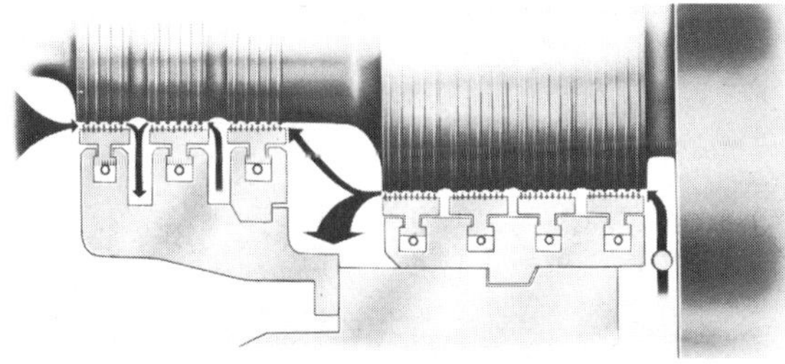

Fig. 3-12. Step-Type Labyrinth Steam Seals (Westinghouse)

Step-type labyrinth steam seals permit efficient sealing where the shaft passes through the casing, eliminating the maintenance required by solid seals.

Both the high-pressure and the low-pressure end of the turbine are sealed by step-type labyrinth steam seals. The sealing segments are spring backed. This type of mounting permits close clearance between the seals and the rotating shaft.

The glands are provided with leakoff connections, one of which (downward arrow at left) is connected to a vacuum source. This vacuum source maintains a pressure slightly below atmospheric, near the outer portion of the gland, and thereby prevents steam leakage to the turbine room even during start-up.

For condensing turbines, low-pressure steam is admitted to the seal to prevent air leaking in.

Fig. 3-13. Top of a Turbine Cylinder Showing Labyrinth Seals (Westinghouse)

The three seals in the foreground prevent leakage to outside of casing. There is also a shaft seal on each of the six rows at stationary blades to prevent leakage past blades. The steam chest is at far end.

Governors

There are two governors employed in most turbine installations. One regulates the rotor speed and prevents a "run away" rotor and ensures steady running irrespective of the load imposed on the machine. The other regulates the rotor speed, as does its mate, but it is also provided with a *manual trip-lever* in case of an emergency. The speed of the turbine is usually controlled by regulating the steam supply, and this throttle is usually oil or electrically operated, and under the control of the governor. Fig. 3-16 shows a typical governor and control throttle valve arrangement. Fig. 3-17 illustrates a much larger control mechanism.

Turbine Applications

For most *stationary installations,* turbine speeds must be reduced by reduction gearing. See Fig. 3-16. This increases the output force because of the principle of levers. In steam turbine electrical power generating stations, the turbine is connected directly to

Fig. 3-14. Turbine Cylinder with Rotor in Place
(Westinghouse)

Compare with top of casing shown in Fig. 3-13.

High-speed journal bearings are usually the babbitt lined, solid backed type, which rapidly dissipate heat. Bearing surfaces may be relieved with shallow markings to eliminate oil whip. For high speed and heavy loading conditions, a pivoted shoe type journal bearing can be used.

Bearings are sealed from the entrance of moisture or foreign materials by labyrinth type seals with felt inserts.

The thrust bearing and journal bearing covers are readily removable for inspection and maintenance without disturbing the governor or other parts of the turbine.

Fig. 3-15. Kingsbury Thrust Bearings
(Westinghouse)

Steam pressure forces the rotor toward the low-pressure end. Thrust bearings absorb this pressure in the direction of the length of the shaft and accurately position the rotor in relation to the stationary blades.

The Kingsbury pivoted-shoe type bearing, shown above, operates with a thin wedge-shaped oil film between the collar and the shoes of the bearing. The exact shape of the oil film depends on such variables as shaft speed, oil viscosity, and thrust loading.

The thrust shoes are mounted to allow free pivoting on hardened buttons. The several shoes adjust automatically to maintain proper alignment with the thrust collar by means of leveling blocks or leveling rings.

Fig. 3-16. Single-Stage Geared Turbine (opened)
(Westinghouse)

The geared turbine combines a rugged, compact speed-reduction unit solidly coupled to the turbine. This combination has the advantage of the efficiency of a high speed single-stage turbine to drive slower equipment such as pumps, fans, compressors, line shafts and generators.

Geared turbines vary in size from small 5 horsepower units to 150,000 kw turbine-generator giants.

the generator as in Fig. 3-17. The turbine shown also illustrates a tandem-compound double-flow. See also Fig. 3-18.

The turbine in *marine installations* may drive an electrical generator which in turn powers the electric motors used to turn the propeller. Sometimes gear reduction is used with clutch mechanisms to control speed. In the latter case, an additional turbine is needed to power the ship in reverse. The former installation is quite easily controlled since it is necessary to control only the electrical input to the motor that powers the ship.

Steam turbines attain maximum efficiency between 20 to 28 percent but only when run at very high speeds. Their efficiencies are a little higher than the best reciprocating systems while providing many operational advantages. Turbines can be built in larger sizes than reciprocating engines, some generating more than 160,000 horsepower.

Terms to Understand

impulse turbines
reaction turbines
pressure drop
compound turbines
Giovanni Branca
Gustave De Laval
centrifuge
Charles Parson
multi-stage turbine
Charles Curtis
velocity-compound turbine
velocity reduction
nozzle
Heinrich Zolly
eddies
centrifugal balance
end-tightening
labyrinth packing
stator blades
rotor
journals
bearing
trip-lever
reduction gearing
clutch mechanism
turbine efficiency

Study Questions

1. Compare the reciprocating steam engine with the steam turbine.
2. What is an external combustion engine?
3. Why is it important to be able to control the steam cut-off of a locomotive?
4. What are the advantages of turbines over reciprocating engines?
5. What was Giovanni Branca's contribution to the development of the steam turbine?
6. Charles Parson introduced the multi-stage turbine. Analyze its operation.
7. How did DeLaval's turbine differ from Parson's turbine?
8. What is meant by "impulse" and "reaction" turbines? Explain their principles of operation.
9. Why is the steam introduced at the small end of a turbine?
10. Analyze the necessity of balancing the rotor of a turbine.
11. List some of the critical points in the operation of a turbine.
12. Explain the principle of labyrinth packing as it is used to prevent steam leakage.
13. What are some of the operating controls employed on a turbine?

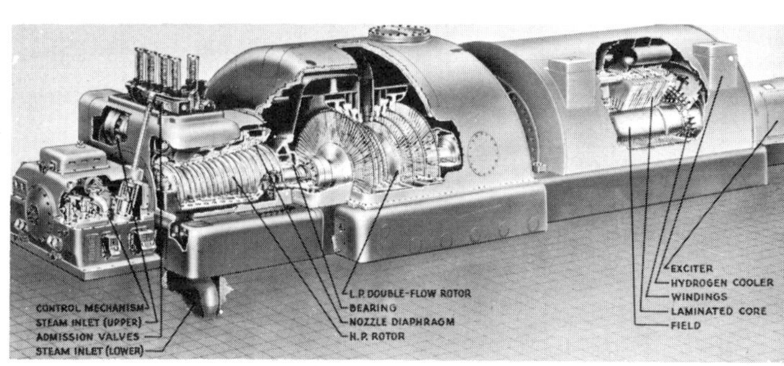

Fig. 3-17. Steam Turbine-Generator Unit (General Electric)

This is a tandem-compounded, double-flow hydrogen-cooled unit. Steam from the high-pressure (H.P.) rotor expands and is channeled to the center of the low-pressure (L.P.) rotor. Here half of the steam goes each way. The electrical generator unit is at the right.

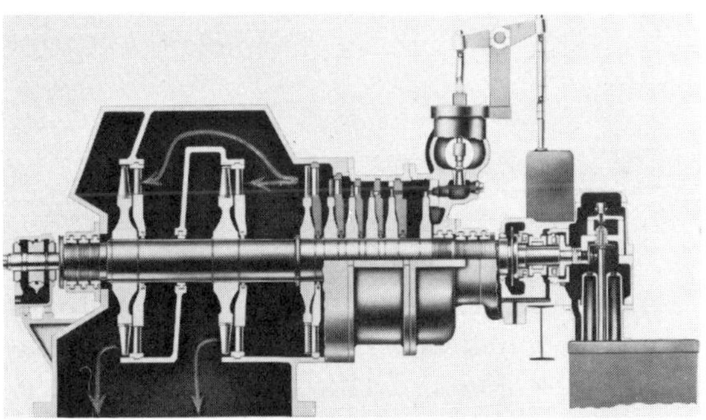

Fig. 3-18. Double-Flow Turbine (Westinghouse)

This double flow turbine is designed for high steam flow. The exhaust system of the first unit splits between two duplicate rows of blades, providing high efficiency and maximum mechanical simplicity.

The multi-valve bar lift steam chest controls the amount of steam entering the turbine. Included is a special valve and seat design for maximum part-load efficiency.

Fossil Fuel Steam Generators

The conventional *boiler* is a closed vessel in which water under pressure is transformed into steam by the application of heat. All popular present-day fuels are hydrocarbons, usually from underground fossils. Burning these fuels releases an abundance of heat energy, and the boiler must transfer this heat to the water in the most efficient manner. Most large commercial or industrial boilers are known as *steam generators*.

This chapter is devoted to steam generators fired by coal, oil, or gas. Steam generators heated by atomic reaction are explained in Chapter 6. As boiler capacity limits the amount of usable power available, technological growth closely parallels boiler development. So this chapter will also summarize some of the major effects increased power has had on the growth of technology in this century.

Fuels and Chemistry

All things are comprised of either elements or compounds. There are 103 known elements. Elements cannot be broken down without losing their identity. Compounds are combinations of elements. The smallest unit of an element is the atom and the smallest unit of a compound is the molecule. Most substances are compounds. It has been proven that elements combine in a definite and predictable fashion. In a chemical reaction, usually a metallic element combines with a nonmetallic element to form a molecule or a compound. In each of these situations, energy usually in the form of heat is either emitted (exothermic) or required (endothermic).

Principles of Combustion

When substances chemically combine with oxygen (most often obtained from the air), they release heat and sometimes light. Such a chemical change is rapid oxidation. The more rapid the reaction the more noticeable is the emission of heat and light energy. The reaction may occur so slowly that the reaction heat is not obvious. Combustion almost always produces byproducts such as water, carbon dioxide, or carbon monoxide. If the combustion is not chemically complete, particles may be emitted and these are commonly referred to as *pollutants*.

Heat of Combustion

The heat given off per unit weight of fuel is known as *heat of combustion*. The heat produced is a uniform value for any specific fuel.

Calorific Value of Fuel

All heat engines convert heat energy into mechanical energy. Their efficiency is determined by the proportion of heat supplied as compared to the mechanical output or the useful work done. This heat is obtained by the combustion of some fuel, i.e. coal, oil, gasoline, gas. The heat produced by one pound of fuel is referred to as its *calorific value*. To calculate the total heat supplied to an engine, the weight of the fuel used during a certain period of time should be multiplied by its calorific value.

When the exact chemical composition of any fuel is known, it is possible to estimate its calorific value if the chemical equation for combustion is figured. This estimate is for complete combustion.

Characteristics of the Ideal Boiler

1. Simplicity of construction combined with excellent workmanship, using materials which give low maintenance, highly efficient heat transfer or insulation, and the necessary structural strength—all at moderate initial cost.
2. Good water circulation with sufficient space for steam and water.
3. A fire box for efficient combustion of fuel and maximum rate of heat transfer.
4. Elimination of expansion and contraction difficulties by the proper placement of expansion joints.
5. Accessibility for easy maintenance and repair; standardization of parts.
6. Responsive to overloads and sudden demands.
7. An adequate safety factor.
8. Delivery of clean steam.

Heat Transfer Methods

A steam generator may be considered a heat transmission and control system. The transmission of heat requires a knowledge of methods by which heat moves. The kinetic molecular theory has been used to explain this phenomenon.

Since matter is made of atoms and molecules that are constantly in motion, it is believed that these collide with each other, and that when this happens energy is transferred by momentum or impact. As the temperature of the substance is increased, the molecular action increases causing the molecules to strike with greater force and frequency. The kinetic energy that causes increased molecular movement is transferred from one molecule to another.

There are three ways heat is transferred to water: radiation, conduction and convection. The percentage of the heat coming from each depends upon the boiler design. These are illustrated by the three types of arrows in Fig. 4-1.

Radiant heat travels in rays directly through space from a hot to a cold body, and depends on the temperature difference and the color of the body which receives the heat. This absorption increases with temperature difference, with darker colors, and with area exposed. Reflectors change direction of radiant heat travel.

Heat absorbed by *conduction* is that heat which is transferred from the source to the tube by direct physical contact. It depends on the conductivity, or heat carrying qualities of the materials through which the heat must pass. Heat insulation conducts heat poorly.

Convection heat is carried from hot to cold body by movement of the conveying substance. The hot boiler gases convey heat to various boiler tubes containing water, as the gases rise through the boiler.

In a boiler, all three forms of heat transmission occur simultaneously and they cannot be divorced from each other. If the boiler is not properly arranged and insulated, much heat

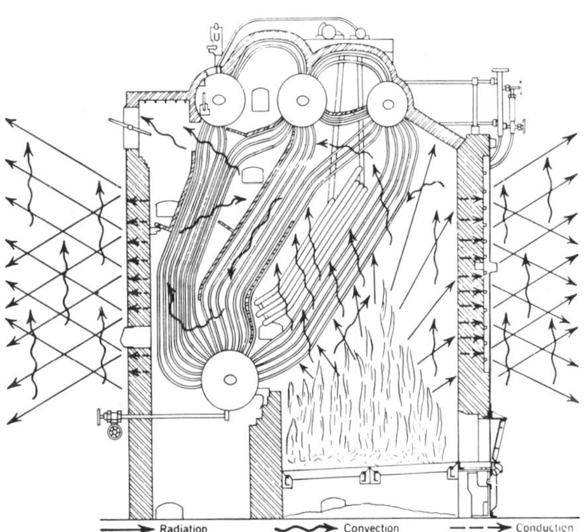

Fig. 4-1. Heat Transfer in a Boiler (Johns-Manville)

Fig. 4-2. Vase Shaped Roman Water Heater of Cast Bronze (© Science Museum, London)

is lost by convection up the stack, radiation and convection to walls, conduction through the wall, and radiation and convection outside the wall.

Primitive Boilers

The steam boiler dates back to before the invention of the steam engine, even earlier than the cauldron beneath Hero's reaction turbine of 1,900 years ago shown in Fig. 2-1. The first boiler was probably a cooking pot made of copper. In the ruins of Pompei, which was destroyed by Vesuvius in 70 A.D., a water heater was found with an internal fire box, which had a small side door through which fuel was fed. Its *fire grate* was made of water tubes. Fig. 4-2 shows another Roman

Fig. 4-3. Model of Haystack Boiler (1850) (© Science Museum, London)

Fig. 4-4. Waggon Boiler (1769)

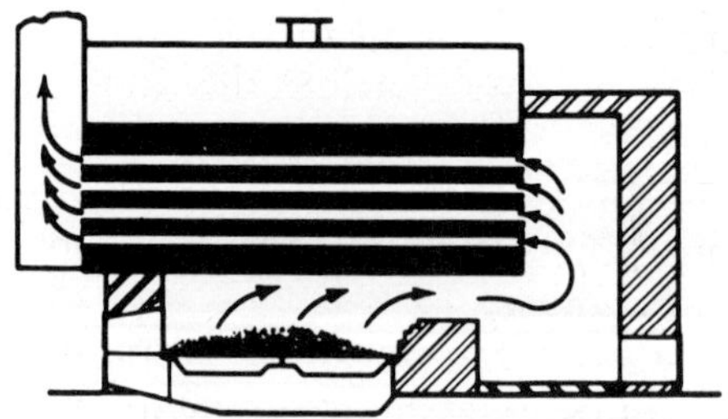

Fig. 4-5. Fire-Tube Boiler

water heater, in which water surrounded the bed of coals.

The *shell boilers* of the last century were essentially a large enclosed kettle filled with water and heated at the bottom. These boilers were not very efficient and often acquired their names from their shape: the haystack, beehive, wagon, or balloon boilers. See Figs. 4-3 and 4-4. Their inefficiency and dangers prompted many to seek a design that would be safer and more efficient. To improve efficiency, it was necessary to increase the surface of water exposed to the heat source.

This was done in two new designs. First, the *fire-tube boiler,* shown in Fig. 4-5, permitted hot gases to flow through tubes surrounded by water. Second, the *water-tube boiler,* shown in Fig. 4-6, permitted the hot gases to flow around water-carrying tubes.

Early Fire-Tube Boilers

Early attempts at increasing boiler efficiency involved using internal flues such as employed in the cylindrical Cornish boiler. Later, more flues were used as found in the Lancashire boiler.

Cornish Boiler

Along with the design of the *large single-flue boilers* for locomotive use, a similar boiler was designed for stationary use to supply steam for pumping engines in the Cornish tin mines. The Cornish boiler, Fig. 4-7, is a long cylindrical vessel almost completely enclosed in a setting of refractory brick work. The flue gases travel from the firebox along the single flue to the back of the boiler. Here they divide and return along the side flues to the front end. A single flue under the shell then carries them to the chimney.

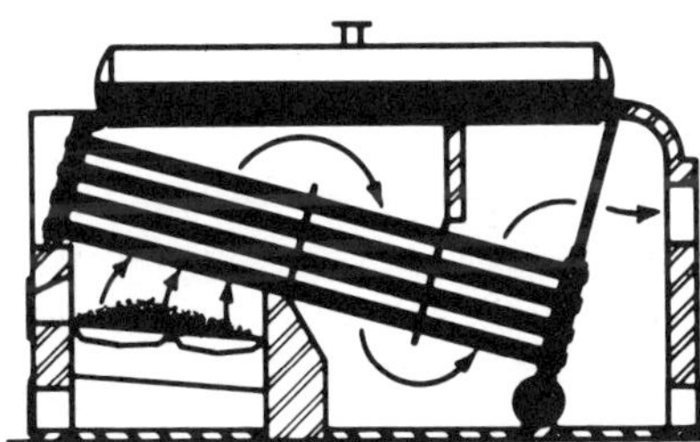

Fig. 4-6. Water-Tube Boiler

Lancashire Boiler

Similar to the Cornish boiler in construction was the Lancashire boiler. However, two flue tubes and fire boxes were fitted into the cylindrical shell. Additional heating surface was provided by *cross tubes* called *Galloway tubes,* see Fig. 4-8. A variant of this boiler was the *Yorkshire Boiler.* It had a flue increasing in diameter toward the rear, permitting better heat distribution throughout its length.

In 1804, Richard Trevithick designed a *return-tube boiler,* see Fig. 4-9. The success of this boiler led to the design, in 1826, of a *multi-tubular* boiler that permitted the products of combustion to pass through a nest of

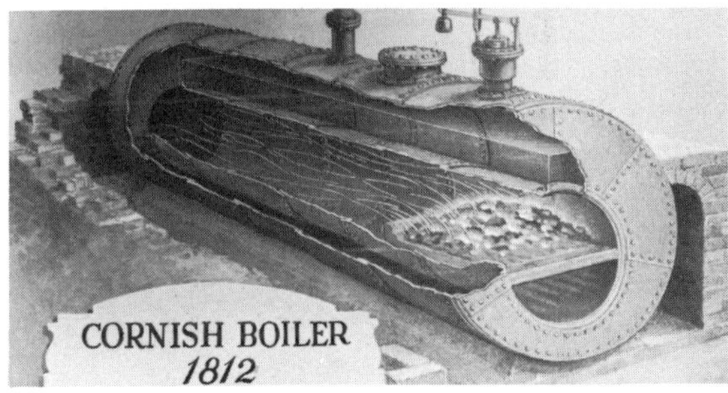

Fig. 4-7. Cornish Boiler (1812)

Fig. 4-8. Model of Galloway Boiler and Setting (© Science Museum, London)

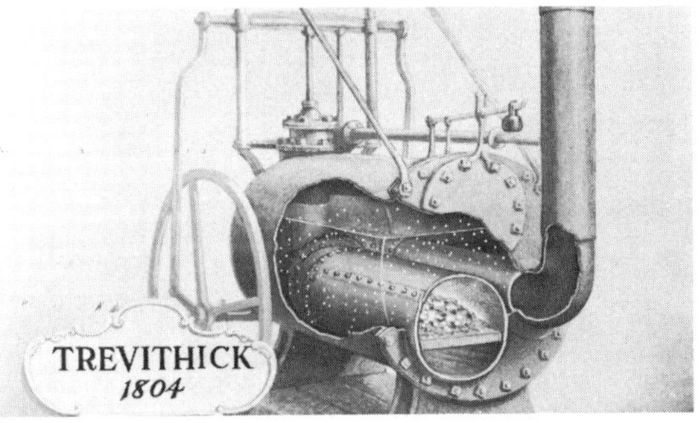

Fig. 4-9. Trevithick Horizontal-Tube Boiler (1804)

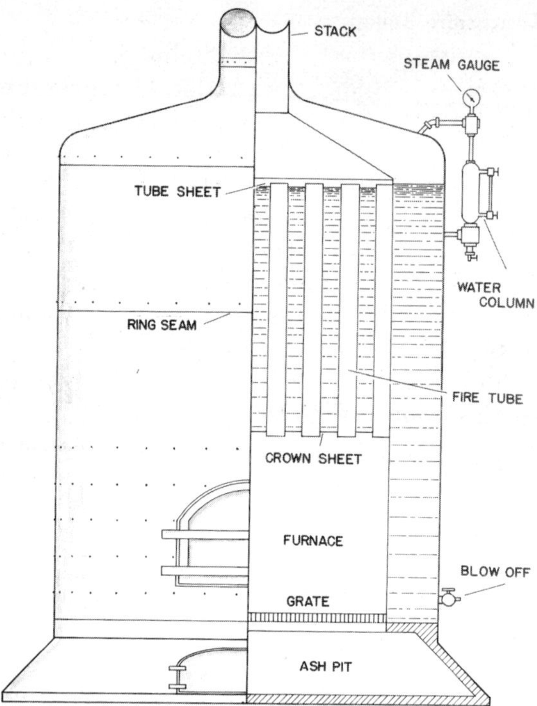

Fig. 4-10. Submerged-Tube Type, Vertical Fire-Tube Boiler

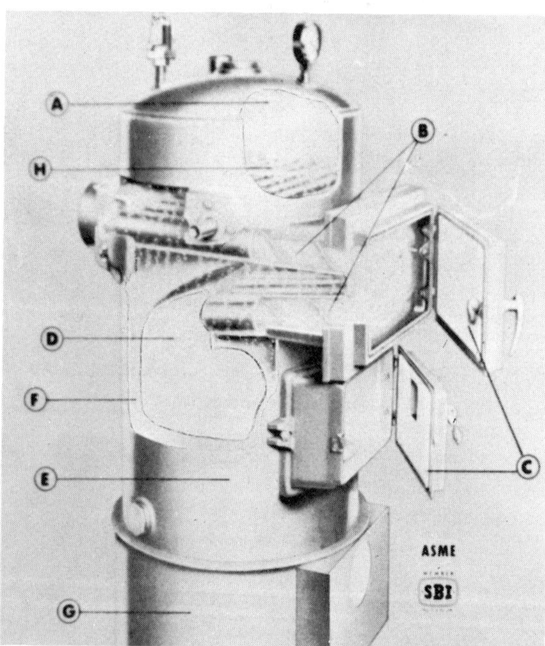

Fig. 4-11. Firebox Type, Horizontal Fire-Tube Boiler (ASME)

(A) Steam, (B) Fire Tubes, (C) Inspection and Clean-Out Doors, (D) Firebox, (E) Shell, (F) Water Jacket, (G) Base for Burner, (H) Hot Water Heater

tubes surrounded by water. George Stephenson was first to use this type of boiler in the *Rocket* at the historical locomotive trials held in Rainhill in 1829. The multiple fire-tube boiler became identified with successful locomotive applications.

Modern Fire-Tube Boilers

Today, fire-tube boilers are classified as *vertical, locomotive,* or *horizontal.* They are also classed as either internally or externally fired, determined by the location of the combustion chamber.

Vertical Fire-Tube Boilers

A vertical fire-tube boiler is shown in Fig. 4-10. It consists of a cylindrical shell with an enclosed firebox held together with *stay bolts.* Tubes extend from the *crown sheet* above the firebox to the upper *tube sheet.* The holes in each sheet receive the ends of the tubes which are *rolled* or beaded over them. The sheet is firmly held between the rolled bead on the tube (inside) and its flanged end outside. These boilers are of two types, the *exposed tube* and *submerged tube,* as determined by the normal water level.

Since boilers of the vertical tube type are usually portable, they are used for hoisting devices, tractors, and shovels, as well as for small stationary plants. They range in size from 5 to 75 boiler horsepower. Their tubes are from 2 to 3 inches in diameter, having pressures up to 100 psi, diameters from 3 to 5 feet, and heights from 5 to 15 feet.

Locomotive-Type Boilers

As boilers are an integral part of the steam locomotive, they are explained near the end of Chapter 5, and only special construction details are given here. Locomotive-type boilers are constructed with a long cylindrical shell fronted with the rectangular firebox. The entire furnace is surrounded by a water jacket. It is fastened to the furnace sheet by stay bolts to the shell of the boiler. In this boiler, an elaborate use of *stay bolts* is required.

The locomotive-type boiler is self-contained and requires no setting. It is limited in size, and sometimes the firebox volume is increased to improve operations and efficiency. The rear end of the firebox comprises one sheet and the other sheet is at the end of the cylindrical section. The tubes are rolled into the tube sheets and flared over. The boiler is built in sizes up to 250 boiler hp, 350 psi of pressure, with 2 to 4 inch diameter tubes. They allow the hot gases to pass through directly to the *stack*. Locomotive boilers are most economical and more rapid steamers than vertical boilers, but they are inaccessible for cleaning, inspection, and repair.

Horizontal Fire-Tube Boilers

These have the tubes carrying exhaust gases arranged horizontally or nearly so. Horizontal fire-tube boilers are of several kinds, the most common being the *firebox type unit*, Fig. 4-11, and the horizontal return tubular boiler (HRT).

The *horizontal-return tubular boiler* has a long cylindrical shell suspended conveniently on the side walls of the furnace. Legs set on rollers permit expansion and contraction. Sometimes these boilers are suspended by means of hangers from overhead beams. In this arrangement, the problem of expansion and contraction proves no hardship on the brick foundation and reduces maintenance. Ends are connected to the boiler by either riveting (the old method) or fusion welding (the more modern method). The required length of the boiler is sometimes obtained by joining several smaller units together.

The boiler setting includes grates, bridge wall, and combustion space. The grates are set under the front end of the boiler. Products of combustion are made to pass between the bridge wall and shell to the rear end of the boiler. Gases return through the tubes to the front end of the boiler, where they connect to the smoke box, connecting two stacks.

The economic boiler and the Scotch marine boiler are both variations of HRT boilers. These will be covered individually.

The economic boiler is a type of horizontal fire-tube boiler where the lower tubes are shorter and end in a tube sheet at the rear of the furnace. See Fig. 4-12. Gases pass from the furnace on the updraft principle: hot gases rise to the rear, return through the upper tubes to the stack. The shell of the boiler is fastened by straps or seams to secure the desired length of boiler. This type of unit is considered more economical in the burning of fuel than the standard HRT boiler.

Tubes and flues are used chiefly as a means of increasing the heating surface. In addition, they give considerable strength to the unit. Sizes below an external diameter of four inches are usually referred to as *tubes* and those above a four inch external diameter are referred to as *flues*.

Tubes are usually rolled into position by means of an expander and then *headed* (flanged) over. Flues are riveted into position. The various sizes of tubes and flues depend to a degree on the fuel burned, tube spacing, staggering, and circulation.

These boilers are often used in stationary installations with flues ranging from 1½ inches to 6 inches in diameter, shell casing from 3 feet to 10 feet in diameter, and lengths from 10 feet to 20 feet, and pressures from 25 to 175 psi.

Fig. 4-12. The Economic HRT Boiler
(American-Standard)

The Scotch marine boiler, another type of HRT boiler, is self-contained, requires no setting and is internally fired. It has the same characteristics of the HRT boiler, but requires less space and headroom. See Figs. 4-13 and 4-14. The shell is cylindrical and contains the tubes and firebox. Most Scotch marine boilers were hand stoked originally, although today many are mechanically stoked or use oil. They range in diameter from 3 to 8 feet, in lengths from 4½ to 18 feet, with working pressures from 50 to 200 psi, and up to 350 hp in size.

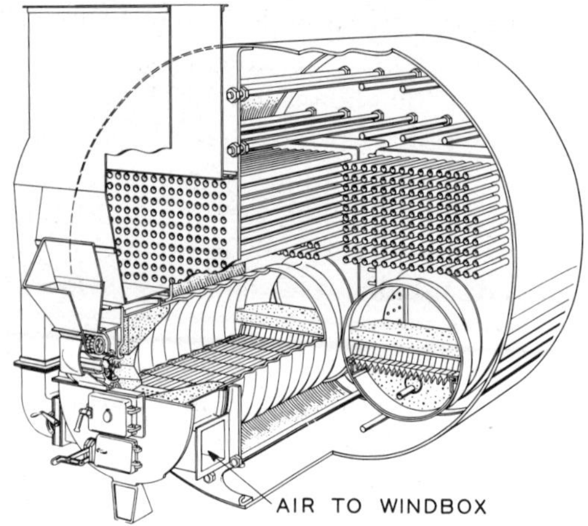

Fig. 4-13. Scotch Marine Boiler (Combustion Engineering)
Fired with a spreader stoker and fitted with two furnaces, this boiler has two separate combustion chambers. Tubes are used as flues for returning the products of combustion from the combustion chambers to the smoke box, covering the upper front of the boiler.

Fig. 4-14. Modern, Medium Sized Fire-Tube Boiler (Ames Iron Works)
This modern, medium sized fire-tube package boiler is one of about a dozen such models made in this country today. They are essentially Scotch marine type boilers with minor modifications, and are complete with all burning equipment, safety controls and standard steam trim. When connected to utilities they are ready to operate. Their compact size, high efficiency, and ease of installation receive acceptance throughout the country and the world.

To summarize, contemporary fire-tube boilers permit the hot gases from the furnace to flow inside steel tubes, approximately 4 inches in diameter, with the water surrounding them. See Figs. 4-13 and 4-14. They employ a drum which serves the purpose of allowing the steam bubbles to be separated from the mass of boiling water, assisting in the delivery of nearly-dry or dry steam. The drum usually surrounds the nest of tubes whose ends are rolled into flat tube sheets. The tubes serve to brace the tube sheets and can be only 20 to 25 feet in length due to structural limitations. Boilers of this type are low in initial cost, are compact, require small headroom, do not require elaborate and costly settings, are easy to clean, and are easy to assemble. But their limitations of 200 to 300 lbs psi and output capacities of only 25,000 to 30,000 pounds of steam per hour restrict them to the smaller installations.

Early Water-Tube Boilers

In 1776, William Blakey improved the Savery engine and included in his patent a novel form of steam generator which is probably the first step in the development of the water-tube boiler. In his boiler, shown in Fig. 4-15, several tubes were alternately inclined at opposite angles with their adjacent ends connected by small pipes.

The first successful user of water-tube boilers was James Rumsey, an American inventor. In 1788, he patented in England several forms of boilers including some of water-tube variety. One of his designs employed vertical tubes, similar to those made at the present time.

The water-tube boiler devised in 1804 by John Stevens made use of small tubes connected at one end to a reservoir as shown in Fig. 4-16. This boiler was actually used to generate steam for the engine of a steamboat operating in the Hudson River. It was not very successful, but it was the forerunner of many such *porcupine boilers.*

The first *sectional water-tube boiler* was designed and built by Jules Griffith in 1821. It had horizontal water-tubes connected to vertical side pipes which in turn were connected to horizontal *gathering pipes* and these were connected to the steam drum. This principle laid the groundwork for modern-day sectional boilers.

The first sectional water-tube boiler with well-defined circulation was built in 1825 by Joseph Eve. See Fig. 4-17. The section consisted of vertical water tubes that had a slight curve. These tubes were connected to a steam drum above and a water space below. The steam and water spaces were connected by outside pipes to insure cycle circulation of the water through the sections and down the external pipes.

In 1826, Goldsworthy Gurney built a number of boilers for use on steam carriages. His boiler design is shown in Fig. 4-18. Small U-shaped tubes were laid sideways and their ends were connected with larger horizontal pipes which in turn were inter-connected by vertical pipes to permit circulation. They were also connected to a vertical cylinder which served as a steam-water reservoir.

In 1856, Stephen Wilcox proposed a major advance in boiler design. His design, shown in Fig. 4-19, incorporated *inclined water tubes* connecting water tanks at the front and rear with steam space above the water level. This permitted better water circulation and more heating surface. His design was inherently safer as well as being more efficient

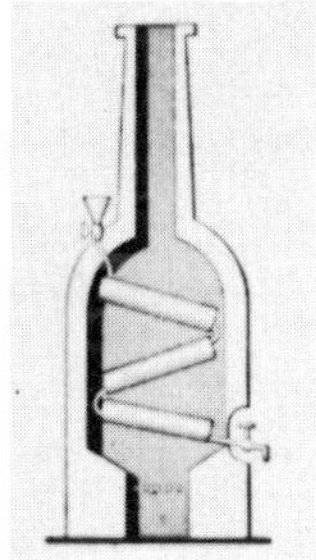

Fig. 4-15. First Water-Tube Boiler, by William Blakey (1766) (Babcock & Wilcox)

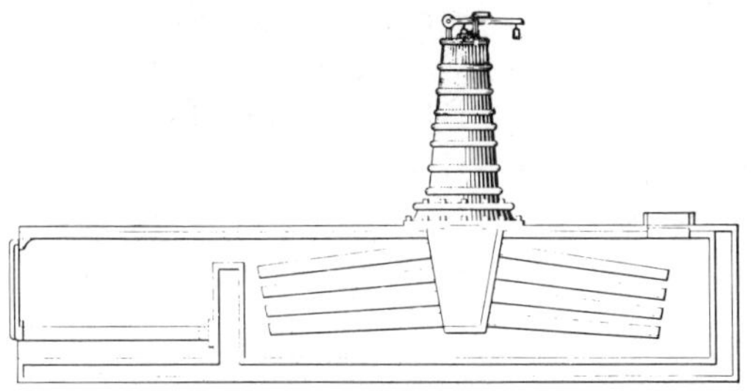

Fig. 4-16. Stevens Marine Water-Tube Boiler, Porcupine type (1804) (Smithsonian Institution)

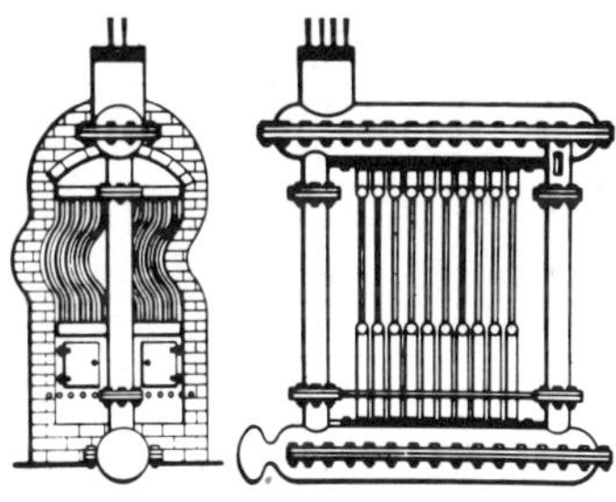

Fig. 4-17. First Sectional Water-Tube Boiler with Well-Defined Circulation, by Joseph Eve (1825) (Babcock & Wilcox)

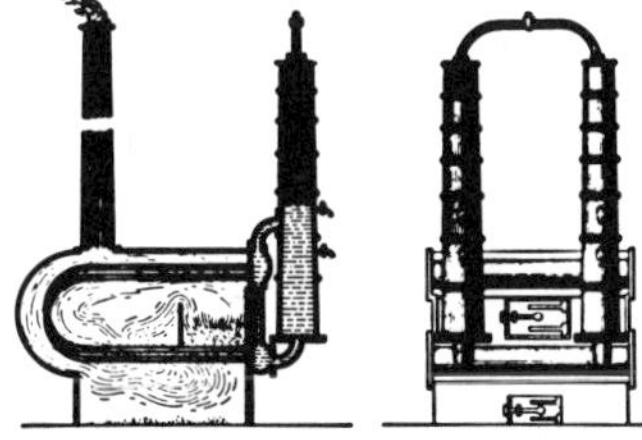

Fig. 4-18. Water-Tube Boiler with Small Tubes Connected at Front by Goldsworthy Gurney (1826) (Babcock & Wilcox)

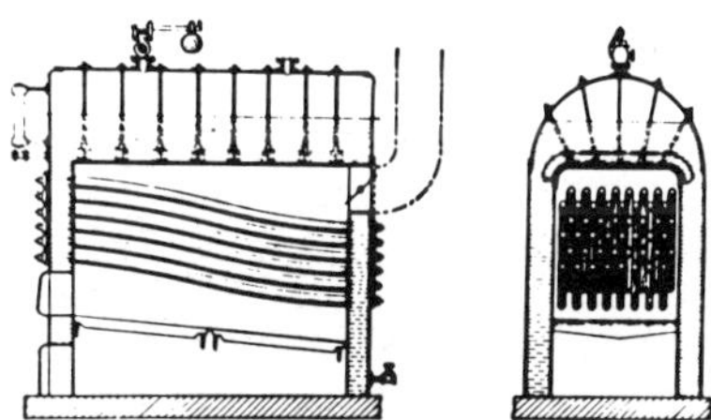

Fig. 4-19. Wilcox Inclined Water-Tube Boiler with Complete Circuit (1856) (Babcock & Wilcox)

than any other steam generator of its day. This prompted its wide acceptance. Soon there were other similar styles, Fig. 4-20.

To summarize, tubes for water or steam are relatively small compared to fire tubes, and their thickness is not necessarily excessive even for extremely high pressure systems. The boiler capacity is readily increased by making tubes longer and adding more of them. Drums can be held to reasonable dimensions and are protected from excessive heat. The water tube principle had cleared the way for the modern era of large high-pressure and high-temperature steam power plants.

Power Brings Modern Era

On September 4, in 1882, Thomas A. Edison opened his Pearl Street Central Station in New York City, see Fig. 4-21. When he ordered the switch thrown here, he ushered in the *age of the cities* by initiating a versatile *power transmission system*. On that day, four water-tube boilers (much like the one in Fig. 4-25) were used to generate *steam energy*. This steam was converted to *mechanical energy* by a steam engine, and the mechanical power was used to generate *electrical energy*. The electrical energy was easily distributed to users over transmission wires. This history-making station opened with 59 customers using about 1,300 incandescent lamps. The boilers at the installation consumed five tons of coal and 11,500 gallons of water daily. These boilers remained in constant use under severe conditions for twelve years until 1894.

As cities expanded in size, real estate values sky-rocketed. New engineering skills, materials, and developments such as the elevator, Fig. 4-22, made it possible for man to build upward. Electricity for the trolley car, Fig. 4-23, took man along the streets with the

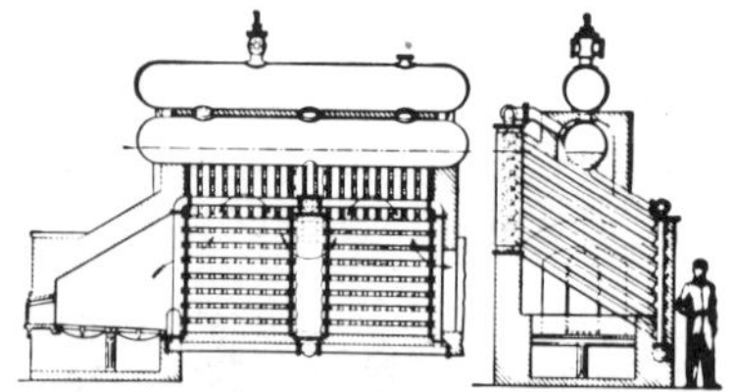

Fig. 4-20. First Water-Tube Boiler with Inclined Tubes in Sectional Form, by Twibill (1865) (Babcock & Wilcox)

Fig. 4-21. Model of Edison's Original Commercial Station for Generating Electric Current

Fig. 4-22. Otis Hotel Elevator—Shown in "Scientific American" (1881)

Fig. 4-23. Early Street Cars Using Power from Overhead Wires

same ease that it took him upward in elevators or lighted his place of work.

The consolidation of business enterprises in the city pushed housing areas to the outskirts of population centers. The trolley now became more important and in many instances charged its way over vacant land to create suburbia. Trolley demands and the need for light prompted the development of many central power stations. Electrical energy was soon used to power many phases of American life.

At the turn of the century, industrial accomplishments on a vast scale had advanced the United States among the world powers. The wheels of American industry now spun faster, improving our standards of living, while, in addition, supplying other countries. The need for technical knowledge swelled the number of students enrolled in colleges from 114,000 to nearly a quarter of a million between 1900-1914.

Aggressive expansion became the hallmark of American industry. The further increase in steam pressures was restricted by the limitations of the reciprocating steam engine. Increase in world trade and demands for more products, prompted industry to look for an efficient alternative to the reciprocating engine. Fortunately, the state of the art of steam generation was sufficiently advanced to be ready for the *new power age* introduced by the *turbine.*

The steam turbine rapidly gained prominence as the major steam-powered source of rotary motion. It offered low cost maintenance, greater overloading tolerance, fewer moving parts and smaller size, which were only a few of the major advantages of the turbine over its predecessor.

Modern Water-Tube Boilers

Modern high-pressure and high-temperature steam power plants typically use some form of a water-tube boiler. These can be classified as *vertical, vertical inclined,* or *horizontal.*

Vertical Water-Tube Boilers

The vertical water-tube boiler usually has two tube banks, separated by a baffle of brick, tile, or steel. Tubes are rolled into the steam and water drums on each end. Hot gases pass over the first bank of tubes creating a water circulation which causes a downward flow in the rear bank of the tubes. This positive circulation is not evident in the fire-tube boiler of vertical construction.

The boiler is supported by lugs fastened to the lower drum with the water feed entering the lower steam drum. These boilers are recognized for their simplicity and ease of inspection and cleaning with pressures from 50 to 225 psi and sizes up to 450 boiler hp or even higher in modern variations. Note in Fig. 4-24, the vertical water-tube arrangement in the larger boiler integrated into a water cooled furnace.

Vertically Inclined Water-Tube Boilers

This boiler is built in a number of designs to meet various requirements. The essential features, however, are very similar.

In 1902, eight Babcock and Wilcox boilers were used to supply steam for the first utility plant completely equipped with steam turbines. Fig. 4-25 shows a model of one of these vertical inclined boilers. It is similar in design to those used in the 1882 Pearl Street station except for extra pipes at the center to superheat the steam after it left the drum. This produced a hotter dryer steam. These 508 hp boilers, the largest built at that time, operated at 180 psi of pressure at a temperature of 530°F, powering each of the 35,000 kw turbines first installed. The station was a

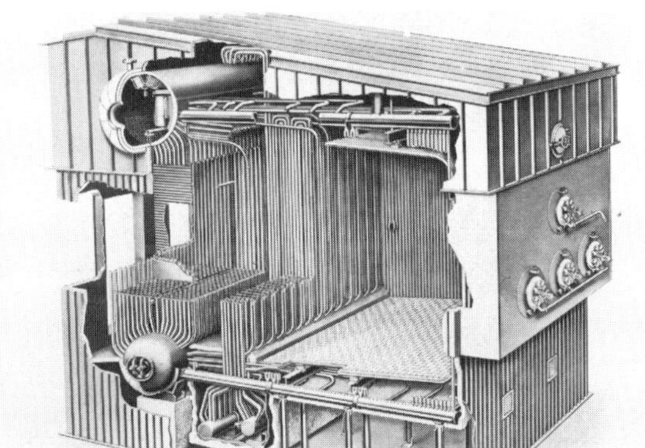

Fig. 4-24. Integral Furnace-Boiler with Superheater (center) (Babcock & Wilcox)

success and proved beyond a doubt the feasibility of turbine power. Its electrical power was sufficient to supply about 40,000 modern homes.

Fig. 4-25. Model of Babcock and Wilcox Boiler, with Addition of Superheater
(© Science Museum, London)

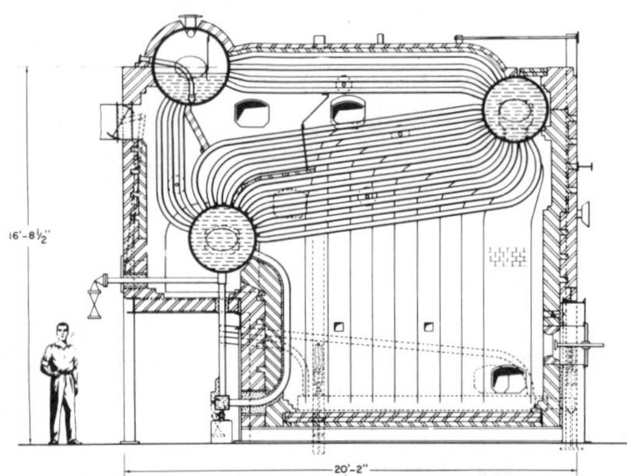

Fig. 4-26. Stirling Three-Drum Boiler
(Babcock & Wilcox)

Fig. 4-27. Stirling Four-Drum Boiler Showing Typical Curved Tube Construction
(Babcock & Wilcox)

By 1906, the *Stirling Boilers* became prominent because of their ability to meet sudden load demands with dry steam even when using poor feed water. See Figs. 4-26, 4-27, and 4-28. Their continuous and economical production of steam was accomplished in low headroom installations.

The basic Stirling design has three drums set crosswise. Upper *steam drums* are connected to a lower *mud drum* (where sediments may collect) by inclined tubes. These tubes have a curved shape at the ends so as to enter the drums radially. *Steam circulators* connect all drums while *water connectors*

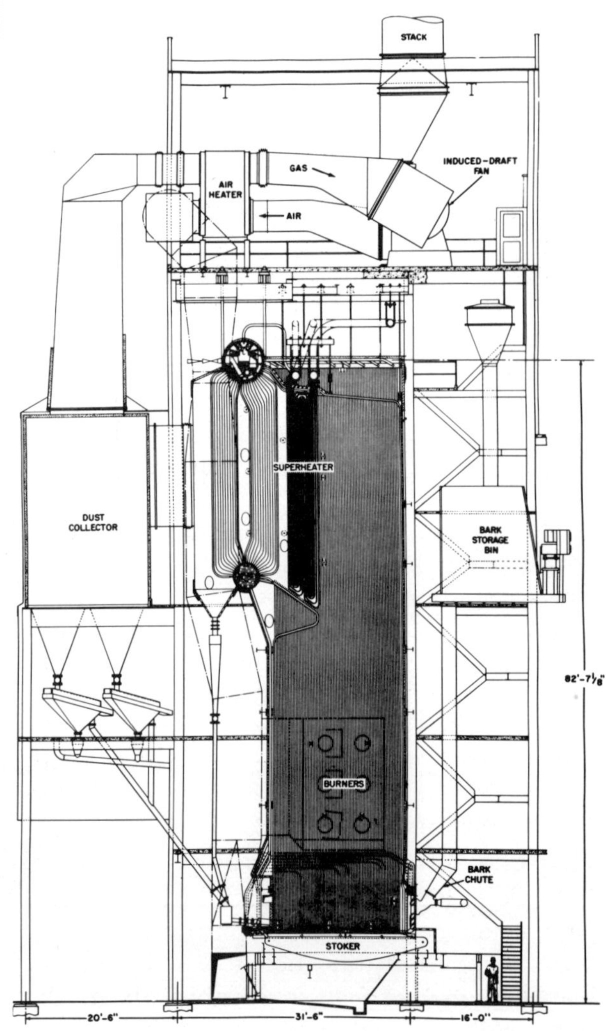

Fig. 4-28. Modern Two-Drum, High-Head, Stirling Boiler at International Paper Co., Moss Point, Miss.
(Babcock & Wilcox)

connect the first two drums. Steam is drawn from the uppermost drum through a *dry pipe*.

The size of the steam drum is the same as that of the mud drum or slightly larger. The upper drums are supported at the end by lugs resting on steel beams. The mud drum hangs free and is suspended by the tubes. The tubes comprise the entire heating surface with the exception of a small amount of drum surface. Baffling is so arranged that approximately 75% of the absorption takes place in the first bank of tubes. After the water leaves the trough it flows down the rear bank of tubes to the mud drum replacing that which was evaporated in the front section.

The steam generated in the first pass goes to the middle drum where water and steam are separated. The *dry pipe* permits the generated steam to pass to a rear drum before it goes to the steam line. The evaporated water in the second bank is replenished directly from the mud drum. Boiler drums range in size from 36 to 54 inches in diameter with units from 200 to 3,000 hp.

In general, these *vertically inclined boilers* are simple in construction, have independent expansion of parts, are fairly rapid steamers, and are easily cleaned and repaired. They usually have excellent circulation and require less headroom than vertical boilers.

Horizontal Water-Tube Boilers

These are often small cast iron sectional boilers as used in apartments, offices, and school buildings, see Fig. 4-29. They are self-contained and simple in assembly. Because of their sectional construction, they are frequently used where space limitations prevent the installation of other types. The unit is

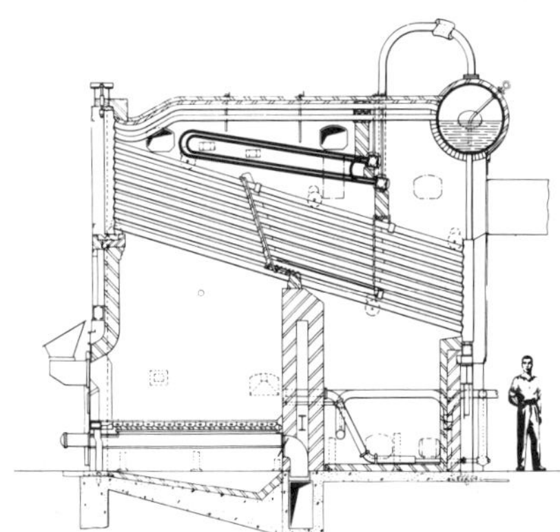

Fig. 4-29. Horizontal Water-Tube Cross-Drum Boiler (Babcock & Wilcox)

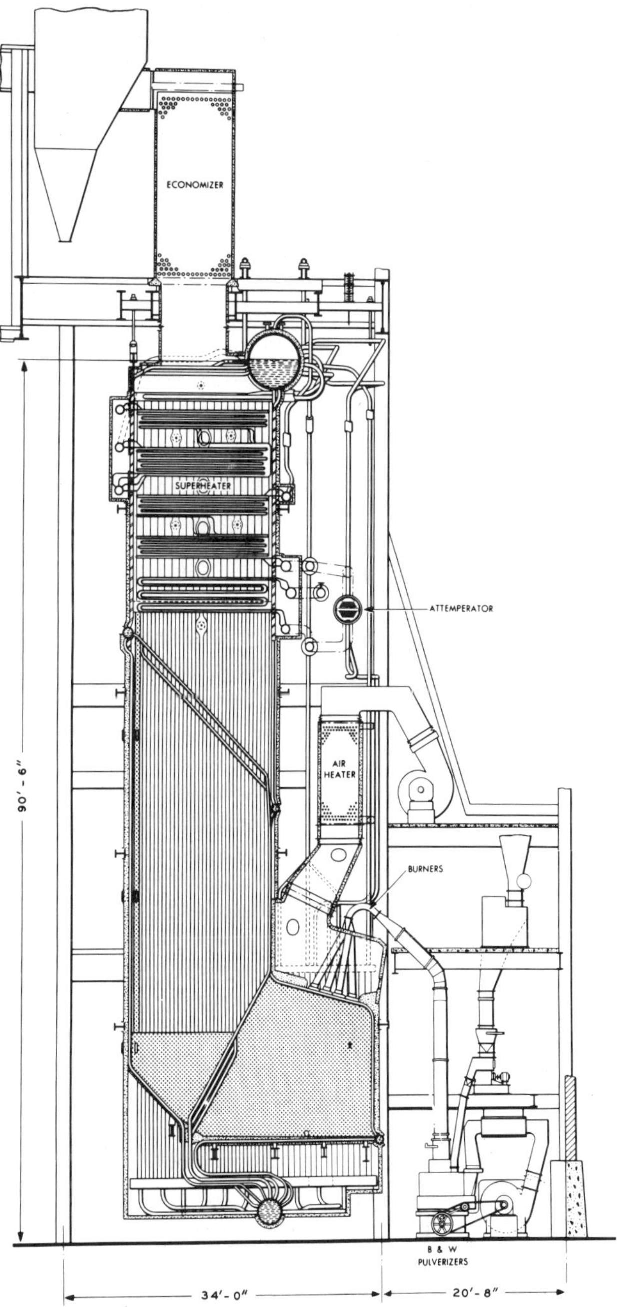

Fig. 4-30. High-Head Cross-Drum Boiler (Babcock & Wilcox)

compact, requires a minimum of space, and meets low headroom requirements. It is usually a small four-pass horizontal-tube boiler which, because of its compactness, is rather difficult to service and maintain.

The *high-head boiler* shown in Fig. 4-30 is another variation of the horizontal water-tube type. These may have the steam drum arranged either parallel with the tubes, called a *longitudinal drum,* or at right angles to the tubes, called a *cross drum.* Tubes are expanded into vertical *water legs* or *box headers* at each end of the tube, with the water legs held by hollow stay bolts and connected to the shell by flanged and riveted joints.

The drum is supported to provide for expansion and contraction. The mud drum is located inside the steam drum. It consists of a long trough into which the feed water passes. The feed pipe enters the front end and emerges from the rear head. Tubes are 3 to 4 inches in diameter with drums 2 to 4 feet in diameter. The length of the drum is 15 to 20 feet. High-head boilers have capacities upward from 100 hp.

Horizontal-drum water-tube boilers may have inclined or vertical headers and most are sectional in construction. The tubes are staggered with respect to each other, and are flanged into headers. Each downtake and uptake header is connected by seamless tubes. The drums usually range from 30 to 60 inches in diameter. The steam drums are usually fitted with an *internal feed pipe, steam baffles,* and *dry pipes.*

Water leaves the drum and passes through the *rear headers,* up the tubes to the *front headers,* to the *circulators,* and back to the steam drum. The liberated steam returns to the drum where it passes to the dry pipe and out to the *superheater.*

These units are built in any size up to 25,000 sq. ft. of heating surface with pressures from 100 to 1,500 psi, with tubes from 1½ inches to 4 inches in diameter. These boilers are rapid steamers, have good circulation, are responsive to overloads. They are safe because of their sectional construction and free from expansion and contraction difficulties. In general, they are easy to repair, maintain, and inspect.

Developments During World War I

Major marine boiler improvements were realized during World War I. The lightweight 3-drum boiler proved invaluable in powering Navy destroyers of that time. This crucial time saw the first *mass production* of boilers. In some marine installations, because of the weight and size limitations imposed, high steam output was realized by employing two or more boilers.

Boiler development was not limited to the maritime alone. Stationary boilers also provided power in huge quantities.

Research, too, went forward solving problems in *caustic embrittlement* or metal fatigue aggravated by higher pressures. It was during these years that *economizers* were first manufactured. An important aid in boiler efficiency, this preheater consists of a bundle of tubes located in the flue gas stream flowing from the exhaust stack. Boiler feedwater passing through the economizer absorbs heat which would otherwise be wasted.

Improvements of the 1920's

The twenties too often are associated with the dramatic symbols of stock ticker tape, the rum runner, and the raccoon coat. More enduring, however, and more significant, were the developments that took place in American industry. Of these, the availability of power was doubtlessly a major factor in sparking an unprecedented national prosperity. America was now using nearly as much electricity as the rest of the world put together. Developing power resources were a tremendous factor in making possible American economic leadership. Sixty-one percent of all telephones were to be found in the United States. Of 27,500,000 automobiles in the world, 22,000,000 were American owned.

The growth of national power capacity to meet the various needs of industry stimulated the development of a variety of boiler *equipment, accessories and controls.*

Larger Boilers

The ever-expanding need for more electrical power in industry and in the home resulted in rapid developments in *central station design.* Higher steam pressures and temperatures promoted higher efficiencies from the coal expended. By 1925, boilers were designed to produce 1400 psi of pressure at 750°F and consumed half as much fuel as boilers designed and produced only 8 years before.

Major changes in boiler design and construction occurred in the late twenties. Previously, as stations increased in capacity, the practice was to increase the number of boilers but this became uneconomical. Boilers were then made *larger and larger,* and soon more efficient means had to be provided to supply and burn the fuel.

Higher Temperatures

The new, larger units with the higher heat release rates and greater wall heights placed a burden on fire brick which proved to be structurally unsafe. Also, the high heats and the fused ash caused deterioration of the brickwork through erosion.

Water-cooled boilers, pioneered by the Bailey Meter Company, overcame these problems. In these water-cooled furnaces, some of the tubes forming the circulation system of the boiler are extended downward along the walls of the furnace. This is easily seen in the unit in Fig. 4-24. There they are in the active combustion zone and the water absorbs the intense heat resulting from the burning of pulverized coal (or other fuel) with forced air. The circulating water not only cools the wall but also the absorbed heat generates steam.

The success of these installations led others to be built eliminating much brickwork and maintenance problems. They permitted greater capacity in less space by having much of the heat-absorbing surface around the furnace. By cooling the gases before they enter the boiler bank or superheater, the water-cooled walls also reduced other operating problems.

The *Stirling H Boiler,* Fig. 4-31, was introduced in 1929 to answer the need of industries for a relatively small unit to fit where headroom was limited.

Firebrick then became the source of major concern. Research proved *Kaolin* a suitable material. Kaolin is a white clay with a high degree of refractoriness, (heat resistance), purity, and uniformity. This aluminasilica brick was soon put into process furnaces of the petroleum, chemical, glass, and steel-making industries. Central power installations and marine boilers also used Kaolin.

Automatic Furnace Controls

The next logical step was to develop *automatic controls* to hold optimum furnace conditions. A load increase or decrease causes the boiler steam pressure to fall or rise. The control device causes air and fuel supply to be changed to restore the pressure to normal. Exact changes in load demand are met as the steamflow-airflow meter continuously adjusts the air supply to match the rate of fuel supply for the most economical operation.

Equipment designed to reduce the problems of operating and maintaining boilers became increasingly important as the size and complexity of equipment continued to increase.

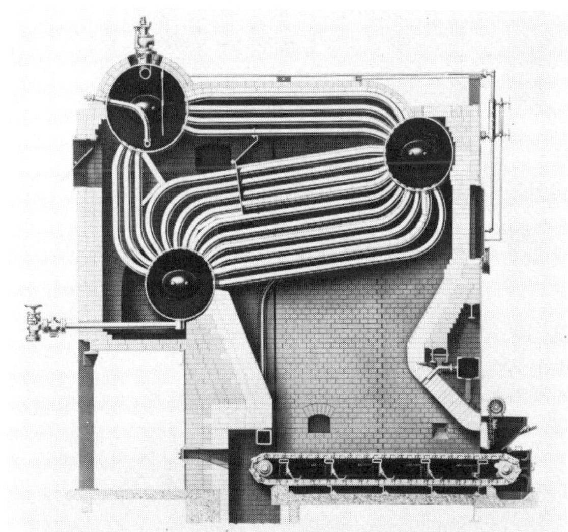

Fig. 4-31. Stoker-Fired Stirling H Boiler Lined with Insulating Firebrick (Babcock & Wilcox)

By 1928, fabricating techniques and the *greatly improved metals* were employed in making boiler tubes. This resulted in better and more efficient boilers for less overall cost.

Improvements of the 1930's

The early thirties were disappointing in contrast to the expanding economy of the twenties. Our economy had taken its worst setback. However, out of these annealing years came a tougher America with an economy that proved reassuringly resilient.

The depression, on the industrial scene, was an ill wind that blew some good. It did intensify emphasis on efficiency and a higher yield for the dollar invested.

In the power field, the accelerated search for economical energy was to bring forth developments of far reaching results. This decade saw the introduction of many significant improvements in steam generating equipment for stationary and marine application; pressures rose to 2,500 psi with temperatures as high as 960°F in many steam generators.

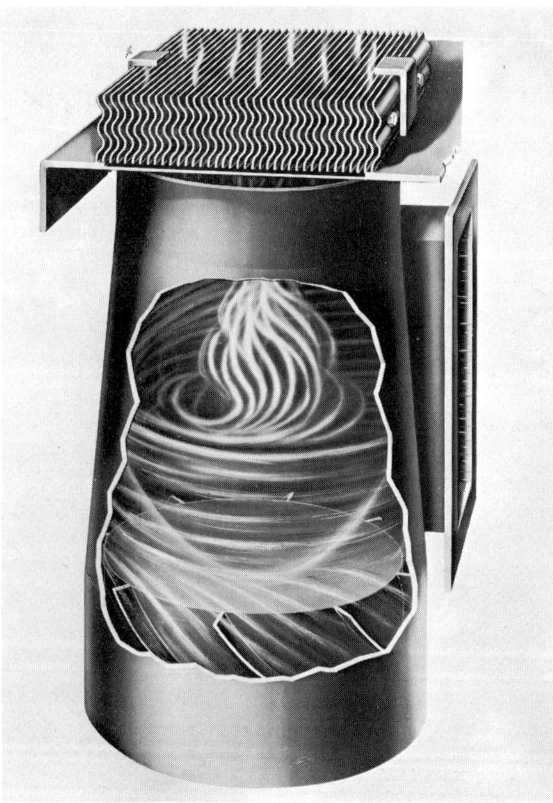

Fig. 4-32. Cyclone Steam Separator Whirling Out Moisture and Impurities (Babcock & Wilcox)

Boiler Fabrication Improved

A major obstacle, the fabrication of the boiler drum, appeared as boiler capacities and pressures increased. The standard method of joining boiler plates was by lapping and riveting, often above the water line. These might be reinforced with butt straps around the drum, or extra strengthening collars. This structural method made a heavy drum that required constant inspection and costly maintenance. The greatest limitation was that riveted construction could not be used on plates thicker than 2¾ inches because no satisfactory method was known of securing a tight joint. This placed severe limitations on the pressure for which the boiler could be designed.

Welding techniques were beginning to improve. Acceptable testing procedures had to be developed that would guarantee the drum without destroying it in the test. After extensive research, it was decided that the x-ray machine could be used to examine the welds. This combination of x-ray examination and improved welding techniques, insured a sound *fusion-welded* power-drum.

Integral Furnace

The need for medium capacity boilers led to the development of a cost saving and efficient boiler similar to the larger steam generators which had water cooled furnaces. This new unit offered the advantages of compactness, low maintenance, and fuel savings and was quickly accepted by industry. It was capable of being fired with stokers or pulverized coal and the then newer fuels, gas and oil. See Fig. 4-24. The *integral furnaces* as they became known, were made available for a wide range of operating conditions from about 5,000 to 350,000 pounds of steam per hour with pressures to 1050 psi at 910°F.

Some industries, such as the paper industry, nurtured the development of a *waste heat* type boiler that recovered the heat and chemicals from paper pulp mill wastes. Note bark chute in Fig. 4-28.

Steam Separator

A new plateau in power progress was the development of the *cyclone steam separator*. Shown in Fig. 4-32. Installed in the boiler drum, the separator used the energy in the steam and water mixture to literally whirl the water and impurities out of the steam. This device made possible the design of natural circulation boilers of high pressure operation. *Pure, dry,* and *clean steam* up to this time was not possible in high pressure systems. The impurities in steam, even in small quantities, caused deposits to build up on the turbine blades requiring constant maintenance and cleaning.

Improvements of the 1940's

The end of the thirties and the beginning of the forties saw the development of the *open-pass* and *radiant boilers* for large central stations. Fig. 4-33 shows the various elements of a radiant-type boiler. Both types are employed in large installations to produce capacities in excess of 300,000 pounds of steam per hour at 1200 to 2200 psi.

Soon after these boilers had been introduced, the *single-boiler, single-turbine* units became the accepted type of installation in central stations. Units of this type were expected to run a year or more without requiring down time for repairs.

The success of the fusion welded boiler spread to *marine boiler design* which opened the way to higher steam pressure without prohibitive weight. The increased installation efficiency demanded higher pressures and temperatures to obtain the optimum power from the turbine. This increased the cruising range as well as speed obtainable from a given fuel supply. To meet the increasingly congested conditions aboard marine craft and still retain the advantages of superheat control, a two-furnace single-uptake type boiler was developed. It operated at pressures in excess of 580 pounds at a temperature of 825°F.

Light Firebrick

A firebrick weighing one-eighth to one-fourth as much as ordinary firebrick combining high heat resistance was developed next. This brick was designed to satisfy the Navy requirements for a light refractory brick that could withstand direct exposure to high temperature furnace gases and at the same time serve as efficient insulation. Their use made it possible to design furnaces with light, thin walls, less supporting steelwork, and lighter foundation. In addition, the low heat storage of insulating firebrick was of great value to many industries which demanded intermittent operation of oil or gas fired furnaces. These furnaces could now be heated and cooled quickly, saving time and fuel.

Marine Boilers

World War II created a demand for marine boilers for the Navy and merchant ships. Production increased from two or three boilers a week to more than 30. From 1942 to the end of the war, approximately 5,400 major steam-powered vessels were built. Of the

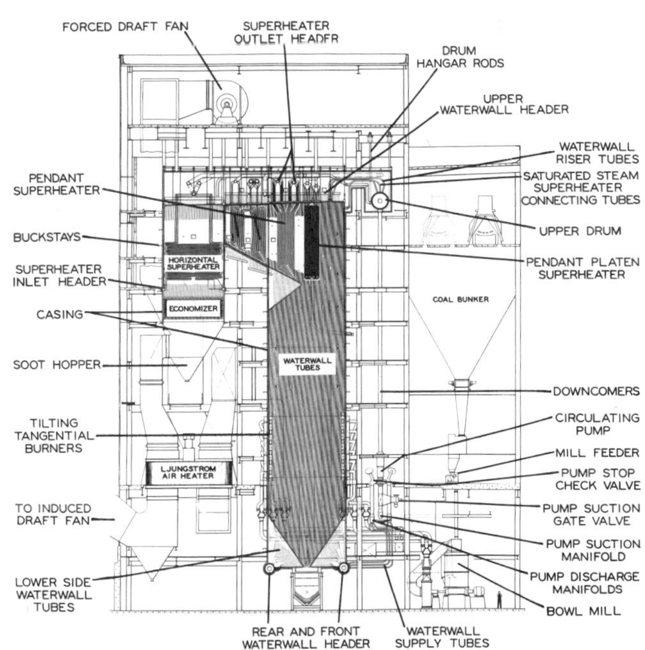

Fig. 4-33. Controlled Circulation Boiler, Cyclone Fired (Combustion Engineering)

boilers in these, only 1800 were not built by Babcock and Wilcox. See Figs. 4-34, 4-35, and 4-36.

To give some idea of the progress realized in marine boiler developments, the boilers used for vessels in the super-carrier class, the *Midway, Coral Seas,* and *Franklin Roosevelt* could generate enough power for a city with a million population. These ships carry enough fuel oil to heat 3,000 homes a year.

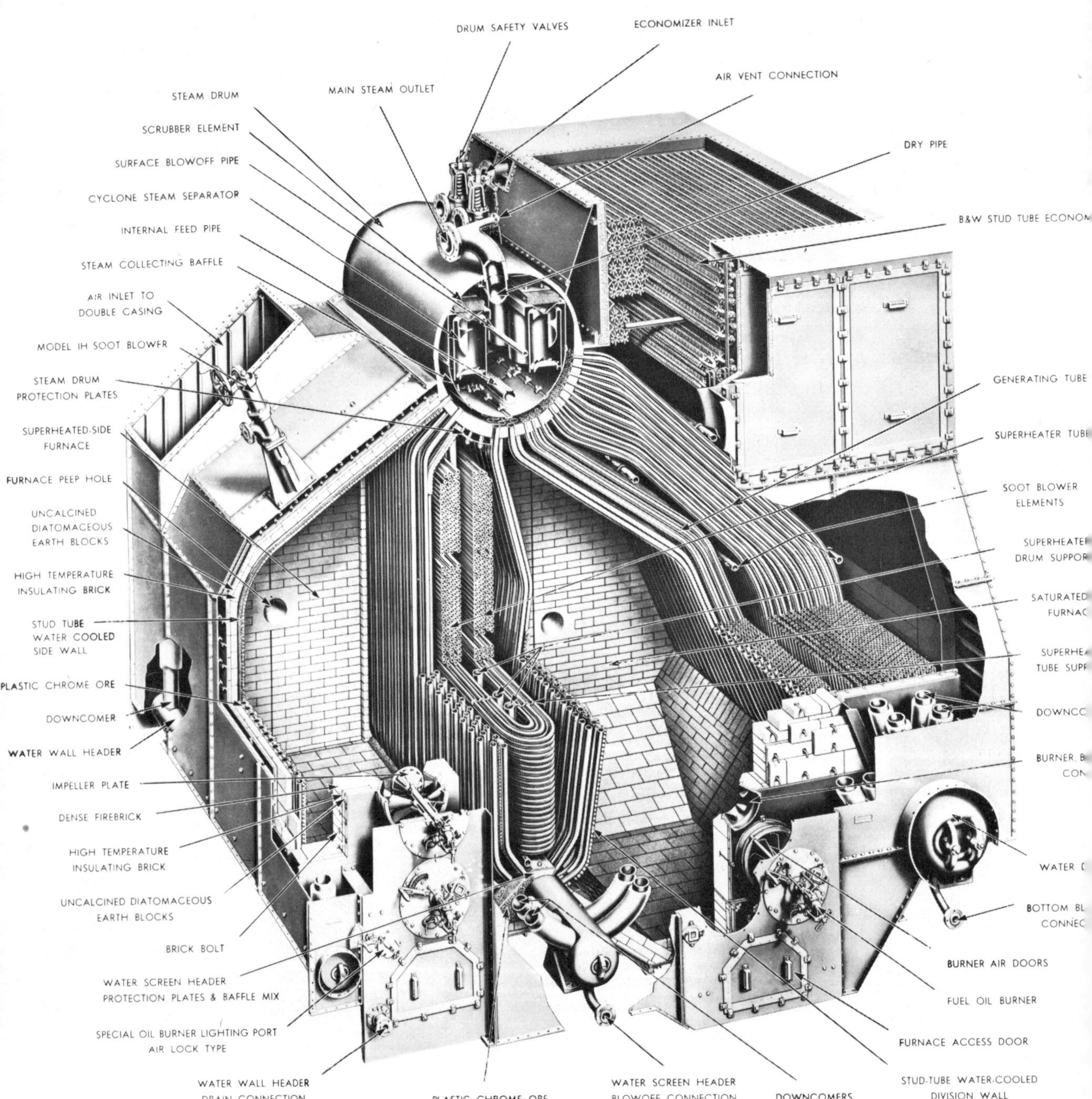

Fig. 4-34. **Single-Uptake Controlled-Superheat Marine Boiler** (Babcock & Wilcox)

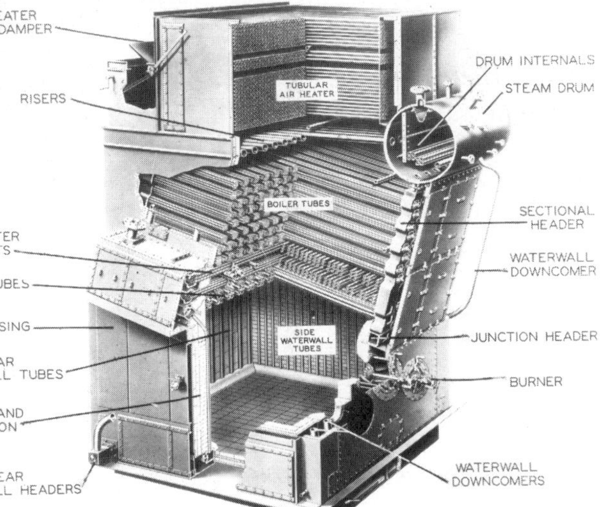

Fig. 4-35. Marine Sectional Header Boiler (Combustion Engineering)

Marine engineers adapted various types of water-tube boilers to fit into the restricted space available on shipboard.

One of the early water-tube boilers was this cross-drum type which had generating tubes extending between a row of rear headers arranged vertically and connected to the drum, and a row of uptake headers at the front of the boiler.

The design was ideally suited for mass production and was on many Liberty Ships in World War II.

The boiler shown was designed for capacities up to 150,000 pounds of steam per hour and pressures to 850 psi.

Fig. 4-36. Marine Boiler with Vertical Superheater (Combustion Engineering)

After World War II, boiler designs were modified to meet the high temperature and pressure demands of the larger engines, as a means of achieving more profitable operation.

Two of these boilers were usually installed. Each was designed for a normal evaporation rate of 43,000 pounds of steam per hour at 600 psi and 855°F at the superheater outlet. The boiler was 88% efficient.

Improved Efficiency

An important part of the wartime effort of boiler manufacturers was to increase the efficiency of boiler operation and public utilities. See Figs. 4-37, and 4-38. This was done to give more power to the nation at a time of crisis. There was an increasing necessity to use low-quality high-ash fuels for generating steam and for keeping most of the coal ash in the furnace, instead of permitting it to go up the stack. This prompted the development of the cyclone furnace.

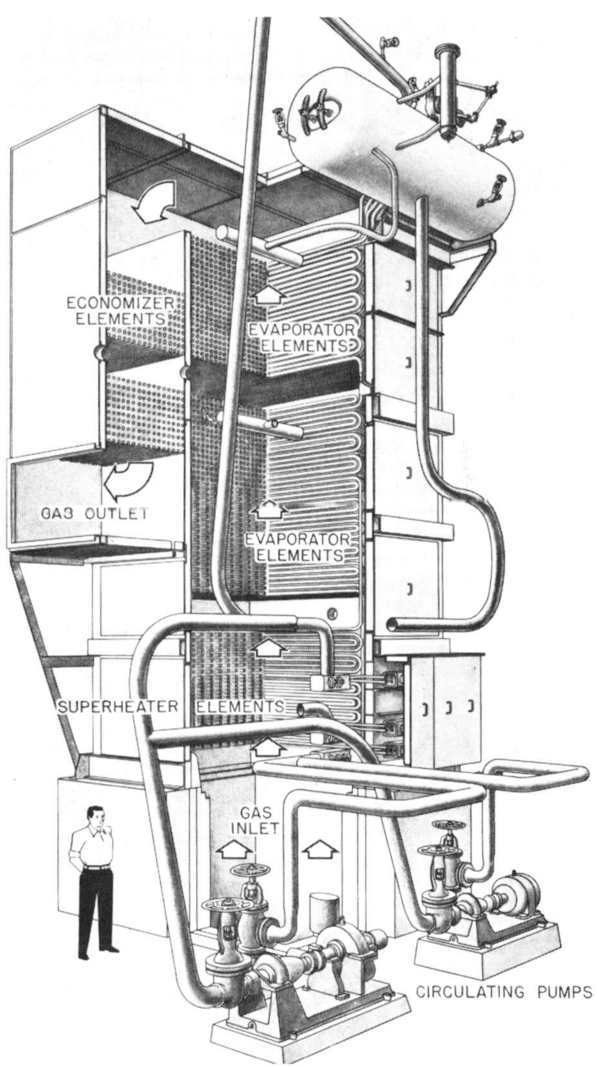

Fig. 4-37. Controlled Circulation "Waste Heat Boiler" to Reclaim Heat From Open Hearth or Chemical Process (Combustion Engineering)

Fig. 4-38. Chemical Recovery Unit
(Combustion Engineering)
This waste heat chemical recovery unit burns black liquor, a residue from paper pulp operations, and recovers pulping chemicals while generating large quantities of steam. The water-cooled low maintenance installation uses a secondary tangential air system for better furnace turbulence. The absence of baffles and widely spaced tangent-tube panels permit access for cleaning by retractable blowers.

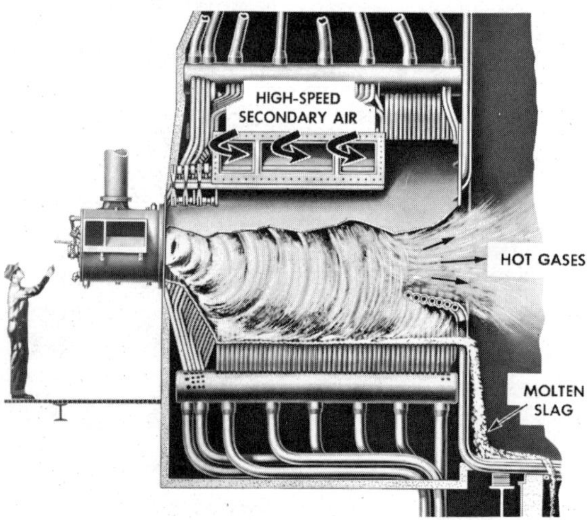

Fig. 4-39. The Cyclone Furnace
(Babcock & Wilcox)

The *cyclone furnace,* Fig. 4-39, gave more functional furnace design, improved operating conditions with *reduced air pollution.* Increased turbulence gave better combustion and caused slag to drop away from heating gases. These advantages were obtained with reduction in capital and operating costs.

It must be realized that all industries in the country were part of a team to produce materials for the war effort. Boiler, tube, and refractory manufacturers, in addition to making their specialties, were engaged in making and developing many other components of metal, ceramic, and rubber. This development permitted tremendous industrial expansion that later was to permit a higher postwar standard of living. The signing of the treaty on the *U.S.S. Missouri* in 1945, released the tremendous energies that had been directed to the production of war materials for a new purpose—buildings, automobiles, white shirts, swimming pools, transistors, air conditioners, penicillin, fertilizers, and plastics.

Fig. 4-40. Modern Power Generating Station with Several Single-Turbine, Single-Boiler Combinations

Developments After World War II

The pent-up desires for peacetime goods were released in a surge of buying keeping industry engaged in satisfying demand. Although this vast growth was accompanied by a doubling of living costs, standards of living increased.

On the engineering front, important developments occurred with boiler design. Larger turbines were developed.

Today, *single-turbine, single-boiler combinations* as in Fig. 4-40, are producing several times as much electricity as was formerly produced by a generating station with many boilers.

Fig. 4-41. Controlled Circulation Twin-Furnace Reheat Boiler (Combustion Engineering)

This *boiler* is representative of integrated units which collectively meet all the capacity, pressure, temperature and fuel burning requirements of the electric utility industry. The tilting action of the tangential burner system is illustrated. In one furnace the burners are tilted upward and in the other, they are tilted downward. Such action provides superheat and reheat temperature control. The man standing on the platform is six feet tall.

These units are capable of 800,000 to 3,850,000 pounds of steam per hour, at pressures of 1450 to 5,000 psi and steam temperatures from 1000 to 1200°F. They are designed for indoor or outdoor construction, natural gas, pulverized coal, or oil firing and single and twin furnace design.

Recently, important developments have been made in the progress toward the production of electricity at the lowest possible cost. These involved the development of *subcritical pressure* steam generators. See Fig. 4-41.

A pressure of 3,206 pounds is known in engineering as the *critical* pressure. Water in a boiler operating at this pressure does not bubble or boil as it converts to steam, but changes instantaneously from water to steam when it reaches 705°F. Such a boiler has no drum for collecting steam and water, but is composed of a system of groups of independent, continuous tubes. Water is forced under pressure into one end of the system of tubes and comes out the other end as super-heated steam. Since forced-flow, (*once-through* or *one-pass*) boilers, could be operated either above or below critical pressure. Babcock & Wilcox refer to it as a *universal pressure boiler.* See Fig. 4-42. Combustion Engineer-

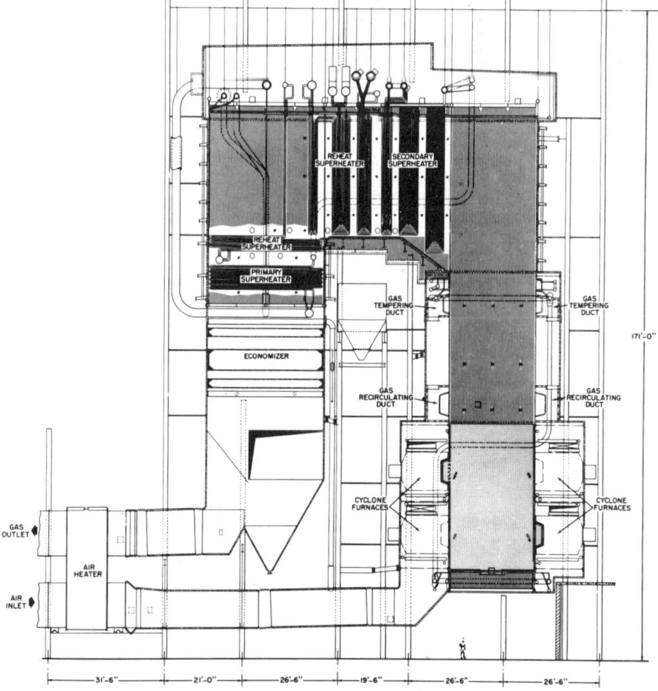

Fig. 4-42. Universal Pressure Boiler (Babcock & Wilcox)

ing's supercritical boiler is referred to as the *combined circulation unit.* These two corporations produce 80 percent of the stationary and steam generator plants.

Supercritical Universal Boilers

Typical of these new *supercritical universal boilers* are the following installations:

One of the first constructed was the Philo Plant of the Ohio Power Company on the American Gas and Electrical Systems. This unit delivers steam at 4,500 pounds pressure at a temperature of 1,150°F to the turbine, generating 120,000 kilowatts of electricity.

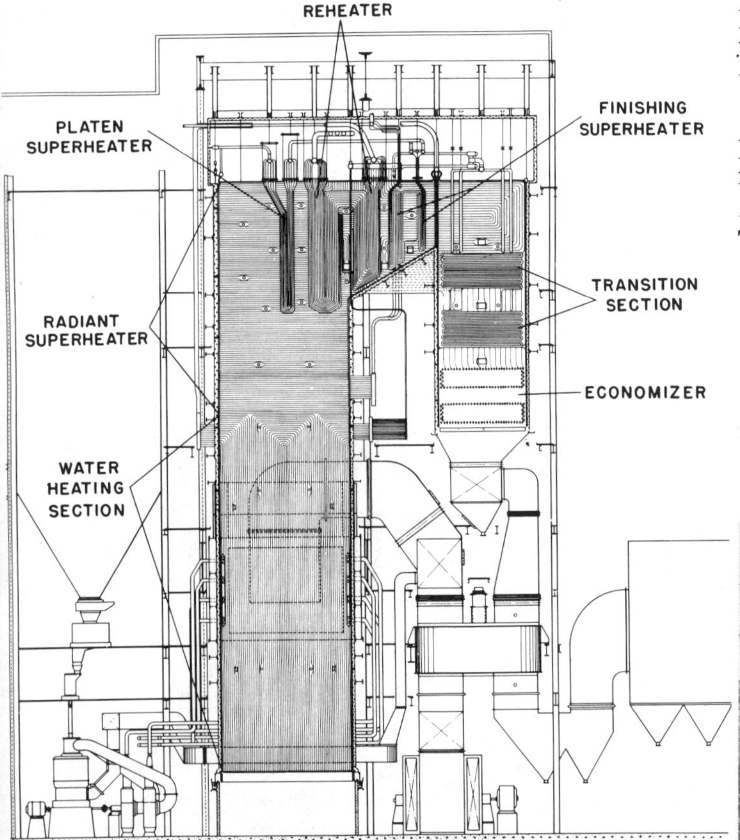

Fig. 4-43. The Avon Monotube Steam Generator (Combustion Engineering)

This unit uses pulverized coal in its dual furnaces which are corner fired, using tilting tangential burners. The unit will deliver 1,715,000 pounds of steam per hour to the turbine throttle at 3,500 psi and 1100°F with a single reheat to 1050°F. The boiler has no drum and is of the forced-circulation once-through type.

Cleveland Avon Station

Another *monotube* or *once-through* boiler was employed at the *Avon Station* for the Cleveland Electric Illuminating Company. This unit was placed in operation on December 18, 1959. See Fig. 4-43. It contained a number of innovations in the design of the steam turbine which was made of *ferritic steel.*[1] Main stream inlet conditions of 3515 psi pressure and 1100°F temperature demanded that the turbine components be constructed of *austenitic*[2] or ferritic materials.

Since being placed into operation, the performance of the plant has exceeded all expectations. Newer materials and operational practices that demanded more costly fabrication techniques were justified because of the thermal gains economically.

The turbine generator, a tandem-compound single-shaft unit operates at 3,600 rpm. See Figs. 4-44 and 4-45. It is rated at 215,000 kw with a capability of 250,000 kw. The steam flows from the turbine main stop

[1] 2.25 percent chromium, 1 percent molybdenum, .25 percent vanadium.

[2] Austenitic steels are very expensive and difficult to fabricate to the turbine. They contain carbon in solid solution at room temperature, are tough, non-magnetic, and work-harden rapidly when cold worked, yet change characteristics at higher temperatures.

Fig. 4-44. Turbine-Generator, a Tandem Compound Single-Shaft Unit, at Avon Station (Westinghouse)

Notice the super and very high-pressure turbine on right and high-pressure, intermediate, and low-pressure turbine to its left.

valves through the following units in order: super pressure (SP) and very high pressure (VHP) elements, to the boiler reheat stage, back to the high pressure (HP) turbine element, the intermediate pressure (IP) and low pressure (LP) elements, and then to the condenser.

Philadelphia Eddystone Unit

To complete our study, reference must be made to the *Eddystone Unit* of the Philadelphia Electric Company, Fig. 4-46. This unit represents an outstanding development in the technology of power generation and is designed for steam conditions of 5,000 psi, well above the *critical pressure* barrier and a new peak value for use in electric power generation. This pressure is slightly more than double the maximum in common use.

Much that was experimented with and employed in the Cleveland Avon installation was incorporated in this unit. See Fig. 4-47.

Starting with this pressure and any presently feasible initial steam temperature, reheat is essential to avoid excessive exhaust stage moisture with undue blade erosion and impingement losses. In this situation, as in the Avon unit, there are two stages of reheat. The

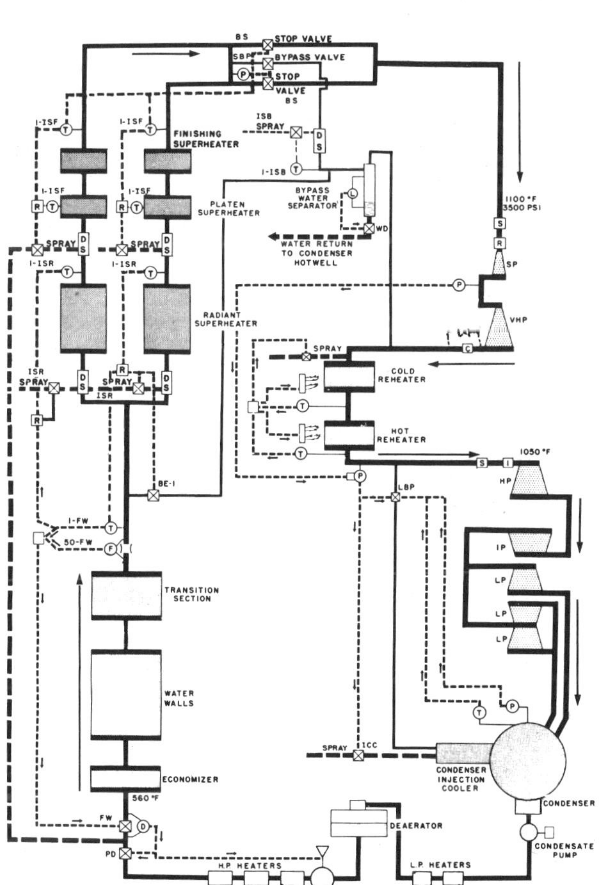

3500 PSI SUPERPRESSURE SINGLE-REHEAT CYCLE

Fig. 4-45. Flow Diagram of Monotube 3500 psi Superpressure Unit

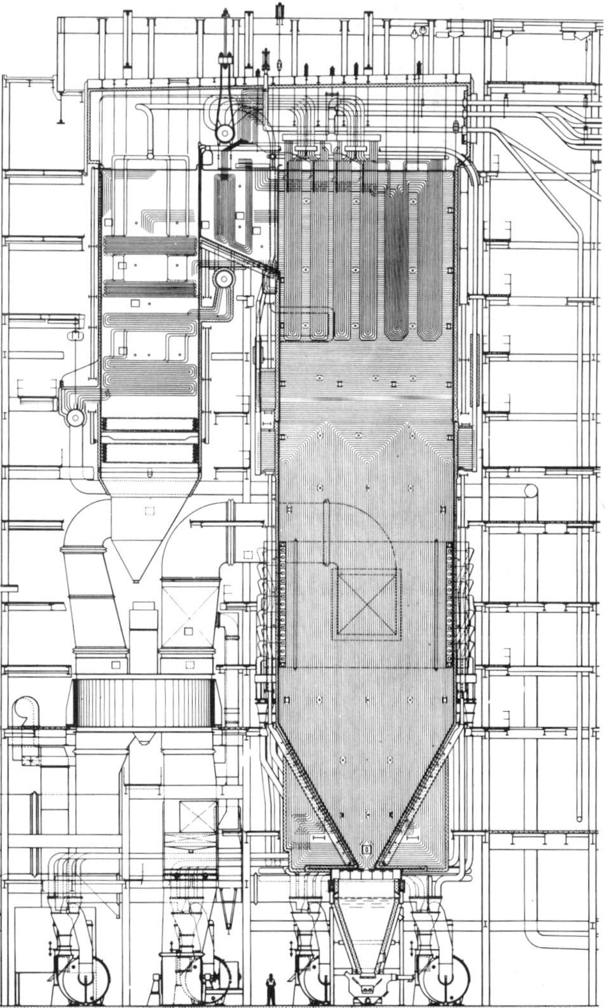

Fig. 4-46. 5000 psi Monotube Steam Generator, Eddystone Station (Combustion Engineering)

steam will be reheated twice to 1050°F with corresponding turbine stage pressures at full load being 1133 and 283 psi.

The turbine is rated at 325,000 kw and is designed for inlet steam conditions of 5015 psi at 1200°F. Two stages of reheat are used to hold 1050°F. Initially, nine stages of extraction feedheat were contemplated and corresponding extraction connections were provided. The system will heat feedwater regeneratively to 551°F at rated output, this temperature increasing to about 563°F at the discharge of the high pressure boiler-feed pump.

Fig. 4-47. Eddystone Unit of the Philadelphia Electric Company (Westinghouse)

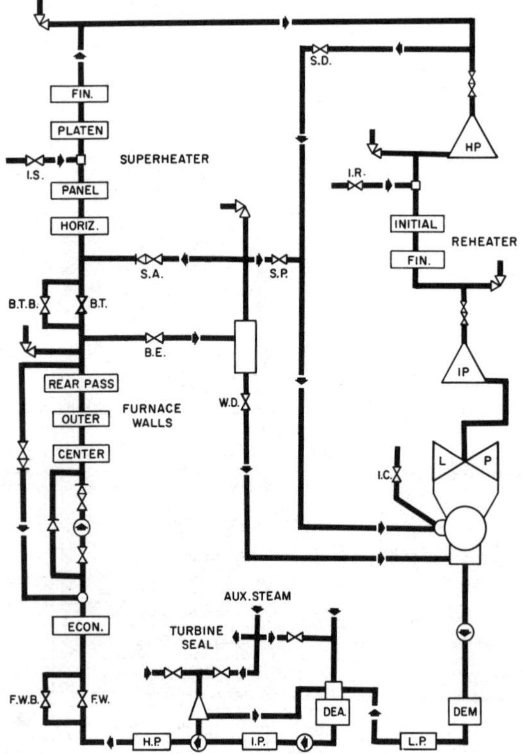

Fig. 4-48. Simplified Flow Diagram of Bull Run No. 1 (Combustion Engineering)

Bull Run Steam Generator

The largest unit for supercritical pressure ordered to date in the United States, and possibly anywhere in the world, is the TVA Bull Run Number 1 Steam Generator. It yields a primary steam flow of 6.4 million pounds per hour at 3500 psi and 1000°F, with a single reheat to 1000°F. Its heat output of about 6800 million BTU per hour for a turbine capability rated at 900Mw (Mega watts) classifies it as a giant among all classes of steam generators. This steam generator is not only interesting because of its size, but because it is the first of a second generation of supercritical units. Unlike the first generation units such as the previously discussed Eddystone and Avon which had to be designed with a host of critical questions unanswered, the second generation supercritical units incorporate in their design the results of operating experience on systems with supercritical fluid and once-through controls.

Boiler Turbine System

The basic flow of this steam generator is similar to that of other systems, Fig. 4-48. Water enters the feedwater valve FW, passes into the ECONomizer, then through the circulating pump and its associated isolating valves to the furnace where it flows in a series through the CENTER wall, the OUTER wall, and finally through the enclosure walls of the REAR gas PASSages. At this point the steam passes through a system of boiler throttling valves BT, and continues through four sections of HORIZontal and pendant or hanging superheaters before reaching the steam leads to the turbine through an outlet piping system. The steam is then returned to the boiler for reheating in a two-section reheater, and then it is returned to the turbine. The condensate passes through a filter DEMineralizer and a string of low pressure heaters (L.P.) to an open DEAerator. The turbine-driven feed pump then returns the feedwater through a string of pressure heaters to the feedwater valve.

Steam Generating System

The general arrangement of the steam generator is shown in Fig. 4-49. The unit consists of two identical dry-bottom furnaces, each with identical associated convection surfaces. Each furnace is subdivided along its full height by a center wall creating two distinct combustion chambers, each served by four tangential burner boxes located close to the corners on the front and rear furnace walls.

Furnace Protection

Obviously, the unit requires very large quantities of fuel and air, and the need to protect these units against dangerous firing conditions must be emphasized. Special efforts have been extended to develop and engineer a furnace safety system. The safety system monitors the functions of furnace

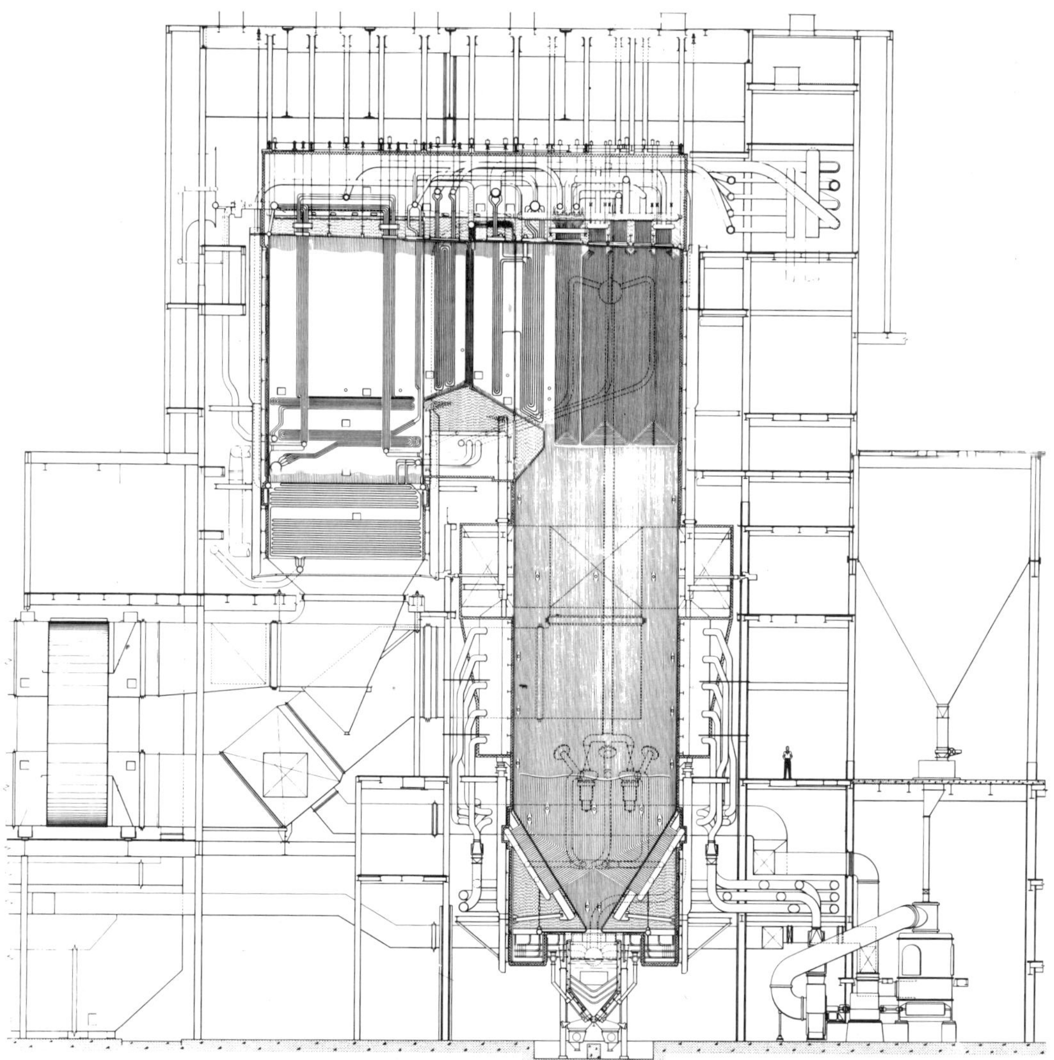

Fig. 4-49. Combined Circulation Twin-Furnace Boiler—Bull Run Number 1
(Combustion Engineering)
Note the comparative size of the man as drawn.

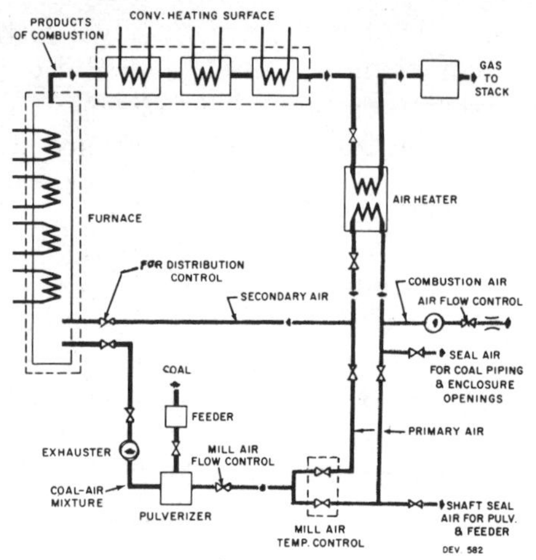

Fig. 4-50. Flow Diagram, Fuel, Gas, and Air System

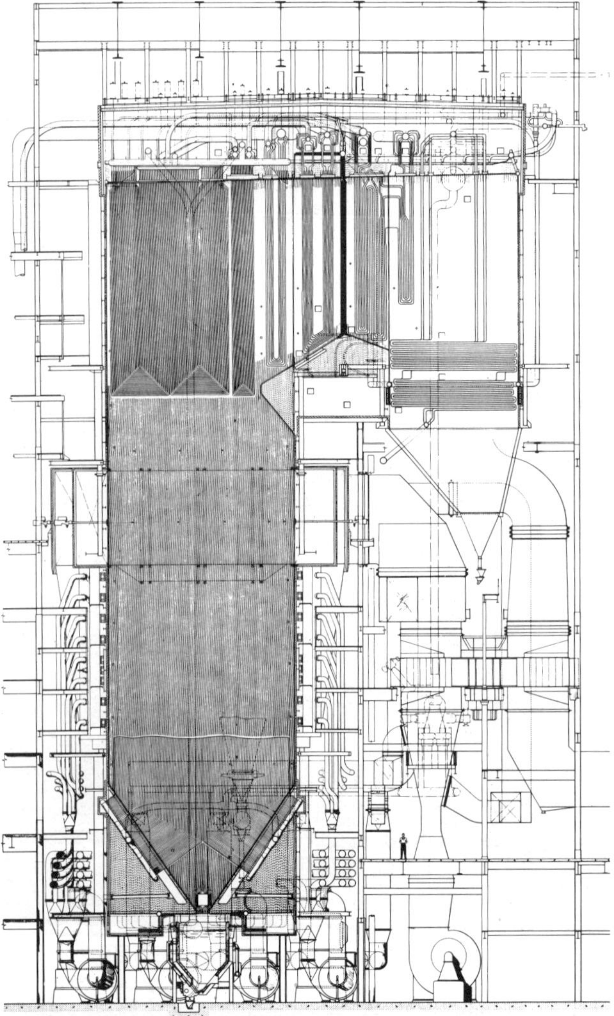

Fig. 4-51. Keystone Steam Generator
(Combustion Engineering)

purging, start-up air control, burner programming and flame detection, and contains permissive interlocks for manual or automatic operations, Fig. 4-50.

Fuel Air and Gas System

The Bull Run steam generator requires about 316 tons of coal per hour to sustain maximum continuous load. Ten coal pulverizing mills are provided, five for each furnace, with eight being capable of handling the top load. Their arrangement with respect to the pressurized furnace follows principles used in other units. The mills are pressurized from the force draft fan with the exhauster used as a booster to the furnace. Primary air, both cold and hot, is taken from the combustion air ducts entering and leaving the air heater. Control dampers establish proper mixing to maintain constant coal air mixture temperature of 180°F to the exhauster. The fuel air stream is divided among the eight burners serving two combustion chambers.

Control System

The coordinated control system regulates feedwater flow, fuel and air input, spray injection, reheat control equipment, and the turbine governor motor as required to maintain proper unit output at the desired steam pressure and temperature.

Keystone Steam Generator

The Keystone Steam Generator uses a single furnace design. In the industry the single furnace design is considered more advanced than the twin furnace. The Keystone Steam Generator serves a turbine capability of 900Mw from a single furnace and represents the ultimate in advanced design. The following are some of the engineering features of the Keystone unit.

General Arrangement

The general arrangement of the Keystone Steam Generator is shown in Fig. 4-51. The dry bottom pressurized furnace is divided into two essentially square chambers by a full height center wall. The two combustion chambers thus created are each fired by four burner boxes. Each box contains eight tilting tangential burners. The furnace envelope is designed with low surface and volume heat release rates for the range of coals to be burned. Each half of the upper furnace is subdivided by four pendant superheater panels that serve not only to cool the furnace exit gases, but to improve gas flow distribution prior to entry into the superheater and subsequent convection sections.

Furnace System

The physical dimensions of this unit pose some structural problems that, although common in some areas of structural design, are not as common with boiler structure. The furnace width is approximately 90 feet and the total boiler depth of approximately 95 feet with outboard columns is much greater than heretofore. Framing of this main support steel required special consideration.

Fuel Air and Gas System

The Keystone unit has eight pulverizers, six of which are capable of carrying full load. By referring to Fig. 4-52, it can be seen that air to the pulverizers is taken from the hot air leaving the air preheaters and the cold air entering the preheaters. The proper proportion of each is regulated by the mill air temperature control to provide the heat necessary for drying and to maintain a constant coal air temperature leaving the pulverizer of 180°F. The coal air mixture from each pulverizer supplies one complete level of eight tangential burners. These, in turn, supply both halves of the furnace to give identical combustion chamber characteristics. The total air from the force draft fan is metered by a venturi section of duct between the fan and the preheater. A portion of this air is diverted for pulverizer tempering air, pilot torch air, and for sealing the various furnace and equipment openings against internal pressure. Air is preheated by three Ljungstrom air preheaters.

Fuel Burning System

The burners located in the front and rear walls are arranged to fire tangentially into a selected firing circle and form an adjustable fireball in the two combustion chambers, one in each half of the divided furnace. Through proper location of the burner group, it was possible to obtain uniformity of peripheral heat absorption in the furnace walls. The burners at each corner are arranged for mini-

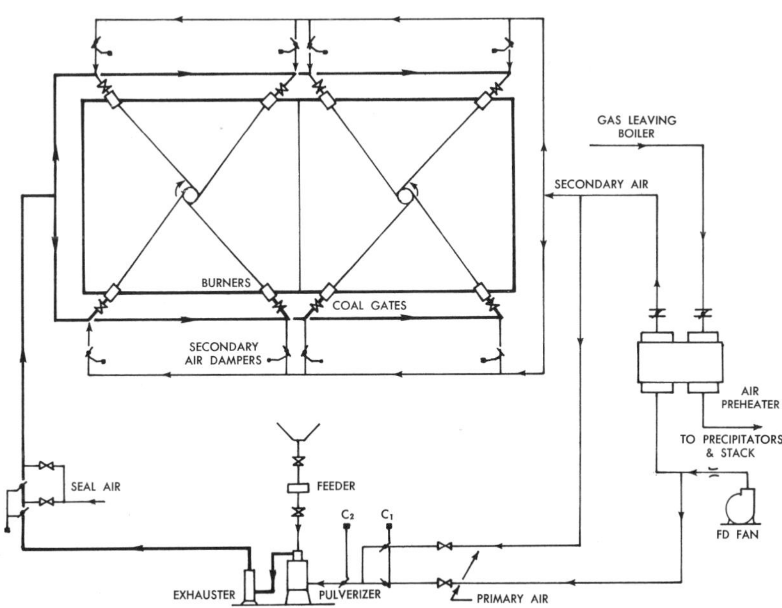

Fig. 4-52. Fuel, Air, and Gas Flow Diagram
(Combustion Engineering)

mum use for auxiliary fuel. They are interlocked and monitored for maximum reliability and safety. Each burner corner (Fig. 4-53) consists of eight coal nozzles, each supplied with a separate pulverizer, one warm-up torch, and nine ignition torches with four optical flame scanners. Light off of the Keystone system begins with ignition torches followed by higher energy warm-up torches and ultimate lighting off of the coal stream, all at common elevation or pressure. With a stable coal fire thus established, subsequent coal streams can be safely ignited with high energy torches. Every step of this procedure is governed by stringent safety rules developed through experience and intensive laboratory testing. This is necessary because it is ascertained that the

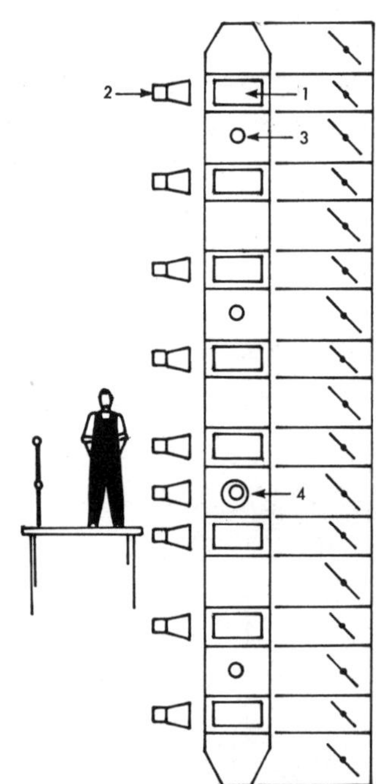

ITEM	1 COAL NOZZLES	2 IGNITERS	3 SCANNERS	4 WARM-UP GUNS
PER CORNER	8	9	4	1
PER FURNACE	32	36	16	4
PER UNIT	64	72	32	8

Fig. 4-53. Schematic Burner Arrangement (Combustion Engineering)

greatest percentage of boiler mishaps occurs during start up.

Reheat Temperature Control

Reheat temperature control is accomplished in each furnace by positioning the tilting burners in response to temperature error. Spray-type de-superheaters are employed for use in emergencies and under abnormal operating conditions.

Controlled System

The traditional division of controls into four areas of feedwater, combustion, steam temperature, and turbine output made different contractors responsible for each area. This system was satisfactory for drum-type steam generators, but recent boiler and turbine specifications have revealed certain limitations. The need for a unified, specifically designed control system embracing all the divisions mentioned is epitomized in the Keystone plant because of its combination of size, once-through design, supercritical pressure level, transient response requirements, and compatibility requirements for computer control.

Fluid Systems

The feedwater passes through the economizer, enters the mixing vessel, and flows to the circulating pump through a single downcomer. (See Fig. 4-55.) Flow then proceeds upward through the center wall down through the external links again through the outer furnace walls. After passing down through the external links, the feedwater follows parallel upward paths through the extended side walls and the rear pass walls. From this point, the once-through fluid flow path is through the boiler throttle valve arrangement (BT and BTB) and then through the panel platen and finishing superheaters. Cold reheat steam to the boiler is reheated in two sections and returned to the turbine.

Safety Protection

The following safety protection equipment is provided on the Keystone Steam Generator:

1. Isolable power control valves are provided at the superheater outlet, set at the pres-

sure part design pressures at the point of connection.

2. Spring-loaded safety valves are located at superheater and waterwall outlets.

3. Automatic pressure override opens the boiler throttle valves at the pressure point design pressure at the valve location.

4. Automatic pressure actuated firing trips are set at 6% above design pressure in two locations, at the superheater outlet and the furnace wall outlet.

5. A mechanical position-limiting stop on the pump bypass valve permits total isolation of the economizer from the remainder of the steam generator.

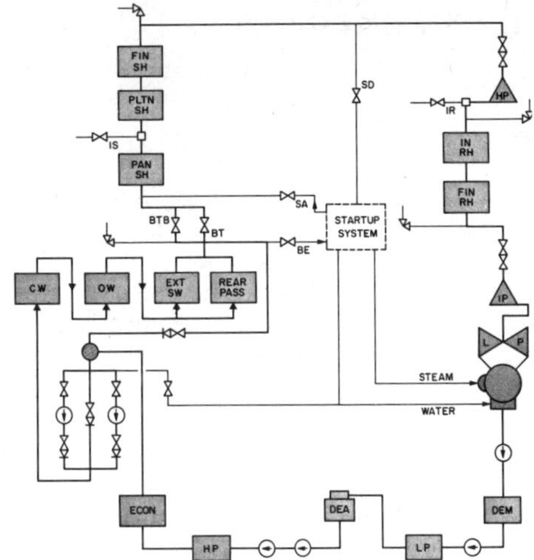

Fig. 4-55. Overall Boiler Flow Diagram

Fig. 4-54. Coordinated Control System Signal Flow Diagram

Terms to Understand

boiler
chemical energy
fire box
furnace
steam generator
heat transfer
insulation
convection
radiation
conduction
fire grate
shell boiler
fire-tube boiler
water-tube boiler
Cornish boiler
Lancashire boiler
Galloway tubes
Trevithick
return-tube boiler
multi-tube boiler
Stephenson
vertical boilers
locomotive boilers
horizontal boilers
exposed tube
submerged tube
stay bolts
fusion welding
grates
bridge wall
combustion space
smoke box
stack
economic boiler
tube sheet
updraft principle
tube
flue
expander
staggering
Scotch marine boiler
internally fired
hand stoked
mechanically stoked
William Blakey
Savery engine
James Rumsey
John Stevens
reservoir
porcupine boiler
sectional water-tube boiler
Jules Griffith
gathering pipes
Joseph Eve
Goldsworthy Gurney
Stephen Wilcox
tube bank
lower drum
vertically inclined boiler
Thomas Edison
elevator
trolley
Babcock & Wilcox
Stirling boiler
transversely
baffling
mud drum
longitudinal drum
cross drum
slings
stay bolts
water legs
rear header
economizers
caustic embrittlement
Kaolin
Stirling boiler
depression
fusion weld
integral furnace
cyclone steam separator
open pass boiler
radiant boiler
cyclone furnace
single turbine-boiler combination
supercritical pressure
universal pressure boiler
monotube boiler
Austenitic steel
ferritic steel
super pressure (SP) turbine
very high pressure (VHP) turbine
high pressure (HP) turbine
intermediate pressure (IP) turbine
low pressure (LP) turbine
condenser
reheat cycle
extraction fuel heat

Study Questions

1. What are the three most common types of boilers? Explain disadvantages of each.

2. In what way is heat transmitted in a boiler?

3. Analyze the properties of an ideal boiler.

4. How is a boiler's efficiency increased?

5. Trace the general technical evolution of the modern steam generator.

6. In what ways do vertical and horizontal water- or fire-tube boilers differ? When is each preferred?

7. How does a locomotive boiler differ from stationary boilers?

8. Describe the components of a simple boiler.

9. Compare the characteristics of water tube and fire tube boilers.

10. Analyze the economic, technological and sociological pressures that interplayed to evolve the modern steam generators.

11. What is the purpose of a mud drum found in some boilers?

12. Analyze how the efficiency of steam generators are increased.

13. Analyze the desire for increased pressure and heat of steam output.

14. What is the purpose of a cyclone steam separator?

15. How does the open pass or radiant boiler differ from conventional boilers?

16. What is meant by critical pressure?

17. Describe the characteristics of a universal pressure boiler.

18. Describe the interrelationships of controls on a supercritical pressure generator.

19. Analyze the safety systems on the Bull Run and Keystone generators.

CHAPTER 5

Steam Power Plants

Having become familiar with the principles of steam generators and steam engines individually, one can now apply these principles to the various types of steam power installations, the various accessory units, the necessary controls, and their operation. Some of these typical installations are *stationary power plants, marine power plants,* and the *steam locomotive*.

Today, steam power electrical generating units have become quite large, 250-350 *megawatts* being common. The size of steam systems is growing at a tremendous rate. Labor and fuel costs have increased in recent years. Construction and operating labor costs do not increase directly with unit size. Labor and fuel costs suggest, and system sizes often permit very large and highly efficient, although costly, steam generating units and prime movers. Thus, in the *overall operational considerations* of capital, operating labor, fuel and maintenance costs a higher capital cost may reflect a lower total cost in the long run.

The development of *nuclear steam generation* equipment is now common also. In the nuclear plant, heat from a nuclear reaction is substituted for the heat obtained when conventional fuels are burned. Nuclear plants will be considered separately in Chapter 6.

Along with the development of large steam power units exists the need for *heavy strong piping* to safely withstand the high pressures and temperatures. In addition, the postwar technological advances in jet propulsion, chemical processing, and atomic energy, led to demands for new types of tubular products and to the improvement in quality of existing types. New materials and steel alloys have been developed with new operations and processes of manufacture complementing their development.

Aspects of Boiler Design

There are two important aspects of boiler design in a particular installation–*structural* and *thermal.* Both must be considered in designing a total installation for the most efficient output for the investment of fuel and for the maximum safety in its use.

Structural aspects concern the materials used, the fabrication method, and the provisions for service and maintenance, including proper safety apparatus.

Thermal aspects are concerned with the best transfer of heat from hot gases to water. Fig. 5-1 shows the various heat losses and

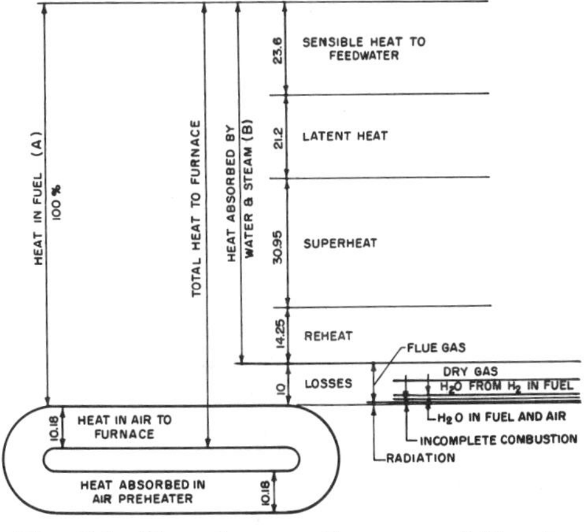

Fig. 5-1. Heat Sources, Losses, and Uses in a Steam Plant (Combustion Engineering)

uses. Enough heat must be available for each use. Boiler design is governed by thermal laws concerning heat transmission per square foot of surface.

Boiler Economy

Modern boilers incorporate several special units to improve their thermal efficiency and economy of operation. These are the economizer, feedwater heater, the air heater, and the superheater.

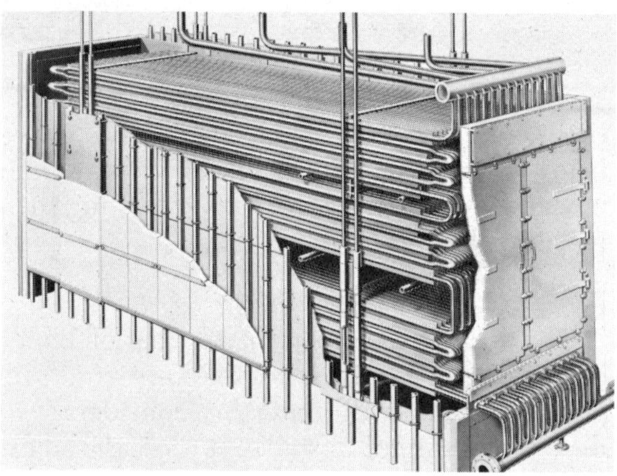

Fig. 5-2. Economizers, Fin-Tube Type
Note water wall (tubes in sides) which also aids in heating feedwater. Economizers are usually made of steel tubes with extended surfaces. They are vulnerable to oxygen corrosion from feedwater passing through them before entering the boiler. This may be combated by treating feedwater electro-chemically.

Fig. 5-3. Continuous Loop-Type Economizer
(Erie City Iron Works)

The *economizer* uses the exhaust gases which are still relatively hot. Heat of combustion is not completely absorbed or transferred to the boiler water. If nothing were done, this heat would be lost up the stack. However, if water tubes were situated between the boiler and the *breeching,* or stack connector, these gases could be employed to preheat the cold water before the water enters the boiler. Figs. 5-2, 5-3, and 5-4 (also many in Chapter 4 beginning with 4-30) show economizers.

There are two popular types of *feedwater heaters:* the direct contact type and the closed type. In the direct contact type, the feedwater comes in contact with the steam. In the closed type, the steam is passed through a series of tubes submerged in the feedwater. Another closed type has the water circulating through tubes with steam passing around the tubes on the outside. These systems are referred to as steam tube or water tube water heaters.

Air heaters, or *pre-heaters,* use the still relatively hot exhaust gases coming directly from the economizer. These heat the air which is used for combustion in the furnace. See Figs. 5-5 and 5-6 (and ones in Chapter 4 such as 4-28 or 4-33) for more details.

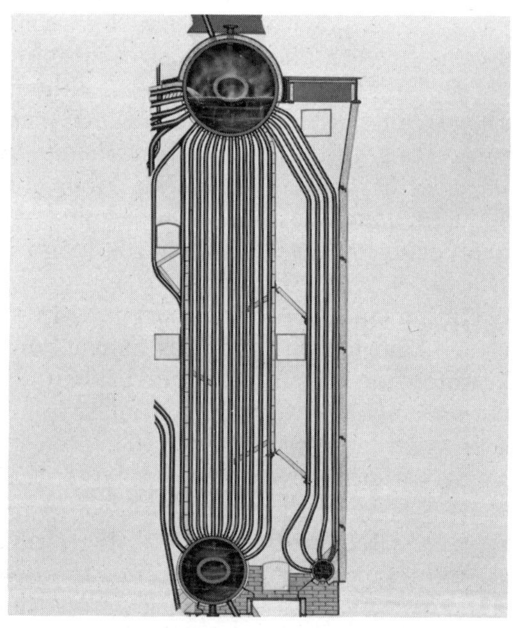

Fig. 5-4. Integral Economizer
(Erie City Iron Works)

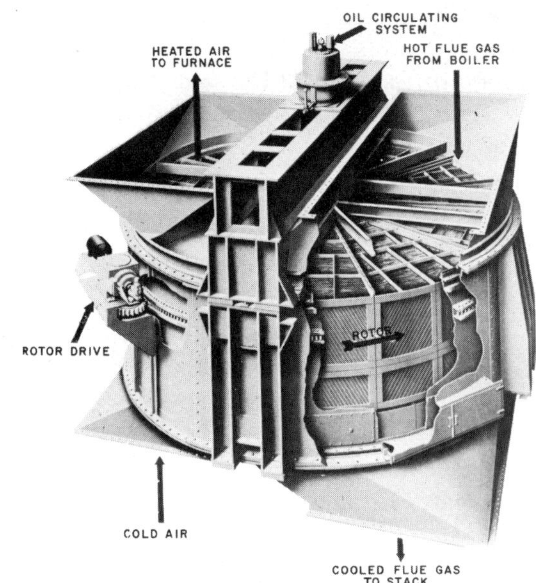

Fig. 5-5. The Ljungstrom Air Heater
This is a regenerative type of air heater. Tubular heaters are the recuperative type. The Ljungstrom unit shown is most popular but requires odd shaped ducts and the care of additional machinery. Tubular air heaters are necessarily very large and have corrosion tendencies which may force total shut down.

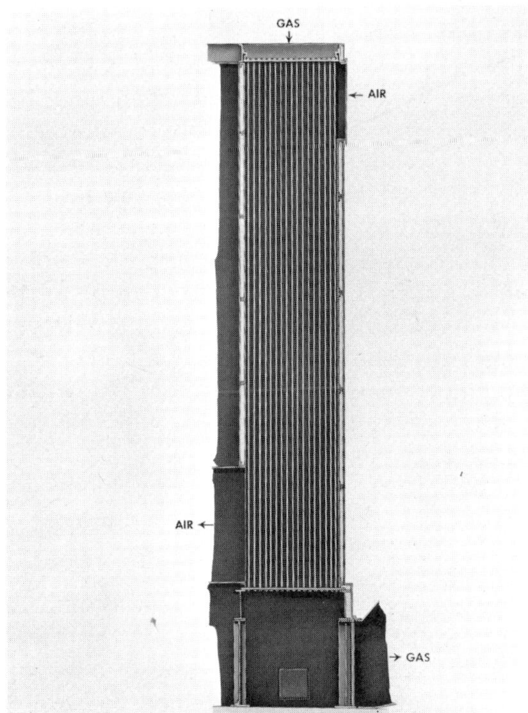

Fig. 5-6. Parallel-Flow Tubular Air Preheater
(Erie City Iron Works)

Superheaters are used in large installations. These are a special bank of tubes located near the hottest spot of the furnace. These tubes take the steam after it leaves the boiler and before delivery to the engine. They cause the steam to absorb more heat than it received during the initial boiling process. This superheated steam is drier and hotter and contains more latent energy. It can be used better in the steam engine, increasing the installation's total efficiency. Fig. 5-7 shows a

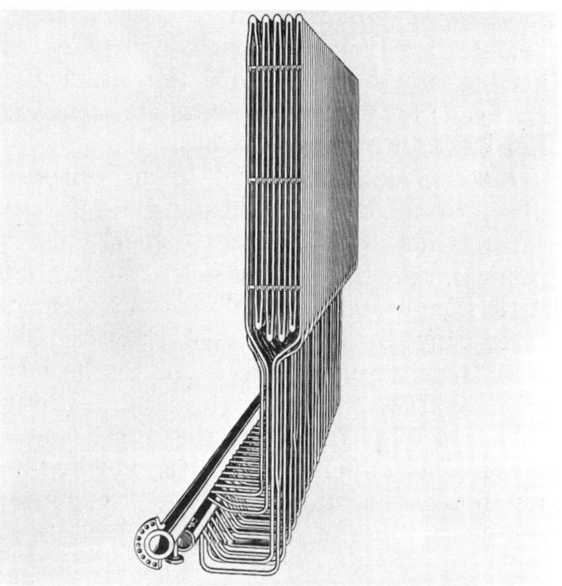

Fig. 5-7. Superheater (Combustion Engineering)
The purpose of a superheater is to raise the temperature of steam generated by the boiler to some point above saturation. Increased superheat improves performance of the prime mover because decreasing moisture to about 12 percent in the last stages of the turbine increases blade life.

Most superheaters are made of alloy tubing of rather small diameter (1½-2″) to maintain high steam velocity and sufficient pressure drop to ensure good steam distribution and to combat erosion.

Since the amount of tubing required depends on rate of heat absorption, the most economical arrangement would be closely spaced tubes near the fire, but such a design would not operate at starting, before steam is generated.

Straight tube boilers, *pendant superheaters*, as shown, are usually used between tube banks. Tube spacing is dictated by slagging tendency of the ash in the fuel.

Superheaters may also be located in the furnace walls where they receive virtually all their heat by radiation.

superheater unit. Others can be seen in the boilers illustrated in Chapter 4.

Placement within the boiler will determine whether it is a convection or radiant superheater. The convection type receives its heat from the stack gases whereas the radiant type is heated directly by the furnace flames. Sometimes there is more than one superheater within a boiler installation. Often these units are combined in order to provide steady heat regardless of the variation in steam pressure. Some large superheaters are divided into two sections, a primary and secondary superheater. These two sections usually are connected through an attemperator which uses feedwater to attemporate (regulate) temperature between the two sections.

Most modern industrial steam generator plants require both superheated and saturated steam. Often the superheated steam must be brought down to saturated steam temperature. A de-superheater accomplishes this temperature change by using the cool feedwater. The spray type de-superheater atomizes the feedwater into the steam flow by using a venturi tube and spray bar where the direct contact de-superheater permits the steam flow to bubble through a controlled amount of feedwater.

Superheaters

In a single-pass superheater, the saturated steam flows from the saturated header through the superheater element into the superheater outlet header. In a multi-pass superheater, the headers are diaphragmed to allow the steam to make several passes to assure good steam distribution through all elements. Marine superheater design demands a judicious balancing of economic and practical factors. There must be a sufficiently large temperature difference between the combustion gases passing over the superheater surface and the steam within the surface to result in a superheater of economic proportion. At the same time, there are practical limitations on the superheater metal temperatures with provision made to arrange the superheater elements in such a way as to prevent slag accumulation.

Usually screened tubes are located ahead of superheaters to obtain reasonable metal temperatures, while at the same time allowing a certain amount of direct radiation to be absorbed by the superheater tubes. This results in a more uniform temperature curve at the superheater outlet. Some boiler designs have the superheaters located in back of the main generating bank. Such an arrangement requires a relatively greater amount of heating surface and a much more elaborate system for controlling superheater outlet temperature. Still another arrangement uses a second furnace which allows the steam temperature to be controlled by varying the firing of the superheater furnace. Such a design permits a wide range of control, but there are many inherent complications in the operating procedures. Most two-drum bent-tube boilers are designed with the superheaters within the generating bank with either horizontal or vertical superheaters. Most designs include access space within the superheater banks in order to permit convenient access for inspection, cleaning, and maintenance.

De-Superheaters

For most modern boilers all of the steam generated by the boiler is passed through the superheater, and auxiliary steam requirements are met by de-superheating. This auxiliary steam is used for purposes such as heating, cleaning the cargo tanks, and in evaporators which are used to keep the cargo tanks free from moisture. De-superheaters can be of the internal or external type. The internal type consists of tubular elements with necessary terminal connections to be installed within the drum of the boiler. The external type consists of a direct or indirect heat exchanger mounted in the steam line with feedwater most often used as the cooling medium.

Condensers

Condensers are extremely essential in maritime installations. They preserve the clean boiler water that is so necessary since salt water cannot be used in a boiler. Salt water is always used, however, as the cooling water within surface condensers. Distilled water is excellent feedwater for the boiler, and the condenser eliminates the necessity of carrying a large water supply for the boiler.

Feedwater Purifier

Modern steam generators demand that the feedwater be cleaned of impurities. These impurities consist of solids such as dirt and organic matter as well as those natural chemical ingredients that cannot be removed by conventional filters. The degree of impurity in the feedwater will determine the size of the water filter and purification system. Some of the chemical filtering systems are quite elaborate, involving several types of neutralizing salts which are added to the water and then removed as the impurities are separated out.

The expense of the feedwater purifier is necessary in order to insure that the steam boiler will have sufficient life expectancy to yield a return on the required investment. Without the feedwater purifier, the steel of the boilers would corrode, become brittle, calcify, or have a slag build-up on the interior walls, prohibiting a heat transfer. Any of these would cut down on the efficiency of the steam generating unit. Of course, the contaminants would also affect the purity of the steam. Impurities in the steam, even in small quantities, can cause deposits to build up on the turbine blades requiring constant maintenance and cleaning, again affecting the unit's efficiency. A major effort in treating the feedwater is aimed at removing the natural gases found in the water. These gases are separated from the water in a deaerator. The deaerator is similar to a huge caldron in which the water is boiled and the vapor is permitted to condense on its top forming droplets which are permitted to fall back into the feedwater.

The amount of feedwater delivered to the steam generator is proportionate to the amount of water lost due to evaporation. Several methods of feedwater control have been used, the most popular being the balanced-flow feedwater system. The balanced-flow control determines the amount of water in the boiler and the rate of steam flow out of the boiler, and compares this with the feedwater flow into the boiler.

Safety Valves

Because steam is generated under high pressures, the boiler must be completely enclosed except for the steam, water, and fuel pipes. *Safety valves* are required to be installed and regulated.[1] The purpose of the safety valve is to prevent steam exceeding the safe limits of the boiler. In general practice, the safe *working pressure* of the boiler is but a small fraction of the bursting pressure. It may be no more than one-tenth. The valve orifice should be large enough to prevent unsafe pressure buildup. The valve should be permitted to lift off its seat upon reaching its working pressure and not an instant before.

Dead-weight safety valves are fitted to stationary boilers. This type of valve is fitted with a high and low water whistle alarm so that in the event of high or low water level, a simple lever device and float mechanism would cause it to blow. The *lever safety valve* is widely used for stationary land boilers. To prevent the weight on the lever from accidentally shifting along the arm, a set screw is usually used. The *ball and socket* valve was usually used in locomotive installations and the tension on the spring determines its *blow pressure*.

Gauges

The *water gauge* is nothing more than a device, sometimes as simple as a glass tube, that will indicate the level of water within the boiler. Too much water will reduce the steam space capacity causing a situation that will prohibit the steam generated to boil off properly. This could be dangerous. Also, excessive water requires too much fuel to be expended in bringing the water up to boiling temperature. This cuts down on boiler efficiency considerably. Too little water on the

[1] In 1680, Denys Papin designed and patented a steam digester using a high-pressure boiler for cooking purposes. To avoid an explosion, he added a device which may be considered the first safety valve on record.

other hand leads to boiling off or burning out the boiler.

To determine the *head* or pressure of the steam generated, a *steam gauge* is employed. The most widely used steam gauge is the *Bourdon spring-tube type,* Fig. 5-8. This unit consists of a curved tube with an oval cross section. One end of the tube is connected to a pointer by means of links, chains, or gears while the other end is attached to the pressure connection. Movement of the pointer is directly proportionate to the distortion of the tube caused by the pressure of the gas within. As the pressure increases, the tube straightens out and this moves a rack and pinion through connection linkage to position the pointer or recording device.

Mechanical gauges for water and steam have been superceded by more accurate electronic devices that not only indicate but also record the conditions as they exist in the boiler. Modern steam generator systems employ computerized controls to compare conditions as they exist to standards and correct any deviation automatically. These electronic systems are most sensitive, accurate, and quick to react. They work tirelessly and are rapidly taking over the job of constantly monitoring gauges, freeing stationary engineers for other responsibilities.

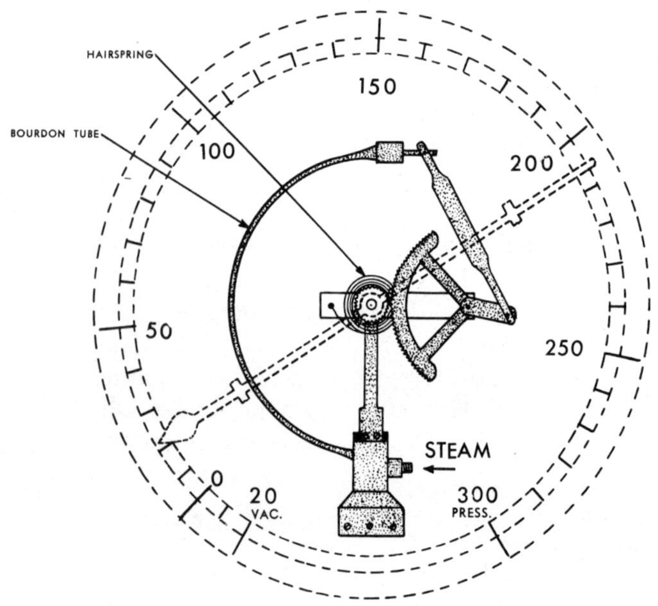

Fig. 5-8. Bourdon Steam Gauge

Control of Combustion

In commercial practice, combustion of fuel and air is accomplished at elevated temperatures. The process, if it is to proceed without interruptions in service and with the highest efficiency, requires the designers and operators of equipment to consider the following principles:

1. *Control of air supply* depends upon the fuel, equipment and operating conditions. It is determined by exhaustive research and tests before recommendations are given by the manufacturer. Too much air results in an excessive amount of hot gases being discharged with a corresponding high loss of heat up the stack. A deficiency of air allows an undue proportion of the fuel to pass from the furnace unburned. It, therefore, is important that best proportion of air and fuel be determined and maintained in order to secure high efficiency.

2. *Mixing of air and fuel* must be as complete as possible. Each fuel particle must be surrounded with air to ensure its proper burning. If the air distribution is poor, there will be an excess of air in some places and a deficiency in others.

3. *Proper temperature for combustion,* to cause rapid oxidation, must be maintained. This burning must take place while the fuel and air mixture is at high temperature. When the flame comes in contact with the relatively cool boiler tubes and shell, the carbon particles are deposited in the form of soot. When boilers are operated at low temperatures, the combustion is incomplete causing excessive smoking.

4. *Time required for combustion* is determined by the air supply, mixing, and temperature. In all cases, an appreciable amount of time is needed to complete the process. When the equipment is operated at excessively high ratings, the time may be insufficient to permit complete combustion. This results in fuel waste in the form of solids or combustible gases.

5. *Control of primary and secondary air* is vital. *Primary air* enters through the coal grates or is blown in with the atomized fuel. *Secondary air* enters through the firebox door or is blown in around or opposite the fuel sprayer. It must be provided in such quantities to cause complete combustion. If there is a deficiency of secondary air, smoke will be emitted and the efficiency will be reduced. In general, the rate of flow of primary air controls the rate of combustion, and secondary air determines the efficiency of the combustion process.

Combustion is a chemical process which takes place in accordance with natural laws. Fuels must be analyzed for their heating value, burning behavior, and pollutant potential. With the proper air-to-fuel ratio, exhaust contaminants in the air can be reduced. Today's power generating stations continually sample the exhaust gases. Certain cities where air pollution is a problem restrict the use of coal with a high sulfur content.

Types of Fuel

Typically, boilers may be fired by any of three common fuels: coal, oil, or natural gas. Usually the most economical fuel is selected. Lump coal requires special stokers for feeding the burners. Coal can also be pulverized and handled in pipes much like fuel oil or gas. Each of these fuels has special handling problems which will be considered separately.

Stokers for Coal

Today, most coal steam generating plants use some type of stoker or mechanical grating system to supply the neessary fuel for combustion. Very few installations still use *hand stoking*. Hand stoked boilers are rated below 300 boiler hp because of the human limitations. Mechanical devices are classified according to the method employed in introducing fuel into the furnace: chain grate and traveling-grate stokers, overfeed, side feed, underfeed, spreader stokers and pulverizers.

Chain and traveling grate stokers employ an endless chain which is constructed to form the fuel bed porous enough to ensure air passage for combustion. The coal is usually fed by a gravity feed hopper on the front of the traveling chain. The burning progresses as the grates move along with only refuse reaching the back end. See Fig. 5-9.

Overfeed and side-feed stokers consist of an inclined grate sloping from the front to the rear of the furnace at an angle of 30 to 45°. See Fig. 5-10. The coal hopper is located in front of the furnace and feeds coal by a reciprocating feed plate. The coal, because of gravity and the movements of the grates, moves down the stoker. Ashes are removed from the furnace by means of a dump grate located at the bottom of the grates. Some overfeed stokers have coal admitted from the sides and are called side-feeders.

Underfeed stokers force the coal up underneath the burning fuel bed, as the name implies. Small and medium boilers are supplied

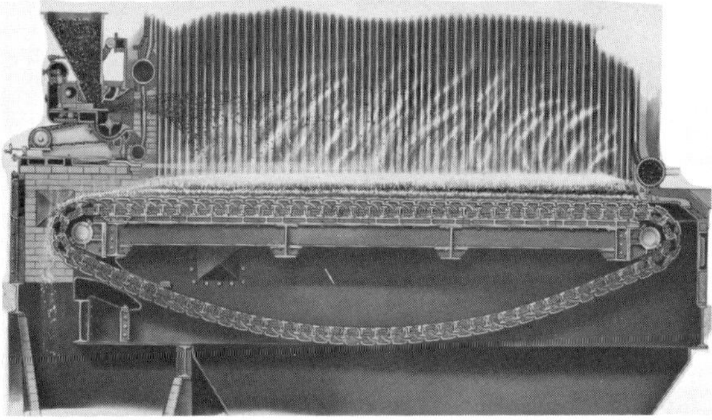

Fig. 5-9. Traveling Grate Stoker with Continuous Ash Discharge—Side View (Erie City Iron Works)

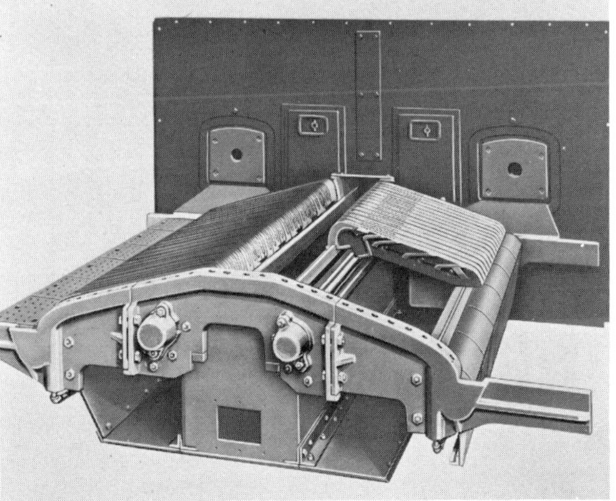

Fig. 5-10. Side-Feed Stoker for Bituminous Coal (Combustion Engineering)

with single or multiple retort stokers. The coal drops down a hopper into a worm screw feed and is driven into the retort for combustion.

Spreader stokers consist of a variable feeding device (a mechanism for throwing coal into the furnace), and grates with suitable air openings. See Fig. 5-11. The coal is sprayed from openings located in the front wall, causing the fine particles of coal to burn in suspension. The larger particles fall to the grate where the combustion is completed. Air enters the grate openings under pressure created by the forced-draft fan. A portion of this air is used to burn the thin layer of fuel on the grates. The remainder passes into the furnace where it is utilized in the combustion of fuel. Most of the fuel is burned in suspension. In the model illustrated, ashes are dumped by periodically tipping the grates as shown in the center section.

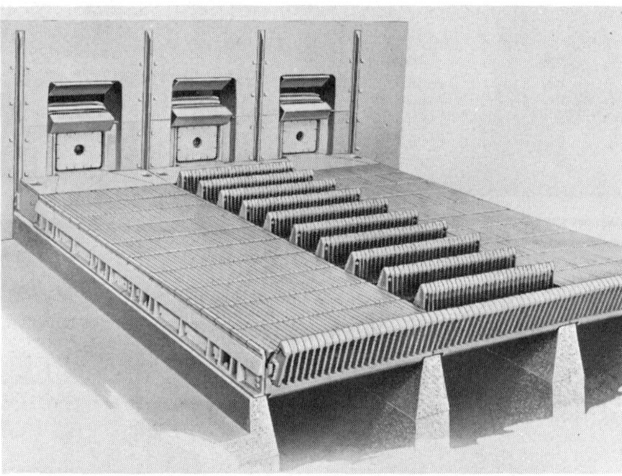

Fig. 5-11. Dump-Grate Spreader Stoker (Combustion Engineering)
Model illustrated is designed for a variety of coals as well as such combustible waste as sewage, sludge, refuse, pulp mill liquor, sugar cane waste, bark, saw dust, coffee grounds, or process gases. Feeds boilers having capacities up to 300,000 lbs. of steam per hour.

Fig. 5-12. Raymond Bowl Mill and Exhauster for Pulverizing Coal (Combustion Engineering)
Coal is dropped down center pipe into a rotating bowl and thrown outward where it is pulverized by three spring-loaded rollers. Air piped from the fan at the right moves the fine particles to the hopper below the bowl. The duct to the burner connects above the motor shaft.

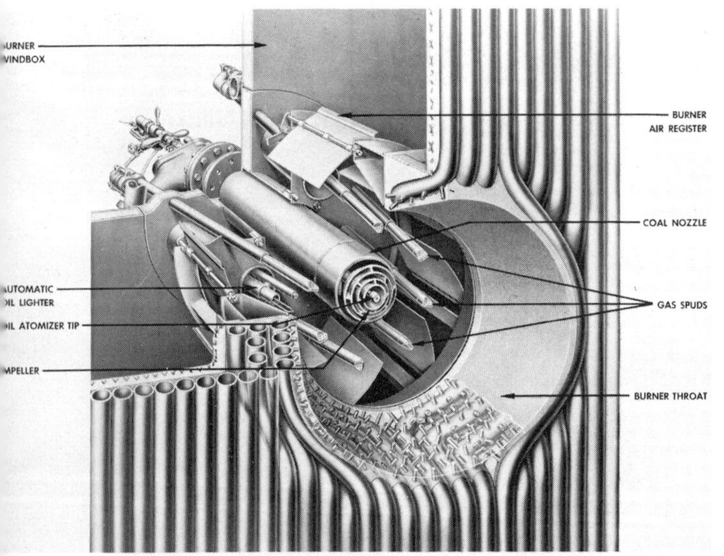

Fig. 5-13. Circular Burner for Pulverized Coal, Oil, or Gas (Babcock & Wilcox)
Note the circular air register, water-cooled throat and membrane-wall. Unit can be adapted to burn any one fuel.

Atomized Fuels

The *pulverization of coal* is a means of exposing a large surface area to the air and consequently accelerating combustion. Electric generating steam plants were the first to use *pulverized fuel.* In this system, the coal is dried in a drier using exhaust gases. It then drops into the mill which pulverizes the coal to a degree of fineness that will be easily used in the furnace. A popular mill, typical of larger pulverizers, is shown in Fig. 5-12. The pulverized fuel, as it comes from this mill, is blown by compressed air into bunkers located above the burners. Speed of the feeders is varied by the fireman. The pulverized fuel, when discharged by the feeders, is carried along by a current of air and blown into the furnace through the burners automatically. See Figs. 5-13, 5-14, and 5-15.

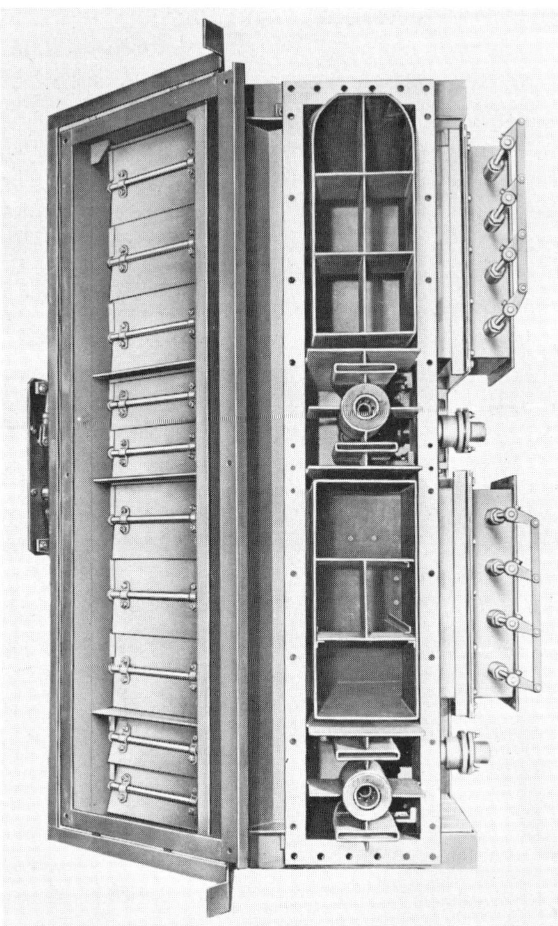

Fig. 5-14. Tangential "T" Burner for Oil, Gas, or Coal (Combustion Engineering)

Unit is located in wall or corner of furnace; crossing blasts from four corners create turbulence and the mixing needed for complete combustion.

Fig. 5-15. Plan View of Tangential Burner Firing (Combustion Engineering)

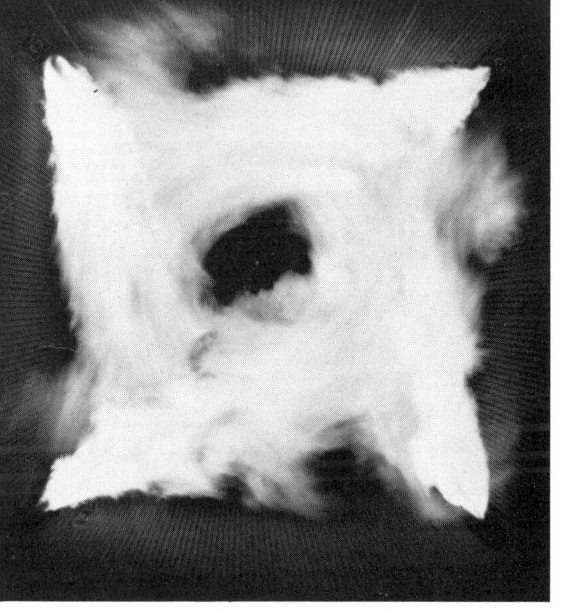

Fig. 5-15A. Actual Photo of Tangential Burner Firing (Combustion Engineering)

Fuel oil is quite popular and requires consideration in the selection of equipment, grade of oil, and attention to operating details. Plant storage depends upon the oil consumed per day, availability of supply, and transportation facilities. Oil-heating equipment must be adequate to liquefy the heaviest oil in spite of extremes of maximum consumption rate and maximum cold. The oil pump must deliver the quantity specified to the burner. Pumps usually are installed in duplicate to provide for two different sources of power, one run by steam and one by electricity. The burners must be designed to provide good atomization to assure quick and thorough mixing of fuel and air. Burners are classified according to the method employed. For example, the atomizing agent may be steam, air, pressure, or rotary motion. See Fig. 5-16. Oil can be stored above or below the ground. Each method has its own problems of feeding and receiving.

Natural draft in the beginning was most prevalent. Today, *forced draft* caused by bladed fans or squirrel-cage blowers is widely used to ensure proper combustion. In the case of secondary air, forced air draft ensures proper air flow throughout the boiler.

Fig. 5-16. Cross-Section of Horizontal Turbulent Burner for Oil or Pulverized Coal
(Combustion Engineering)
Turbulence comes from rotary motion of primary air (in cylinder with spirals) around fuel pipe, as well as the swirling secondary air in the outer funnel.

These fans may be steam or electrically operated, but must be able to function at variable rates to compensate for partial as well as full capacity output of the boiler.

Fly Ash and Grit Removal

The average generating station burns in excess of 7,000 tons of coal daily. Power generating stations employ a variety of methods to rid flue gases of grit and dust. In addition to mechanical cleaning by a screen, a popular device known as a "cyclone separator" is used. This separator carries the gases in a special path causing them to whirl about in a chamber utilizing centrifugal force to separate the particles from the gas. A spray of water is sometimes used.

Mechanical devices are quite primitive and inefficient compared to the electrostatic purifiers that are popular today. These purifiers charge the particles of dust electrostatically and then collect the dust on a grid or screen, employing an unlike charge between grit and grid. These screens are periodically cleaned by using electrical vibrators or hammers, commonly referred to as *rappers.* The rapping causes the dust to fall from the filters into a bin below. The grit then is removed by high pressure water or air jets into underground sluicing pipes and then to surface or water vehicles. Storing this ash is costly. Suitable storage areas are fast becoming scarce; therefore, it is imperative that new ways of utilizing or disposing of this waste product be found. The available ash disposal methods include pile storage, filling up gravel pits, and occasionally selling the ash to be used as a supplementary building material, especially for roads. In general, all of these disposal methods are unsatisfactory in the long-term view and occasionally uneconomical. Many research institutes are working on projects trying to determine a use for the by-product of the power generating system.

The solids contained in the flue gas include two different kinds of particles: fly ash consisting of inorganic particles such as slag beads, oxides, sulfates, as well as phosphates of all metals, such as iron, aluminum, calcium, magnesium, sodium and potassium; and fly coke consisting of fine coke or coal particles. One university reports that they have used this ash as an ingredient in making concrete blocks. These blocks were proven to be of comparable strength to regular blocks while exhibiting the advantage of lower weight. The problem of trying to find what to do with slag is compounded because each fuel has a different slag composition, and therefore, has to be treated uniquely.

Typical Stationary Power Plant

The water-tube boiler in a stationary installation may be fired by any one of the three fuels: coal, oil, or natural gas. The fuel is fed into the furnace by a burner that is capable of handling most fuels. The proper combustion, paramount for high efficiency, is controlled electronically from a panel located in a control room. In some older installations, control of burners and air blowers is done manually, necessitating an elaborate communication system of speaking tubes, phones, and gauges between boiler and engine room.

Components and Their Functions

Since coal requires extensive handling equipment and special ash and dust removal units, it will be used as the fuel in this discussion of the typical stationary power plant sketched in Fig. 5-17. The coal is loaded into overhead hoppers by conveyor belts and by gravity. It is fed into the pulverizing mills which reduce it to the consistency of fine flour. From the mills, the powdered coal is dried and then blown into the furnace by air.

Above the tube bank is the superheater and behind the boiler, the economizer. It is

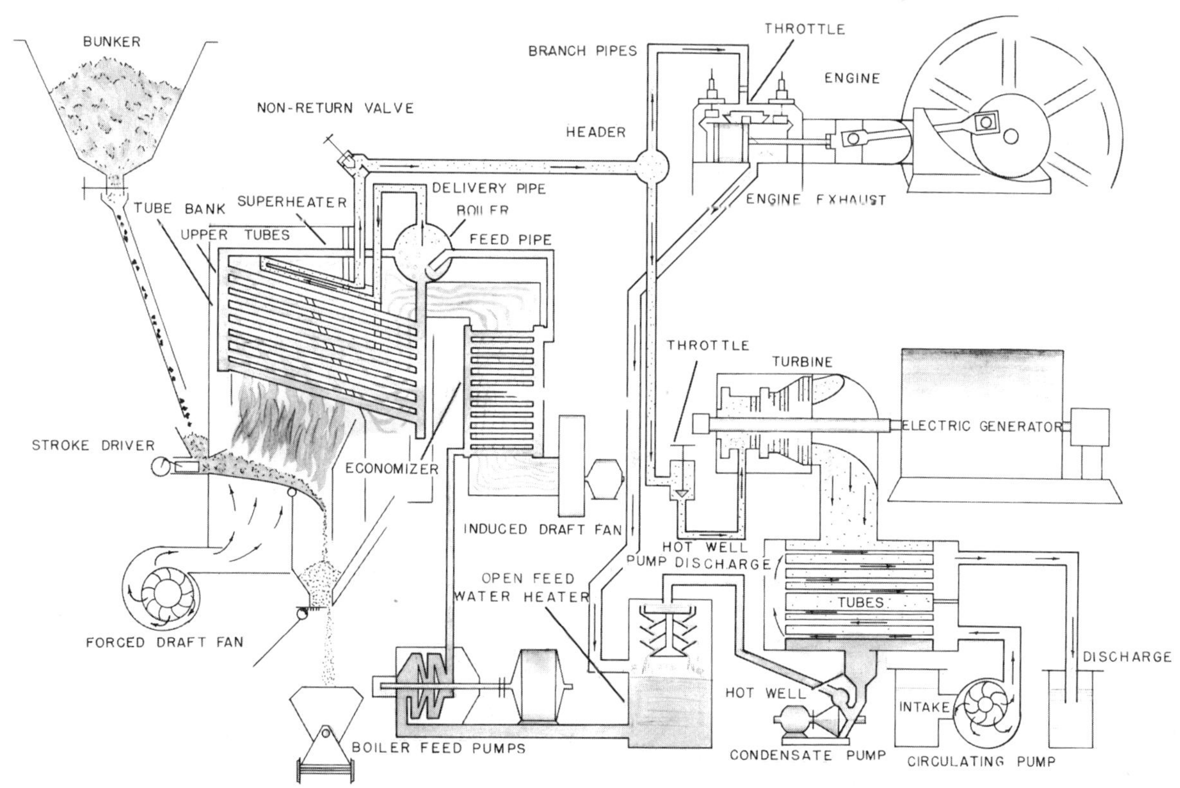

Fig. 5-17. Steam Power Plant

This illustrative installation burns coal and shows the components needed to run a turbine-generator as well as a reciprocating steam engine which will furnish mechanical power.

obvious that since the paths for the hot gases and air are so complicated, fans are required to maintain the necessary draft. A forced draft fan is shown in the basement and an induced draft fan is shown at the base of the stack. This balances the former and draws the gases out of the economizer after having passed over the boiler, superheater, and economizer.

The boiler is aptly called the cross-drum type, since we only see a cross section of the drum. From the economizer, there is a feed pipe filling the boiler with hot water. The water level in the drum is maintained slightly higher than the upper tubes. Above the water in the drum is a space in which steam is generated and the delivery pipe receives the dry steam.

Dry steam then passes through the superheater, which always has a safety valve so a main stop and a *non-return valve* are placed at this outlet. These valves, as the name implies, either stop the steam supply from the boiler, or, when open, prevent the return of the steam flow to the boiler. In case pressure drops for some reason the necessity of these valves cannot be underestimated—especially if more than one boiler is used and all deliver steam into the same header. In some installations this is the case. A number of boilers insure against an entire shut-down for maintenance and repair. The reason for the valves should now be quite clear. They prevent the steam from being pushed into the other boilers if the pressures in these should not be equal.

Steam and air meters, draft gauges, water gauges, and pressure gauges are all necessary accessories. These provide the fireman with an indication of how much steam is needed in the engine room. He adjusts the fuel supply by regulating the proper fuel pumps to meet the engine demand. Every such change in fuel input must be accompanied by a change in air supply. Air supply is regulated by dampers. In some installations, this is done electronically from a *central control room.*

Grit removal equipment is rather complicated and is very necessary. The average generating station may burn up to 7,000 tons of coal daily and this can prove to be a health hazard. Different methods or a combination of them are used to rid flue gases of grit and dust. In one dust arrester, the flue gases are cleared by centrifugal force. Another device, which is known as the *cyclone separator,* carries the gases in a special path which causes the foreign matter to separate from the gas and veer out. Some devices use water sprays in the chimney, while others give an electrostatic charge to the particles as they rise up the flue. They are then collected on a screen which has been given an unlike charge. These screens are periodically cleaned by a *rapping* with electric hammers. The rapping bar causes the dust to drop into collectors below. Grit and furnace ashes are usually removed by high pressure water jets in underground *sluicing pipes* to bunkers. They are then carried away by barges, railway cars, or trucks.

Engine Room Operation

Steam in the *header* is always ready for use. It is kept at the proper pressure and temperature to be used by the selected prime mover. These are fed by *branch pipes.* In Fig. 5-17, a turbine and reciprocating steam engine are shown. At the inlet to each, there is a *throttle valve* which permits the shutting off of the steam. Each machine has a governor to control the revolutions per minute based on the engine load.

In this illustration, the turbine is connected to an electric generator. It is shown exhausting into a surface condenser with a circulating pump for the cooling water. The steam is made to condense on the outer surfaces of the tubes within the condenser shell. This permits the condensate to collect in the *hot well* and not to mix with the cooling water. Condensate is then pumped to the feedwater system. The partial vacuum, which is created by the cooling steam, sucks the spent steam out the turbine exhaust.

Cooling water intake and exhaust (lower right, Fig. 5-17) are shown as tunnels which would be located apart from one another in a river, lake, or other large body of water. However, if water is scarce, the cooling water may be air-cooled and then recirculated.

The reciprocating engine in the drawing is of the uniflow type. Its large flywheel may be connected to a generator, compressor, pump, or other machine.

Heat Balance

Condensate from the *hot well* is lukewarm and could be heated to advantage before admission into the economizer. Auxiliaries, such as feed pumps, forced and induced draft fans, condenser and hot well circulating pumps, and fuel pumps usually are steam driven and their exhaust steam is used for heating the condensate. In some systems, a portion of the steam is extracted from the turbine or boiler to heat the condensate. In this system, the exhaust from the engine has been used for that purpose. The *hot well pump* discharge and the engine exhaust are at the same pressure and, therefore, they can be mixed in an open-feedwater heater. The condensate trickles over trays and the exhaust steam is admitted directly into the same place. There, the steam that condenses is mixed with the condensate and the water. It comes out of the heater warmer than in the hot well. The economizer then has less heating to do and consequently can be made smaller than if it were supplied cold water. The amount of heat required to warm the water must balance the amount of heat in the exhaust steam, hence the term *heat balance*. There are many ingenious and complicated schemes that engineers use to accomplish this.

The exhaust steam of plants which serve hotels, hospitals, industrial plants, clubs, and office buildings may also be used for heating in the winter.

Development and Operation of Large Steam Generators in the United States

The magnitude of the United States power system may be realized when we consider that one-third of the world's electric generating capacity is installed in the United States. This capacity of 230,000Mw is about equal to the combined capacity of the next five leading power-producing countries. Historically, the industry's output has shown a remarkably steady increase, with further rapid expansion predicted for the decades to come. This power consumption has not only been due to the population growth, but even more importantly to the continuing rise in per capita demand. Electricity is being used increasingly for residential use due to more home appliances, air-conditioning, and all-electric homes. An important consideration in the development of the United States power industry is the role of private enterprise. More than three-fourths of the electric power capacity is furnished by some 400 investor-owned companies, with the balance being furnished by government-financed organizations.

Current Trends

The most apparent trend during the last decade is the development of large size units. The major incentive for this trend is the cost reduction possible, in both initial investment and operation. Fewer boilers, turbines, and generators are needed, and also other associated power plant components, such as condensers, evaporators, heaters, pumps, fans, pipings, valves, and so forth.

Power Pooling

Power pools serve as many as ten utilities organized to coordinate both their day-to-day operations and the planning of future generation and transmission facilities. This permits each independent power producer to better perform its basic function which is the reliable delivery of the cheapest possible kilowatt hour of electricity. It also permits these utilities to capitalize on the economies of size, reserve capacity, peak diversity, and energy supply. There are today some 25 power pools in the six major interconnected operating groups. Many variations exist in the complexity of contractual agreements between members of such pools, particularly as to power dispatch. All of them have the effect of emphasizing the economics of bigger blocks of generation.

Minemouth Plants

The natural coal reserve in the United States is indeed large, although extensive coal fields adapted to low cost mining techniques are considerably more restricted. More coal lies west of the Mississippi than to the east and, while mineable at low cost, is far away from major load centers. The coals mined in the east and midwest are generally classified as high-grade bituminous, but among them are some coals which have caused considerable problems due to their ash behavior. Coal is now used to produce about two-thirds of the total thermal electric generation, and recent developments have emphasized the minemouth plant.

Gas and Oil Fuels

Next to coal, natural gas accounts for more than 27% of total thermal generation and must be considered an important factor in the development of steam generators. Natural gas reserves are heavily concentrated in five states: Texas, Louisiana, Oklahoma, Kansas, and New Mexico. It is expected that a major proportion of the new reserves developed during the next decade or so will be in or near these areas. The extension of pipe lines from these sources has put natural gas to use for electric power generation in almost every state. Gas has a competitive edge in the south-central region where boilers are designed specifically for natural gas firing, with oil as an emergency fuel. The capital cost reduction obtainable compared to units with full load alternate fuels, either coal or oil, is substantial.

The use of residual fuel oil in electric generation is generally restricted to areas where water-borne transportation is available, the northeastern part of the United States, Florida, and California. Steam generators using residual oil as fuel are most always designed to accommodate gas and/or coal as alternate fuels. The availability of fuel oil, however, provides a competitive influence on other fossil fuels, the extent of which greatly depends on the international and domestic policies as well as the world market.

Standardized Cycle Conditions

There is a tendency in the United States to standardize design equipment and operating cycles. More than 80% of all capacity purchased during the past decade employed only three subcritical pressure levels and one for supercritical operation. With increasing unit size, more and more capacity was purchased at the higher pressure levels. There has been a general trend to select 1000°F for both primary and reheat steam. More than 85% of all utility steam generating systems purchased during the last year was at that level. A few utilities, notably those which in the past have selected cycles with steam temperatures of 1050°F and higher, have employed supercritical cycles with double reheat either at 1000°F or with reheat steam temperatures of 1025° and 1050°F. The economic justification of a particular cycle is based on an evaluation of many specific cost variables derived from data obtained by experience and extrapolation (inferred knowledge).

Standardizing a cycle condition has an effect on steam generator design by promoting practices in component design, material selection, and arrangement of heating surfaces which can be followed in general through several units providing economic benefits.

Common Attributes of Marine and Stationary Practice[1]

Both marine and stationary power plant designers have benefited greatly by the interchange of technical information. Marine boilers operate successfully at much higher heat release rates and smaller furnace volumes than field-erected stationary boilers. Where problems have been similar, the solutions have been resolved comparably. Where the problems and situations are different, each has retained its distinctive characteristics.

Marine Power Plants

The steam engine used in marine transportation is centrally located within the hull of

[1] W. C. Freeman and E. W. Lutt, *Marine Boilers*. Combustion Engineering, Inc., Windsor, Conn.

the ship. Basically, the steamship power plant resembles stationary ones. The turbine engine has replaced the reciprocating engine and in nearly all cases these are multiple expansion and condensing engines.

Trends in Increasing Marine Boiler Capacity[2]

The industry's present trend toward larger tanker and bulk carrier steamships has resulted in startling changes in propulsion machinery arrangements especially with regard to boiler capacity and configuration (arrangement). In rather rapid succession, 100,000 DWT (Dead Weight Tonnage) tankers were dwarfed by 150,000 DWT ships which, in turn, recently lost the distinction of being the largest to a 209,000 DWT tanker. It is projected that before long there will be tankers of 300,000 DWT class coming off the ways of Japanese shipbuilders to be followed by units of 500,000 DWT and larger. The power plant requirements for these mammoth ships have increased from 20,000 SHP (shaft horsepower) to the 35,000 SHP range with some designers considering employing horsepower ranges in the 40 and 50,000 SHP range.

Coupled with the sharp rise in the size of ships and related horsepower requirements, there is an interesting and important change in the design configuration. The change consists of applying two concepts. First, the installation of only one propulsion boiler and second, on a more limited basis, the application of the reheat steam cycle. The advantages in applying one or both of these two design features have been the subject of many articles and technical papers. Boiler technology, especially in the area of construction, has been changing rapidly. Major changes have taken place before the implications of these changes are understood. There is general agreement between the United States and the United Kingdom that the furnace refractory material should be eliminated in new marine steam generating systems. Also, there is common agreement to require wider spacing of superheater elements and the application of welded wall construction.

There is a developing school of thought which differs widely on the matter of basic marine boiler configuration for large capacity and reheat systems. This design approach supports the single boiler. It is certainly easy to understand the increase in boiler size associated with the increased horsepower. What is difficult to understand is the use of a single boiler rather than two boilers as is the custom in conventional moderate horsepower marine installations. Actually, the single boiler concept has taken a long time to be accepted. The first single boiler installation was in the United Kingdom just after World War II. The success of this unit has led major companies to request that single boiler units be constructed for them. Previously, these units were built in England. However, United States shipyards now are accepting contracts for single boiler systems.

The popular single-boiler design is the culmination of over 30 years of steady development and improvement. The vertical two-drum, bent-tube marine boiler commonly referred to as the D-type boiler, Fig. 5-17A,

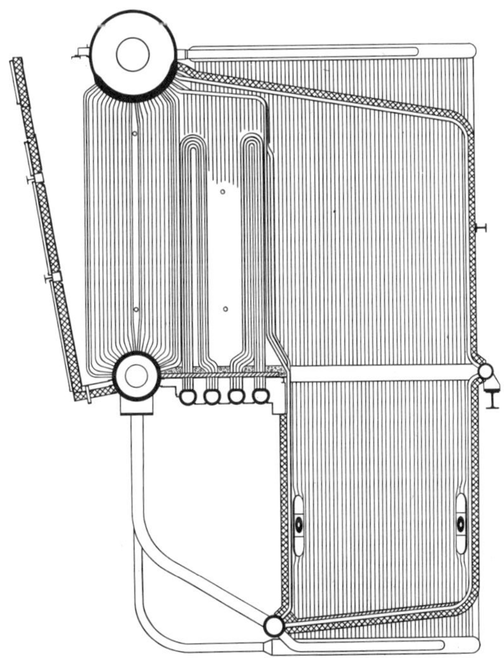

Fig. 5-17A. D-Type Boiler

[2] L. E. Triggs, *On Increasing Marine Boiler Capacity; Some Important Considerations for Single Boiler Ships.* Combustion Engineering, Windsor, Connecticut, 1967.

was built in the 1920's and gained wide acceptance in the 30's. Manufacturers provided their own variations of detail, but the basic design arrangement was the frame of reference for all manufacturers since its introduction.

There is now a definite trend toward designs which have completely water-walled furnaces as exemplified by the V2M-5 design, Fig. 5-17B. This particular configuration employs many unique features, one of the most significant being that it completely eliminated all exposed refractory. In a recent survey conducted by the United States Maritime Administration, it was found that over 30% of boiler repair and maintenance cost on newer ships is directly attributed to brick work. This is quite significant when one considers that the same report indicates that repair and maintenance costs for boilers on older ships represent about 30% of the total shore maintenance costs for the entire power plant. This particular boiler has welded wall construction. It provides for the elimination of the double casing construction since the pressure parts, when welded together, establish a gas-tight integrity. This basic design configuration is presently being installed in naval and merchant ships built in the United States, and in some merchant ships built in Europe and Japan. Initially, there was a variation of the design which included tangent-tube water walls and double casing when shipbuilders were hesitant to accept the welded wall feature. The majority of boilers built today of the V2M-8 configuration are of the welded wall design. When the V2M-8 design was introduced, it was projected that the design would be appropriate for single boiler installations. It was anticipated that if any significant increase in horsepower was required, it would be most likely accomplished by introducing another boiler. However, in a swing which defied prediction, the marine industry has within a short period of time accepted the

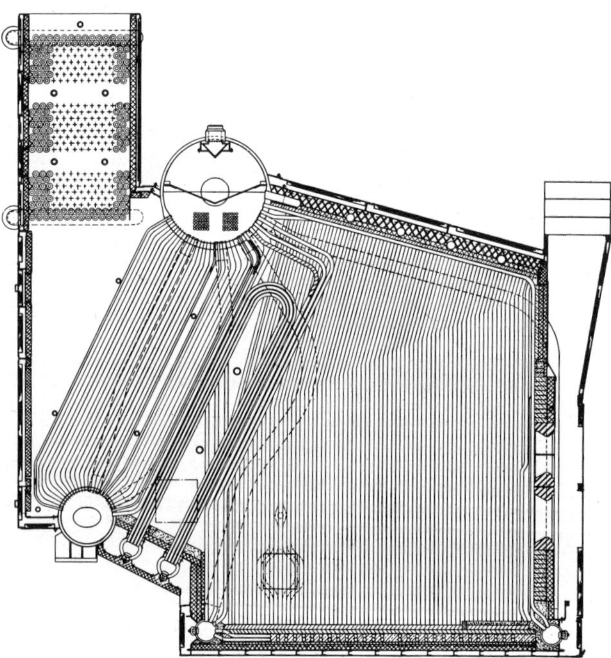

Fig. 5-17B. Sectional Elevation Plan of V2M-5 Design

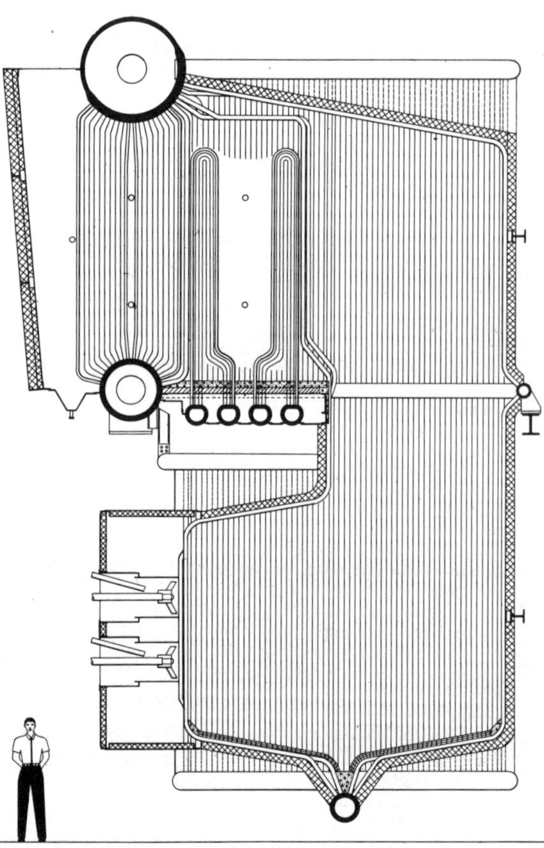

Fig. 5-17C. Sectional Elevation Plan for V2M-9 Design

single boiler concept for larger ships. This trend forced boiler designers to carefully examine all existing designs to determine whether they would adequately meet the greatly increased evaporation rates.

Large Capacity Single Boiler for Marine Use

Figure 5-17C shows the arrangement of a V2M-9 design which is proposed for large capacity, single boiler, high horsepower requirements. In fact, the top half of the V2M-9 is a V2M-8 without a furnace floor, retaining the same basic configuration with regard to boiler and superheater. The increase of furnace volume was accomplished by extending the furnace downward. By increasing the furnace size in this way, the vertical distance between the water and steam drum centers was not increased over existing designs. Disengaging the furnace from the boiler results in the ideal situation; many variations of furnace shape can be used without affecting the boiler bank and superheat arrangement. Figure 5-17D is a typical V2M-9 variation that could be used in conjunction with tangential burners. Comparing it to Fig. 5-17C, note that fuel burning equipment is located in the lower part of the furnace. In the design shown in Fig. 5-17E, the burners are located in the roof of the furnace. Considerable satisfactory service experience with roof firing has been accumulated with the V2M-8.

Particular attention must be given to preventing the formation of gas pockets in the roof of this type furnace because of a serious explosion hazard. If any gas pockets are thought to exist, they must be carefully purged by drawing all the unburned gas out of the furnace with the force draft fan. This limitation has not diminished the popularity of this roof firing furnace.

The V2M-9 is supported under the water drum and mid-point header complex. The relatively light-weight lower furnace is hung from a mid-point in the header complex. There is no weight-carrying support located under the furnace, only guides to prevent the furnace from moving fore and aft. This system

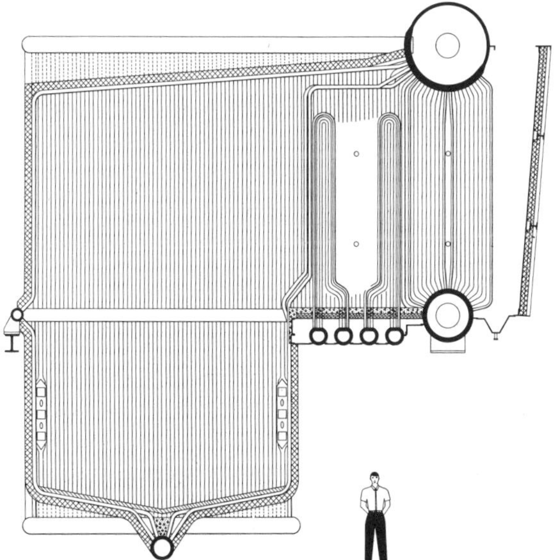

Fig. 5-17D. Sectional Elevation Plan for V2M-9 Arranged for Tangential Firing

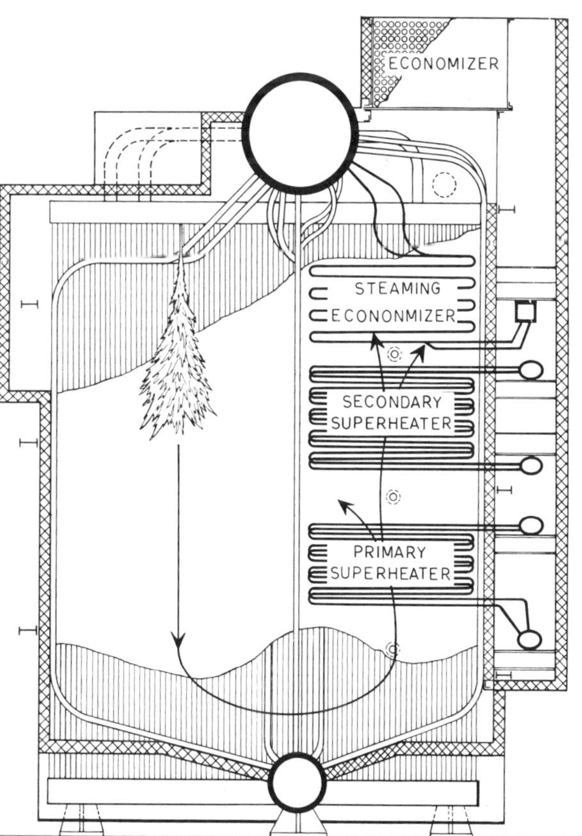

Fig. 5-17E. Section Elevation Plan, Typical "Radiant" Design

provides for thermal expansion downward for the lower half of the furnace and upward for the upper half of the furnace from the midpoint center support. This support arrangement also locates the boiler center of gravity very close to the major foundation located under the water drum. Figure 5-17F shows the arrangement of this boiler in the machinery space of a 180,000 DWT tanker.

Controls and Instrumentation

It is essential that the shipboard boiler plant be fitted with adequate instruments to enable the operating personnel to raise steam, maintain design conditions for steady steaming, secure the boiler units, and to promptly detect malfunctions and failures. It is desirable to have the boiler instruments situated on a gauge board which also includes the combustion and feedwater controls, with duplicate instruments for principal variables provided at the main throttle station gauge board.

Shipboard boiler controls can be classified into two basic groups: controls which regulate continuously, and controls which act to perform a prescribed operation when a limiting condition has been exceeded. Regulating types of controls include combustion, boiler water level, fuel oil temperature, fuel oil viscosity, blowdown, and superheat temperature. Combustion controls of a pneumatic or electric type are widely used for merchant ships while naval vessels use pneumatic controls exclusively. Different systems available offer varying degrees of automatic control. Generally, the combustion control system maintains constant steam pressure by controlling the flow of air and oil to the boiler. The more advanced controls transmit the air and oil loadings simultaneously, but with a slight lag between air and oil. The air will lead the oil as the boiler load is increased, and the oil will lead the air as the boiler load is decreased. Such an arrangement makes it possible to minimize the emission of smoke during a maneuvering.

In the past, ships were fitted with feedwater regulator control systems which operated solely as a function of the drum water level. However, as boiler steam conditions and evaporation rates were increased to meet the requirements of higher power propulsion plants, it was determined necessary to have a two-element control. In this situation impulses of drum water level and steam flow are combined to give a more accurate response during maneuvering conditions. These systems are installed on many cargo ships and

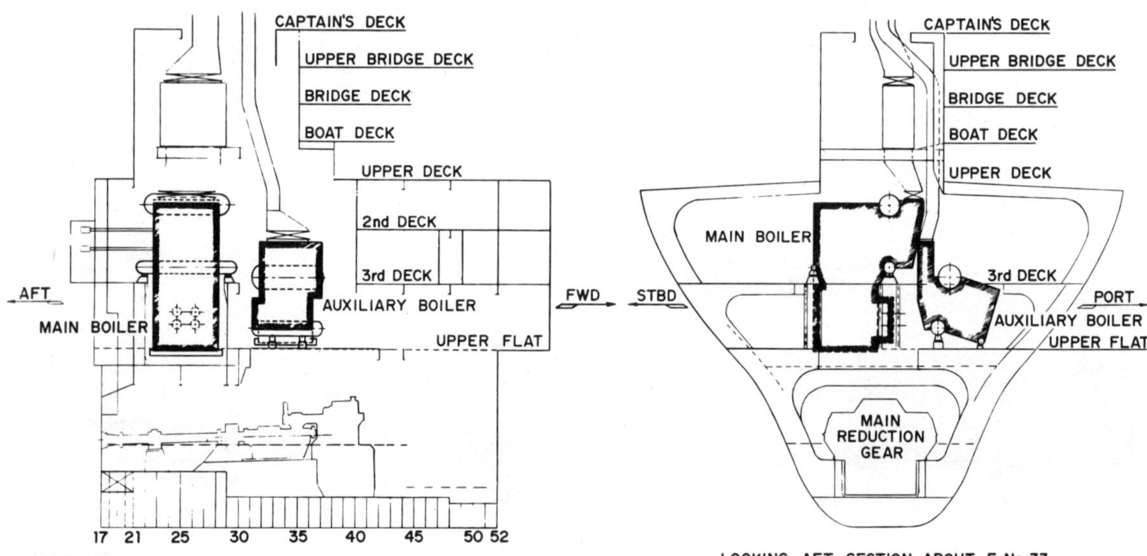

Fig. 5-17F. Arrangement of the V2M-9 in the Machinery Space of a 180,000 DWT Tanker

have proven to be reliable. In addition, some types of ships, specifically naval vessels and high-power passenger ships, are fitted with three-element feedwater controls. In the three-element systems, drum level, feedwater flow, and steam flow are measured and transmitted to the regulating valve in the feed line.

Many controls serve to operate or present a warning signal when dangerous conditions exist. Controls of this type include high water level alarm, low water level alarm, low stack temperature alarm, and fuel oil shut-off for forced draft fan failure.

Fuel Burning

Fuel Oil

Oil burners for marine boilers must be capable of burning the fuel oil within a furnace of minimum dimensions. Therefore, the design of the furnace and the location of the burner must go hand in hand. The burner must also provide for efficient firing over a wide range of oil flow rates and be able to change load rapidly to meet maneuvering requirements. For ships which require a substantial proportion of their operating time in maneuvering operation, it is essential that the boilers be fitted with burners which are able to vary the firing rate over a wide range without the need of changing atomizer tips.

Before the oil can be burned, the oil must be atomized and at the same time mixed with an ample supply of air to permit combustion. A burner consists of two parts: (1) the atomizer which serves to deliver a flow of atomized oil to the furnace, and (2) the register which serves to supply a flow of air to the furnace. The burner barrel contains a sprayer plate, oil chamber, and an orifice tip which set together to produce a fine oil spray.

The straight mechanical oil burner consists of a burner atomizer which converts the potential energy of the oil pressure into a flow of atomized oil particles. The oil flow is regulated by varying the supply pressure. On some installations this is accomplished manually and on others it is done automatically.

The return flow oil burner functions with a constant pressure oil supply and the atomizer barrel contains a passage which permits a portion of the oil to return to the fuel oil service pump section. The firing rate is varied by regulating the control valve in the return line. This type of burner achieves a much wider range than the straight mechanical burner.

The steam atomizing burner utilizes a flow of steam which mixes in the atomizing tip with the oil flow. A portion of the energy in the steam serves to break up the oil particles for better atomization. This burner has a high turndown ratio and offers the advantage of being able to efficiently burn low quality fuels.

Although various other burner designs have been developed, none has the acceptance to the extent that it may be considered popular.

Coal

While a vast majority of shipboard installations are fired by oil, there still remain some uses where the economic conditions make it desirable to burn coal. Modern coal-fired marine boilers are fitted with stokers. They are similar to the stationary coal feed systems, but on a smaller scale.

Atomic Fuels

Atomic fuels may become popular for marine use. A pound of uranium possesses the same energy as 4.5 million pounds of coal.

Engine Components

If a reciprocating engine is the power source, it is usually located so that its weight is divided over the center beam of the ship. The *screw* or propeller is directly attached to the flywheel because the rpm of the engines can be controlled. Sometimes a small engine is located to the rear of the main engine for reverse movement.

Today, turbines are usually employed because of their many advantages. Having no pistons or connecting rods jerking back and forth, turbines run more smoothly than the reciprocating engines and are more efficient, produce more power for the fuel consumed, and take less space.

Some turbines are connected to the propeller shaft by reducing gears. High rpm of the turbines and the slower rpm of the screw make this reduction necessary. If a turbine is to work efficiently, it must revolve at a very high speed. Since a turbine cannot run backwards, the vessel must employ a small turbine for reverse direction.

Sometimes, a turbine is connected to an electrical generator whose output is connected to an electric motor for driving the screw. With this type of system, the electrical power can be controlled to the motor and easily reversed with a switch. This eliminates the need for the small reverse turbine.

The turbines employed at present can be divided into two major types – the *impulse* and the *reaction turbines*. This classification is based on the number of rows of blades and how the steam energy is used.

Different turbines employ these two major principles in various ways (see Chapter 3). They have one important principle in common – that of changing a high-pressure, high-temperature gas to lower pressures and temperatures while extracting the kinetic energy to do work.

Steam Locomotive Power Plant

The steam locomotive has been, until recently, a popular, stable, remarkable, and dramatic means of transportation on land.

From the point of view of a power plant, the steam locomotive is unique and interesting. Compactness, high power, and wide ranges in load are very important. Weight, space, weather, and severe service conditions, are all obstacles that were surmounted by the locomotive engineer and designer. The locomotive itself is a movable steam power plant consisting of fuel source, operator's cab, water supply, cylinders, and pistons coupled to the wheels.

The steam locomotive is a wonderful facet of our country's socio-economic history. Its glamour was evident in developing the West. It served as a main artery of transport during both world wars. Top priority is always given to the offensive strategy involving the demolition of an enemy railroad and the protection of one's own lifeline.

Just a little more than two centuries ago such problems as the placement of the boiler horizontally or vertically plagued the designers. Of course, the horizontal boiler was chosen because of its greater efficiency, ease of maintenance, and transport. The boiler size and diameter grew until it reached its limit. Higher and wider locomotives just would not pass through existing tunnels or navigate curves. Cylinder and wheel connections, heaters, superheaters, variable valve gears, automatic stokers and train controls were added. This makes a complicated contrivance, quite refined and efficient. And this was wonderfully dramatic, as anyone who ever witnessed close-up, a steam locomotive exhausting and grinding to a halt, and then puffing and spitting to churn up speed will attest. In fact, many model railroad layouts show preference to steam locomotives rather than diesel types.

Types of Locomotives

There were three main types of locomotives: *freight*, *passenger*, and *switch engines*. They were built to serve such requirements as speed, heavy loads, and economy. Trains are classified by wheel arrangement from front to rear, see Fig. 5-18. Thus, a locomotive with a two-wheel pilot truck (pony wheels), six driving wheels, and a two-wheel trailing truck, was referred to as a 2-6-2. It was also referred to as a *Prairie* type. If the trailing wheels were missing, it was called a *Mogul* or a 2-6-0. If the pilot wheels were left off as well, it would become a 0-6-0 switcher capable of navigating the sharp curves found in railroad yards.

As a rule, steam freight locomotives employed smaller drivers than passenger engines. This gave them greater power. Passenger engines had larger drivers giving them greater speeds, and they seldom employed trailer tracks to support the firebox.

Tenders varied a great deal. Those used for short runs were much smaller than those employed for heavy freight work because they had to carry more coal and water. Trucks on the latter had 4, 6, or 8 wheels and usually had mechanical stokers for the firebox.

Before we look inside to see what makes it go, let us look at the locomotive and learn to recognize the exterior nomenclature in order to be able to appreciate this ingenious piece of mechanization. See Fig. 5-19.

Locomotive Description

At the front of the locomotive is the pilot truck, just behind the cow catcher (16). On the pilot beam is mounted the coupler. The cylinder is topped by the valve box or steam chest. The steam chest encloses the valve rod which leads to it. Just behind are the valve hangers and valve gear. From the cylinder comes a piston rod leading to a cross-head attached to the first wheel. From this wheel, the side rod is connected to the other drivers.

The stack of the boiler prominently shares the top of the boiler with the sand dome. The sand dome stores a ton or more sand for starts on icy tracks and emergency stops. The following smaller dome, the steam dome, houses the whistle controls and the throttle valve. Bell whistle and safety valves complete the top boiler exterior.

Along the side of the boiler are the running boards. They suspend high pressure air drums needed for brakes. Forward of the cab is a large section of the boiler called the firebox. This houses the fire, grates, and the flue which takes the heat past the water tubes. A superheater is also contained here. The superheater

Fig. 5-18. 2-8-2 Steam Locomotive
(Collection of M. C. Wikman, Flanders, N.J.)

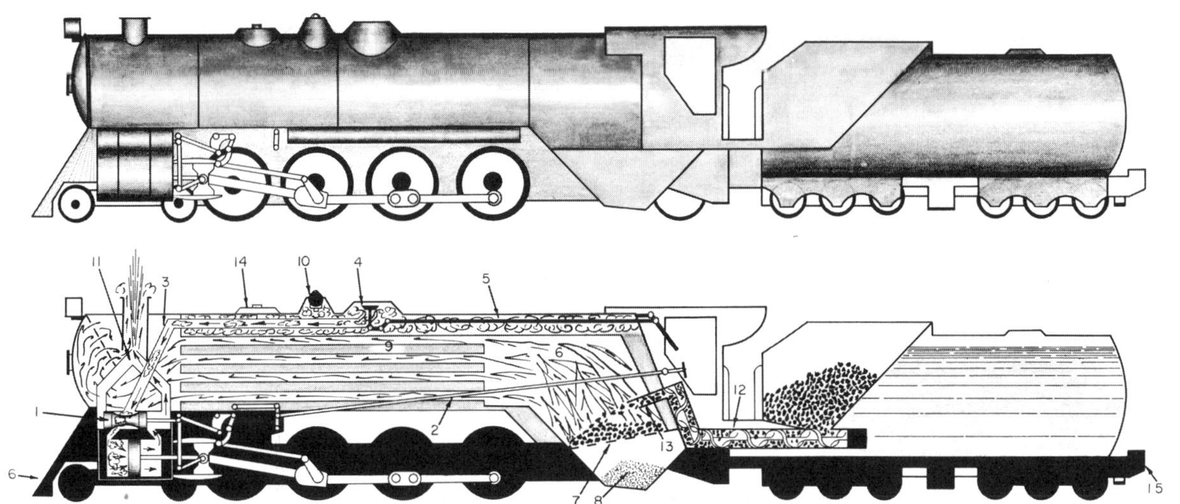

Fig. 5-19. Sectional View of a Typical Steam Locomotive with Major Parts Labeled

1. Steam Chest and Valve
2. Reversing and Variable Cut-Off Linkage to the Valve Gear
3. Steam Pipe
4. Throttle Valve
5. Superheater
6. Firebox
7. Grates
8. Ash Pit
9. Flue
10. Steam Dome
11. Stack
12. Mechanical Stoker
13. Stoker Feed-Pipe
14. Sand Dome
15. Tender
16. Cow Catcher

heats the steam so that it will acquire live-steam or perfect gas properties. Note that there is no condenser. Steam locomotives usually have no condensers because of the prohibitive additional weight. It is usually easier to take on new water as the old water is consumed by the boiler.

Two views of the locomotive are given, an outside view and a section. The inside arrangement of the principal parts is shown including the steam chest and cylinder where the propelling force of steam is absorbed by the piston and is transferred to the wheels.

Locomotive Operation

The working of the stationary steam engine was explained in Chapter 2. The locomotive engine works in the same way. Referring again to the Fig. 5-19, try to evolve the mechanics of the steam locomotive. It should be easy for you to recognize the cylinder, valve cylinder, main piston, valve piston, connecting rods, and the side rods joining all the wheels which distribute the tractive force among them.

When the locomotive starts from a standing position, the greatest force is required to overcome its inertia. More steam is admitted to the cylinder since the steam cut-off is made late. This is accomplished by a series of links and levers that actuate the valve so that the cutting-off of the steam admission can be made later in the stroke. This causes more steam to be admitted into the cylinder. This very important feature of the locomotive is called the *variable cut-off.*

As the speed of the locomotive increases, the cylinders require steam more frequently and the consumption is increased. This demand is usually evident at speeds in excess of 10 mph. The variable cut-off must gradually be made to occur earlier in the stroke. This reduces the portions of steam taken at each reversal of the piston and gives the boiler time to replenish with fresh steam that which was drawn off into the cylinders. Of course, the less steam taken by each stroke the smaller the force exerted. Thus the force can be adjusted to cause no further acceleration of the locomotive and it then proceeds at a constant speed. This, of course, also is affected by resistance due to friction of the train and changes in grades.

The late cut-off, which is necessary to start the train, causes the steam to rush in and out of the cylinders with great speed and noise. The noise is the loud chugging accompanied by puffs of smoke that make the steam locomotive so compelling to watch. At high speeds, the exhaust steam is at a lower pressure causing a much less violent and noisy escape.

Control of the variable cut-off is accomplished through a complicated system of links driven from a cross-head and main crank, see Fig. 5-19. The locomotive engineer can, also, with the same mechanism, cause the train to reverse. This can be seen by again referring to the diagram. Suppose the valve was moved back. This would cause the admission port in the forward end to be closed and the exhaust port to be opened. In the rear end, the admission port would be open and the exhaust port closed. The steam would now act on the back of the piston, pushing it forward, pulling the connecting rod and crank, turning the wheels clockwise, and causing the locomotive to move in reverse.

The *throttle* shuts off the steam when the locomotive must be stopped. The steam, as you can see, comes to the cylinders through a pipe, at the end of which is fitted the throttle valve which can be opened or closed from the cab by means of a long rod and hand lever. With one hand, the engineer is able to pull on the throttle lever, open the throttle valve, and permit the steam to go from the boiler to the cylinders. His other hand can control the variable cut-off, varying the admission of steam as need demands. See Fig. 5-20.

In the beginning, *hand stoking* was satisfactory, but as the locomotive increased in size, the appetite for fuel also increased until *mechanical stoking* was necessary. This device usually consists of a hollow tube through which a large screw turns. The screw extends from the tender to the firebox. The fireman need only control the speed of the stoker so that the supply of coal be adequate. The amount of coal is based on the demands of the boiler. The fireman also watches the water level gauge in the boiler and can add water from the tender.

Naturally, it isn't long after the train is in motion that it must *slow up or stop.* The engineer controls the braking mechanism from the cab. See Fig. 5-20. The brakes are actuated by *air pressure* produced by steam-driven air pumps. They are located under the middle of the running board. From these tanks air pressure is transmitted through pipes and flexible hose connections between all cars and brakes on each wheel. When the engineer wishes to stop, he *releases the throttle* and opens the *air valve.* The open valve causes the brake shoes to rub against the wheels stopping the train.

The reciprocating engine was not very efficient. It caused railroad engineers to look for another prime mover as an answer to economical power demands. The *turbine* and

Fig. 5-20. Inside the Cab of a Steam Locomotive
(Collection of M. C. Wikman, Flanders, N.J.)

diesel engine (see Chapter 11) were their next sources of locomotion. However, the reciprocating steam engine may be still used for long hauls, up sharp grades, or where fuels are relatively cheap. In any case, if the locomotive should ever completely leave the scene as a prime mover, its glamorous tradition will surely be retained by the model railroader who finds it as exciting as ever.

Turbine Locomotive

The steam turbine engine employs a boiler to generate steam. Steam releases its energy to a turbine which is geared to axles. This is accomplished within a shell that permits streamlining to reduce air resistance. One wheel receives its energy from the turbine with the side rod driving the other drivers. This locomotive makes a steady hissing sound since the steam is employed within to do work.

Mercury Vapor Turbine

The hotter the steam generated by the boiler and the hotter the steam sent to the turbine the more efficient the installation. To raise efficiency, some stationary systems employ mercury vapor in place of steam. Mercury is an element that is liquid at ordinary temperatures, although it is denser than lead. The mercury boiler generates mercury vapor at 884°F. The vapor activates the turbine and then is condensed in a heat exchanger. The exchanger also doubles as a water boiler. The steam from this exchanger-boiler is used to run another turbine.

Although this system is quite efficient, it has one major disadvantage – mercury vapor is poisonous. Any leak in the system can prove dangerous to the operators.

New Directions for the Steam Engine

Steam engines were sidetracked from the main line of automotive research years ago because of their bulk and relatively high cost. Today, steam engine designers claim that their steam power plant will be smaller, cheaper, and quieter than the gasoline engine. Above all, it will cause far less air pollution. Two firms have been chosen to install steam engines in California highway patrol cars for a year's road test. The president of one of these firms claims that the technology for steam-powered family cars is here.

The internal combustion engine beat out the steam engine as the prime mover for the automobile because it was smaller, cheaper and safer. The tin lizzie sold for $900 compared to $3,000 to $4,000 for a Stanley Steamer. Also, steam engines were dangerous in those days. A large volume of water was heated to generate a small amount of steam. Boilers were relatively weak and there were frequent explosions. Technology today permits a large amount of steam to be developed from a small amount of water, perhaps a couple of pints of water in small coiled tubes. If a tube were to burst, the problem would be only a leak not an explosion. Most importantly, smog production was not a problem in the old days. The internal combustion engine gave off clouds of smoke, but nobody cared because there were relatively few of them. Today there are millions of cars on the road and pollution is a problem. In the steam engine virtually all the fuel is burned and little, if any, pollution escapes into the air.

Steam Powered, Low-Pollution Locomotion[3]

Inventors and engineers have always strived to get more power from an engine with less fuel, at less cost, lower weight, in less space. In the first decades of the automobile industry, these goals led away from the steam and electric power units to the internal combustion reciprocating engine. Had the early designers been directed to develop an engine that would pollute less, the evolution of the internal combustion engine and specifically the automobile power plant might have been quite different.

The 19th century was the most active age in the development of prime movers in our entire history. It produced the conception of all the basic power cycles that are contending today for acceptance as the basis for producing the cleanest prime mover. One of the first theories to have widespread acceptance was the Rankine cycle or steam engine principle. This was followed by the development of the Otto cycle fundamental to the internal combustion reciprocating engine, the Brayton cycle fundamental to the gas turbine and the Sterling and Diesel cycles. All of these cycles employ heat energy to do work in some imperfect way. The theorist's ideal, explained in the Carnot cycle, can never be achieved in practice.

[3] Adapted from copyrighted materials provided by Research Development Department, Lear Motors Corporation, January, 1972. Reproduced with permission.

Early Steam Power Units

Founded in 1968, Lear Motors established the objective of developing a low-pollution prime mover that could be employed for means of locomotion, especially in automobiles. It was thought that the external combustion Rankine or steam cycle held the most promise for further development because combustion was continuous and therefore could be easily controlled. Accordingly one of the first investigations was to determine why steam powered automobiles had previously been unsuccessful. Many reasons were found:

1. The early automobiles used low pressure and temperature which obviously were inefficient.
2. Low efficiency made closed-loop or full condensing impractical, necessitating adding water every few miles.
3. Early steam cars were complex yet lacked the advantage of modern electronic controls.
4. Their physical size demanded that every conceivable space be used to provide for the power plant.
5. Early steam cars required up to one-half hour to get up steam. A surprising fact was that the steam cars of the twenties had pilot lights that kept the engine and the radiator system warm in sub-zero weather. If these cars had slow steaming boilers, the pilot light was also used to maintain pressure overnight. The pilot light system required only about a quart of fuel per night. This was a relatively small price to pay for a warm, ready-to-go automobile.

6. The main reason for the steam car's failure was its cost. The Stanley Steamer was the most popular steam car because it was produced at the lowest cost. At peak production, the Stanley Company produced 600 cars per year. Ford at that time was producing over a million cars per year. Because of the low production rate, steam cars cost much more than the Ford Model T.

By the late twenties Ford was producing 4 million cars per year and his selling price eliminated 80% of the car companies before the great depression. The only companies that survived the depression were those that had a line of low-priced cars to sustain the losses incurred in producing luxury or high-priced automobiles. In Lear's analysis, the problem finally boiled down to developing a simple low-priced steam system that could be mass produced. When a production rate is in the millions, price then is mostly determined by the cost of materials. With mass production methods and low cost materials, the goal is to develop a new engine that will surpass the reciprocating internal combustion engine in terms of reliability, power-to-weight ratio, efficiency, and produce lower pollution emissions.

Turbine Electric System

Lear Motors investigated the feasibility of six power systems, three of which were turbine electric systems. In these, a turbine powered a large brushless alternator which generated electrical energy transmitted to drive motors at the wheels. These systems did not require conventional transmission and drive lines. The electric traction motors were conceived and designed, utilizing high speeds and stronger magnetic fields. These motors exhibited their maximum torque at zero speed, making them almost a perfect propulsion choice to drive a motor vehicle — capable of delivering a smooth stepless power from a standstill to maximum speed, with an efficiency competitive with present automatic transmissions. The drive motors were electronically controlled with almost no waste of power in the controlled system. If the power was not needed by the traction motor, it was then not generated by the alternator. The drive motors were brushless, variable speed units, linked to the alternator by a solid state control system.

Control of the electric drive was simple and reliable. The voltage and current levels required by the motors were regulated by control of the alternator's field. A tachometer mounted on each motor monitored speed and synchronized it with the firing frequency of the silicon controlled rectifiers. Complete studies of vehicle applications for turbine systems with electric drives were carried out for passenger cars as well as commercial application. Very attractive layouts were possible by mounting four drive motors at the respective wheels providing an all-weather four-wheel drive system. Further breakthroughs may be made in the implementation of an electric drive system, whether it be battery powered or turbine-alternator powered.

Two different types of power turbines were developed: a gas turbine and a vapor turbine. The gas turbine was a single shaft turbine instead of the two-shaft designs employed by most automotive gas turbine designers. Dynamometer tests were conducted on this turbine engine to determine feasibility and potential for use as a low-pollution power plant. Based on these tests it was concluded that a suitable gas turbine based on the Brayton cycle would be impractically expensive. Attention was then directed to the development of the vapor turbine. The vapor turbine system is similar to the steam turbine and employs the Rankine cycle.

The chief difference between the vapor turbine and steam turbine is the choice of working fluid. In one case it is water to steam, and in the other it is an organic fluid. The organic fluid is relatively inexpensive, safe, and non-toxic. It freezes at minus 40°F and will give good efficiency at the low vapor temperature of 600°F. It condenses at the same temperatures and pressures as water and has a high molecular weight. This fluid allows for the development of a simple, efficient turbine design that did not require a gear reduction system. Organic fluid systems can give an efficiency that is competitive with present gasoline automobile power plants, but only water can tolerate the very high temperatures necessary to yield the efficiency really desired. Both systems require a boiler, condenser and pumps.

Involute Expander Engine

Lear also refined an engine that employed the Rankine cycle in a rather unique way. First developed as a compressor, the unit worked equally well as an engine and is known by several names, including *helical screw motor, involute expander* and *Lysholm motor*. See Fig. 5-21. This pressure motor combines the best qualities of a turbine and piston engine, and operates as a positive displacement engine rather than a simple force device. This engine exhibits a high efficiency at low horsepower levels, which is characteristic of reciprocating engines, but it also has the smooth continuous power of a turbine. There is no reciprocating motion or recompression which are the two chief causes of vibration and noise in the conventional reciprocating engine.

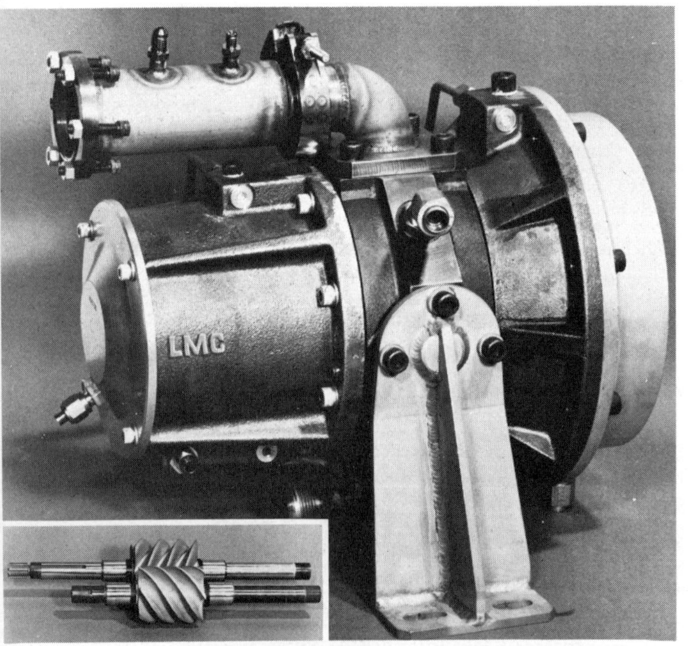

Fig. 5-21. First Stage of a Two-Stage Involute Expander Motor (Lear)

The involute expander engine consists of two helical screw rotors running in mesh on parallel shafts. Each meshing thread on the rotors forms a small cavity, which enlarges with rotation much like a piston travelling down a cylinder. Steam is introduced into the small cavity at one end and then expands, to be exhausted at the other end. A 300-horsepower motor of this type would occupy less than a cubic foot and weigh approximately 100 pounds. It has a maximum torque at zero speed or stall condition and is capable of a wide speed range. With these characteristics neither a torque converter nor shifting transmission is required. The only shortcoming of these steam handling involute screw-type engines is the very high manufacturing precision required. Lear Motors is still conducting tests and advancing the state of involute expander technology. In Fig. 5-22 is a conception of this system applied to a motor vehicle.

Reciprocating Steam Engine

Another power plant under development was a conventional piston steam motor – a 6 in-line engine of the single-acting type. It used poppet valves and many other parts common to the modern day internal combustion engine. This engine's chief advantage is its close identity with the present technology and production methods. It was felt that with the cost of a relatively short engineering and tooling phase this engine would power the first steam systems and would incorporate the

Automotive Installation Concept

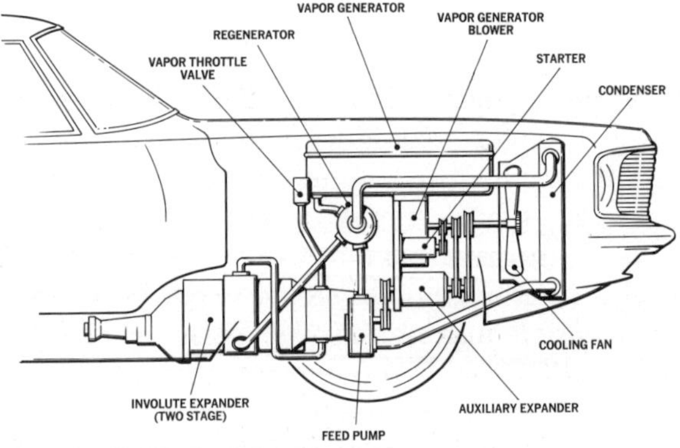

Fig. 5-22. Involute Expander System (Lear)

virtues of the past steam engine such as smooth and quiet power and also high torque at low speeds and wide efficiency range. Static testing trials led to an installation of this reciprocating steam engine in the front of a passenger car which was intended for use as a police patrol vehicle. However, the engine's large size made it necessary to install the radial inflow vapor generator in the trunk of the car. Although this power system would have met both State and Federal pollution criteria the layout was not up to the desired standards so it was set aside.

Vapor Turbine System

The most promising engine developed by Lear Motors is a straight vapor turbine power plant. It has been installed in a demonstration bus for the California Department of Transportation. This bus developed sufficient horsepower to supply all drive and auxiliary systems and propel the bus up a 19% grade with a 50% overload of passengers. (A 19% grade is the steepest hill in San Francisco.) See Figs. 5-23 and 5-24.

When the driver turns on the key, this activates the starter, combustor fan, and fuel pump. Refer to Fig. 5-25. A spark plug ignites the fuel and air mixture and the resulting flame heats the water which is encased in thin tube coils in the boiler. The steam generator or boiler consists of a continuous coil of tubing surrounding the burner. The burner has an integrally mounted combustor blower. Viewed with the boiler lid off, the tubes appear to be tightly stacked in uniform layers. After the boiler is fired up, steam is produced within 30 to 60 seconds. The steam is then metered to the turbine by a special throttle

Fig. 5-24. Vapor Turbine Installation in a Bus (Lear)

Compare with Fig. 5-28.

Components & Flow Diagram

(REAR VIEW)

Fig. 5-23. Vapor Turbine System (Lear)

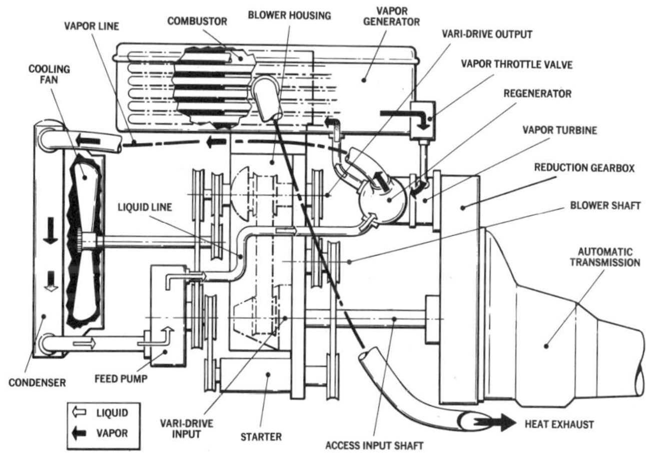

Fig. 5-25. Vapor Turbine System Diagram (Lear)

or valving mechanism. The turbine contains multiple nozzles which emit high velocity steam against the turbine wheel blades. See Fig. 5-26. The turbine shaft transmits power to a reduction gear box which drives an automatic transmission, Fig. 5-27.

After the steam has passed through the turbine it goes to the regenerators. See Fig. 5-25. These units serve two functions: they preheat the water going to the boiler and precool the vapor or steam on its way to the condensers. The condensers reduce the steam to

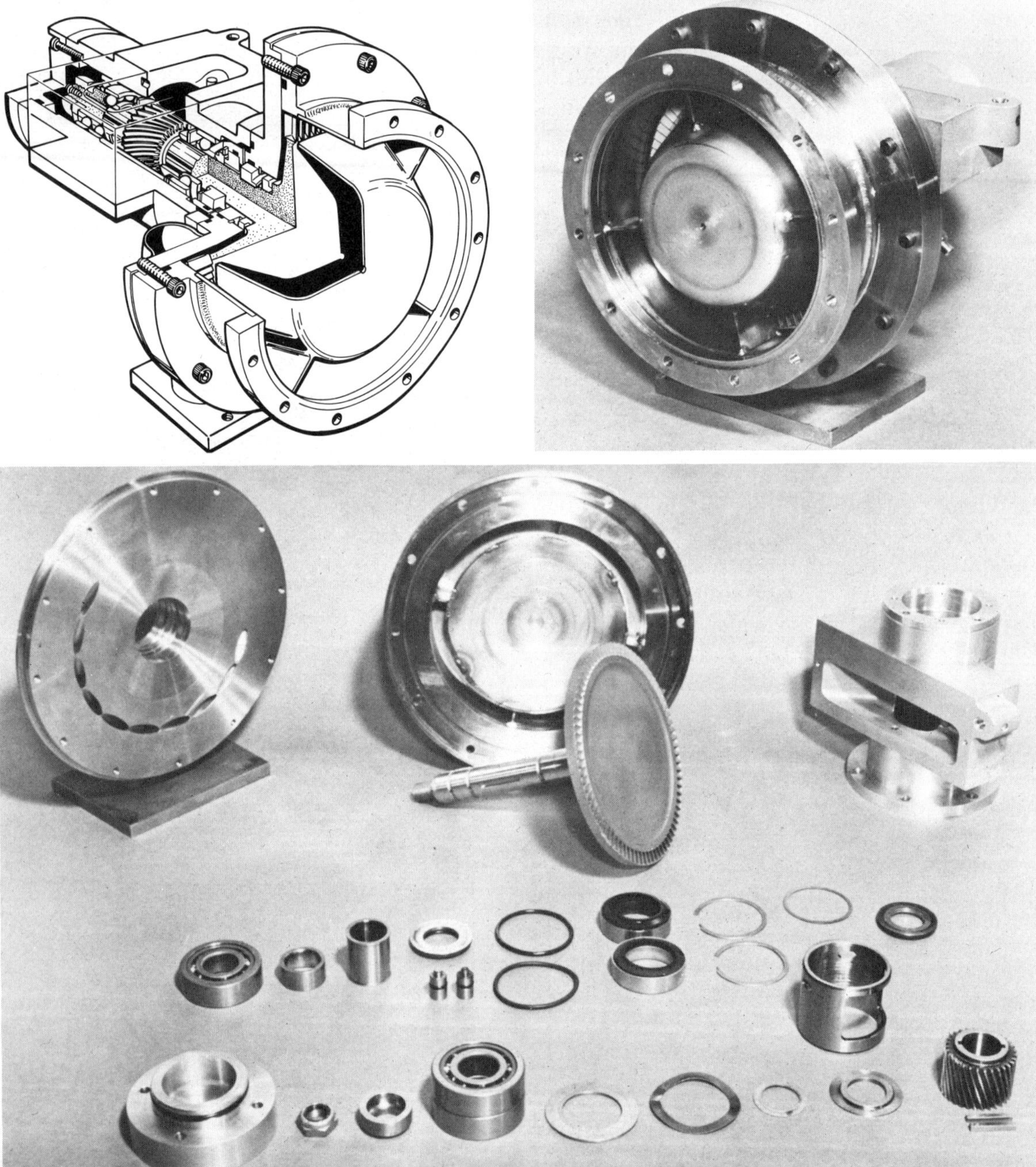

Fig. 5-26. Vapor Turbine and Components (Lear)

a liquid state which drains to the makeup tank or reservoir. The water is then pumped up to boiler pressure and returned to the boiler tube coils for reuse. The operation of this vapor turbine system for vehicular power is no different than the basic operation of a conventional steam turbine system. Auxiliary systems for the operation of the turbine and accessories are driven by a shaft extending from the reduction gear box. A combination of mechanical and electrical components make up the fully automatic control system. Standard elements familiar in present day vehicles are required to operate the power system.

Vapor Generator, Condenser, and Accessories

The turbine wheel is three-tenths of an inch wide and 5.4 inches in diameter at the shrouded tips of the 80 blades which are three-tenths inch long. See Fig. 5-26. Supersonic nozzles and impulse type blades give good performance over the turbine's operating speed range of 15,000 to 55,000 rpm. A double-reduction gear train reduces the turbine speed by a ratio of 11.7 to 1 to permit the use of a present day automatic transmissions.

In both the turbine and the gear train, ball and roller bearings are used. For production, simpler specially designed fluid-film bearings are envisioned and further optimization of the design of the turbine blading is needed. Integrated with the turbine housing is its unique area-modulated control throttle, a series of cam-operated blades metering the proper amount of vapor to the nozzles. Changes in the throttle position affect the fuel delivery to the vapor generator through a solid-state, throttle rate control. This signals the system to increase or decrease the heat input according to the transient power requirements.

Fig. 5-27. Vapor Turbine and Gearbox (Lear)

The vapor generator is no larger than a tire with a 26-inch diameter, and is made of steel tubing wound in a spiral pattern around a central burner. Outer rows of tubing are finned to improve heat transfer and a series of passages is provided in the monotube system to provide quick startup response and fast control. The steam generator is simply designed and built. Where necessary it is air-cooled for durability and heat shielded to provide complete combustion for minimal emission. A proprietary burner design provides full vaporization and fast emission of readily available fuels. The air-cooled condenser that reduces the vapor to a liquid is made of aluminum. Though it looks like an automobile radiator, the condenser has four and one-half times as much surface area for heat dissipation. Variable speed servo motors power the turbine accessories: the fan, feed pump, the blower for the burner and others. They constantly adjust the output of these components to suit the demands for power being made by the turbine.

Characteristics of Performance

The vapor turbine system, as employed for vehicular power, is a remarkable industrial accomplishment. It retains the virtues of classical steam engines such as silence, smoothness, high stall torque, toughness and multi-fuel capability. In principle, the engine could easily outlast the vehicle in which it is installed. It offers small size, light weight, moderate cost and above all, clean combustion. Tests over the latest Federal emissions driving cycle have shown that the exhaust pollutant levels are markedly lower than the standards set for 1975 and 1976. The establishment of these very difficult standards did indeed encourage the development of a radically new and improved power system by organizations outside the established automotive industry.

The vapor turbine system is especially suitable for marine applications, because of the ready availability of water as a condensing medium.

The Stirling Engine[4]

Although the Stirling engine is not a steam engine, it is an external combustion engine. It is capable of burning a wide variety of liquid hydrocarbons, such as unleaded gasoline, diesel fuel, or kerosene. The Stirling engine burner is in continuous operation; and with sufficient fuel and an adequate air supply, the unit is designed to assure essentially complete combustion. Therefore, the engine emits virtually no odor and low amounts of carbon monoxide and smog-forming hydrocarbons. Presently the emission of oxides of nitrogen is about half of the present gasoline engine. The Stirling engine is also significantly quieter than conventional gasoline and diesel reciprocating engines.

[4] G. Flynn, W. Percisal, F. Earl Heffner, *GMR Stirling Thermal Engine*. General Motors Research Laboratories, 1966.

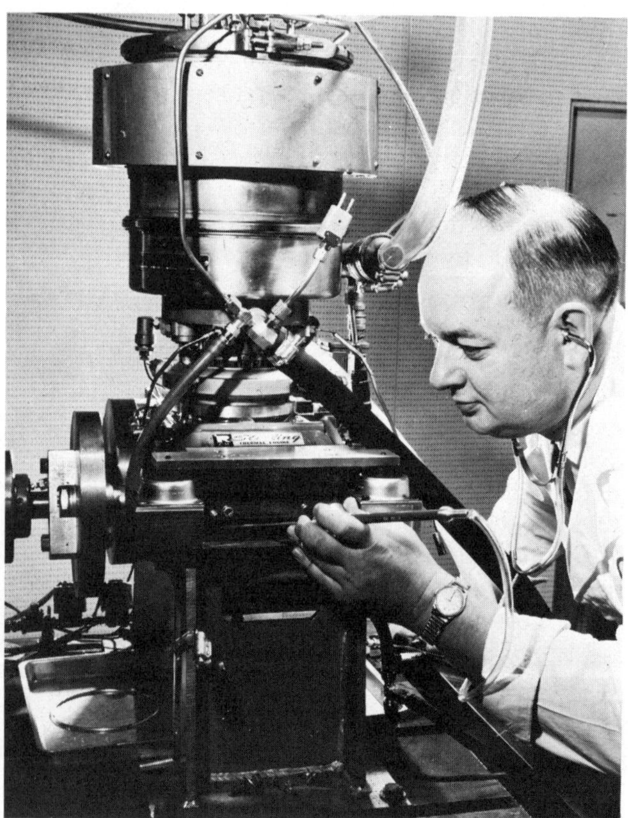

Fig. 5-28. Inspecting a Modern Eight-Horsepower Stirling Thermal Engine (G.M.)

The Stirling engine was invented in 1816 and was manufactured in small quantities for many years. It served in a variety of applications requiring simple, safe power sources. Electric motors and gasoline engines took over because the Stirling engine was too inefficient and too bulky.

In 1937, the Phillips Company of the Netherlands revived the Stirling engine and with the help of modern technology, developed a Stirling cycle engine that could compete in efficiency and output with present internal combustion engines. In the meantime General Motors' research had begun an extensive study of external combustion engines, including both vapor and gas cycle engines. After ten years of independent research, General Motors' research made a formal agreement with Phillips for an intensive cooperative research and development program on the Stirling engine. The new Stirling engine evolved from the application of modern thermodynamics and heat transfer principles with a new understanding of how the engine really works. In addition, improvements in materials, bearings, lubricants, and seals reflected an increase in output efficiency and durability of the engine. In the past ten years of research, General Motors has accumulated some 15,000 hours of operating time on experimental Stirling power plants ranging from eight horsepower, single-cylinder engines to 400 horsepower four-cylinder engines (Fig. 5-28). These engines were built and designed for a diversity of applications: to power army portable power units as well as for torpedoes, submarines, and other quiet and lightweight power plant uses.

At the present time the Phillips Company is working with German and Swedish manufacturers on Stirling engines for the world market. Phillips also is doing military-sponsored engine research. General Motors is continuing research on the basic Stirling engine and its components and is concentrating on the demonstration of potential engine application for low smog intracity bus propulsion and for quiet engine generator systems for the recreational vehicle market, such as boats in the 15-20 horsepower range.

Efficiencies are equal to or better than those of present internal combustion engines. For engines of several hundred horsepower, the Stirling will be about the size and weight of a similar diesel engine. In small sizes of tenths of horsepower, it will be larger but more efficient than similar output gasoline engines. In special applications it is capable of as much as 200 horsepower per cubic foot of engine or more than ten times the specific horsepower of normal mobile gas turbines or turbocharged diesels. Like any heat engine employing the thermodynamic cycle, it produces power by compressing the working gas when it is cold, letting it expand to do work when it is hot. The modern Stirling engine employs a metal mesh regenerator, which is the key to the engine's efficiency. The heat this regenerator recovers would otherwise be lost or dumped into the cooling system. It took many years of experience in heat transfer and regenerator design to develop this mesh regenerator.

Engine Operation

The Stirling thermal engine consists of five major components: the engine heater, the regenerator, the engine cooler, the displacer piston, and the power piston. The arrangement of these five major components is shown in the schematic. (See Fig. 5-29.) The heater consists of a bank of closely spaced stainless steel tubes brazed into the cylinder head and the regenerator. These tubes are kept hot by burning fuel in an external combustion system. The regenerator is a mass of fine wires sealed within eight individual cups located around the outside of the engine. The cooler is formed from bundles of small tubes surrounded by an annular chamber through which water is circulated. These cooler tubes form gas paths from the regenerator back to the cylinder.

The displacer piston is a hollow steel shell which fits loosely in the cylinder. Its motion is controlled through the displacer piston rod connecting it to the drive mechanism in the crankcase. There is very little pressure difference between the top of the displacer piston and its bottom, and a small leakage of gas between the displacer and the cylinder wall can be tolerated. Therefore, the displacer piston requires no rings or other sealing device. The top of the displacer piston operates at approximately the same temperature as the heater, while the bottom operates at approximately the temperature of the cooler so the piston walls are made as thin as possible to reduce heat losses due to conduction. In addition, the piston has two internal horizontal baffles to reduce radiant heat loss through the piston.

The power piston must provide the work of compressing the gas and deliver the work of expansion so it experiences considerable pressure differences between its upper and lower extremities. It therefore fits more closely into the cylinder and is equipped with suitable

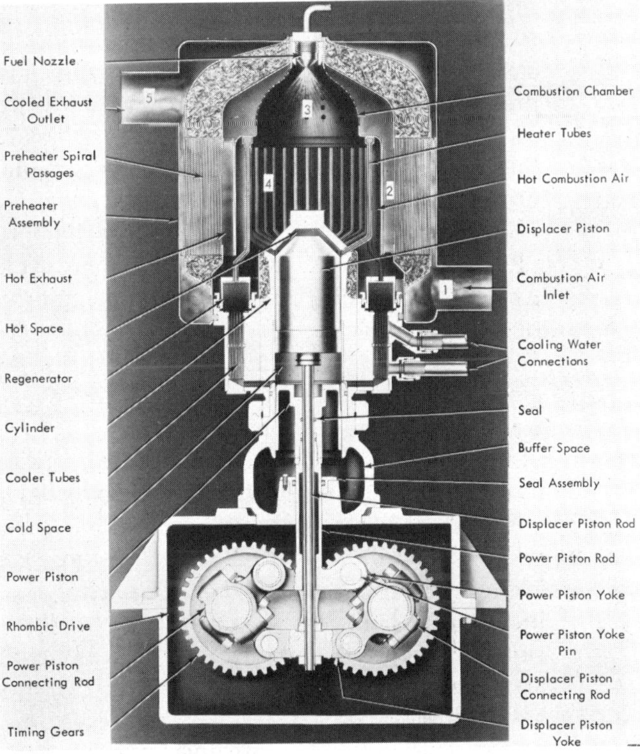

Fig. 5-29. Schematic of a Stirling Engine (G.M.)

rings and other sealing means to prevent gas leakage. The power piston is located entirely in the cold zone of the engine. This allows more latitude in the selection of sealing means than usual pistons in conventional engines which experience very high combustion temperatures. Force is transmitted from the power piston to the rhombic drive mechanism by the power piston rod as shown. This power piston rod is hollow, and the displacer piston rod passes through it.

Note that there is a buffer space below the power piston and above the seal assembly at the top of the crankcase. The engine is designed to operate at high pressure, and the buffer space is provided so that a thermodynamically inert volume of working fluid can be trapped below the power piston. The mean pressure of this gas in the buffer space is kept near the mean pressure of the working fluid above the power piston and serves to reduce the loads on the drive mechanism. Present engine assemblies have established the mean pressure at about 1,000 lbs. per square inch. The seal assembly shown at the power piston rod seals this buffer pressure while the crankcase is vented and operates at atmospheric pressure. It is also evident that a seal is required between the displacer piston rod and the inside of the power piston. A conventional O-ring is used at both locations.

The small numbers within the schematic (Fig. 5-29) indicate the combustion gas cycle. At point *1* cold combustion air from a suitable blower enters. It is then heated in the counterflow preheater, becoming hot combustion air at point *2*. Fuel is then introduced by the nozzle and burned at point *3* and the products of combustion give up energy to the working fluid in the heater tubes at *4*. The exhaust gases then pass through preheater tubes where they are cooled by the incoming air before being exhausted at *5*. It must be remembered that in the actual engine construction these components are annular elements arranged symmetrically around the cylinder center line.

The operation of the Stirling engine is completely governed by the relative motion of the two pistons, and it is most easily described by considering these piston functions. First, all of the working gas is contained in the total volume that is the sum of the volumes of the engine's five working spaces and their connecting passages. These spaces are: (1) the variable volume of hot gas space in the cylinder above the displacer piston, (2) the internal volume of the heater, (3) the gas volume of the regenerator, (4) the internal volume of the cooler, and (5) the variable volume of the cold working space between the pistons in the cylinder. The total volume occupied by the working fluid is, therefore, completely governed by the position of the power piston. Since the displacer piston always occupies the same volume, its position cannot change the volume of the system. Therefore, the gas volume change necessary to effect compression or expansion is accomplished by motion of the power piston and is independent of the position or movement of the displacer piston.

The displacer piston serves to control the location of gas within the total volume established by the power piston. When the displacer piston is at the top of the cylinder, most of the gas is in the cold spaces. Downward movement of the displacer piston forces the gas through the heat changer circuit up through the cooler, regenerator, and heater into the hot spaces. The net effect of this downward motion of the displacer piston is to move most of the gases up from the cold space into the hot space. Moving the displacer piston down heats the gas. Reverse motion of the displacer piston upward from the bottom of its travel transfers most of the working gas from the hot space downward through the heater, regenerator, and cooler into the cold space and effects the cooling of the gas.

The primary function of the power piston is to compress and expand the working fluid, and the primary function of the displacer piston is to heat and cool the working fluid. Only the gas contained in the active spaces above the power piston goes through the thermodynamic cycle that converts part of the heat from the heater into work at the power piston. The gas contained in the buffer space below the piston is the same kind of gas as the working fluid, but it accomplishes a thermodynamic purpose and serves only to balance the forces of the mean pressure of the supercharged working fluid.

The working fluid in the Stirling engine is usually hydrogen or helium, and the Stirling cycle is usually described by the sequence of piston positions shown in Fig. 5-30. With the power piston at bottom dead center (BDC) and the displacer piston at top dead center (TDC) the gas contained in the cold space is at maximum total volume. The first process in the ideal cycle is an isothermal compression. This is accomplished by movement of the power piston from bottom dead center to top dead center without moving the displacer piston, position *1*. The next process is the heating of the gas at constant volume. This is accomplished by moving the displacer piston from top dead center to bottom dead center without moving the power piston, position *2*. The third process is an isothermal expansion and is accomplished by moving the power piston from top dead center to bottom dead center without moving the displacer piston. The cycle would then be complete by returning the displacer piston to top dead center to cool the gas at constant volume. The above description of the piston motion is based on the theory that heat is transferred into and out of the working fluid through the cylinder walls during the isothermal process. In actual practice, however, the heating and cooling of the working fluid is accomplished by the suitable movement of the displacer piston.

The actual engine operations during the expansion and compression strokes are quite like those described for the ideal engine with relatively large time for heating during the expansion points *3* and *4* and relatively small time for cooling during compression points *1* and *2*.

Except for flow losses through the heat exchanger, the static pressure of the working fluid is constant in the engine working spaces at any given moment. The magnitude of this pressure is determined by the Gas Law Relationship and the distribution of

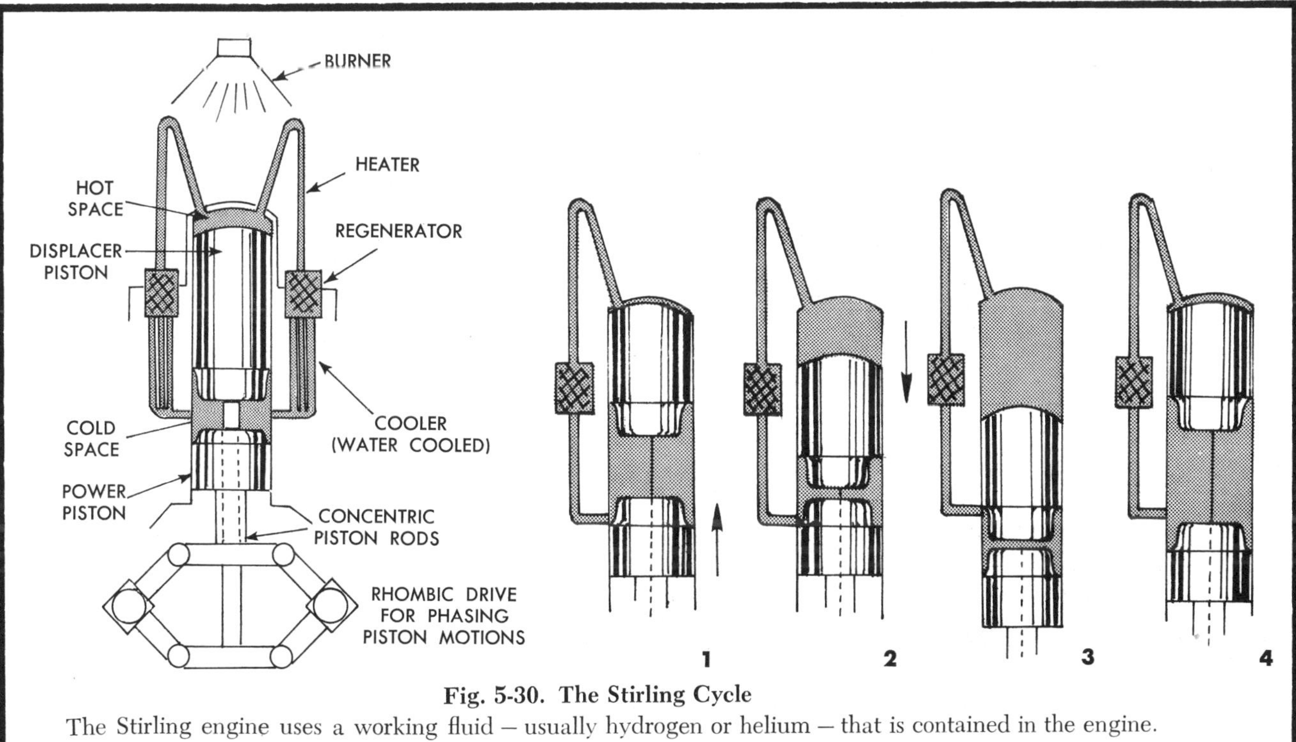

Fig. 5-30. The Stirling Cycle

The Stirling engine uses a working fluid – usually hydrogen or helium – that is contained in the engine.

the mass of working fluid in the various spaces of the engine, and this is influenced by motions of the pistons. If the displacer would move the gas from hot spaces to cold spaces with no motion of the power piston, the gas pressure would drop. Also, the power piston could change the gas pressure with no motion of the displacer piston by a change in the total volume of the gas. With the actual simultaneous motion of both pistons, a combination of these basic effects is produced. A unique characteristic of the Stirling thermal engine (and one that tends to indicate the degree of perfection with which it performs the thermodynamic conversion of heat to work) is the capability of the engine to function as a heat pump when work is put into the crankshaft instead of being taken from it as is the case in normal engine operation. If the engine is operated by driving the crankshaft with an external force or machine, the Stirling thermal engine will operate as a heat pump pumping heat from the heater to the cooler. In a few moments of operation the heat pipes will be sufficiently cool to cause frost to form from moisture in the air, and the engine will continue to refrigerate the surroundings as long as power is supplied to the crankshaft. This theoretical principle of being able to reverse cycles is easily explained thermodynamically. It is actually rather rare to find an engine that can perform such a feat.

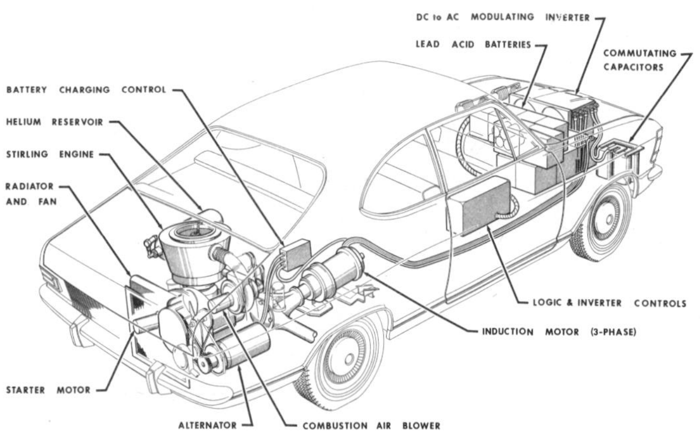

Fig. 5-31. The Stir-Lec I (G.M.)

Fig. 5-32. Small Stirling Engine Installed in Rear of the Stir-Lec I (G.M.)

Stirling Engine Electric Hybrid Car

The Stirling electric car is an experimental vehicle designed by General Motors to explore the feasibility of using this low emission engine and an electric drive system in a small car, Fig. 5-31. For this study a 1968 Opel Cadet was modified to use a variable speed alternating current electric motor to drive the rear wheels through reduction gears and the differential, Fig. 5-32. Batteries provide electric power to the motor through electronic circuitry that gives the variable frequency required for speed control. A small Stirling engine driving an alternator supplies energy to recharge the batteries. In the experimental test vehicle, the Stirling engine drives a three-phase alternator, the output of which is rectified to charge the batteries. The vehicle drive motor is a three-phase induction motor capable of providing about 20 horsepower over a three-to-one speed ratio. The battery power is modulated and inverted to provide variable frequency to the drive motor. The total weight with two passengers is approximately 3,100 lbs., which is about 1,100 lbs. more than a conventional vehicle with two passengers. The vehicle can accelerate from 0 to 30 miles per hour in 10 seconds and achieve a top speed of 55 miles per hour. In this first experimental car none of the components, the motor, the battery, or the engine, was optimized; and therefore, all limits indicated could be improved.

Terms to Understand

overall operational considerations
structural considerations
thermal considerations
breeching
economizer
preheaters or air heaters
superheaters
safety valves
working pressure
water gauges
steam gauge
Bourdon spring-tube gauge
oxidation
combustion considerations
primary air
secondary air
stoker
chain grate
overfeed stoker
underfeed stoker
retort
hopper
spreader stoker
pulverized coal
forced draft blowers
cross drum boiler
non-return valve
central control room
grit removal
cyclone separator
rapping bar
sluicing pipes
header
throttle valve
vacuum
heat balance
flywheel
hot well
feed pumps
marine power plant
marine condenser
screw
reverse turbine
locomotive power plant
2-6-2
pilot truck
driving wheels
trailing truck
prairie locomotive
mogul locomotive
switcher locomotive
tender
cow catcher
steam chest
steam dome
sand dome
running boards
air drums
stack
throttle valve
firebox
side rod
inertia
variable cut-off
mercury vapor engine
Rankine cycle
gas turbine
vapor turbine
steam turbine
involute expander engine
helical screw
condenser
vapor generator

Study Questions

1. Analyze why modern stationary power plants employ more than one fuel.
2. Discuss the advantages and disadvantages of the three most common types of fuel, coal, gas, and oil.
3. Describe briefly how each type of fuel may be stored and eventually fed into the furnace.
4. Name and give the purposes of various appendages of a modern water tube boiler.
5. Why is it necessary for modern steam generators to employ forced draft fans?
6. How do the superheater and economizer increase efficiency?
7. Describe how the water is caused to pass thru the steam generator, made into dry steam, used in an engine and returned to its source.
8. Describe the functions of draft gauges, water gauges, pressure gauges, steam and air mixers.
9. Describe the operation of a Bourdon spring tube pressure gauge.
10. Briefly describe the various methods of grit removal from the flue gases of modern power plants.
11. How is proper combustion accomplished in large boilers?
12. Why the necessity and urgency for smoke control?
13. Describe what is meant by heat balance.
14. Describe the operation of a steam power generating plant.
15. Analyze how the marine power plant is similar to stationary power plants and how it differs from these plants.
16. Why is oil more popular as a fuel than coal in marine power plants today?
17. Marine engines may be of a reciprocating or turbine variety. Analyze the advantages and disadvantages of each type engine including how each is employed.
18. Analyze the idiosyncrasies of a steam locomotive power plant. Include a list of unique demands made on this prime mover.
19. Analyze the part the steam locomotive played in the development of our nation.
20. Briefly describe the three main types of locomotives.
21. Describe the appearance and function of each part of a steam locomotive.
22. What is meant by "variable cut-off" of the reciprocating steam engine? Why is it necessary?
23. How does the engineer reverse the engine?

24. Briefly describe how the engineer brakes the train.

25. Analyze limitations of the reciprocating steam locomotive that prompted its passing.

26. Briefly describe the operation of a steam turbine locomotive.

27. What are the goals of performance for a transport power plant?

28. Why was internal combustion chosen over steam and electric power?

29. What has been a critical problem with external combustion propulsion systems?

30. Describe the vapor turbine system.

CHAPTER 6

Atomic Fuel Steam Generators

Recently, man has learned to harness the most amazing source of power—the energy locked within the atom. Even before Hiroshima was leveled by the destructive power of the first atomic bomb, man was attempting to tame this energy for peaceful purposes. He now has learned how to use this incredible source of power for the good of mankind. By controlling its heat, power can be provided for turbines on land and sea, all over the world.

The nuclear reactor is used to generate steam to operate conventional steam turbines. These turbines may be used to power electric generators as shown in Fig. 6-1, or to drive propellor screws of marine craft through gear reduction units. Thus, nuclear power can be used to satisfy a mechanical energy demand.

Today, nuclear generating stations are delivering electricity into power networks in many countries and their numbers are increasing every year. In the United States at least five such plants are in operation, nine are under construction and nine more being planned or developed. These will generate a total of two million kilowatts of power.

Nuclear energy is being used to power marine vessels such as the *USS Enterprise*, Fig. 6-2, submarines such as the *USS Nautilus, Triton, George Washington,* and *Thomas*

Fig. 6-1. Yankee Atomic Electric Plant, Rowe, Mass.

Fig. 6-2. Nuclear Powered Carrier, USS Enterprise (U. S. Navy)

Fig. 6-3. USS Ethan Allen, Second Generation Polaris Submarine (U. S. Navy)

Prior to the successful harnessing of the atom for propulsion, submarines were severely handicapped in underwater endurance. The oil-consuming diesel engines require air to burn their fuel. Therefore, the engines could be operated only when the craft was on the surface, or when the snorkel—a breather pipe—was raised. The snorkel, of course, was easily detected. When submerged a conventional submarine must derive power from storage batteries. With no means of recharging other than by snorkeling the submerged endurance was limited to a few hours.

Atomic engines overcame the handicap that plagued submarines. The nuclear power plant is, in its simplest terms, a steam engine of fantastic endurance.

The Nautilus, George Washington, Triton, and their sister ships operate on a tiny chunk of enriched uranium. The controlled nuclear reaction of the fuel causes tremendous heat. This heat boils water, converting it to steam which is used to drive large turbines. These turbines turn the propellers and turbogenerators which satisfy the electrical needs of the crew. The atomic engine, needing no oxygen, is capable of underwater subsistence limited only by the endurance of operating personnel.

Edison, Figs. 6-3 and 6-4, and the merchant ship *NS Savannah,* Fig. 6-5. These vessels could remain under power for months, even years, without refueling. Nuclear power is now being considered for rocket and satellite propulsion systems.

Special Components

Atomic Fuel

Power for these new turbo-electric stations and ships is provided by substances which we must regard as *fuel,* expended to provide heat in the same way as oil or coal. Current *atomic fuels* are the elements *uranium, plutonium* or *thorium,* or combinations of these. One ton of these atomic fuels, however, is equivalent to 2,300 tons of coal, or 300,000 gallons of oil. Nearly three million times as much heat is produced by a nuclear reactor using uranium fuel as is produced by an ordinary furnace burning coal or oil. This ratio will become even greater as technology improves on present methods. The burning of coal or oil is a chemical action, but the extrac-

Fig. 6-5. Nuclear Powered Merchant Ship, Savannah (Babcock & Wilcox)
Maiden voyage to Europe was in June, 1964.

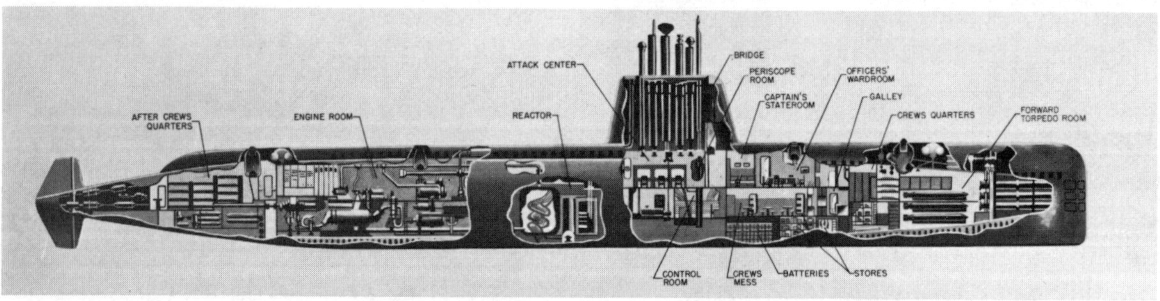

Fig. 6-4. Interior of USS Nautilus, First Nuclear Submarine (U. S. Navy)

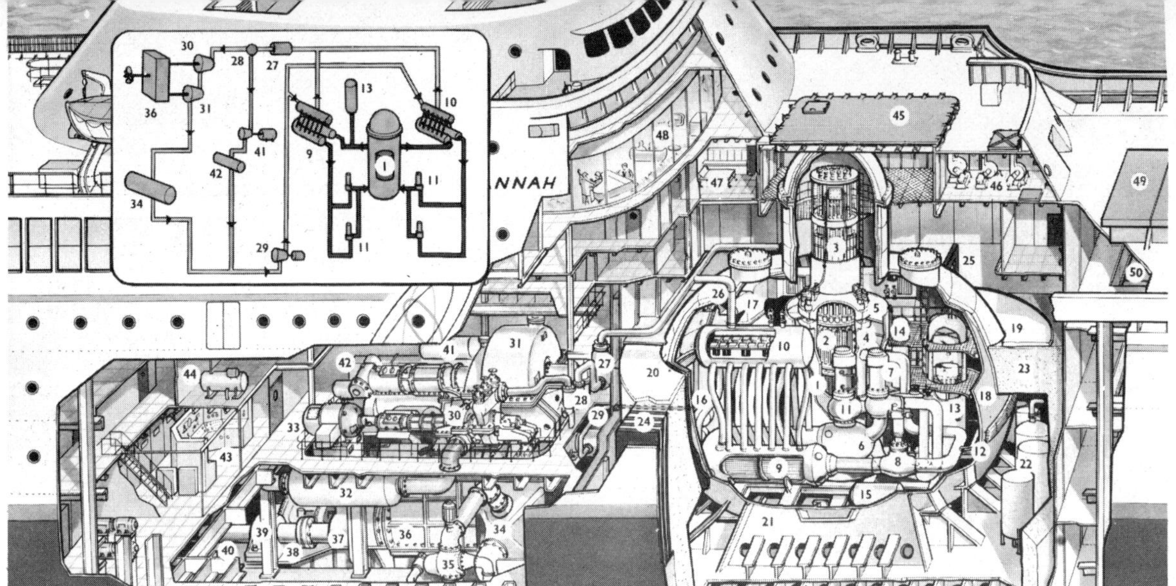

Fig. 6-6. Nuclear-Steam Power Plant of NS Savannah—Note Diagram on Inset (Nuclear Engineering, London)

1. Core
2. Control rods
3. Control rod mechanism
4. Reactor shell
5. Lead neutron shield
6. Primary inlet
7. Primary outlet
8. Gate valve
9. Heat exchangers (2)
10. Steam drums
11. Primary pumps
12. Pressurizer surge line
13. Pressurizer
14. Condensing tank
15. Drain tank
16. Let-down coolers
17. Cooling ducts
18. Steel containment
19. Lead shielding
20. Polyethylene shield
21. Vessel support members
22. Water treatment plant
23. Concrete shielding
24. Steel and redwood collision mat
25. Anti-roll brackets
26. Secondary steam outlet to turbines
27. Main steam separator
28. Throttle valve
29. Main feed pumps and secondary return
30. High-pressure turbine
31. Low-pressure turbine
32. Steam separator
33. Take-home motor
34. Main condenser
35. Main condenser pump
36. Reduction gears
37. Thrust bearing
38. Coupling
39. Propeller shaft bearing
40. Propeller shaft
41. Turbo-generators (2)
42. Auxiliary condenser
43. Control center
44. Water heater and tank
45. Reactor hatch
46. Fan room
47. Sick bay
48. Main lounge
49. Cargo hatch
50. Cargo hold

Fig. 6-7. Heat Exchanger of the Savannah's Nuclear Reactor (Babcock & Wilcox)

Fig. 6-8. Tubing for a Heat Exchanger on NS Savannah (Babcock & Wilcox)

Workman grinds welded sections. Marked areas have been X-rayed for safety. Reactor-heated water circulates through tubes in U-shaped exchanger (bottom) at 1750 psi and 520°F. It does not boil because of the extreme pressure. This heats secondary water in steam drum (top) forming steam at 490 psi and 347°F to drive the various turbines. Reacter, exchanger, and related units are contained in a heavy steel vessel shielded with lead, polyethylene, and concrete.

A total of 1624 ¾-inch stainless steel tubes 27 feet long were used. Each was most carefully made and tested because it must contain the high pressure of the primary water.

tion of atomic heat is a very different chemical process requiring different types of furnaces and boilers. Figs. 6-6 through 6-12 show a complete nuclear-steam power plant including the *fuel,* the atomic furnace or *reactor,* the boilers or *heat exchangers,* as well as conventional steam turbines, condensers and related units.

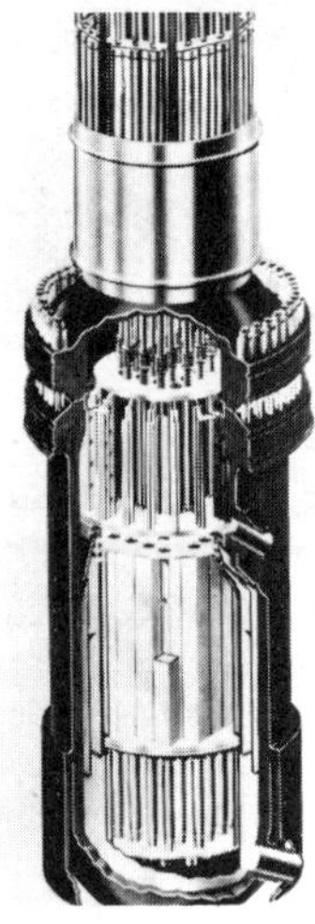

Fig. 6-9. Interior View of Pressurized Water Reactor on NS Savannah (Babcock & Wilcox)

Fuel element units are located in lower third. Control rods (finned, near center) are withdrawn to increase reaction. Hoisting mechanism is at top. Collar around middle unbolts for loading the fuel elements.

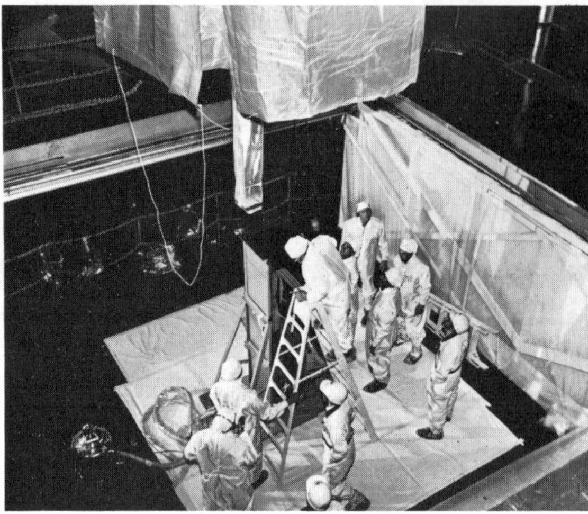

Fig. 6-11. Fuel Loading Procedures Start in Hold of Savannah (Babcock & Wilcox)

Conditions must be hospital clean. Fuel element is removed from packing case and lifted into nylon shroud overhead for protection. Shroud and element are then hoisted to top of reactor.

Fig. 6-10. View of Top of Fuel Elements If Covering Were Removed (Babcock & Wilcox)

There are 32 square fuel elements about 90 inches long. Each is made up of 4 bundles containing 41 rods (5 rows of 5, plus short rows of 4 around edges). Each rod contains about 130 pellets of uranium oxide enriched with about 4½% of uranium 235—a total of 8,060 kilograms of uranium fuel. Fuel elements are separated by 21 control rods which absorb neutrons. The further they are raised the more heat is generated. Water surrounding the container is circulated in the primary loops of heat exchangers.

Fig. 6-12. Fuel Element Is Positioned Over Opening of Loading Cover (Babcock & Wilcox)

The shroud forms a protective tent. Man at left measures radio-activity rate at all times. Polyethylene cover is removed as element is lowered into reactor. Note double eccentric discs in cover to position opening. About one hour is required to install each of the 32 fuel elements. One loading lasts about 300,000 miles—or 3½ years. It develops 22,000 hp, carries 10,000 tons, 60 passengers in luxurious quarters, and a crew of 110 at 21 knots. Length is 595½ feet, displacement 22,000 tons.

Nuclear Reactor

In a nuclear reactor, the fuel is used in a carefully arranged pattern to cause a controlled reaction. This reaction, called *fission,* creates a tremendous amount of heat in the heart of the reactor. Several types of reactors will be explained in this chapter.

Heat Exchanger

Heat from the reactor is used to produce steam in a boiler called a *heat exchanger.* Usually two piped circuits come to the exchanger. The *primary loop* uses a liquid (such as water or liquid sodium) or a gas (such as carbon dioxide) to carry heat from the reactor to the exchanger. This causes water in the *secondary loops* to become steam which is carried to the turbines, back through condensers and the condensate is returned to the exchanger. The reactor, primary loop, and exchanger must carefully be sealed to guard against radioactivity. The turbine may be used to turn generators or power the ship through gear reduction units.

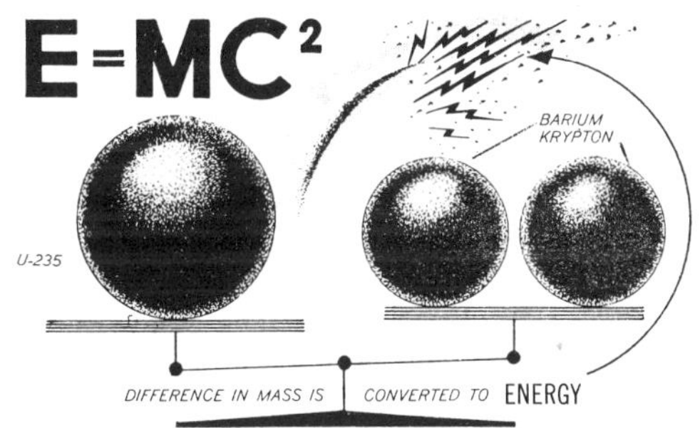

Fig. 6-13. Einstein's Formula Shows Energy Comes from Loss of Mass (G.M.)

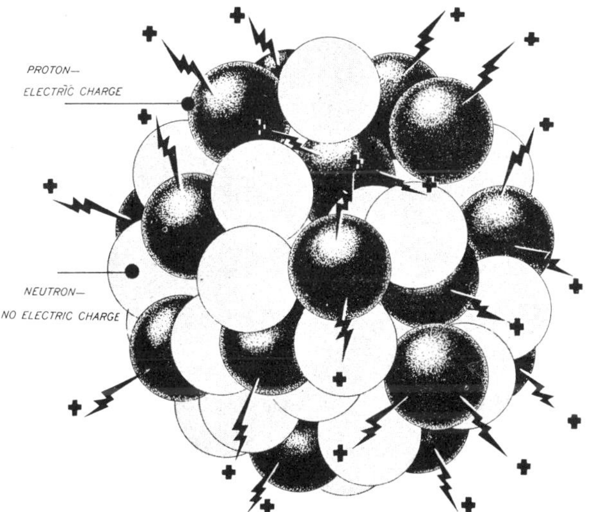

Fig. 6-14. The Positive and Neutral Charges in the Nucleus Held Together with Great Force (G.M.)

Source of Atomic Power

To understand how atomic fission generates heat requires an elementary study of the structure of the atom. Release of energy by fission results from changing about .1% of the weight of the fissioned uranium into energy.

This was understood by Albert Einstein, who in 1905, announced his basic equation $E = MC^2$. It was obtained not through experiment, but by mathematical computation. Einstein's contention was that energy and matter actually are one and the same. This is illustrated in Fig. 6-13. His equation states that when matter is converted completely to energy, the amount of energy (E) is equal to the mass (M) times the square of the speed of light (C^2). As C^2 is tremendously large, very little matter must be converted to produce huge quantities of energy. A loss of one ounce would give as much power as produced by the great Hoover Dam plant in an entire month.

Atomic Structure

The *atom*[1] is the smallest part of an element. It is so incredibly small that it is beyond comprehension, just as the solar system and outer space is so unbelievably large.

As small as the atom is, we know that it is not a solid sphere of matter, but it is made of a very complicated structure. The heart of the atom is the *nucleus,* from which *nuclear power* gets its name. This is composed of even smaller particles called protons and neutrons as shown in Fig. 6-14. Circling in orbits around the nucleus, like planets around

[1] Since the history and physical study of the atom is so wide and complex, only the terms needed to provide an understanding of how the atom is employed to generate heat are given here. Other sources should be consulted for a more detailed and comprehensive study of the atom's potential.

the sun at tremendous speeds, are little particles called *electrons.* These electrons are so small that the atom itself is composed mainly of empty space. It is hard to believe that an atom of iron is predominantly composed of empty space, but the answer lies in the amazing speed of the electrons.

The atom's *electrons* carry *negative* charges of electricity. *Protons* in the nucleus carry equalling *positive* charges of electricity. Thus, an atom is electrically neutral, always containing the same number of protons as electrons. Not until 1932 was it discovered that the nucleus of most atoms also contains particles having about the same weight as protons but having no electrical charge. Being electrically *neutral* they are called *neutrons.* The nucleus of most elements (other than hydrogen, the lightest) has at least as many neutrons as protons, see Fig. 6-14.

Although the number of protons balances the electrons in an atom, the actual number varies with the element. For example, hydrogen has one proton, helium has two protons, and so on. The largest atom found in nature, uranium, contains 92 protons and 92 electrons. The number of protons determines the substance or element, such as gold, lead, oxygen, or hydrogen. But some elements have forms which do not have the usual weight. This is because their number of *neutrons* is different. These different forms of an element having different weights because of extra neutrons (but identical numbers of protons or electrons) are called *isotopes.* The hydrogen atom shown at the top of Fig. 6-15 has two isotopes. One is called *heavy hydrogen* or *deuterium* because it has a neutron not normally in the hydrogen atom.

Uranium has several isotopes as shown at the bottom of Fig. 6-15. All contain 92 protons. The atom shown in the center contains 143 neutrons, making a total of 235 particles in the nucleus—hence, the name *uranium 235* or *U-235.* But uranium metal, which is obtained by refining the uranium ore dug from the ground, is not composed entirely of these 235-weight atoms. In fact, they are in a minority of *one in every 139 atoms* of uranium. Early experiments showed this rare U-235 isotope to be the source of heat energy. The majority of the remaining atoms are isotopes of uranium 238, having 3 additional neutrons and the usual 92 protons.

Atomic Heat Energy

Where does the heat come from? Fig. 6-16 represents an atom of U-235 with its nucleus and surrounding electrons. If a stray neutron traveling at tremendous speed is made to penetrate the barrier of electrons and to enter the nucleus, the nucleus immediately becomes unstable and splits into two smaller nuclei.

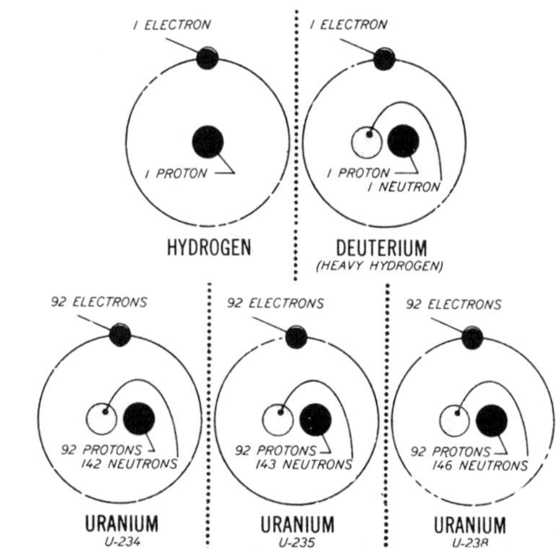

Fig. 6-15. Various Isotopes of Hydrogen and Uranium (G.M.)

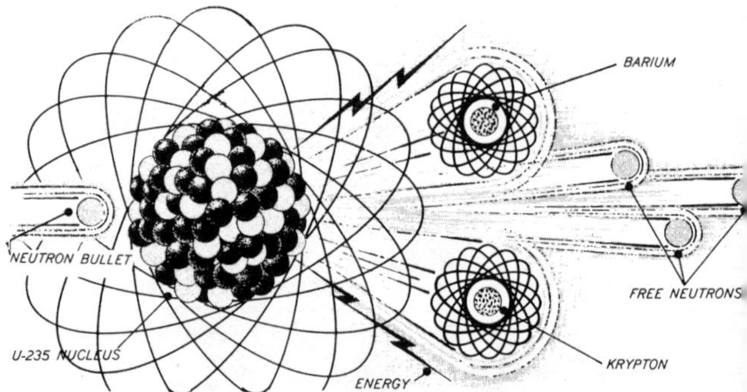

Fig. 6-16. Fission of the U-235 Atom (G.M.)
The splitting produces Ba-137, Kr-83, free neutrons to continue the chain reaction, and tremendous energy from the loss of weight.

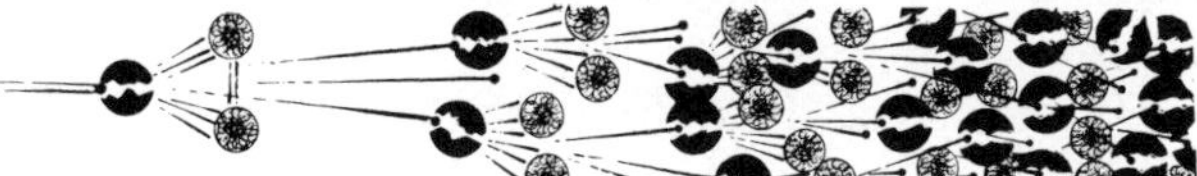

Fig. 6-17. Free Electrons in a Chain Reaction (G.M.)

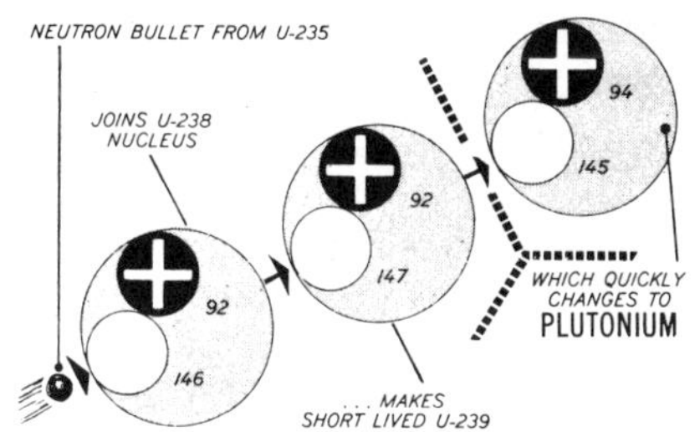

Fig. 6-18. Fusion of U-238 Produces Pu-242 (G.M.)

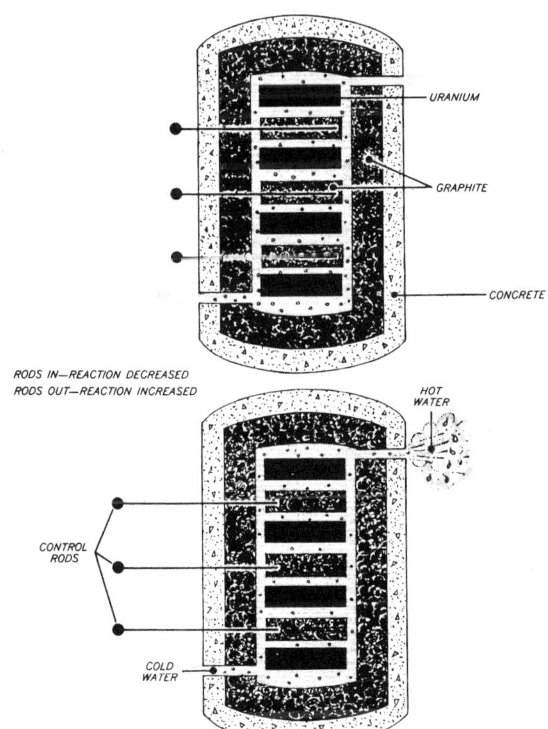

Fig. 6-19. Experimental Reactor Using Carbon Moderator and Neutron-Absorbing Control Rods (G.M.)

The reactor slows down the chain reaction so heat generated can be controlled properly. Uncontrolled reaction is an explosion.

Fission

This splitting is called *nuclear fission.* The energy stored in the new nuclei is much less than that of the original U-235 atom, and the surplus is given off as heat. The nuclei are driven apart at tremendous speeds and are absorbed as they collide with surrounding atoms—the effect of which converts more energy into heat. See Fig. 6-17. In addition to the 2 nuclei, one, two, or three loose neutrons are given off. Each neutron can produce another fission of a U-235 atom. The process constitutes a *chain reaction* producing tremendous heat in fractions of a second. However, this fission occurs only in one of every 139 uranium atoms—in only the U-235 isotope.

Fast-Fission Fuel

The U-238 isotope (the predominate one in uranium metal) behaves a little differently, as shown in Fig. 6-18. When the invading neutron strikes it, it does not split, but captures that neutron which later changes the atom into an artificial element called *plutonium,* or *Pu-242.* These new plutonium atoms behave like U-235 atoms. However, unlike the scarce U-235 they can be used as a concentrated *fast-fission nuclear fuel.* Uranium, having both U-235 and U-238 atoms gives a means of generating tremendous heat and, at the same time, a means of generating fast-fission plutonium fuel.

Control

Remember though, that at least one neutron from each fission must hit a U-235 nucleus. In order that the chain reaction shall be continuous, the neutrons must be slowed down so that they are more likely to cause a fission of the U-235 atom than be captured by U-238 atoms. This is accomplished by forcing the free neutrons to move through a *moderator,* which is often made of pure graphite. See Fig. 6-19. The *moderator* slows down the speed of the neutrons without being otherwise affected. Also needed is a throttle device to control the amount of heat produced. Neutron absorbing *control rods* moved in between fuel particles decrease the reaction. Withdrawing the rods as shown in the second position of Fig. 6-19 increases reaction speed and gives maximum heat. Much experimentation was required to determine proper control.

The Nuclear Fuel Cycle[1]

Nuclear fuel, like any other fuel, is used for creating heat; but unlike any other fuel, it is manufactured into an integral system used to extract heat and is retained in this system for many years. Nuclear fuel is manufactured to purity standards similar to those used for medicines and drugs, and to tolerances as exacting as a watch but in tonnage quantities. It is not depleted of all of its energy during its first lifetime. Nuclear fuel is sealed and performs its job for many years without exposure to air. Nuclear fuel is most unique in that it creates additional fuel while it is being consumed. As you would expect, there is a very interesting story behind such a fuel.

[1] Adapted from V. J. Rinaldi, "The Nuclear Fuel Cycle," Westinghouse Technical Paper, 1968.

Uranium was first discovered in 1789 by a German chemist, H. M. Klapwroth. The earth's crust is estimated to contain uranium in a proportion of about four parts per million; therefore, it is as plentiful as lead and much more plentiful than silver or mercury. Conventional fuels create heat by exothermic chemical reaction, mostly by oxidation, and they are consumed in the process. An understanding of nuclear fuel must begin with the realization that it differs from conventional fossil fuels. The key to understanding is *time*. The economics of fossil fuels hinge exclusively on purchase price. Nuclear fuel is used for years and then reused. Nuclear economics present an almost unlimited opportunity for management variations, with its cost tied to the method of its use as well as to its procurement. Since nuclear fuel is not completely expended during its first lifetime in a reactor, it must be removed, purified, replenished, and refabricated periodically. This creates a *fuel*

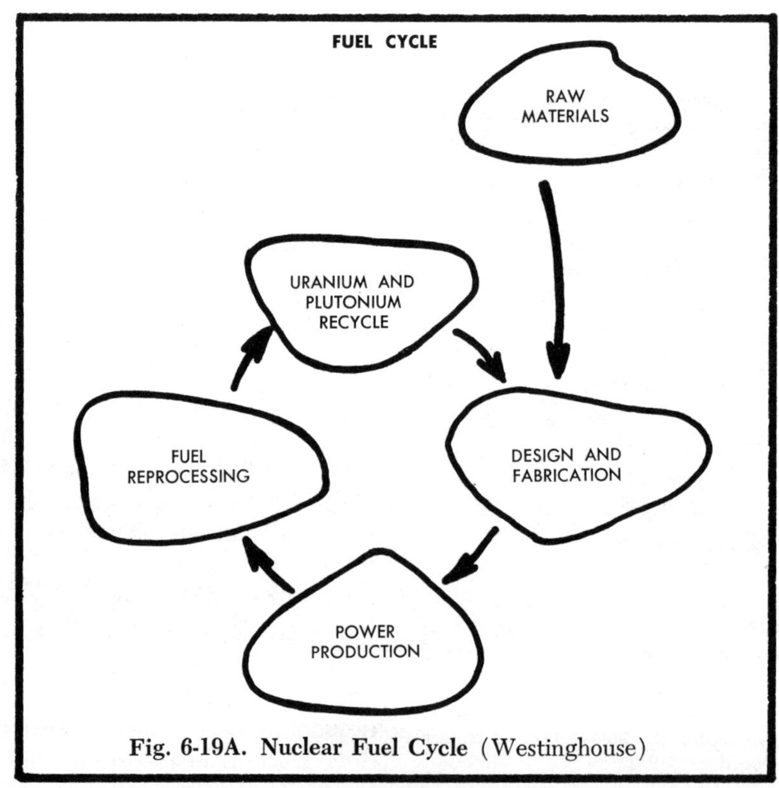

Fig. 6-19A. Nuclear Fuel Cycle (Westinghouse)

cycle, Fig. 6-19A. There is more than one fuel cycle, but the enriched uranium cycle is utilized by practically all reactors today. The fuel cycle begins at the uranium mines in the Colorado plateau region in the southwestern United States and at the Reactor and Fuel Design Organization which specifies how uranium will be used.

Raw Materials

The U.S. uranium mining industry consists of some 500 mines capable of producing over 14,000 tons of uranium oxide per year. Once the uranium ore bodies have been located, suitable mining techniques are chosen. The mining techniques used include both underground and open pit. See Fig. 6-19B. The

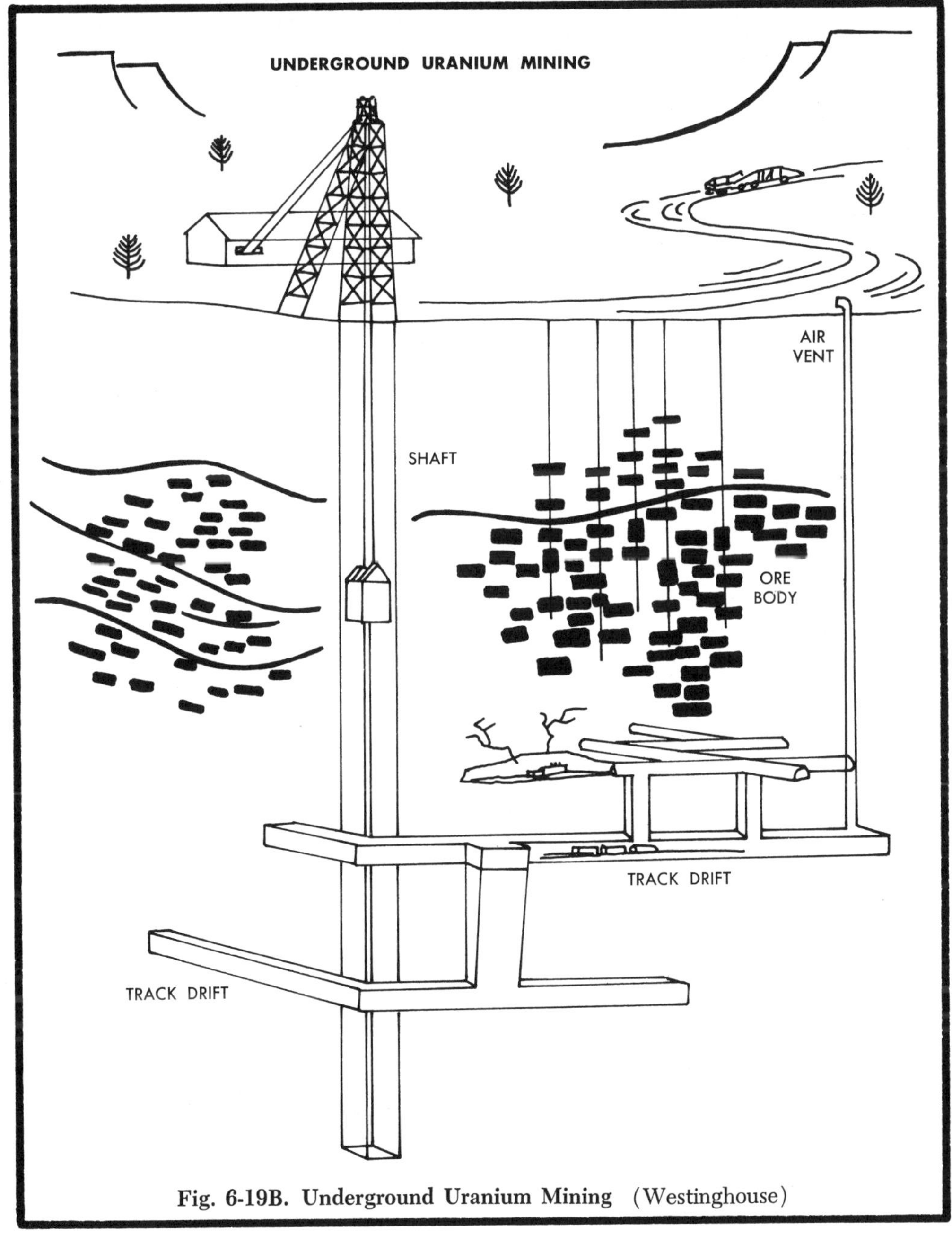

Fig. 6-19B. Underground Uranium Mining (Westinghouse)

average United States mine has an uranium assay of .25%. This means that each ton of ore contains about five pounds of uranium. The uranium processing mills (Fig. 6-19C) are designed to extract this uranium in a form commonly called "yellow cake," which is crude oxide or salt concentrate assaying approximately 70-90% U-308. It is on this basis that this commodity is bought and sold.

It is the process of fission of certain atoms by thermoneutrons that creates the energy in nuclear reactions. One of these fissionable atoms is U-235. Present water reactor designs call for uranium to contain 3-4% of U-235, by weight. Natural uranium as it is mined and

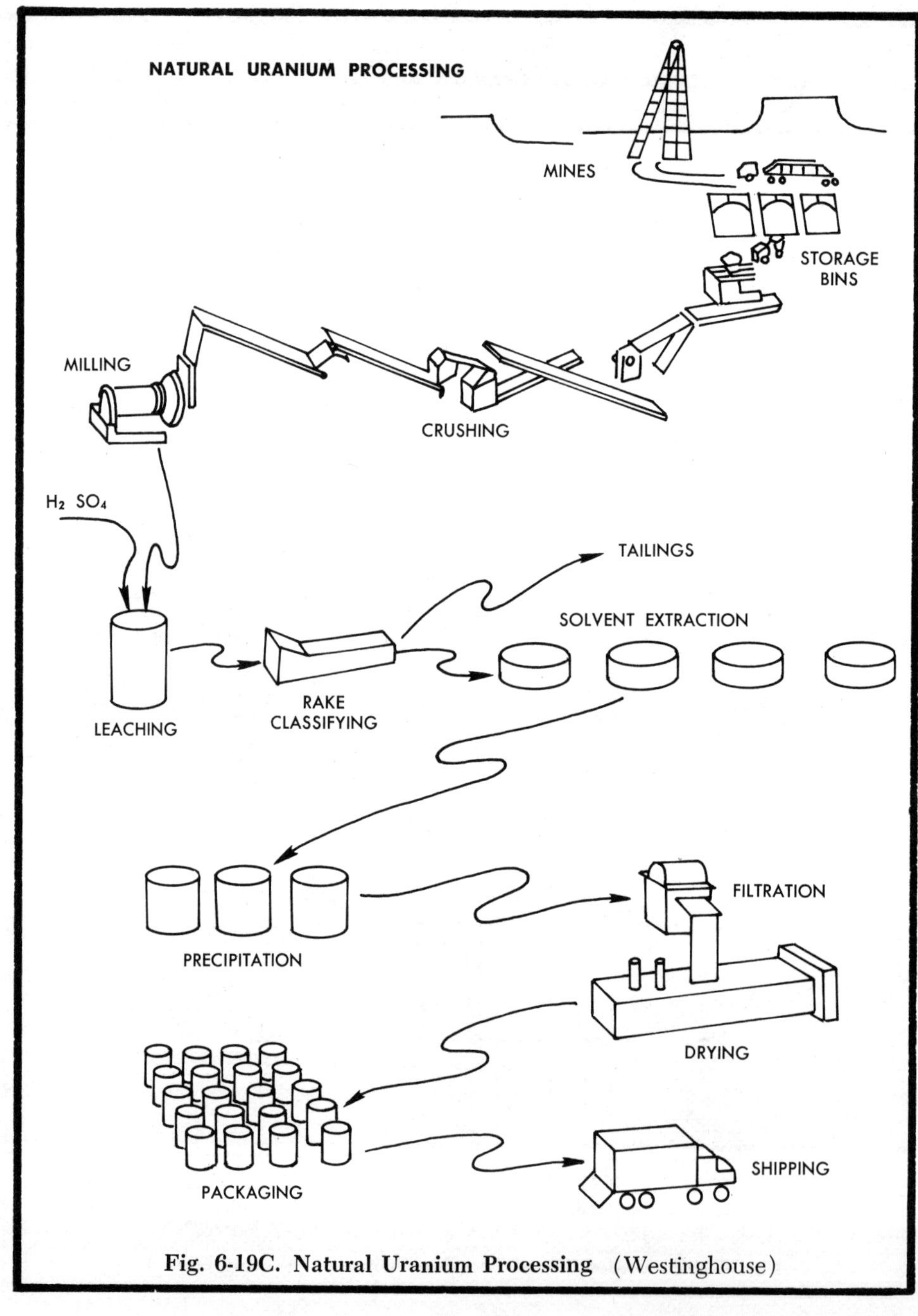

Fig. 6-19C. Natural Uranium Processing (Westinghouse)

milled contains only about .7% U-235. The remaining 99.3% is U-238. Therefore, the isotopic assay in the natural uranium must be altered. The United States Government developed and constructed gaseous diffusion plants for the purpose of altering the natural mix of isotopes to produce uranium enriched in the isotope U-235.

This step, called *fluorination,* is presently performed by only one commercial firm, Fig. 6-19D. Their plant capacity is sufficient to handle the forecast fuel load into the early 70's. Once the uranium has been converted to UF6, it is ready for enrichment, the last step in the uranium raw material preparation. Enrichment alters the naturally occurring iso-

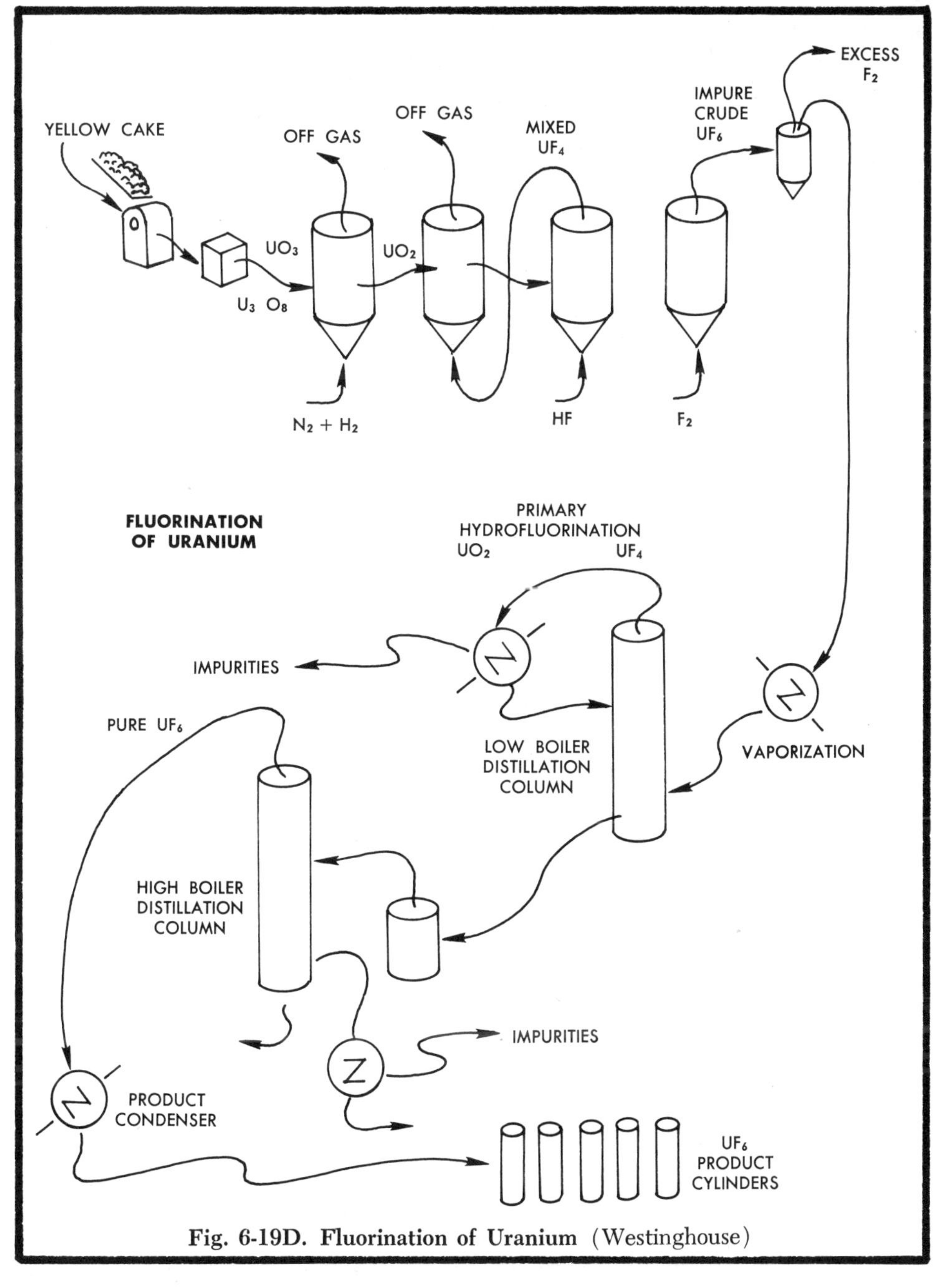

Fig. 6-19D. Fluorination of Uranium (Westinghouse)

topic assay of uranium, and it is accomplished by gaseous diffusion (Fig. 6-19E).

The principle on which gaseous diffusion is based was discovered in 1829 by Graham. The average velocity of gas molecules at any temperature depends on their mass. Differing isotopes will then have differing velocities which, though small, are very important. The amount of separation by different molecules through a membrane is equal to the square root of the ratio of weights of the gas molecules. In a special gaseous diffusion stage container, the UF6 gas is pumped into a tube whose walls are a porous barrier through which the gas is diffused. To obtain material of 3% U-235 enrichment from natural uranium of .7% U-235, the diffusion process must be repeated through hundreds of stages.

The United States Atomic Energy Commission has three diffusion plants. They are located in Oak Ridge, Tennessee; Paducah, Kentucky; and Portsmouth, Ohio. These remarkable installations represent an investment of over $2 billion and consume immense quantities of electricity for the gas and vacuum pumps and the associated equipment. In 1962 they required 47 billion kilowatt hours of electricity or about 5% of the total amount of electrical power generated in the United States. It is estimated that the present capacity of these diffusion plants is adequate until the 1980's. The enrichment of the uranium to the required U-235 assay ends the raw material portion of the fuel cycle.

There is, however, one important reactive material which should be discussed. Uranium fuels must be contained within the reactor in a cladding (lining or coating) capable of withstanding several years of high pressure, high

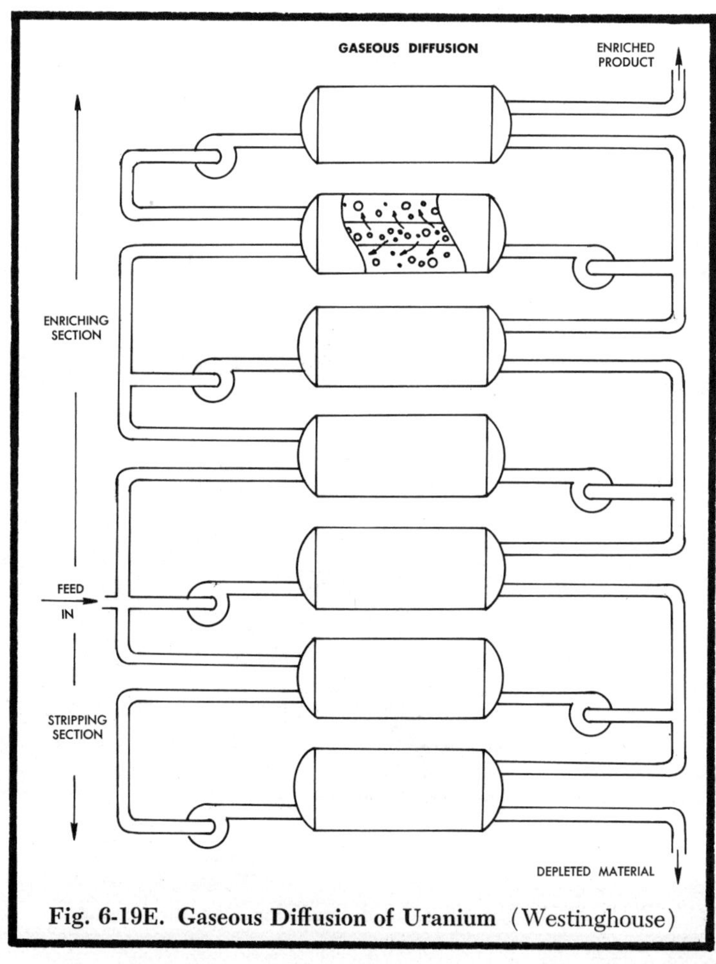

Fig. 6-19E. Gaseous Diffusion of Uranium (Westinghouse)

temperature, high flow, and high radiation. Such strength and corrosion resistance are not uncommon, but the clad must have one important nuclear characteristic – low neutron cross section, for it must allow neutrons to pass through it. The more transparent the cladding is to neutrons the better. Zirconium combines strength, corrosion resistance, and low cross section. Until recently zirconium was a rare and expensive material. The decision of fuel designers to utilize it as a cladding for commercial power reactors has created an expanding market for zirconium alloys, and the large scale zirconium production has resulted in relatively economical prices. Zirconium is a metallic element whose atomic weight is 91.22. It has a lower thermoneutron cross section than any metal of comparable structural quality, and is an abundant element in the earth's crust. (See Fig. 6-19F.)

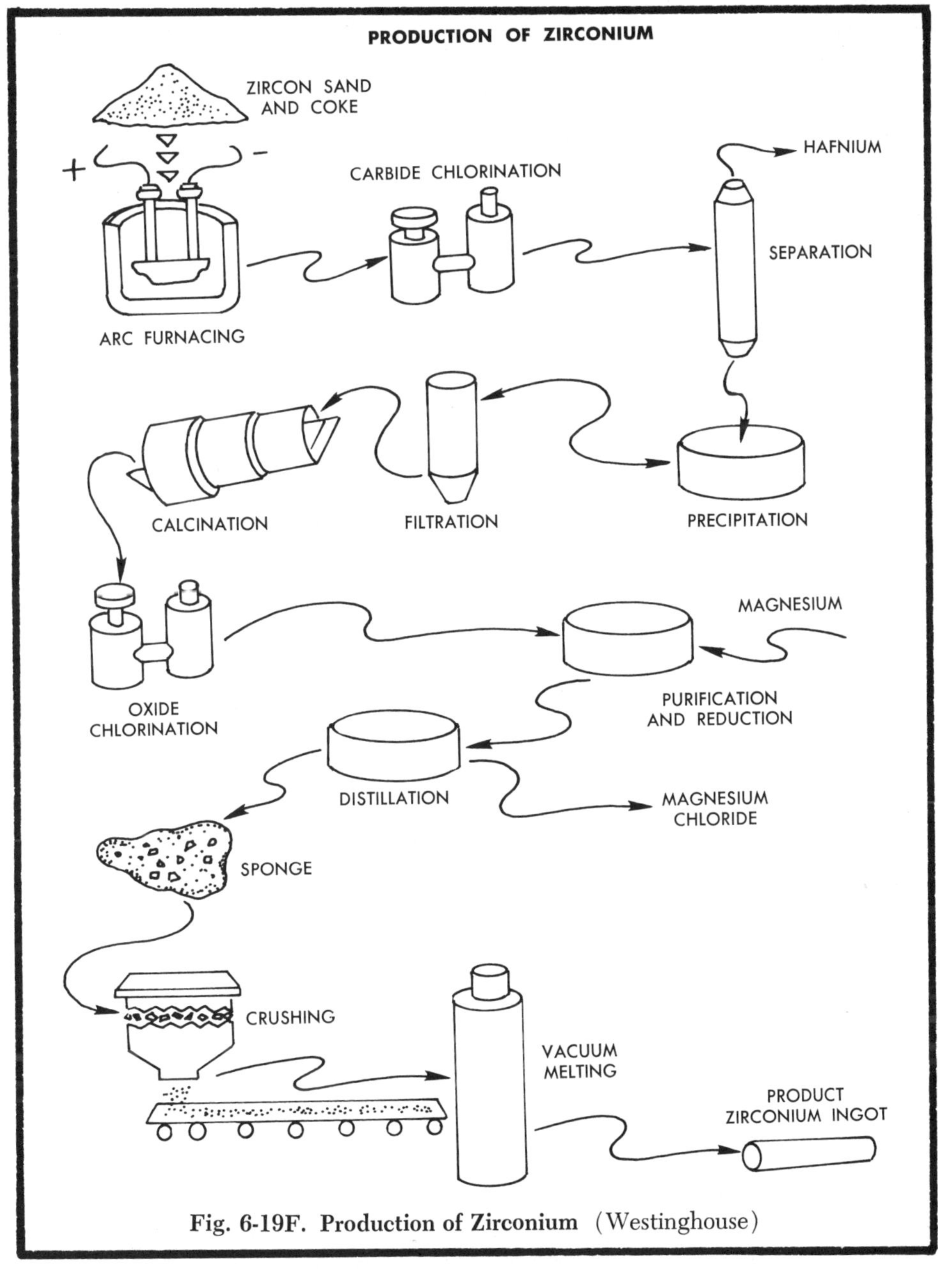

Fig. 6-19F. Production of Zirconium (Westinghouse)

The fuel elements are received at the reactor site and are carefully and individually placed into the reactor vessel (Fig. 6-19G), and the production of electrical energy is ready to begin. During power generation (heat production) the U-235 is consumed. Energy and fission products are created. Each fission produces approximately three neutrons, one of which may escape. One may be captured by a U-238 nucleus to create plutonium, and the last may cause fission of yet another U-235 nucleus. Over the life of the fuel, the U-235 content is gradually depleted and plutonium is gradually built up. As plutonium is created within the fuel, it then can also fission and contribute to the production of energy.

The inner region of the fuel contains the lower enrichment; the outer the highest enrichment; and annually the center fuel is removed and new fuel is added. Approximately

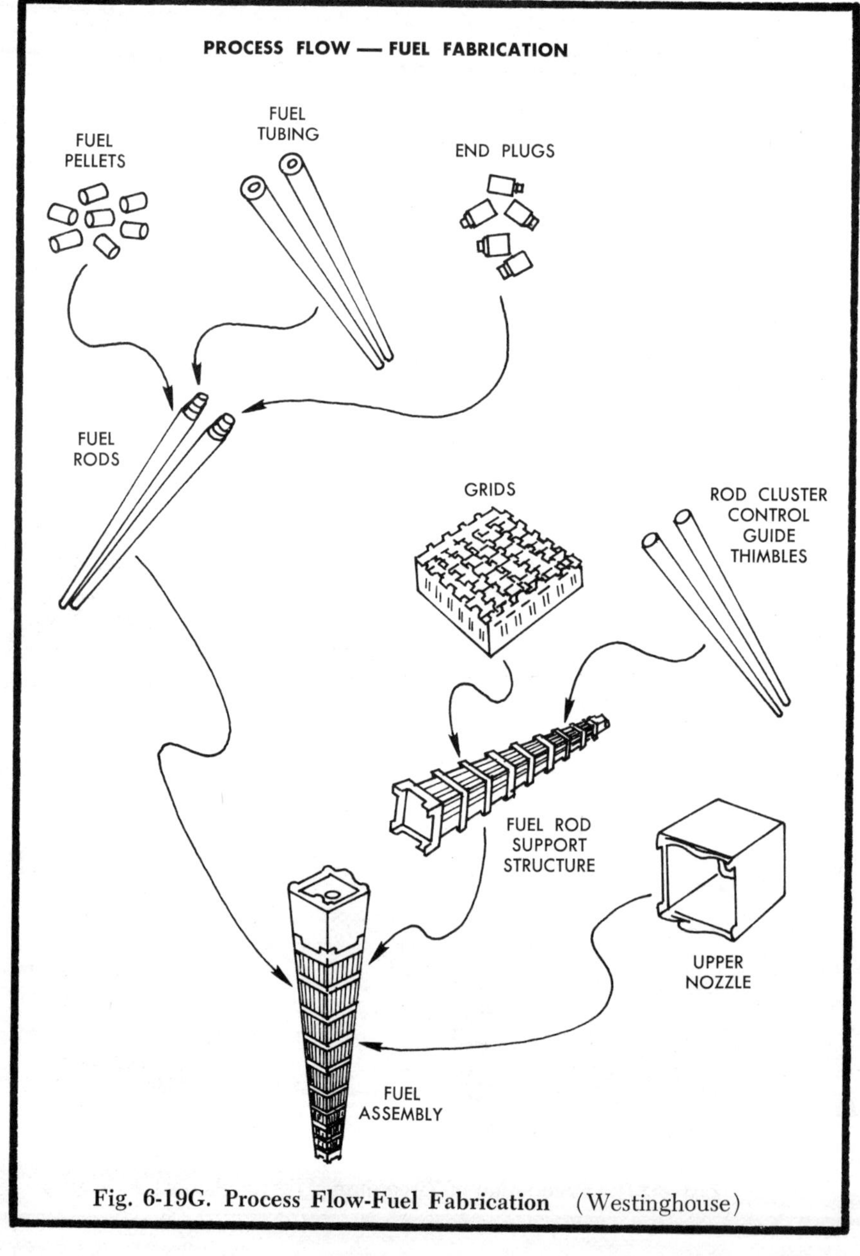

Fig. 6-19G. Process Flow-Fuel Fabrication (Westinghouse)

one-third of the fuel is replaced. The remaining fuel is shuffled into the center of the core in a pattern, whose determination is based on the mode of operation during the previous cycle. The designation of the enrichment of new fuel and the shuffling pattern are a part of the management of the nuclear fuel called *core management* (Figs. 6-19H and 6-19I). This management is unique to the long life-nuclear fuel. Conventional fuels permit no such opportunity for control.

In order to realize the minimum overall fuel cost, attention must be given to all of the economic, technical, and scheduling considerations in the entire fuel cycle. The nuclear fuel designer, manufacturer, and the utility or user must work closely in selecting a suitable operating cycle optimizing total energy extracted from the fuel, maximizing specific power, and achieving the best neutron economy. At the end of the third cycle it becomes economical to remove the oldest region of the fuel, purify it, replenish it, and refabricate it.

When spent fuel is removed from the reactor, it is highly radioactive. It must be handled remotely. Much of the spent fuel handling is done under water. Water is an active shield, allows good visibility, and effectively removes residual heat. The spent fuel is removed from the reactor and placed in an underwater storage tank. The fuel placed into the reactor contained 3% U-235 and 97% U-238. The spent fuel removed from the reactor contains approximately 1% U-235, 95% U-238, 1% plutonium, and 3% fission products. The products contained in the spent fuel are a result of the fission of uranium and plutonium. Over 200 isotopes of 35 elements are found in fission products with atomic weights ranging from 72 to 160. Some of these isotopes are stable. Many are radioactive, and there is a wide range of radioactive activity and half lives. The half-lives of many of these are meas-

INITIAL LOADING PATTERN

Fig. 6-19H. Initial Loading Pattern (Westinghouse)

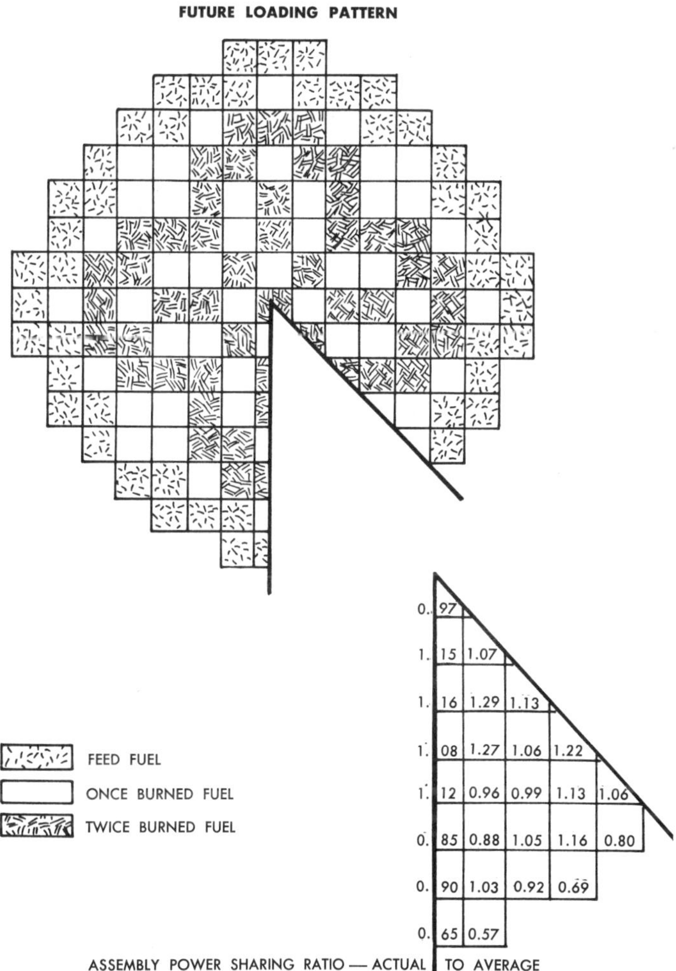

Fig. 6-19I. Future Loading Pattern (Westinghouse)

ured in days, which means that once the fuel is removed from the reactor and placed in storage much of the radioactivity dies quickly. Spent fuel is not thrown away, for these spent assemblies contain much valuable fuel material; and it is at this point that the business of nuclear fuel becomes a cycle.

Reprocessing

After the fuel has cooled for three to four months, it is loaded under water into heavily shielded casks. These leadlined casks are used to transport the fuel to a chemical reprocessing plant.

In reprocessing the fuel is transferred from the storage pool to a cell where the assembly can be mechanically disassembled. The fuel rods are sheared into short pieces after the end fittings have been removed. These pieces are placed into a dissolver where nitric acid selectively dissolves the fuel and leaves the cladding. The resulting fuel-bearing acid solution is treated by solvent extraction to separate uranium and plutonium from the fission products. The uranium and plutonium are subjected to further extraction steps to purify them of fission products. Many of the isotopes being recovered as fission products are put to use for medical and industrial uses; and as technology further develops, more value will be placed on further reducing the fuel cycle costs.

The uranium from reprocessing presents very few problems for reuse. It can be re-enriched and reused in the same manner as before. Plutonium is a different matter. Like uranium it is a heavy metallic element which has fissionable isotopes; it is highly toxic and hazardous to handle. Its use as a fuel, therefore, presents problems in handling and fabrication not encountered with uranium fuels. It can, however, be handled and fabricated quite safely using semiremote techniques which do not bring the workers in direct contact with the fuel. Under certain situations and with certain design adjustments, plutonium can be used interchangeably with uranium.

Pressurized Water System

The initial application of atomic power was certainly unique. On May 31, 1953, the first atomic engine was operated in the desert near Arco, Idaho. At that time, the big problem was controlling the abundance of heat energy from atomic fission and using it to generate steam. Questions involved were the correct concentration of fuel, its spacing, type and amount of moderator, the number, spacing and material of control rods and nature of safety precautions.

This nuclear reactor, or atomic power plant, safely produced a substantial quantity of controlled power.[2] It served as a prototype for such *pressurized water* atomic power installations as the Yankee Atomic Electric Company at Rowe, Mass., The Belgian Atomic Utility at Brussels, Belgium, The Consolidated Edison plant at Indian Point, New York, the first atomic submarine, the *USS Nautilus*, and the *NS Savannah*.

A pressurized water system has purified water circulating in the *primary loop system* which contains the nuclear reactor in which heat is produced. The water must be kept under very high pressure (about 1500 psi) to prevent boiling. The *secondary system* is the usual boiler system, forming steam, carrying it to the turbine and back for reheating. See Fig. 6-20. A cylindrical container houses the primary system.

Pressure Vessel

Within the container is the pressure vessel in which the reactor is enclosed. See Fig. 6-21. This vessel is a cylindrical structure formed of carbon steel plates and forgings. The inside surfaces are made of stainless steel to provide corrosion resistance. Thermal shields prevent excess heat generation in the vessel wall from the gamma ray radiation given off by the reactor core. The top and bottom sections are shaped like hemispheres. The top section or closure head is bolted

[2] This plant was built by Westinghouse Electric Corp., under the direction of the United States Atomic Energy Commission.

onto the main part of the vessel. It has openings for control rods and instrumentation.

Control

Control of the reactor is maintained by moving neutron-absorbing control rods in and out of the atomic fuel core. These rods are made of alloys of silver and cadmium, steel and cadmium or boron, or of the metallic element, hafnium. They readily absorb neutrons and thus can retard the fission chain-reaction which is the heat-producing process. Dropping the control rods into the reactor slows the atom splitting; their withdrawal speeds up the reaction.

For a complete shut-down, a special burnable or soluble "poison" (moderator) is injected directly around the fuel rods.

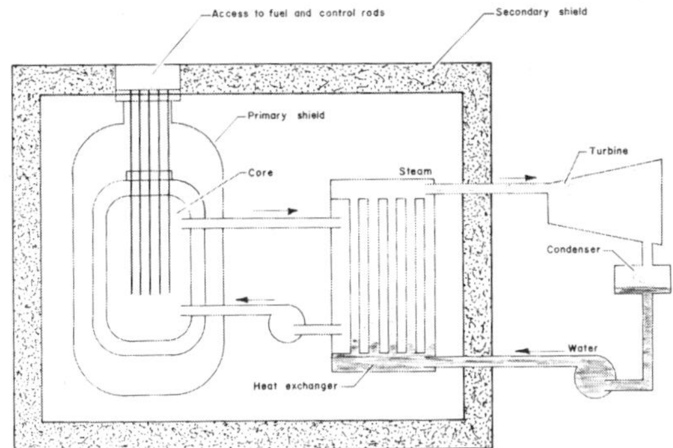

Fig. 6-20. Pressure Water Reactor

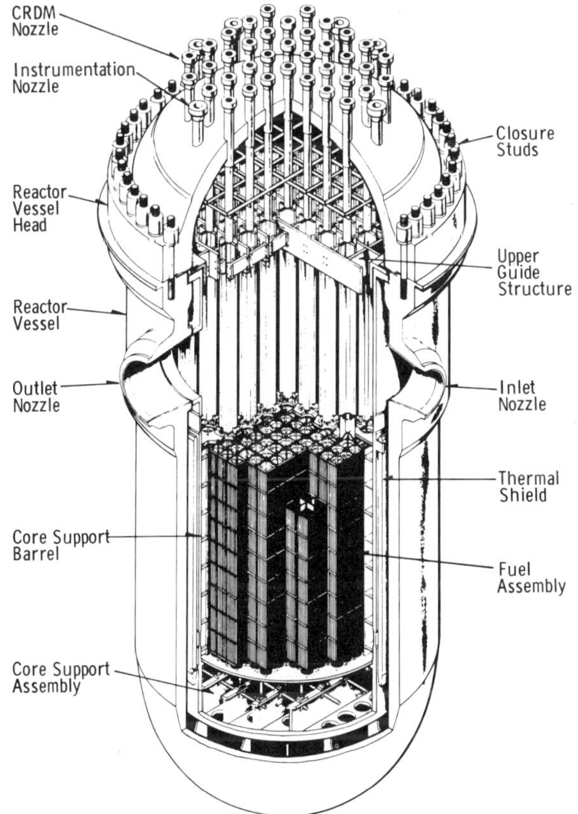

Fig. 6-21. Sectional Details of a Reactor Vessel (Combustion Engineering)

Fuel

The *core* or heart of the reactor is where the heat is produced. It is made up of a geometrical pattern of uranium fuel elements.

The core of the pressurized water reactor plant uses slightly enriched uranium oxide. Just enough metallic uranium is added to the uranium oxide that the number of neutrons emitted in the fission process equals the number necessary to generate the fissions, thus maintaining a nuclear chain reaction. The *fast particles,* or atomic fragments emitted in the fission process, have great speed and mass and yield high kinetic energy. As they strike the surrounding atoms of uranium they generate heat. The heat is conducted through the uranium and enclosure to the water coolant. The heated water flows out at high temperatures through piping near the reactor top. It is kept under 1485 to 1760 pounds of pressure per square inch to prevent steam from forming within the reactor. Stainless steel pipes penetrate the wall of the reactor core vessel and carry this *purified pressurized water.*

Energy Transfer

From the core, the hot water or coolant rushes through the *primary loop system,* to the heat exchanger. See Fig. 6-22. Inside the exchanger it passes through a series of stainless steel tubes. Water in the secondary loop flows upward over the outer surface of the hot tubes and immediately turns to steam because of its relatively low pressure of 400 to 500 psi. The primary coolant becomes radioactive and cannot be sent to the tur-

1. Chemical bldg.
2. Fuel handling bldg.
3. Overhead crane
4. Equipment hatches
5. Equipment removal shield door
6. Removal rails
7. Removal trolley
8. Decontamination wash
9. Decontamination room
10. Fuel transfer pools
11. Water gates
12. Sphere ventilation
13. Ext. radiation shield
14. Containment sphere
15. Polar crane
16. Elevator
17. Reactor tool shaft
18. Refuelling console (normally unattended)
19. Rotating plugs
20. Refuelling hoist

Fig. 6-22. Steam Generator and Heat Exchanger for Indian Point Plant (Babcock & Wilson)
Unit is 40 feet long, and contains 10 miles of one-inch stainless steel tubing. (See 40 and 41.)

Fig. 6-23. Nuclear-Electrical Power Plant at Indian Point, New York (Nuclear Engineering, London)

21. Storage pit hatch
22. TV cameras (3)
23. Fuel transfer manipulator
24. Tube upper valve
25. Storage pit
26. Transfer tube
27. Transfer tube lower valve and shuttle
28. Reactor vessel
29. Reactor core
30. Control rod drives
31. Reactor pit
32. Sump
33. Sump pump
34. Blowdown tanks (2)
35. Reactor inlet
36. Reactor outlet
37. Gate valves
38. Check valves
39. Pumps
40. Steam generators
41. Steam drums
42. Steam to superheaters
43. Pressurizer
44. Sphere vent to stack
45. Acess doors
46. Sphere supports
47. Nuclear service bldg.
48. Sphere vent plenum
49. Service ventilation
50. H_2SO_4 storage tanks
51. Transformer yard
52. Oil fired superheaters (2)
53. Economizers (2)
54. Airheaters (2)
55. Blowers (2)
56. Flues to stack (2)
57. Stack
58. 10-ton jib crane
59. Controlled start pipe
60. Superheated steam to turbines
61. Condensate tanks (3)
62. Service water tank
63. Deaerators
64. Deaerator tanks
65. Evaporators
66. Boiler feed pump
67. Boiler pump room
68. Elevators
69. Ventilation room
70. Central control room
71. Terminal board room
72. Battery room
73. Water treatment
74. Turbine hall
75. Turbine-generator
76. Main steam valves
77. Loading well covers
78. Administration block
79. Take-off tower
80. Transmission towers

bine, so the *secondary water* is used as a vehicle to transmit the heat energy to the turbine. Notice that the primary coolant loop and the secondary water steam loop are independent and closed circuits. No coolant or water is lost. As the hot coolant gives up its heat to the water in the heat exchanger, it is pumped back into the reactor and heated again. As the steam leaves the turbine, it is passed through a condenser liquifying it for return to the exchanger and conversion to steam once more. This is a continuous process that will furnish electricity as long as the nuclear fuel in the reactor lasts.

This steam is dried by passing through conventional steam separators. It may be superheated by a fossil-fuel furnace before being piped into the steam turbine which turns the generator that produces electrical energy. See Fig. 6-23 for a view of all com-

Fig. 6-24. Power Distribution Equipment at Morris, Illinois Nuclear Power Station (General Electric)

Fig. 6-25. Calder Hall Nuclear Power Station, Britain's First (U. K. Atomic Energy Authority)

Fig. 6-26. Diagram of Calder Hall Nuclear Power Station (U. K. Atomic Energy Authority) ponents of such a plant. The generated electricity is transmitted through an adjacent *switching yard,* through transformers and over high tension wires on its way to homes and industries. See Fig. 6-24. This type of reactor is being employed in installations with outputs up to 250 megawatts.

English Atomic Power Stations

The first atomic power station in the world to generate electricity on a commercial scale was the Calder Hall station near Windscale, England, opened on October 17, 1956. See Fig. 6-25, 6-26 and 6-27. The steam turbines, condensers, electrical generators, cooling towers, and so on, are of conventional types. Only "boiler houses" are different.

Let us inspect one of the four reactors to learn more details of reactor design. At the same time some differences will be contrasted with the systems already illustrated.

Moderator

At the core of the reactor is the moderator made up of more than 58,000 pieces of graphite. See Fig. 6-28.

Fig. 6-27. Dump Condensers and Turbine at Chapelcross (U. K. Atomic Energy Authority)
This station near Annan, Scotland is a duplicate of the Calder Hall plant.

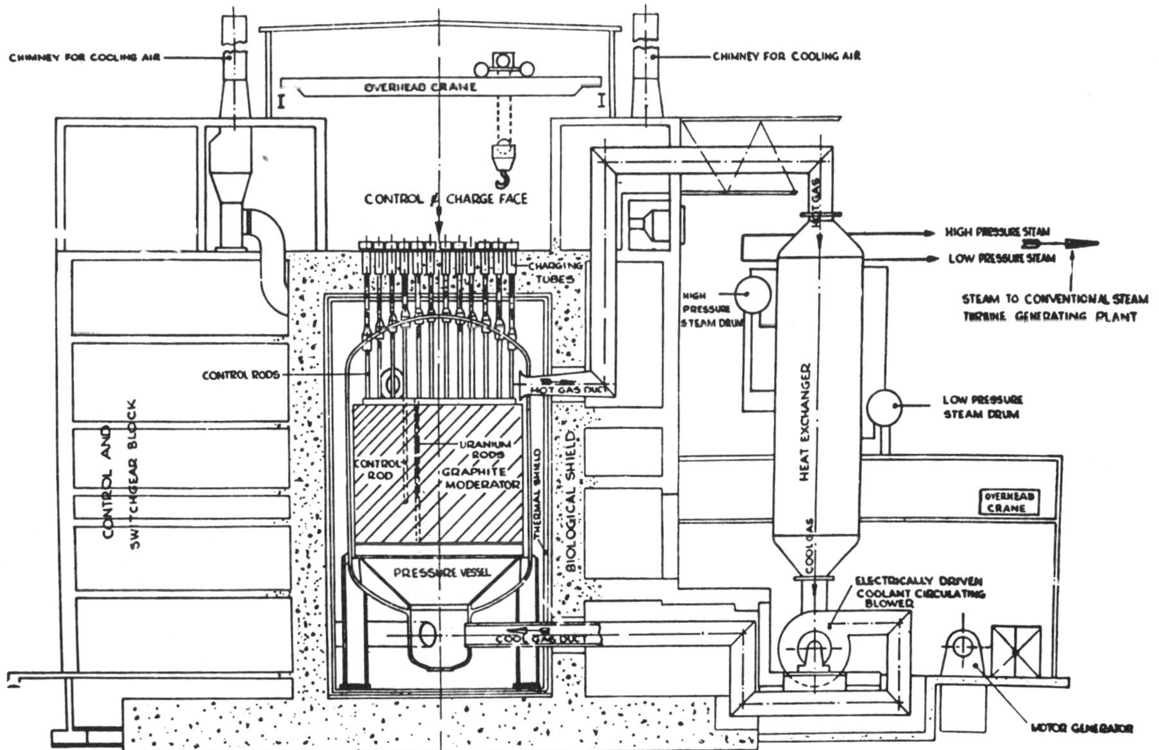

Fig. 6-28. A Calder Hall Pile with Pressure Vessel and a Heat Exchanger (U. K. Atomic Energy Authority)

In the graphite, running from top to bottom, are 1,700 channels into which the uranium fuels are lowered. Each element consists of a uranium rod about one-fourth inch in diameter and 40 inches long. This is sealed in a container fitted with fins to assist in heat transfer to the exterior. Six elements each on top of the other make a channel. This provides more than 10,000 elements in the moderator which is 36 feet in diameter and 27 feet high.

The moderator is enclosed in a steel casing with walls more than two inches thick. This casing is fitted with four large pipes at the top and bottom through which CO_2 gas is pumped at pressures of about 100 psi and at the rate of about one ton per second. This is the gas that transfers heat from the reactor to the heat exchangers. The heat exchangers are located at each corner of the reactor building. These exchangers comprise the *steam boilers* of the installation.

Shield

Surrounding the pressure vessel is a *biological shield* made of concrete seven feet thick for the walls and eight feet thick for the roof. This structure is lined with thick plates of steel to protect the concrete from the heat. Between the plates and concrete there is a six foot gap through which cold air is circulated. This shield is a protection against any harmful effects of gamma rays given off by the fission process.

Charge Tubes

The concrete roof is provided with openings through which charge tubes are placed into the moderator 30 feet below. See Figs. 6-29 and 6-30. Each charge tube serves 16 fuel channels. The fuel elements are raised and lowered through these charge tubes by special devices to prevent the escape of CO_2 gas during these operations.

Control Rods

Under each charge tube, there is a boron steel control rod located in a separate channel and suspended on a cable operated by a winch. Boron has the property of absorbing neutrons. The further the control rods are lowered into the moderator, the less is its heat energy output. In the event of overheating, or other emergency, these boron rods fall into the channels automatically, causing the reactor to stop operating.

The main function of Calder Hall station is to produce *plutonium* recovered from used uranium fuel rods. Less than one percent of the uranium fuel is used to provide heat for the turbines. With improved techniques, by 1966, it is expected that Great Britain will be generating one-fourth of her electricity from nuclear reactors. This will save 20 million tons of coal a year.

Other Atomic Fuels

Plutonium as a Fuel

Plutonium as a nuclear fuel produces a *fast-fission* nuclear reactor. The first such

Fig. 6-29. Calder Hall Reactor Charging Floor and Fuel Unit Basket (U. K. Atomic Energy Authority)

Fig. 6-30. View of the Pile Control Room at Chapelcross (U. K. Atomic Energy Authority)

reactor was built at Dounreay, in the North of Scotland. The Dounreay installation requires no moderator to slow down the neutrons, and all of the plutonium rods are potential fuel so less fissile material is required.

With all plutonium, there is no U-238 present to absorb the stray atoms. But because of the high proportion of fissile atoms in the plutonium, there are more stray neutrons. These stray atoms must be captured. This is done by surrounding the core with rods of U-238. See Fig. 6-31.

Each fission of a plutonium atom produces an average of 2.5 neutrons, as with U-235. One neutron keeps the chain reaction operating. An average of one out of four neutrons is lost to convert the surrounding U-238 into plutonium. Thus, for every atom of plutonium that is split, one and one-quarter new plutonium atoms are produced. For every four atoms burned, there are five more new ones produced. Hence, the term *fast-fission breeder reactor* is derived. This reactor uses no moderator and breeds plutonium fuel faster than it is consumed.

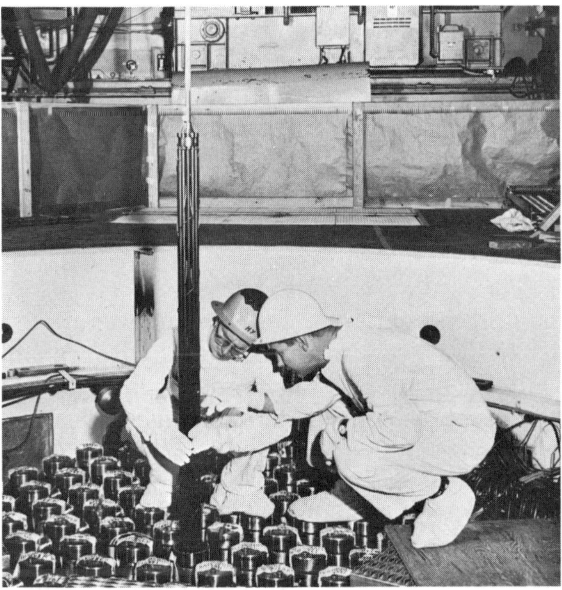

Fig. 6-31. Technicians Load Fuel Element Into the Plutonium Recycle Test Reactor
(General Electric)
This view is in the Hanford plant at Richland, Washington, just before it went "critical" or started its first chain reaction. It is an important step in learning to use plutonium fuel.

Liquid-Metal Heat Transfer

This highly concentrated fission produces great quantities of heat. This heat must be removed and transferred by a medium of *liquid metal*—sodium, or potassium. Gas is unable to do this. This liquid is pumped through the core and transfers heat to the exchangers within the biological shield. The shield is very necessary because the metal is rendered radioactive as it is heated in the reactor core.

The purpose of the large sphere is to prevent the escape of radioactive particles should there be an accidental sodium fire, since sodium burns explosively.

Thorium as a Fuel

Thorium, Th-232, is another natural element which can be used as an atomic fuel. Its atoms will not split, but like U-238, can capture neutrons. It then becomes an isotope of uranium known as 233, another artificial nuclear fuel.

Heavy Water

In some reactors, the moderator may be *heavy water* instead of graphite. Heavy water is water in which each hydrogen atom is twice as heavy as usual because it has a neutron (ordinary hydrogen has none). See Fig. 16-8. The heavy water acts both as a moderator and as the medium through which heat is transferred in the heat exchanger.

Other Types of Reactors

Swimming Pool Reactor

Another type of reactor is known as the *swimming pool reactor,* see Fig. 6-32. This consists of an open aluminum alloy tank filled with ordinary or heavy water in which is placed a concrete casing. Uranium rods, enriched with U-235, are suspended in the tank and used for research purposes.

Homogenous Power Reactor

In the *homogenous power reactor,* enriched uranium fuel in the form of uranium sulphate is dissolved in water. This serves as both the coolant and the moderator. The solution is pumped at high pressure through the core vessel to the heat exchanger. The stray neutrons are reflected by heavy water housed in an outer pressure vessel.

Fig. 6-32. Swimming Pool Reactor

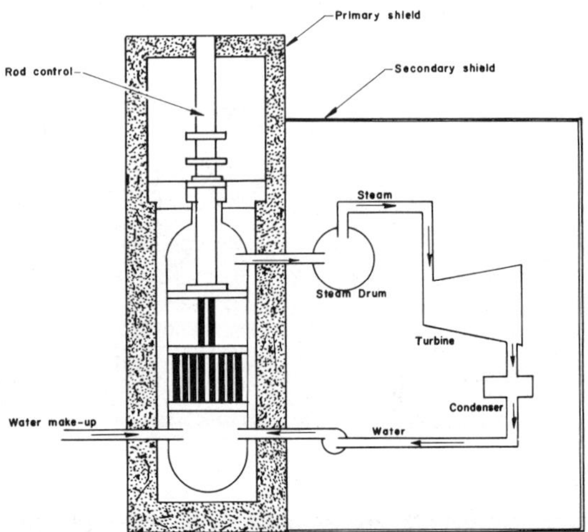

Fig. 6-33. Boiling Water Reactor

There are other types of reactors, all operating on the same principle, but varying in the method of transfering the heat from the core to generate steam.

Boiling Water Reactor

In the *boiling water reactor,* for example, steam for the turbine is generated by direct contact since the water circulates through the core. See Fig. 6-33.

Hot Gas Closed-Cycle Reactor

Up to now, we have been discussing nuclear powered *steam* turbines. But the heated gas from the reactor can also be used to power gas turbines using a *closed cycle principle.* See Fig. 6-34 for a similar diagram. Air, nitrogen, and carbon dioxide can be used in closed-cycle nuclear gas generators. The problem is that all these gases become radioactive when they are heated in the reactor. Helium, however, does not, and it also has high heat-transfer capacity. The cost, however, is rather high, but becomes practical by making the system leakproof.

Fusion

Finally, we must discuss the ultimate source of power for steam and gas turbines—the *fusion* of heavy hydrogen. Heavy hydrogen is obtained rather cheaply from the sea. In fusion the atom is not divided but rather built up. The atom generates heat during the process.

The ordinary hydrogen atom consists of one proton with one electron circling around it. If, however, two atoms of hydrogen are united chemically, their nuclei, in this case the two protons, remain unchanged with two electrons circling around them. Energy content of the two atoms is less than that of the individual atoms—therefore, heat is given off.

In every 6,000 atoms of hydrogen, there is one isotope known as heavy hydrogen or *deuterium.* Deuterium contains one electron, one proton, *and one neutron.* When chemically combined, the heavy nuclei is circled by two electrons with the inevitable loss of heat. But, if the two heavy hydrogen atoms—isotopes—can be made to collide at tremendous speeds, the two nuclei will momentarily combine and then divide. This action leaves a single atom with two electrons circling a nucleus of two protons with one neutron escaping. The new atom is helium. The process is one of *nuclear fusion* instead of fission, or simple combustion. The resultant heat, due to the change of energy content, is multiplied some 50 million times. This is what happens in a hydrogen bomb and on the surface of the sun.

The difficulty in bringing about nuclear fusion is in achieving the required initial temperature of several million degrees centigrade. Temperatures in excess of five million degrees centigrade have been achieved for a few seconds. This, however, is not enough. It is estimated that a temperature of 100 million degrees centigrade will be required to cause heavy hydrogen to move rapidly enough for fusion, and when this is achieved, turbogenerators will have an inexhaustible source of power.[4]

Nuclear Power for 1980 and Years Beyond

To predict the form of nuclear power in the years beyond the 1980's requires examination of present trends, the extra-polation of those trends in modified form into the future, and an estimation of man's ingenuity. What is happening at present is relatively obvious. Electric power requirements in the United States continue to increase at a rate of about 7% a year. This means that the utilities systems must, roughly, double in size every 10 years. This estimate of growth is shown in Fig. 6-35 and projected out to the year 2000. What the actual kilowatt hour consumption will be in the year 2000 is difficult to predict; however, with today's electrical energy consumption at over 1 trillion kilowatt hours a year, a projected growth through 1980 to 2.2 trillion kilowatt hours per year and a prediction of some 6 trillion kilowatt hours consumed in the year 2000 seem reasonable. It is estimated that by 1980 there will be close to 175,000 megawatts of nuclear power installed and that by the year 2000 nuclear power plants will constitute at least 50% of the total capacity of 1 million to 1.5 million megawatts, Fig. 6-36.

Among the many factors which will influence the growth of nuclear power is the fact that light water reactor converter plants are presently being purchased in quantity. These reactors employ slightly enriched uranium, which is acquired in gaseous diffusion

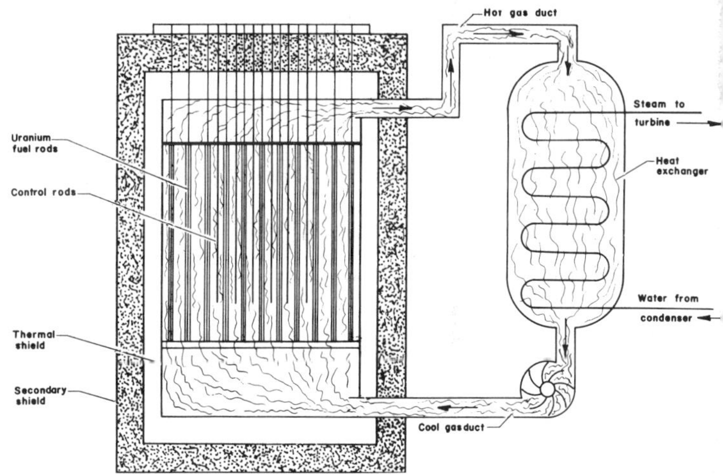

Fig. 6-34. Hot Gas Closed-Cycle Reactor

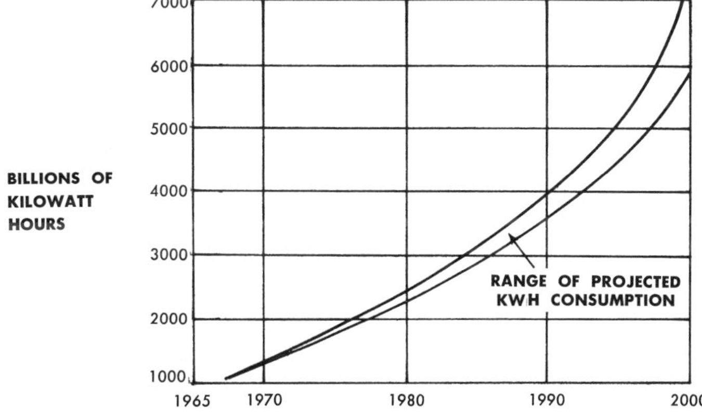

Fig. 6-35. Electric Energy Consumption

[4] Richard Post, "Controlled Fusion Research—An Application of the Physics of High Temperature Plasmas", *Review of Modern Physics,* Vol. 28, No. 5, July, 1956, pp. 338-362.

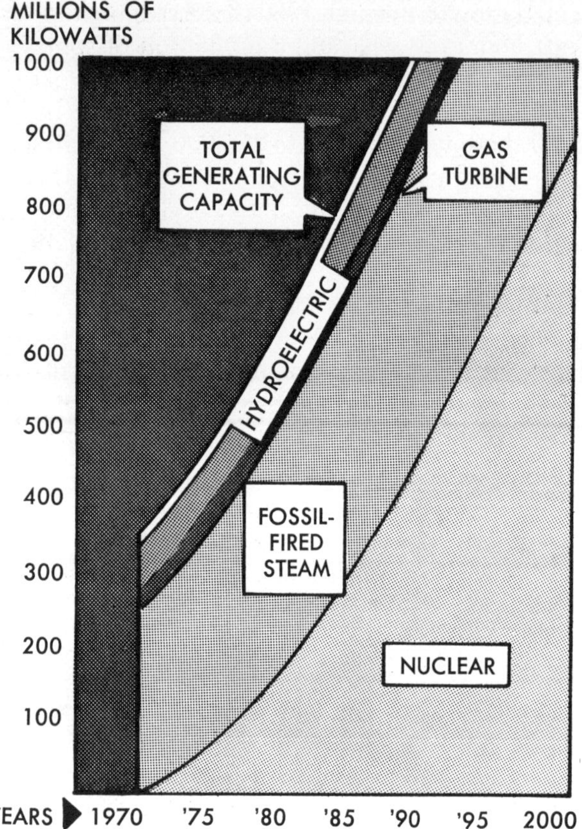

Fig. 6-36. Trends in Future U. S. Electric Utility Generating Capacity

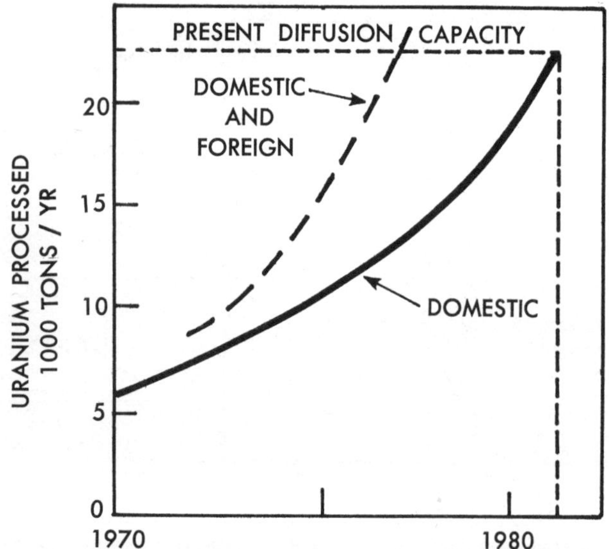

Fig. 6-37. Natural Uranium Consumption Rate

enrichment facilities. As shown in Fig. 6-37, present enrichment facilities can handle about 20,000 tons of the uranium per year. At the projected rate of growth, this capacity will be exhausted in the late 70's or early 80's.

It will be necessary to make decisions on expanding enrichment facilities or making the capital investment required to develop other nuclear systems which do not have this requirement. Another factor affecting future nuclear power is the quantity and cost of natural uranium required to meet the demand. If all of the projected nuclear load growth between now and the year 2000 is met by installing light water converters, the supply of low cost uranium could be completely exhausted. If, on the other hand, much of the new capacity installed after 1980 is in the form of high-gain breeder reactors, the costs may still rise, but the ore requirements will be lower, with virtually no mining required after the year 2020.

Typical utility systems have an average load of about 60% and can conveniently base load only 30-35% of their installed capacity. The remainder of the system must provide for the load demands that peak at certain times of the day and at certain times of the year. A reactor system such as the fast breeder reactor has a very low incremental fuel cost and relatively high capital cost. It will perform admirably in base load regions. However, if the load factors drop off appreciably, the higher fixed charges with the fast breeder reactor plant and fuel inventory make the cost of power relatively high. On the other hand, a converter reactor with low capital cost and relatively good fuel cycle cost will not quite compete with the fast reactor in the base load portion of the curve, but will have superior performance at lower load factors. Thus from a utility viewpoint, the system should be, as illustrated in Fig. 6-38, composed of plants which will provide for baseload, swingload, and peakload, producing the lowest total power cost for this system as a whole. This, of course, will require more than one type of nuclear reactor plant.

The important factors which will influence the application of nuclear power are: (1)

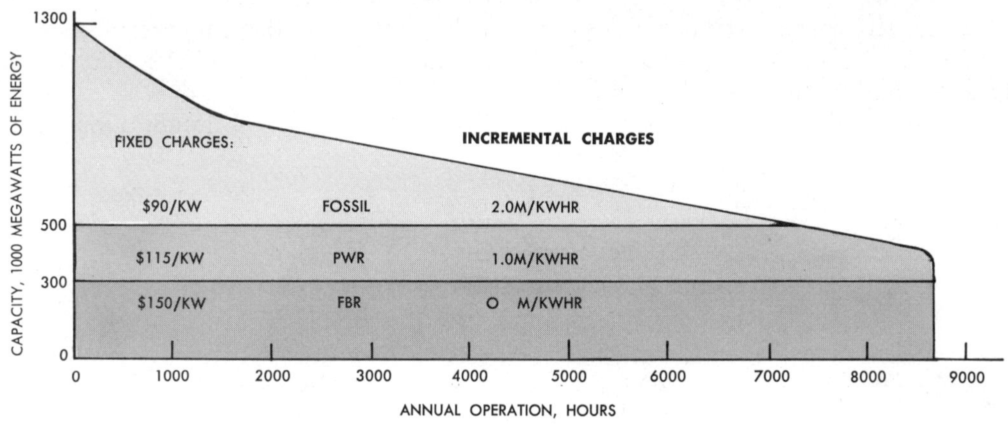

Fig. 6-38. Estimated Load Duration Curve

continued overall system and nuclear growth; (2) limited diffusion plant capacity; (3) ore requirements and available ore resources; (4) the size and disposition of the light water reactor plutonium stockpile; and (5) the optimum types of reactors for various utility system requirements.[5]

[5] J. C. R. Kelley, Jr., A. J. Hoffmeister, "Nuclear Power for 1980 and Beyond," *Westinghouse Technical Paper,* 1969.

Terms to Understand

atom
nuclear reactor
turbo-electric station
uranium 233, 235, 238
plutonium 242
thorium 232
fission
exchanger
$E = MC^2$
nucleus
electrons
protons
neutrons
isotopes
chain reaction
fuel cycle
assay
fluorination
gaseous diffusion
zirconium
cladding
loading pattern
radioactive
moderator
control rods
U.S.A.E.C.
core of reactor
pressurized water reactor
primary loop system
secondary loop system
switching yard
gamma rays
boron rod
biological shield
charge tubes
Calder Hall
Dounreay
Chapelcross
breeder reactor
liquid metal exchanger
heavy water reactor
swimming pool reactor
homogenous power reactor
boiling water reactor
closed cycle
fusion
helium
deuterium
fusion temperature

Study Questions

1. What are the advantages of atomic fuels as opposed to fossil fuels? What are their limitations?

2. Analyze the ways nuclear energy is and is expected to be used.

3. Analyze the structure of an atom.

4. Discuss the operation of a nuclear reactor.

5. What are the properties of uranium that make it a desirable atomic fuel.

6. What is meant by atomic fission?

7. Explain how the atomic reaction is controlled in the core by the "moderator".

8. What is the principle of the "heat exchangers"? What materials are commonly used?

9. Explain the difference between "fission" and "fusion".

10. Describe the operation of a nuclear power plant.

11. Analyze the various moderators used in some reactors.

12. Analyze why atomic fusion would provide a better means of acquiring energy than atomic fission.

13. Outline the preparation stages of uranium.

14. Discuss fuel management of atomic generating plants.

15. Describe the process of gaseous diffusion.

16. How is reuse of uranium managed?

Selected Readings for Part II
External Combustion Converters

Ames, Maurice, *Science For Progress Series,* (Englewood Cliffs: Prentice Hall, Inc., 1956)

Beebe, Lucius, and others, *The Age of Steam,* (New York: Rinehart & Co., Inc., 1957)

Church, Edwin F., *Steam Turbines,* (New York: McGraw-Hill Book Co., 1935)

Croft, Terrell W., *Steam Engines, Principles and Practices,* (New York: McGraw-Hill Book Co., 1939)

Crouse, William H., *Understanding Science (Steam Turbines),* (New York: McGraw-Hill Book Co., 1948)

Dickinson, Henry W., *James Watt, Craftsman and Engineer,* (Cambridge, England: The University Press, 1936)

Edison Electric Institute Committee on Environment, *Major Electric Power Facilities and the Environment.*

El-Wakel, M. M., *Nuclear Power Engineering,* (New York: McGraw-Hill Book Co., 1962)

Frisch, Otto R., *Atomic Physics Today,* (New York Basic Books, 1961)

Gerard, Geoffrey, *Book of Power Stations,* (New York: Frederick Warner & Co., 1962)

Glasstone, Samuel, *Principles of Nuclear Reactor Engineering,* (Princeton: D. Van Nostrand Co., Inc., 1959)

Hart, I. B., *James Watt and the History of Steam Power,* (New York: H. Schuman, 1949)

International Conference on the Peaceful Uses of Atomic Energy, *The World's Requirements for Energy: The Role of Nuclear Energy,* (New York: United Nations, 1956)

Jones, James B., and Hawkins, George, *Engineering Thermodynamics,* (New York: John Wiley & Son, 1960)

Lucas, Walter A., and others, *100 Years of Steam Locomotives,* (New York: Simmons-Boardman Publ. Corp., 1957)

Molloy, Edward, *Steam Engines and Boilers,* (New York: Chemical Publ. Co., 1941)

National Coal Policy Conference, Inc., Series of Reports on America's Fuels and Energy Future: No. 1 – *COAL: Key to Meeting Future Electric Power Demand;* No. 2 – *COAL's Answer to Fuel Shortages: 200 Million Tons of New Production Annually;* No. 3 – *EXPANDED RESEARCH: Only Answer to Cleaner Air and Adequate Energy Supplies,* (Washington, D. C. 20036)

Pickard, James K., and others, *Power Reactor Technology,* (New York: Van Nostrand, 1961)

Power-Generation Systems, Energy Systems Engineering, (New York: McGraw-Hill Book Co., 1967) (By the editors of POWER)

Research Development, (Lear Motors Corporation, 1972)

Russell, Charles R., *Elements of Energy Conversion,* (Elmsford, New York: Pergamon Publishing Co., 1967)

Sandfort, John F., *Heat Engines, Thermodynamics in Theory and Practice,* (New York: Doubleday, 1960)

Skrotzki, Bernardt G. A., *Electric Generation: Steam Stations,* (New York: McGraw-Hill Book Co., 1956)

Solberg, H. L., and others, *Elementary Heat Power,* 2nd Ed., (New York: John Wiley & Son, 1962)

Steam, Its Generation and Use, (New York: Babcock and Wilcox Co., 1955)

The Story of Steam, (New York: Babcock and Wilcox Co., 1957)

United States Atomic Energy Commission, *Atomic Energy Facts,* (Washington: Government Printing Office, 1957)

United States Atomic Energy Commission, *Civilian Power Reactor Program, Part I,* (Washington: Government Printing Office, 1960)

Valentine, James M., *Teach Yourself Atomic Physics,* (New York: Macmillan Co., 1961)

Wilson, Mitchell, *Energy,* (New York: Life Science Library, Time, Inc., 1963)

Woodruff, Everett, Lammers, Herbert, *Steam Plant Operation,* (New York: McGraw-Hill Book Co., 1950)

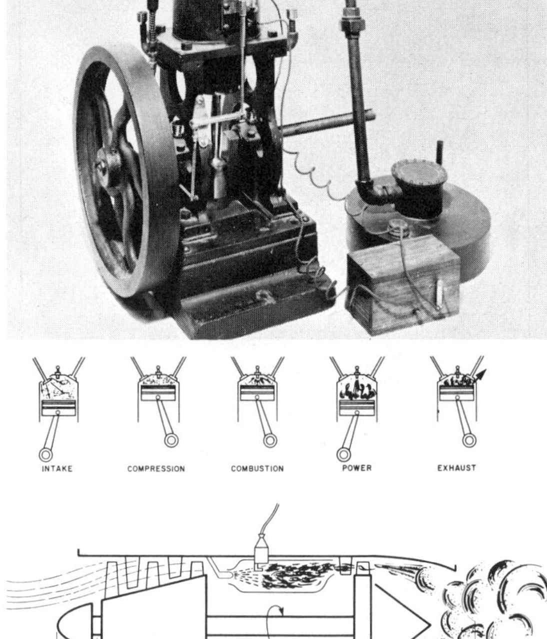

INLET COMPRESSION COMBUSTION TURBINE EXHAUST

1884 Barrett Gasoline Engine (Smithsonian), **Internal Combustion Principle** (GE), **Fan-Jet Engine** (P&W), **Chrysler Turbine Car, X-15 Rocket Plane** (USAF)

PART **III**

INTERNAL COMBUSTION CONVERTERS

The potential energy of a fuel is released
by burning within the engine itself
then *directly converted* to mechanical power
by pistons or by turbines.

Chapter

Internal Combustion Engines

The previous section concerned the external combustion engine (or E.C.E.) in which the burning of fuel, and the generating of heat energy occurs outside the prime mover. See Fig. 7-1. In this section, we will devote our attention to prime movers that convert the energy created by burning fuel and air within a combustion chamber located in the engine proper. They are referred to as *internal combustion engines* (or I.C.E.). The hot expanding gases may be employed to turn turbine rotors, push down pistons, or be used to cause locomotion by the reaction principle. The real working medium is air heated to increase its pressure.

Most people are familiar with the *internal combustion reciprocating engine.* It powers automobiles, boats, lawn mowers, home generators, and many other devices. It is heard and sometimes watched with awe, as it propels aircraft through the sky, large and small marine craft over the ocean, and trucks, buses, and tractors over black ribbons of highway. Modern man has learned to take this prime mover for granted. The only time he stops to try to understand this machine is when it fails to respond to his call.

Internal Combustion Variations

The many types and names of these engines can be quite confusing, but interesting if they can be properly identified. Such engines might be mobile or stationary, marine or aircraft, reciprocating or turbine, developing ⅓ hp or 3,000. They may be diesel or gasoline, L or I head, jet (or reaction), air cooled or water cooled, compression or spark ignition, two cycle or four cycle, fuel injected or carbureted, use a battery or a magneto. They may have one cylinder or many. Multi-cylinder engines may be in-line, horizontal, slant, radial or V-type. See Fig. 7-2. Study of

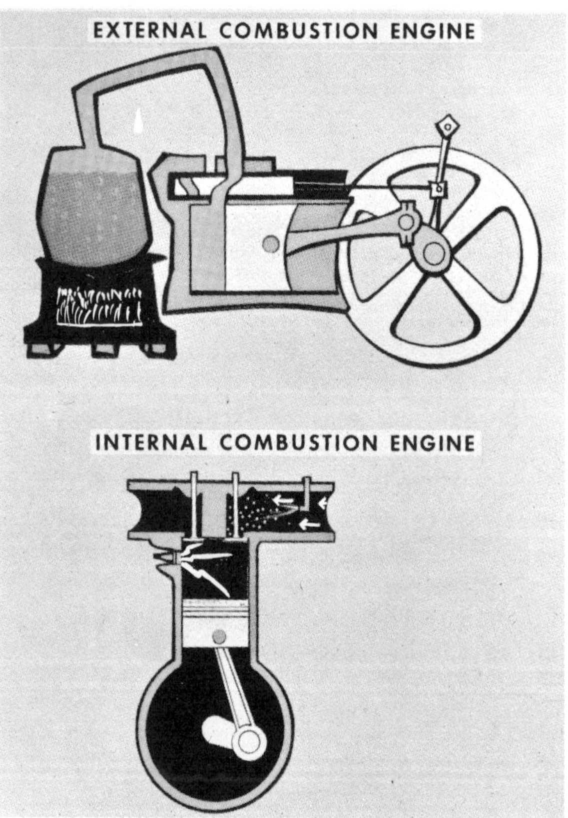

Fig. 7-1. Internal and External Combustion Reciprocating Engines (Ford)

man's technological advances using these forms of internal combustion engines to provide power for present day needs can also be very interesting.

Compared with External Combustion

Before discussing the development and principles of operation of the more popular kinds of reciprocating *internal* combustion engines, let us note the similarities that exist between these and the *external* combustion reciprocating engine.

The most important similarity between the two types of engines is that they are both *heat engines,* since both transform heat energy to mechanical energy. Also, both engines accomplish the conversion of heat energy into mechanical energy by generating a reciprocating motion using a crankshaft and one or more connecting rods.

The fundamental difference between the external and internal engine is where the fuel is burned. Their names suggest where this will take place. The *steam engine* is referred to as an *external combustion engine* because the fuel is consumed entirely *outside* of the cylinder(s) or engine proper. The *internal combustion engine* is so named because the burning takes place *within* the engine proper or within the cylinder or cylinders. The rate at which the combustion occurs also differs widely in the two types of engines. In the steam engine, the *fuel burns slowly* and the resulting heat is used to generate steam. Steam acts as an intermediate working substance which conveys the energy into the cylinder and uses it to move the piston. In the internal combustion engine, no such intermediate material is necessary. The *fuel burns rapidly* within the cylinder and the resulting expanding gases yield some of their energy to the piston causing it to move downward.

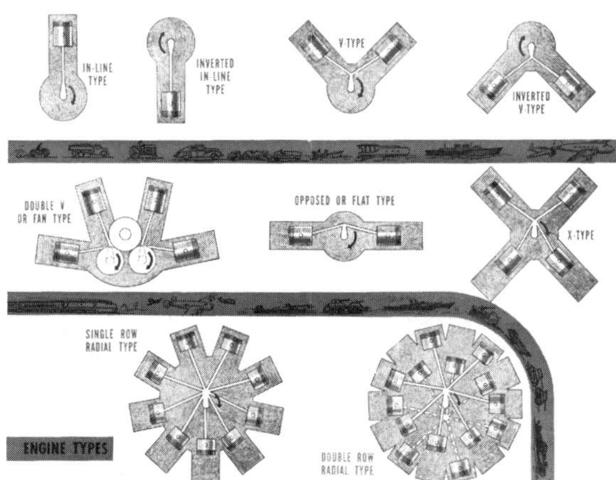

Fig. 7-2. Some Types of Internal Combustion Piston Engines (G.M.)

Early Developments

The first reciprocating internal combustion engine was made by Christian Huygens, a Dutch scientist. He devised the piston engine using a gunpowder explosion as mentioned in Chapter 2. The explosion fired the piston upwards and the gases thus formed were cooled until a partial vacuum was produced. As the cylinder pressure was then less than atmospheric pressure the piston was forced downward. Then the process was repeated. Because of hazards, the engine was never used, but provided inventors with a fundamental idea that was worth further investigation. Because of fuels then available, the developmental work for reciprocating engines which followed, involved the external combustion engine.

Static Spark Ignition

In 1799, Philip Lebon, a French artisan, devised and patented the first successful gas (not gasoline) engine. He compressed a charge of gas and air into a separate container and then passed the mixture into the cylinder on first one side of the piston and then the other.

The mixture was ignited by an electrical spark so that it worked much like the double-acting steam engine (then known for about 11 years). The pumps and the electric generator for the spark were driven by the engine. Coal gas was used as fuel although it had not yet been introduced as an commercial product for lighting. The gas was specially prepared for the engine. The only source of electric spark known at that time was static electricity. This was very unreliable and much depended on atmospheric conditions. The engine worked well, but because of the difficulties, was not adopted for any practical purpose.

Gas Flame Ignition

In 1823, Samuel Brown invented a gas engine that used a constantly lighted gas flame situated outside the cylinder to ignite the gas and air mixture within the cylinder. Part of the burned gases escaped through valves in the piston. By cooling the cylinder by water, a vacuum was created within and permitted atmospheric pressure to push the piston down. The basic mechanism of a later model is shown in Fig. 7-3. This engine found usefulness in pumping water and propelling boats. An experimental boat on the Thames attained a speed of 8 mph. The expense of producing gas fuel prevented it from remaining in competition with the steam engine.

Separate Compression Pump

William Barnett, in 1838, patented a gas engine which compressed a mixture of air and gas by employing a separate pump. Similar gas engines were designed during the following 20 years, but they all were too expensive and cumbersome to operate.

First Practical Engine

In 1860, Pierre Lenoir constructed the first practical gas engine, shown in Fig. 7-4. This engine was similar to a double-acting horizontal steam engine; a mixture of gas and air was drawn into the cylinder and ignited by an electric spark from an induction coil. However, this spark was unreliable, irregular, and defective, and produced an overall engine efficiency of 4 percent. A slide valve similar to that of a steam engine was used for admitting the gas and air mixture. It also allowed the escape of burned gases. High heat caused by combustion within the cylinder made valve adjustment difficult. These engines were rather crude, but many were made and used.

Four Cycles

Beau DeRochas, in 1862, patented the foundation for the modern, internal reciprocating engine. He described the principle of his engine in the following order: 1) suction or drawing in of gas and air mixture, 2) compression of mixture, 3) ignition to occur at the dead point and the expansion to occur during next forward stroke, 4) exhaust or expulsion of burned gases from the cylinder.

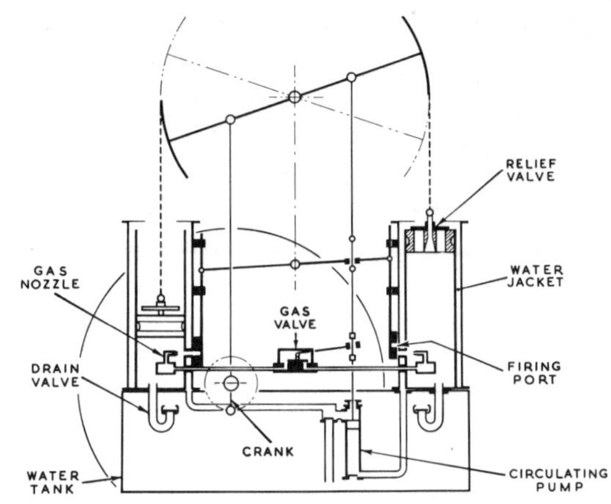

Fig. 7-3. Brown Gas Engine (1826)
(Science Museum, London)

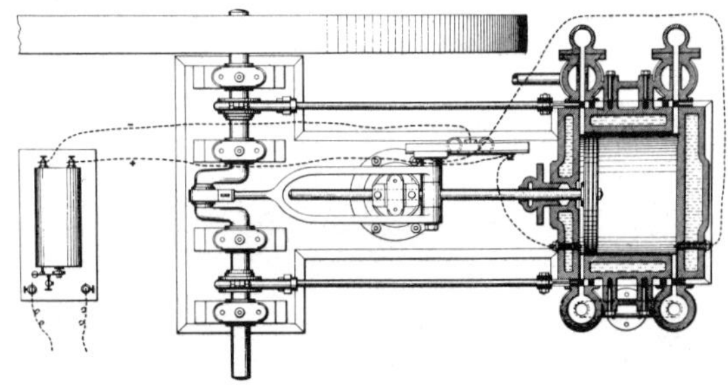

Fig. 7-4. Lenoir Gas Engine (1860)
(Science Museum, London)

He, furthermore, stated the four conditions necessary for the most economical results: 1) maximum possible volume of cylinder with minimum surface area, 2) piston speed as high as possible, 3) early cut-off, 4) high initial pressure.

It was not until 1876, that Dr. N. A. Otto designed the highly successful engine shown in Fig. 7-5, which employed the DeRochas principles. Today, these four strokes are known as the Otto cycle because of this engine. It was much more efficient than the Lenoir engine, using only 25 cu. ft. of gas per hp as compared to 96 cu. ft. of gas per hp for the Lenoir.

Operation of Otto Engine

Otto employed an outside flame for igniting the mixture within the cylinder and a slide valve for regulating the cycle of operations. He also used water to cool the cylinder. A slide allowed passage to the cylinder inlet and the gas and air inlets through openings in the slide. During the first part of the intake strokes, air only was admitted, then both gas and air. The slide was moved backward and forward by a crank on a side shaft driven at half of engine speed by gear reduction. (In Fig. 7-5, this horizontal shaft is just above the ball governor, partially in dotted lines.) During the return stroke, the exhaust port was closed and the mixture was compressed. As the slide valve moved across, the chamber was filled with gas from the supply pipe. As the valve passed back the gas was ignited by the continuous external flame. The burning gas was carried until it caused the mixture in the cylinder to become ignited. On the fourth stroke, the burned gases were driven out through the exhaust port. It was kept closed by a spring-held valve which was opened by a lever mechanism operated by a cam on the side shaft.

Hot Tube and Spark Ignition

In 1879, Atkinson used *hot-tube ignition* in a gas engine. A wrought iron tube was opened at its lower end. A small hole was drilled through the wall of the cylinder and closed at the upper end. It was kept red hot by a gas burner. When the mixture within the cylinder was compressed, a portion passed into the tube, was ignited, and flashed back into the cylinder firing the complete charge.

This novel ignition system gave way to the electrical spark plug as the electrical generator and this method of ignition became more reliable.

Gas as a Fuel

Today, the gas engine is not used to any great extent, because it is less efficient than

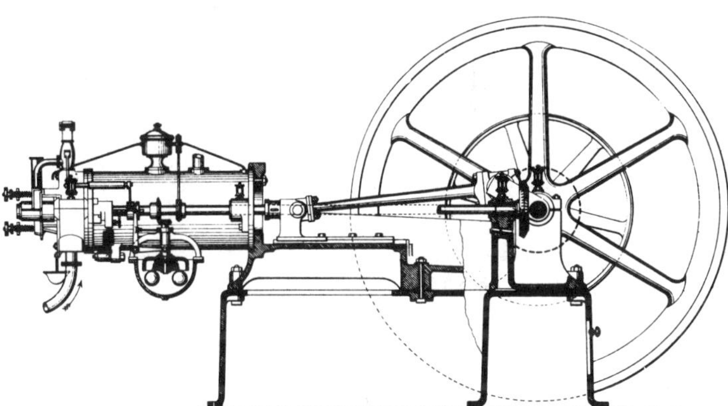

Fig. 7-5. Otto Gas Engine (1876)
(Science Museum, London)

Fig. 7-6. Daimler's First Gasoline Engine (1885)
(Smithsonian Institution)

the gasoline engine and because the gas requires a much larger storage space than liquid fuel. Gas engines are used, however, where a supply of cheap gas is available. During World War II in Europe, buses, trucks, and conventional passenger vehicles used "producer" gas. This was generated by burning coke, coal, or wood in self-contained gas generators. These generators were usually located in the back of the vehicle and the driver of the vehicle stoked them periodically as the engine called for more fuel.

Gasoline Engine

Because of the high cost of gas, some engine designers experimented with various liquids, and devised contrivances to vaporize them. Success was not achieved until 1885, when Gottlieb Daimler, Manager of Otto's engine works, patented the first gasoline engine. See Fig. 7-6. It worked on the 4-stroke cycle principle just as Otto's gas engine, but the gasoline was vaporized by the carburetor before being admitted to the cylinder. Daimler applied his engine to a rather crude motorcycle and later to cars.

Oil Engine

In 1889, Priestman and Hall constructed the first oil engine. In it, oil was vaporized by heating it in a small container before it entered the cylinder. The mixture of oil vapor and air was then ignited as before by an electrical spark.

Herbert Akroyd Stuart, in 1890, procured a patent for the compression ignition engine shown in Fig. 7-7. This engine was fitted with a cylinder extension called a vaporizer. This vaporizer was heated externally before starting. During the induction stroke, only air passed into the cylinder, and this was compressed to about 35 psi. At the end of the compression stroke, a small quantity of oil was forced into the vaporizer by a pump, which promptly ignited. After running for a period of time, the external heat was no longer necessary on the vaporizer. In 1891, the firm of Hornsby and Sons, Ltd., of Grantham, started manufacturing these engines known as the *Hornsby-Akroyd* engine. Compare this commercial model, shown in Fig. 7-8, with the experimental model shown in Fig. 7-7. Inch rules (alternate inches black and white) compare sizes.

Diesel Engine

In 1892, Rudolph Diesel secured a patent for a new type of compression ignition engine. This engine did not have a vaporizer, but employed *compression* high enough to ignite the mixture of oil and air. The first successful diesel engine was built in Augsburg in 1897. It not only used a cheaper fuel than gasoline but proved to be more efficient and

Fig. 7-7. Model of Akroyd Crude Oil Engine (1890)
(©Science Museum, London)

Fig. 7-8. Hornsby-Akroyd Crude Oil Engine (1893)
(©Science Museum, London)

quickly became extremely popular. See Fig. 7-9.

Vehicular Use

By 1897 considerable work was carried on in Germany, France, England, and the United States, in the development of overland vehicles driven by the internal combustion engine. Many vehicles employed a vertical engine situated at the front under a hood and mounted on a modern-type chasis. Others were patterned on the familiar horse-drawn figure which they were expected to replace. Some of these early engines employed a sliding gear transmission (operated by the right hand), clutch, brake, and foot accelerator. It cannot be considered that the motor car was the product of any one inventor or any group of inventions.

Fig. 7-9. Early Diesel Oil Engine (1909) (Science Museum, London)

Fig. 7-10. Olds Gasoline Engine (1903) (Smithsonian Institution)

After 1900, the *internal combustion engine* had a profound effect on the evolution of mechanically propelled road vehicles. See Fig. 7-10. Since the steam engine had been too bulky as a source of power for such vehicles, this new engine, a small lightweight unit that could supply more power per weight than the steam engine, was seen as the answer to the problem. It should be realized, however, that the evolution of the internal combustion engine was conditioned by the increasing supply of cheap fuel and also by cheap steel. New developments in the production of crude oil and studies on the nature and combustion of gases which had begun in the eighteenth and continued into the nineteenth century also helped.

The twentieth century saw the internal combustion engine as something that had come to stay. Easily seen are the improvements that have been made by the re-designing of the *carriage* and the engine parts. The two World Wars stimulated the use of trucks and automobiles and helped build up the strong demand for cheaper and simpler vehicles, able to attain higher speeds.

The many demands imposed on man to do work has caused him to employ this versatile prime mover in many ways. His ingenious use of this engine has permitted him the luxury of free time and better living conditions.

Compression vs. Spark Ignition

As has been mentioned, there are two main types of ignition in reciprocating internal combustion engines. These are *spark ignition* (or SI), used in gasoline engines, and *compression ignition* (or CI) as used in diesel

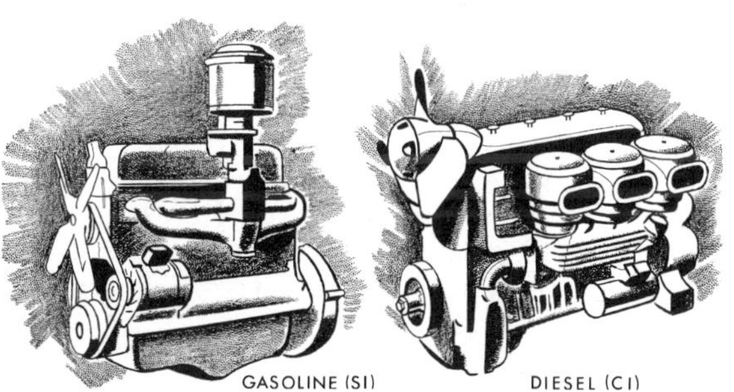

Fig. 7-11. SI and CI Engines (G.M.)

engines. Fig. 7-11 shows that in general appearance, these engines look almost alike. However, they are quite different in the method of mixing air and fuel and in the method of igniting this mixture.

In the gasoline engine, the mixture is made in a carburetor outside of the cylinder. It is drawn into the cylinder and compressed by the piston moving up within and then ignited by an electric spark.

On the other hand, the piston in the diesel engine compresses only air as the piston moves upward within the cylinder. This increases the temperature of the compressed air to about 1000°F. The fuel is then forced into the combustion chamber and is ignited by the temperature caused by compression.

Both types of ignition are possible in engines using either a four-stroke cycle or a two-stroke cycle. Let us now compare spark ignition with compression ignition in four-stroke engines, and then in engines with two-stroke cycles.

The Four-Stroke Cycle

Figs. 7-12 and 7-13 compare the cycles of a four-stroke *gasoline* engine and a four-stroke *diesel* engine. (A stroke is one movement of the piston within the cylinder. "Four-stroke cycle" is often shortened to "four-cycle".)

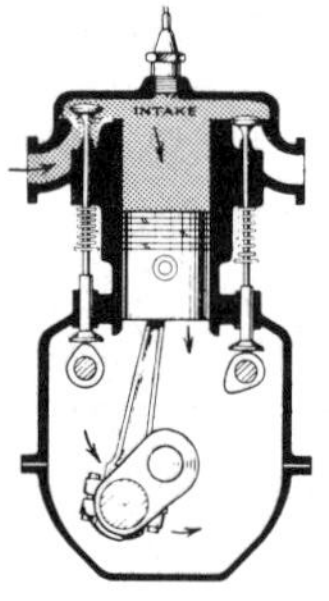

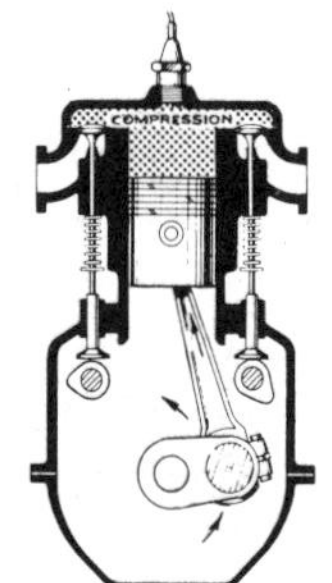

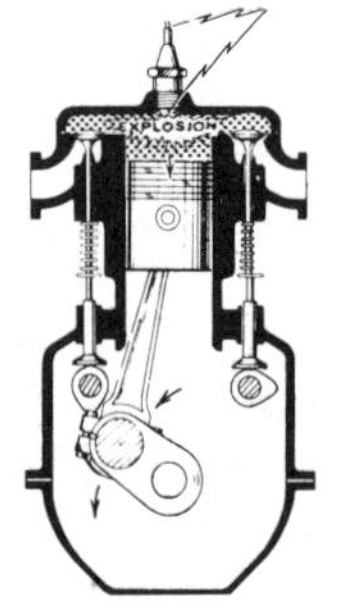

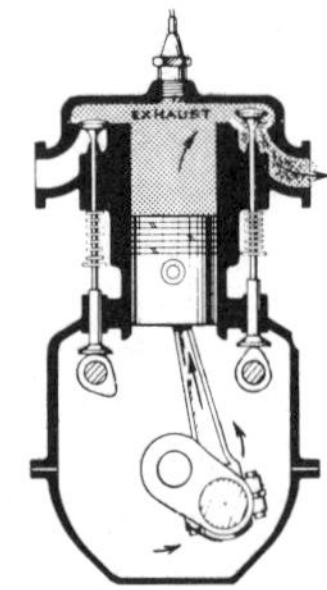

Fig. 7-12. Four Strokes of a Gasoline (SI) Engine (Lawn-Boy)

On the downward stroke of the piston, a partial vacuum is created; the intake valve opens and atmospheric pressure forces the *gas and air mixture* to fill the void.

The intake and exhaust valves are closed as the piston starts upward compressing the mixture at from 70 to 125 psi or 1/10th of the space it would ordinarily occupy.

The compressed fuel and air is ignited by an *electric spark*. The heat of combustion causes an expansion of gases within the cylinder, which forces the piston downward.

The exhaust valve opens which permits the burned gases to escape as the piston moves upward, readying the cylinder for another cycle.

Intake **Compression** **Power** **Exhaust**

On the downward stroke of the piston, a partial vacuum is created; the intake valve opens and atmospheric pressure forces *air* in to fill the void.

The intake and exhaust valves are closed as the piston moves upward compressing the fuel to approximately 625 psi or 1/15th of the space it would ordinarily occupy.

High compression creates enough heat to ignite *fuel* forced into the cylinder. Combustion heat expands gases within the cylinder, forcing the piston downward.

The exhaust valve opens which permits the burned gases to escape as the piston moves upward, readying the cylinder for another cycle.

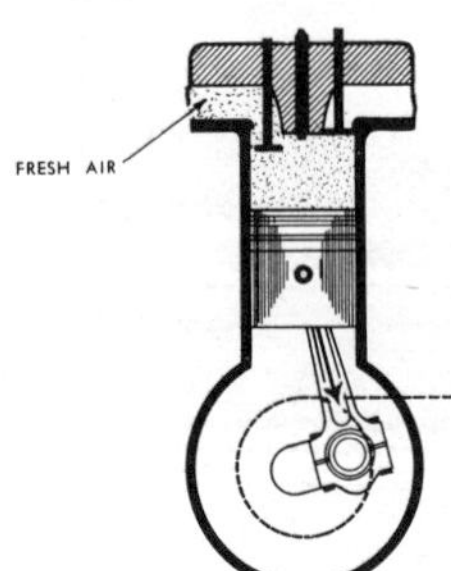

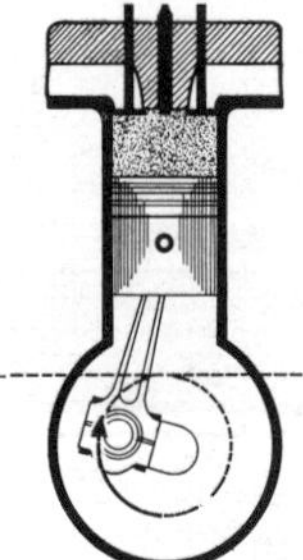

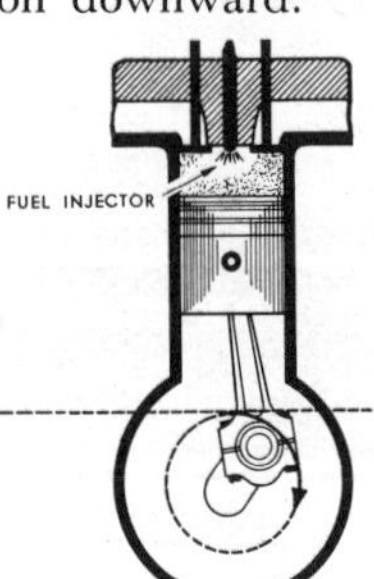

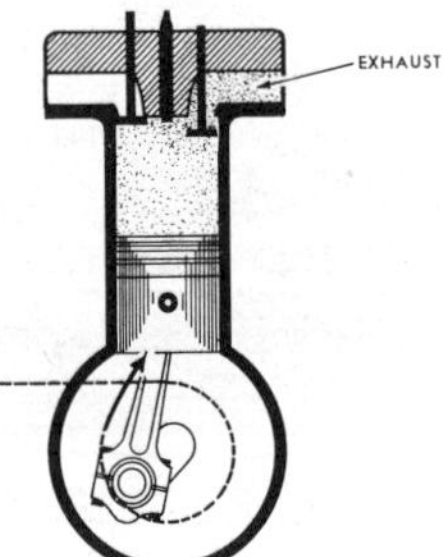

Fig. 7-13. Four Strokes of a Diesel (CI) Engine

Two-Stroke Cycle

Fig. 7-14 shows the basic parts of a modern small engine with a four-stroke cycle. In this engine, there is one power stroke for every four strokes of the piston or for every two revolutions of the crankshaft. It would be advantageous to have a power stroke for each revolution of the crankshaft or for every two movements of the piston—a two-stroke cycle. This would give a more powerful and smoother running engine. Fig. 7-15 compares the phases of a four-stroke cycle and a two-stroke cycle during two revolutions of the crankshaft. A modern small engine having a two-stroke cycle is shown in Fig. 7-16. Note that this engine lacks the usual valves so is lighter in weight besides having fewer moving parts. See Fig. 7-17.

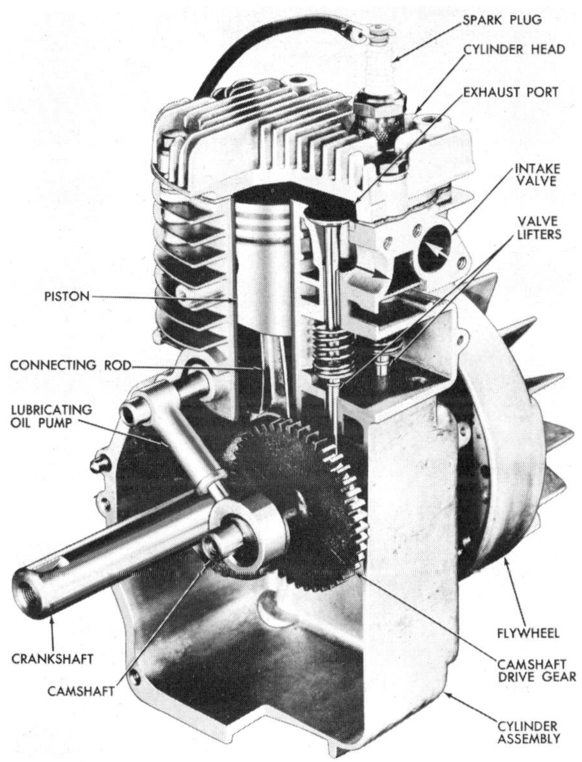

Fig. 7-14. Small Vertical Engine with Four-Stroke Cycle (Tecumseh)

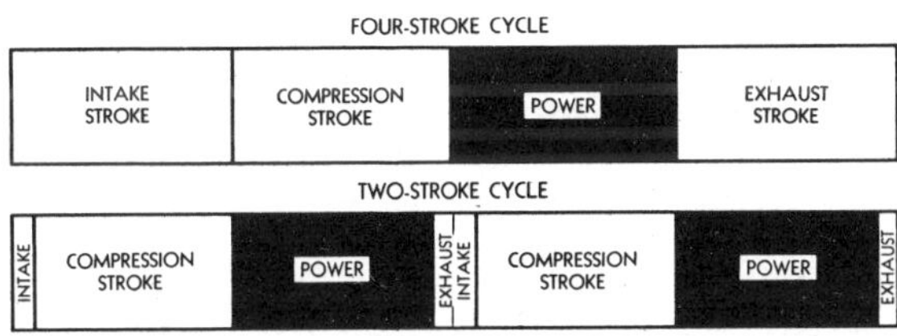

Fig. 7-15. Four-Stroke and Two-Stroke Cycle Compared (G.M.)

Development of Two-Stroke Cycle

In 1878, Sir Dugald Clerk constructed a two-stroke cycle engine which was exhibited at the 1881 Paris Exhibition. Clerk's engine had exhaust ports or holes in the cylinder walls, which were covered and uncovered by the moving piston. The combustion chamber was conical in shape and the mixture of gas and air was forced in by a separate pump. At the end of the power stroke, the exhaust ports were uncovered, and at the same time a fresh charge was pumped into the cylinder. As the piston moved forward, it compressed the mixture and then ignition took place at the time it reached the top of its stroke.

In 1891, John Day invented the valveless-type two-stroke gasoline engine that is popular today in powering model airplanes and

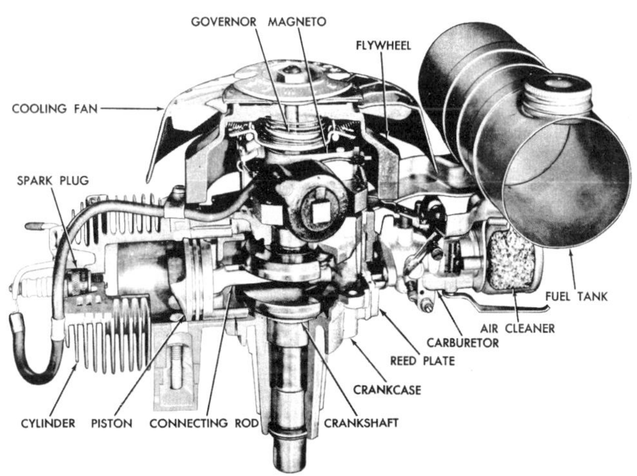

Fig. 7-16. Small Horizontal Engine with Two-Stroke Cycle (Tecumseh)

boats, small compressors, and household equipment.

The two-stroke cycle is not satisfactory for large gasoline engines although the principle is employed in large marine diesel engines.

In the two-stroke spark-ignition engine, the inlet side exhaust ports are designed so that a fresh charge first fills the cylinder, with none escaping out of the exhaust, for a particular speed and load. See Fig. 7-18. But in practice, with a varying load, some of the exhaust gases remain in the cylinder diluting the fresh gas and air charge, cutting down on power; or, some of the charge escapes out the exhaust port, wasting fuel, and cutting down on engine efficiency.

The diesel engine, however, only compresses air. Fuel is injected at the end of the compression stroke, so that if some of the fresh air charge escapes, no fuel is wasted. So, the two-stroke cycle diesel engine is quite popular because it is smoother running than the four-cycle engine. See Fig. 7-19. However, in larger gasoline engines, because of greater efficiency, and flexibility, the four-stroke cycle is most popular.

Two-stroke cycle spark-ignition engines are popular for powering model aircraft, boats, lawnmowers, and outboard motors. These engines must be light in weight for portability and the thirst for fuel is not prohibitive because of their relatively small size.

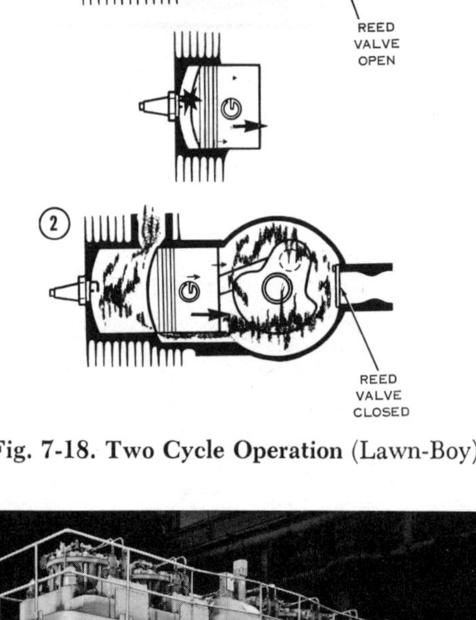

Fig. 7-18. Two Cycle Operation (Lawn-Boy)

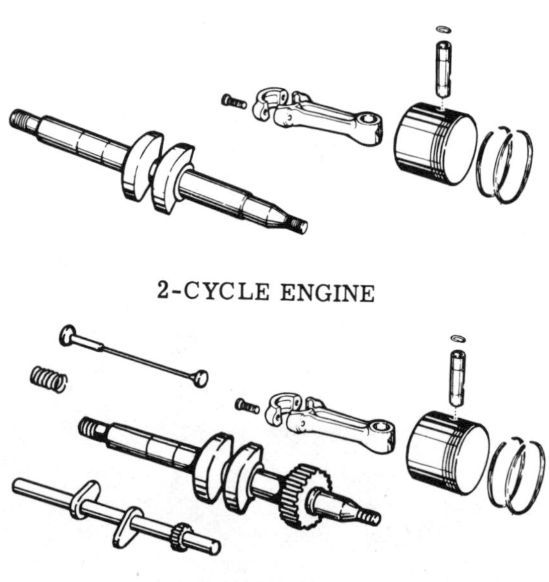

Fig. 7-17. Moving Parts of Four-Cycle and Two-Cycle Engines Compared. (Lawn-Boy)
Four-cycle engines require an oil sump, and a circulation system. This is unnecessary in two-cycle operation because oil is mixed with fuel.

Fig. 7-19. An Eight-Cylinder, Two-Cycle Diesel Engine Powers the Ship, Alexander T. Wood (Nordberg)
This engine is typical of the large two-stroke cycle engines. These engines, built with 5 to 12 cylinders are rated from 4500 to over 12,000 horsepower. They meet the demands for heavy continuous service in marine, utility and industrial plant and power generation.

Two-Cycle Operation

In this engine, the piston takes over some of the valve functions that are found in four-cycle engines by covering and uncovering ports or openings in the side of the cylinder wall, and thus acts as a valve in filling and emptying the cylinder. This is shown in detail in Figs. 7-20 and 7-21.

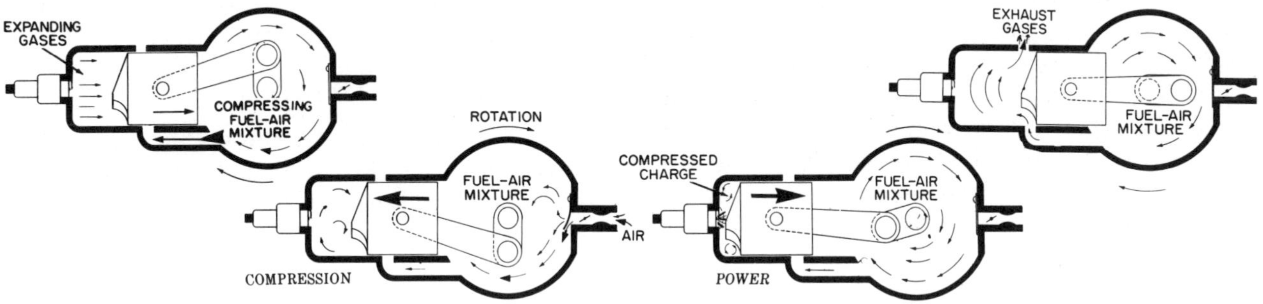

Fig. 7-20. Two-Stroke Cycle of Small SI Engine (Tecumseh)

Intake and Compression Stroke

As the piston moves upward in the SI engine, the fuel-air mixture is compressed above it, while a partial vacuum is created in the crankcase drawing in the fuel-air charge from the carburetor for the next compression stroke. Most small two-cycle SI engines employ reed valves, as shown in Fig. 7-22. These valves are thin metal flaps which allow air flow inward but spring back to prevent its return. They permit the mixture of gasoline and air to enter the crankcase as the partial vacuum is created by the upward-moving piston.

In an engine using a *blower* or a *scavenger* as in the diesel diagramed below, the fresh charge (which is just air in a diesel engine) is forced through intake ports into the cylinder at the beginning of the upward stroke of the piston. This forces out the spent gases before compression actually takes place. Not all of the spent gases from the previous stroke are removed in either case.

Power and Exhaust Stroke

In the SI engine, the mixture is ignited electrically; in the CI engine, the fuel ignites as it is injected into the air heated by high compression.

As the piston is moved downward by expanding gases, the exhaust port is uncovered permitting the spent gases to escape. The piston is also compressing a new charge in the crankcase and, as the intake port opens, a fresh supply rushes into the cylinder.

The intake and exhaust ports are opposite one another. A deflector on top of the piston directs the fresh charge upwards away from the spent gases leaving through the exhaust port.

Blower-type engines usually have one or more exhaust valves at the top of the cylinder. These open when the piston nears the bottom of the power stroke permitting the spent gases to leave. Then, as the piston moves further downward, the intake ports are uncovered and the cylinder is replenished for the next cycle as shown below.

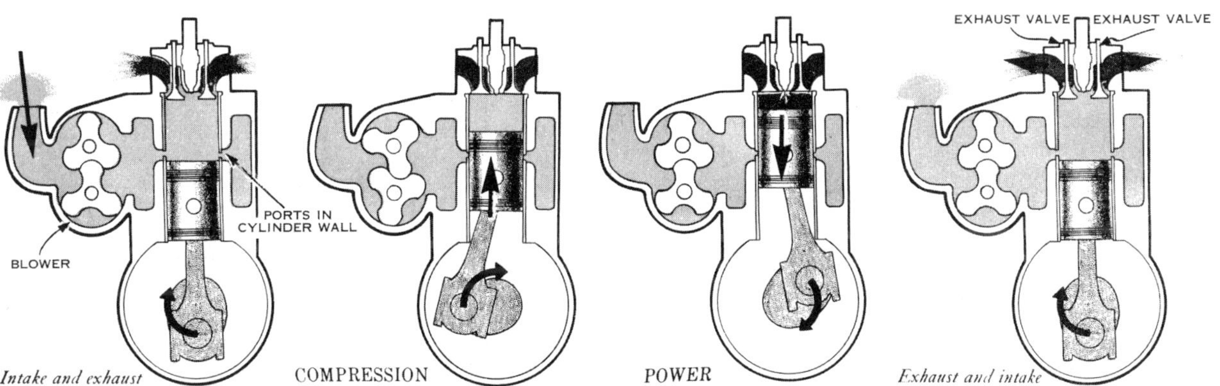

Fig. 7-21. Two-Stroke Cycle of Diesel Engine (G.M.)

Glow Plug Ignition

The popular small model airplane and boat engines employ the diesel principle with a heater called a *glow-plug*. The glow-plug preheats the cylinder and when the mixture is compressed in the combustion chamber, it reaches the combustion point more easily. Once the engine is running and the cylinder is hot enough to maintain firing, the electrical connections can be removed and the engine runs on the diesel principle. The plug is so designed that it remains red hot (although not electrically connected) by absorbing heat from combustion. See Fig. 7-23. This glow plug principle is also being used in some large compression ignition engines. It features easier starting, particularly in cold weather, and better combustion. See Fig. 7-24.

Impact of the Gasoline Engine

The main source of vehicular locomotion today is the gasoline engine. Presently, more than 72,000,000 vehicles are registered in the United States.

Many believe that the automobile industry determines the economic climate of our whole industrial society. This is easily realized when one reflects on the many varied and diversified industries involved in the production of the automobile. See Fig. 7-25.

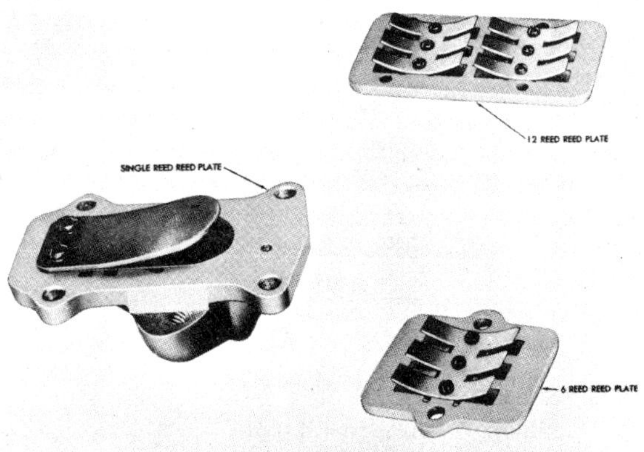

Fig. 7-22. Reed Plates (Tecumseh)

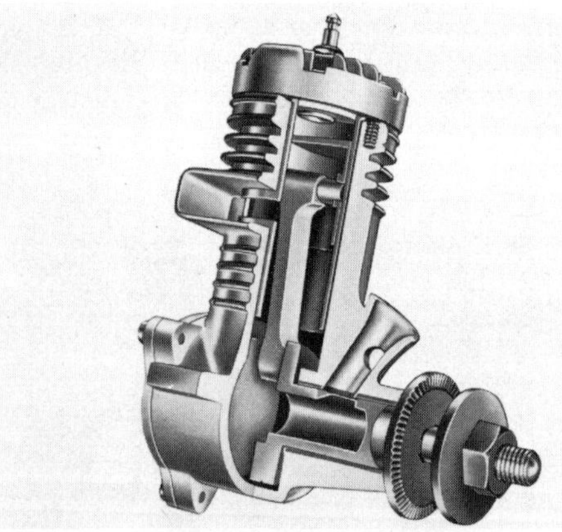

Fig. 7-23. Two-Cycle Model Airplane Engine Showing Parts

Note the glow plug, cylinder wall liner, connecting rod and crankshaft, piston, and the exhaust port. The simple needle carburetor is not shown. Some of these engines develop up to one-third horsepower.

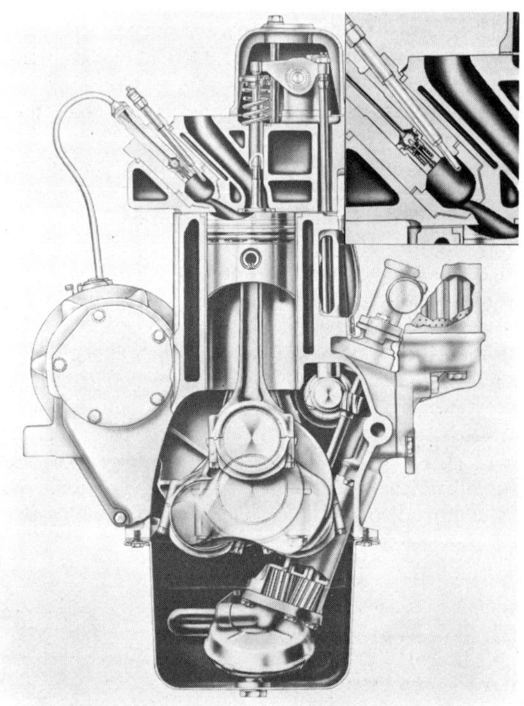

Fig. 7-24. Glow Plug in Diesel—Insert Shows Plug Protruding into Pre-Cup Chamber (International)

Location of glow plug in pre-cup aids cold weather starting. This design heats the fuel-air mixture in the pre-cup instead of heating only the air. Single orifice nozzle gives improved economy. Initial combustion occurs in the pre-cup where fuel is sprayed directly into the turbulent air charge. The gases then expand into the cylinder, resulting in more complete combustion.

Certainly, there has been no other prime mover that has responded so willingly for the benefit of the young and old and provided them with the facility of travel with relative comfort and speed. Ribbons of asphalt and concrete have tied the continent into a "neat package", providing many with employment in service industries, tourist accommodations, and other related jobs.

Terms to Understand

external combustion engines, E.C.E.
internal combustion engines, I.C.E.
reciprocating engine
combustion speed
Christian Huyghens
Philip Lebon
Samuel Brown
William Barnett
Pierre Lenoir
Beau De Rockas
N. A. Otto
Atkinson
Gottlieb Daimler
Priestman and Hall
Herbert Stuart
Hornsby-Akroyd
Rudolph Diesel
compression ignition
spark ignition
carburetor
combustion chamber
4-stroke cycle engine
2-stroke cycle engine
Dugald Clerk
John Day
glow plug
intake
compression
combustion or power
exhaust
reed valve
blower or scavenger

Study Questions

1. Describe the principles of operation of a 4-cycle I.C.E.

2. Discuss principles of operation and the differences between internal combustion and external combustion engines.

3. Analyze the limitations of each.

4. List some uses of reciprocating internal combustion engines.

5. How is the engine used to do work?

6. What types of coupling or transmission systems are employed?

7. Analyze the similarities between reciprocating I.C.E. and E.C.E.

8. Describe the operation of Christian Huyghens' first internal combustion engine.

9. Briefly discuss the development of the I.C.E.

10. Analyze the principles outlined by Beau DeRochas for his I.C.E.

11. Analyze this statement: The modern reciprocating I.C.E. was the product of many inventions.

12. Describe the principles of operation of a 2-cycle I.C.E.

13. What are the main differences between the diesel and gasoline reciprocating engines?

14. Compare the advantages and disadvantages of 2- and 4-cycle gasoline engines and diesel engines.

15. What is meant by a scavenger or blower exhaust system?

16. What is the principle of the glow plug?

17. In a diesel engine with a piston having a 6-inch diameter, the effective pressure during the working stroke is 200 psi. The piston moves 6 inches at 500 rpm. What is the horsepower of the engine?

18. Why is a diesel engine more efficient than a gasoline engine?

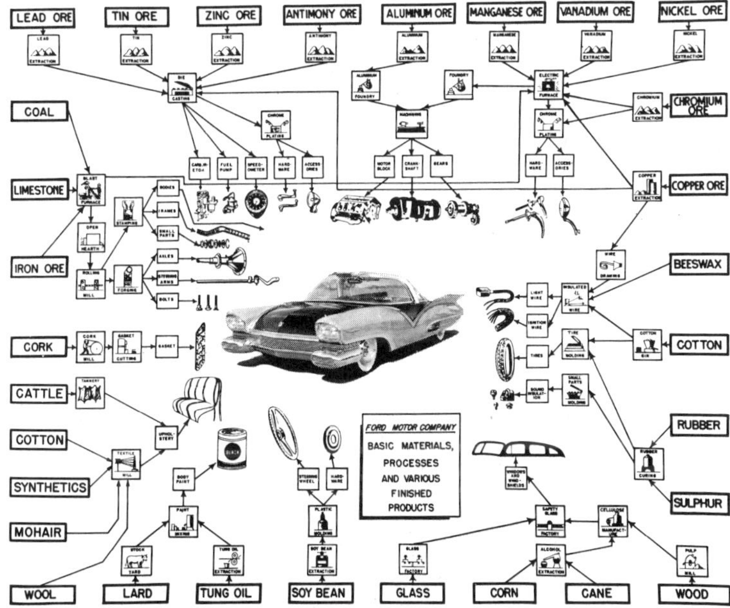

Fig. 7-25. Basic Materials, Processes, and Products in Automobile Manufacturing (Ford)

Reciprocating Engine Design

The demands imposed on prime movers such as the reciprocating SI and CI engines, are so varied that many designs and modifications are to be expected to provide adaptability to satisfy the numerous needs. Some of the considerations and changes made by engine designers will now be discussed to provide a better understanding of these heat engines.

Engines and Air

Anyone who has used these internal combustion engines realizes that he must provide the engine with fuel, but he may not have bothered to concern himself about the necessity for air. This is only natural, as fuels cost money and air is for the taking.

Enormous Demand for Air

In many ways, the problem of providing the engine with sufficient air is more difficult than providing it with fuel because of the huge quantities necessary for proper operation. Theoretically, the modern gasoline engine should be provided with about 15 parts of air to every one part of gasoline by weight. This may vary somewhat depending on whether fuel economy or power is the main consideration. So about 15 pounds of air is required for every pound of gasoline. But, gasoline weighs about 600 times as much as air at sea level, or, in other words, the air takes up about 600 times more space than does the equivalent weight of gasoline. Thus, for every cubic foot of gasoline we must furnish 600 times 15, or 9,000 cubic feet of air. This is enough air to fill an average house or a balloon more than 28 feet in diameter at sea level. In aircraft engines this problem is even more complex because of rarified air at higher altitudes. To get the same amount of air at 17,000 feet the volume must be doubled and at 59,000 feet the volume must be ten times that at sea level. It can be seen that air volume is difficult to handle as compared to fuel volume.

It is important to realize that the only reason we are interested in providing so much air to the engine is to provide the fuel with the necessary *oxygen* for combustion. Air, as you may realize, is a mixture of 21 percent oxygen and 78 percent nitrogen and 1 percent of other gases. The nitrogen and other inert gases go through the engine and out the exhaust unchanged—only the oxygen is utilized.

Admission of Air

Later, we will discuss the various methods of getting this air into the cylinder. The most common method is through openings on the top of the cylinder that are covered or

Fig. 8-1. Air and Gases Admitted by Valves or Ports

uncovered at proper intervals by mushroom-shaped lids called *poppet valves.* Air admission is also obtained through *ports* or openings in the side of the cylinder that are open or covered as the piston moves up and down. There are also other arrangements such as the *sleeve valve.* It is so called since it employs a sleeve that slides between the piston and the cylinder wall that controls the flow through the ports in the side of the cylinder. *Reed valves,* the spring flaps commonly used to control movement of the fuel-air mixture in two-cycle engines, were described in Chapter 7.

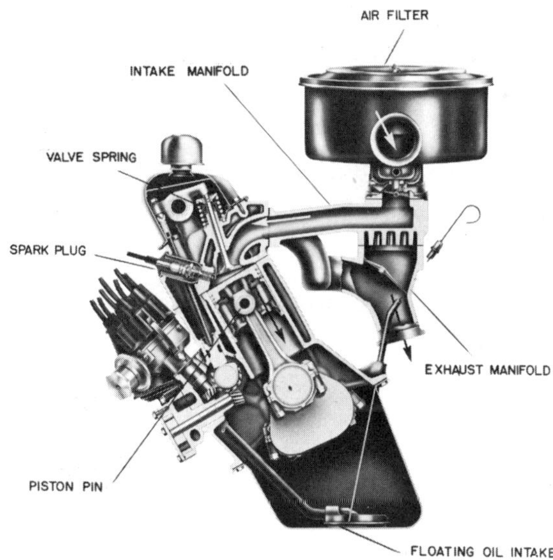

Fig. 8-2. 30° Slant of This Inline Engine Allows More Room for Air Intake and Carburetor (Valiant)

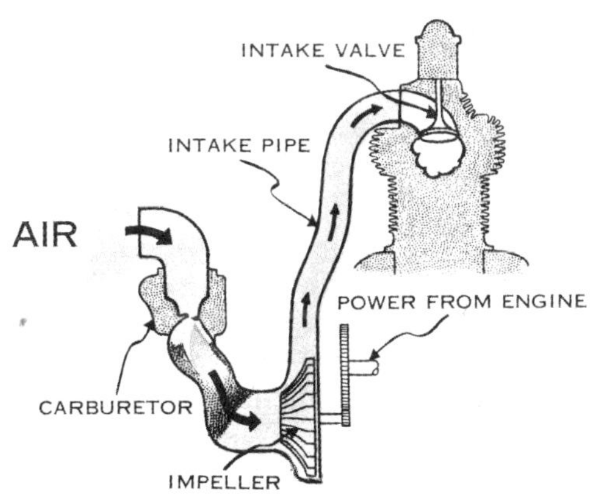

Fig. 8-3. Aircraft Supercharger System (G.M.)

Supercharging

In most engines, atmospheric pressure forces air into the partial vacuum formed in the cylinder when the piston makes its intake stroke. See Fig. 8-2. Some engines employ an impellor, called a *blower* or *supercharger* to force air into the cylinder. Fig. 8-3 diagrams a typical aircraft supercharger system. Figs. 8-4 to 8-6 show how a supercharger is utilized on a large diesel engine. Most diesel engines have a blower for air intake to promote more efficient scavenging of exhaust gases. One type is shown in Fig. 8-7.

Atmospheric pressure at sea level is about 14.7 psi. This pressure is neither felt nor seen and sometimes is never thought of as being present. Yet, this great ocean of air surrounding the earth is pressing down on us at all times. As we have already learned, when a void is created with less pressure in it, the atmospheric pressure will push to fill it up. If we climb a mountain or go up in an airplane, the atmospheric pressure will decrease just as

Fig. 8-4. General Purpose Locomotive (Electro-Motive)

This combination high speed and heavy drag locomotive uses the turbocharged G.M. engine in Fig. 8-5 to achieve its wide range of speed and power. The engine runs a heavy generator which powers electric motors driving the wheels. Simple cab controls (inset) are mostly electrical.

the pressure of the ocean decreases when a diver approaches the surface. Supercharging is even more important at high altitudes, so there are many complications in supplying air to an aircraft engine. This will be discussed in detail in Chapter 12.

Fuel

Today's petroleum fuels are a product of both man and nature; and, more often than not, are given little thought or appreciation as to how and where they are made. Except for water, petroleum is the most plentiful liquid of nature. It contains more energy than any non-atomic explosive. In fact, computations show that the energy in a gallon of dynamite would run a modern car approximately three miles, as compared to perhaps 18 miles on a gallon of gasoline.

Petroleum

Petroleum is a *hydrocarbon,* a complex union of hydrogen and carbon atoms. The fuels that we extract from it are various other hydrocarbons. Man has learned to extract from petroleum a number of fuels, lubricants

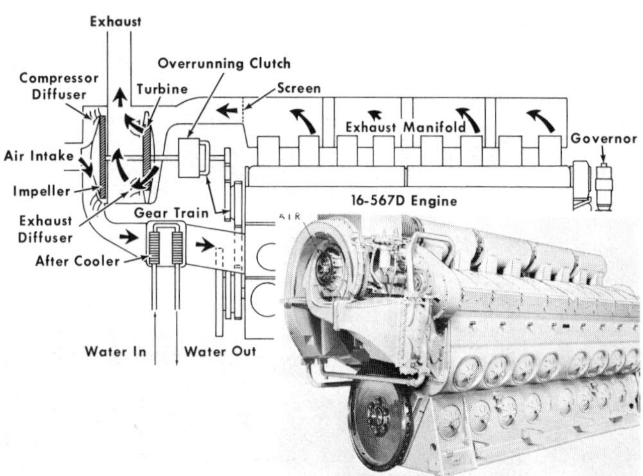

Fig. 8-5. Turbocharged Diesel Engine (Electro-Motive)

This 16 cylinder, two-cycle CI engine develops up to 2850 hp and is used for locomotives, tug boats, ships, generators and oil drilling. The turbine turning the air impeller is driven by a gear train from the engine at slow speeds and by exhaust gases at high speeds.

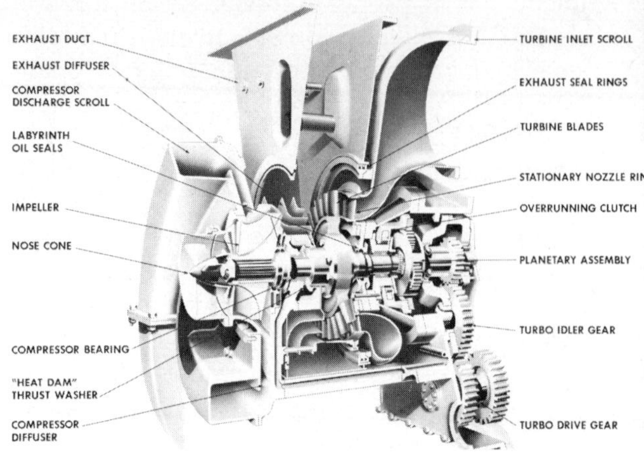

Fig. 8-6. Turbocharger for G.M. Diesel Engine Supplies Engine Air (Electro-Motive)

When exhaust gas energy turns turbine faster than the gears can, the overrunning clutch disengages the gears. This increases efficiency especially at high speeds and at high altitudes when the demand for air is enormous.

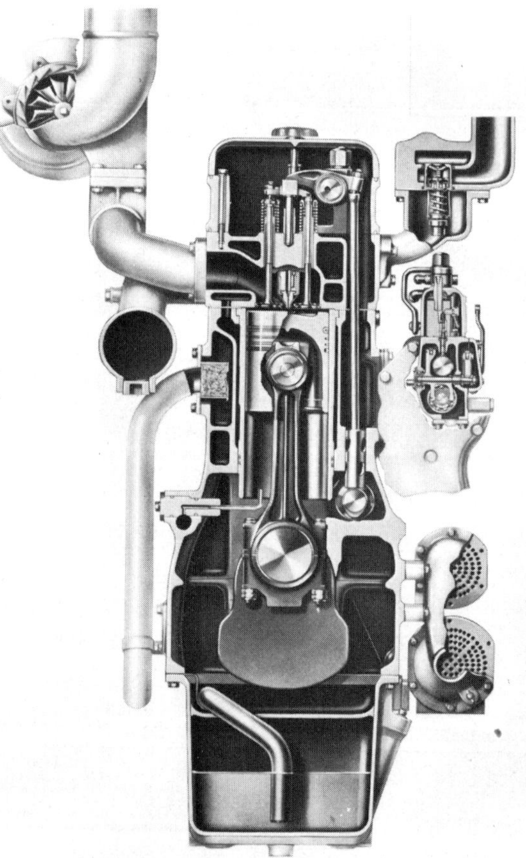

Fig. 8-7. Diesel Engine—Note Turbocharger, Intake and Exhaust Valves (International)

Table 1
Comparison of the Demand for Various Fuels With Amounts Produced without Special Cracking

Type of Fuel	Distillation Producible	Amounts Needed
Gas (Refinery Fuel Gas, Chemical Raw Materials, Liquified Petroleum Gas)	5%	4%
Gasoline (Aviation and Motor Gasoline)	20%	53%
Light Fuel Oils (Jet Fuel, Kerosene, #1 and #2 Heating Oil and Diesel Fuel)	25%	36%
Residual Fuel Oils	50%	7%
(#3 and #4 Heating Oil)	(40%)	(0%)
(#5 and #6 Heating Oil)	(10%)	(7%)
Total	100%	100%

and tars. This is done by *distilling, cracking,* and by *polymerization.* Distilling and cracking use heat to divide the raw oil into products with various degrees of volatility from aviation gasoline to residual tars, Fig. 8-8. In polymerization, the raw petroleum is first cracked into basic chemical "building blocks" which man can then combine to reconstruct the quantities of fuel, diesel and fuel oil, and other derivatives in proportion to his needs. For example, Table I shows man uses far more gasoline than could be obtained by the simple distillation of petroleum. At the same time we burn practically none of the thinner residual fuel oils. Polymerization permits improved products as well as satisfying our actual needs without waste. Other refining processes produce lubes, waxes, grease and asphalt products.

Compression Ratio

In discussing fuels, it is necessary to understand *compression ratio.* This is the ratio of the space above the piston in the cylinder when the piston is at *bottom dead center* (B.D.C.) to the volume of the space above the piston when the piston has moved to *top dead center* (T.D.C.) See Fig. 8-9. The higher the compression ratio, the more we squeeze or compress the mixture and the more power is derived. If a mixture is compressed so that it exerts a pressure of 250 psi before combustion, we will get several times more power than if the mixture was compressed at 100 psi.

The reason for the increased power from increased compression can be explained if we realize that the fuel and air is made of minute particles of matter called *molecules.* As you probably know, everything in the world is composed of these tiny building blocks of matter that cannot be seen with the most powerful microscopes because of their size, approximately seven ten-billionths of an inch in diameter.

These molecules are always in a state of flux or motion, traveling at an average speed of 1,000 mph at room pressure. As they race about, they constantly strike each other and the walls of the container.

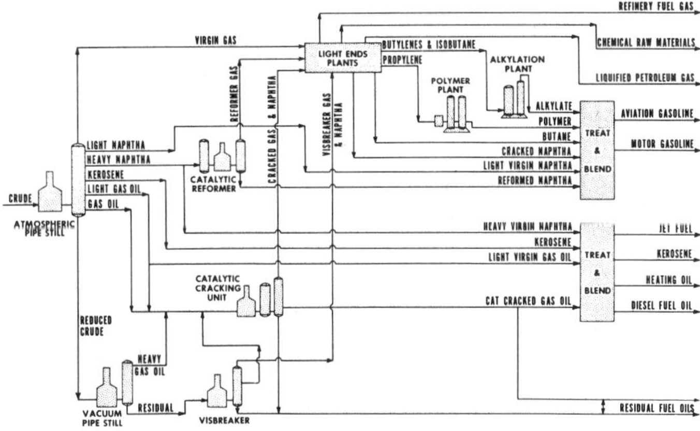

Fig. 8-8. **Typical Fuel Products Flow Plan** (Esso)

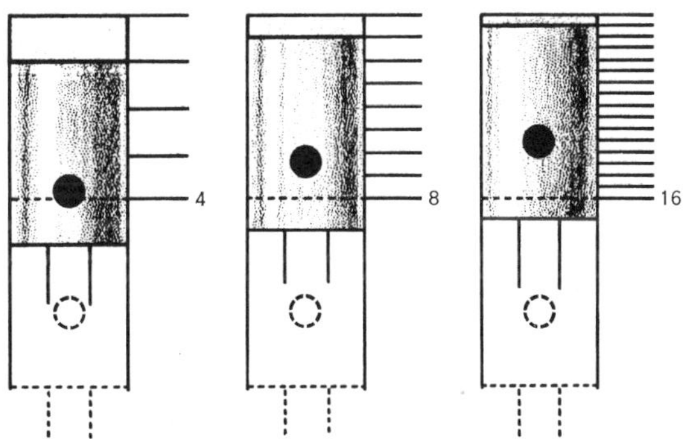

Fig. 8-9. Compression Ratios (G.M.)

Fuel and Air Mixture

Now, suppose we have a mixture of fuel and air in the cylinder. The molecules will beat against the walls and top of the piston. As the piston moves upward, the molecules are squeezed together. This causes them to strike one another and the surrounding metal more often because less space is available to them. The increased pounding results in increased pressure and higher temperature.

When the compressed mixture gets hot, it means the molecules are moving faster. The faster they move, the more frequently they strike the cylinder walls, and the top of the piston. Thus, two things give an effect of greater pressure in the combustion chamber; namely, the compressing of the mixture in a smaller space, and the speeding up of the molecular movement.

Spark Ignition

In the SI engine, the piston moves to *top dead center* and compresses the mixture to where the heat caused by compression is just below that which would cause self-ignition. This usually is not higher than 10 to 1 ratio, as shown in Fig. 8-10. An outside electric spark causes the mixture to combust.

Compression Ignition

In the CI engine, the air alone is compressed into such a small space that the temperature increases to where it ignites the fuel injected into it. This usually is higher than a 16 to 1 ratio as shown in Fig. 8-10. The burning mixture then will cause the already rapidly moving molecular particles to speed up their movement tremendously and the billions and trillions of tiny blows on top of the piston collectively cause the piston to move downward with great force.

As the piston moves downward, the rapidly moving molecules have more space to travel and, therefore, hit the top of the piston less often. The speed of the molecules decreases because part of their energy has been expended. The spent gases are expelled and the cylinder is now ready to start a new cycle as a new change of air enters.

Pinging

Twenty to thirty years ago, a 4 to 1 compression ratio in SI engines was common, while today a 10 to 1 compression ratio is not unusual. Most of the increase in power and economy which we enjoy today is due to the increase in compression ratio.

Why not raise the compression ratio more, say to 15 to 1? The answer is simply that the present day fuels will not permit it.

When the compression ratio of an SI engine is raised too high, *detonation* takes place. This premature firing is also known as *knocking* or *pinging*. It is not only annoying, but it means a loss of power and, worse, may cause engine damage. For many years this knocking was a mystery, but it was finally traced to an improper burning of the fuel—too much of it, too fast, at one time. Instead of burning smoothly, the fuel would explode causing the knock. See Fig. 8-11.

Octane Rating

Today, the *octane number* is a common specification for grades of gasoline. The basis for determining this rating of gasoline is quite complicated, but the higher the octane

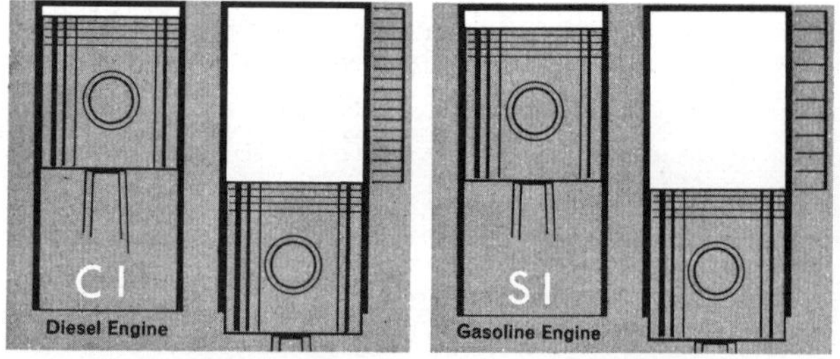

Fig. 8-10. CI and SI Compression Ratios (G.M.)

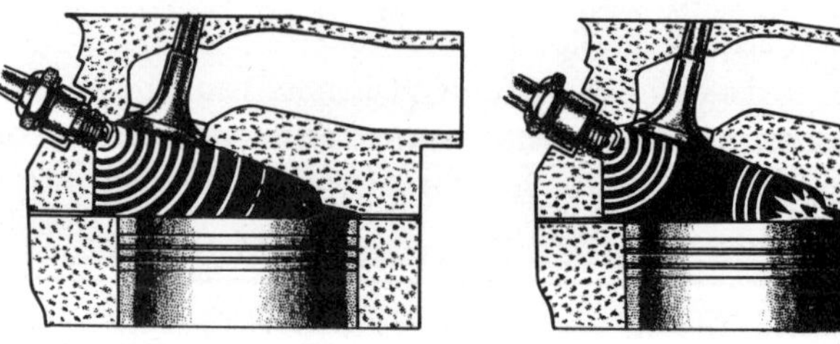

Fig. 8-11. Normal Combustion (left) and Detonation

rating, the less its tendency to knock.[1] A higher octane gasoline is required in high compression engines and, all things being equal, it is a better gasoline. Today, fuels in excess of 100 octane rating are not uncommon. At one time, these fuels were considered aviation fuels, and previously, 100 was the highest number of the scale, but some high performance engines demand fuels with higher ratings. Major brands of "regular" automobile gasoline have an octane rating of about 90 to 92, "premium" grades about 97 to 99, and in some brands, a "super" grade of about 101. Octane ratings vary with the seasons, the altitude of the area, and the brand. Other necessary qualities include controlled volatility, lack of residues such as gum, anticorrosiveness, anti-icer, and cleanliness.

Diesel Fuels

Diesel fuels, like gasoline, are hydrocarbons made from petroleum. They have many things in common with gasoline, but the property of burning is just the opposite. Because ignition is different, the fuel is made to burn as fast as possible instead of at a low, steady rate as with gasoline. The cylinder is filled with air and at the *top dead center* of piston travel, fuel is injected into the combustion chamber. The highly compressed air is very hot, in excess of 1000°F., and the finely sprayed oil burns immediately.

From this we can see why the diesel fuel must burn as rapidly as possible. There should be no time-lapse between the time the fuel is injected and the time it begins to burn. Such an interval would permit tiny drops to accumulate in the cylinder before burning. This would cause the fuel to burn all at once, resulting in a knock similar to the gasoline detonation. If the first tiny fuel droplet begins to burn immediately upon entering the chamber, the tiny droplets that follow will also burn forcing the piston down in an ever-increasing flow of power.

[1]Basically, the octane number is found by comparing knocking properties of the fuel with known mixtures of *isooctane* and *normal heptane* in various proportions. Isooctane, C_8H_{18}, once was considered perfect in antiknock qualities, and normal heptane, C_7H_{16}, the poorest. The octane number is the percentage of isooctane in the mixture which has the same knocking properties as the fuel being tested. Numbers above 100 are an extension of this scale.

Cetane Rating

Diesel fuels are graded by the *cetane* rating. This indicates the length of time between injection and combustion. The higher the cetane rating, the more quickly the fuel is ignited and burned. The higher the cetane rating, the better the fuel from the ignition and combustion standpoint. Available diesel fuels are between 30 to 60 in cetane rating.

A popular misconception is the belief that diesels run well on cheap, low-grade fuels, and that this constitutes the principle reason for the economy with which they can be operated. It is true that diesels have been run on such "fuels" as sawdust, oat hulls, and buttermilk, but these performances were strictly stunts. Dr. Diesel's first engine, designed to run on powdered coal, proved so powerful that the engine blew up during a trial run and almost killed its inventor.

Modern diesel engines have fuel requirements that are just as critical as the gasoline engines and, in general, burn a light, highly refined fuel oil which costs about the same at the refinery as does the gasoline used popularly today. The lower retail price of diesel fuel results almost entirely from its lower tax rate. Also it is usually sold in larger quantities, making lower markups feasible.

Gasoline and Diesel Efficiency

Gasoline and diesel engines differ in relation to engine speed and efficiency. At most times, engines are not run at full power or full speed. The slower the speed at which the gasoline engine is run and the less power used, the less its efficiency. In the diesel engine, the efficiency increases as the power output decreases. This is easily explained.

Fuel-Air Ratios Compared

A mixture of fuel and air is compressed in the cylinder of a gasoline engine. This mixture must be correct for proper ignition to take place. Too much fuel, a rich mixture, or too little fuel, a lean mixture, may not burn. The mixture of 15 pounds of air to one pound of gasoline is desirable no matter how little or wide the throttle is opened.

In the diesel engine, air alone is compressed until its temperature is beyond 1000° F. Fuel oil is then sprayed into the cylinder where it promptly combusts regardless of the quantity of oil emitted. Speed and power are controlled by the amount of oil sprayed into the cylinder. The amount of air is constant. The fuel to air ratio is not too important and varies with the throttle setting.

Heat Loss Compared

Therefore, in the gasoline engine, the fuel must always burn in the same proportion of air regardless of how much mixture is used in the cylinder. If the engine runs at one-quarter power, the cylinder is only partly filled with the mixture, but the temperature of the combustion is the same as if it were at full load.

In the diesel engine, the quantity of air is always constant. Speed and power are controlled by the amount of fuel sprayed into the cylinder. Therefore, at low power, one part of fuel may heat 3 or 4 times as much air as in a gasoline engine (45-to-1 or 60-to-1 rather than the 15-to-1 air-fuel ratio). Thus, the temperature in the diesel usually is not as high as that of the gasoline engine.

With higher temperatures heat flows easier and faster. So it follows that the higher temperature of the gasoline engine transfers heat to the cooling water more rapidly than the cooler running diesel engine. Therefore, because the heat transferred to the water is wasted, the diesel wastes less heat and employs proportionately more heat to push the piston down. The temperature in the cylinder of the gasoline engine is nearly the same regardless of the speed and load, whereas, in the diesel engine, a decrease in temperature is expected as the load and speed decrease.

The diesel wastes less heat at both full and part throttle because the temperature within the cylinder is always lower than in the gasoline engine insuring higher engine efficiency.

Cylinder and Block Design

In single-cylinder engines, only one of four or one of two strokes furnishes the power that is required for the engine to coast through the rest of the cycle. Actually, power is being exerted on the piston less than one-fourth or one-half of the time since the force resulting from combustion is almost entirely dissipated before the piston reaches its lowest point. The motion of such engine is not very smooth, as it consists of a series of power surges separated by coasting periods. The inertia of a flywheel or the driven mechanism may in some degree smooth out the pulsating motion. Figs. 8-12 to 8-14 show the main parts of some one-cylinder engines available for light utility use.

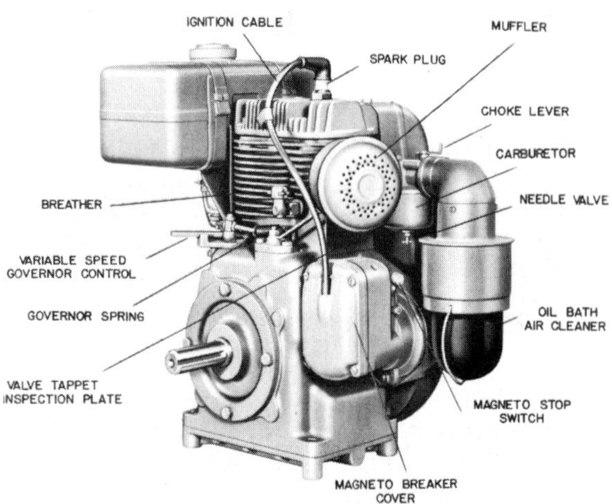

Fig. 8-12. One-Cylinder Horizontal-Shaft Gasoline Engine with Four-Stroke Cycle (Wisconsin)

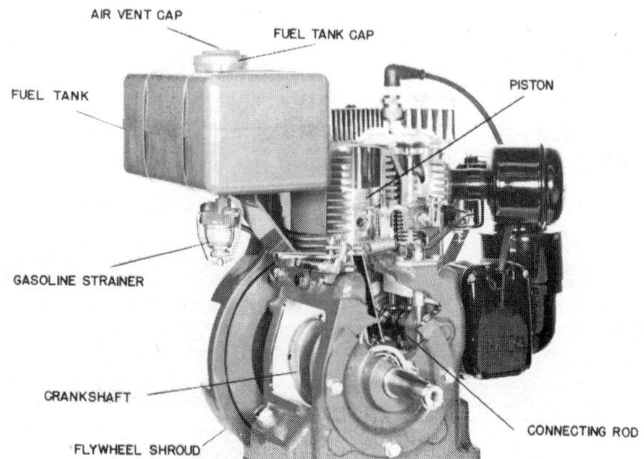

Fig. 8-13. Same Engine Showing Interior (Wisconsin)

Multicylinder Engines

Both smoother and increased power may be obtained by using engines of more than one cylinder. In this way, the coasting periods between power strokes may be shortened. In fact, four-cycle, four-cylinder engines are designed to provide a power stroke every half revolution of the crankshaft. However, because force is not exerted through the entire power stroke, the four-cylinder engine has times when there is no power being applied to the crankshaft. In a six-cylinder engine, the power strokes overlap slightly. With more cylinders the overlap increases. On the other hand, the multicylinder engines are more costly to run, other things being equal.

Cylinder Arrangements

Multicylinder engines may have their cylinders arranged in a variety of ways depending on shape, area available, and weight factors. The major sections of a typical engine are labeled in Fig. 8-15. By looking at the

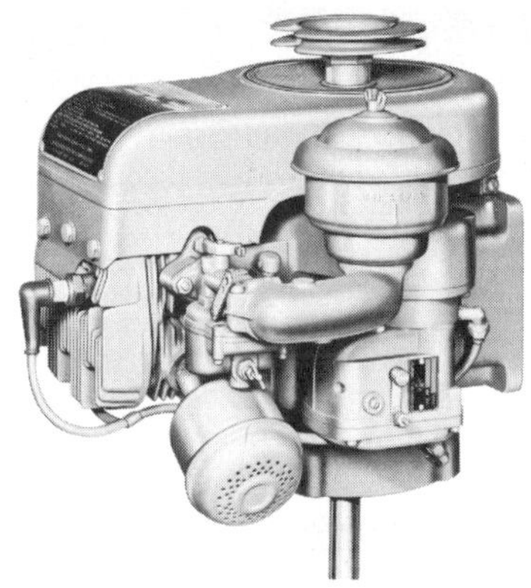

Fig. 8-14. Main Components of Vertical-Shaft Engines are Rotated 90° (Wisconsin)

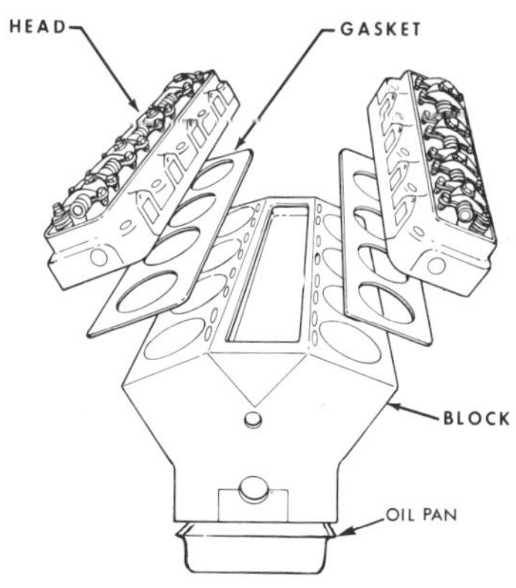

Fig. 8-15. Main Sections of V-Type Engine (Ford)

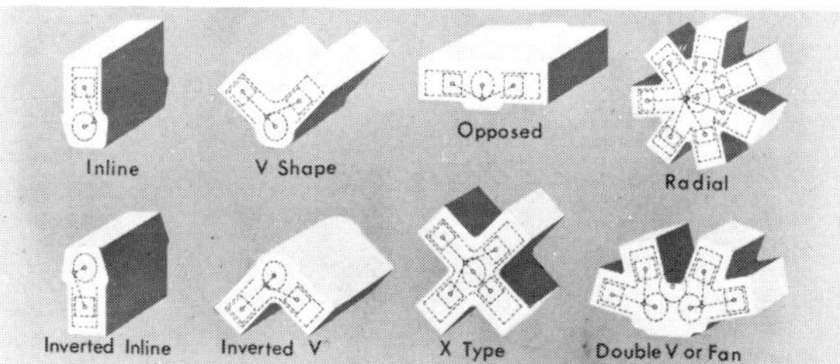

Fig. 8-16. Engine Cylinder Arrangements (Socony-Mobil)

Fig. 8-17. Horizontal Opposed Two-Cylinder Four-Cycle Engine Developing 18 hp (OMC)

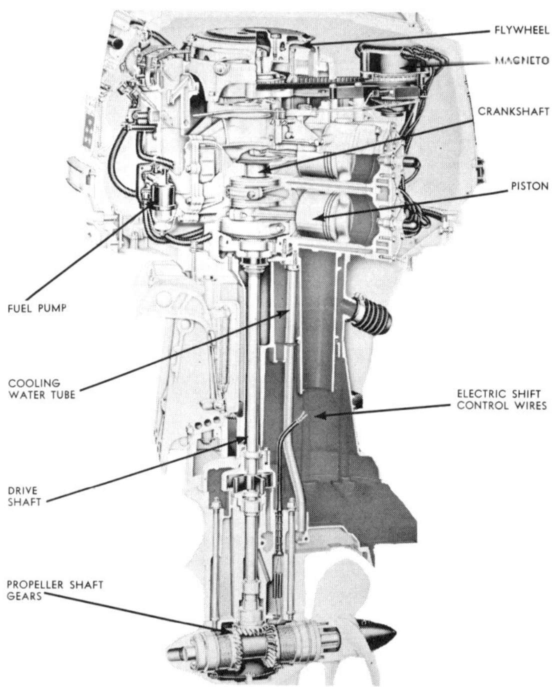

Fig. 8-18. Horizontal V-4 Outboard Marine Engine with Four-Stroke Cycle, 75 hp (Johnson)

block of an engine, the arrangement can be seen. The cylinder configuration determines the name given the engine, such as V, in-line, inverted, vertical, horizontal, slant, opposed, radial, or X. Fig. 8-16 defines these terms. The number of cylinders is also a part of the designation. For example, in-line slant-six, V-8, and seven-cylinder radial are all common designations. Figs. 8-17 to 8-25 show common types of multicylinder gasoline engines developing from 18 to 3500 hp.

Fig. 8-19. In-line Slant-Six Automobile Engine, 145 hp (Chrysler)

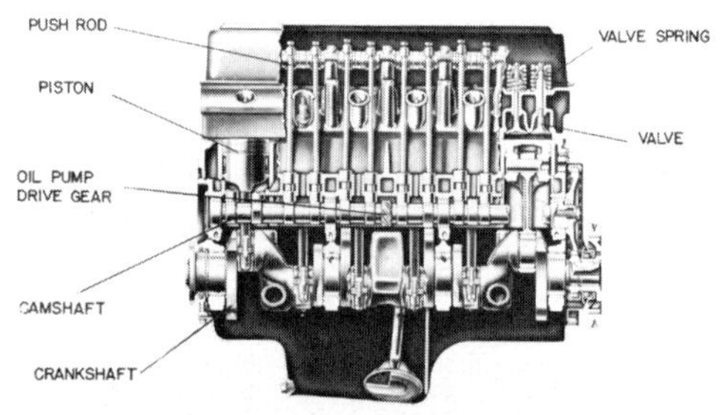

Fig. 8-20. Interior of Engine in Fig. 8-19—See Also Fig. 8-2 (Chrysler)

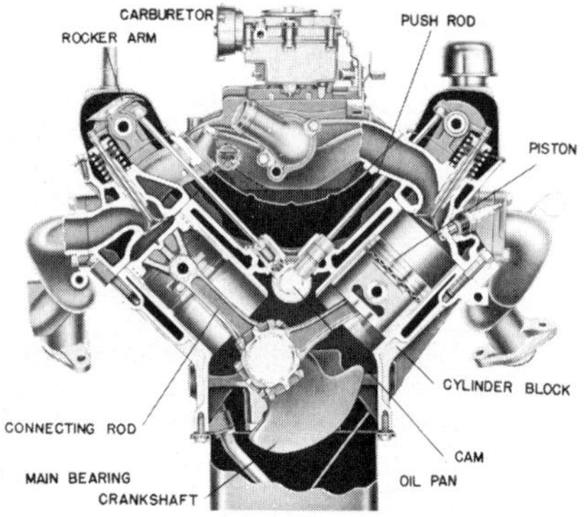

Fig. 8-21. Cross Section of Typical Overhead Valve V-8 Automobile Engine, 355 hp (Buick)

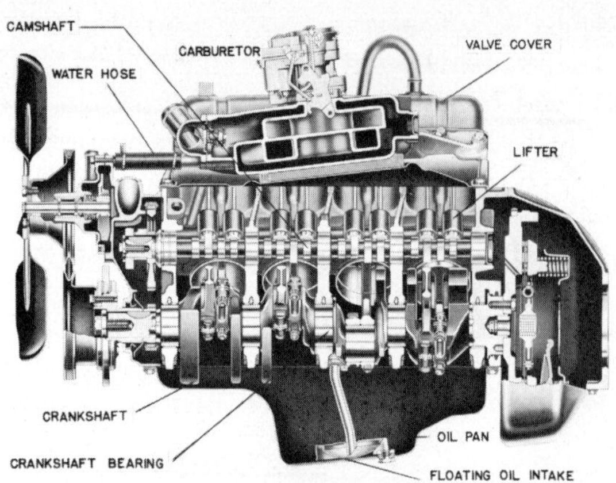

Fig. 8-22. Side View of Engine in Fig. 8-21 (Buick)
Note water pump on same shaft as radiator fan at left. This circulates water through cavities in block and head to cool the engine.

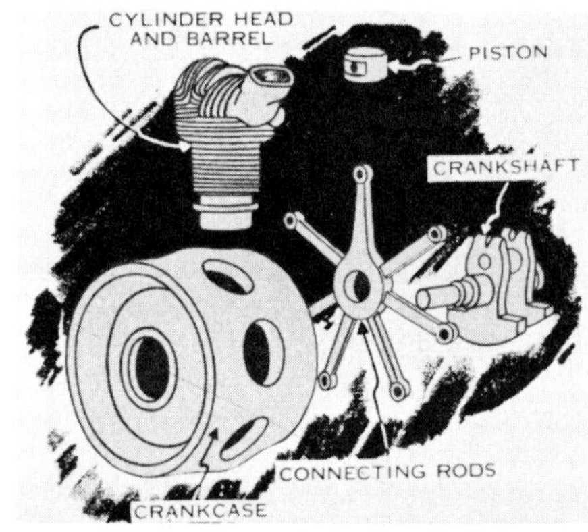

Fig. 8-23. Main Parts of a Radial Engine (G.M.)
Crankshaft has only one throw—for the heavy vertical master rod. Other connecting rods in the bank are fastened to the master rod. Cylinders are heavily finned for air cooling.

Fig. 8-24. Nine-Cylinder Radial Wasp Engine, 600 hp (Pratt and Whitney)

Cylinder Cooling

It can be easily determined if the cylinders are air-cooled or water-cooled. *Air-cooled engines* are recognized by radiation fins on the head and cylinder. Sometimes separate fans or blowers driven by the engine force air around the cylinder to insure cooling. Air cooling is used on small engines, where weight must be kept at a minimum, or where airflow is enough to keep engine temperature within desired limits. See Figs. 8-23, 8-24, 8-25.

Fig. 8-25. Twenty-Eight Cylinder (4 Staggered Banks of 7) Radial Wasp Major Engine, 3500 hp (Pratt and Whitney)

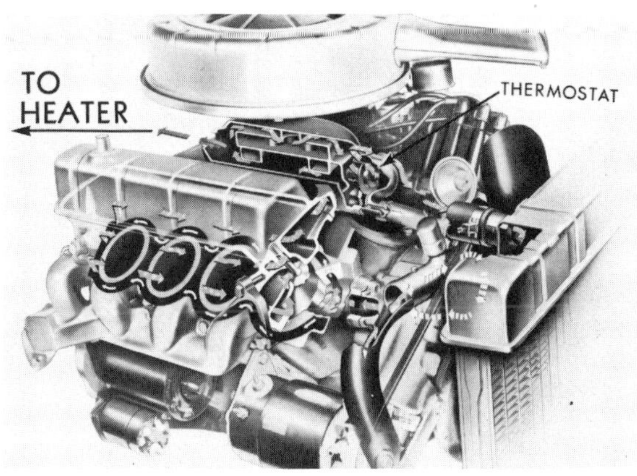

Fig. 8-26. Water-Cooled Circulation (Buick)
This is the same engine shown in Figs. 8-21 and 8-22. Cold water circulates around cylinders absorbing heat. This hot water then surrounds the intake manifold to heat the incoming fuel-air mixture (which is more commonly heated by the exhaust manifold). Hot water is also taken back to the heater for passengers. The thermostat prevents circulation through cooling radiator until engine has warmed up.

Water-cooled engines are heavier looking, have no radiation fins, and usually have a radiator to permit heat to dissipate from the water. See Fig. 8-26. Circulation of water around the cylinder walls and through water jackets is caused usually by a centrifugal pump. In some instances, water is circulated and then exhausted after it has absorbed the engine heat. This is possible only where a supply of water is readily available, as in marine use or with water pumps.

Cylinder Size

Diameter of the cylinder as well as the number of cylinders is related to the power potential of an engine. Cylinder diameters may range from less than one-half of an inch for model engines to more than a foot for marine diesel engines. Multicylinder engines may be preferred to a single-cylinder engine of the same horsepower if the engine is to run at high rotation speeds. This is due to the fact that the engine would have smaller pistons, rods, and other parts. Thus, all the parts would be lighter and more able to reciprocate at high speeds and thus gain

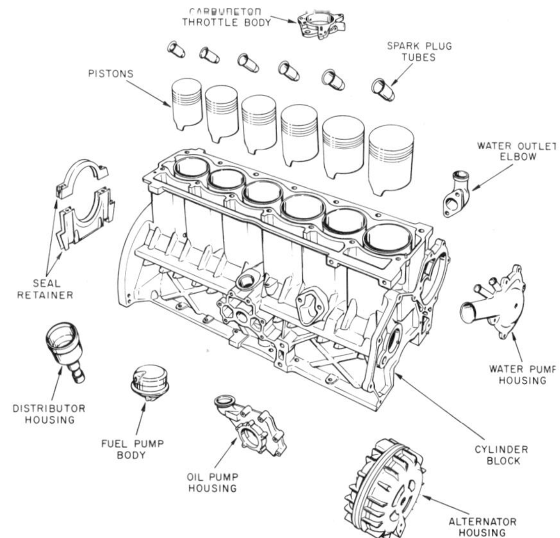

Fig. 8-27. Aluminum Usage in 225-Cubic Inch Engine (Dodge)
This reduces weight by 80 pounds, improving performance, fuel economy, and permitting easier steering with less load on front wheels.

power. A single-cylinder engine may be more desirable where a steady, slow or moderate rpm is needed with no need for rapid acceleration.

Use of Aluminum

In some engines aluminum is employed for engine blocks, pistons, and cylinder heads, with only bearing surfaces and inserts made of cast iron or hardened steel. Figs. 8-27 and 8-28 show how aluminum components are used to reduce weight. In addition, the combination of aluminum (to readily dissipate heat) with the wearability of steel makes an engine that will tolerate higher compression and rpm. Frequently these advantages more than offset the extra cost of the aluminum.

Engine Block Design

Valve placement is also a distinctive factor in cylinder design. See Fig. 8-29. The four basic arrangements are known as a T-head, L-head, I-head and F-head.

The T-head was used in the early days of the internal combustion engine when the cylinders were cast individually or in pairs. In this arrangement, the intake valves and the exhaust valves both are in the block but on opposite sides of the cylinder.

The L-head arrangement has both intake and exhaust valves in the block on the same side of the cylinder. This design found favor for many years, particularly when cylinders were cast in block form with detachable heads.

The I-head, often referred to as valve-in-head or overhead-valve engine, is now the most popular design. This design has both valves located above the cylinder in the head.

The F-head design has been employed in some fine engines but never received wide acclaim. It is a combination of the L and I head design. The intake valve is located in the head and the exhaust valve is in the block beside the cylinder.

Fig. 8-28. Lightweight Industrial Engine (OMC)
This four-cycle, air-cooled single-cylinder engine develops 9 hp and features overhead valves and die-cast aluminum components.

Engine Valves

Valves come in various designs. *Sleeve, rotary, slide, reed* and *poppet* valves each have various applications. Fig. 8-30 shows the common poppet valve. Valves are an inte-

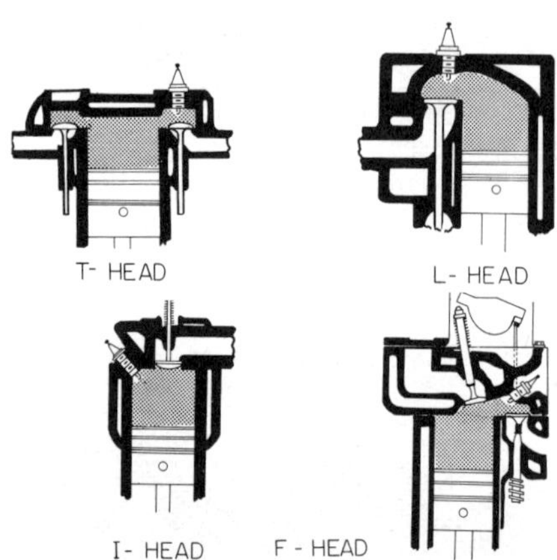

Fig. 8-29. Valve Arrangements

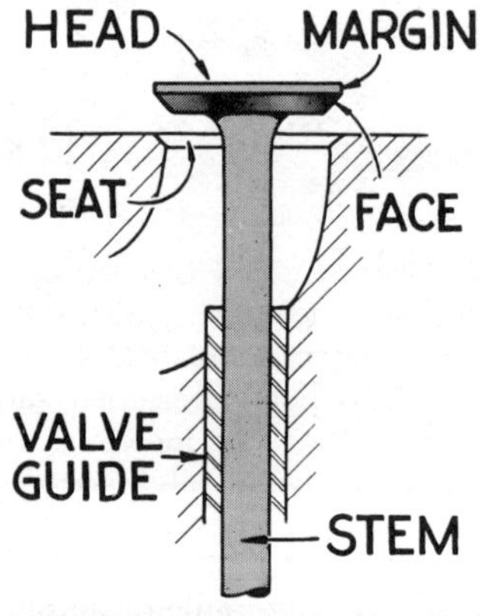

Fig. 8-30. Poppet or Mushroom Valve

gral and important part of the engine and their design demanded tremendous ingenuity. Although they are quite efficient, they operate under many problems. Valves operate under brutal conditions. They are usually situated in the combustion chamber where the temperature may momentarily reach as high as 5,000°F. The exhaust valve must then open to permit the spent fiery gases to escape. The only cooling that a valve receives is the heat dissipation possible through the valve guides and the cylinder block when the valve is seated. This is no great span of time. If a four-cycle engine is operating at 2,000 rpm, a valve opens 1,000 times per minute to permit hot gases to escape. Not much relief from heat is possible in such a brief exposure to the block or head.

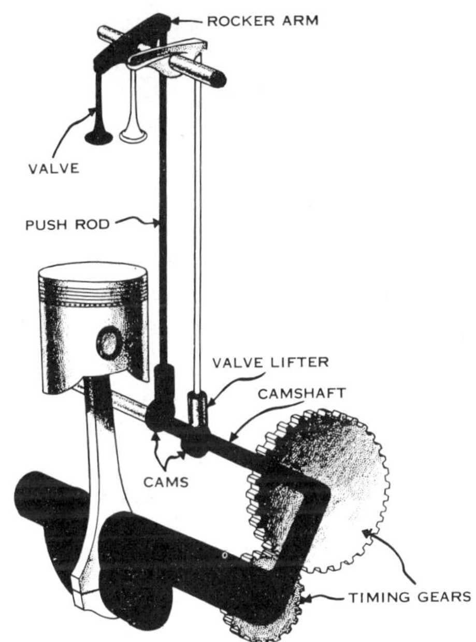

Fig. 8-31. Overhead Valve Operating Mechanism (G.M.)

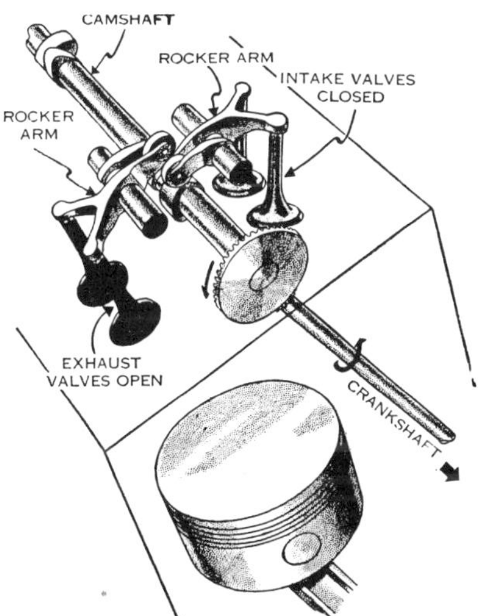

Fig. 8-32. Overhead Camshaft Has No Pushrods (G.M.)

Exhaust Valves

It is, therefore, necessary to make exhaust valves of heat resistant alloy steel and often to fill the inside of the stem and head with mineral salts to help them dissipate the enormous amount of heat. The valves are kept light because excess weight is undesirable for reciprocating engines at high speeds. The valves close rapidly and are kept seated by employing very strong springs. Often the valve seats are made of a heat resistant alloy

Fig. 8-33. Timing Chain and Sprockets (Buick)

in the form of inserts which are set in the cylinder block.

Intake Valves

The punishment taken by the intake valve is a little less severe. The cool incoming gases and the fact that the valve remains closed or seated at the peak of combustion give it a rather charmed life.

Camshaft Location

The valves are opened by cams as shown in Fig. 8-31. The camshaft is usually geared directly to the crankshaft. A four-stroke cycle requires two revolutions of the crankshaft for one of the camshaft, so the camshaft timing gear must have twice as many teeth as the gear driving it. This section describes the location of camshafts in relation to various valve arrangements. The design of the cams and the camshaft will be explained on pages 139 and 140.

The *L-head engine* has the valves located to the side of the cylinder and the camshaft is located below them. One push rod for each valve rides on a cam and directly lifts its valve to open it. A *T-head engine* requires two camshafts—one for the intake valve and one for the exhaust valves.

I-head engines or overhead valves require a single camshaft with the mechanism shown in Fig. 8-31. Long push rods ride on each cam. These raise one end of a rocker arm, the other end of which depresses the valve. Sometimes, to reduce the weight of the valve and rocker assembly, the camshaft is mounted directly over the valves, Fig. 8-32. This method is satisfactory but adjustment is more complicated. It is operated by gears or chains which are more difficult to time properly. The valves in an *F-head engine* are operated off one camshaft with a short and long push rod operating the valve and a rocker arm respectively.

Valve Timing

The exact timing of the opening and closing of the valves is paramount for engine efficiency. Long gear chains and trains wear appreciably faster and are usually to be avoided. See Fig. 8-33.

Operational speeds make the accuracy of valve opening and closing exacting. The importance of timing becomes even more critical as the engine speed increases. For this reason valve *overlap* is employed to compensate for the time required for gases to flow through the manifolds. Valve overlap means that both intake and exhaust valves may be open at the same time in any one cylinder.

In theory, the intake valve should open when the piston is just starting downward and should close at the exact instant it starts upward. Both valves are closed during compression with the exhaust valve opening at the end of the power stroke. This is not the case, however, in high speed engines, although low speed engines may find this timing satisfactory.

In Fig. 8-34, the timing diagram of a typical high speed engine, it will be noted that the intake valve opens 10° *before* top dead center (T.D.C.) while the exhaust valve does not close until 30° *after* top dead center. Therefore, the valves are open together during 40° of the crankshaft rotation.

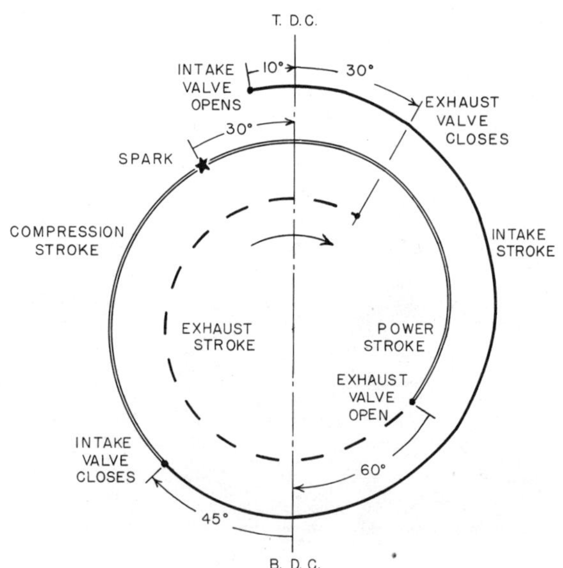

Fig. 8-34. Valve Action During the Four-Stroke Cycle

Combustion and Compression

As previously emphasized, other things being equal, the more that gas and air are compressed in the cylinder by the piston, the greater the power. The *compression ratio is computed on volume* as shown in Fig. 8-35. If the original volume is compressed into one-eighth the space, the ratio would be 8 to 1. The degree of compression is dependent upon the volume within the cylinder, the size of the combustion chamber, and the distance the piston travels in one stroke.

Altering Compression

The compression ratio can be altered quite easily. The ratio can be increased by grinding or *shaving off the face of the head,* bringing the cylinder head closer to the block and thus decreasing the combustion chamber. The ratio can be decreased by moving the head away from the block by employing two gaskets or one which is oversized. Also, if the combustion chamber volume was changed by *welding on or grinding away metal,* the ratio would be altered.

The same result would be obtained by adding to or subtracting from the *piston's length* above the wrist pin. Often engines designed to operate at high altitudes are equipped with longer pistons. Sometimes, the compression ratio is altered by employing a crankshaft with a *longer throw* than the original one to increase the distance the piston travels.

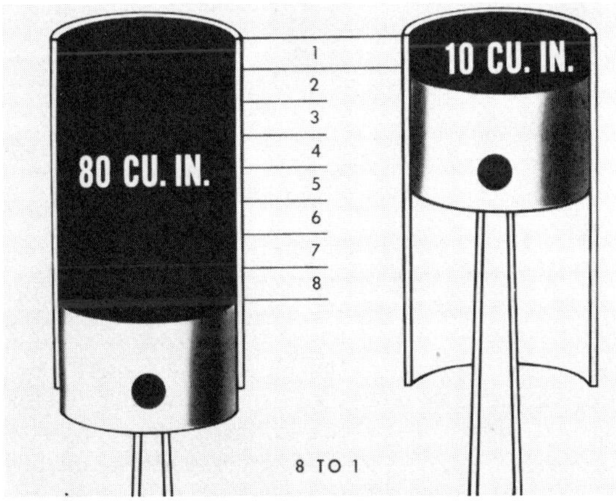

Fig. 8-35. Compression Ratio of 8 to 1 (Ford)

As we have described, a limiting factor of compression is imposed by the characteristics of the fuel used. The higher the compression, the greater the tendency for the fuel to pre-ignite or ping. Much time, money, and experimentation have been expended on this phenomenon. It is believed that this knocking is the irregular and too rapid expansion of the gas and air mixture. The vibration of the combustion chamber emits the characteristic noise.

Leaded Gasoline

Research has promoted an additive, *tetra-ethyl lead,* to the gasoline to slow down the rate of combustion or expansion. In this way, an *expanding* force rather than an *explosive* one is placed on the piston.

Today, the compression ratio in many cars exceeds 10:1, and with newer additives, better fuels, improved piston and combustion chambers, and fuel injection, this ratio may gradually increase until it approaches the diesel compression ratios of 16:1, or 18:1. Today, some racing and sports car engines employing special fuels have a compression ratio of 14, 15, or 16 to 1.

Combustion Chambers

Research findings show that for complete control of atomization and combustion of the gas-air mixture, it must flow turbulently into the cylinder. This promotes a more even distribution, prevents separation of gas and air in the combustion chamber and checks pre-ignition. Irregular shapes of the piston head and combustion chamber increase turbulence and promote a more uniform burning. Increasing the surface area of the combustion chamber also facilitates the dissipation of heat. In the popular "L" head engines, the part of the combustion chamber farthest from the spark plug is smaller to avoid stagnation of the mixture and to increase total surface area. See Figs. 8-2 or 8-21. This wedge shape also helps prevent preignition.

Fuel Injection

A leading automobile manufacturer and a petroleum company have jointly developed a multi-fuel engine which they say is now ready for production. See Fig. 8-36. The developers claim that a standard six-cylinder car will be capable of traveling more than 40 miles on a gallon of kerosene or furnace oil.

The new principle involves shooting the low grade fuel directly at the spark plug causing a swirling turbulence in the combustion chamber, Figs. 8-37 to 8-39. This high concentration of fuel around the ignition plug causes a more complete combustion than is possible with today's best high octane gasoline. This new design means high fuel economy, very few exhaust fumes, no-knock performance, and besides, the ability to burn most fuels.

The new engine combusts only 3 parts fuel to 100 parts air—so lean that a spark plug would not ignite it in a conventional engine. The mixtures and efficiencies are compared with usual SI and CI engines in Fig. 8-40.

Fig. 8-36. Multi-Fuel Injection Engine (Texaco)

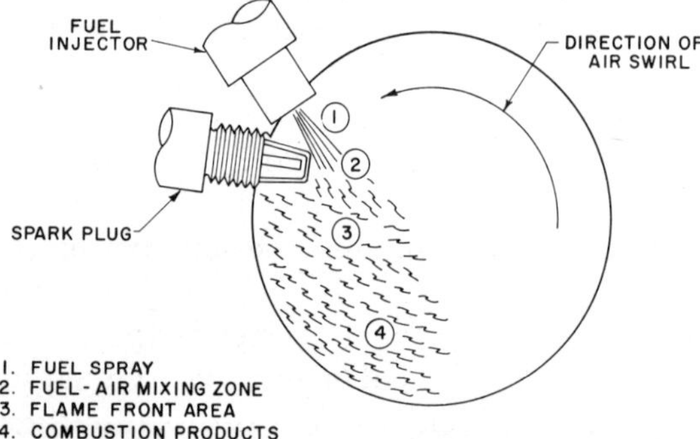

Fig. 8-37. Texaco Combustion Process

The TCP is a combination of fuel injection, positive ignition and swirling air. Fuel injection begins near the end of the compression stroke. The first of the spray is ignited by the carefully timed spark nearby. This establishes a flame front and fuel is burned as fast as it is injected.

Fig. 8-38. Multi-Fuel Injection Cylinder Head (Texaco)

Note fuel injector, spark plug, and valves. Operating cycle is much like a diesel except for the ignition. Cans on injectors contain ignition breaker points operated directly by the nozzle valve.

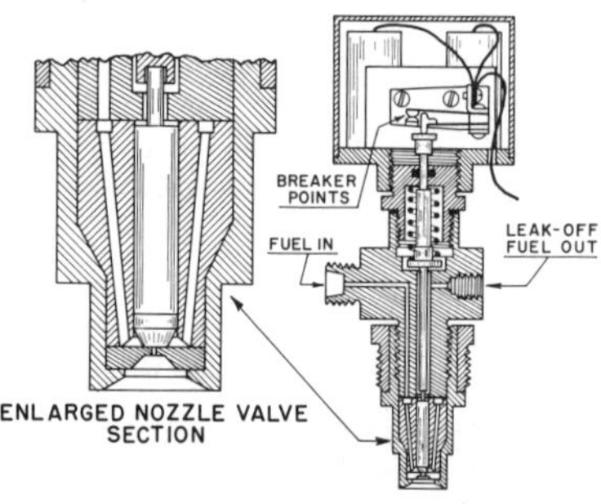

Fig. 8-39. Nozzle Assembly with Ignition Breaker (Texaco)

Although distributor ignition systems have been used, more accurate timing results when the beginning of injection is used to actuate the spark. Injection actuated ignition is not limited to the nozzle valve operated breaker system shown here.

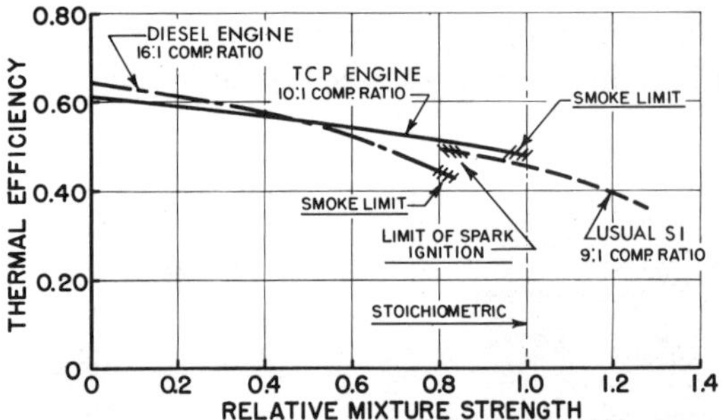

Fig. 8-40. Operating Ranges and Theoretical Efficiencies of Several Engine Cycles (Texaco)

Note that the *usual four-cycle spark ignition engine* (dashed line at lower right) requires a relatively rich mixture of fuel. Both the experimental TCP engine (solid line) and diesel engines operate over a wide range of leaner mixtures with better thermal efficiency. The TCP process also eliminates specific octane or cetane ratings as necessary fuel qualities and permits a wide range of fuels.

Other major manufacturers and engineering colleges are working on similar multi-fuel engines. One of these is shown in Fig. 8-41.

Pistons

The force of the expanding gases is absorbed by the pistons. These in turn transmit the reciprocating force through the connecting rod to the crankshaft where the force is converted to rotative motion. Pistons also guide one end of the connecting rods, aligning their movement. In two-cycle engines, pistons also perform as port covers or as valves.

Fig. 8-41. New Automotive-Type Multi-Fuel Engine for Army (Avco)

These engines developed by Lycoming start unaided at temperatures as low as −25°F. This four-cylinder model is lightweight, air-cooled, and runs on diesel fuel, low grade gasoline, kerosene, or jet fuel. An eight-cylinder model is also being developed.

Fig. 8-42. Piston Shapes (G.M.)

Pistons operate under extremely severe thermal and mechanical conditions and must be made and installed accurately. They must be strong enough to withstand the constant pounding of the exploding gases. Yet they also must be as light as possible to reduce inertia as they change direction every stroke. They must fit snugly to prevent the escape of expanding gases and yet freely to reduce friction to a minimum while not slapping and rocking within the cylinder.

Piston Characteristics

The piston head or *crown* is the surface that is exposed to the explosive force. It may be flat, recessed, convex, concave, or shaped in a variety of ways to promote turbulence of the gases within the firing chamber as well as to absorb the greatest amount of the energy of the expanding gases. Some typical shapes are shown in Fig. 8-42.

In some small and inexpensive engines, pistons are *lapped* to fit the cylinder snugly yet freely. Lapping is a simple process where a part is fitted in position using a fine abrasive. Under limited working conditions of time and speed, lapped pistons perform satisfactorily.

Ordinarily, pistons are equipped with *compression rings* as in Fig. 8-43. These rings are located in grooves near the top of the piston and provide a seal between the piston and cylinder wall without noticeably increasing friction. Sometimes, a wide grooved *oil ring* is located below the others in a groove that has holes drilled into it. This allows oil to circulate from the inside of the piston, by splashing through this ring to the outside of the piston wall, and lubricating the wearing surfaces.

The side of the piston is known as the *skirt*. This forms a bearing area which absorbs side thrusts caused by the connecting rod as it moves up and down. This thrust is more pronounced on the side opposite the crank throw as it moves down on the power stroke. The lesser thrust is on the other side of the crank throw as it moves up during the compression stroke. Pistons are internally reinforced to absorb these thrusts adequately. See Fig. 8-44.

Sometimes, the piston hole or *wrist pin hole* is located off-center as much as one-half inch to lessen the effects of side thrust on the cylinder wall. Sometimes this hole is undercut around it to prevent *seizing* if the piston were to overheat and expand excessively.

Also, in some cases the skirt is lengthened to increase the bearing surface on the sides of the cylinder that will bear the thrusts, distributing its force over a greater area. Pistons with such extensions are called *slipper* pistons.

Piston Variations

In alloy pistons, it is necessary to relieve the thrusts by cutting slots into the skirts. These slots may be vertical or diagonal, and may be of one or more segments. In this way, the pistons can be fitted more closely when cold because they can expand freely when hot. (Cast-iron pistons never have split skirts).

In some pistons, inserts of alloy steel are cast into the aluminum. Such pistons are skeleton like and undercut around the piston hole. In others, a steel *land* or ring is cast into the head of the piston. In both types, the purpose is to control the rate of expansion of the aluminum.

Many times, piston skirts are ovally ground. This insures greater thrust surfaces when the piston is cold, and as it becomes hot, the skirts become more round further increasing the bearing surfaces.

Often, pistons are tapered with the top ground smaller than the bottom. In this case, as the piston becomes hot, causing a more pronounced expansion at the top, the taper will insure uniform diameter all the way down. When the piston is not tapered, it is necessary to slightly undercut the surfaces or lands between the rings because less clearance is needed due to the unequal heating and expanding of the piston.

The amount of clearance between the piston and cylinder varies with the engine design, cooling system, material, and purpose. Generally, the tolerance between surfaces is about .00075 to .001 of an inch for cast iron pistons. Aluminum pistons are fitted more closely.

Piston Rings

Piston rings have been designed in the many shapes shown in Fig. 8-45. The simple cast-iron ring of eccentric or concentric shape, with a butt, miter or step-joint was common. This type was made by casting iron tubes of the approximate size and then turning them down on a lathe to the desired dimension. They were then turned inside and cut apart at the proper width. Finer

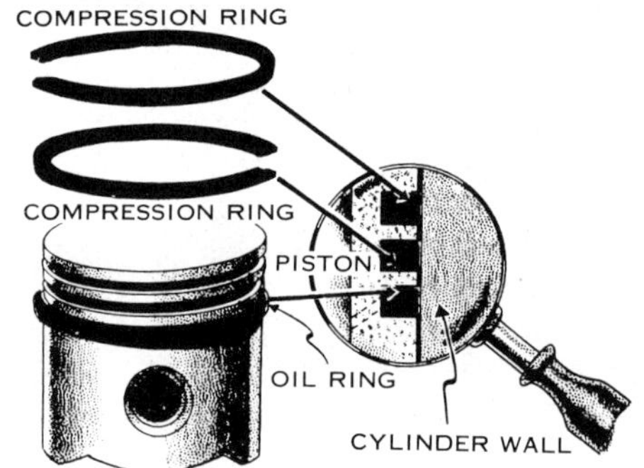

Fig. 8-43. Piston Rings (G.M.)

Fig. 8-44. Piston with Connecting Rod (Buick)

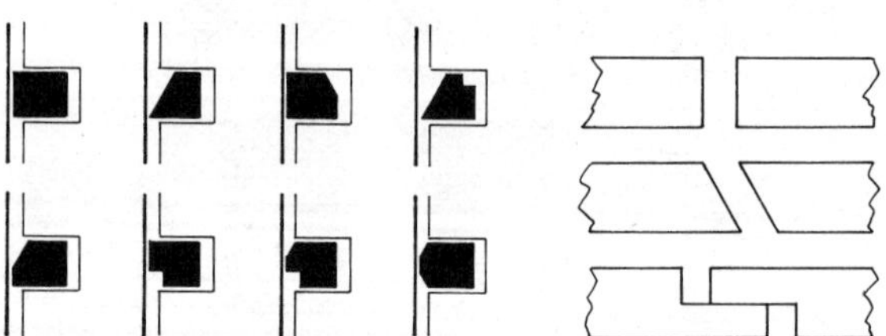

Fig. 8-45. Ring Cross Sections (left) and Joints

metals and newer centrifugal methods of casting have made this method extinct.

Today, rings are made of fine steel as well as cast iron. Designs are often quite unique, based on a particular purpose. Sometimes, they are plated with chromium or other metals to increase their wearing qualities. All are heat-treated to provide a uniform tension of 8 to 12 pounds of pressure on the cylinder wall.

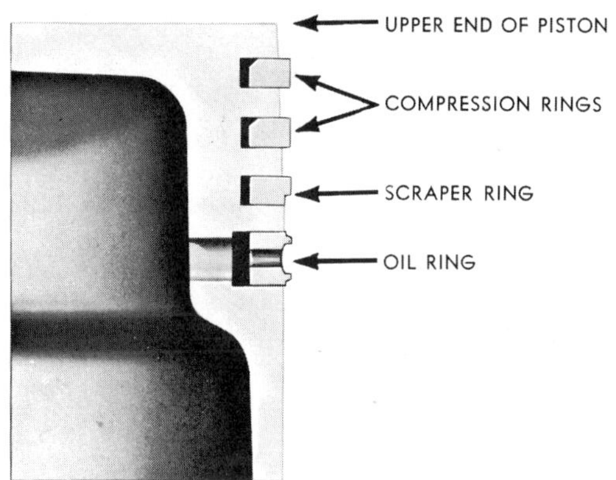

Fig. 8-46. Piston Cross Section Showing Rings
(Wisconsin)

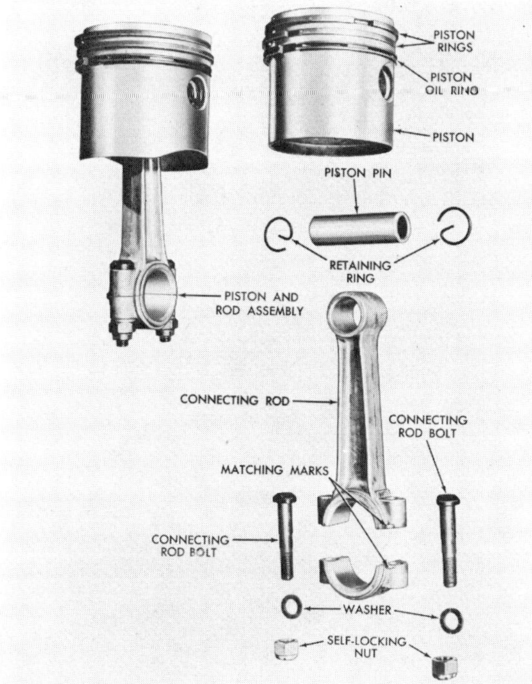

Fig. 8-47. Piston and Connecting Rod Parts
(Tecumseh)

Compression rings are designed to prevent leakage of compression and explosion pressure in one direction and to control the flow of oil in the other direction. This could be easily accomplished if it were not for the expansion, distortion, and warpage of the pistons as they operate. The ring must perform under difficult conditions while subject to high temperatures, pressure, and vacuum.

The top compression ring is usually rectangular with a cut made into its inside top corner. See Fig. 8-46. This missing corner causes the ring to twist in its groove so the outside lower edge presses more firmly against the cylinder wall. Beveled rings do the same thing. The purpose of these cuts is to insure a better seal because of the higher pressure of an abbreviated area of contact. Such rings come with installation instructions, because they must be placed in the groove of the piston correctly. The cross section of the second compression ring may be rectangular, dado-cut on the inside or outside, or beveled to provide localized pressure.

Oil rings are usually the lower one or two rings. The piston grooves are slotted as well as the oil rings to permit oil to move freely in or out and thus lubricate the cylinder wall. Sometimes, oil rings are backed with expander rings that are also slotted to permit oil passage. The oil rings are grooved to provide localized contact insuring greater contact pressure. Excess oil will be scraped from the cylinder wall into the grooves and deposited in a thin film where needed.

Care must be exercised when installing rings to make sure that the joints are staggered to insure proper compression and operating conditions.

Piston Pins

Wrist pins (piston pins or gudgeon pins) are used to fasten the connecting rod to the piston. See Fig. 8-47. There are three main types. In one, the pin is anchored in the piston, and is free to turn in the bushing in the upper end of the connecting rod. In another type, the pin is tight in the rod but free within the piston bearing. In a third type, the pin is not held in either the rod or piston and moves freely in both. In these the pin is held by lock rings inside the skirt or plugs outside to prevent side to side movement which would score the cylinder wall.

Wrist pins are hollow steel pins which are case-hardened on the outside. They must be replaced if worn, not being adjustable. Because of the limited wear in the short arc of connecting rod oscillation, the bearing surface may be made with a bronze bushing or anti-friction metal insert. The one major complication in using inserts is the different rates of expansion of the different metals.

The main reason for the various locations of wrist pin bearings is to develop a long wearing surface. The greater the bearing surface, the better the distribution of wear. Bearing surfaces can be increased by increasing the diameter of the pin. However, if it is too large, the weight is increased and the bearing loads correspondingly increased. If the pin is made light by decreasing its diameter, the bearing surface may not adequately carry the load. In some designs, the wear is over three bearing surfaces, in some on two, and in some on one large bearing surface. Each design has its own merits and provides design engineers with much reason for discussion. In any case, the most prevalent problem is the inherent heat, because wear is proportionate to the heat of any bearing. The slightest wear of these surfaces causes an annoying thumping sound in the engine.

Connecting Rods

The energy that the piston receives must be transferred to the crankshaft where the reciprocating motion is changed to rotating motion. This is done by the *connecting rod.* The movement of the piston, the swing of the crankshaft, and the placement of the piston in relation to the throw determine its size and shape. Some connecting rods are straight while others are offset.

The wrist pin bearing at the small end of the connecting rod has just been explained. The large split bearing at the opposite end fits the crankshaft. See Fig. 8-48. These *connecting rod bearings* are similar to the *main bearings* supporting the crankshaft and are just as critical. The various types of bearings used in both of these places as well as in other major bearings will be explained in the next section.

Bearings

The internal combustion engine has many parts that rotate within another. Note the four main bearings in the inverted block in Fig. 8-49. To increase wearability and to re-

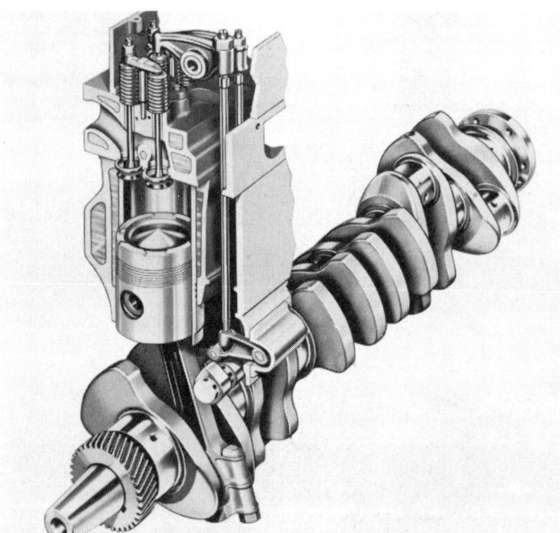

Fig. 8-48. Related Cylinder Parts and Crankshaft (Cummins)

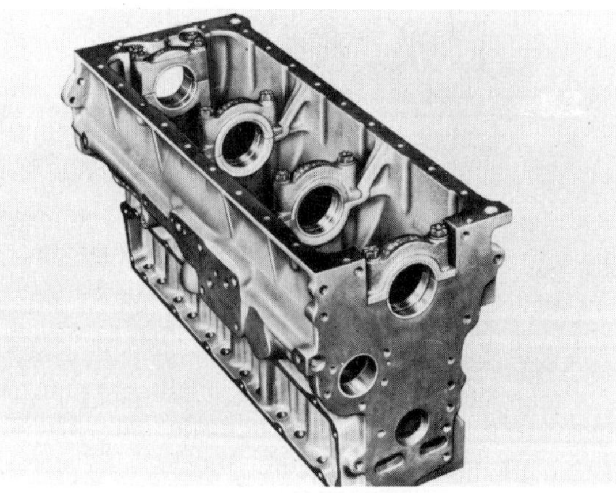

Fig. 8-49. Deep I-Block Crankcase for Either Gasoline or Diesel Engines (International)

duce friction to a minimum, several types of *bearings* are employed. Three main varieties of bearing surfaces are: the old poured babbit type, the newer precision inserts, and anti-friction bearings using balls or rollers.

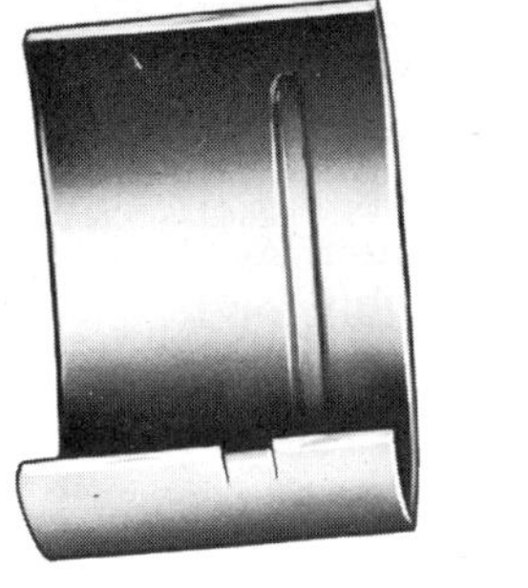

Fig. 8-50. Precision Insert Bearing (International)

Fig. 8-51. Parts of a Tapered Roller Bearing (Timken)

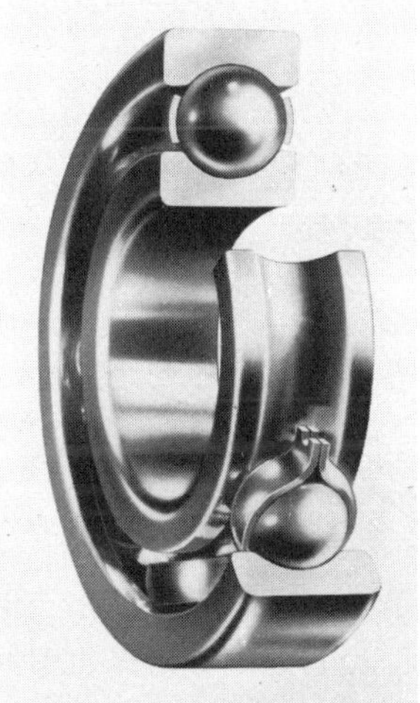
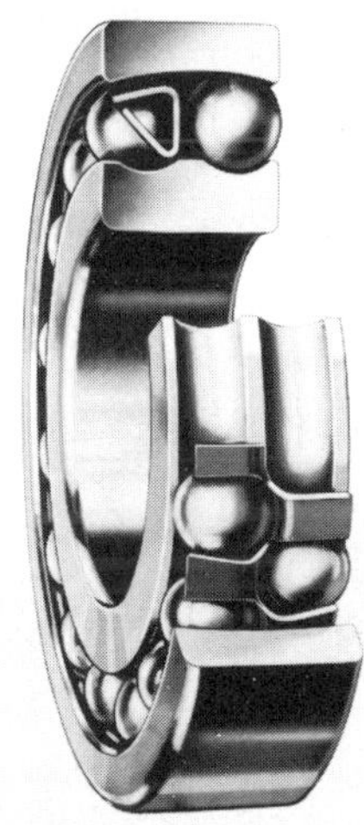

Fig. 8-52. Deep Groove Ball Bearings (SKF)

Babbit Bearings

Years ago, most main and connecting rod bearings were made of babbit, a soft metal alloy made of tin, copper, antimony, and lead. The percentages of each varied, but tin was always the major element. These bearings were cast into their prepared seats, and they remained there until they were melted out. Today, babbit *inserts* are popular, much easier to replace, and can be bought in many sizes.

Precision Insert Bearings

Today, the most widely used type of bearing is the *insert bearing,* Fig. 8-50. It is precision made of layers of metals and various alloys. Alloys of cadmium, silver, copper-lead, as well as babbit alloys are used in these newer bearing inserts.

It is interesting to note that the success of any bearing surface depends upon the light film of lubricating oil that is kept between the surfaces. The space left between the two surfaces is small, measuring in the thousandths of an inch, and will vary with the type of lubrication system used.

When inserts or poured babbit bearings are used, the seat is usually split to facilitate assembly and removal. This would mean that each bearing would be made of two matched parts and must be handled accordingly. When assembled, precision instruments are required to insure the proper amount of bearing crush, seating pressure, as well as the necessary clearances to insure proper wear.

Anti-Friction Bearings

Anti-friction bearings have rolling rather than sliding contact points and therefore require less lubrication than surface or plain bearings. They may be operated at a high speed. They run cool, exhibit low starting friction and are capable of handling high shock or impact loads. All anti-friction bearings contain four basic parts—the outer race which is fixed to the housings, the inner race which is usually pressure fitted to the shaft, the hardened steel balls or rollers, and usually cages or retainers that keep them located evenly within the races. These are shown in Fig. 8-51.

Some common types of anti-friction bearings are: deep groove ball bearings, conical-race ball bearings, cylindrical roller bearings (needle bearings), and tapered roller bearings. See Figs. 8-52 to 8-54.

Fig. 8-54 contrasts a *thrust bearing,* designed for heavy forces on the end of the shaft but little crosswise, and a *radial or journal bearing,* designed for a rotating load with little end thrust.

Each type of bearing finds specific applications. *Deep groove ball bearings* are used where high speed radial loads are found with little thrust. The *self-aligning ball bearing* has a cone to remove end play, and take some end thrust, and is used for slower speed, higher load conditions such as on bicycles. Ball bearings are less costly than roller bearings. Because of the small contact area between balls and raceways, they are usually employed for light to moderate loads.

Roller bearings have greater contact area over which to dissipate the load. They can handle moderate to heavy loads and can withstand high shock and impact loads.

The *cylindrical roller bearings* will take much heavier radial loads having no end thrust. The *tapered roller radial bearing* again has a cone adjustable to remove end play and can be used for the heaviest load conditions such as front wheel bearings on an automobile.

Rotative-Reciprocative Changes

The reciprocative motion of the piston is changed to usable rotative power by the crankshaft. Part of this rotative power is then used by the camshaft to cause the valves to reciprocate. Thus a *cam* is a circular inclined plane (often egg-shaped) which changes rotary motion into back and forth motion. A *crank* is an eccentric which may either change back and forth motion into rotary motion or vice versa.

Let us now take a closer look at the form and function of the camshaft, and the crankshaft, and note their relation to timing and firing order.

Camshafts

The important function of the valves and various arrangements of the camshaft which operates them have already been explained. This section will explain the design of a camshaft such as shown in Fig. 8-55. Each valve requires its own eccentric *lobe* or *cam* for lifting it at just the right time in the running cycle of the engine. The camshaft is a series of cams, each located beneath a valve, and made to rotate on a common shaft. These cams open and close the intake and exhaust

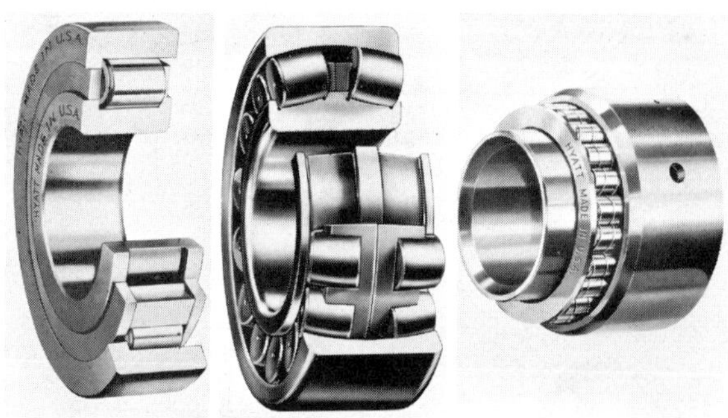

Fig. 8-53. Cylindrical Roller Bearings
(Hyatt, SKF)

The center bearing is a *spherical* roller bearing. It is similar to the self-aligning double-row deep-groove ball bearing except each roller has a *line* contact rather than a point as do the balls. This allows it to carry a much heavier load. The wide bearing at the right has helical grooves in the rollers. These are alternately right-hand and left-hand grooves which move the lubricant back and forth across the cases.

Fig. 8-54. Thrust Bearing (right) and Radial Bearing (left), Both with Tapered Rollers
(Timken)

valves for each cylinder at the time necessary to insure its proper working cycle. Cams are egg shaped with the shaft at the heavy end.

Because the camshaft usually runs at a slower speed and has no great reciprocating stress on it, it is much smaller and has smaller bearings than the crank shaft.

The camshaft is usually made of steel that has been case-hardened to prevent rapid wear of the bearing surfaces. Camshafts are simple looking but demand the ultimate in mathematical and engineering design. They not only open and close the valves, but keep them opened or closed until they perform the function of emptying or filling the cylinder. In other words, they control the volumetric efficiency of the engine.

The design of the cams varies with the purpose of the engine. For quiet engine performance, it is preferred to have a gradual opening and closing of the valve controlled by a cam of squat appearance. Racing engines have cams with a more pronounced nose to speed valve action. These run more noisily and wear out much more rapidly.

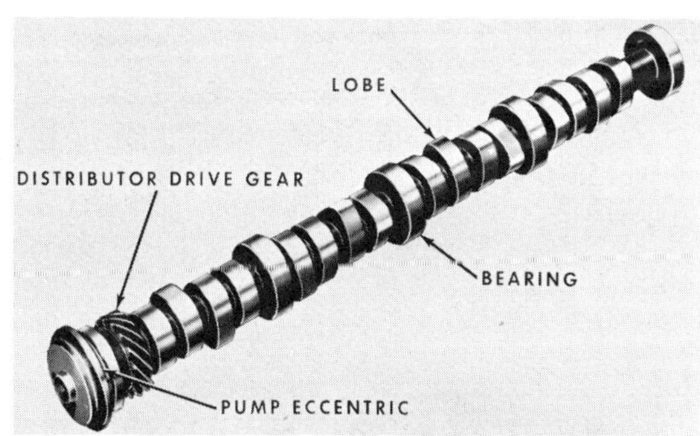

Fig. 8-55. Parts of a Camshaft (Ford)

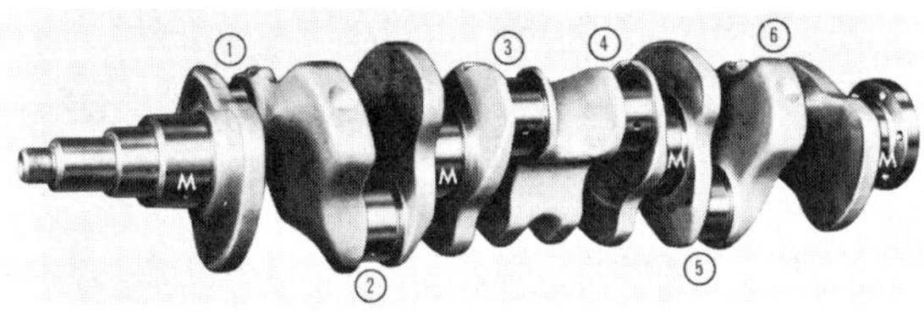

Fig. 8-56. Crankshaft for Six Cylinder Truck Engine (International)

Note that pairs of throws are located between the four main (M) on-center bearings. Throws 3 and 4, 2 and 5, and 1 and 6 are in same radial location, but one of each pair is 2 strokes ahead in its 4-stroke cycle. The valve action and cam lobes are timed differently for each cylinder. The crankcase for this is shown in Fig. 8-49.

When any cam is worn, the entire camshaft is replaced. At one time, each cam was fastened separately, but now are cast as a unit, tempered, and precision ground.

The camshaft is run from the crankshaft. It has been noted that in a four-stroke cycle, the crankshaft revolves twice for one turn of the cam shaft, so the camshaft timing gear has twice as many teeth as the driving gear. If only two gears are employed, the camshaft will rotate in the opposite direction of the crankshaft so a third or *idler gear* usually is used. If chain driven, it will rotate in the same direction as the crank shaft.

Camshafts are usually located below the valves as in Fig. 8-48. However, in the overhead camshaft engine it is located above the cylinder head. This type is open-chain driven and the valve stems ride directly on the cams. This design avoids the use of rockers, lifters, and similar parts, and provides excellent valve action at high speeds. It is, however, costlier, noisier, and more difficult to adjust.

Crankshafts

Engine crankshafts are generally quite similar. Each piston gives its energy to a throw, or off-center bearing. It is at this point that reciprocating movement is converted to rotating motion. Each throw is usually counterbalanced by a weight to provide a smooth, vibrationless motion at high speeds. Such balance is *dynamic balance,* because it must prove out at operating speeds.

A single-cylinder engine will have one throw. Multicylinder engines will have as many throws as there are pistons. The firing order of the engine will determine the angle of the throws of the crankshaft and of the lobes on the camshaft. On most automobile engines, pairs of crank throws will have the same position, but one of the pair will fire two strokes later than the other. Thus, in a six-cylinder engine there are three pairs 120° apart, and firing is spaced evenly around the two revolutions, making a cycle. See Fig. 8-56.

An *opposed* two-cylinder, four-cycle engine will have a crankshaft with throws that are opposite each other, or 180° apart, and will fire alternately. If this same crankshaft were used for a *two-cycle opposed* engine, the firing of each cylinder would occur at the same time. This same crankshaft could be used on a two-cylinder, two-cycle alternate firing engine, if both cylinders were located on the same side. Usually, the power stroke of each cylinder is designed to come at such a time as to insure an even distribution of power during each revolution of the crankshaft.

Firing Order

Firing orders vary with the engine. In four-cycle, four-cylinder engines, the firing order may be 1-2-4-3 or 1-3-4-2. In any case, one power pulse is obtained every half revolution. Similar variations can be found in other multicylinder engines. Usually the front cylinder fires first, and each follows in an order that locates each firing as far as possible from the previous one. This minimizes engine vibration. V-type engines start with the first cylinder in one of the banks. Firing orders for common automobile engines are given in Fig. 8-57.

ENGINE FIRING ORDER CODES

In all cases LEFT BANK is driver's side.
The left side of listings is the front of the vehicle.

A Code
FRONT 1 6 2 5 8 3 7 4

B Code
FRONT
1 3 5 7 Right Bank
2 4 6 8 Left Bank
Firing Order 1-2-7-8-4-5-6-3

C Code
FRONT
2 4 6 8 Right Bank
1 3 5 7 Left Bank
Firing Order 1-8-7-3-6-5-4-2

D Code
FRONT
2 4 6 8 Right Bank
1 3 5 7 Left Bank
Firing Order 1-8-4-3-6-5-7-2

E Code
FRONT 1 5 3 6 2 4

G Code
FRONT 1 3 4 2

H Code
FRONT
1 2 3 4 Right Bank
5 6 7 8 Left Bank
Firing Order 1-5-4-8-6-3-7-2

I Code
FRONT
1 2 3 4 Right Bank
5 6 7 8 Left Bank
Firing Order 1-5-4-2-6-3-7-8

J Code
FRONT
5 3 1 Right Bank
6 4 2 Left Bank
Firing Order 1-4-5-2-3-6

Make, Year, Model	Fire Order
Buick	
1946-52	A
1953 "40"	A
1953 All other-61	B
1961 "Special"	D
Cadillac	
1946-48	C
1949-61	D
Chevrolet & Corvair	
1946-61 (6 cyl. ex. Corvair)	E
1955-61 (V-8)	D
1960-61 Corvair	J
Chrysler	
1946-54	E
1946-50 (8 cyl.)	A
1951-61 (V-8)	D
De Soto	
1956-54 (6 cyl.)	E
1952-61 V-8	D

Make, Year, Model	Fire Order
Dodge & Dart	
1946-61 (6 cyl.)	E
1953-61 (V-8)	D
Edsel	
1959-60 (6 cyl.)	E
1958-60	I
Ford & Falcon	
1947-61 (6 cyl.)	E
1947-57 (V-8)	H
1958-61 (292 V-8)	H
(All other V-8)	I
Lincoln	
1957-58	H
1959-61	I
Mercury & Comet	
1960-61 (6 cyl.)	E
1949-57	H
1958-61 (292 V-8)	H
(All others)	I

Make, Year, Model	Fire Order
Oldsmobile	
1946-50 (6 cyl.)	E
1946-48 (8 cyl.)	A
1949-60 V-8	C
1961 F-85	D
All others	C
Plymouth & Valiant	
1946-61 (6 cyl.)	E
1955-61 V-8	D
Pontiac	
1948-54 (6 cyl.)	E
1948-54 (8 cyl.)	A
1955-61 V-8	D
1961 (4 cyl.)	G
Rambler	
1950-61 (6 cyl.)	E
1957-61 V-8	D
Studebaker	
1948-61 (6 cyl.)	E
1951-61 V-8	D

Fig. 8-57. Engine Firing Orders (A-C)

Lubrication

Friction cannot be removed, but we can reduce it to a controllable degree with proper friction-reducing lubricants. If these lubricants were accidentally withheld, bearing surfaces would melt due to the extreme heats caused by the high rpm of the engine.

These lubricants are made from the same crude oil as gasoline. Some lubricants are made by mixing petroleum oils, animal fats, and vegetable oils, silicones, and other manufactured ingredients. They all, however, provide a thin film between two surfaces. Their main purpose is to reduce friction and thus excessive wear and heat. Lubricants, in general, serve to seal all parts and guarantee proper function. If a continual flow of lubricant is used, it also washes away rough particles worn from surfaces. These functions are illustrated in Fig. 8-58. Any contamination

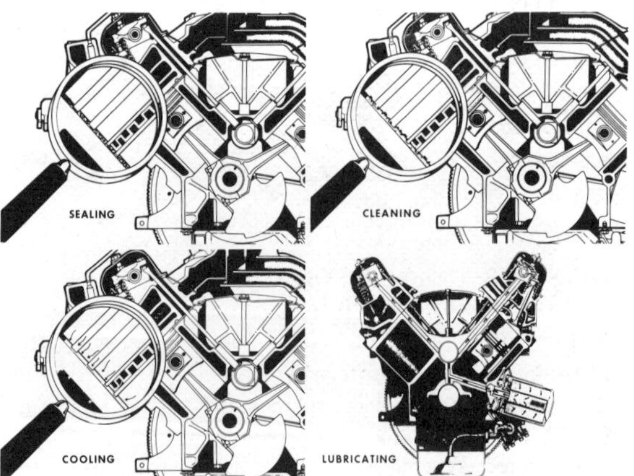

Fig. 8-58. Four Functions of a Lubricating System (Ford)

may then be filtered out by a replaceable oil filter in the system, Fig. 8-59.

Weights and Classifications of Oil

Lubricating oils must function in tremendous physical and temperature extremes. They are made in varying weights to insure proper lubrication at any specific temperature range and physical condition. Lighter oils stiffen less at low temperature, whereas the heavy oils are not too thin at high temperatures. The *Society of Automotive Engineers* (S.A.E.) has determined specifications of oils. The lighter weights (thinner oils) have lower S.A.E. numbers. SAE 10 would be a thin oil used for low temperatures or tight bearings. SAE 30 is a heavier oil used for warmer weather or on loose bearing surfaces. The SAE number has nothing to do with the quality of the oil.

Some oils have other designations such as "W" or "H" added to the SAE number. These indicate a slightly different range of the oil. W or winter weights (5W, 10W) are for use at lower temperatures. The H indicates heavy duty oils to be used where conditions are quite severe. Multi-range oils (5W-20, 10W-30) remain as thin as the low number in cold yet also have high temperature characteristics of the larger number.

There are *motor oils* for three classes of service in gasoline engines: ML for motors having *light* and favorable operating conditions; MM for *moderate* conditions; MS for use where problems of high cylinder temperatures, bearing corrosion, or sludge deposits are *severe* because of engine design or fuel characteristics.

A new system of identification for motor oils has been adapted by the American Petroleum Institute's lubrication committee. In broad terms, API has substituted the use of the letter "S" for passenger car and light truck

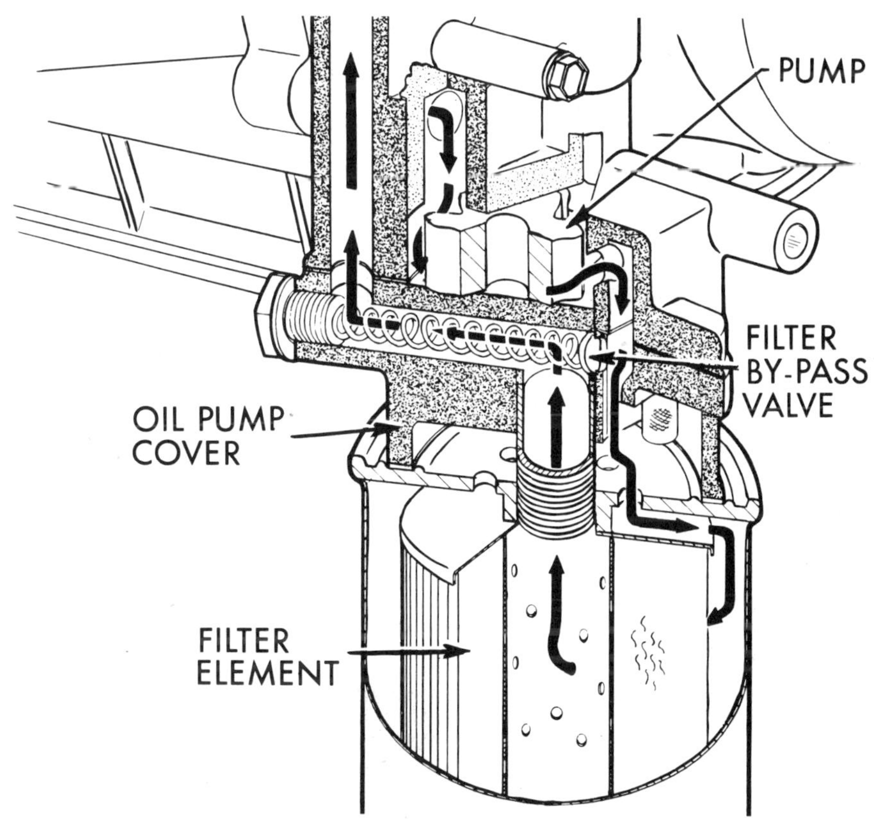

Fig. 8-59. Oil Filter and Oil Pump (Buick)

oils and "C" for heavier, commercial vehicle lubricants. The "S" designation replaces the "M", and the "C" replaces "D". See Fig. 8-60.

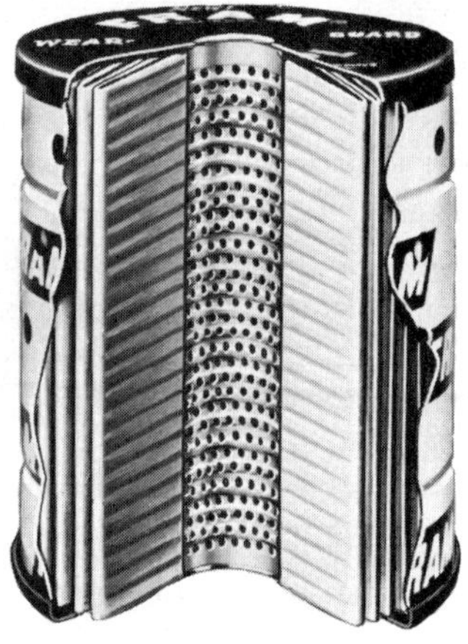

Fig. 8-60. Cut-Away of Replacement Oil Filter Cartridge (Fram)

Variations in Motor Oils

Today, lubricating oils contain many additives to increase their effectiveness. For instance, *detergents* are added to keep the engine clean. *Inhibitors* are added to retard the deterioration of the chemical structure of the oil. *Dispersives* are added to keep in suspension certain contaminants and prevent their collecting and forming sludge. Still other additives in the multi-range oils allow them to flow freely at low temperatures, without thinning under extremely hot working conditions.

Usually, the manufacturer of the engine recommends the type of oil that should be used. It is based on temperature, working conditions, and clearances that will insure maximum efficiency. For instance, a new engine would run hard and hot because of the tight-fitting parts and usually requires an SAE 20 oil in warm weather, a SAE 10W for

NEW	OLD	OIL CLASSIFICATIONS DEFINED
SA	ML	Utility gasoline and diesel engine service. Engines operated under mild conditions.
SB	MM	Minimum duty gasoline engine service.
SC	MS-1964	Gasoline engines 1964 through 1967 models; cars and trucks operating under engine makers' warranties.
SD	MS-1968	For 1968 gasoline engine warranty service; cars and trucks beginning with 1968 models and operating under engine manufacturers' warranties.
CA	DG	Light duty diesel engine service.
CB	DM, Supp-1	Moderate duty diesel engine service.
CC	DM, MIL-L2104B	Moderate duty diesel and gasoline engine service; typical of lightly supercharged diesel engines operated in moderate to severe duty.
CD	DS, Series 3	Severe duty diesel engine service; typical of supercharged diesels in high-speed, high-output duty.

Fig. 8-60. Oil Classification Systems
(Commercial Car Journal)

cold weather and light use, and in extreme cold may require a 5W oil to facilitate starting. After much use, this same engine might require heavier oils such as SAE 30 in the warm weather and SAE 20W for cold weather.

Generally speaking, the engine manufacturers recommend the lightest weight oil that will do the job. In this way, the oil viscosity will not detract from engine power in starting and is easily circulated to all parts of the engine.

The thin film of oil, although only a fraction of a thousandth of an inch thick, is made of many layers of oil molecules. These molecules rotate one over the other much like ball bearings and reduce friction to a tolerable degree by holding the friction producing surfaces apart. These mirror-smooth bearing surfaces, if magnified, would look very rough, and it is imperative that they be kept apart to lessen friction and to insure long life.

Methods of Lubrication

There are two major methods of circulating oil to the moving parts: *splashing* and by *force pumping.* In some engines, a combination of both methods is employed.

In the *splash system,* the rotating crankshaft splashes the oil to the bearing surfaces as it rotates in the bath of oil in the crankcase. Sometimes a dipper is fastened to the connecting rod to ensure adequate splash lubrication. See Fig. 8-61.

The *constant level splash system* employs the principles of the simple splash system already mentioned plus a pump to keep the oil supply in the splash reservoir at a constant level. Another system similar to the splash system uses a *slinger* Fig. 8-62, driven by the cam gear. The slinger is situated in the oil well and slings the oil for proper lubrication.

Lubrication by *ejection pumping* is popular on some small engines, Fig. 8-63. It depends on a cam-operated pump spraying oil on the rotating connecting rod. Some of the oil enters the bearing of the connecting rod while some is thrown about within the crankcase.

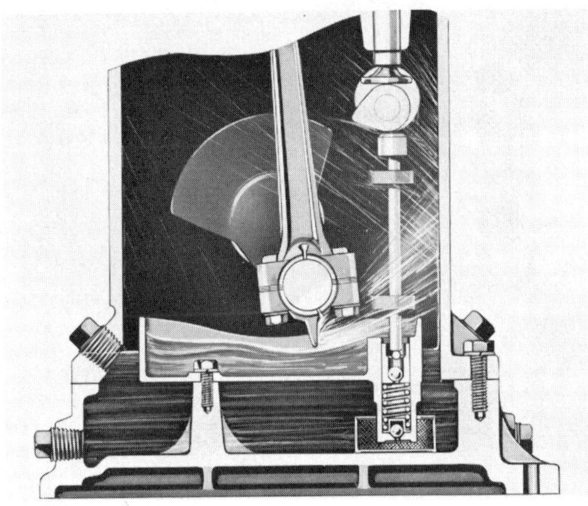

Fig. 8-61. Constant Level Splash System—Crankshaft Splashes Oil to Bearing Surfaces (Wisconsin)

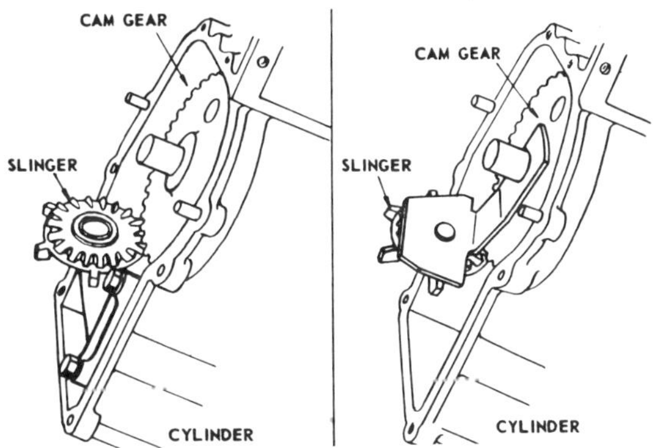

Fig. 8-62. Oil Slinger for Small Engines (Briggs & Stratton)

Fig. 8-63. Ejection Pumping Oil System (Wisconsin)

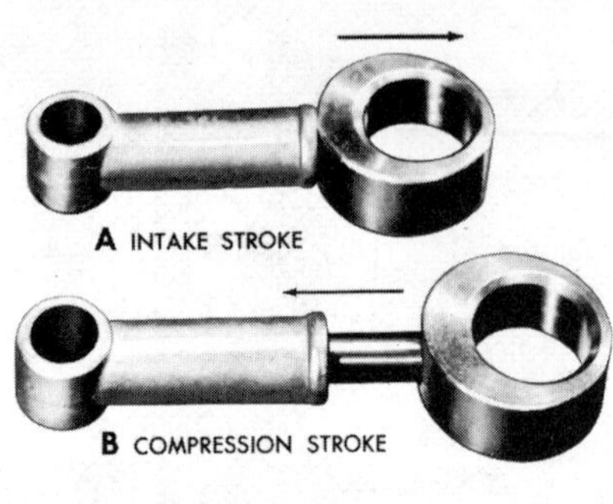

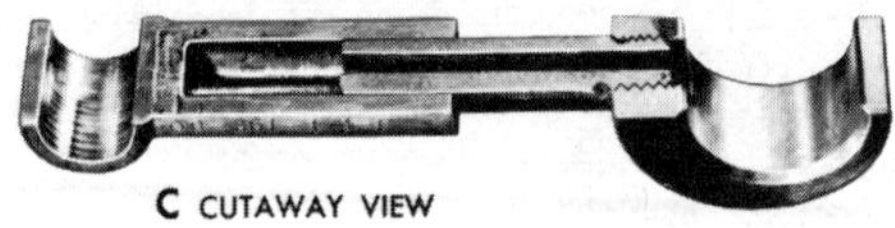

Fig. 8-64. Barrel-Type Oil Pump

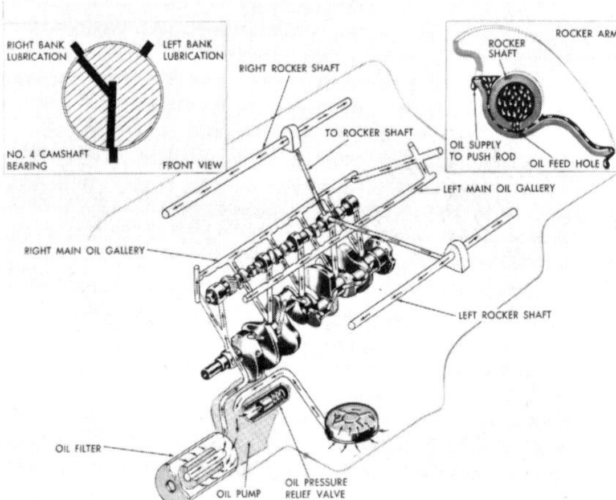

Fig. 8-65. Oil Pressure System and Flow Paths (Chrysler)

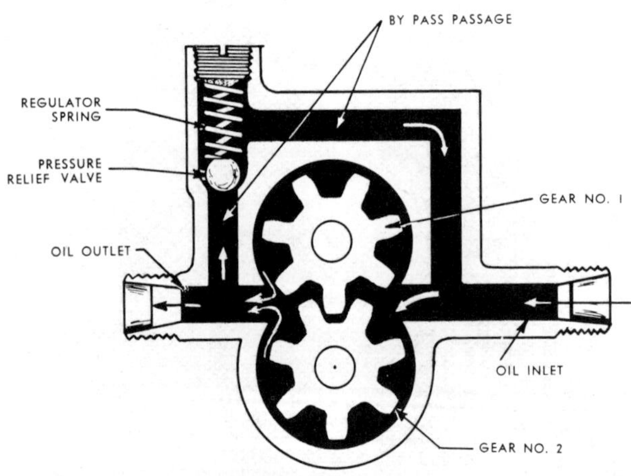

Fig. 8-66. Gear-Type Oil Pump

Various *partial pumping systems* are employed to force oil through capillaries to important bearing surfaces contained in the crankshaft, main bearing, and the connecting rod assembly. One type of pump is called a *barrel-pump,* and is activated by an eccentric driven by the crankshaft. See Fig. 8-64. When the pump's plunger is pulled out, the oil is drawn through an opening into the chamber. When the plunger is pushed in, the oil is forced under pressure into the various lubrication passages and openings.

Larger engines employ a *full pressure lubrication system* such as diagramed in Fig. 8-65. Oil is delivered to the necessary bearings, through passages to main, connecting rod and camshaft bearings, valve tappets, rockers and so on, under pressure. A *positive displacement gear type pump,* Fig. 8-66, is most popular because of its relative simplicity of design and dependability. Of course, a splash or ejection system sometimes is employed in conjunction with the full pressure system, Fig. 8-67.

In 2-cycle engines, *lubricating oil is mixed with the fuel.* As the mixture is drawn into the crankcase on its way to the cylinder, the oily mist coats all parts, working into the bearings and providing the necessary lubrication.

Oil Filter Systems

Most all manufacturers of internal combustion engines use some type of oil filter. The protection afforded the lubrication system returns dividends in the form of decreased maintenance and longer engine life.

The oldest popular oil filtration system has been the *bypass type,* Fig. 8-68. Some oil is withdrawn from the lubrication system and bypassed through a filter before *returning* to the crankcase. The amount of oil withdrawn ranges from 5 to 10 percent of the pump delivery depending on the viscosity of the oil, type of filter, and its condition.

Oil is pumped by a gear pump from the oil pan to the oil gallery which supplies the bearings. A pressure regulating valve located near the pump opens at the setting found suitable for the particular engine. The excess oil delivered by the pump will be returned to the crankcase. The oil to be filtered is taken from any point on the pressure side of the system, and directed through the filter. The average system will filter approximately 30 gallons of oil per hour or pass the entire crankcase of oil through the filter 15 to 20 times per hour. At this rate, dirt is removed as it is collected and formed by the engine.

Most automotive manufacturers have now adopted the *full flow filtering system,* or the *shunt-type filter system.* See Figs. 8-69 and 8-70. These were necessitated by closer manufacturing tolerances, higher engine speeds, and thin steel-backed anti-friction bearings. Each of these systems passes oil through the filter *before* it goes to the bearings. Therefore,the flow of the filter must be 5 to 10 times greater than the bypass or partial-flow filter. To accommodate this flow rate, the resistance to oil flow was decreased, proportionately cutting the filtration properties of the filter. This type of filter is in effect more like a strainer than a filter.

These systems include an oil pump provided with a pressure regulating valve, a filter that can receive all the oil as it is directed to the bearings, and a pressure operated bypass valve to permit oil to return directly to the crankcase in order to regulate the pressure in the system.

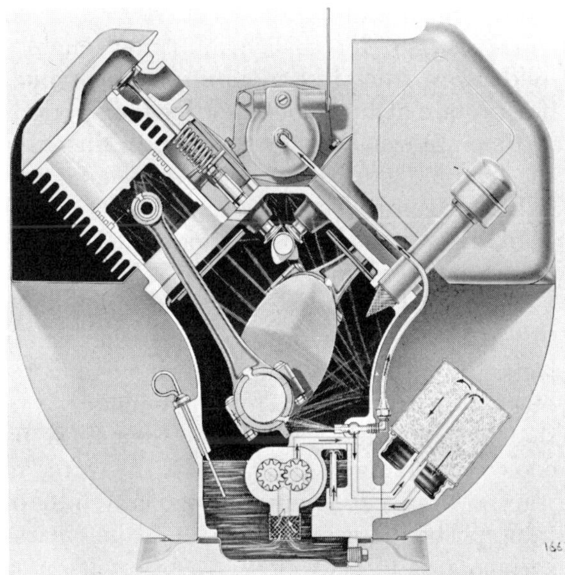

Fig. 8-67. Full Pressure and Ejection Combination Oil System in Light V-2 Engine (Wisconsin)

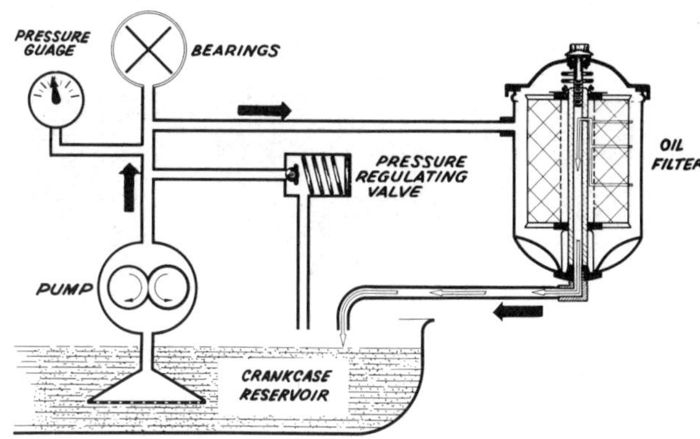

Fig. 8-68. Bypass Oil Filter System (Fram)

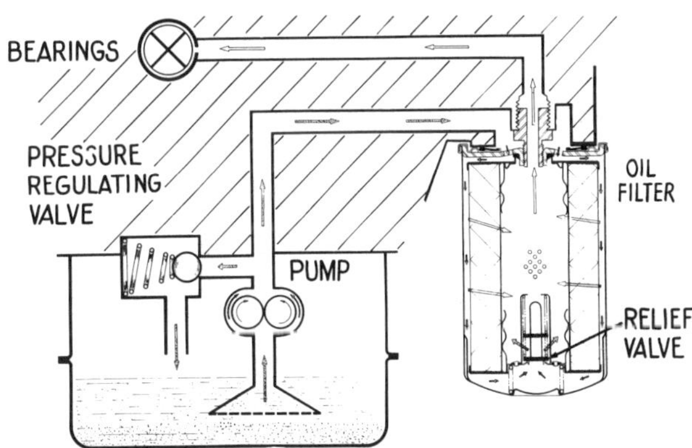

Fig. 8-69. Full-Flow Oil Filter System (Fram)

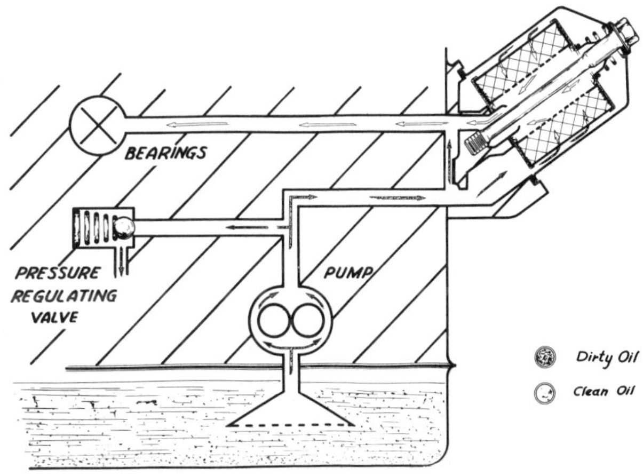

Fig. 8-70. Shunt-Flow Oil Filter System (Fram)

Cooling Systems

If it were not for the cooling system, the extreme temperature of combustion, (approximately 5000°F.) would melt many parts of the engine. This cooling system does nothing more than to cause the heat of combustion to be dissipated in metal, water, or air, and to automatically, thermostatically permit the engine to run continually at its best operating temperature of about 200°F.

Fig. 8-71. Fabricating Cooling Fins to Cylinder Barrel—Note Cast Fins on Head (Curtiss-Wright)

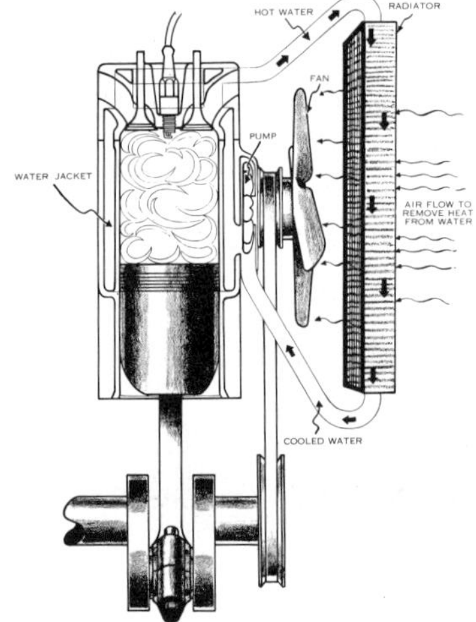

Fig. 8-72. Water Circulation Between Jacket and Radiator (G.M.)

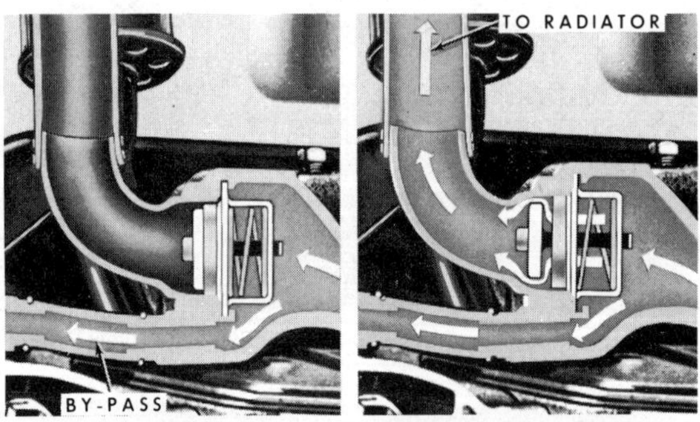

Fig. 8-73. Thermostat Operation (Ford)

Air-Cooled Engines

The most popular small internal combustion engines that are used to power lawnmowers, chain saws, small power generators, motorcycles, some small cars, as well as the large airplane engines, are air cooled. Regardless of the kind of engine, 2-cycle or 4-cycle, single or multi-cylinder, this cooling method is most satisfactory. It is almost fool-proof because it requires no moving parts and, therefore, no maintenance. See Fig. 8-71.

The head and cylinder block have fins cast into them. Most of the radiation surface is where the heat is greatest—at the head and top of the cylinder. These fins increase the metallic surface area through which the heat may be radiated to the cool surrounding air. Usually a cover or *shroud* channels air flow over the fins. A fan is a very necessary part of such engines located away from fast moving air. These engines are seemingly hot to touch, yet they run comparatively cool at approximately 200°F.

Water-Cooled Engines

The larger internal combustion engines used away from fast moving air and which must rotate at high speeds or for long periods of time are usually water-cooled. In this way, the running temperature of the engine can be better controlled.

In water-cooled systems, water jackets surround each cylinder. See Fig. 8-72. Usually, a centrifugal water pump is used to circulate the water continually through the water jackets. In this way, the high heat of combustion is transferred to the cylinder wall then to the water. The water then must be cooled in a radiator that permits the water to transfer its heat energy to its labyrinth of tubing. The honeycombed structure increases surface area of each pipe. This permits, as a result, more rapid and greater cooling efficiency and it also increases structural rigidity. The surrounding air again absorbs this excess and wasted heat energy.

Greater temperature control is accomplished by putting a water thermostat in the system, as shown in Fig. 8-73 and 8-74. In this way, the water is not permitted to circulate to the cooling radiator until optimum running temperature is reached. In cold weather this permits running temperature to be reached more quickly as well as maintaining the higher temperature needed for efficient carburetion or for operation of a passenger heater.

To be efficient, the water cooling system must be kept clean. Rust, dirt, and lime sometimes cause hot spots by collecting on the inside surfaces acting as an insulator. The metal, at this point, will become very hot and could distort or burn through. Minor accumulations of scale and trash can be flushed away with chemicals. The manufacturers' directions should be followed.

If the engine is to be subject to cold weather, certain antifreeze additives are used to prevent the water from freezing. See Fig. 8-75. As was mentioned, water expands when frozen and this expansion can crack the engine block. Some engines of today have blow plugs designed to pop out of the block as the water freezes. In this way, the block is less apt to crack. Other additives prevent rust and rubber deteriorations. Naturally, these chemicals are desirable and well worth the nominal initial cost because they will increase engine life.

Exhaust System

Hot exhaust gases must escape efficiently from heat engines. In the external combustion engine these exhaust gases flow up and out the stack. In small internal combustion engines exhaust gases exit directly into the atmosphere if the accompanying sound is not of a magnitude that demands muffling. Because of the annoying level of noise most engines require some type of muffler (or sound deadener). This muffler is frequently nothing more than a cannister that contains an inner cell that breaks up the sound passage permitting it to dissipate its energy within the muffler before it is permitted to escape. The size of the muffler is proportionate to the size of the engine.

In multi-cylinder engines the exhaust gases are collected by the exhaust manifold from

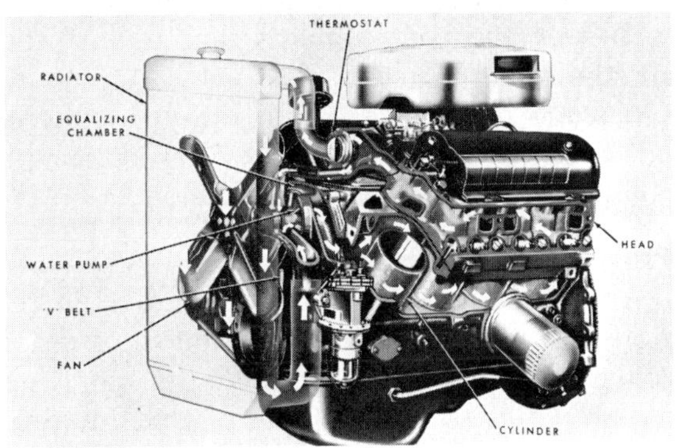

Fig. 8-74. Water-Cooled V-8 Engine (Ford)

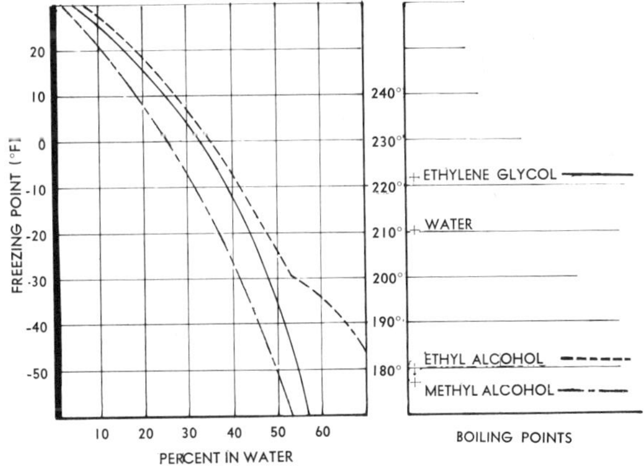

Fig. 8-75. Antifreeze Boiling and Freezing Points

Find lowest cold weather temperatures at left margin. Follow across to diagonal line for the antifreeze to be used, then down to determine the percentage needed in water. (Thus, for protection to 0° use ⅓ ethylene glycol and ⅔ water—half and half (50%) would be adequate to −34°F.) Ethylene glycol is known as permanent type because it is not very volatile, having a higher boiling point than the water. As the alcohols have lower boiling levels they evaporate some but are less expensive. Alcohols also require a special low temperature thermostat—usually 160° rather than 180°.

each cylinder's exhaust valve or port, Fig. 8-76. From the manifold the gases pass to the exhaust muffler and from the muffler they flow out the tailpipe. Some cars have a single-exhaust system and some have a dual-exhaust system, Fig. 8-77.

At one time the only purpose of the exhaust system was to permit the hot exhaust gases to escape efficiently while moderating the noise of the escaping gases. As concern is expressed to reduce the contaminants that pollute the air, the exhaust system must not only provide a passage of hot gases into the atmosphere, but include measures that will reduce the pollutants emitted from the engines.

Exhaust Emission Control

Air pollution and air contamination in regions of high population have led the federal government to establish minimum operating requirements for hydrocarbon engines: hydrocarbon emissions to 275 parts per million and carbon monoxide to 1.5%.

One method of reducing automobile engine air pollution is to inject air into the exhaust manifold causing the unburned compounds to burn more completely. The thermactor exhaust control system, Fig. 8-78, uses an air pump that is operated off the fan belt. The limitation of this system is that when exhaust emission is at its highest during idle and deceleration of the engine, the air pump speed is decreased. The effect of the system to control or lower contaminants is thereby reduced at a time when it is needed most. Also, the considerable amount of hardware added to the engine creates more parts congestion under the hood of the car.

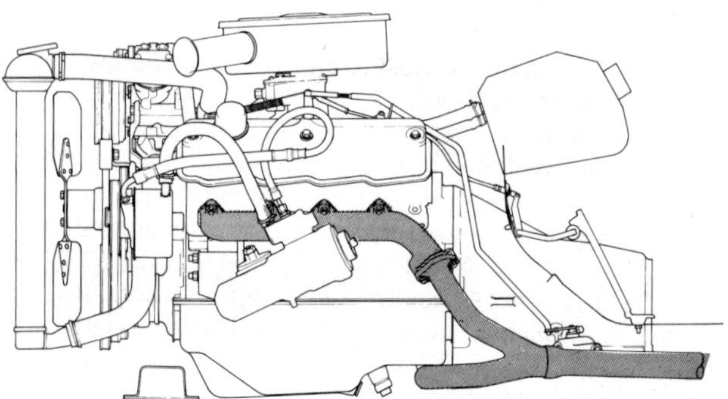

Fig. 8-76. Multi-Cylinder Engine Exhaust Manifold (Dodge)

Typical of the more advanced automotive exhaust emission control systems is one that provides cleaner exhaust gases at all engine speeds and involves adjusted ignition timing, higher engine speeds, greater internal air flow, special choke calibration, and other more subtle modifications peculiar to each engine. These include revised combustion chamber design, improved manifold heat valves, and new design carburetor metering systems for better carburetion and cylinder distribution.

Research has revealed that the conventional automobile engine exhausts relatively low emissions of hydrocarbons and carbon monoxide at accelerating or cruising speeds, but

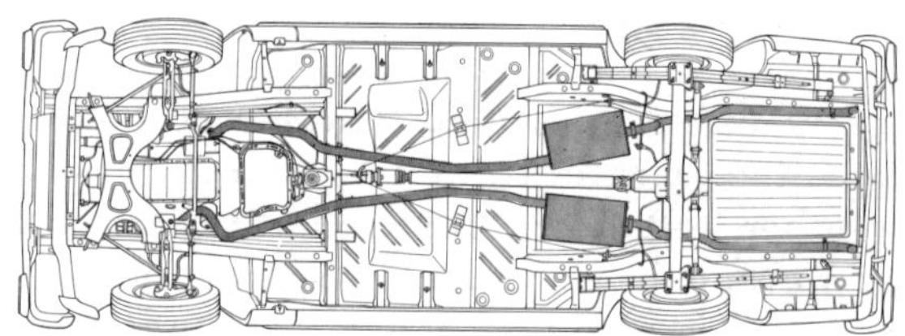

Fig. 8-77. Dual-Exhaust System (Dodge)

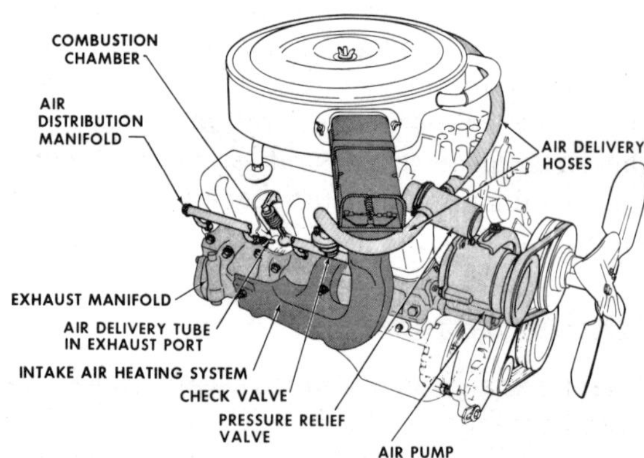

Fig. 8-78. Thermactor Exhaust Control System (Ford)

The Thermactor system reduces hydrocarbon and carbon monoxide emissions by adding a fresh supply of air to the hot exhaust gases as they leave the combustion chambers of the engine. This air, together with the high temperature of the exhaust gases, burns most of the remaining hydrocarbons and carbon monoxide as the gases move through the exhaust manifold and exhaust pipe.

very high emissions when decelerating or operating at low or idling speeds. It was also found that more complete combustion of the fuel-air mixture during periods of high exhaust emissions would lower such emissions not only while decelerating and idling but also during acceleration and cruise.

Most automobile manufacturers today employ some type of exhaust emission control system. They are basically similar, so knowing the principles of operation of one system will help understand all. The Chrysler cleaner air system, referred to as CAP (Cleaner Air Package), Fig. 8-79, changes the conventional carburetor choke and distributor and makes other internal modifications determined by specific engine needs. Most of these are directed toward certain parts of the engine operating cycle, idle, acceleration and deceleration.

Limiting Exhaust Emissions at Idle and Acceleration

For the engine to reduce its exhaust emissions at idle, it must approach the more efficient combustion conditions that exist at cruising speed. In the cleaner air system this is done by increasing idle speeds and the air flow necessary to maintain them, providing a cleaner mixture of fuel and air, and retarding spark ignition. The result is that the engine receives a fuel/air mixture similar to the mixture it would receive if it were cruising. The engine burns this mixture much more completely. The carburetor is set to deliver as lean a mixture as the engine will tolerate without affecting performance. A new carburetor device called the idle mixture limiter makes certain the idle mixtures will stay within an acceptable emission limit no matter how the idle mixture is adjusted. The maximum range of lean to rich adjustment is reduced to half that of the conventional engine.

The spark plugs are timed to fire later than normal in the compression stroke. Retarded timing provides two favorable conditions leading to more complete combustion, Fig. 8-80. First, to compensate for the power reduction resulting from the retarded spark, air and fuel flows are increased creating a charge density that resembles that existing at cruising speed. Second, the retarded spark increases the exhaust gas temperature causing additional burning of hydrocarbons and carbon monoxide in the exhaust manifold.

Another modification applies to cold starting and warm-up operation. Conventionally a rich fuel mixture is necessary for the engine to fire and reach a smooth operating condition. The choke valve is closed when the engine starts and opens gradually as the engine warms up, and a less rich air/fuel mixture is

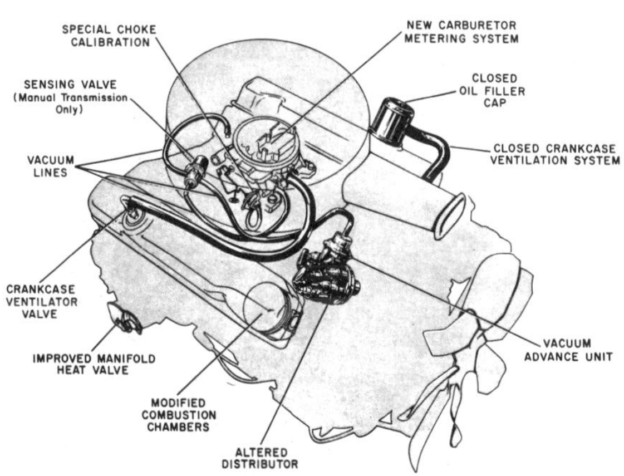

Fig. 8-79. Cleaner Air System Shown with V-8 Manual Transmission (Chrysler)

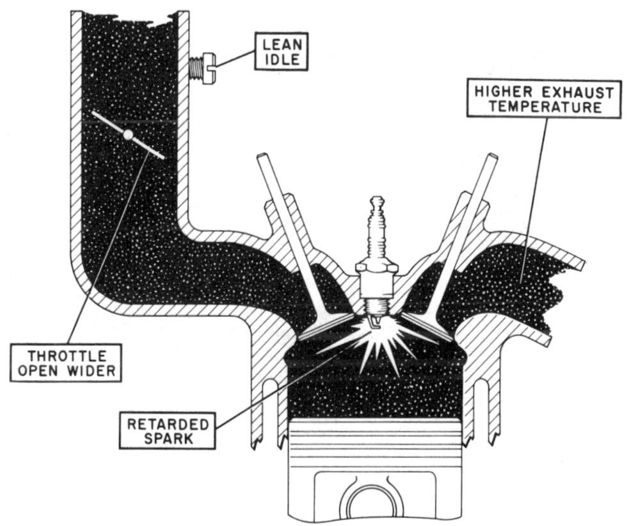

Fig. 8-80. Retarded Timing (Chrysler)

required for smooth, economical operation. In an engine equipped with the cleaner air system, improved manifold heat valves, carburetor metering, and cylinder distribution permit the choke to be calibrated to open sooner than in previous engines. This, of course, reduces the total fuel consumed at warm-up. The total effect of these modifications is a substantial decrease in exhaust emission of carbon dioxide and hydrocarbons — more than 50% over nonmodified engines.

Limiting Exhaust Emission During Deceleration

The emission due to deceleration consists primarily of hydrocarbons of partially or unburned fuel vapors. Two combustion factors, low air/fuel flow and a relatively high dilution of the fuel mixture by exhaust gases, contribute primarily to this problem. The low air/fuel flow occurs as soon as the driver eases up on the accelerator. Normally the throttle blade inside the carburetor is nearly closed just as it would be during idle, severely restricting air flow from the carburetor to the combustion chambers. Engine speed at this time is high, depending on how fast the car was cruising at the time deceleration began. The low air/fuel flow and high engine speed combine to create a relatively strong vacuum in the intake manifold. As the intake valve opens, exhaust gases from the previous charge which were still escaping from the closing exhaust valves are drawn toward the intake side. These exhaust gases mix with the charging mixture, weakening it and thereby causing the charge to burn rather poorly and often leaving pockets of unburned fuel to escape out the exhaust, raising hydrocarbon emission.

In engines equipped with cleaner air system modifications, the throttle blade at idle is opened wider than normal. During deceleration this permits greater air flow and lowers the intake manifold vacuum. Consequently, the tendency for the exhaust gases to mix with the incoming fuel mixture is reduced. Another factor improving combustion during deceleration is advanced timing which provides more complete combustion under conditions of very high manifold vacuum, Fig. 8-81. These very high manifold vacuum conditions occur only during deceleration and primarily in vehicles with manual transmission. In a car with an automatic transmission, the slip characteristics of the torque converter in the automatic transmission allow the engine to slow down much more rapidly as the vehicle is decelerating, thereby quickly reducing the high manifold vacuum. On vehicles

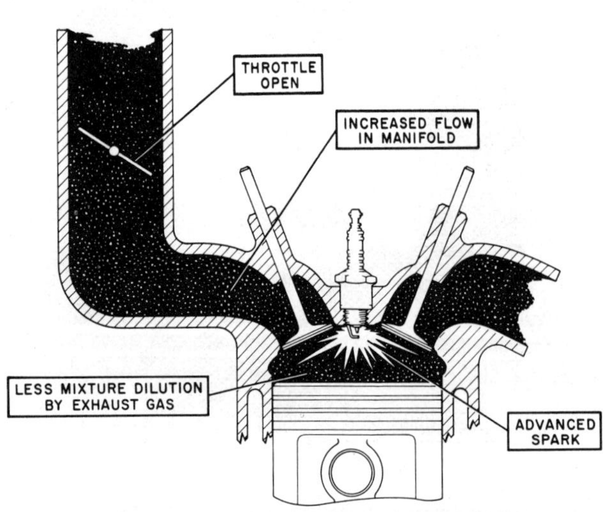

Fig. 8-81. How Cleaner Air System Limits Emissions on Deceleration (Chrysler)

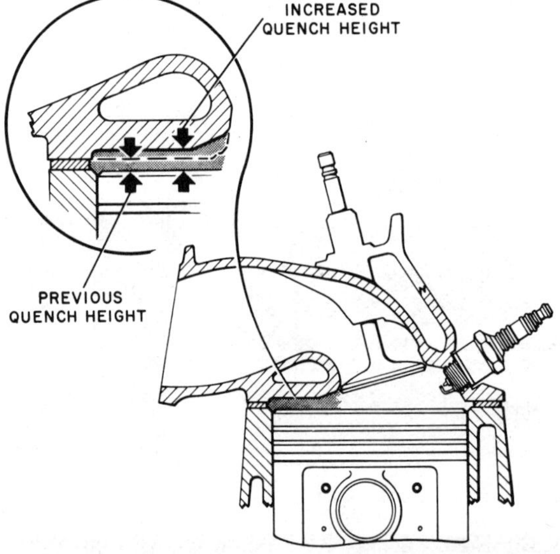

Fig. 8-82. Increased Quench Height (Chrysler)

equipped with manual transmission, engine slow down is not as rapid during deceleration. High manifold vacuum exists longer; therefore spark is advanced at this time. This is accomplished by a special distributor vacuum control valve which reacts to manifold pressure during deceleration to advance timing until the engine reaches the low speed range.

The distributor vacuum control valve is nothing more than a switching device placed in the vacuum hose circuit between the carburetor and the distributor vacuum spark advanced unit, thus dividing the circuit in two, Fig. 8-82. It also adds a third vacuum hose leading to the intake manifold. When the engine is accelerating at part throttle or cruising, vacuum is present at the spark port in the carburetor throttle body. The control valve shuts off the opening to the manifold and routes carburetor vacuum directly to the vacuum spark advance unit for early sparking. When the engine is decelerating, carburetor vacuum is low, but intake manifold vacuum is very high. The control valve then shuts off the circuit leading to the carburetor and relays manifold vacuum to the spark advance unit. Thus in all operating ranges, the necessary spark advance is provided automatically.

A number of additional internal refinements aid in lowering emissions. Among the noticeable improvements are:

1. *A new heat valve and gasket* to provide better distribution of exhaust gases against the underside of the intake manifold so that engine warm-up is quicker, allowing earlier leaning out of the fuel/air mixture.

2. *Increased quench height* in the combustion chamber so that any gradual build-up of carbon deposits will not unduly restrict complete combustion. This design also prevents the metal walls of the combustion chamber from dampening the flame as it travels outward from the spark plug.

3. *Single idle mixture screw* which means that it is no longer necessary to balance the fuel mixture between the barrels of the carburetor when adjusting idle. Balance is preset and sealed. A single idle mixture screw raises or lowers the level of mixture simultaneously in both barrels without affecting balance.

4. *Adjustment idle air bleed* provided in some carburetors incorporates a secondary air bleed that can be adjusted to smooth out engine operation in the transfer range between idle and acceleration.

5. *Bypass air slot* built into the carburetor side wall adjacent to the throttle valve. During closed throttle at idle, it carries air to a key spot below the throttle valve best suited to break up the concentration of raw fuel.

CAP: Includes Closed Crankcase Ventilation

The cleaner air package (CAP) is designed to control crankcase emission as well as exhaust emission. In this sense, it serves as an extension of the positive crankcase ventilation (PCV) system. Introduced on some engines in 1963, PCV on engines not equipped for the cleaner air system had a ventilated oil filler cap. Manifold vacuum pulled fresh air through the cap into the crankcase where it was used to sweep blow-by, unburned, and partially burned fuel vapors out of the crankcase into the carburetor near a special ventilator valve. From the carburetor, the vapors were carried into the combustion chamber for burning. With the cleaner air package, the filler cap is not vented. Instead it is connected by a hose directly to the carburetor air cleaner so that if an extensive amount of blow-by vapors is coming from the crankcase or the vent valve should become stuck, the extra blow-by gases will be routed right back through the engine via the air cleaner rather than allowed to escape.

A System, Not a Device

Obviously, the "cleaner air system" is not any single device or group of devices that can be bought and applied by any mechanic. It is a highly-developed, sophisticated system of engine modification that has one purpose: to reduce emissions to an acceptable level. This system, although rather complex, requires no additional maintenance beyond the normal recommendations made for engine care.

Controlling Fuel Evaporation Emissions

The Ford Motor Company introduced in the 1970 cars the first control system for fuel evaporation emission. This control system seals the vents in the fuel tank and carburetor to prevent escape of fuel hydrocarbons. Depending on the operating conditions, the system collects the evaporates from the fuel and returns them to the fuel supply after condensing them, sends the vapors to the engine for burning, or stores the vapors for future burning, Fig. 8-83. The Ford fuel seal system (Fig. 8-84) includes the following major components:

1. A flat vapor collector unit is attached to the top inside wall of the fuel tank. It is so designed that the liquid fuel never completely covers the collector regardless of the vehicle angle; therefore, it is always able to function.
2. A vapor separator is installed in the wall of the vehicle's trunk and separates all liquid fuel from the vapors and permits it to return to the fuel tank.
3. A three-way valve controls the flow of fuel vapors within the system and permits air to enter the fuel tank to replace the fuel as it is consumed. The previously provided air vent in the filler cap is sealed.
4. In the engine compartment a vapor storage subsystem is provided, Fig. 8-85. It consists of a cannister filled with a supply of charcoal pellets that absorb the fuel vapors, giving them up later to the engine induction system as the engine vacuum pulls fresh air over the pellets and into the air cleaner.

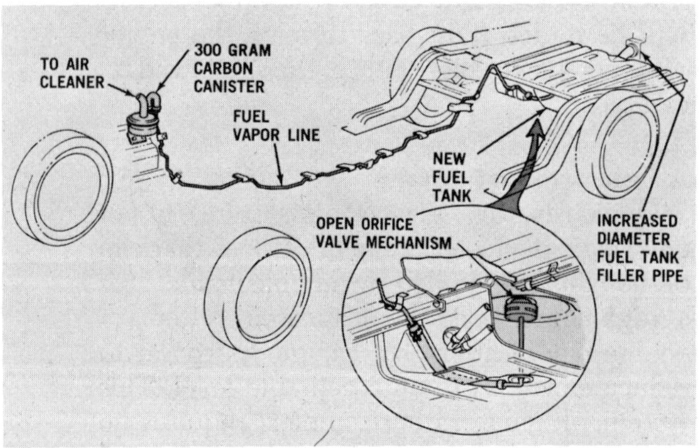

Fig. 8-83. New Fuel Evaporation Emission Controls (Ford)

Research for the Future

The automotive industry's research programs range from basic science research into the nature of combustion processes to engineering development of hardware to implement experimental emission control concepts. They include the continuing investigation of low-emission power plants such as the gas turbine and the rotary combustion engine. They also include modification of old power plants such as steam and electric. They include modification of present fuels as well as the development of new fuels, new devices, and attachments that will reduce pollution that is emitted from the present reciprocating engine. Two innovative ideas designed to reduce pollution from present internal combustion engines are high temperature furnaces and catalytic converters.

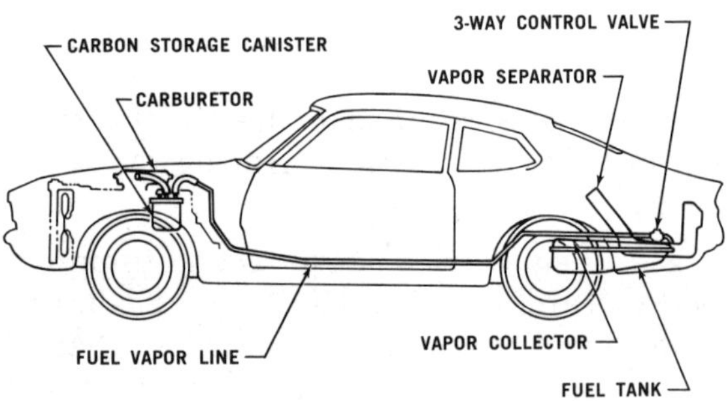

Fig. 8-84. Fuel Seal System (Ford)

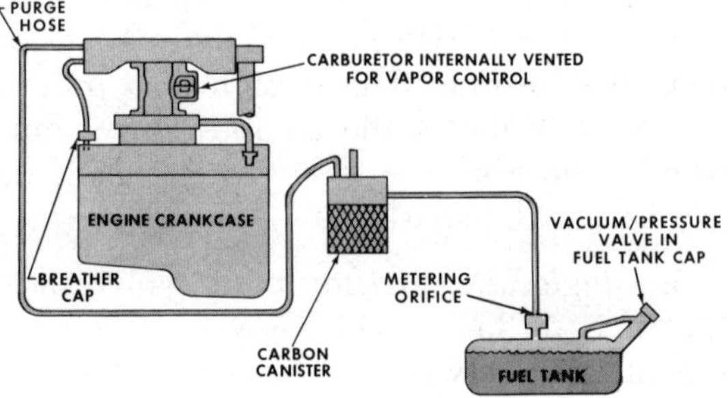

Fig. 8-85. Evaporative Emission Control System (Ford)

The Inter-Industry Emission Control Program

The Ford Motor Company and Mobil Oil Company established a joint research program in 1967 to reduce automobile emissions. They have been joined by five major oil companies and four foreign automobile manufacturers. This multimillion dollar program is an effort to develop the technology necessary in both the automotive and petroleum industries to virtually eliminate emission from the gasoline engine. A result of their collective efforts has been the development of a catalytic converter system which includes a container of a granular chemical compound through which the engine's exhaust gases are permitted to pass as they move out the exhaust system. See Fig. 8-86. An oxidizing catalyst speeds up the burning of hydrocarbon and carbon monoxide. A reducing catalyst takes the oxygen from the nitrous oxides. The life of this catalytic material is shortened by lead in the present fuels which quickly coats and plugs up the pores of the granules. The success of this system will depend to a major degree on providing nonleaded fuels for automotive use.

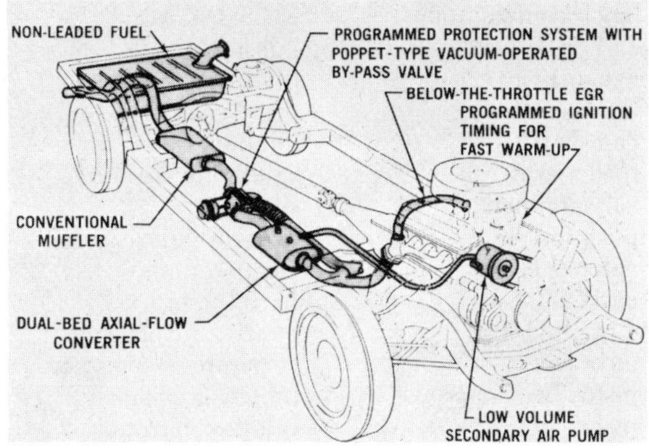

Fig. 8-86. Dual Catalyst Converter System (Ford)

The Thermal Reaction System

Another promising development provides a high temperature furnace in which the pollutants are burned up as the exhaust gases move through it, Fig. 8-87. The reactor will replace the conventional exhaust manifold. It is designed with a considerably larger volume than the conventional manifold in order to provide sufficient time for the gases to mix with the air and burn. A supplementary air pump supplies oxygen from the atmosphere to promote burning. This system demands a significant advance in material technology due to the high temperature produced in the thermal reactor and the light gauges of metal needed for fast warm-up.

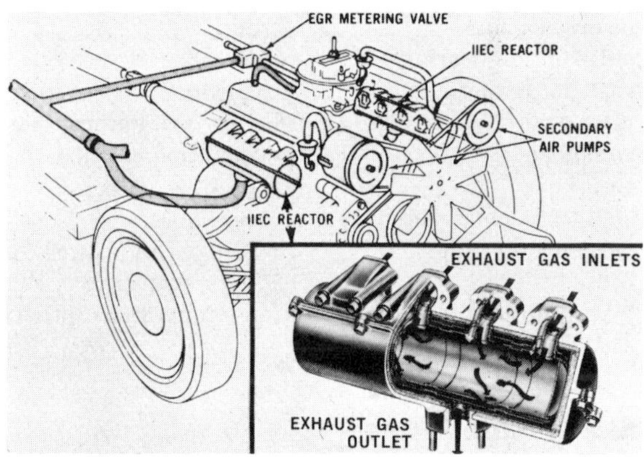

Fig. 8-87. Thermal Reactor System (Ford)

Combustion Systems

We have now discussed each major component of the internal combustion engine, such as the block, piston, piston rings, connecting rod, camshaft, crankshaft, internal bearings, lubrication, and cooling system. We must now introduce to this grouping of parts, a mixture of fuel and air, and an ignition system to make the engine operational.

At the point of combustion systems, SI engines and CI engines separate since combustion principles are their only major dissimilar characteristic.

Terms to Understand

15 to 1 by weight	cracking
Air—21%-78%-1%	polymerization
combustion ratio	compression ratio
poppet valve	dead center T.D.C., B.D.C.
ports	molecules
sleeve valve	detonation
reed valve	knocking or pinging
supercharger	octane rating
sea level air pressure	cetane rating
petroleum	engine efficiency
hydrocarbon	lean/rich mixture
distilling	

block configurations
L, I, F, T, heads
exhaust valve
intake valve
camshaft
rocker arm
valve tappets
push rod
valve overlap
gaskets
tetraethyl lead
turbulence
piston head or crown
piston ring
piston skirt
gudgeon pin or wrist pin
connecting rod
babbit bearings
insert bearings
anti-friction bearings
case hardening
idler gear
cam gear
throw
counterbalance weight
dynamically balanced
firing order
SAE number
10W-30
ML, MM, MS
lubricating oils
detergents
dispersives
inhibitors
splash lubrication
slinger
pressure lubrication
ejection pump
barrel pump
positive displacement pump
bypass filtration
full flow filtration
water-cooled engines
radiator
air-cooled
cooling fins
shroud
pollutants
exhaust control systems
idle mixture limiter
deceleration exhaust
positive crankcase ventilation
fuel evaporation emission
catalytic converters
high temperature furnace

Study Questions

1. What are some of the considerations in selecting a reciprocating combustion engine as a source of power?
2. Why is air sometimes a problem in using I.C.E.?
3. Analyze the various types of methods of getting air into the cylinder.
4. How does the theory of differential pressure enter into the operation of an I.C.E.?
5. How is gasoline obtained from crude oil?
6. What is the difference between cracking and polymerization?
7. What is the significance of compression ratio?
8. Explain how compression ratio affects the efficiency of an engine using the molecular theory.
9. Analyze the significance of octane rating.
10. How does cetane rating differ from octane rating?
11. How does engine speed affect engine efficiency? Diesel, gasoline engines?
12. Analyze the advantages of a multi-cylinder engine.
13. Analyze the ways multi-cylinder engines may be arranged.
14. Analyze the cooling methods employed for I.C.E.
15. Discuss the L, I, F, T, head designs.
16. Analyze the various valve designs.
17. Discuss the conditions and the purpose of a valve system.
18. What methods are employed to activate the valve system?
19. How is the timing of the opening or closing of the valves achieved?
20. What is meant by "valve overlap"?
21. How does the cylinder size affect the engine rating?
22. Analyze how the compression ratio may be altered.
23. Discuss the problems of combustion chamber design.
24. Analyze the operating conditions of a piston.
25. Describe some of the characteristics of a piston.
26. Analyze the types and necessity of piston rings.
27. What is the function and design consideration of the connecting rod?
28. Analyze the various types of bearings used in I.C.E.
29. Analyze the purpose of the camshaft and how it is rotated.
30. How does the shape of the cam affect the operation of the valves?
31. How does the shape of the crankshaft affect the operation of the engine?
32. Analyze the purpose of the lubrication system.
33. Discuss the various types of lubrication systems.
34. What is the significance of the SAE numbering systems for oil? Do they indicate the quality of the oil?

35. Analyze the two lubrication filtering systems employed in modern I.C.E.

36. Analyze the physical and thermal characteristics of the two types of cooling systems.

37. What is the purpose of the thermostat?

38. Trace the flow of the cooling fluids found in I.C.E.

39. What systems have been devised to reduce exhaust emissions?

40. Contrast performance of high and low exhaust emission engines.

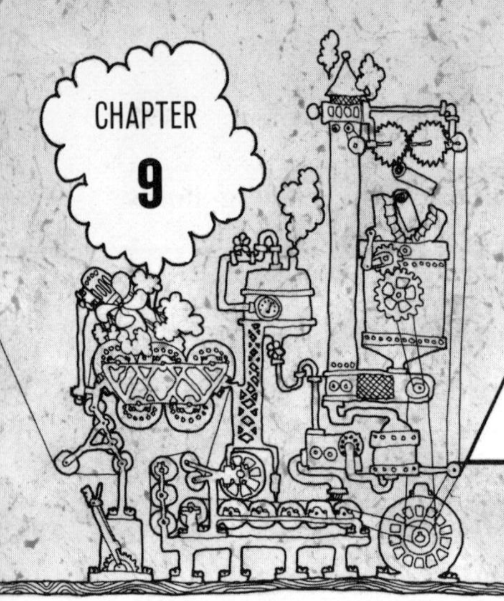

Spark Ignition Engines

In the gasoline engine, fuel and air are mixed in the carburetor in proportions that will insure starting and running under various load conditions. In the modern engine, fuel is atomized or sprayed and thoroughly mixed. This basic function is demonstrated in Fig. 9-1. Then it is vaporized in the intake manifold before being drawn into the combustion chamber, compressed, and ignited to release its potential power. This chapter explains the various types of carburetors, and ignition systems.

Carburetors

In yesterday's engine, the carburetors used were much simpler in design and depended on simple vaporization of the available gasoline. For instance, some of the early engines drew air into the engine that had simply *passed over* a surface of gasoline. In this way, enough gasoline vapor was taken into the engine to cause combustion. Other engines drew air into the cylinder that passed over wicks dipped into the gasoline. These carburetors were crude and were soon improved.

Needle-Valve Carburetor

The simplest modern carburetor uses a *spray bar* or *needle valve,* Fig. 9-2. It is popular in model engines as well as in some small engines that power home appliances. It involves the use of a needle valve that will control the flow of gasoline out of a tube situated in the air passage to the combustion chamber. Although effective, these carburetors are too erratic to use on larger engines. Their ability to mix fuel and air is greatly affected by the height of the fuel supply above the mixing valve, the speed of the engine, and the quality of the fuel.

These problems were solved by employing carburetors of much more complicated design. For instance, the height of the fuel supply above the mixing valve was made constant by

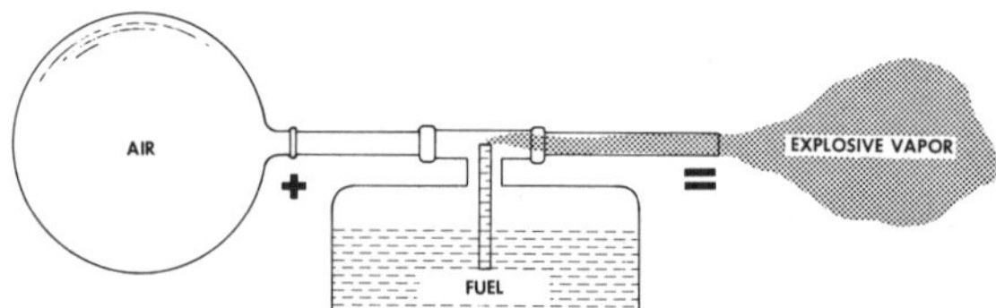

Fig. 9-1. Basic Function of a Carburetor

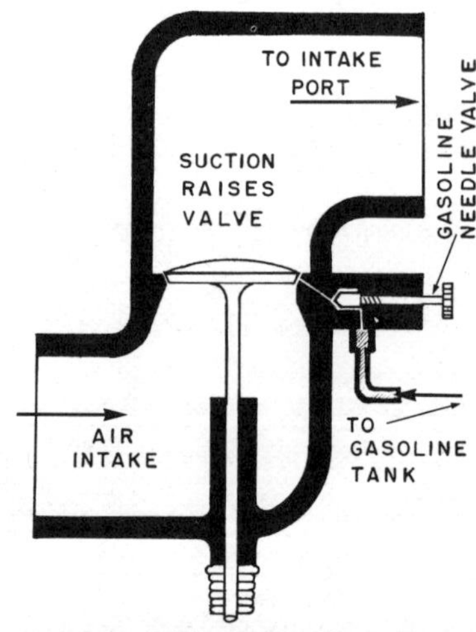

Fig. 9-2. Simple Needle-Valve Carburetor

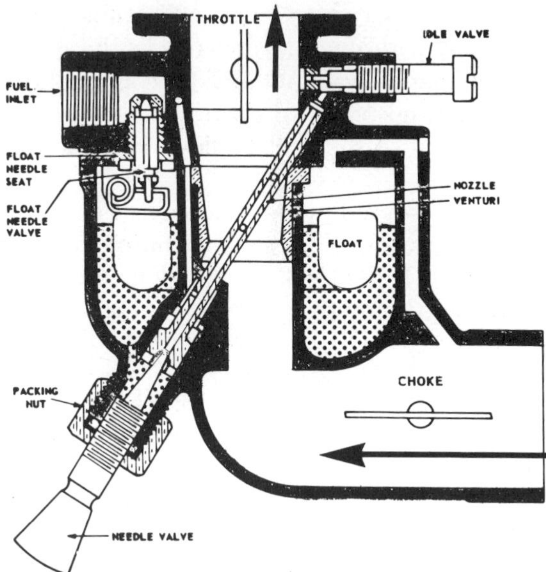

Fig. 9-3. Float-Type Carburetor for Utility Engine
(Briggs & Stratton)

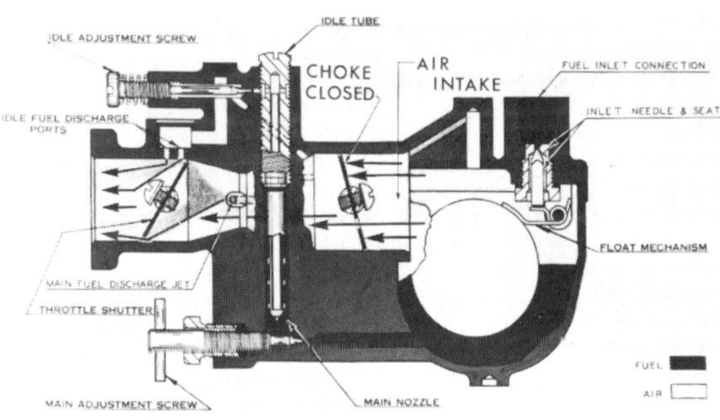

Fig. 9-4. Choked Position of Small Carburetor
The choke is used for cold starting. The valve blocks air flow causing increased suction at both *idle discharge ports* and at the *main fuel discharge jet.* The result is a very rich mixture.

utilizing a *float and reservoir* arrangement. See Fig. 9-3. In this design, the gasoline is pumped to a chamber which is part of the carburetor. The float within the chamber rises and falls with the level of the fuel. When the designated height is reached, a needle valve, mounted on the float, shuts off the supply. Then, as fuel is consumed, the float drops, drawing the needle valve up, permitting more gas to enter the chamber until it reaches the set height again.

Demands of Carburetion

The gasoline engine demands varying proportions of gas and air for proper operation. When the engine is started, it is usually cold and requires a rich mixture of gas in proportion to air, Fig. 9-4. When it reaches operating temperature, such a mixture would be too rich and would cause the engine to run poorly.

Another demand occurs when an engine is idling or operating at low speeds, Fig. 9-5. The mixture must be richer than when operating at normal running speeds and power. When acceleration or more power is required of the engine, the carburetor must respond with increased fuel mixtures, Figs. 9-6 and 9-7. These desired proportions of gas and air must be maintained as the volume of intake varies with the speed and load of the engine. All of these demands must be satisfied although the volume of air through the carburetor may increase more than 100 fold as the engine accelerates from idling to full load.

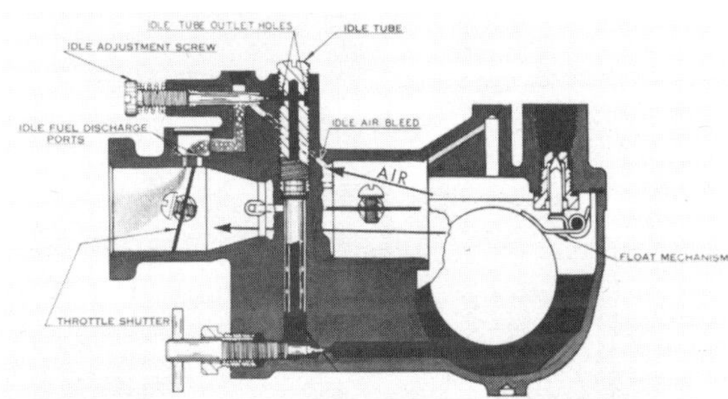

Fig. 9-5. Idling Operation of Small Carburetor
Throttle is closed cutting off normal flow. Engine suction draws fuel and some air from one idle discharge port. Special screw adjusts for best idle.

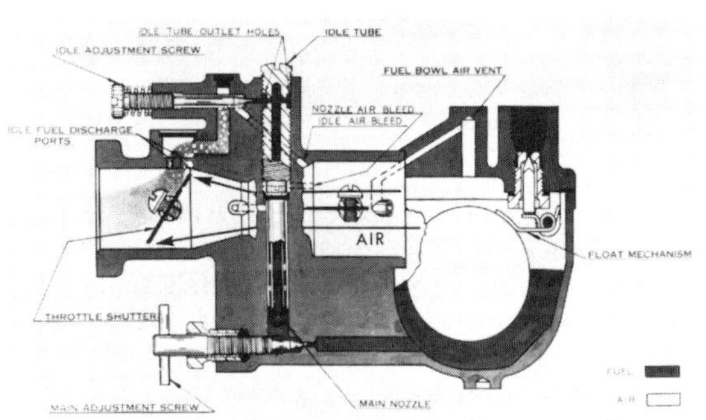

Fig. 9-6. Low Speed Operation of Small Carburetor
Slightly open throttle causes fuel to discharge from both idle ports. Normal air flow begins.

Still another demand may be imposed by the volatility of different fractions of gasolines distilled from petroleum. These fractions found in today's gasolines may vaporize at 100°F. to 400°F.

Principles of Operation

Each cylinder during the intake stroke creates a partial *vacuum*. The difference between this *suction* and atmospheric pressure causes the air and fuel mixture to move through the carburetor and into the combustion chamber.

The principle by which the moving air draws the fuel from the jet within the carburetor is known as *Bernoulli's Principle*. This principle is interesting and important. It is also used over an aircraft wing to provide the lift keeping it in flight. It applies to all fluids in motion, either gaseous or liquid.

The fundamental principle states that when the *speed of a fluid is great, its pressure is small; and when the speed is small, its pressure is great*. Fig. 9-8 shows that the same volume of fluid must pass all points when flowing through the tube. For this to happen, the fluid must move faster through the constriction; and in doing so creates a partial vacuum. Then as the fluid moves on, the speed again decreases. Now, if a tube were connected with one end located in the gasoline, this partial vacuum at B in combination with the atmospheric pressure on the fuel at A would cause the fuel to flow into the air stream.

This constricted tube is known as a *venturi*. In some more complicated carburetors, two or three such venturis are used in order to acquire maximum draw on the fuel jet.

Maintaining the Proper Mixture

The density of the liquid fuel does not change materially with changes of pressure, while air, like all gases, is compressible. The rate of delivery of fuel will vary depending on the pressure, e.g., the velocity at which the fuel leaves the jet varies as the square root of the difference between the jet and the atmospheric pressures. Also, the velocity of the air passing the throat of the carburetor varies as the square root of the pressure difference between the cylinder intake and the atmospheric pressures. The rates of the fuel and air delivery differ because the density of air changes while that of the fuel does not. As a result, as more air flows through the carburetor, the fuel flow also increases but at a much more pronounced rate. So, in a simple carburetor,

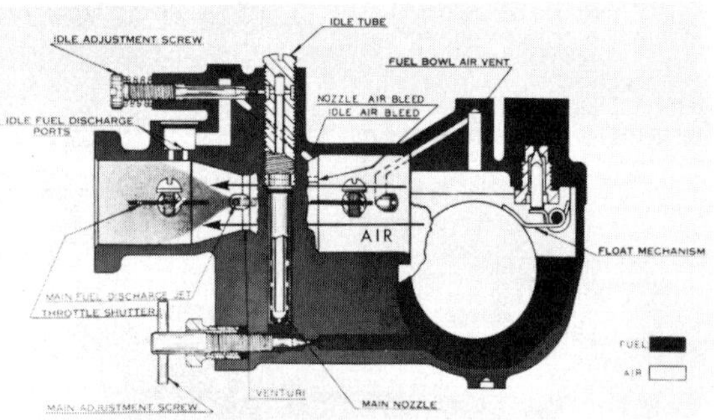

Fig. 9-7. Full Speed Operations of Small Carburetor (Figs. 9-4 to 9-7, Tecumseh)

Throttle butterfly valve is completely open allowing full air flow. The narrow throat (*venturi*) causes increased air speed with lowered pressure. The *main fuel jet* is at point of lowest pressure causing fuel to spray into air stream varying with amount of air flow. At slower speeds more air is drawn through the *nozzle air bleed* allowing the fuel to be metered more freely, as required at less than full speed.

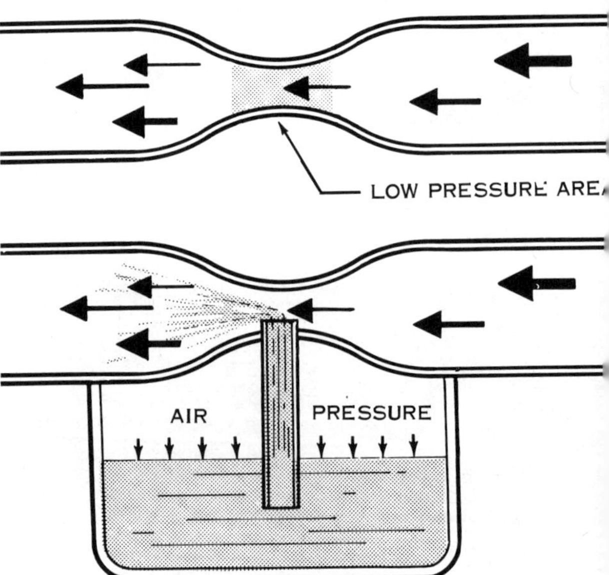

Fig. 9-8. Bernoulli's Principle in a Carburetor

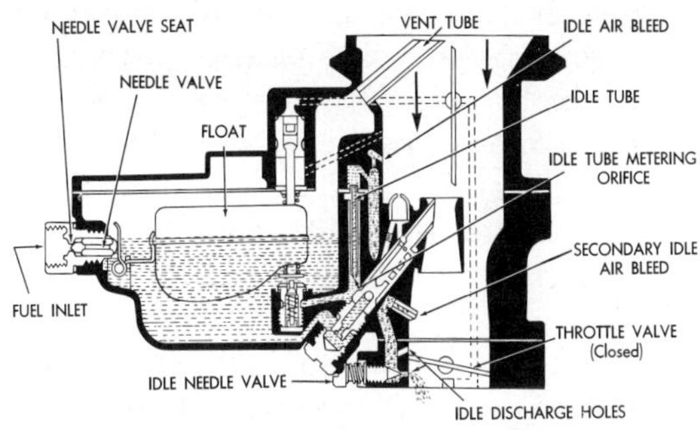

Fig. 9-9. Automotive Carburetor, Idling

When the throttle is closed engine vacuum draws the fuel out of the *lower idling jet.* The *secondary air bleed* aperture causes the fuel to atomize more evenly. The *float* maintains an even fuel level in the chamber.

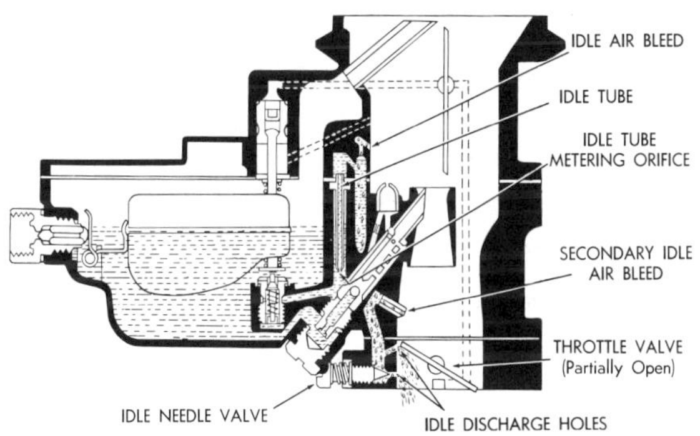

Fig. 9-10. Automotive Carburetor, Quarter Throttle

When the throttle is partially open the fuel is drawn out of *both idling jets.* The engine runs faster and delivers more power.

the mixture would be much too rich under full throttle.

In such a carburetor, the proper proportion of fuel and air will be provided at only one rate of flow. Its idling mixture would then be too lean and its full throttle mixture too rich. Therefore, in a practical carburetor, means must be provided to insure the optimum mixture for all throttle conditions.

In idling conditions, air flow in the venturi is too low to cause a flow of fuel from the main jet, so a special fuel outlet known as the *idling jet* is located with its orifice situated close under the edge of the throttle valve when the valve is closed. The vacuum created by the intake stroke of the cylinders can not pass above the closed throttle, so suction is strong at the *lower idle discharge jet.* See Fig. 9-9 for a typical arrangement. This causes fuel to be drawn from the *float chamber* through an *idle tube* and past the *idle needle valve.* Part of the suction also draws in air, which bubbles into this idle fuel system helping to control the volume of gasoline. This air is drawn in through the *idle air bleed,* and the *secondary idle air bleed* and passes with the fuel out the lower discharge hole.

When the throttle is opened slightly, there is also flow from the upper discharge hole, giving more power and faster idling speeds. See Fig. 9-10. As the throttle valve opens

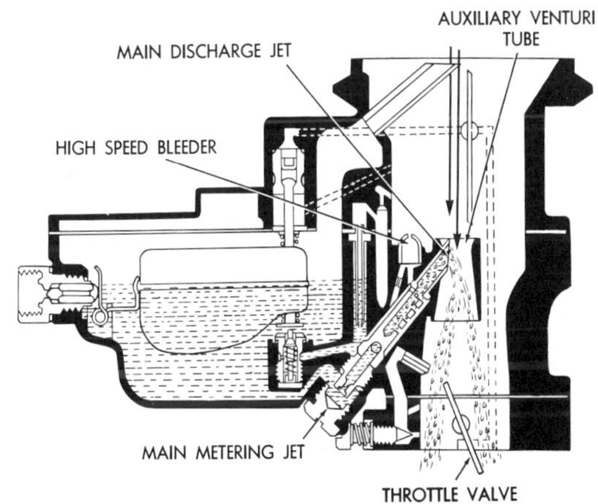

Fig. 9-11. Automobile Carburetor, Half Throttle

Here, the fuel is drawn out the *main discharge jet* giving normal power range.

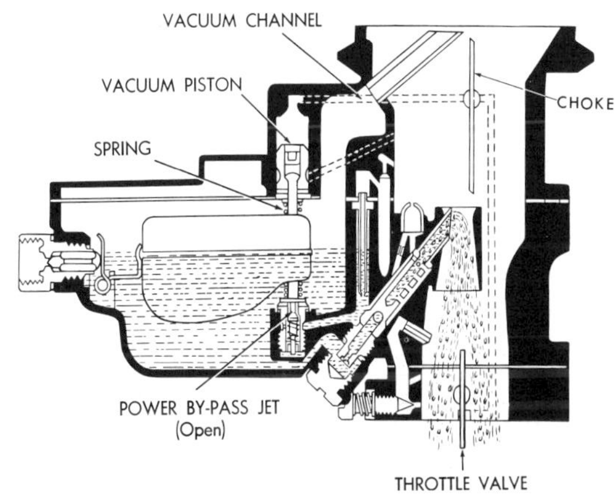

Fig. 9-12. Automotive Carburetor, Full Throttle
(Figs. 9-9 to 9-12, Chrysler)

When the throttle is full open, the *power bypass jet* will deliver maximum fuel.

more and more, there is less difference in pressure above and below the throttle. This causes less air to bleed through the idle jets allowing a gradual increase in fuel flow and power.

At the same time, however, as air begins to flow through the venturi in the throat of the carburetor, fuel begins to flow out of the *main discharge jet.* See Fig. 9-11. This same air flow reduces the suction on the idle discharge holes, reducing all flow in the idle system. Above about quarter throttle the idle system no longer functions, and all fuel comes from the *main jet system.* Unless there is some compensating system the mixture will become too rich at higher throttle settings.

Regulating Fuel-Air Ratio

Several methods have been used to correct unequal increase in delivery of fuel and air.

Air-bleeds are used on the typical carburetor illustrated here, to compensate for the increased richness of mixture. See Figs. 9-10 and 9-11. This system requires a primary venturi, an auxiliary venturi, a main jet, a high speed bleeder, and a secondary or power bypass jet. The *main discharge jet* provides a control of fuel mixture from one-quarter to three-quarters throttle, by permitting a small amount of air to enter the *high-speed bleeder.* Air holes or *bleeder holes* are located in the upper section of the main discharge jet at a point below the level of fuel in the jet. This reduces the surface tension of the fuel and helps fuel to flow at low suction, while at high suction, the resulting turbulence restricts fuel flow through the main jet. When maximum power is demanded, Fig. 9-12, a *vacuum piston* opens the *power bypass* jet which allows fuel to bypass the main metering jet delivering the proper mixture for full power. This gives three separate carburetion systems: idling, part-throttle, and full-throttle.

An *auxiliary air valve* compensated for the unequal increase in delivery rates of fuel and air in the early stages of carburetor development. As the throttle is opened, the engine rpm increases providing greater suction. This increased suction opens a spring loaded auxiliary air valve permitting more air to mix with the increased flow of fuel and providing a better mixture ratio of gas to air.

The *double nozzle* is another method of controlling the mixture throughout the operating range. In addition to the main jet, an *auxiliary jet* provides a constant rate of discharge.

The auxiliary jet is supplied from a standpipe similar in construction to the idle tube of Fig. 9-10. This standpipe receives its fuel from the float chamber. The main jet receives its fuel directly from the float chamber. The top of the standpipe is open and the supply of fuel to it is constant because of the constant level of fuel in the float chamber. The rate of fuel which may be drawn from the auxiliary nozzle will, therefore, be constant. At high engine speeds, the proportion of fuel delivered by the auxiliary jet will be less than at low engine speeds. Therefore, it compensates for the natural tendency of the main nozzle to deliver a rich mixture at high speeds.

Special Carburetion Needs

Several other refinements are necessary in carburetors. The *choke* reduces air intake, producing the richer mixtures required in cold operation. The choke, shown in outline in Fig. 9-12, is a *butterfly* type of valve much like the throttle valve but is near the throat entrance ahead of all fuel nozzles. It may be operated manually by a lever or, on auto matic chokes, by a thermostat.

The *accelerating pump,* Fig. 9-13, gives immediate response for throttle demands for

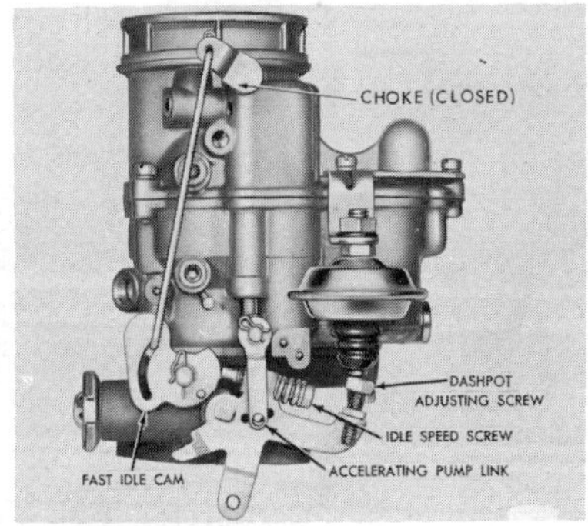

Fig. 9-13. Downdraft Carburetor Showing Adjustments (Ford)

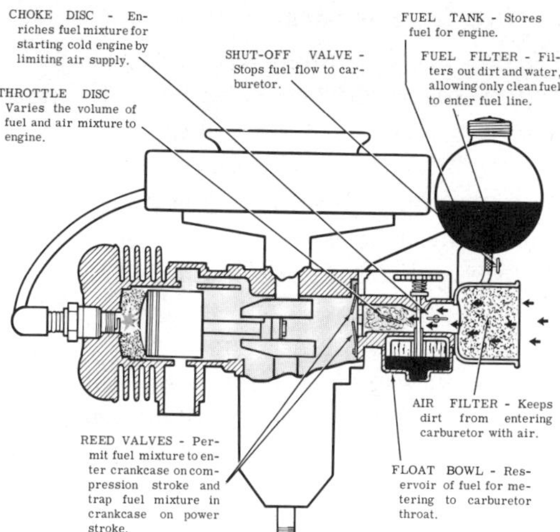

Fig. 9-14. Crossdraft Carburetor on Small Two-Cycle Engine (Lawnboy)

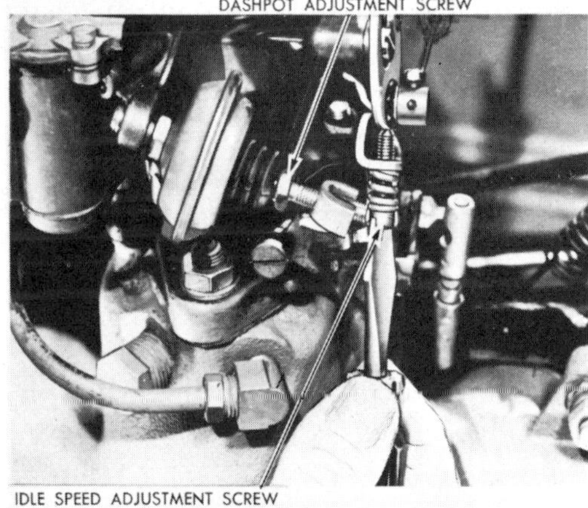

Fig. 9-15. Idle-Speed Carburetor Adjustment (Ford)

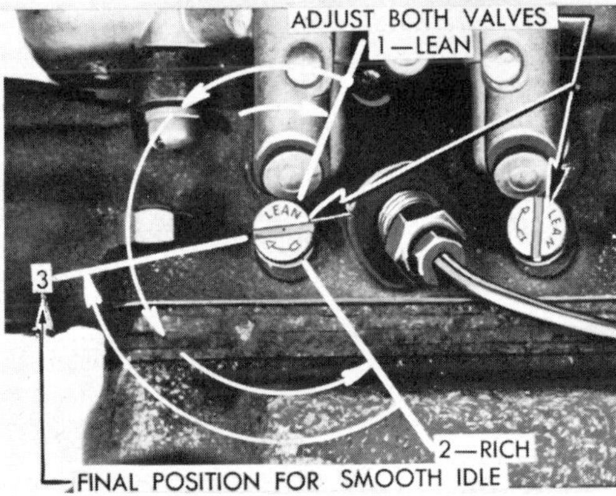

Fig. 9-16. Idle Mixture Adjustment—Four Barrel Carburetor (Buick)

increased power. It consists of a barrel pump which squirts extra fuel into the carburetor throat whenever the throttle setting is increased.

The *dash pot,* Fig. 9-13, is a small air cylinder preventing too fast a return of the throttle to minimum setting. A fast return may cause the engine to stall because the load on the engine (particularly with automatic transmissions) may not diminish at the same rate.

Carburetor Draft

Whether a carburetor is updraft, downdraft, or sidedraft, is determined by where the air enters.

The early carburetors were *updraft* carburetors permitting air to enter through the bottom and exiting with the atomized fuel from the top into the intake manifold. See Fig. 9-3. One disadvantage of this design was that the fuel must be lifted up by air friction. This required a small diameter mixing tube so that the air velocities, even at idling speeds, would be adequate to lift and atomize the fuel. At high speeds, the small tubes restrict the amount of fuel that can be delivered and the maximum potential of the engine is never quite reached.

The *downdraft* carburetor was designed to overcome the limitations of the updraft carburetor. In this design, the air enters through the top and passes with the metered atomized fuel out the bottom into the manifold. See Fig. 9-9 to 9-13. The fuel flow in this situation does not depend on air friction; therefore, the tubes can be larger in diameter. Fuel flow now is not restricted at high engine speeds which allows the engine to easily acquire its potential.

Still another, the *side draft* or *crossdraft* carburetor, is popular in European cars, on stationary plants, and on small utility engines. See Figs. 9-4 to 9-7, and 9-14. These engines usually have the intake manifold cast within the block. An advantage of this unit is that it does away with one right angle turn in manifolding.

Carburetor Adjustments

Today, few carburetor adjustments can be made. Most of these control idling. In the early carburetors, the fuel flow could be controlled through the entire performance range. These required expert manipulations and demanded constant readjustment. Usually today, only idling mixture can be adjusted, see Fig. 9-13.

Before any adjustment is undertaken, the ignition, manifold, and carburetor seals should be checked. The carburetor should be clean and in top operating condition with the float levels properly set.

The *idling speed adjustment* is easily undertaken. Some idle speed adjustment screws are shown in Figs. 9-13, 9-15 and 9-16. It should be done with the engine at operating temperature. It is set for the lowest rpm without causing the engine to falter. Turn the adjustment devices to the extremes and then reset between these points for best idle speed. This specification can be found in manuals and tested with a tachometer. The idle speed screw may work against a *fast-idle cam,* Fig. 9-13. This cam has a raised section giving a faster idling speed whenever a cold engine is being choked.

Idling speed can be adjusted more accurately using a vacuum gauge attached to the intake manifold. The adjusting screw is then turned for the maximum gauge reading.

Many engine condition factors besides idle speed will also effect the amount of intake manifold vacuum, however. Compression ratio, valve conditions, and faster engine speeds will also influence the reading. All readings for tune-up purposes should be done at idling speed.

Multi-Barrel Carburetors

Some automobile manufacturers, to please the more demanding owners, have provided their engines with *two- and four-barrel carburetors.* These are nothing more than two or four separate carburetors contained within a single casing. In this way, each carburetor is required to serve fewer cylinders. The engine usually will respond more quickly and be more powerful because of this feature. In this case, each carburetor must be adjusted as described.

Engine Governors

Most small appliance engines employ an engine speed governor to keep the engine speed at a constant rate under varying load conditions. Speed governors also keep the no-load engine operating speed within safe limits. This rate is determined by the manufacturer and should not be altered by tampering with the governor.

The two most popular governor systems are either *centrifugal* or *pneumatic,* Fig. 9-17.

The *centrifugal or mechanical system,* shown at the left is much like the *flyball governor* invented by Watt and previously discussed. The spring loaded weights are pulled outward by centrifugal force as they rotate. Their movement draws a pin (running through center of the shaft) in or out, closing or opening the throttle through mechanical linkage.

The *pneumatic system,* shown at the right, employs an air vane which is located within the shroud covering the flywheel blower near the flywheel. The engine speed determines the amount of air blown against this vane; the greater the speed the more air, the slower the speed the less air. The vane is connected by mechanical linkage to the throttle.

In both systems, the spring load placed within the linkage is critical and determines the governor setting.

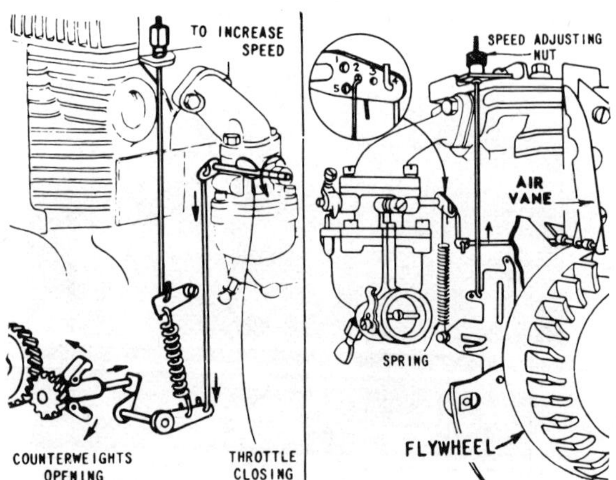

Fig. 9-17. Centrifugal (left) and Pneumatic Governors (Briggs & Stratton)

Fuel Feed Systems

There are several popular methods of getting the fuel from the tank to the carburetor. Some are more complex than others, but all will deliver a constant flow of fuel with certain advantages and limitations. Each system will contain a fuel tank, fuel line and air cleaner. See Fig. 9-18 for a typical arrangement of fuel system parts.

The method employed getting the fuel to the carburetor determines the name of the system: *vacuum, gravity feed, fuel pump,* and *pressurized tanks.*

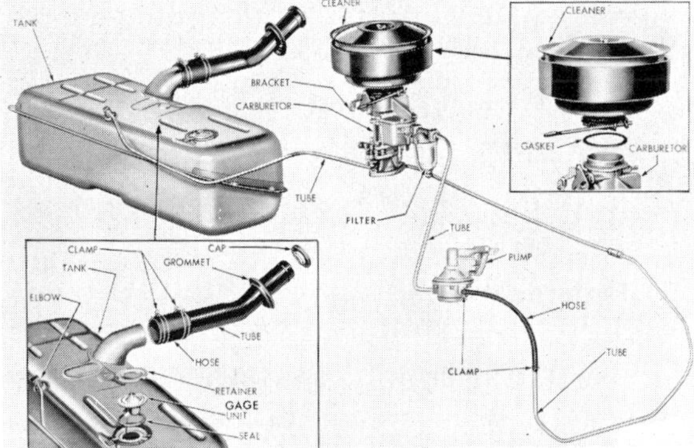

Fig. 9-18. Pumped Fuel Components for Automobile (Chrysler)

Vacuum Systems

The *vacuum system* is the simplest and may be used on small engines. The fuel is located below and close to the carburetor's nozzle or spray bar, Fig. 9-19. Atmospheric pressure forces fuel into the partial vacuum of the venturi. Operation varies some with the level of the fuel in the tank, as fuel flows easier when it must be lifted the lesser distance.

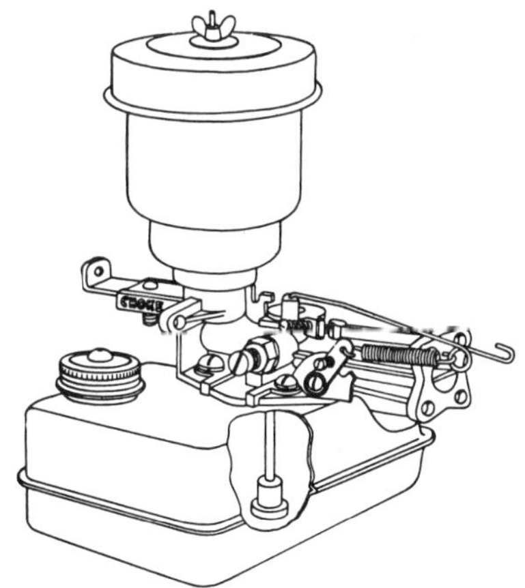

Fig. 9-19. Suction Feed Fuel System (Briggs & Stratton)

Gravity Feed Systems

The *gravity feed system* must have the fuel supply situated above the carburetor. See Fig. 9-14. Some type of metering system must be used to control the flow of fuel and prevent flooding of the carburetor. A float within a float chamber is connected to a valve. As the float moves down, the valve is opened permitting more fuel to flow. When the proper level is reached, the valve is closed. This system operates nicely and adjusts for various conditions rather quickly.

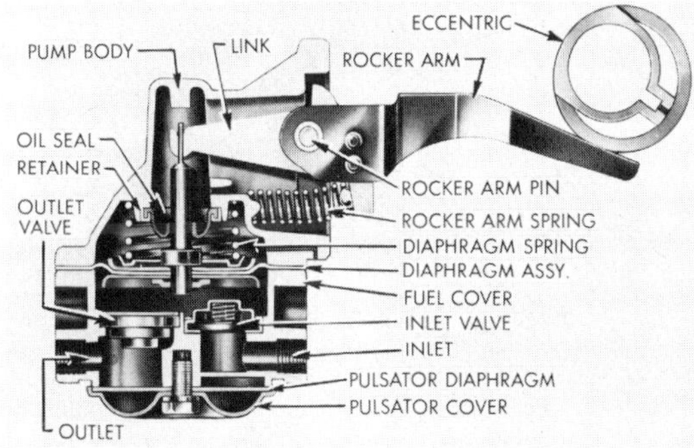

Fig. 9-20. Fuel Pump (Buick)

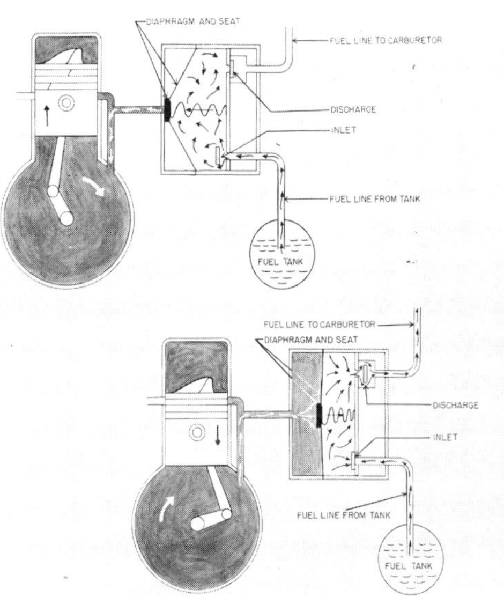

Fig. 9-21. Crankcase-Pressure Fuel Pump (Johnson Motors)

Fuel Pump Systems

The *fuel pump system* is used on most larger engines. In small engines, the fuel tank can be situated above the carburetor's float chamber so fuel is gravity-fed. In larger engines, this is not a popular location for the tank because of the safety factor and the prohibitive size of a 10-20 gallon tank.

A *fuel pump* is employed when the tank is located below the float chamber. See Fig. 9-20. The pump usually is situated in the lower half of the block. Its diaphragm is activated through a *link* by a *rocker arm* riding on a cam on the camshaft. The rocker arm works with a stiff *rocker arm spring* to move a flexible *diaphragm* located at the base of the pump. When the diaphragm moves upward a partial vacuum is created drawing in gas from the fuel line that is connected to the fuel tank. As the diaphragm is returned by the diaphragm spring, the inlet check valve is closed and the trapped fuel is forced through the outlet valve toward the carburetor.

The reason the diaphragm is spring activated is the need to relieve pressure when the carburetor float cuts off the fuel flow even though the pump arm moves continuously. When fuel flow stops, the pressure created by the pump equals the pressure of the spring and, therefore, the diaphragm does not move. A pulsator smooths out the outlet pressure, and the pump output is determined by the amount of fuel needed by the carburetor. Usually there is a glass globe reservoir nearby through which the gasoline can be observed as it goes to the carburetor.

Crankcase pressure operates a fuel pump on some two-stroke cycle engines. See Fig. 9-21. The diaphragm is moved by the changing pressure in the crankcase permitting fuel to be drawn through and forced out *monoflow (check) valves.* These two valves are called the *inlet* and *carburetor valves.*

Pressurized Fuel System

A *pressurized fuel system* is employed in some outboard marine engines to force fuel from a fuel tank which may be located quite a distance from the carburetor. These engines will have two lines located between the engine and the fuel tank—one is for air and the other is for fuel. The entire unit must be air tight so that the air pressure created in the crankcase by the downward moving piston can force the fuel to the carburetor.

Common troubles such as water in the gas line, dirt in the form of sedimentation, and the lack of gasoline can be observed without dismantling any part of the engine by looking in the *glass settling bowl.* If this bowl is removed, it should be reseated properly, usually with a new gasket to insure a perfect seal.

Fuel Injection System[1]

Electronic fuel injection is now available in Volvo and selected Volkswagen cars. Their popularity will prompt the major domestic automobile manufacturers to follow suit and offer such systems in the near future.

An electronic fuel injector system was developed for use in the 1968 Volkswagen's fastback and squareback sedans, Figs. 9-21A and 9-21B. The heart of the system is an electronic control unit, Fig. 9-21C, with more than 200 electronic components, including transistors. It is housed in a small metal case which fits inside the left rear fender of the

[1] Adapted from Werner Buttgereit, Christoph Voges, Christoph Schilter, *Exhaust Emission Control by Fuel Injection: The VW 1600 with Electronically Controlled Fuel Injection System,* SAE, 1967.

Fig. 9-21A. Engine with Electronic Fuel Injector System—Computer at Upper Left (Volkswagen)

vehicle. The electronic control unit determines the amount of fuel to be injected according to engine speed, engine load (intake manifold pressure), and engine temperature.

When the ignition switch is turned on, current is supplied to the control unit via a main relay 3. See Fig. 9-21D. The unit also controls the fuel pump *1* to which current is supplied via pump relay *2* when the engine is operating. The control unit opens the injector valves *6* electrically in pairs – group 1, cylinders 1 and 4; group 2, cylinders 2 and 3. The

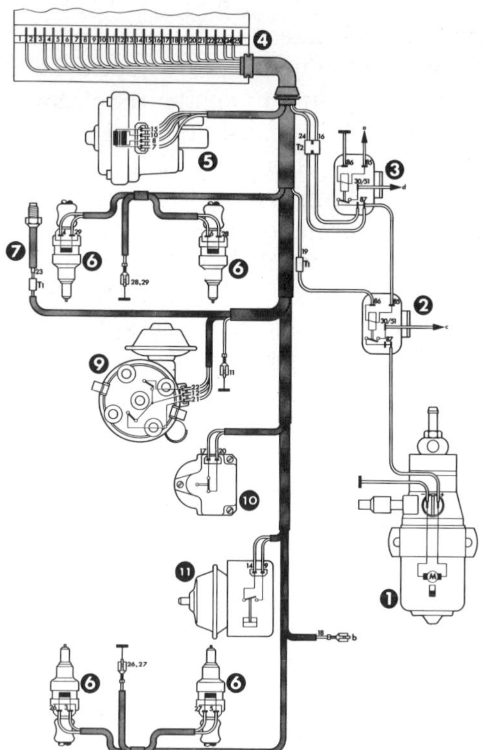

Fig. 9-21D. Schematic of Electronic Fuel Injection System (Volkswagen)

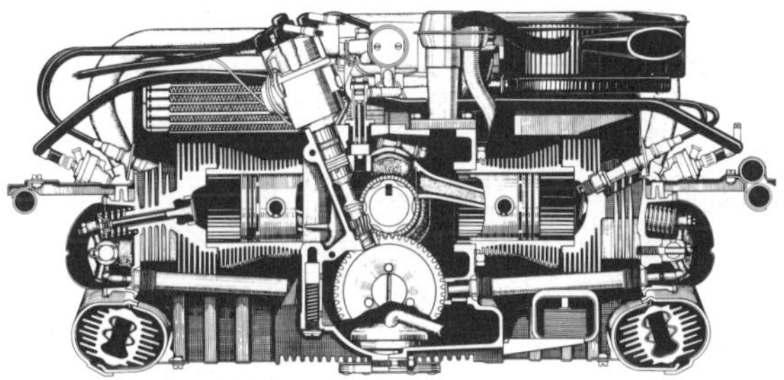

Fig. 9-21B. Cutaway Drawings of Electronic Fuel Injector System Engines (Volkswagen)

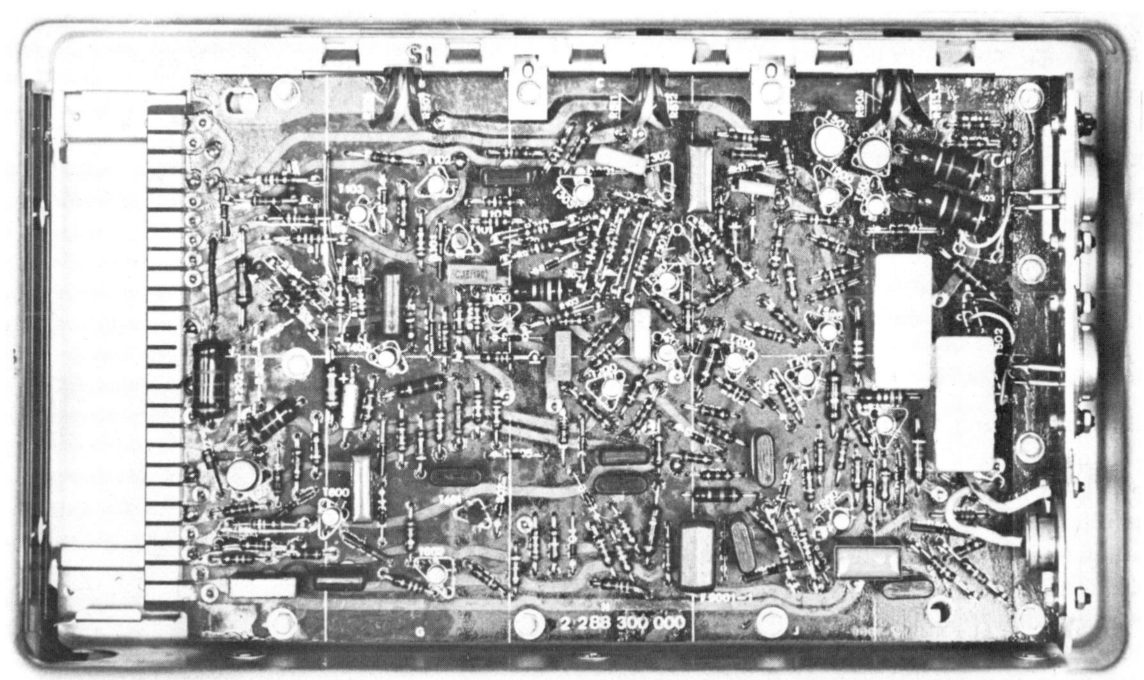

Fig. 9-21C. Cover of Computer Removed to Show Components (Volkswagen)

amount of fuel injected depends upon the length of time the injectors are kept open and is metered according to engine requirements. This is possible because the injectors are under constant fuel pressure. The duration of injection is determined by the control unit, the data or information process being fed by sensing devices mounted on the engine.

The control unit is mounted in the left air duct and is connected by a cable harness to the sender units. These units include: the pressure sensor, *5,* which controls the basic fuel quantity by measuring the intake manifold pressure; the pressure switch, *11,* which controls the fuel enrichment and is operated by the differential between the intake manifold and the ambient air pressure; the temperature sensor one, *8* in the crankcase; and temperature sensor two, *7* in the cylinder head control mixture enrichment for cold starting and during the warming-up period. Trigger contacts, *9,* in the distributor feed a signal to the control unit when and into which cylinder group fuel is to be injected. The throttle switch, *10,* cuts off the supply of fuel on deceleration.

The distributor, which was developed especially for the fuel injection engine, houses the normal contact points and triggering contacts for the cylinder's injectors. Ignition timing on the fuel injection engine is set at 0° top dead center. By choosing the fuel volume as the variable dependent upon the absolute pressure at the intake manifold, the system requires no altitude correction. Variations in barometric pressure, which occur at increased altitude, have no influence on the mixture richness.

Maintenance and Troubleshooting

Except for periodic fuel filter changes, the electronic fuel injection system requires no maintenance. Only normal engine maintenance need be carried out. The life expectancy of each component is at least as long as the life expectancy of the engine itself. To avoid difficulties in troubleshooting, the unit has been developed so that push button checks can be made of all important circuit functions.

Conclusion

Test results show that the electronically controlled fuel injection systems perform their fuel metering and fuel distribution functions so that these engines fully comply with existing gas exhaust standards without need for auxiliary equipment. It is particularly interesting that this result was achieved with full interchangeability of parts. There are no adjustments to be made within injection systems, nor is matching to the individual engine necessary.

Air Cleaner

Before the air is taken into the carburetor and then into the engine proper, it must be cleaned of dust or grime or any abrasive particles that may injure the close fitting parts by abrading them. An air cleaner is provided for this purpose. It usually covers the carburetor air intake and it may be a dry or an oil bath filter. See Figs. 9-22 and 9-23. In any

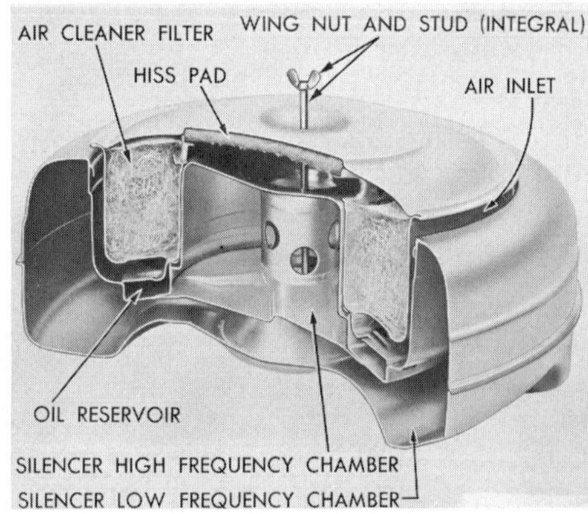

Fig. 9-22. Oil-Bath Type Air Cleaner (Chrysler)

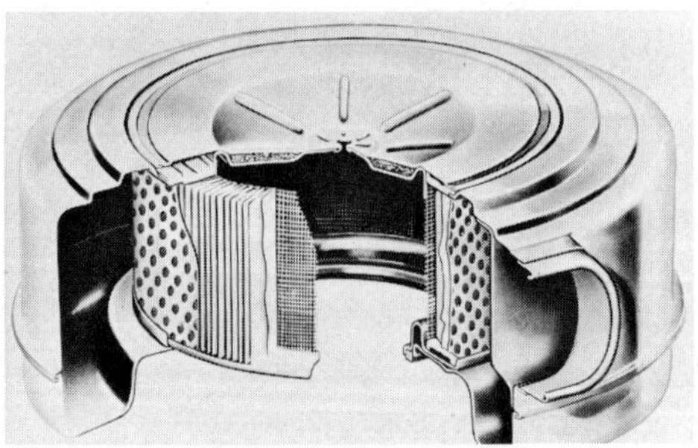

Fig. 9-23. Dry Type Air Cleaner with Replaceable Element (Ford)

case, the filter must be kept clean to insure its proper function and to permit the air to pass through with little resistance. These filters may be cleaned in white gasoline. The oil level in the oil bath air cleaner must be maintained to insure proper air cleaning.

Ignition Systems

The electrical principles employed by the modern gasoline engine are to be discussed more fully in Chapters 10, 16, 17 and 18. We must now describe the necessary ignition units, but their electrical theory will be explained in more detail later.

Breaker Points

Providing the igniting spark is quite a chore for the electrical system, because it must be done with precision and rapidity. For example, a 6-cylinder engine driving a car 60 mph, requires 9,000 igniting sparks per minute or 150 per second must be distributed at just the right instant to each cylinder. To accomplish this, a switching device with breaker points is used. The breaker point cam has a flat for each cylinder, see Figs. 9-24 and 9-25. The breaker points are closed for less than 4.5 thousandths of a second, and on a thousand mile trip they open and close more than 7 million times.

The size of the *gap* between the open points determines how long they will *dwell* or stay closed. The relationship between gap and dwell (cam angle) is shown in Fig. 9-26. Tune-up specifications usually give the gap (.020 to .030″) but it can be set more accurately with a *dwell meter*. Points usually dwell closed about half of the time. Thus the dwell angle would be about 30° for a six-cylinder engine (½ of 360°/6) and about 22½° for eight cylinders.

During the time the points are closed a low-voltage current is building up. The instant the points *open*, the magnetic field caused by the low voltage, collapses. This induces a high-tension current of about 25,000 volts in a secondary winding of a coil having many turns. This high-tension current is carried by a well insulated wire to the spark plug projecting into the cylinder. The current jumps a gap between electrodes at the bottom of the plug and this forms the spark which ignites the fuel-air mixture.

Some spark ignition systems depend on an outside energy source, a *battery*. Others use *a magneto*, a self-contained generator.

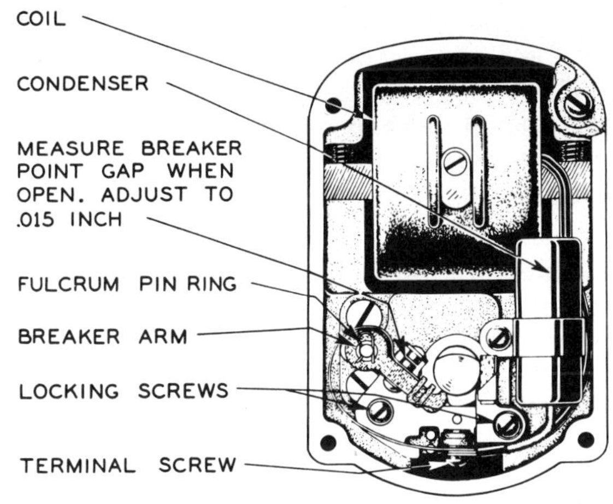

Fig. 9-24. Magneto Distributor Components, Single-Cylinder Engine (Wisconsin Motors)

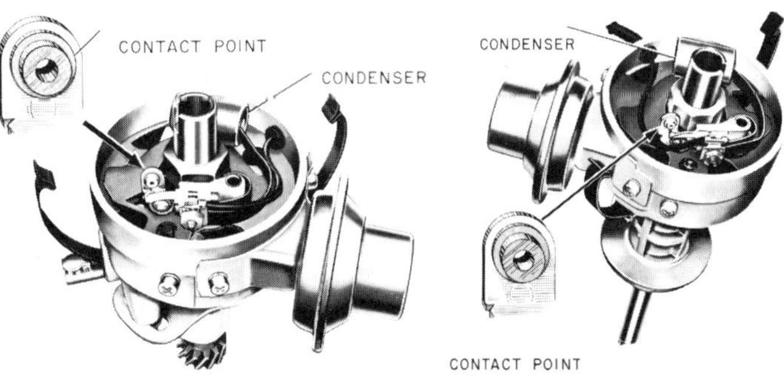

Fig. 9-25. Distributor Components, Six-Cylinder (left) and Eight-Cylinder (Dodge)

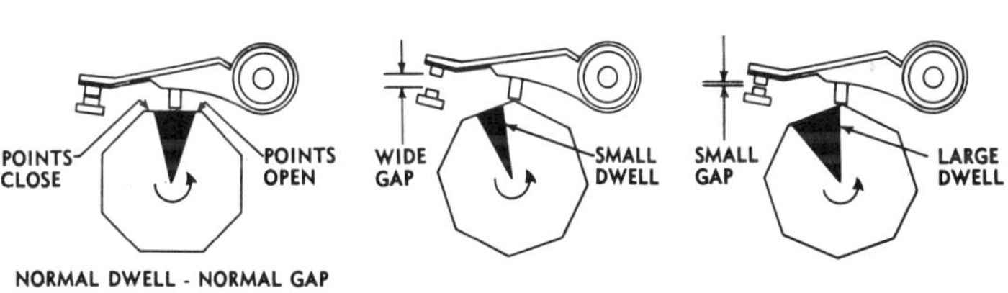

Fig. 9-26. Breaker Point Gap, Dwell and Cam Angle (Slep Electronics)

Magneto Ignition Systems

The most simple device for generating the igniting spark is the magneto. There are basically two types of magnetos: the *low-tension type* which generates a low voltage that must be then stepped up or multiplied by a separate coil; and the *high-tension type* which generates and steps-up voltage without the assistance of an external coil.

The difference between a magneto and a generator is that the generator has an *electro-magnetic* field requiring an *outside* source of electricity to excite it. Magnetos use *permanent magnets* for this field. Some telephone systems have used low-tension magnetos to ring the bell.

Advantages of Magneto Systems

There are several advantages of the magneto ignition systems as compared to the battery-demanding systems. First of all, they are more portable and lighter because they do not require a battery. Secondly, they provide a spark that is hotter as the engine speed increases. Newer magnetic alloys have greatly increased and improved their performance.

Principles of Operation

A flow of electricity can be generated if a conductor or wire is caused to move through a magnetic field. If either the coil or the field is *revolving* the current flow *alternates.* That is, the current gradually builds up in one direction, falls off, builds up in the opposite direction, and falls off again. This *cycle* (shaped like a sine curve) is repeated each revolution. This output has the same form as an AC generator, but usually does not have enough current for lights or other accessories. Generation theory will be explained in Chapter 18. Magnetos use a strong permanent magnet and a coil made of many turns of finely wound wire to generate current. The movement necessary to cause the wire to cut the magnetic field can be obtained in three ways. If the *coil revolves* in the magnetic field, it is known as the *shuttlewound magneto.* If the *permanent magnet rotates,* it is known as the *revolving magnet magneto.* In a rotary *inductor magneto,* both the magnet and coil are in stationary positions, and the movement of the magnetic field is made by making or breaking the magnetic field. This may produce a *pulsating* current.

Low-Tension Magnetos

The earliest type of magneto was the low-tension shuttle-wound magneto. It still is popular on industrial engines, see Fig. 9-27. A U-shaped magnet has the primary coil revolving between its poles. This armature also has the breaker points revolving with it, and they are timed to open the circuit at the peak voltage of a cycle. The *breaking* of the primary current produces a high tension current in the secondary winding of the coil. This current is then directed through the distributor to the proper spark plug.

The breaker points can be connected either in series or parallel with the armature as shown in Fig. 9-28. In the series hook-up, the magneto simply serves as a low current

Fig. 9-27. Low-Tension Magneto

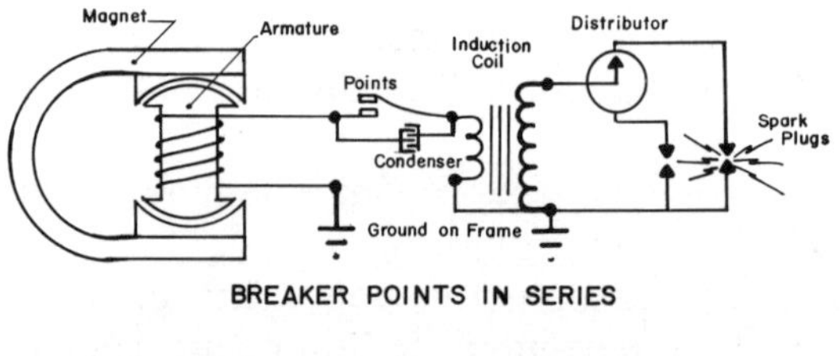

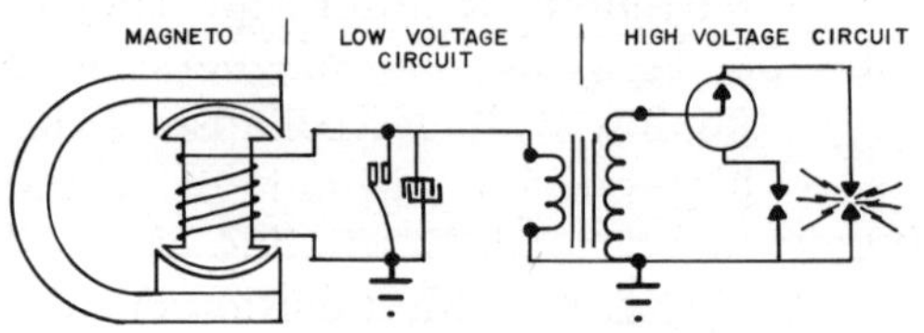

Fig. 9-28. Low-Tension Magneto Circuits

source, because the resistance of the primary is included in the circuit. In the parallel (or shunt) hook-up the resistance of the primary is not constantly in the circuit permitting a heavier build up of current flow. When the breaker points are opened, the high current surging through the primary produces a high inductive effect.

Conventional High-Tension Magnetos

The conventional magneto is a high-tension shuttle-wound magneto which needs no external induction coil to step up the voltage. The primary and secondary windings are wound one over the other and form the armature that is rotated within the magnetic field. As the electricity is generated by their rotation, breaker points (which are shunted across the primary winding) open and induces a current in the secondary winding. Because of the greater number of turns in the secondary, the voltage is increased. This voltage is taken off of the rotating armature on a collector ring and directed through the distributor to the correct spark plug.

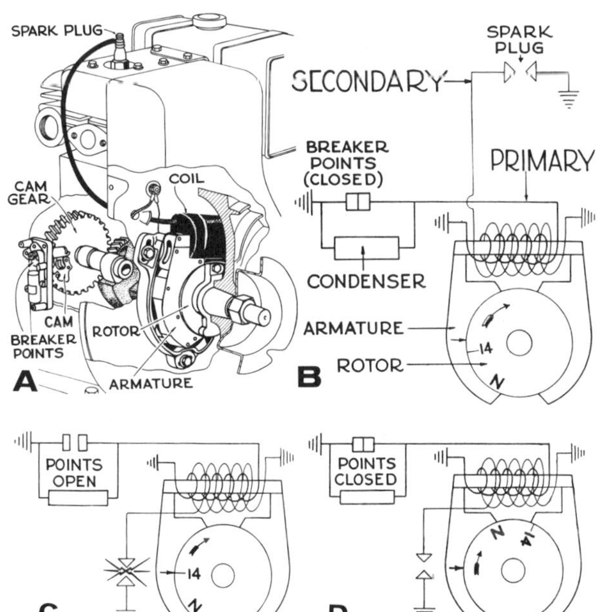

Fig. 9-29 Revolving-Magnet Magneto Ignition System (Briggs & Stratton)
B, C and D show timing sequence as N pole passes armature segment.

Sometimes a portion of the primary is rotated while the balance of the primary, the secondary, breaker points, and condenser are stationary. The rotating primary on the armature is connected by a collector ring to the stationary primary, and the circuit is completed through the breaker points to the ground.

Rotary Inductor Magnetos

This type of magneto has both the magnet and coil in a stationary position. Electricity is induced in the primary by breaking and perhaps reversing one or both ends of the magnetic circuit. When one end of the magnetic field is simply broken, the energy induced in the coil varies from maximum to minimum but does not reverse or alternate direction.

Revolving Magnet Magnetos

Since the advent of better magnetic alloys, the revolving magnet magneto has virtually replaced the conventional magnetos. This design is more simplified, sturdier with less moving parts, easier to maintain, and is more compact and lighter because the *coil*, *condenser*, and *breaker points* are stationary. See Fig. 9-29. Note that the *armature* is also stationary and has two segments which are semicircular extensions of the laminated steel core in the coil.

The magnet turning in the *rotor* causes the stationary primary winding to cut its field twice for each revolution. This is done as each end of the magnet passes a segment of the armature. Because of this, an alternating current is induced to flow in the primary each time the breaker points are closed completing the circuit.

The intensity of the induced current is greatest each time a complete reversal of magnetic flux occurs. This timing is shown at B, C and D in Fig. 9-29. As the N magnetic pole approaches the armature segment (B) the current induced in the primary envelops the secondary with a magnetic field. At the moment of highest intensity (timing marks align as at C), the breaker points are caused to open, breaking the primary circuit. This causes the surrounding field to collapse, inducing a high-tension voltage in the secondary because of its greater number of winding. The high voltage is directed to the proper spark plug through the distributor. There are about 100 times more turns in the secondary winding. At D, the N pole is leaving the armature, completing half of the cycle, and the points are already closed in preparation for the next firing.

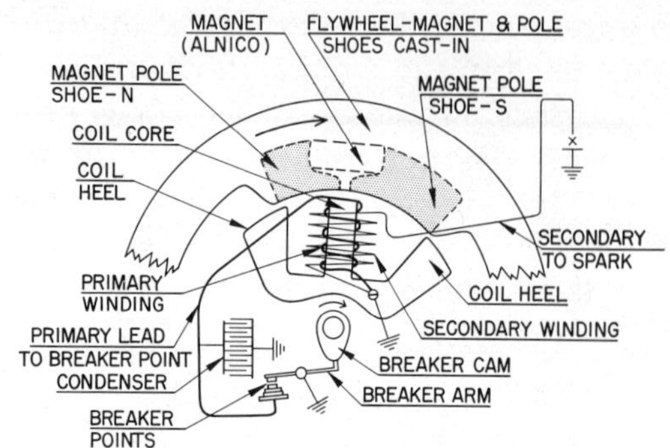

Fig. 9-30. Flywheel Magneto (Johnson Motors)

Flywheel Magnetos

Small gasoline engines used on lawn mowers, garden tractors, generators, pumps, and so on, use a flywheel magneto. This is simply an integral revolving-magnet magneto built into the flywheel or flywheel shaft. In a typical arrangement, shown in Fig. 9-30, the magnet is cast in the flywheel and revolves around the rest of the magneto as the flywheel rotates.

The Condenser

The condenser that is shunted across the breaker points in all of these circuits absorbs the self-induced voltage caused by the collapsing magnetic field. This, in essence, promotes a more rapid collapse of the primary field and prevents arcing which will cause pitting and rapid deterioration of the breaker points. In electronics, the condenser is now called a capacitor, but the name and its symbol have not changed in engine usage.

High-Tension Safety Gap

In the high-tension magneto, it is necessary to provide the secondary winding with a safety gap. This protects the secondary wire insulation from excessive voltage in the event the wire should be disconnected from the spark plug causing an incomplete circuit. The voltage then would jump the safety gap and relieve the strain on the secondary insulation.

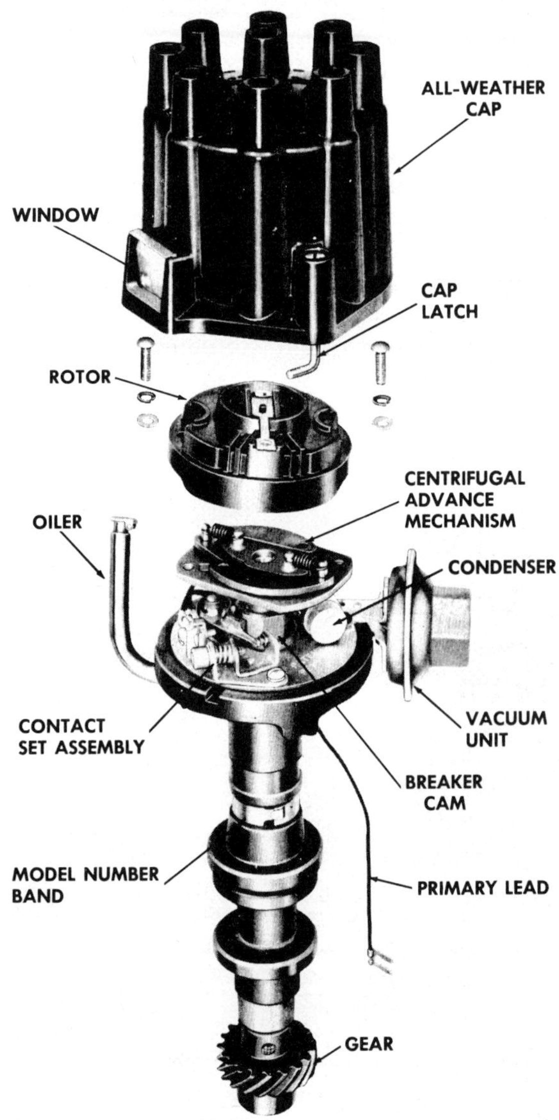

Fig. 9-31. Distributor Components for Eight-Cylinder Engine (Delco-Remy)

Spark Advance

In either a magneto system or a battery ignition system, the ignition spark must fire earlier (be advanced) with higher engine

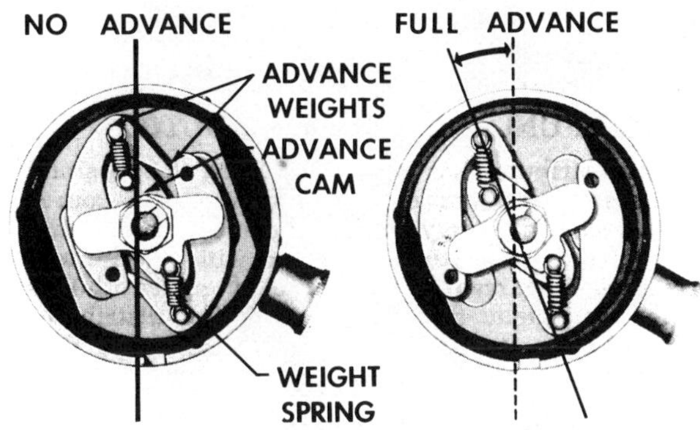

Fig. 9-32. Centrifugal Advance Mechanism (Delco-Remy)

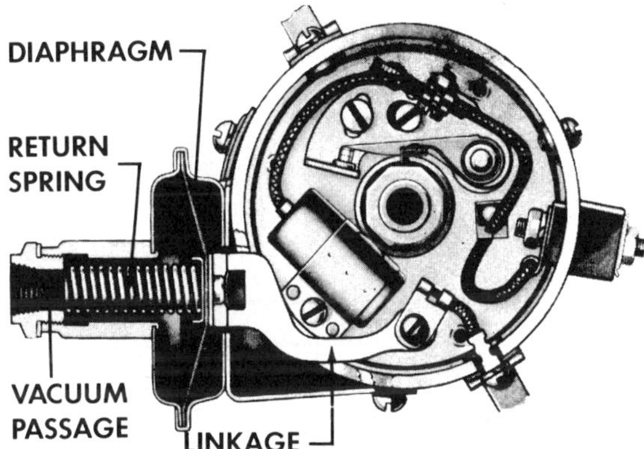

Fig. 9-33. Vacuum Advance Mechanism (Delco-Remy)

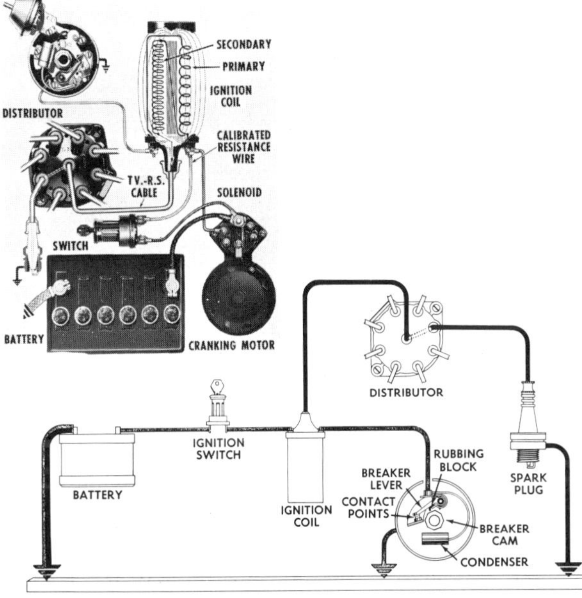

Fig. 9-34. Battery Ignition System (Delco-Remy)

loads and speeds. Because the breaker points control the spark, the timing can easily be accomplished by advancing or delaying the time of their opening. This is done by rotating the mounting for the points. The amount of advance or retard is limited because the intensity of the spark decreases rapidly as the points are timed for other than when maximum current is built up in the primary.

Once it was necessary to advance the spark manually after starting the engine, and perhaps even more for higher throttle settings. Now, automatic advance is standard. This is done either centrifugally or by vacuum. Often there is a combination of these systems as in the distributor shown in Fig. 9-31. The *centrifugal advance* has two weights under spring tension similar to centrifugal governors. These weights swing outward at higher speeds, advancing the breaker cam on its driveshaft, as shown in Fig. 9-32. The *vacuum advance* uses suction from the intake manifold to slightly rotate the entire distributor mechanism, thus advancing the points on the cam as in Figs. 9-33 and 9-34. The vacuum advance is more effective at idling and slow speeds while the centrifugal advance gradually increases according to the cam shape required by engine characteristics.

Distributor

The distributor is in the high-voltage cir- Figs. 9-31 and 9-34, which channels the timed high-tension surge of electricity to the correct spark plug. Several of these figures show a distributor for an eight-cylinder engine. There are eight lobes on the breaker cam, and sockets for eight spark plug wires. The metal finger on the rotor carries the charges from the coil wire at the center of the cap to the circle of sockets around it.

Battery Ignition Systems

The battery ignition system finds popularity where a battery is available to provide electrical energy to start the engine. In the modern automobile, the battery also powers other conveniences, such as radio, heater, and lights. This system employs a low-voltage and a high-voltage circuit similar to the magneto systems previously mentioned. See Fig. 9-34. A generator keeps the battery charged.

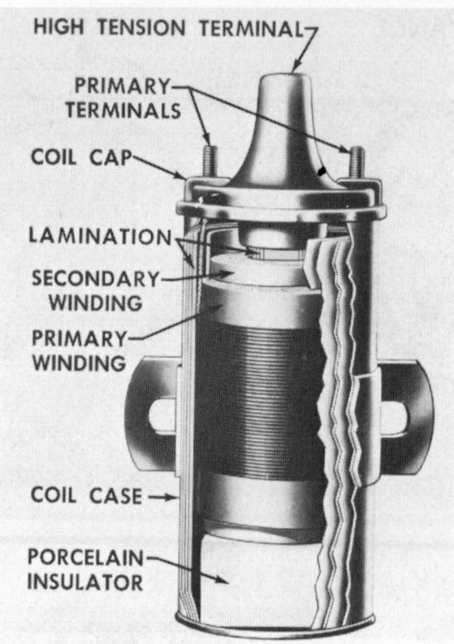

Fig. 9-35. Ignition Coil

Ignition Coil

The ignition coil has two windings on a single core of laminated steel. The low voltage current from the battery flows through the primary windings producing a surrounding magnetic field. The secondary winding is under the primary, and has many thousands of turns of fine wire. See Fig. 9-35. The primary circuit is broken by the breaker points opening just as the cylinder reaches top dead center of its power stroke. This causes the magnetic force to collapse around the secondary, inducing a much greater voltage than in the primary. This high voltage is then directed to the proper spark plug by the distributor. The only major difference in this and the magneto system is the voltage source. Here, a battery furnishes the low voltage.

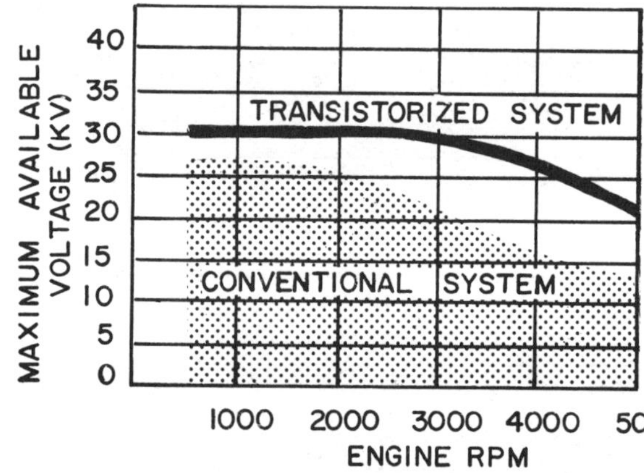

Fig. 9-36. Transistor Ignition holds Better Voltage at High Speeds

Transistor Ignition Systems

Today the industry is testing the potential of *transistorized* ignition systems. These replace or aid the conventional breaker points with a semiconductor electronic switching device which has no moving parts. Several advantages have been claimed: (1) more current is made available to fire the plugs, Fig. 9-36; (2) breaker point deterioration and malfunction are minimized or eliminated; (3) the troublesome condenser is removed.

Transistorized ignition (TI) systems are slow in being adopted as standard on cars, but TI is offered as an *option* by most car manufacturers. If TI follows the same acceptance pattern as the alternator (its immediate predecessor in major changes) it will first be offered as costly options. Then eventually it will become standard equipment as the market broadens and individual cost decreases. Presently there are many independent manufacturers of transistorized ignition kits for both 6 and 12 volt systems. These companies offer kits from $25 to $125, depending on the type and complexity. See Fig. 9-37.

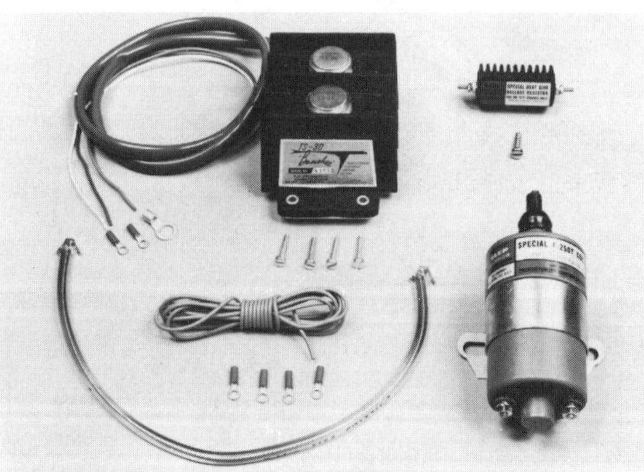

Fig. 9-37. Transistorized Ignition Kit (Slep Electronics)

Conventional ignition systems are finding it hard to keep pace with the increasing engine speeds, higher compression ratios and engine temperatures. Today, systems have been developed to a point where maximum performance nearly has been reached. Engine manufacturers are demanding something better. Conventional ignition systems produce 300 to 400 sparks per second, any demand beyond this point results in point bounce and ignition breakdown. Some TI systems show no appreciable breakdown below 530 sparks per second. An engine with transistorized ignition is capable of achieving even more than 8,000 rpm without ignition breakdown. This simply means there is enough ignition to fire plugs at much faster speeds. For this reason many *racing vehicles* are being converted to TI.

Breaker points in conventional systems deteriorate under high currents and must be replaced every 10,000 miles. In fact, with the condenser, the points are one of the most important replacements of any tune-up job. Full primary voltage and current pass through the points. This causes an oxide to form on the contact surfaces as well as deep pitting, thus impeding current flow. The result is that shortly after tune-up, less current and voltage is made available to the plugs resulting in progressively poorer starting and engine performance. Thus, *longer consistent service* is the reason truckers, fleet owners, and average car buyers consider TI.

The transistorized systems eliminate erosion of the points and blurring of the switching function because 90 percent of the current flow is controlled by the power transistor. Breaker points in most cases use only 10 percent of the primary current to switch the power transistor on or off. Although this lesser amount of current greatly increases breaker point life, the gap still must be set periodically to allow for wear of the rubbing block. Some users have reported that breaker points have lasted 60,000 miles with consistently good performance. And as firing is cleaner, it is also claimed that spark plugs can last this long.

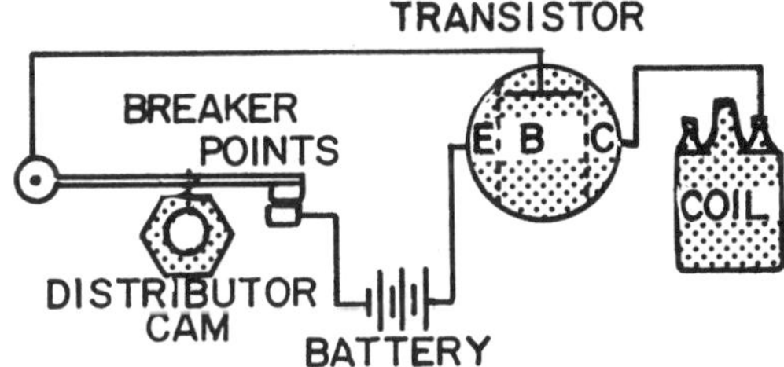

Fig. 9-38. Simplified Diagram of a Regular Contact-Controlled Transistorized System

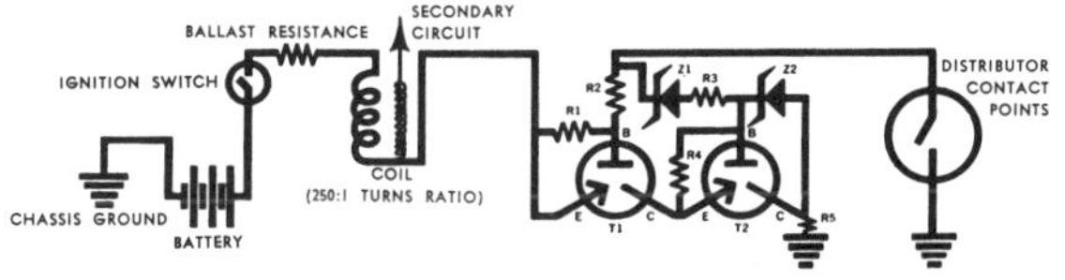

Fig. 9-39. Typical Contact-Controlled Transistor Circuit (Slep Electronics)

Fig. 9-39. Typical Contact-Controlled Transistor Circuit (Slep Electronics)

When contact points close, a small current activates the base (B) of both transistors (T_1, T_2) so current will flow through them (E to C). This completes the primary circuit of the coil. When it is interrupted, high voltage flows in the secondary winding of the coil. Zener diodes (Z_1, Z_2) protect the transistors from any surges of reverse current flow. The five resistors (R) reduce various paths of current flow so the correct relationship exists between bases and emitters.

Transistorized Systems

There are three types of transistorized systems in use: the regular *contact-controlled system*, the *capacitor-discharge system* and the *magnetic-pulse system*.

Transistorized ignition systems consist of a distributor without a condenser, a high voltage coil—similar to conventional ones but with a different turns ratio (250:1 or more), a ceramic ballast necessary only for 12 volt systems, and a transistorized package made up of special power transistors enclosed in a specially designed heat sink made of aluminum. A typical kit is shown in Fig. 9-37.

Contact-Controlled System

In a regular contact-controlled transistorized ignition system, the transistor takes over the role of the distributor breaker points. The points are used only to trigger the *base* (*B*) or switching element of the transistor, Fig. 9-38. Thus, breaker points handle only 2/10 to 8/10 ampere as compared to the 4 or 5 amperes of conventional ignition systems. When the points are closed, the base is electronically triggered so that full primary current flows from the battery, across the *emitter* (*E*) to the *collector* (*C*), around the primary windings and back to the battery through a ground connection. The high tension current is taken as usual from the center terminal of the coil, through the distributor rotor and to the individual spark plugs. Fig. 9-38 has been simplified to show the basic principle. Fig. 9-39 shows an actual wiring diagram of a $40 kit producing a 30,000 volt spark. By using 400:1 or 500:1 coils (at extra cost) the output can be increased to 45 kv or 55 kv (a kv is 1000 volts). This higher voltage could increase high-speed performance but probably at the expense of burning spark plugs at slower speeds. It is important that positive and negative connections are not reversed to the transistor unit.

Capacitor-Discharge System

The *capacitor-discharge system* is a variation of the contact-controlled system. It is especially capable of firing badly gapped or fouled plugs.

This system is a regular contact-controlled system with additional parts as shown in Fig. 9-40. These units increase the voltage with a second coil and stores it in a capacitor, for use the instant the spark is needed. The system is installed in addition to the conventional systems. By reversing the connector plug, the conventional system can be used normally, providing a spare ignition system. This is especially useful if an electron tube should burn out.

Fig. 9-41 shows that the circuit to the left of the T_2 transformer is similar to most transistor systems. The added components at the right, a rectifier tube (V_1), a capacitor (C_1), and a thyratron gas tube (V_2) build up a greater current surge yielding a hotter spark.

Magnetic-Pulse System

The *magnetic-pulse distributor system* is currently made by only two companies. It employs a magnetic distributor that does away with the conventional breaker points entirely.

The magnetic distributor resembles any standard distributor on the outside. Inside is

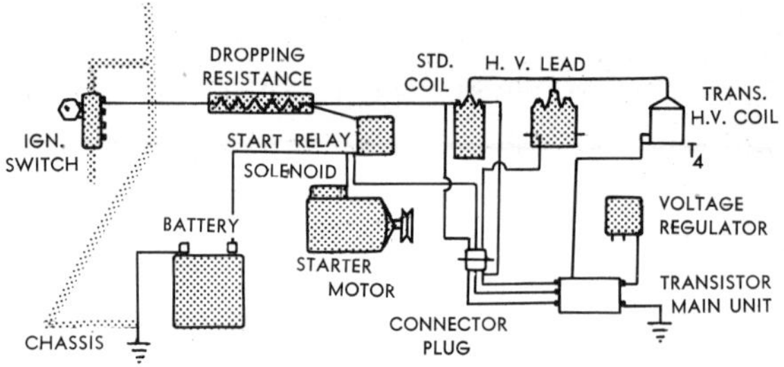

Fig. 9-40. Capacitor-Discharge Ignition
(Tung-Sol)

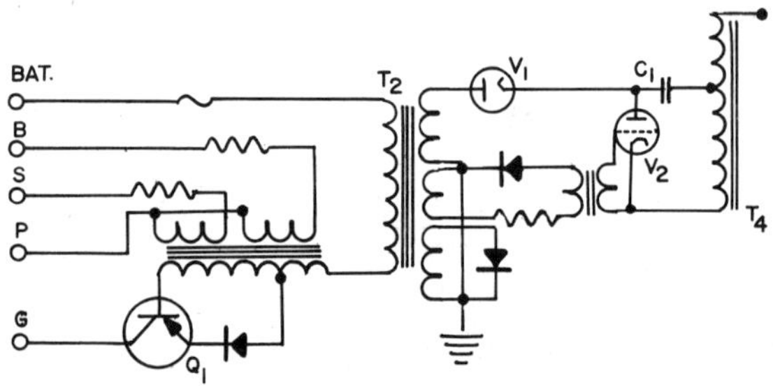

Fig. 9-41. Capacitor-Discharge Circuit
(Tung-Sol)

The circuit begins to function as the points open. Current then flows through the primary of the transformer T_2 building up a magnetic field. When the points close, the primary flow stops and the field collapses, inducing a high voltage in the secondary. This voltage is transferred through a rectifier tube (V_1) to the capacitor (C_1), where it is stored until the points open again. During the next cycle a portion of the secondary voltage is applied to the grid of the thyratron tube (V_2) causing it to conduct. The energy previously stored in the capacitor is then discharged through the thratron to the plugs through the coil T_4. The rectifier tube acts as a check valve preventing this discharge from flowing back to T_2 or interferring with the incoming surge being built up.

a different story, Fig. 9-42. Instead of the familiar cam and breaker plate assembly, the unit has a rotating pole piece within a stationary magnet and a coil which picks up the current pulses generated.

The pole pieces each have a number of equally spaced teeth—one for each cylinder. As the distributor shaft rotates and the rotating projections pass the stationary ones, the magnetic field alternately builds up and collapses. Thus a pulsing voltage is induced in the pickup coil at each passing.

Each voltage pulse is conducted to the ignition pulse amplifier where it switches *on* a triggering transistor (T_1), eventually causing the actual switching transistor (T_3) to cut *off*. This action stops current flow thru the ignition coil primary causing the coil to fire the plug. The switching transistor returns to an "on" condition, permitting the coil current to build up again for the next cycle.

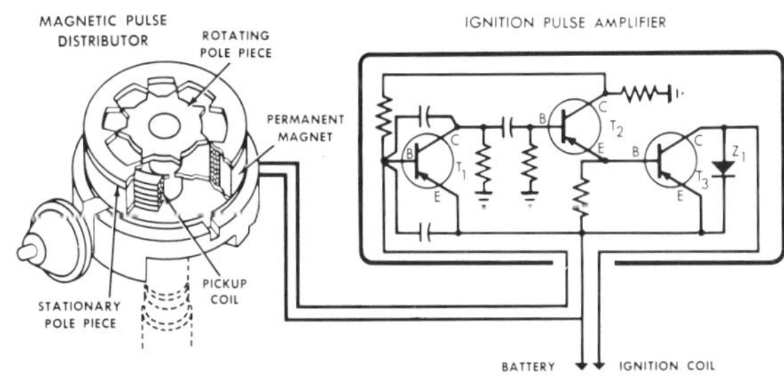

Fig. 9-42. Magnetic-Pulse Ignition (Delco-Remy)

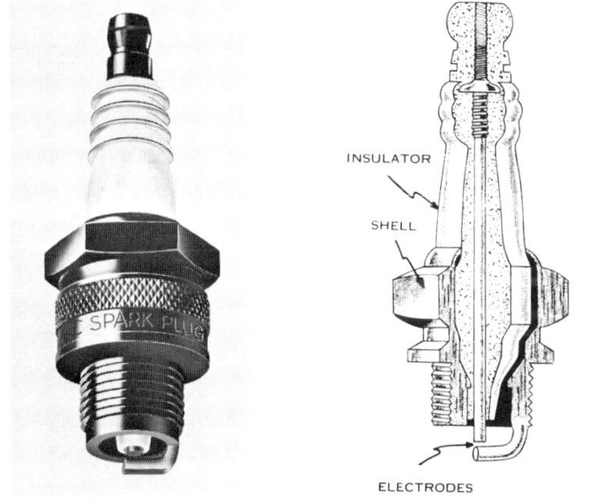

Fig. 9-43. Spark Plug (G.M.)

Installation

Transistor ignition kits can be easily installed with simple tools in an hour or so. Instructions must be followed implicitly. There is one important caution, and that is to avoid overheating the transistors. Transistors do not function properly in temperatures exceeding 170°. At this temperature their life span is decreased immeasurably. Therefore, if the engine runs extremely hot, or if an air conditioning unit is under the hood, it may be best to install the transistor unit under the dash inside the car.

Spark Plugs

The spark plug is a device that provides a gap through which the high tension voltage can jump, causing ignition of the compressed fuel in the combustion chamber. See Fig. 9-43.

The central electrode of the spark plug is connected to the high tension lead from the secondary coil through the distributor rotor. A second electrode, the ground, is attached to the threaded shell. A molded insulator, resembling porcelain, covers all but the ends of the central electrode. This gap between electrodes ranges from .020 to .040 of an inch and can be adjusted by bending the ground or second electrode.

The spark plug gap varies with the engine specifications. The larger gap provides better ignition because it will combust more of the compressed mixture. However, some electrical systems will not fire consistently if the gap is made too large, or if the compression ratio is too high. Understanding this, the manufacturer's recommendation should be followed when setting the gap of a spark plug. At one time, .025 of an inch was standard, but today, with better materials and electrical systems, the larger gaps are finding popularity. The threaded shell permits easy removal and comes in the following thread sizes: ½″ pipe thread, ⅞″ pipe thread, 10 mm, 14 mm, and 18 mm.

Plug Voltage

The voltage necessary to cause a spark to jump the electrode gap depends on the distance between the electrodes, the shape of the electrodes, the cleanliness of the electrodes, the compression ratio, the conductivity of the mixture, and the temperature of the engine.

If the plug is dirty, some of the induced voltage may be lost because it takes an appreciable time for sufficient voltage to build up in order to jump the gap. This can easily be understood if we reflect on how the high tension voltage was induced. The primary circuit surrounds the secondary coil with a magnetic field. This field was made to collapse by opening the circuit at the breaker points. This will induce a high tension voltage in the secondary winding of the coil which grows from zero to its maximum and then back to zero. The entire cycle may take only .020 of a second. The voltage capable of jumping the gap is gradually built up, and if any foreign matter is permitted to collect at the plug electrodes, this voltage will leak off causing no spark or an inefficient spark. The loss of peak voltage across the gap can be prevented by keeping the plugs clean and properly set.

Plug Characteristics

The spark plug must be of correct length in order to extend into the combustion chamber correctly. See Fig. 9-44. The engine manufacturer specifies the proper length of the spark plug. If the plug is too long, it may be damaged by the rising piston and, if it is too short, its electrodes may be shielded by the surrounding head, resulting in misfiring.

Spark plugs can be purchased for various *heat ranges*. See Fig. 9-45. *Hot plugs* extend further into the combustion chamber and because of their additional length, become hot more rapidly and stay hot. This is due to the fact that the heat of combustion is caused to travel a greater distance up the shell (and electrode) before it is dissipated in the head and in the water jacket. If the engine is to run at slow to moderate speeds for short periods of time, a hot plug may be desirable.

If the engine is to run for long periods of time under full load, a *cold plug* is needed. Cold plugs have short shells to facilitate cooling by the head and water jacket.

If the improper sized plug is used, *pre-ignition* may occur because of the hot plug being used steadily under load. Cold plugs tend to foul because they cannot burn off carbon and other deposits as efficiently as they should. The manufacturer's recommendations are based on the fuel used and the work performed by a particular engine.

Plug Fouling

As was indicated, the proper type of plug will remain just hot enough to burn off any deposits of lead or carbon that would cause fouling, and yet not hot enough to cause pre-ignition. Some common operating conditions are shown in Fig. 9-46.

A black soot on the electrodes of a spark plug indicates *carbon deposits*. If these deposits are heavy, they will cause the engine to miss or run roughly. Usually, carbon fouling is the result of a running of the engine for long periods of time at very slow speeds or a running of the engine with too rich a mixture. Adjusting the speed and mixture of

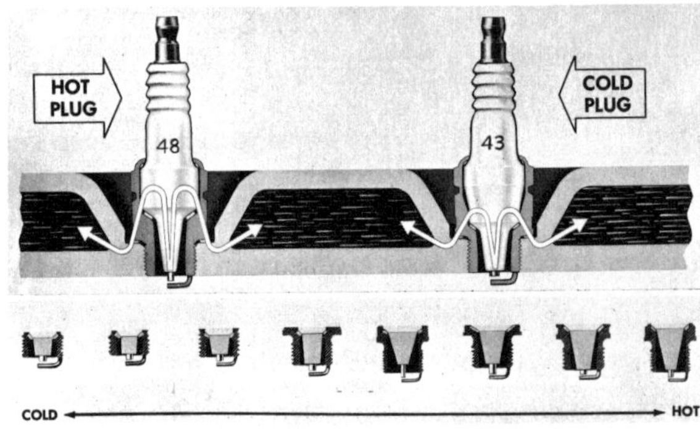

Fig. 9-45. Spark Plug Heat Ranges (G.M.)

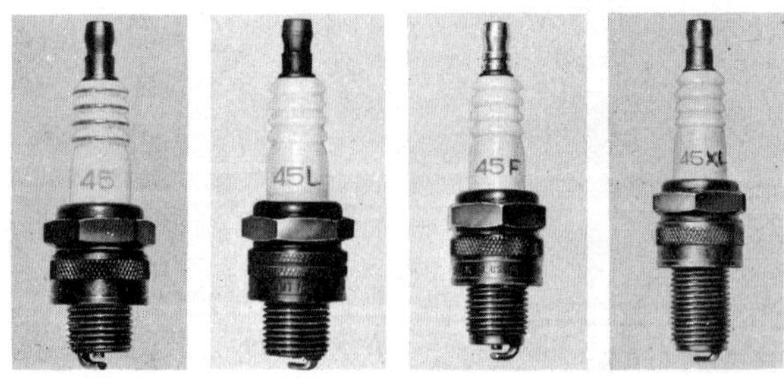

Fig. 9-44. 14 mm Spark Plugs with 3/8", 7/16" 1/2" and 3/4" Reaches (G.M.)

the engine or using a hotter plug will remedy this problem.

Lead deposits will appear as a crust of tiny globules depending on the fuel, operating conditions, and running time. Lead deposits are caused by the tetraethyl lead used in the fuel to prevent engine knocking at high speeds. Lead fouling will permit the engine to run smoothly at slow to moderate speeds, but at high speeds, it will cause missing to occur. This happens because the higher running temperatures melt the lead deposits which then provide a path of least resistance for the high tension charge to short circuit the plug since these deposits are actually salts.

It is possible, sometimes, to burn off these deposits by causing the engine to run at a speed just below that which would cause missing. Then, as the engine becomes hotter and the plugs become cleaner, the speed of the engine should be increased until the engine is running with no fault at its maximum.

Cleaning and Installing Plugs

If the spark plug is removed and found dirty, it can be easily cleaned by employing a mild abrasive. A small pillar-file or emery board, similar to those used to file fingernails, will suffice to clean the electrodes. A service station sometimes employs a sand-blasting machine to clean dirty plugs. If the plug is old or cracked, it must be replaced since an old plug demands too much voltage and a cracked plug may short the voltage from the electrodes.

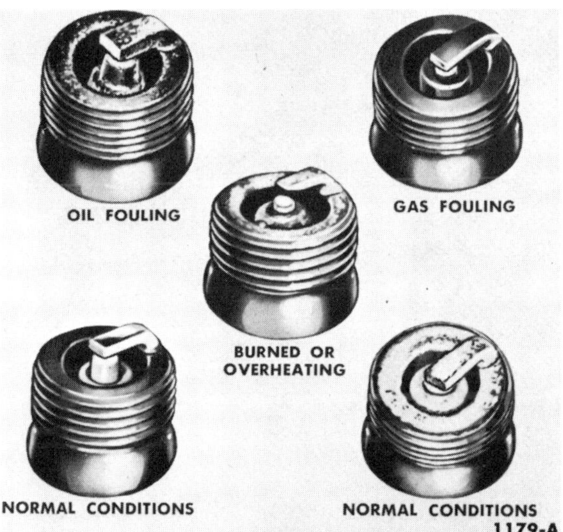

Fig. 9-46. Spark Plug Inspection Shows Operating Conditions (Ford)

After checking the plug gap for recommended setting with a feeler gauge, and correcting the gap by bending the outer electrode to the proper setting, the threads on the outside of the plug and on the inside of the block must be cleaned of foreign matter. Particular attention must be given to the gasket seats on the plug and head. An improper seal will permit compression leakage, and if this is caused by dirt, the dirt may act as a heat insulator and cause the plug to run hot. A new gasket should be placed on the plug, and the plug should be carefully located within the hole.

A torque wrench should be used to draw the plug in correctly. A 25 to 30 lb. *torque* is usually recommended although there are many exceptions. In any event, the plug should be tightened only enough to crush the new gasket. The high-tension cable is then replaced after making sure that it is clean. A rubber shield over the plug and cable, if used, will help prevent leakage caused by the accumulation of oil and grit on the plug.

New Rotary Combustion Engine

The Wankel engine is a radically new internal combustion piston engine. It was designed in 1956 by Felix Wankel, a German mathematician. He showed it to a German small car manufacturer, N.S.U. Werke. They looked at the idea sketches and went into action. Three years later, it was no longer just another idea; N.S.U. needed more money and more research facilities to speed up development. In March, 1960, they entered into a licensing agreement with Curtiss-Wright Corporation in the United States. Its possible applications appear to be broad: land, air or marine vehicles and utility engines of many sizes.

Currently there are two automobile manufacturers using Wankel rotary engines in pro-

A. Exterior Design

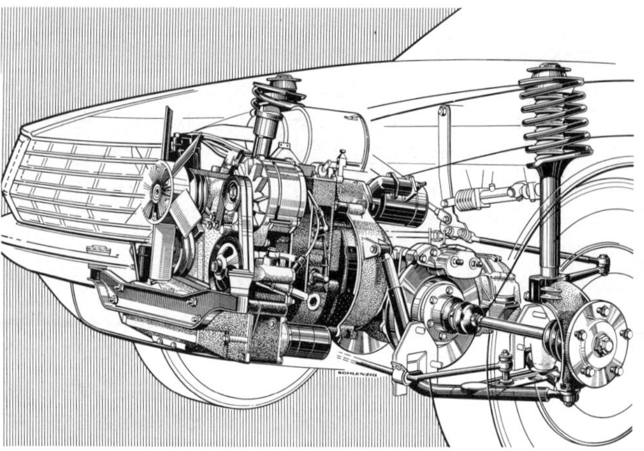

C. Details of Front-Wheel Drive Mechanism

B. Partly Sectioned View of Power Pack

Fig. 9-47. The NSURO 80 (Wankel)

duction cars: N.S.U. of Germany and Toyo Kogyo of Japan. The N.S.U. engine delivers 113.5 brake horsepower while the MASDA R-100 engine delivers 120 horsepower. Both cars are reported to have attained speeds in excess of 100 miles per hour and produced over-the-road fuel consumption of 25 to 30 miles per gallon. Mercedes-Benz and Citroen are operating experimental cars with Wankel engines and a number of other manufacturers are engaged in testing and developing rotary engines. General Motors is doing intensive research and development studies on the rotary combustion engine and expects to have some production models available by 1974. The latest experimental Wankel is a diesel version announced by Rolls-Royce. Funded by the British Ministry of Defense, the firm developed a two-stage rotary engine with a large lower rotor and chamber that is geared and ported to a small upper rotary and chamber. The first chamber draws in air, compresses it and ports it to the second chamber for further compression and ignition. Spent gas then goes back to the first rotor and is exhausted.

The NSURO 80

In the new front-wheel drive NSURO 80 (Fig. 9-47) the NSU Wankel Twin Rotor Engine is the power plant, producing 113.5 bhp. The engine is reported to operate quietly, with a gentle hum and give excellent performance, especially at high speeds. The engine requires fewer moving parts than conventional reciprocating engines and is capable of burning lower octane gasolines efficiently.

Epitrochoidal Design

The Wankel engine differs greatly from conventional engines. See Fig. 9-48. The crank throw (a simple eccentric bearing) is shown as (e) and the rotor radius is shown as (R). The relationship of these basic design factors generates the *epitrochoidal shape* of the housing as the rotor is revolved about the shaft eccentric by its stationary timing gear (2). The rotor turns at one-third the speed of the crankshaft. Each of the three faces of the rotor in turn receives a power impulse. Ignition occurs as the eccentric of the fast-turning crankshaft passes under the spark plug. Timing marks on the rotor gear and on the end housing stationary gear aid in assembly so this timing is correct. Each face of the rotor has a dished-out section and this, along with the walls of the rotor housing, forms the combustion chamber.

This engine is unique. It obtains the familiar intake, compression, power and exhaust cycle by a triangular-shaped rotor. This rotary piston revolves epitrochoidally around the eccentric. The three tips of the rotor remain in constant, snug contact with the chamber walls, dividing the open spaces into three sections which are constantly changing size and shape. The only other moving part is the crankshaft. Besides great simplicity of design, there is little or no vibration. There are no

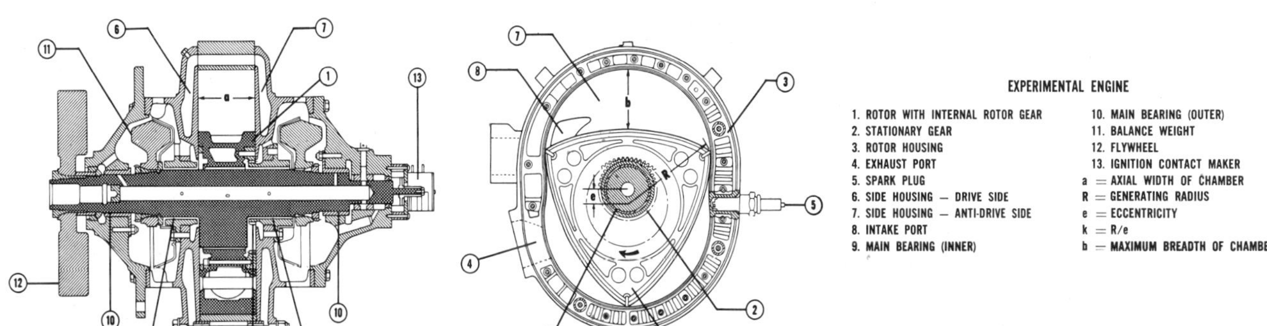

Fig. 9-48. Wankel RC Engine, Development Model
(Curtiss-Wright)

problems of heat dissipation, no hotspots, no detonation; all of which plague reciprocating engines. In Figure 9-49 the parts of the rotating combustion engine are compared with a standard reciprocating engine. The Wankel has 40% fewer parts, roughly one-third the bulk and half the weight of a comparable reciprocating engine.

Advantages

The Wankel has been refined greatly in recent years. Multi-rotor units predominate in commercial and experimental autos. There are carburetted and fuel injected designs that use diesel fuel, gasoline (premium, regular and non-leaded), jet-fuel, and various exotic mixtures. Many engines have two spark plugs per rotor and use multiple ignition systems. Most Wankel engines are liquid cooled but there are air-cooled units, both large and small. The Wankel design is capable of running at very high speeds for long periods of time. It exhibits a high power to weight ratio. An exceptionally good torque curve indicates effective power at all engine speeds. It is extremely versatile; for example, there is almost no limit on compression ratio, maximum RPM, type of fuel feed and method of cooling.

Curtiss-Wright has concentrated work on a 100 hp, 5,500 rpm engine having a combustion chamber of 100 cubic inches or 1,600 cc. They are also developing a 160 hp at 8,000 rpm unit which is rated as most promising. See Fig. 9-50. The company hopes to soon be able to mass produce the 1,600 cc unit.

Several automobile manufacturers, including General Motors and Ford, have development rights to the Wankel.

Principles of Operation

Three chambers are formed by the sides of the rotor and the wall of the housing. Their shape, size, and position are constantly being altered by the rotor's clockwise rotation and the faster rotation of the eccentric. The usual four-stroke cycle occurs with the simple

ROTATING COMBUSTION ENGINE

RECIPROCATING ENGINE

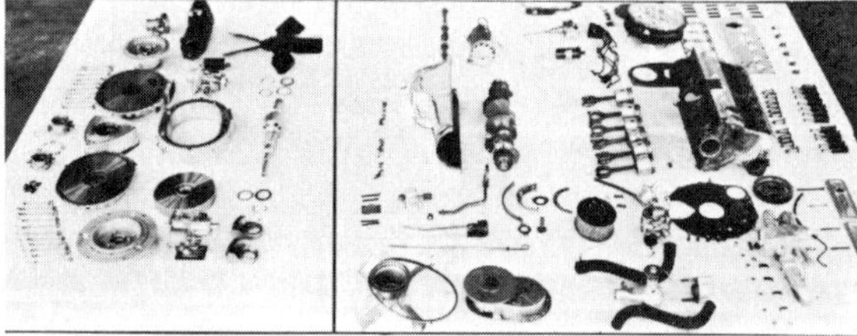

Fig. 9-49. Rotating and Conventional Engine Parts Compared (Curtiss-Wright)

The rotating combustion (RC) engine has only two rotating parts, the mainshaft and rotor. There are no valves, cams, or pistons to accelerate and decelerate, and no reciprocating forces to be counterbalanced.

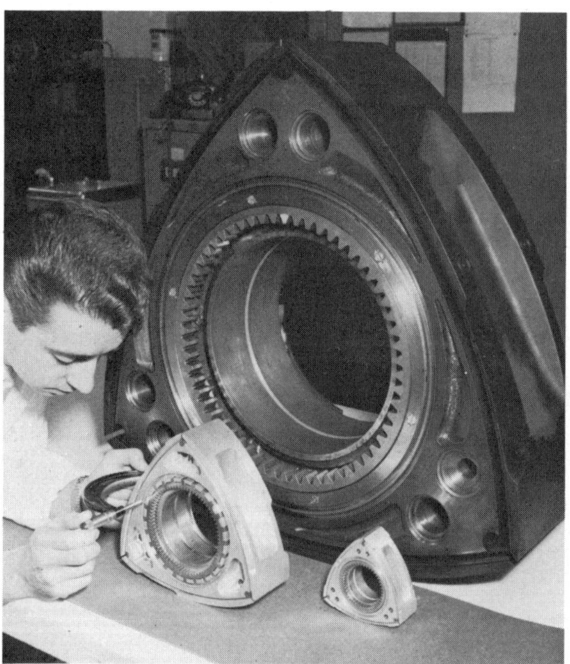

Fig. 9-50. Rotors for 8.6, 60, and 1920 Cubic Inch RC Engines (Curtiss-Wright)

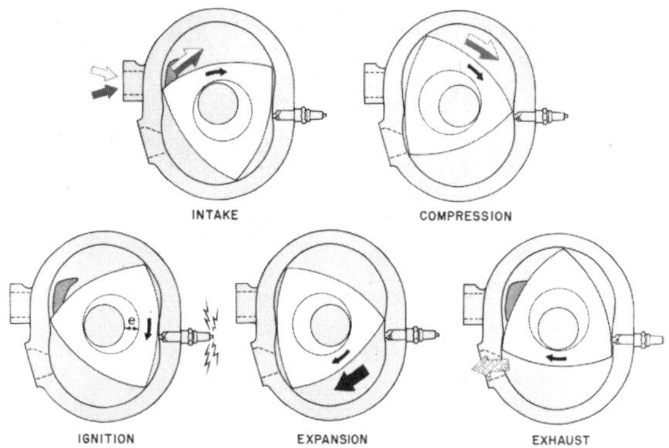

Fig. 9-51. Rotating Combustion Cycle
(Curtiss-Wright)

valving and power stroke frequency of the two-stroke cycle. See Fig. 9-51.

The rotor opens the intake port (which has no speed-restricting valve mechanism) and fuel and air enter, as in any four-stroke cycle engine. The rotor continues on, closing the intake port by passing beyond it and compression begins, followed by ignition, combustion and expansion for the power stroke until the apex seal opens the exhaust port. The exhaust cycle then takes place, again with no speed-restricting valve mechanism, and the cycle is complete.

Similar combustion events occur on the other faces in series, providing three power impulses for each rotor revolution. To produce the rotating motion, the crank throw or eccentric must be in a position to transmit the combustion force into shaft motion as each face of the rotor passes the spark plug. Note in Fig. 9-50 (ignition) that the throw (e) is just passing the spark plug. It must do this for each of the three rotor faces, so it turns at three times the speed of the rotor. Thus, the crankshaft revolves once for each power (expansion) stroke. There are three power impulses for each revolution of the rotor.

The engine is unique in that the power impulse is spread over approximately 270° of crankshaft rotation, compared to 180° of the conventional reciprocating two-stroke cycle engine.

The engine features four-stroke cycle operation, greater power impulse, high rpm yield

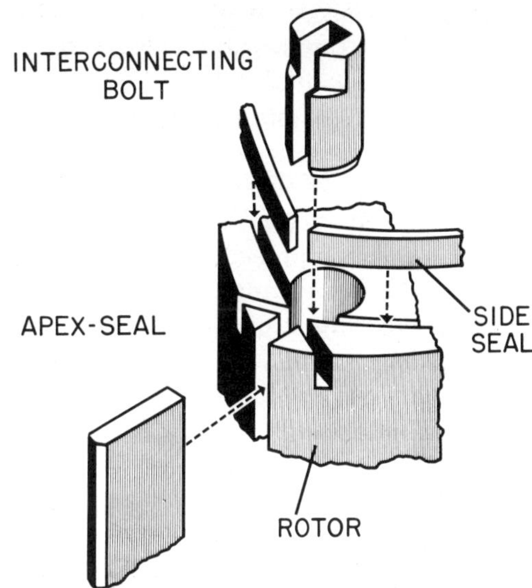

Fig. 9-52. Seals for RC Engine
(Curtiss-Wright)

and a very high specific ratio of power to displacement. This permits lighter, smaller engines for a given horsepower than any other positive displacement power plant. Also, the single rotor has instantaneous torque characteristics that are nearly equivalent to a four cylinder reciprocating engine. A rotating combustion engine with twin rotors is better than a four cylinder engine. The engine virtually has no size limitations. At this development state, it compares favorably in performance yet is lighter and more compact than the conventional reciprocating engine which has been under development for about 85 years.

To make this simple principle into an efficient engine, it is necessary to seal the chambers of one rotor face from the adjacent chambers and faces. Apex sealing is not as difficult as it might seem because the seal has no radial motion. Theoretically, this is because the epitrochoidal housing wall is generated by the rotor apex and the only radial motion comes from the manufacturing tolerances of the parts. Seals are also required on the rotor side faces. See Fig. 9-52.

So far most apex seals are made from carbon or sintered carbon and aluminum backed by stainless steel rings. These materials could change as engine manufacturers change the surface material on the engine chamber walls. Compression seals on the sides of the rotor are generally made of piston ring cast iron and do not present the design problems found with apex seals.

The advantages of this engine seem to make its future most attractive. Its light weight and small size offer unprecedented potential in emergency, standby, and continuous power generation, and for pumping units, compact tractors, balers, harvesters, loaders, combines and marine engines concealed in the stern well or under the deck.

From the emission standpoint, the Wankel presently produces a much greater quantity of unburned hydrocarbons than does the reciprocating engine, especially at low speeds. However, this is relatively easy to control because the small engine size leaves plenty of room under the hood for a thermal reactor to be located close to the exhaust ports for maximum efficiency. The more harmful and difficult to control nitric oxides and other oxides of nitrogen emitted by the Wankel are very low in comparison to those from the reciprocating engines. Rotary engines are expected to be able to meet standards of anti-emission legislation.

Terms to Understand

carburetion
vaporization
atomized
spray bar or needle jet
float and reservoir
fuel-air variation
Bernoulli's Principle
venturi
throttle jet
idle jet
idle air bleed
throttle valve
main jet
auxiliary air valve
auxiliary jet
high speed bleed
power bypass choke
butterfly valve
accelerating pump
dash pot
various draft carburetors
single- and multi-barrel carburetors
idle mixture screw
idle speed screw
fast idle cam
centrifugal governor
air-vane governor
vacuum fuel system
gravity fuel system
pump fuel system
diaphragm
fuel pump pressure
pressurized fuel system
air cleaners
fuel injection
electronic fuel control
breaker points
battery
magnetos
low tension
high tension
shuttlewound
revolving magnet
rotary inductor
series hook-up
parallel hook-up
conventional magneto
primary/secondary winding
armature
flywheel magneto
condenser
high-tension safety gap
ignition timing
breaker cam
centrifugal spark advance
vacuum spark advance
distributor
rotor
battery ignition
ignition coil
spark plug
hot plug
torque
Wankel engine
epitrochoidal
frontwheel drive
detonation

Study Questions

1. Discuss the purpose of the carburetor.
2. Explain how differential pressure is used in carburetion.
3. Analyze the various types of carburetors.
4. What are the demands imposed on a carburetor by varying loads and speeds?

5. Explain Bernoulli's Principle and how it is employed in carburetion.
6. Describe the various components and their function in a simple pump-fed carburetor.
7. Describe the function of an engine governor.
8. Analyze the popular governor systems.
9. Analyze the popular methods of getting the fuel to the carburetor.
10. Describe the operation of the fuel pump.
11. Analyze the purpose and popular types of air filters.
12. What are some of the demands imposed on an electrical system?
13. Describe the operation of the magneto electrical system.
14. Analyze the various types of magneto systems.
15. Analyze the necessity and methods of ignition timing.
16. How does a battery ignition system differ from a magneto system?
17. What is the function of the ignition coil?
18. Analyze the characteristics of various types of spark plugs.
19. Describe the operation of the Wankel engine.
20. What are the advantages of electronic ignition?
21. How do you rate the potential use of the Wankel engine?

CHAPTER 10

Engine Electrical Systems

Many engines, even small ones, will have an electrical system to gain the convenience of electrical starting or other accessories impossible to have with a magneto. See Fig. 10-1. The automotive electrical system will be studied here because it is typical, with minor variations, of those found on many other engine installations. The electrical system provides power for starting, for spark ignition (when needed), for lighting, and for various controls, auxiliary accessories and instruments. Components in the electrical system include the storage battery, generator or alternator, devices for regulating voltage and current flow, starting motor, ignition system (covered in Chapter 9), electrical accessories, wiring and solenoids or other switching devices. Fig. 10-2 shows the wiring typical in a modern automobile.

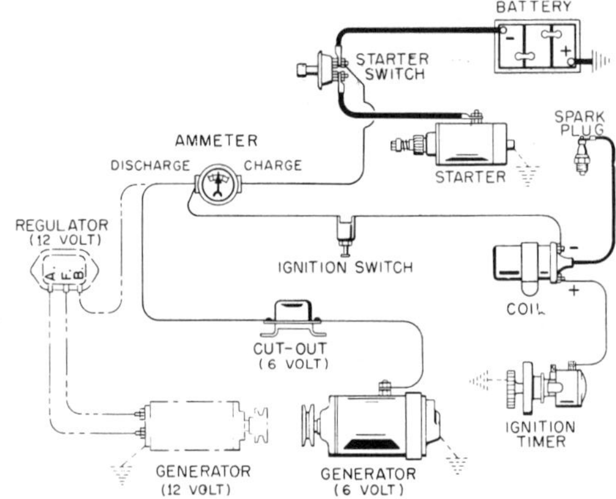

Fig. 10-1. Small Engine Electrical System (Wisconsin)

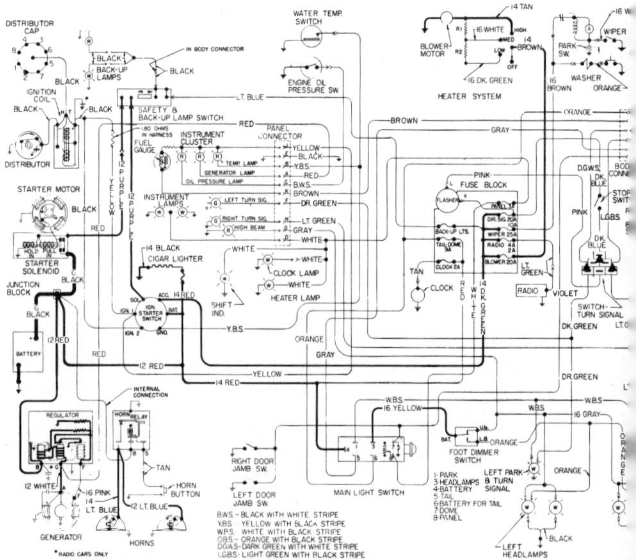

Fig. 10-2. Automotive Electrical System (Buick)

Storage Battery

The lead-acid battery is used as a source of electrical potential because it can be used and recharged repeatedly. It provides the electrical energy needed to start the engine and to keep it running at idling speeds. Above idling speed, the engine's generator provides enough electrical power to satisfy the demands of the ignition system.

The lead-acid battery is commonly called a *storage* battery. This is actually a misnomer because the battery does not store electricity. However, by electro-chemical action, it converts chemical energy into electrical energy.

The potential current of the battery depends on the type and amount of acid and electrodes used.

Each cell of a lead-acid storage battery will produce about 2 volts regardless of the size. The larger cells will provide longer cell life because they can produce more electrons when needed. A battery is made up of 3 or 6 cells depending upon the voltage desired. These cells are connected with a plate strap and a vertical lug protruding from the plate. See No. 7 in Fig. 10-3. Both the negative and positive plates are connected to their own groups in this way, and the portion of the strap that extends up through the cell casing constitutes the post or terminal of its respective group in the battery. Batteries are rated by the amount of amperes they can produce per hour. A 60 ampere-hour battery can produce half of what a 120-ampere-hour battery can produce. Usually, the more plates a battery has, the greater ampere-hour rating and the greater the cost.

Composition of Lead-Acid Battery

The lead-acid battery is made of positive and negative plates consisting of special lead alloys that are contained in grids of lead, tin, and antimony. These flat, rectangular grids are filled with either gray-colored sponge lead for negative plates, or brown-colored lead peroxide for positive plates. They are bound together to form the electrodes of the positive and negative terminals.

In the cell, these plates are alternated with a porous insulator between them to prevent their touching or shorting out. These separators can be a thin layer of wood, plastic, fibre, or any material that will not react in the electrolyte but will allow the electrolyte (sulphuric acid) to react with the plates chemically. Sometimes, they are ribbed on the side facing the positive plates to provide more volume of acid to react with the plate, increasing the efficiency of the cell.

Initially, the battery must be charged by an outside direct current source. This creates an electrochemical unbalance between the positive and negative terminals. The difference of potential will cause a flow of electrical energy in a conductor if it is placed between the two poles, because of their desire to become electrically balanced. This electrical energy can be made to do work as in the case of the starter, ignition system, lights, radio, and other electrical accessories.

The battery case is usually made of molded rubber or some similar composition. This material does not react with the acid, is mechanically strong, and is able to expand and contract with various temperature conditions.

Checking the Battery

Each cell has one screw cap through which the electrolyte and distilled water is added. These caps have vent holes in them to permit the gases created by charging to escape. Over a period of time, evaporation and the charging process can cause the water supply to become low. Water must be replenished

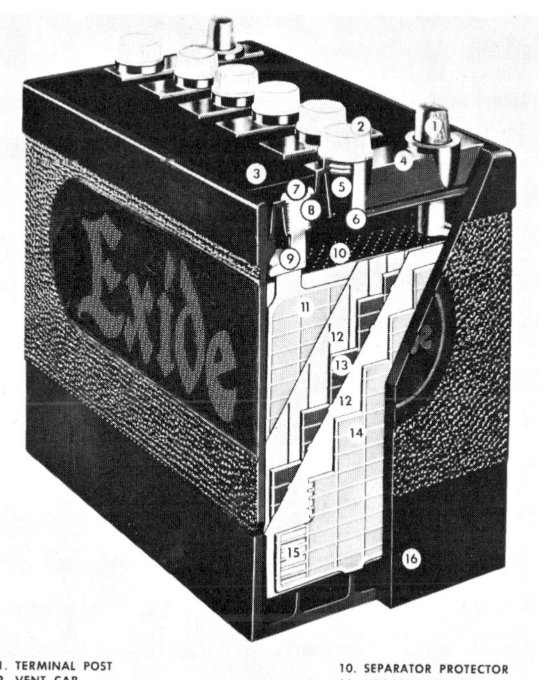

1. TERMINAL POST
2. VENT CAP
3. SEALING COMPOUND
4. CELL COVER
5. FILLING TUBE
6. ELECTROLYTE LEVEL MARK
7. INTER CELL CONNECTOR welded to...
8. LEAD INSERT in cover and...
9. PLATE STRAP
10. SEPARATOR PROTECTOR
11. NEGATIVE PLATE
12. SEPARATOR
13. POSITIVE PLATE
14. NEGATIVE PLATE with active material removed to show...
15. PLATE GRID
16. CONTAINER

Fig. 10-3. 12-Volt Automobile Battery (Exide)

when its level does not completely cover the cell plates. Newer caps do not permit much evaporation and the batteries need refilling only after long intervals.

Specific Gravity of Battery

The specific gravity of the electrolyte can indicate the condition of the cell or battery. Specific gravity indicates the relation of the weight of a liquid to an equal volume of water. A specific gravity reaching 1.260 to 1.300 at 80°F indicates a fully charged battery. Many battery testers omit the decimal point so would read 1260 to 1300.

Specific gravity is taken by using a hydrometer as shown in Fig. 10-4. This is nothing more than a glass calibrated float. The depth the float sinks into the solution tested indicates its specific gravity. The float will sink further into solutions having a lower specific gravity than those having a high specific gravity. Temperature must be considered when the specific gravity is taken. Temperature corrections are made by adding or subtracting .004 specific gravity for every 10°F change in temperature *above or below 80° F.*

In a battery, the specific gravity of the electrolyte decreases during the discharge of the cell. This is caused by the cell using the sulphuric acid as well as forming more water. In this condition, the positive plates may be damaged during freezing temperatures. When the battery is fully charged, sulphuric acid is formed and the water is used. In this situation, there is little chance of the battery liquid freezing.

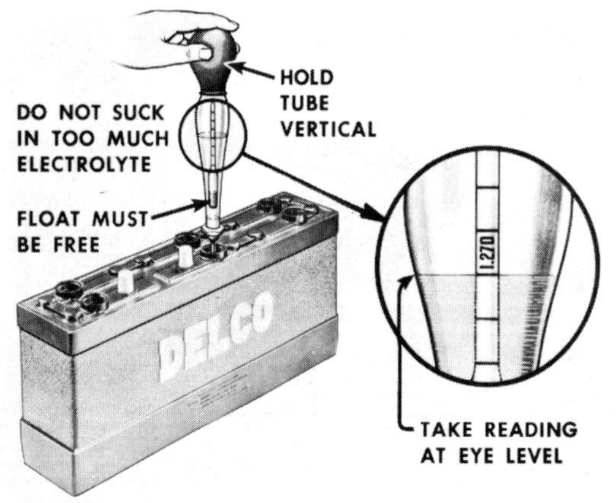

Fig. 10-4. Using a Hydrometer (Delco-Remy)

Charging the Battery

A cell or battery is charged with a controlled direct current. Usually, a commercial charger can be regulated to provide a direct current output that will give a quick or trickle charge. In either case, the charging voltage is constant and the same as the cell or battery potential. Battery chargers run off motor generators or alternating current. In any case, the alternating current must be changed to DC by rectifiers (selenium, silicon, or some other dry disc). Various transformers and electronic filters are usually used to produce a filtered direct current for charging.

Connecting Battery to Charger: To charge a battery, the terminals and the battery case must be cleaned. The leads from the charger must be connected to the proper terminals on the battery—*positive to positive* and *negative to negative.* If this is not done, the battery could be ruined.

Safety Precautions: During charging, the vent holes must be kept open because gases are formed and they must be permitted to escape. Also, the temperature of the battery must be watched to prevent overheating. This could cause the plates to buckle. The charging temperature should never exceed 110°F—if it does, the charging rate should be reduced.

Charging Rate: To determine the charging rate, "a rule-of-thumb" is to set the amperage rate of charge to one-half the number of plates in the cell. A 15 plate cell would be charged at 7.5 amperes, a 17 plate cell would be charged at 8.5 amperes, and so on. When several batteries are charged in series, the battery with the least number of plates is used as the amperage index. As the battery is being charged, it should be constantly checked every hour with a hydrometer. If the reading does not vary for 2 or 3 hourly readings, the battery has received its maximum charge. Today, rapid charging is popular. It is efficient if it is done properly with all precautions taken to prevent the plates from warping. Quick charging can be accomplished in 30 minutes, but it is not well accepted by many mechanics as the best way to charge a battery because of the generation of excess heat and gas.

Trickle-charging is designed to maintain a charge in display batteries. The charging rate of one ampere is very low, but, if maintained over too long a period, can ruin a battery. Care must be taken to rest a battery during trickle charging usually twelve hours on and twelve hours off will prevent damage from overcharging.

Generators

In those engines which use an electric starter and a battery operated ignition system, provision must be made to re-charge the battery. The generator does this job. Fig. 10-5 shows the major components of such an electrical system using a generator.

The generator converts mechanical energy to electrical energy in much the same way as a magneto. The main difference is that the generator uses an *electromagnet* instead of a *permanent magnet* to develop the field. The generator collects the electrical energy with brushes on a commutator or split rings instead of using the energy directly from the coil. The generator induces a flow of electrical energy of moderate voltage with high amperage (or quantity) while the magneto generates a high tension voltage surge in very small quantities.

Generator Operation

The generator, like the magneto, operates on the principle of a conductor made to cut through a magnetic field. An electrical current flows if the circuit is completed. The generator consists of the *field coils* (which supply the magnetic field) and the *armature winding* (which rotates and cuts this field). The armature is the means by which the induced voltage is collected through *brushes* riding on the *commutator*. See Fig. 10-6.

The field coil consists of a soft iron core around which many coils of wire are wound. This electromagnet receives its electrical energy from the current induced in the armature. These field coils may be connected in series, parallel, or series-parallel with the armature. See Fig. 10-7.

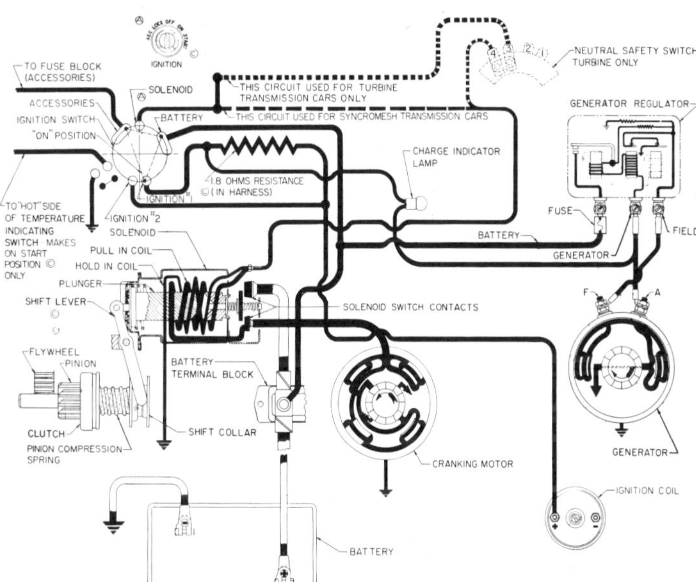

Fig. 10-5. Battery Operated Ignition System (Buick)

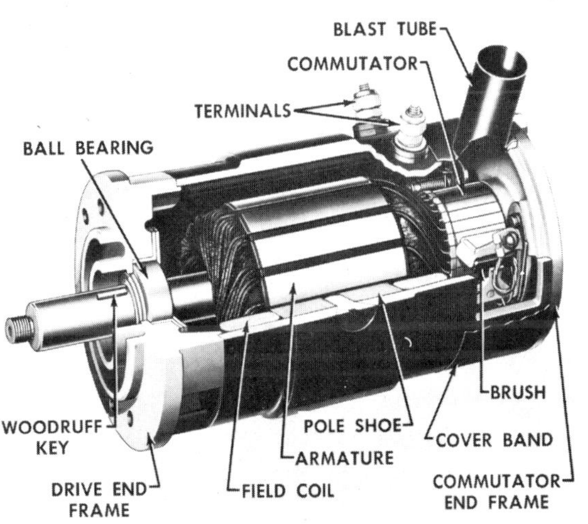

Fig. 10-6. Automotive Generator

In a *series-wound generator* (A in Fig. 10-7), all the current in the circuit passes through the field and armature. Any resistance introduced into the circuit increases the current flow and results in increasing the strength of the magnetic field and causes the voltage to vary.

In *shunt-wound generators* (B in Fig. 10-7) the field coil is in parallel with the armature. The armature and field coil have separate circuits. The current flowing through the field depends upon the resistance of the field and the voltage at the brushes. As long as the voltage at the brushes remains constant, the current in the field remains constant and the generated voltage is constant. This type, and its variations which will be explained later, is the most popular.

In the *series-parallel generator,* known as a *compound generator,* various generating characteristics can be achieved. These are accomplished by selecting different size windings for the shunt and series coils, and by varying the internal connections (C and D in Fig. 10-7). For instance, if the series field opposes the shunt field, increasing the speed of rotation will cause a decrease in current.

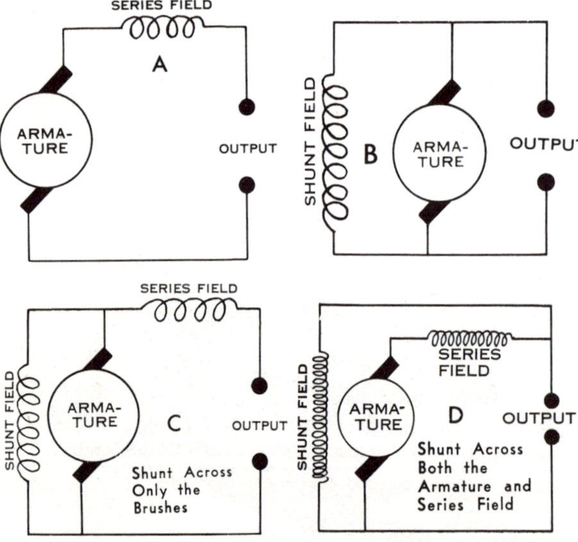

Fig. 10-7. Generator Field Coil Arrangements
A. Series wound; B. Shunt or parallel wound; C. short-shunt compound wound; D. Long-shunt compound wound; (D and C also called series-parallel).

The armature of the generator shown in Fig. 10-6 consists of many insulated coils of wire placed in insulated grooves cut around a soft iron core which rotates within the field coils.

The ends of the armature coil are connected to a current collecting device. This can be either segments of the *commutator,* or a pair of one-piece *slip rings,* either type being in contact with *carbon brushes.* The brushes are connected to a power consuming device to complete the circuit. When the armature is made to rotate, the armature coil cuts through the magnetic field of the field coil. The current thus induced will flow out one end of the armature, through the brushes to the consuming device and back to the other end of the coil completing the circuit.

Types of Generated Current

The output of generators may be either a form of *direct current* (*DC*) or *alternating current* (*AC*). Direct current flows in one direction only, while AC is constantly reversing or alternating directions. In automotive systems DC is required for battery charging, but AC can be used if it is first *rectified* (changed to DC). The AC generator will be explained first because it is most simple, because it is now the most common, and because all mechanically generated current (not coming from batteries) is alternating in its basic form.

AC Generator

The AC generator is also known as an *alternator.* Fig. 10-8 shows a simplified form of a traditional alternator. There is a strong magnetic flux flowing from the N to the S pole of the field. The armature is a coil of wire ABCD revolving in this field. The coil is connected to slip rings which revolve with the coil. Current is collected by brushes J and H for use externally (L).

In view A, the coil ABCD being vertical is not cutting any lines of magnetic flux so no current is being generated. After a quarter turn, view B, it is cutting the greatest amount of magnetic flux so there is a strong flow of electrons in one direction. After a half turn (C) the coil is again vertical so current flow has tapered off to zero. After three quarters of a turn (D) the sides AB and CD have reversed position from view B so electron flow has again reached a peak but in the opposite direction. The graph gives a picture of this cycle. The number of cycles completed in a second is known as the *frequency* of the current. Frequency depends on the speed of rotation and the number of pairs of magnetic poles cut in a revolution.

Car manufacturers have introduced a new type of alternator that is more efficient and is replacing the conventional direct current generators. This alternator has a revolving field rather than a revolving armature, and is diagramed in Fig. 10-9. This arrangement eliminates the need for large brushes (long a source of wear and a matter of deep concern for automotive engineers). It also provides charging rates at engine idling speeds. This is an important consideration for the growing electrical requirements in cars.

An actual alternator, shown in Fig. 10-10, has six pairs of field poles in the rotor so six cycles are generated in one revolution. The alternating current is rectified to a form of direct current by *silicon diodes* before it leaves the unit. As these rectifiers are sensitive to excess heat they must be fitted into a *heat sink*. This sink has fins and is made of a metal which readily conducts heat to speed its dissipation over a larger area. The capacitor grounds possible radio interference.

DC Generator

Until recently, nearly all automobiles and self-starting engines used a direct current generator to charge the battery. This generator is much like the conventional alternator shown in Fig. 10-8, except that an insulated segmented ring (commutator) is used in place of the two, one-piece slip rings. Fig. 10-11 diagrams such a DC generator. Each end of the coil is connected to a segment and brushes make contact with these segments.

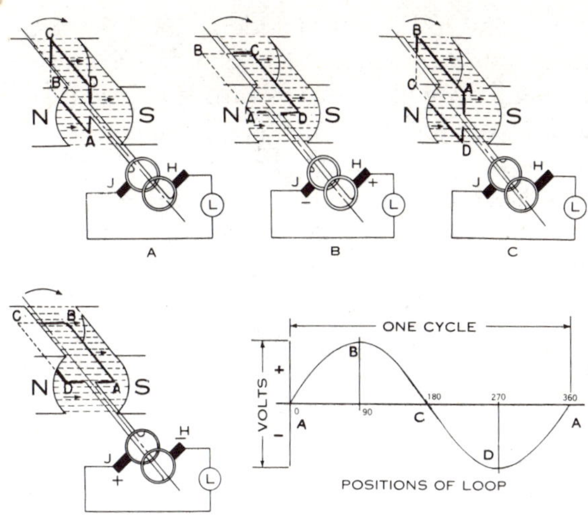

Fig. 10-8. Generation of Alternating Current

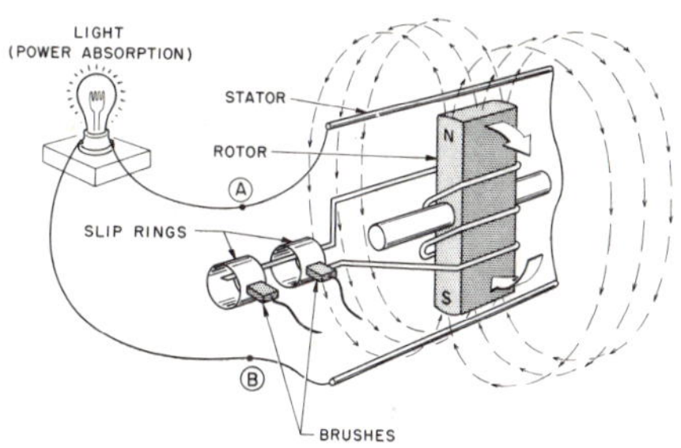

Fig. 10-9. Simplified Automotive Alternator (Chrysler)

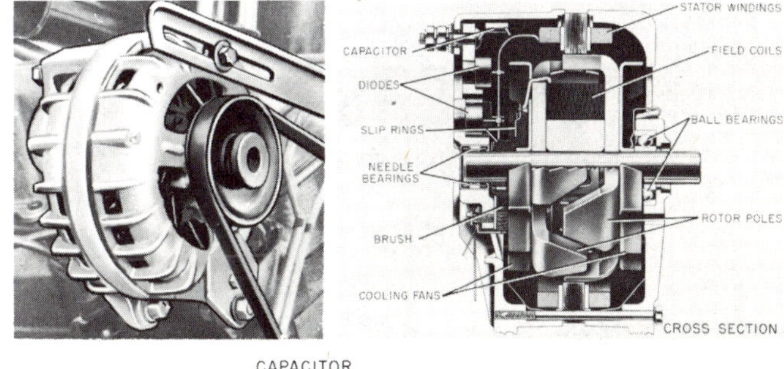

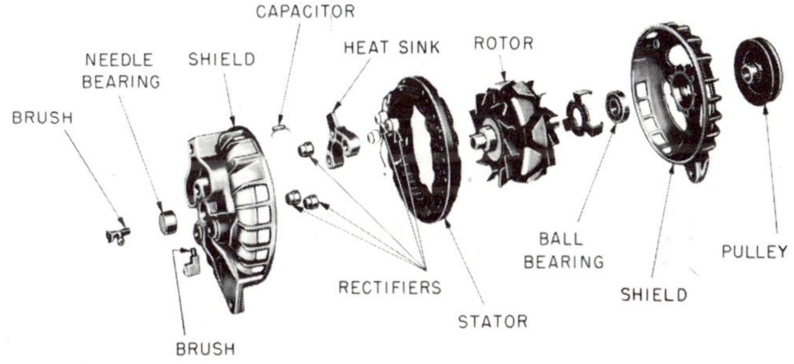

Fig. 10-10. Automotive Alternator (Chrysler)

At view A, Fig. 10-11, side AC of the armature coil is rising past the S pole creating a strong flow of electrons toward the B segment of the commutator. This flow is picked up by the negative brush. At view B, a half revolution later, the opposite side of the armature is rising past the S pole creating a strong flow of electrons toward the A segment of the commutator. However, as the split rings have also made a half revolution, this electron is still picked up by the same brush. This causes the electricity to flow in one direction in the external circuit.

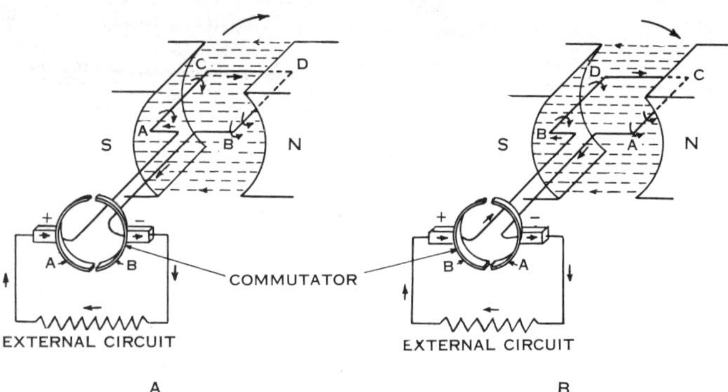

Fig. 10-11. Generation of a Pulsating Direct Current

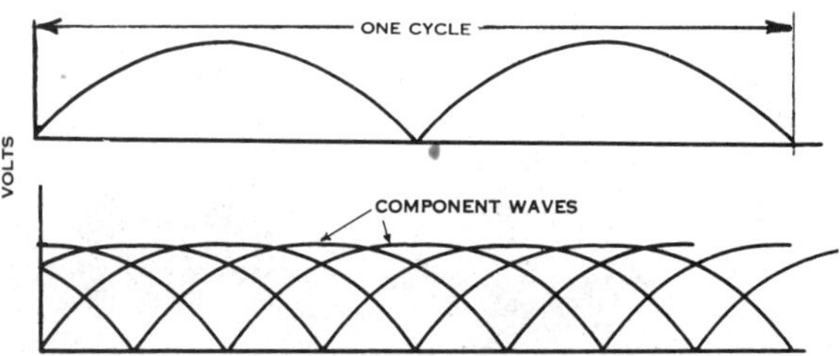

Fig. 10-12. Voltage Curve of Single Coil Generator (above) and One with Four Coils

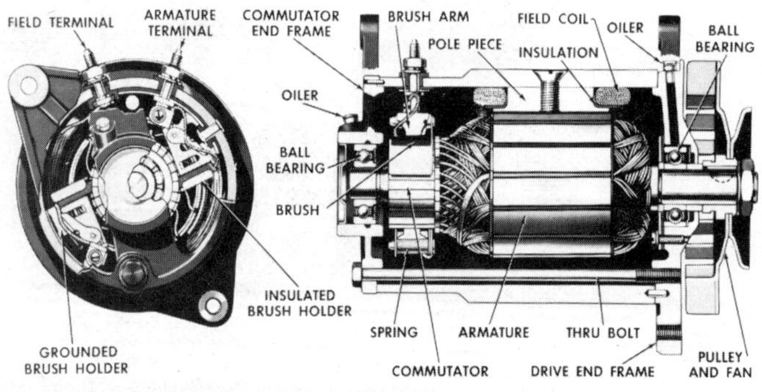

Fig. 10-13. DC Generator (Buick)

Although the current is flowing in one direction the intensity varies from zero to peak voltage and back to zero each half cycle. The commutator segments merely reverse the second half of the cycle to the same direction as the first half. This forms a *pulsating* direct current (PDC) as shown at the top of Fig. 10-12. Pulsations can be reduced greatly if several coils are spaced around one armature with their ends connected to individually insulated segments. At the bottom of Fig. 10-12 is shown the component voltage of an armature with four coils. Instead of having two peaks per revolution, there are eight. Fig. 10-13 shows a DC generator with 14 armature coils and 28 commutator segments. In this way, a relatively smooth electrical output can be achieved.

There are a number of variations in DC generator internal circuits to improve the output at various uses and speed ranges. Some various types to be explained are: several shunt variations, the third brush, the interpole, the bucking field and the split field types.

Three-Brush Generator

The three-brush generator utilizes armature and field reaction to control output. Armature current is caused by the interaction of the magnetic fields surrounding the conductors of the field and armature.

The magnetic field surrounding the armature as it conducts the generated current causes the magnetic flux to become uneven as the armature coils revolve through it. The flux seems to become more concentrated in the direction of rotation. As the armature coil cuts through this denser field, a higher voltage will be generated within the coil than within those cutting through the less dense portions of the magnetic field.

The three-brush generator has a third brush that is connected to one end of the field winding while the other end of the field winding is connected to the negative (F) brush as shown at the left in Fig. 10-14. The voltage applied to the circuit is controlled by the position of the third brush. The voltage will be increased as the third brush is moved closer to the nearby main brush and decreased as it is moved away. In other words, moving the third brush in the direction of rotation will cause the field current to increase, and moving it in the opposite direction will cause the field current to decrease. This controls the generator output because the voltage generated is dependent upon the extent of the magnetic force of the field coil which is controlled by the voltage it receives.

Three-Brush Output: Although the output of the three-brush generator is dependent upon the voltage applied to the field, the armature voltage is dependent upon the resistance to which it is connected. If the generator is operated with no load, the voltage generated may be so great that it may burn itself out. To prevent this a fuse is usually placed in the field circuit.

If this type generator is used to charge a battery, it provides a higher charging rate when the battery approaches full charge and a lower charging rate when the battery is in a discharge condition. This condition is not excessive in generators having up to a 20 ampere maximum output. Another undesirable characteristic is the tendency of the generator to work best at high speeds. If this were not corrected for slower speed ranges, the generator output would decrease rapidly.

Shunt-Type Generator

At the right of Fig. 10-14 is shown the internal wiring of a common shunt-type generator. The insulated-shunt generator (Fig. 10-15, left) is identical except the case and neither brush is grounded.

While the shunt-type generator satisfies the demands of charging a battery at low speeds, at high speeds the same generator output would be excessive. This is due to the fact that the generated voltage is proportionate to the speed of armature rotation and the magnetic strength of the field magnet. Therefore, it is necessary to provide some means to reduce the field strength as the armature speed increases to keep the charging voltage and amperage within limits. An external voltage and current regulator is this limiting device, and will be explained later.

Interpole Generator

As the armature rotates generating a flow of current, it builds up a magnetic force that surrounds its conductors. One method of neutralizing the magnetic effect is to provide *interpole coils* as shown at the right of Fig. 10-15. These are small electromagnetic pole shoes, made of heavy copper wire, mounted between the regular field coils. The heavy winding is made in such a way as to cause its magnetic field to be in opposition to that created by the armature field. Because the current in the interpole is always equal to that in the armature, the correct neutralizing force is provided—thus eliminating the arcing

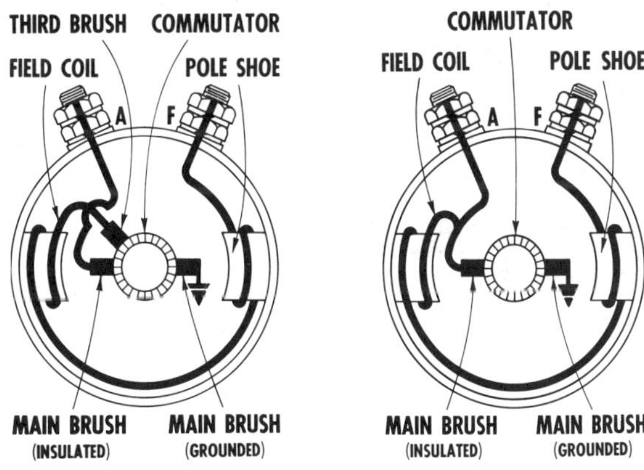

Fig. 10-14. Three-Brush Generator (left) and Common Shunt Type (Delco-Remy)

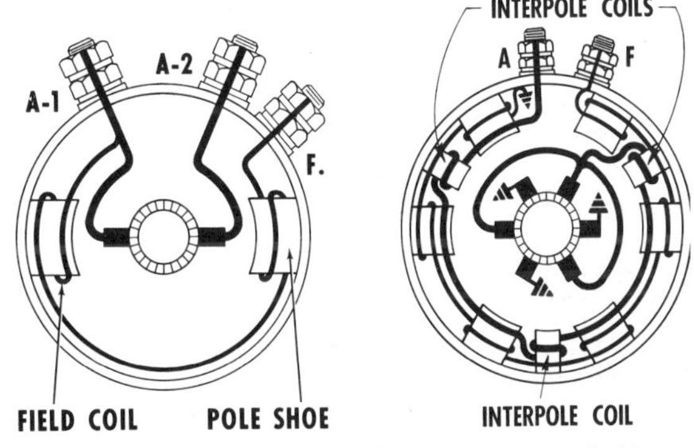

Fig. 10-15. Insulated-Shunt Generator (left) and Interpole Type (Delco-Remy)

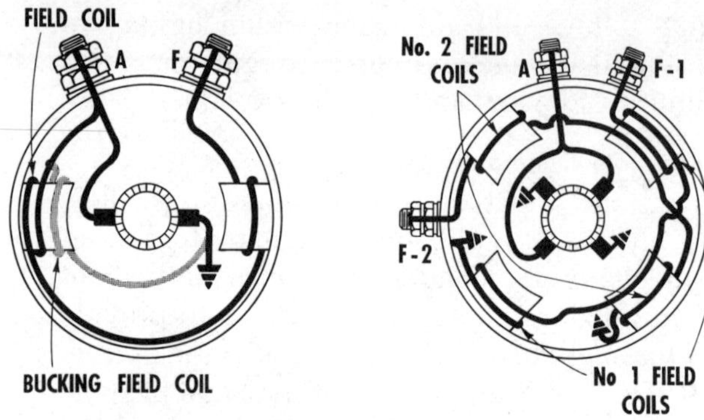

Fig. 10-16. Bucking-Field Generator (left) and Split-Field Type (Delco-Remy)

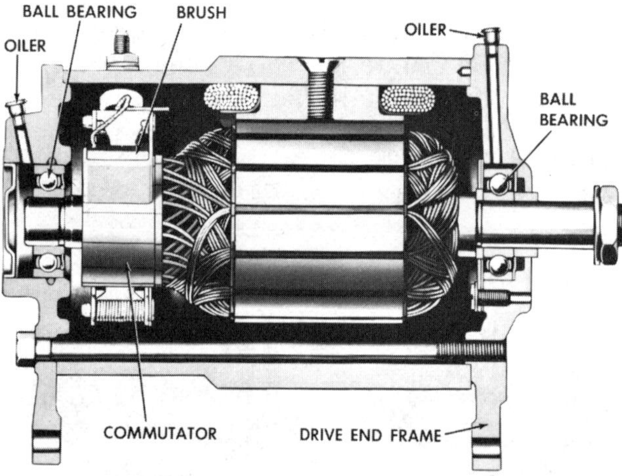

Fig. 10-17. Motor-Generator (Delco-Remy)

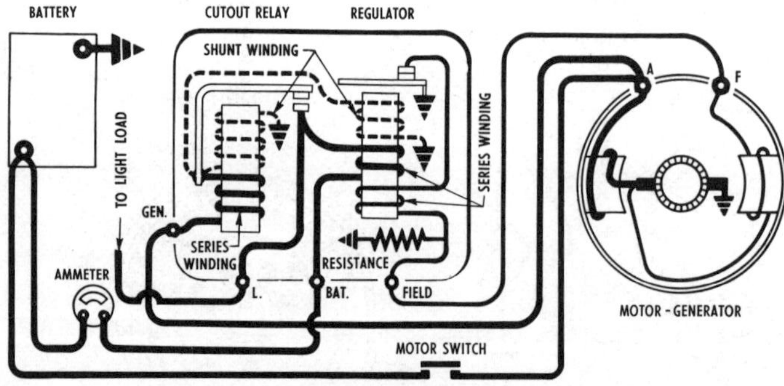

Fig. 10-18. Wiring Diagram of Motor-Generator and Regulator (Delco-Remy)

Operation of the cutout relay and the combination current-voltage regulator are explained in the *Generator Control* section of this chapter.

that would normally occur due to the commutated coils cutting the lines of force. This provides the brushes and commutator with additional serviceable life.

Bucking-Field Generator

Another method of controlling the armature reaction is by employing a magnetic field of opposite polarity. This is accomplished by placing a shunt winding in the opposite direction on one field pole and connecting this across the brushes of the armature, as shown at the left of Fig. 10-16. When the normal field is strong at low speeds, the opposing effect will be small, and at higher speeds, the current can be regulated by the voltage regulator. The opposing magnetic effect will be greater than the residual magnetic field. In this way, the current through the field coils can be controlled maintaining a normal voltage.

Split-Field Generator

This is another method of producing high current at low speeds. At the right of Fig. 10-16 is shown a split-field generator. This type has a strong set of field coils for slow speeds and a weak set for higher speeds. Each set has a separate external voltage and current regulators.

Motor-Generator

Some small gasoline engines employ a motor-generator, as shown in Fig. 10-17. This unit serves to crank the engine and to satisfy the electrical needs of the installation as well as to charge the battery.

The motor-generator contains a series and a shunt field. Both fields are used for developing torque when the unit operates as a motor. Figs. 10-18 and 10-19 illustrate the circuitory of a two terminal motor-generator with a two unit regulator. When the unit operates as a generator, the shunt field is the main field and the series field acts as a bucking field, which tends to limit generator output at high speed.

There is also a three-terminal motor-generator using a three-unit regulator. When this unit operates as a generator, the shunt field is the only field functioning because the series field is by-passed. Greater output at low and high speed is achieved in this manner.

The motor-generator functions as a cranking motor when the motor switch is closed. After the engine starts the switch opens the circuit and the unit operates as a generator. In the two-terminal motor-generator, control of the output and system voltage is achieved by using a current-voltage regulator.

Servicing the Generator

Maximum generator life can be easily obtained with proper maintenance. A little lubrication and inspection of the brushes and commutator are needed periodically. Also, cleanliness and sturdiness of the electrical connections determine efficiency.

It is important to check the belt and pulley arrangement, making sure that the belt is clean and not overly worn, and has the proper tension.

If any electrical contact, commutator or brushes are dirty, they can be cleaned by rubbing them with a fine abrasive paper, such as garnet or flint. Do not use emery paper since the abrasive grit breaks down too rapidly and penetrates the area being cleaned. If the brushes are worn below half their original size, they should be replaced. One way of determining this is by comparing them with new brushes. In replacing the brushes, care should be exercised to make sure that they move freely within their holders. New brushes should be shaped to the contour of the commutator with abrasive paper that is stretched over the area they will contact. The brushes are relatively soft and will wear to shape quite rapidly.

Generator Controls

There are several control devices necessary for generator systems. These include the cutout relay, and devices to control generator voltage and generator current. This section will consider the operation and maintenance of these devices.

Cutout Relay

To prevent the battery from discharging through the generator when the engine is idling, a cutout relay is used in the battery-generator circuit. See Fig. 10-20. This relay closes when the speed of the engine turns the armature fast enough to induce sufficient voltage to charge the battery, and opens when there is not sufficient generated voltage to charge the battery.

The typical cutout relay consists of two coils of wire wound on the same core, Fig.

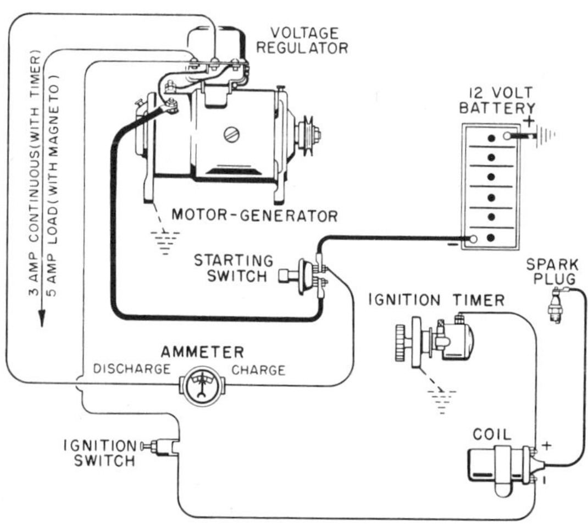

Fig. 10-19. Motor-Generator Electrical System (Wisconsin)

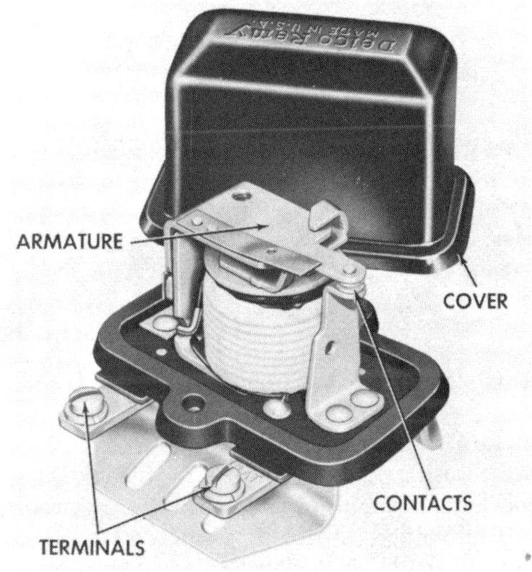

Fig. 10-20. Cutout Relay (Delco-Remy)

10-21. One winding is made of heavy wire and is connected in series with the circuit, while the other is of many turns of finer wire and is connected across the generator.

A hinged arm above the core of the coils contains contact points. When the generator is not producing enough voltage to charge the battery, the contact points are held apart. When there is enough voltage to charge the battery, the current through the coils produces enough magnetism to attract the arm of the core, close the contact points, and complete the circuit between generator and battery. Current flows through the series coils adding to the magnetic force that draws the leaf armature down. When the generator slows down, current reverses and flows from the battery to the generator. This causes an opposite magnetic force in the series winding only, cancelling attraction of the shunt winding. The contact points open as the arm is moved away by a spring, opening the battery-generator circuit.

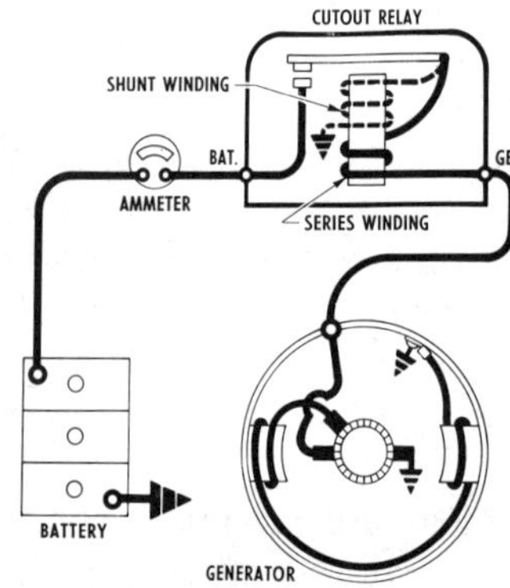

Fig. 10-21. Cutout Relay Wiring Diagram (Delco-Remy)

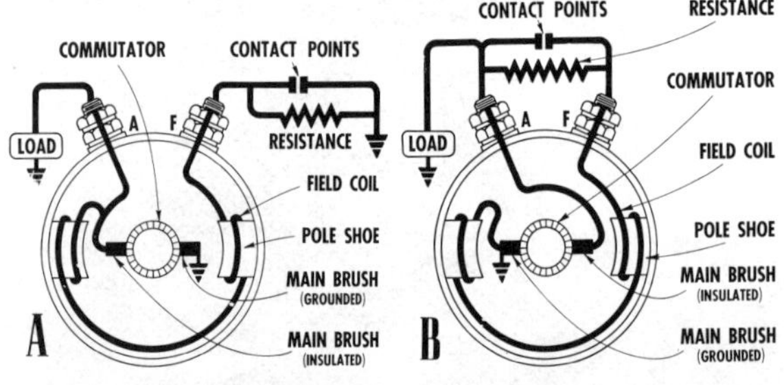

Fig. 10-22. A and B Circuits for Shunt Generator and Regulator (Delco-Remy)

In the A circuit, the field is connected to the insulated brush and is grounded at the external end by the regulator control points. In the B circuit, the field is grounded at the internal end and is connected externally to the insulated brush through the regulator.

Relay Maintenance: The relay, to be effective, must be clean with the gap-opening properly set and the prescribed voltage required for operation maintained.

The cover of the cutout relay must be removed, and the battery must be disconnected before any check can be made. If the points are dirty, they can be sanded with some fine abrasive paper. The gap between the points can be easily adjusted so that they close when the armature is held down by loosening the adjusting screws and raising or lowering the point until properly set. Care should be taken to keep the points in line and the adjusting screws tightly seated.

The operating voltage of the relay can be checked with a voltmeter. One leg of the meter is connected to the generator terminal of the relay and the other to the ground. The reading is taken when the speed of the engine causes the point contacts to close. Increasing or decreasing the tension by bending the spring post will proportionately increase or decrease the working voltage. In this way, the proper voltage is easily achieved.

Three-Unit Regulator

The type of current and voltage regulator must suit the type of internal wiring employed in the generator. The two basic hookups "A" and "B" are shown in Fig. 10-22. Their difference can be best explained if we first understand regulator operation. The regulator that will be discussed consists of a cutout relay, a voltage regulator and a current regulator unit, as shown in Fig. 10-23. *The cutout relay* closes the generator-battery circuit when generator voltage is enough for charging. It opens the circuit when the generator produces less voltage or stops generating.

The voltage regulator unit is a voltage-limiting device that prevents the system voltage from *exceeding* a specified maximum and thus protects all voltage sensitive equipment including the battery. *The current regulator* unit is a current limiting device that limits the output of the generator as so not to exceed its maximum.

Fig. 10-24 is a wiring diagram of the three-unit regulator.

Regulator Cutout Unit

The cutout relay has two windings, and operates in the same manner as the separate cutout previously described. When the generator is not operating, the contact points are held apart by the tension of a flat spring located on the side of the contact arm.

Voltage Regulator

The voltage regulator unit (at right) has a shunt winding of many turns of wire which is connected across the generator output. The winding and core are assembled in a frame. A flat steel armature above the core is attached to the frame by a flexible hinge so the contact points align. When the voltage unit is not operating, the spring tension holds the armature away from the core so the points are closed. This completes the generator field circuit to the ground in an A-circuit regulator. In the B circuit regulator the field circuit is completed to the generator armature through the closed contact points.

Voltage Regulator Action: When the generator voltage reaches the potential for which it is adjusted, the magnetic field produced by the winding overcomes the armature spring tension, pulls down the armature and separates the contact points. This places resistance into the generator field circuit. The field current and voltage are reduced. Reduction of the generator voltage reduces the magnetic field of the regulator shunt winding. The result is that the magnetic field is further weakened and allows the spiral spring to pull the armature away from the core and the contact points again close. This directly grounds the "A" current or connects the "B" circuit generator field circuit causing the generator voltage and output to increase. This action takes place many times a second regulating the voltage to a predetermined value. Most generators in 6 volt systems are designed to provide 7 volts while those in 12 volt systems provide 14 volts.

Current Regulator

The current regulator (center) has a series winding of a few turns of heavy wire through which all generator output passes. The winding and the core are assembled onto a frame. A flat steel armature above the core is attached to the frame by a flexible hinge so the contact points align. When the current reguoator is not functioning, the spring tension holds the armature away from the core so that the points are in contact. In this position the generator field is completed to ground in the "A" circuit and completed to the generator output in the "B" circuit through the contact points of both current regulator points then voltage regulator in series.

Current Regulator Action: When the generator amperage reaches its set value, the magnetic pull of the winding overcomes the

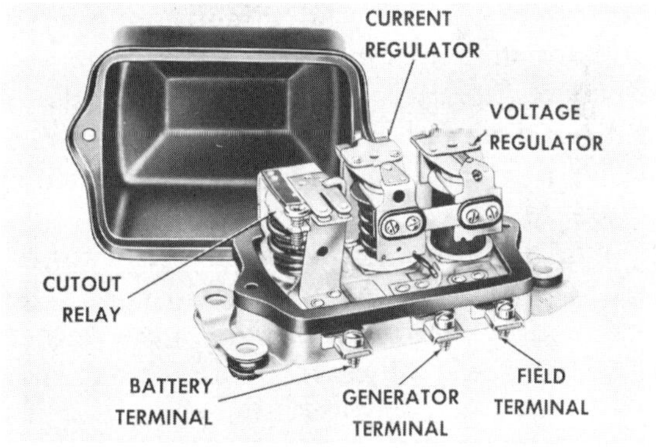

Fig. 10-23. Three-Unit Regulator (Delco-Remy)

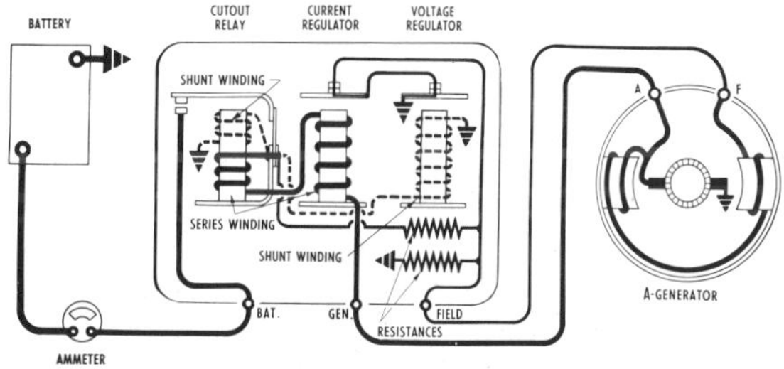

Fig. 10-24. Wiring Circuit of Standard Three-Unit Regulator (Delco-Remy)

spring tension of the armature and pulls the armature down opening the points. This places a resistance into the generator field circuit, the output of the generator is reduced, reducing the magnetic field of the current regulator winding. The result is that the magnetic field is weakened enough to permit the spiral spring to return to the armature upwards closing the contact points. This directly grounds the "A" circuit generator field circuit. In the "B" circuit, the generator field circuit is connected to the generator armature when the points are closed. In both situations the generator output increases. This cycle is repeated many times a second limiting the generator amperage so that it does not exceed its design maximum. Most regulators are designed to provide 36 amperes in 6 volt systems and 25 amperes in 12 volt systems.

Resistances

The current and voltage regulator unit circuit employs two common resistors, the lower one in Fig. 10-24 is inserted in the field circuit when either the circuit or voltage regulator unit operates in the A-circuit, the second resistor is connected to the regulator field terminal and to the cutout relay frame. In the B-circuit the second resistor is connected to the regulator field terminal and ground. In either situation the resistor is shunted across the generator field coils. The sudden drop in field current causes either the current or voltage regulator contacts to open. This is accompanied by a surge of induced voltage as the strength of the magnetic field changes. These surges are partially dissipated by the resistors preventing excessive arcing in the contact points.

Two-Unit Regulator

Now look back at Fig. 10-18 and note how voltage and current regulation can be combined into a single unit with three windings. The second unit of the regulator is the standard cutout relay. When generating, the motor-generator has a short compound (series-parallel) field.

Regulator Polarity

Regulators are designed for use with negative or positive ground systems. Using a regulator having the wrong polarity will cause the contact points to pit badly and yield short life. As a precaution against installation of the wrong regulator all units have the model number and the polarity clearly stamped on the base of the regulator.

In the *standard* generator system the current-voltage regulator resistance is situated between the field and the ground when the points are opened. In another system, the *heavy duty* system, the current-voltage regulator resistance is placed between the field coil and the main insulated brush.

The terms *heavy* and *standard* duty have no bearing on the output of the system. Both systems are designed for light or heavy loads, but their components cannot be interchanged. The systems can be recognized by inspecting the brushes and field coil connections. If the field coil is connected to the ungrounded main brush, the generator system is of the standard type; if the field coil is connected to the grounded main brush, the system is the heavy duty type.

Regulator Maintenance

(1) Mechanical checks and adjustments must be made with the battery disconnected and the regulator preferably off the vehicle. Never connect the contact points by hand with the battery connected to the regulator because this would cause a high surge to flow through the units, seriously damaging them. (2) Electrical checks and adjustments may be made either on or off the vehicle. The regulator must always be operated with the type of generator for which it was designed. (3) The voltage regulator and current regulator must be tested with the generator operating at 3500 rpm. (4) After testing and adjustments, the generator on the vehicle must be polarized before the engine is started.

Polarizing the generator. To polarize in the A-circuit generators after reconnecting the regulator, connect a jumper lead momentarily across two terminals of the regulator—

the generator and battery terminals. This permits a surge of current to flow through the generator and correctly polarizes it. Failure to do this may result in severe damages to the equipment since reverse polarizing causes vibrating, arcing and burning of the contact points.

To polarize "B" circuit generators, disconnect the lead at the regulator field terminal and momentarily touch this lead to the battery terminal of the regulator. This permits the current to flow through the generator which correctly polarizes it. Failure to do this will result in severe damage to the equipment.

Starters

The smaller gasoline and diesel engines are easily started manually by using a hand crank, a rope and pulley device or a spring-load starter to turn the engine over until it begins firing. These devices are relatively efficient, but can be physically taxing if the engine is cantankerous. Larger engines use an electric motor, the starter, to turn the crankshaft until the engine starts.

Electric Starters

Starting motors are extremely powerful for their size. They develop their power by utilizing a great deal of current—200 to 300 amperes. This large current can cause a battery to drain rapidly if the starter is run excessively to turn a stubborn engine. Since high amperage develops a great deal of heat the starter may burn out if it is not rested periodically to permit cooling.

All starters in use today basically look much like the one shown in Fig. 10-25. They consist of a drive mechanism, an armature, commutator, brushes, a field coil, and a frame. The amount of power required determines the number of field poles and brushes. Two pole requires four brushes, four pole requires four brushes, six pole—six brushes in series wound motors. While a starter appears much like a generator, its operation is the reverse because it consumes rather than produces electrical power. Starting motor coils require very heavy wire.

Principle of Operation

All motors are based on the law of magnetism or *like poles repel, unlike poles attract.* The armature coils and the field poles have a magnetic field surrounding them as they conduct electricity. The polarity of the field-coil is fixed, but the polarity of the armature coils can be changed by employing brushes and a commutator. The armature can be made to rotate if its coils have the opposite polarity of the field coils so they will be attracted. Then, at the instant the rotation has cancelled this attraction, the commutator changes armature polarity to make the coils of like polarity so that they will repel. This alternate attracting and repelling of the armature coil by the field coil causes the armature to rotate.

All starter motors are so wound that the field magnet is in series with the armature field. These series-wound motors are capable of starting under tremendous loads while providing maximum torque. On the other hand, shunt-wound motors would start with

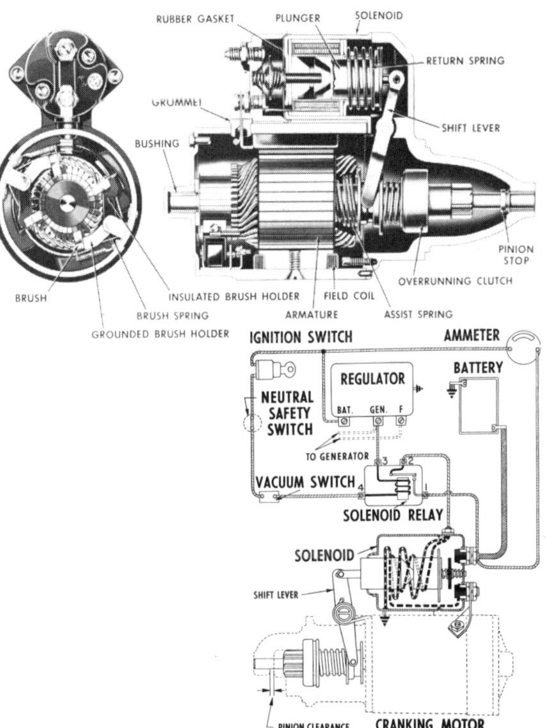

Fig. 10-25. Starting Motor (Delco-Remy)

low torque, and maintain a steady speed. Series-wound motors have been known to destroy themselves, due to centrifugal force, if they are operated with no load.

Starter Solenoid

The starter requires high amperage to turn over a dead engine. This high amperage requires a heavy cable between starter and the battery. A solenoid, an electro-magnetic switch, is used to connect the battery to the starter when the starter switch is closed to provide a more direct path for the current. Another reason for the use of the solenoid is to allow light conductors and electrical currents in the dashboard or control area. Also, a mechanical switch to carry such high amperage is unusually large and more difficult to locate effectively.

The solenoid is activated by a small current when the starter switch is closed. This permits a high amperage from the battery to the starter without any appreciable line loss.

Terms to Understand

lead-acid storage battery
EMF
ampere hour
electrode
plates
electrolyte
specific gravity
hydrometer
fully charged
charging
direct current
generator
field coil
electro magnet
series-wound generator
shunt-wound generator
series-parallel generator
armature
AC generator
alternator
frequency
DC generator
PDC
commutator
brushes
slip rings
three-brush generator
interpole generator
bucking-field generator
split-field generator
motor-generator
cutout relay
voltage, current regulator
polarizing the generator
A, B circuits
electric starters
solenoid

Study Questions

1. Analyze the function and basic characteristics of a storage battery.
2. Analyze the purpose of a generator.
3. What are the various types of generators?
4. Describe the operation of a DC generator.
5. Describe the operation of an alternator.
6. Analyze the purpose and operation of the cutout relay.
7. Analyze the purpose and operation of the current and voltage regulators.
8. Analyze the purpose, operation and characteristics of an electrical starter.
9. Analyze the purpose and operation of the solenoid.
10. Describe the function and operation of the distributor.

Compression Ignition Engines

A diesel engine is an oil burning internal combustion prime mover. It burns a fossil fuel atomized into the combustion chamber. Efficient combustion results from the intimate contact between the extremely fine fuel particles and highly compressed air. The extreme temperatures of compression within the cylinder causes combustion of the fuel without a special ignition system. The rate at which fuel is injected determines the speed and pressure of combustion and thus the power.

As indicated in Chapters 7 and 8, diesel or compression ignition (CI) engines are very similar to gasoline or spark ignition (SI) engines. They differ mainly in that CI requires no ignition system. Diesels use higher compression ratios to ignite a lower grade fuel. No electrical components are necessary for ignition unless the engine is only partly CI in design. Some diesels may use spark ignition for starting. The shape of the combustion chamber, as well as injection timing, pressures, and fuel metering are important.

This chapter will explain the operation of compression ignition, and the various combustion chambers, injector systems, governors, starting systems, and the uses of diesels. Figs. 11-1 to 11-3 locates some of the mechanisms of a compression ignition engine.

Diesel engine components are usually heavier than gasoline engines because of the additional structural strength needed for the higher compression ratio and its additional power. See Fig. 11-4.

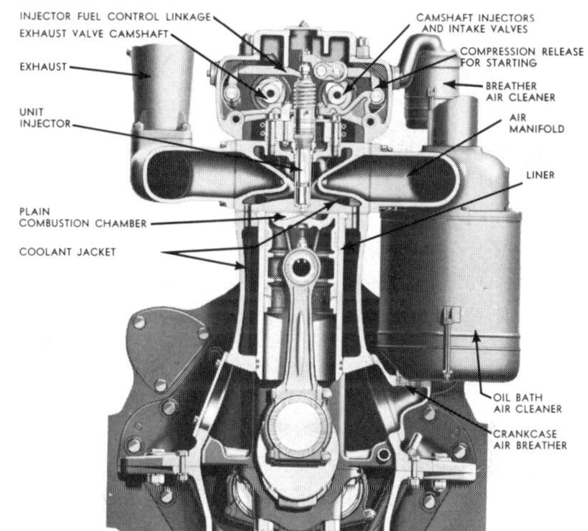

Fig. 11-1. Cross Section of Diesel Engine
(Murphy)

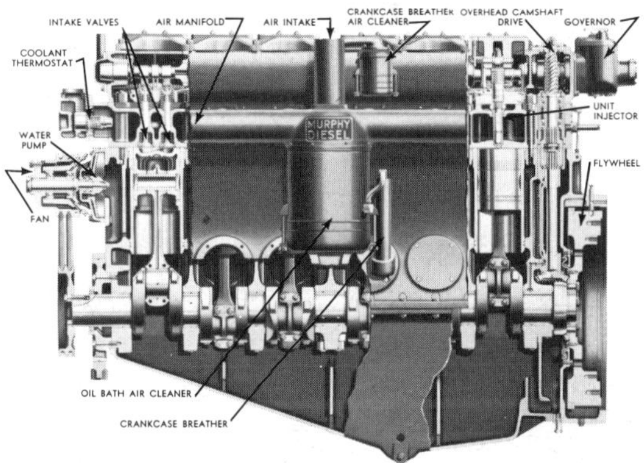

Fig. 11-2. Diesel Engine Mechanism, Side View
(Murphy)

This shows how unit injectors are located at the center of the open combustion chambers. Note the dual overhead camshafts. Four valves per cylinder give better breathing for the 4-cycle operation.

Diesel Operation

The diesel engine uses no carburetor, but employs an injection system to spray the fuel into the air compressed by the piston. This mixture burns and the expanding gases push the piston down producing power. The timing of fuel injection is just as critical as the spark that causes combustion in the gasoline engine. Therefore, the injecting mechanism is connected by gear or chain to the crankshaft.

The fuel injector sprays the fuel into the chamber against the pressure (in excess of 500 pounds sq. in.) of compressed air. The injector nozzle must atomize and force the fuel to mix thoroughly in the entire combustion chamber to produce maximum energy for the fuel expended.

As the diesel has no carburetor to vary the fuel and air mixture to provide engine control, some other method must be used to vary the mixture to control the power and the speed. Since each cylinder takes and compresses a full-charge of air, the power must be varied by the *amount of fuel injected.*

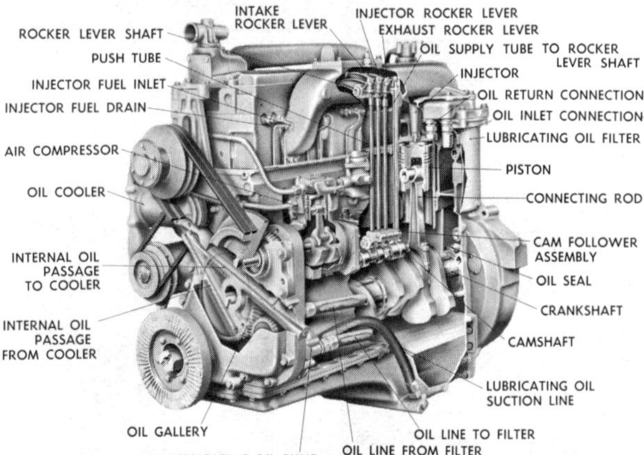

Fig. 11-3. Mechanism of Diesel Truck Engine (Cummins)

Fig. 11-4. Diesel Repair Shop (Santa Fe)

Either of two main systems have been used to inject fuel. In various *solid injection systems* liquid fuel is pumped directly into each cylinder. In the older *air injection systems* compressed air was used to blow fuel into the combustion chamber.

Solid injector systems are used in most modern diesel engines. These systems have various pump and timing arrangements and a nozzle for each cylinder. They are made with such precision that they can provide pressures in excess of 20,000 psi and force fuel into the combustion chambers at speeds greater than 750 mph.

Air injection systems have been used quite extensively for large, low-speed stationary and marine engines. This system has a separate air compressor to blow fuel into the combustion chamber. Such engines can be operated quite economically, but demand more skill to operate than solid-fuel injection systems. Their operation will not be detailed.

There are many variations of combustion chamber designs, nozzle designs and locations, fuel injection timing, as well as duration and pressure. Each is designed to acquire maximum energy from the fuel for a particular range of speeds, power, acceleration, or other working conditions.

Combustion Chambers

At one time, all diesel engines were large and slow-moving, and only one type of combustion chamber was used. This was the plain open-chamber into which the fuel was injected. As the engines became smaller and the speeds higher, various auxiliary combustion chambers were designed for efficiency.

Although there are many designs, the following four types of combustion chambers are illustrative: 1. plain combustion chamber; 2. separate ignition chambers or pre-cups; 3. turbulence chamber; 4. energy cell across from the nozzle. With all these combustion chambers the waterjacket, heat insulation and external head are designed to maintain the best running temperature.

Plain Combustion Chamber

The only contours in a plain combustion chamber are on the piston head which is usually dished as shown in Figs. 11-1 to 11-3 and 11-5. While injectors with a separate pressure pump may have some type of auxiliary chamber, new unit injectors with an integral piston pump develop such tremendous pressures that good combustion is possible without more complex shapes. The recessed cylinder head usually is raised at the center to promote some turbulence and to force air close to the fuel spray of the nozzle. Intake ports of two-cycle diesels are also designed to bring in air in a swirling motion, Fig. 11-5. The nozzle sprays outwards.

Pre-Cup Combustion Chamber

Most of the air is compressed through a narrow throat upward into a separate ignition chamber containing the nozzle, also shown in Fig. 11-6. The narrow throat makes use of the venturi principle to promote turbulence both in compressing the air and forcing the gases of combustion back into the cylinder. The fuel is sprayed into the pre-combustion chamber, where it ignites. The burning mixture then escapes into the main combustion chamber creating complete combustion. The injection of fuel is just before TDC so the main expansion into the cylinder comes when the piston starts downward. Some pre-cups have a glow plug to heat this small chamber to promote easier starting, Fig. 7-24.

Turbulence Chamber

Another variety of pre-combustion chamber is shown in Fig. 11-7. This circular auxiliary chamber holds about a fourth to a half of the compressed air and is connected at its edge to the main chamber. As air is forced through the throat by the piston moving upwards, it speeds into the side chamber setting up a swirling turbulence. Fuel is injected and ignited as it mixes readily with swirling air then expands into the cylinder proper.

Energy Cell

The energy cell is an auxiliary chamber diametrically opposite the injection nozzle as in Fig. 11-8. Since the fuel is injected through the center of the main chamber, it comes in contact with the very hottest air which has not been cooled by contact with

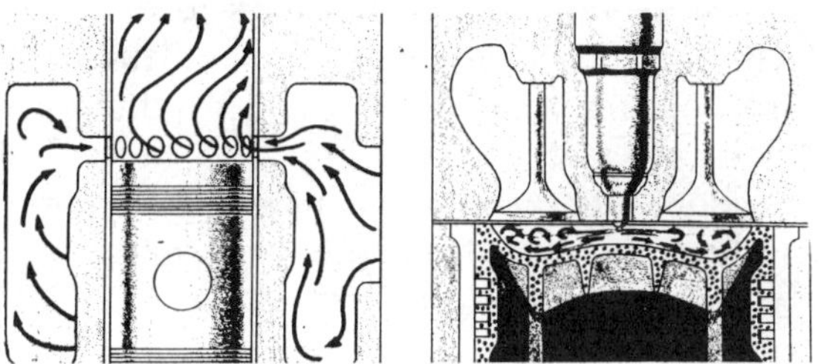

Fig. 11-5. Plain Combustion Chamber (G.M.)

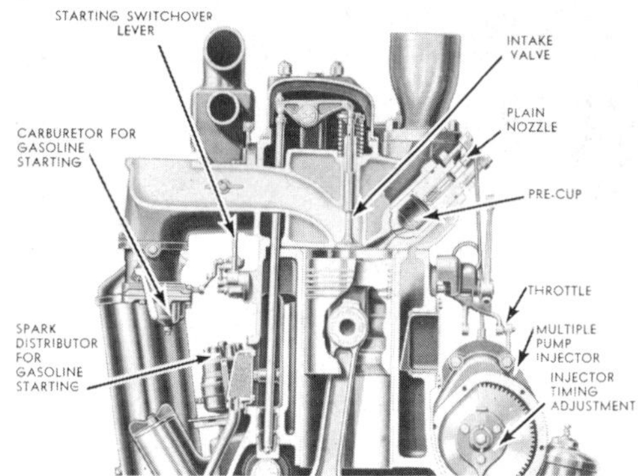

Fig. 11-6. Cut-Away Showing Pre-Cup Combustion Chamber (International)
Also note the provision for starting on gasoline fuel, and the injection timing adjustment on the multiple pump injector and separate nozzle.

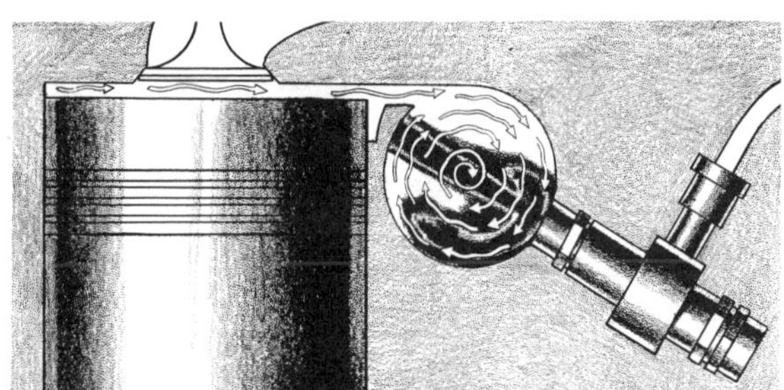

Fig. 11-7. Pre-Combustion Turbulence Chamber (G.M.)

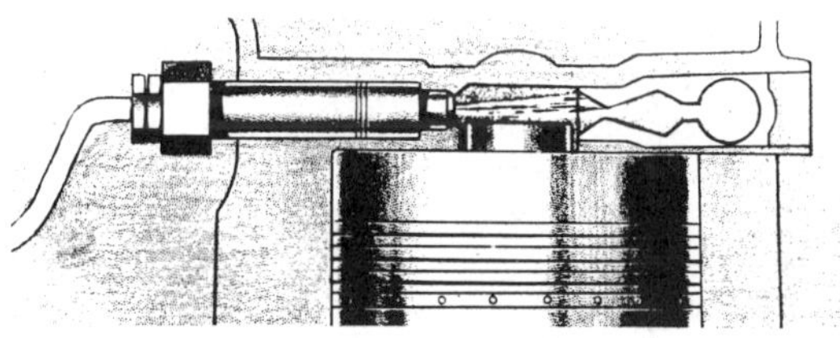

Fig. 11-8. Energy Cell (G.M.)

the walls of the combustion chamber. About 40 per cent of the fuel is mixed with this extremely hot air and begins to burn while the remaining 60 per cent burns within the cell. Pressure in the cell reaches in excess of 1,100 psi, but in the main chamber, the pressure does not exceed 700 psi. The difference of the pressure causes the cell charge to move out into the main chamber, setting up a swirling movement of fuel and air which cleans up remaining unburned fuel.

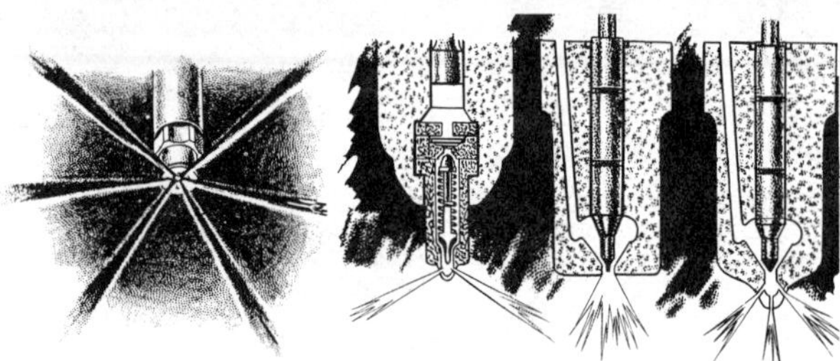

Fig. 11-9. Diesel Spray Nozzles (G.M.)

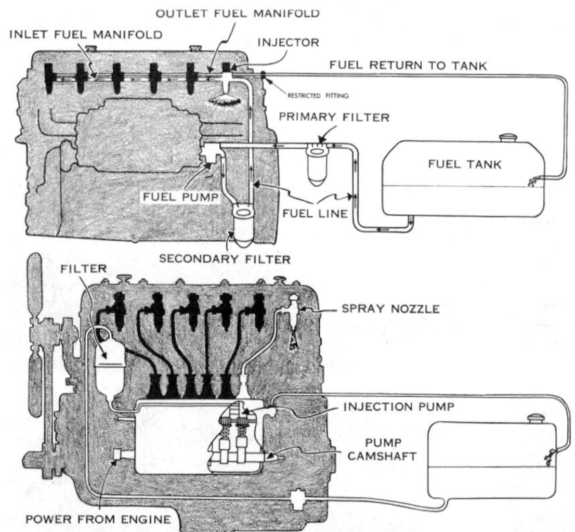

Fig. 11-10. Two Types of Fuel Injection Systems (G.M.)

Top: *Unit injector system* has a separate complete unit for each cylinder. Fuel is circulated to each injector by a low pressure pump. Restricted return keeps a slight feed pressure to the high pressure pump in each injector unit.

Bottom: *Multiple pump system* has high pressure pumps for each cylinder in a separate mechanism. Low pressure fuel transfer pump circulates fuel to injectors. Each injector is connected to its nozzle by a high pressure tube.

Spray Nozzles

The nozzle in the combustion chambers (or any auxiliary chamber) is placed so as to best distribute the force of combustion to the top surface of the piston.

Some nozzles have one central hole with a spray pin causing the fuel to be forced out in a cone-shaped spray, like that of a garden hose. Other injectors have several holes forcing the oil to spray outward. See Fig. 11-9. Most have a needle valve which is opened by the high pressure surge of fuel. This gives a more positive start and cutoff.

Basically, there are three ways a nozzle is combined with the rest of the injection system. *First,* it can be built into a *unit* for each cylinder which contains all needed injection parts (nozzle, pressure pump, throttle controls, timing mechanism). See top of Fig. 11-10. *Second,* only the *timing valve* may be combined with the injector nozzle, and a continuous pressure furnished by a separate pump system. *Third,* the nozzle may simply be a *spray orifice* which receives a high pressure shot of fuel at the instant of injection. See bottom of Fig. 11-10. Any one of these three types of nozzle units may be called the *injector.*

Fuel Injection Systems

The heart of the compression ignition engine is the fuel system because it squirts the proper amount of fuel into the proper combustion chamber against the high internal pressures caused by compression. The fuel system actually performs the operation of both the distributor and carburetor in the spark ignition system.

Some of the components of the fuel system are similar to those in spark ignition engines: fuel tank, filters, fuel transfer pump, and fuel lines. The injectors are a most important component, quite unique to the diesel fuel system. The components required in the injector are a nozzle for each cylinder and at least one high-pressure injection pump, a timing arrangement, and a throttle device to control power and speed. Two fuel systems are compared in Fig. 11-10.

The mechanism for varying the injection into the combustion chamber controls engine speed. This amount of fuel will vary from none at all, to enough to deliver maximum power. This is very critical because of the small quantities involved. In a truck engine, the most injected into a cylinder would be a drop about ⅛ inch in diameter.

Four common solid injector systems are the *unit-injector system*, the *common-rail system*, the *multiple-pump system*, and the *distributor system*. Each will be explained in turn.

Unit-Injector System

A unit-injector system consists of one complete injector unit for each cylinder as shown in Fig. 11-11. This system is most popular because it is trouble free and dependable. However, because of the mechanisms to be built into the head, it is not as readily adapted to any engine as systems having a separate pump and nozzle. The engine must be built around the unit injector.

The unit injector shown in Fig. 11-12 provides all the essential elements of fuel injection for efficient operation. Its piston pump provides the high pressure needed to inject the fuel directly into the combustion chamber. The integral nozzle atomizes the fuel for fast complete combustion. The control lever varies the amount of fuel to be injected for a throttle control. Operation and timing of each unit is direct from the cam shaft.

The fuel is metered by a helix in the pump plunger which allows a varying part of the fuel charge to be bypassed. This reduces the charge injected into the combustion chamber at slow speeds. An arm on each injector controls this bypass. All control arms are linked to the throttle. See Fig. 11-1.

As this system has no central metering or pressure pump, it has no high pressure lines that may rupture.

The injectors may be easily replaced in minutes if they become defective. The system can be easily checked, since the fuel does not flow through a governor, pressure regulator, separate throttle, individual pressure pumps or other such complicated devices. Any component of the unit-injector system can easily be replaced if it malfunctions.

Most unit injectors have both fuel inlet and outlet connections so pumps can circulate flow of fuel. Figs. 11-10 (top) and 11-13 show the low-pressure fuel-transfer pump, and the flow of fuel. The system is self-bleeding of any air, and filters remove any sediment which might clog injectors.

Unit-injector systems may provide 5,000 psi or more without penalties. These higher pressures give better penetration and a more

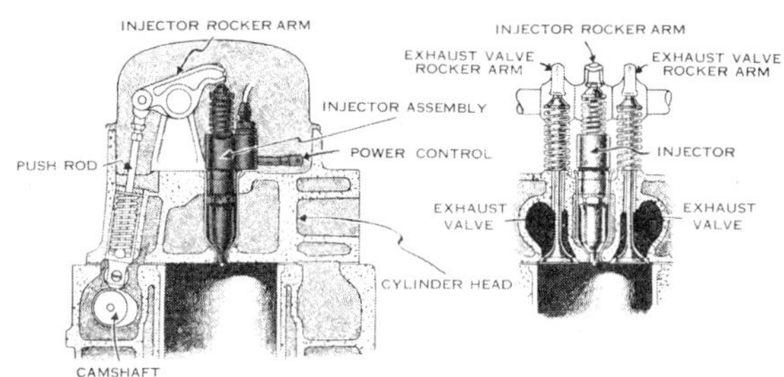

Fig. 11-11. Unit-Injector Mechanism (G.M.)

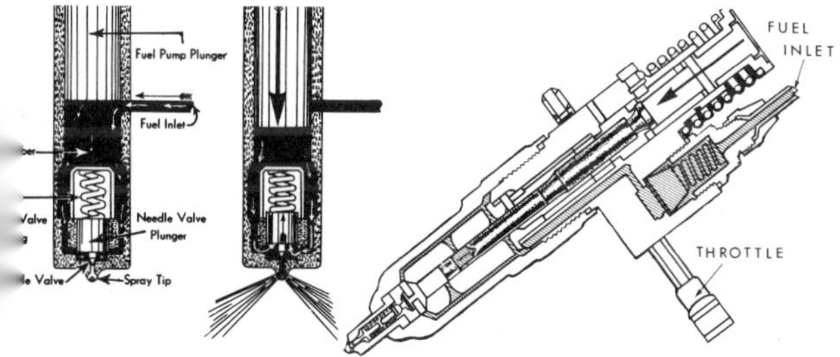

Fig. 11-12. Unit-Injector Operation (G.M.)

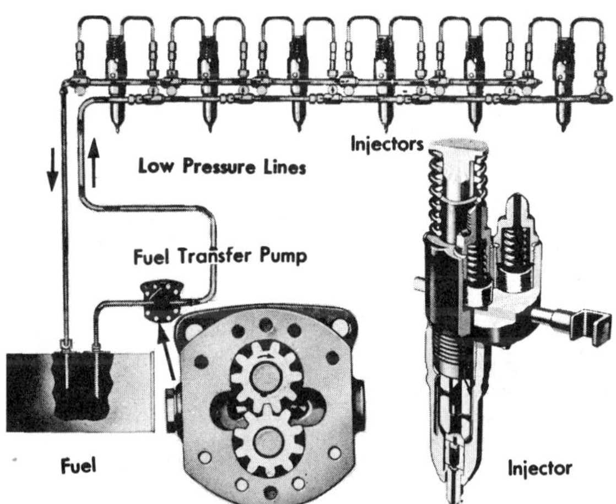

Fig. 11-13. Unit-Injector System (G.M.)

thorough atomization of fuel into the combustion chamber. As a result, plain combustion chambers may be used as no auxiliary chambers are necessary. By doing away with the excess turbulance, a greater amount of the heat of combustion is put into useful work instead of being lost in auxiliary chambers. Consequently, this system can be very economical.

Common-Rail System

The *common-rail* or *pressure-time system* consists of a fuel pump assembly mounted on the side of the engine. This contains a pressure regulator, centrifugal governor, gear type pressure pump, throttle shaft and shut down valve. This assembly is connected by a single high-pressure fuel line to injectors for each cylinder. See Fig. 11-14.

Metering is through a fixed orifice in the injector so is accomplished by varying the pressure of the fuel and the length of the injection period. Pressurized fuel at 2,000 to 3,000 psi is supplied to the injectors and the time for metering is determined by the interval during which the metering orifice remains open in the injector.

This system pressurizes the fuel with a single pump to the common rail. This pressure is maintained by pressure-regulated bypass valves, which permit the surplus fuel to return to the fuel tank. A failure of any of the components can cause the entire system to fail. Like most other systems, if a portion of the pump assembly fails, it is usually the practice to replace the entire assembly.

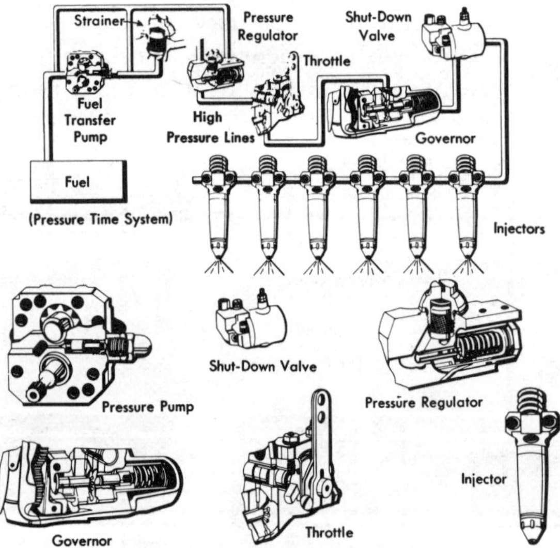

Fig. 11-14. Common-Rail (Pressure-Time) Injection System (G.M.)

An injection nozzle for each cylinder is located in the head and is connected by high pressure tubing to the rail. Each nozzle has a control valve seated by a spring. A cam lifts the valve when injection is desired, permitting the fuel to flow through the nozzles into the combustion chamber. The amount of fuel admitted into each chamber is controlled by the height that the valve is lifted and the length of time it is permitted to remain open. A wedge-shaped device varies the lift.

The common-rail system is very satisfactory for *constant load operation.* It is not well suited for general power applications where the speed must be changed continually, nor is it suited for high speed use.

Multiple-Pump System

The multiple-pump system has a single assembly with *individual pressure pumps for each cylinder* which meter and distribute pressurized fuel through a high pressure line to each cylinder. There is a simple nozzle in each combustion chamber. Such a system is diagramed in Fig. 11-15.

Multi-pump systems are quite popular. The chief objection to them is that high pressure fuel lines between the pump assembly and injectors may rupture, interrupting fuel flow. Servicing is difficult because the pump assembly contains a number of individual pressure pumps. When a breakdown occurs, the practice is to exchange the whole pump assembly, which usually also incorporates the governor and the metering and pressurizing mechanism.

This system is not self bleeding, and as a result, whenever it is disassembled lines must be bled of all air. An *air relief valve* is thus required because the system has a one way flow. Fig. 11-10 (bottom) shows a multiple pump system which is self bleeding except for the high pressure lines.

Most engines using this system must use precombustion or turbulence chambers to assure adequate mixing of air and fuel because the injectors have only one opening through which the fuel passes into the cylinder.

The nozzles may be classified into two classes. One type has a spring-loaded check-valve in the nozzle tip that permits the oil to spray through the nozzle when the tension of the spring is overcome by the oil pressure. The other type has an open tip and depends upon the method of cutting off the fuel at the pump to prevent dribbling through the nozzle. The open-tip nozzle system lessens the tendency of clogging due to foreign matter passing the filters, but the closed-tip nozzle gives more satisfactory injection, and as a result, is more widely used. All nozzles used with the individual-pump system are automatically operated and do not require the cam mechanism used with the common-rail system.

Distributor Fuel System

The distributor system is much like the multiple-pump system except it uses a single pump and a rotating channel to distribute pressure through individual high pressure links to the nozzle in each combustion chamber. Like the multiple-pump system it is mounted on the side of the engine and is driven by a separate camshaft. The single fuel transfer pump has a single plunger that may be high or low pressure. Fuel oil is distributed to each cylinder in proper firing order by a rotating device with holes made to line-up with the proper fuel line—the mechanical counterpart of a spark distributor. See Figs. 11-16 and 11-17. Such an arrangement appears much like an SI engine.

The nozzles used with the distributor system are similar to those used in multiple pump systems. Pressurized fuel in both cases is furnished by the engine-mounted pump assembly and carried by high pressure fuel lines to each injector nozzle. These systems are both one way systems with no return lines, so that *bleeding* is required to prevent overloading or air locks.

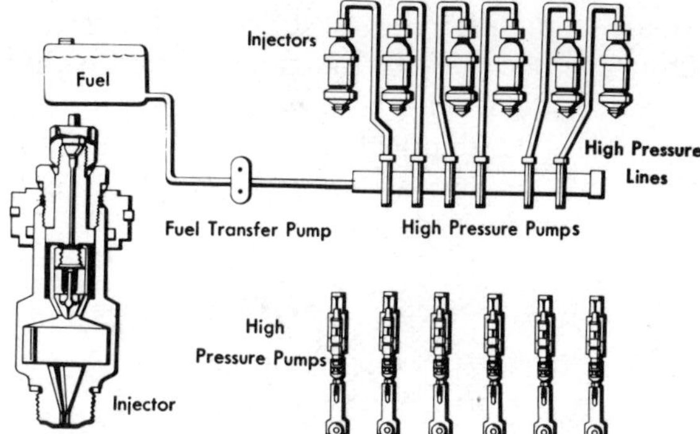

Fig. 11-15. Multiple-Pump Injection System (G.M.)

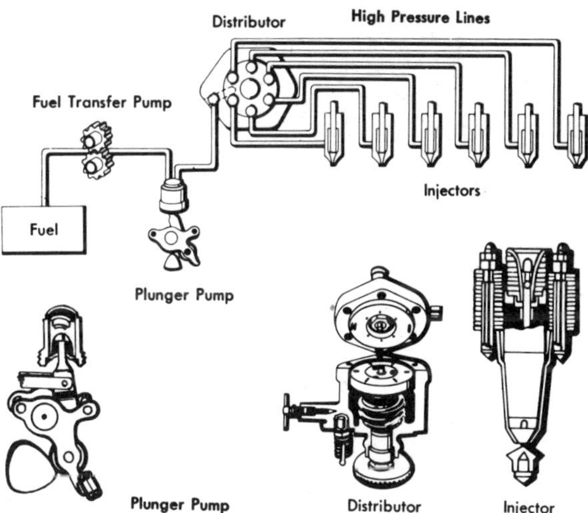

Fig. 11-16. Distributor Injection System (G.M.)

Fig. 11-17. Distributor Injection Unit (International)

Opposed cam-operated plungers in a single cylinder meter equal fuel charges to each cylinder. Unit can be throttle or governor controlled. Maintenance of single pump is simplified.

Long fuel lines such as used in multiple pump and distributor systems could detract from the accuracy of the timing of each fuel injection. The length of each high pressure line must be identical so the timed surge of pressure will not arrive early at closer cylinders. Note length of lines in Figs. 11-17 and 11-18. Sometimes the high pressures expand the fuel lines, resulting in less accurate fuel injection, especially at variable speed applications.

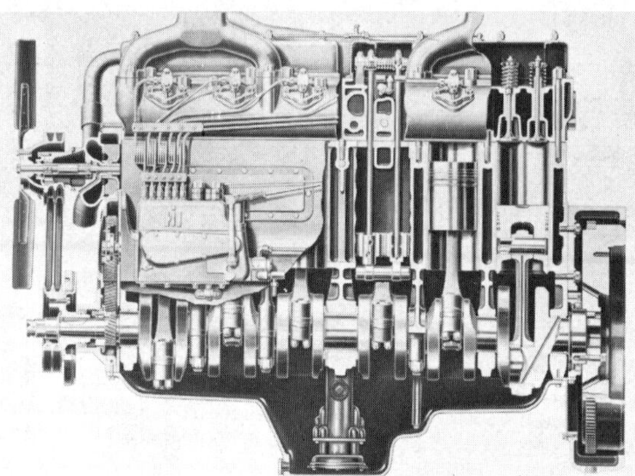

Fig. 11-18. Engine with Multiple-Pump Injection (International)

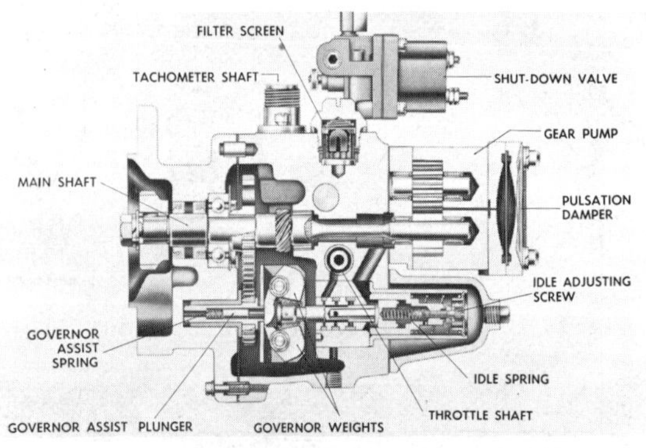

Fig. 11-19. Common-Rail Injection Unit with Governor, Pressure Pump, and Controls (Cummins)

Fig. 11-20. Compressor for Air Starting (Ingersoll-Rand)

Where precombustion chambers are employed, best operation is at high engine temperature. This provides the problem of starting the engine in cold weather, unless it is equipped with heating devices.

Most fuel systems are lubricated and cooled primarily by the fuel flow through them. This is satisfactory, especially when heavier fuels are used. Lubricating difficulties may be experienced when lighter fuels are used, especially when the engine is operated at high speeds.

Governors

In diesels, speed and power output are controlled by a variation in the amount of fuel injected into the cylinder. The governor controls the pump mechanism so that the fuel will be metered according to speed and load. The governor may be built separately or in combination with the pump. Fig. 11-19 shows a combination unit for a common rail system.

The governor is sensitive to varying speeds. Most governors operate on the centrifugal principle. When the throttle is set for a predetermined speed, the governor will maintain the rpm of the engine up to maximum horsepower. The throttle lever controls the governor which in turn controls the fuel supply regulating power output.

Starting Systems

Starting diesel engines of the smaller variety is more difficult than starting a gasoline engine of comparable size. Some very small engines use a hand cranking device, but they are exceptions.

Most diesel engines of small to medium size use electric starting motors or they use gasoline in one of two ways. A small, auxiliary gasoline engine may be so used to turn the diesel through a drive similar to those employed with an electric starter, or the diesel may be so designed that the gasoline may be burned within its own cylinders. In the latter case, provision must be made to decrease the compression ratio from about 16-1 to 5-1 and to electrically ignite the fuel and air mixture. The heavy-duty, slow-speed stationary diesels use compressed air for starting.

Air Starting

Air starting requires a powerful air-compressor unit such as shown in Fig. 11-20. In air-injection type of diesels, the compressor is already a part of the engine.

An air-starting valve is located in the head of each cylinder, and air is admitted from the compressor or storage tank at 400 psi to 1,000 psi into the combustion chamber. Engines using mechanical (or solid) injection need less air pressure for starting. The air is admitted in the proper sequence to the cylinders causing the engine to rotate while the fuel supply is turned off. When the engine speed is sufficient, half of the starting valves are closed and fuel is injected into these cylinders. As soon as these cylinders begin to fire and turn the engine, the remaining air valves are closed and fuel is admitted into the cylinders. The engine now runs on its own power, and the compressor tanks are refilled for another start. The whole starting device is operator-controlled.

Electric Starter

Electric starting systems, such as widely used with gasoline engines, are only adaptable to the smaller high-speed diesels. They must, however, be heavier and provide more starting power because of the high compression ratios. These starters usually require a 24 to 32 volt battery. See Figs. 11-21 and 11-22.

Although they are heavy and bulky, these systems are simple in operation and find acceptance in truck, automobile, tractor, and some small railroad installations, such as shown in Fig. 11-23.

The electric-starting engine is entirely dependent upon the electrical energy stored in the battery. When the unit is in good condition, the starting is quick, easy, and efficient.

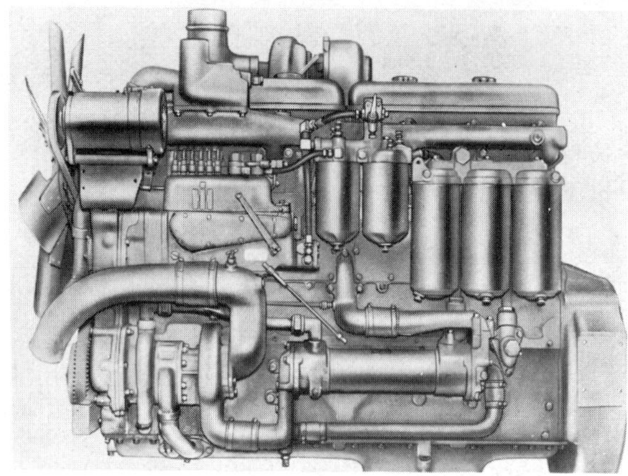

Fig. 11-21. Diesel Engine with 24-Volt System and Electrical Starter (International)
Multiple-pump injector delivers 20,000 psi to multi-orifice nozzles. Turbocharger uses exhaust energy to power blower. Engine has dual intake and exhaust valves, develops 250 hp at 2100 rpm.

Fig. 11-22. Diesel Powered Electric Generator with Electrical Starting (Fairbanks-Morse)

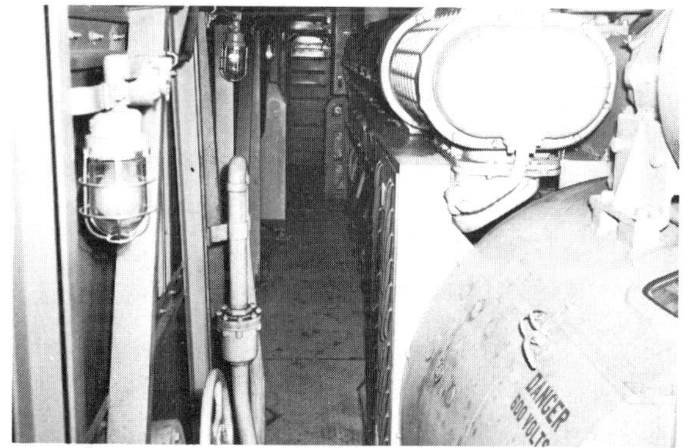

Fig. 11-23. Diesel-Electric Locomotive, Looking at Side of Engine (Santa Fe)

Fig. 11-24. New Diesel Powered Tugs (Nordberg)
Each is powered by a four-cycle diesel engine with 8 cylinders of 13-inch bore and 16½-inch stroke. It develops 1200 hp at 310 rpm and turns an 84-inch propellor with four variable pitch blades. Seven fuel tanks hold 30,000 gallons of #4 diesel fuel.

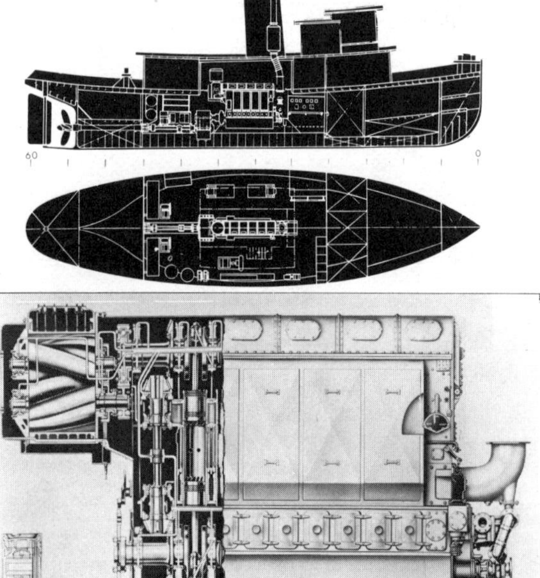

Fig. 11-25. Opposed Piston Diesel Engine—Layout Shows Use in 60-Foot Ship (Fairbanks-Morse)

Fig. 11-26. Reconditioned Ann Arbor No. 6
Two 2550 hp diesels replaced two triple-expansion steam engines on this ship. The conversion increased the capacity and the speed of the vessel.

In cold temperature starting, difficulty may be encountered by the additional resistance caused by the congealed lubricants. The battery can produce only so much amperage before its energy is depleted. It is apparent that the battery must be kept in excellent condition and be completely charged at all times.

At times, the diesel is pre-heated before starting is attempted. This is accomplished by flushing hot water into the water-jackets or by using a *glow-plug* in the combustion chambers.

Auxiliary Gasoline Starter

Some of the smaller-high speed engines use a gasoline engine and a Bendix drive mechanism similar to those used in the automobiles of today. These auxiliary starters are quite practical because they can exert more energy over a longer period of time than is possible with an electric starting system.

The usual method of starting the auxiliary gasoline engine makes use of a compression releasing mechanism to lift either the inlet or exhaust valves. This allows the starting engine to turn the diesel up to starting speed more easily. When starting speed is attained, the valves are returned to their natural position and the engine is operated as in the ordinary manner.

In some cases, the exhaust gases from the gasoline starting engine is used to pre-heat the diesel to facilitate cold weather starting.

Gasoline Starting

As indicated previously, some diesel engines are converted into gasoline engines for starting purposes. The electrical ignition and starting equipment are built into the diesel, but are used only when starting. See Fig. 11-6.

This method provides the surest cold weather and worn engine starting. This is because the engine is thoroughly heated by burning a gasoline and air mixture. During starting, the compression ratio is reduced (by means of a mechanical linkage) from 16:1 to 5:1 for gasoline operation, and the air intake is detoured to flow through a carburetor system before being admitted through the intake valves. When the diesel's starting speed is reached, this mechanical linkage can be released and the engine converted from gasoline to *full diesel.*

Diesels at Work

Diesel engines were, until recently, popular power plants for submarines. Nearly all of the submarines built during the last half century were powered by diesel engines. This condition is now quickly changing with the advent of nuclear power. These CI engines powered the craft on the surface and turned generators which charged huge banks of storage batteries. When beneath the sea, the craft could be powered by electric motors. The demand for huge quantities of air so necessary to operate any heat engine was eliminated by using electric motors.

Marine Diesels

Diesel engines proved useful as power plants for medium sized surface ships such as tugs, Fig. 11-24. For over 30 years, more ships have been built with diesel engines than with steam engines. Some of these installations use two or four diesel engines to develop 10,000 to 40,000 horsepower.

A relatively new and unique diesel power plant of highly simplified construction has been proven successful under most marine operating conditions. This opposed piston engine has 40 per cent fewer wearing parts than comparable engines of equal horsepower and finds application in tugs, tow boats, dredges, yachts, freighters, ice breakers, Navy ships, and submarines.

The engine, shown in Fig. 11-25, has no cylinder heads, valves, and valve-actuating mechanisms, no valves to grind or burn out, no push rods, rocker assemblies or springs to break, wear out or repair; yet, the engine offers reversing or non-reversing power, with a turbo-charger increasing its potential horsepower by 50 per cent. The engine has proven more efficient, economical, smaller in size, and more responsive to varying load demands than comparable engines.

It is interesting to note that diesel powered passenger ships are built with dummy funnels like those used on steamships, although they serve no useful purpose. An exhaust out the stern of the ship would work equally as well if not better. But because shipping companies believe that passengers expect to see stacks, they build them to satisfy. See Fig. 11-26.

Diesel Locomotive

Diesel engines are used to power large land vehicles such as trucks and locomotives. See Figs. 11-27 and 11-28. In fact, the diesel-electric locomotive has almost replaced the steam locomotive in the United States and it won't be long before the steam locomotive will become extinct in other lands. A reason for this is that diesel engines demand less time in the repair shop, have no boiler and fire box to maintain, and start instantly. However, some limitations of diesel engines are a heavier weight because of the higher com-

Fig. 11-27. 2000 hp Lead Diesel Unit (Santa Fe)
Inset shows cab with radio phone to caboose. To increase power this lead unit can be coupled to a number of second or "B".

Fig. 11-28. 2000 hp Road-Switch Locomotive (Santa Fe)

pression ratios, sluggish starts compared to gasoline engines, and reluctance to adapt to changing power. These have kept them from being used in automobiles and airplanes.

Diesel-Electric Combinations

The diesel engine can drive vehicles either directly or through an electric drive. In the latter case, the diesel turns an electric gen-

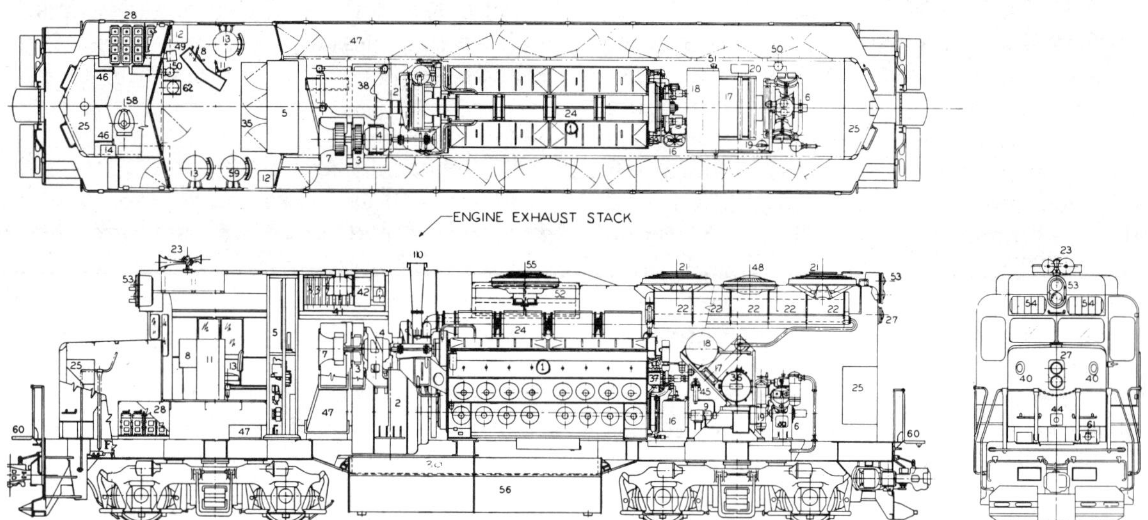

Fig. 11-29. Layout of 2250 hp Diesel-Electric Locomotive (G.M.)
(See Figs. 8-4, 8-5, 8-6 for photos of this compact 56-foot locomotive.)

1. Engine
2. Main Generator
3. Generator Blower
4. Auxiliary Generator
5. Control Cabinet
6. Air Compressor
7. Traction Motor Fan
8. Engineer's Control
9. Fuel Pump
10. Engine Exhaust Stack
11. Air Brake Valve
12. Cab Heater
13. Sliding Seat
14. Hand Brake
16. Lube Oil Filler
17. Lube Oil Cooler
18. Engine Water Tank
19. Fuel Pressure Filter
20. Load Regulator
21. 48″ Fan and Motor
22. Radiator
23. Horns
24. Exhaust Manifold
25. Sand Box
27. Twin Headlights
28. Batteries
30. Main Air Reservoir
35. Trap Door
36. Lube Oil Filter
37. Dual Fuel Filter
38. Engine Air Filter
41. Inertial Air Separator
42. Dust Evacuator
45. Fuel Filter
46. Collision Post
47. Traction Motor Air
48. 36″ Fan and Motor
49. Speed Recorder
50. Fire Extinguisher
51. Engine Water Filler
52. Dynamic Brake
53. Signal Light
55. Dynamic Brake Fan
56. Fuel Tank, 4300 gal.
58. Toilet
59. Third Cab Seat
61. 2nd Engine Plug-in
62. Water Cooler

Fig. 11-30. Diesel Power-Generator Unit
(Murphy)

This unit furnishes both electrical and mechanical power. It can drive a rock crusher through the clutch and independently furnish 100 kw of electricity for other work.

Fig. 11-31. Portable Diesel Generating Plants Develop 12,000 kw by Remote Control
(Sierra-Pacific Power)

erator which powers an electric motor. See Fig. 11-29. The electric motor propells the wheels or propeller shaft. Direct drive is usually preferred for trucks, electric drive for locomotives, and marine installations may employ either system.

Stationary Power Plants

Today, progressive engineering continues with efforts devoted to applying the diesel engine to stationary applications such as central generating stations, industrial power plants, oil pipe lines, pumping lines, flood control, and irrigation pumps. See Figs. 11-30 to 11-32. This prime mover has been successfully used because of operating advantages such as low maintenance, greater efficiency, controlled power, and fuel economy under all loads.

The versatility of this engine is exhibited in a design using natural gas and diesel fuel simultaneously as well as the sole use of conventional diesel fuel. See Figs. 11-33 to 11-36.

Comparative Efficiency

The average efficiency of SI engines from fuel to useful work is about 25 to 28 per cent, with the best engines achieving something like 30 to 32 per cent, an appreciably better average than steam engines. See Fig. 11-26.

Data from the Research Division of the General Motors Corporation indicate that the overall efficiency of the average automobile

Fig. 11-32. Diesel Power for Uranium Mine (Nordberg)

Six 6-cylinder 1200 hp diesel engines power 854 kw generators. Exhaust heats the building.

Fig. 11-33. Radial CI-SI Engines in Generating Station (Nordberg)

These two-cycle radial engines are dual fuel engines. They will burn diesel or any of several gases (natural or manufactured gas, sewage gas, propane, or others) with only a small amount of pilot oil to control combustion. They also have spark ignition for gasoline fuel. Cylinders have a 14-inch bore and a 16-inch stroke and develop 2,000 to 3,200 hp. These 36 engines are part of the world's largest internal combustion engine power plant at Point Comfort, Texas, which produces a half million hp.

Fig. 11-34. World's Largest Dual-Fuel Engine (Nordberg)

The unit produces 8500 hp with a 29-inch bore and a 40-inch stroke. It drives 12,470-volt generator developing 875 kva in Ponca City, Oklahoma.

Fig. 11-35. Dual-Fuel Engines in Pipe Line Pump Station (Nordberg)

These 4-cycle 8-cylinder engines have 13″ x 16½″ in-line turbocharged cylinders which deliver 2,000 hp each at 514 rpm. This Sinclair station at Teague, Texas uses natural gas with diesel oil as pilot fuel.

in everyday driving is about 8 per cent. In other words, 8 cents of every dollar spent on gasoline is expended in actually moving the car along the road. The remainder is consumed in various ways. About 40 per cent is absorbed by the cooling system, 20 per cent is wasted due to incomplete and faulty combustion, 30 per cent is needed to overcome friction of one sort or another, and the remainder produces sound rather than usable power. The principle hope for increasing total efficiency lies in reducing combustion losses by improving techniques of fuel ignition, injection and burning.

The CI engine is a little more efficient because of its higher compression ratio. Another important reason for the CI's low operation cost is the fact that its efficiency remains nearly constant over a relatively wide latitude of speeds. In the gasoline engine, efficiency falls sharply when the speed changes or power falls below that of best energy output. The average CI engine is 32 to 35 per cent efficient. This makes it a popular prime mover of trucks and buses which attain almost twice the fuel mileage of similar vehicles equipped with conventional gasoline engines. Today, CI engines are used in stationary power installations, locomotives, and marine installations because of their higher efficiencies, economy of operation, and low-volatility of fuel.

Fig. 11-36. Dual-Fuel Powered Generators (Nordberg)
These produce electricity at a fuel cost of $ .002841 per kwh in New Roads, La.

Terms to Understand

fuel injector
atomize
turbulence chambers
solid injector system
air injection systems
plain combustion chamber
pre-cup
auxiliary combustion chamber
venturi principle
precombustion chamber
turbulence chamber
air cell, energy cell
external head design
heat insulator
water jacket
nozzle tips
spark ignition system
unit injector system
governor
pressure regulator
throttle
pressure pump
camshaft
helix
common rail
pressure-time system
gear type pressure pump
shut down valve
metering orifice
bypass valves
closed-tip nozzle
cam device
constant load operation
multiple-pump system
self bleeding
air-relief valve
spring-loaded check-valve
dribbling
clogging
distributor system
fuel transfer pump
plunger pump
distributor disc
air locks
air starting
gasoline starting
electric starting
glow plug
Bendix drive mechanism
inlet valves
exhaust valves
compression ratio
push rods
rocker assemblies
turbo-charger
opposed piston engine
electric drive
dual fuel engine
efficiency

Study Questions

1. Analyze the differences of CI and SI engines.
2. Why doesn't the diesel engine need a carburetor?
3. Analyze the purpose and techniques of fuel injection.
4. How do diesel combustion chambers differ from gasoline combustion chambers?
5. Describe the various types of diesel combustion chambers. Describe the various injection systems, their components, and their controls.
6. Describe the various methods used to start CI engines.
7. Analyze and describe some uses for CI engines.
8. Why are diesel engines more efficient than SI engines?

CHAPTER 12

Aircraft Piston Engines

There are three classes of airborne engines: *piston engines* driving a propeller, the several kinds of *airstream reaction engines,* and *rocket engines.* This chapter is devoted to the first type. The second type includes various jet and turbo-prop engines and are covered in Chapter 14. Jet engines are quickly replacing the larger piston engines for longer flights. Rocket engines are reaction engines which do not require atmospheric pressure nor external oxygen for combustion. Therefore they can fly beyond the limits of our atmosphere. These are explained in Chapter 15.

Engines and Flight

Reciprocating aircraft engines differ from their grounded counterparts for a number of reasons. Some of these should be understood before studying their actual mechanical features. Many demands are imposed by the third dimension of flight, and by the thinness of air four, six or eight miles up. Airplanes today fly where temperatures are almost 200° colder than on the ground. And of course, the weight of the engine is a major consideration in such a gravity defying machine.

Aircraft may deviate considerably from straight and level flight and this also restricts engine design. Engine components of some must operate in any position—on end, sideways, or even inverted. This limits the use of such features as open oil reservoirs, floats, or gravity-feed systems. The aircraft engine, more than most prime movers, has become complex to adapt it to its environment and special needs.

The aircraft engine must provide power for lift as well as thrust. *Lift* is the upward force provided by the wings moving through air. Lift must overcome the *weight* of the plane before it will begin flying. *Thrust* is the forward force provided by the action of the propellor. In jets and rockets, thrust comes from the reaction (forward) to the expulsion of gases rearward. Thrust must overcome the *drag* or air resistance of the plane. Drag in airborne vehicles (especially at higher altitudes) is less than surface or marine vehicles at similar speeds. The action of the four main forces acting on a plane in flight is shown in Fig. 12-1.

Airfoils

The cross section of a propellor blade and a wing are similar *airfoils.* Both make use of Bernoulli's principle of air pressures learned

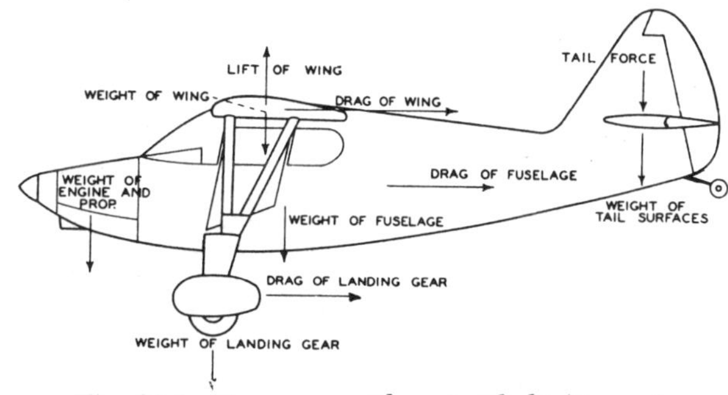

Fig. 12-1. Forces on a Plane in Flight (Zweng)

in Chapter 9. Fig. 12-2 shows this cross section for a wing. The top half has a greater curvature than the lower. Faster flow causes less pressure above the wing than the full atmospheric pressure below. This results in the upward force known as *lift*. Engine power must produce the relative wind over the wing by moving the plane forward.

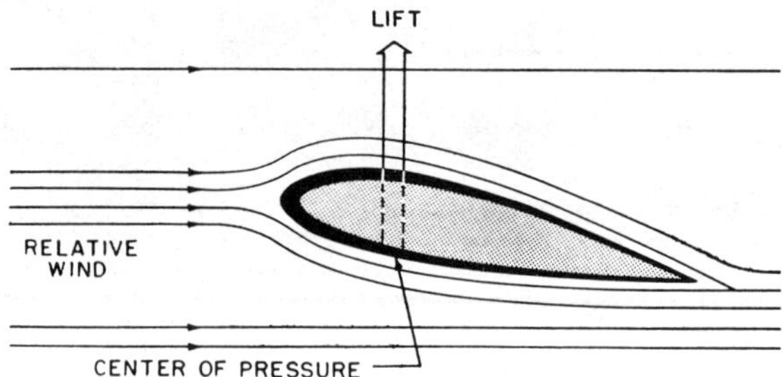

Fig. 12-2. An Airfoil Produces Lift (Zweng)

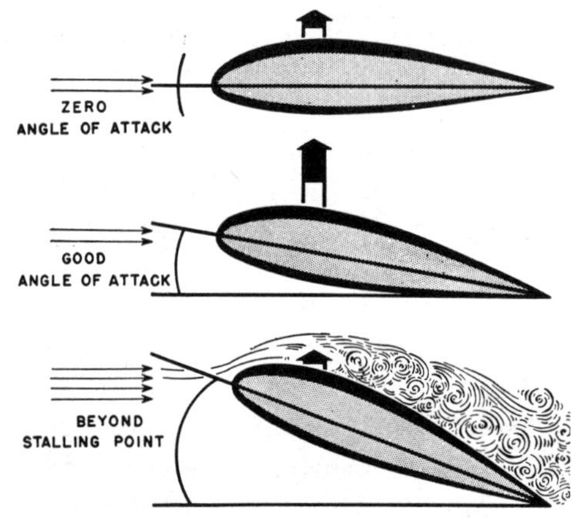

Fig. 12-3. Airfoil in Three Angles of Attack (Zweng)

Fig. 12-4. Flight Deck of C-97 Stratofreighter (Boeing)

Engine instruments for flight engineer are at right. Pilot, co-pilot and flight controls are beyond.

Fig. 12-2 can also be used as the view looking down on a cross section of a propellor blade. The relative wind is caused by the *rotation* of the propellor. The force of the airfoil (the large arrow) is now the forward *thrust*, rather than upward lift. Both the propellor and the airplane wing depend on power from the engine. Neither air foil will function without atmospheric air pressure. Different means are required to penetrate the void of outer space as will be studied in Chapter 15.

Angle of Attack

The *angle of attack* is the amount the leading edge of an air foil is tipped above the straight path of the relative wind. As the angle of attack of the wing is increased slightly, more lift is developed and the plane gains altitude if the relative wind speed is maintained. See Fig. 12-3. This angle of attack (the *attitude* of the airplane) is maintained by the horizontal control surface of the tail. If however, the angle is increased to a point more than about 20°, air no longer flows smoothly over the wing, lift stops, and the plane begins to fall. This is called the *stalling angle* or *burble point*. If the angle of attack is decreased, altitude is lost, speed is increased, and less engine power is needed for lift. *Altitude* in flying is *stored power*—like money in the bank. It can be used to increase speed, decrease power, or to sustain powerless flight for a limited time so that an emergency landing can be made.

The angle of attack of a propellor is known as its *pitch*. Controls for propellor pitch serve the same purpose as the gear shift of an automobile. Propellor pitch determines the speed of the engine within certain load limits. As the pitch is increased, the propellor takes a bigger bite of air, thrust is increased (up to the stalling point of the propellor), and rpm decreases. This is the cruising position giving maximum fuel economy. However, as an automobile needs a lower gear for maximum power, a plane prop needs a low pitch (for higher rpm) to develop maximum power. Automatic variable-pitch props control cruising rpm of larger aircraft engines.

Weight per Horsepower

It can be seen that weight and bulk are enemies of an aircraft power plant. Bulk creates *drag* which opposes thrust. Weight opposes *lift* and the more power used for lift, the less available for thrust. Engines are constantly being redesigned to cut the weight per horsepower.

The importance of the power-to-weight ratio of aircraft engines has promoted prime movers that look different and reflect different materials and workmanship. Lighter metals such as aluminum and magnesium are used whenever possible even though it means greater expense. Each part is shaved to its bare essentials without impairing its efficiency and safety factor. Every pound is being taxed to do more work than a comparable pound in a surface engine.

Safety Considerations

In the air, malfunctioning becomes deadly serious. Workmanship must be as perfect as possible. The result of a loosened connection may likely be an emergency landing or a crash. Yet in spite of all the problems of aircraft engine design, there are a number of reasons for their outstanding safety records. Engine instruments record each aspect of operation—and other devices check the instruments. See Fig. 12-4. Such safety features as dual ignition systems, careful performance checks, regular preventative maintenance, and rigid licensing regulations all contribute to this record of safety.

Let us now consider some features typically found on the larger complex piston engines for aircraft. Smaller engines designed for low altitude flying by less experienced pilots may simplify some of the mechanisms.

Radial Engines

Reciprocating engines vary in size and shape. Opposed and in-line engines resemble, to a degree, the engines found in automobiles. See Figs. 12-5, 12-6 and 12-7.

Fig. 12-5. The Allison V-12 Watercooled Engine (G.M.)

This was the first 1,000 hp engine to pass the 150 hour test. It was a spectacular fighter engine from 1937 to 1947.

Fig. 12-6. Cross Section of the Allison V-12 (G.M.)

Fig. 12-7. Six Cylinder Lightplane Engine (Continental)

Radial engines, such as shown in Fig. 12-8 however, are quite different and have been popular in aircraft. Radial engine design was introduced in Chapter 8, but will be detailed more here.

Fig. 12-8. C-9 Radial Engine—Note Spark Plugs (Curtiss-Wright)

Fig. 12-9. Assembling C-9 Radial Engine (Curtiss-Wright)

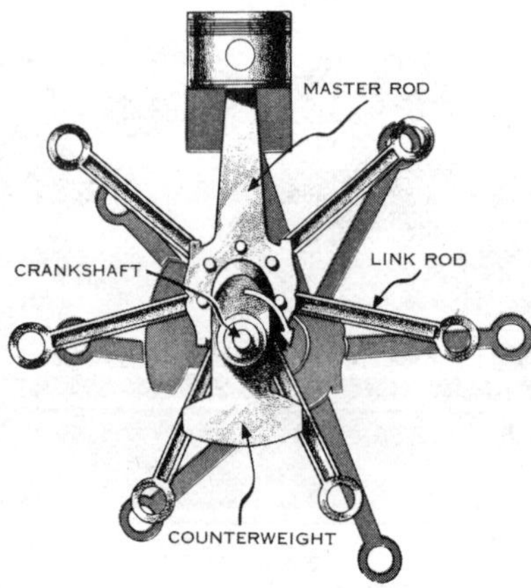

Fig. 12-10. Rods and Crankshaft for Radial Engine (G.M.)

The radial engine has cylinders and pistons so located that they spread out from the center radially as in Fig. 12-9. Some larger radial engines have additional banks of pistons and cylinders staggered behind the first. Each bank can be thought of as a separate engine.

Fig. 12-10 shows there is just one crank or throw for a bank of pistons. It is similar to a single cylinder crankshaft and is counterbalanced by two weights. The other connecting rods are fastened to it in such a way as to cut down on the space required. The master connecting rod has its small end fastened to a piston and its larger end is fastened around the crank just as if it were a single-cylinder engine. This large end is enlarged to provide space around it for other connecting rods. The link (articulated) connecting rods provide a means of transmitting power first to the master rod and then to the crankshaft.

Cylinder Arrangement

The crankcase of a radial engine is similar to a wide ring or hoop. The cylinder barrels fit into holes that are evenly spaced around it. (This was shown at Fig. 8-23.) Each cylinder is capped with a head which includes

Fig. 12-11. Details of Turbo-Compound Engine—Note Fin Area (Curtiss-Wright)

the valves, Figs. 12-11 and 12-12. This typical overhead valve engine with the valves set at an angle makes the combustion chamber peaked at the top. Just as in other such engines, there are push rods and rocker arms. The cams are located around a ring in two rows instead of on a shaft. There is one row for the intake and another for the exhaust valves. As the cam ring rotates, the cam opens one valve after the other. Usually, there are several sets of cams on each track requiring that the ring rotate more slowly.

Cylinder Cooling

The cylinders are arranged radially not only to save space but to provide each with the maximum and equal exposure to the cooling air. Fins around the cylinders provide a means for dissipating the intense heat to the air quickly. Wherever the heat is localized, such as around the exhaust valves, more fins are provided than in other places. This is well shown in Fig. 12-11. Air cooling is quite adequate because of the air being forced over the engine by the propellor and by the fast movement of the plane.

Usually a thermocouple is placed under a spark plug of the hottest running cylinder of each engine to record its *cylinder head temperature*. See Fig. 12-13. The thermocouple has two dissimilar metals which generate a small current in proportion to the amount it is heated. Cowl flaps controlling air flow around the cylinders are adjusted to hold the best cylinder head temperature. Each engine has its temperature gauge and cowl flap controls.

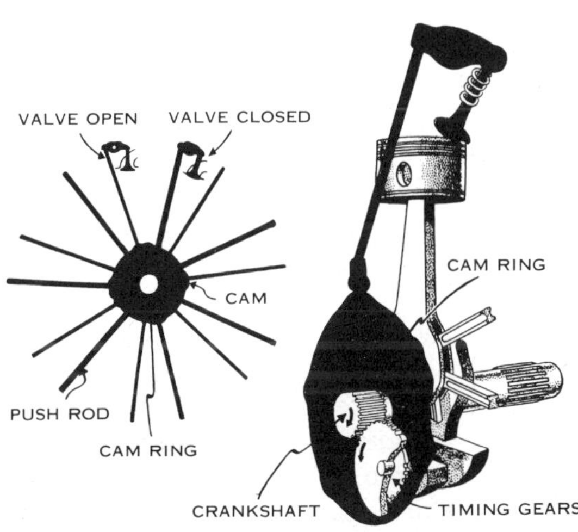

Fig. 12-12. Radial Engine Valve Operation (G.M.)

Compound Radial Engines

To increase the efficiency of the radial engine, a turbine run by exhaust gases may be geared to the engine crankshaft. This is shown in Figs. 12-14 and 12-15. In this way, instead of wasting the energy of the hot

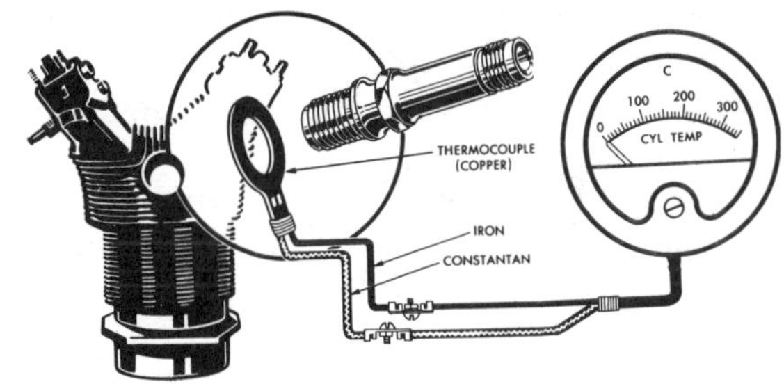

Fig. 12-13. Cylinder Head Temperature Gauge

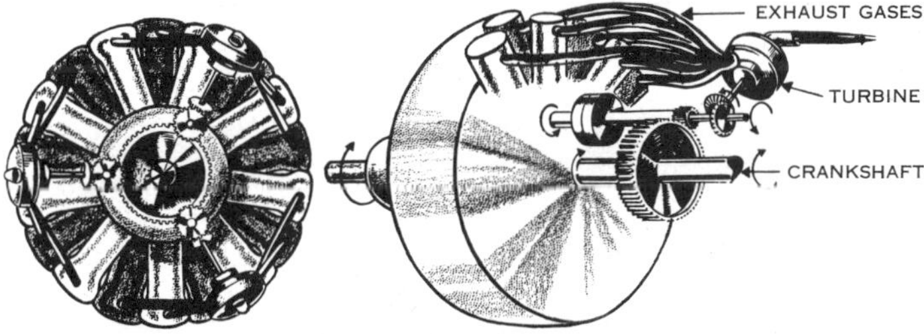

Fig. 12-14. Turbo-Compound Engine (G.M.)

Fig. 12-15. Turbo-Compound Engine on Test Stand (Curtiss-Wright)

expanding exhaust gases, they are employed to rotate the turbine, furnishing additional power for the propellor. Such engines are called turbo-compound engines. The increased weight of the turbine is compensated for by the additional power acquired with practically no additional expense in operation.

Lubrication

The aircraft engine employs a lubrication system similar to that employed in an automobile engine. A pump forces oil under pressure to critical points of wear such as main bearings, connecting rod bearings, and other parts. Cylinders and pistons get their lubrication from the splashes from these other points. The oil reservoir is a tank located outside of the engine because there is no crankcase to speak of in a radial engine. The oil return is facilitated by using scavenger pumps.

If a radial engine has been standing for some time, oil may drain into the cylinder heads of lower cylinders. To check this, props are turned by hand through several turns before cranking the engine.

Oil Temperature: A cooling coil or a radiator is used to keep the oil cool. A temperature gauge indicates the oil temperature for each engine. Oil cooler flaps are controlled to hold the best oil temperature. Abnormal oil temperatures are an excellent indication of impending trouble. With an oil cooling system a single weight of oil can be used even through the air temperature may vary from +100° to −50 during a single flight. In cold weather congealed oil must be heated before starting the engine.

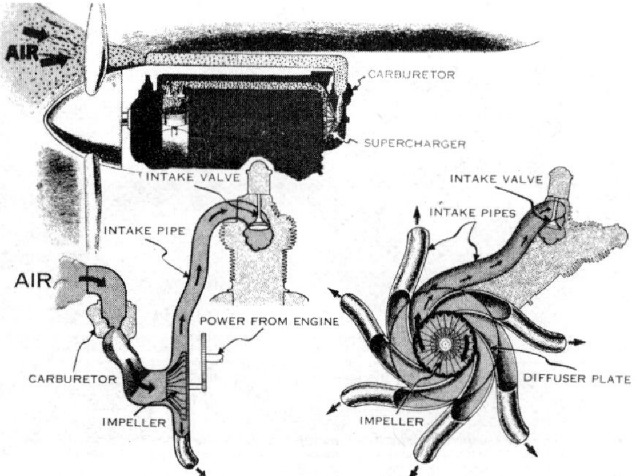

Fig. 12-16. Gear Driven Superchargers, In-Line and Radial (G.M.)

Supercharging

More power can be obtained from an engine if its fuel and air intake is increased. Increasing the intake of fuel poses no problem, but increasing the intake of air is quite a different story.

In most surface engines, atmospheric pressure pushes the air into the cylinders through the carburetor. In aircraft engines, where maximum power is sought with the least expenditure of weight, a supercharger or blower is used rather than making the engine larger.

Supercharger Action

Most large aircraft engines have a supercharger powered by the crankshaft. The blades of the supercharger spinning at extremely high speeds are called an impeller. They throw the air and gas mixture from the carburetor outward by centrifugal force. This mixture is then permitted to build up in the chamber surrounding the impeller. Speed of the mixture slows down in the chamber thus increasing the pressure. From there, it is directed through the manifold into the cylinder by means of valve action. Fig. 12-16 shows this for both an in-line and rotary engines.

The action of the impeller can be compared to that found in a vacuum cleaner. The fan draws in the air from the atmosphere and directs it through the cleaner into the bag. The bag expands and thus exhibits an increase of pressure as the air is caused to build up.

The supercharger in the same manner increases the pressure in the intake manifold to 20 psi or more instead of the usual 14.7 psi. This boost, as it often is called, squeezes more air and fuel into the cylinder yielding as much as 40 per cent more power from the same engine.

Effect on Engine Power

It must be realized that this increase of power has its price. Power is needed to drive the supercharger and this comes from the engine. So, in order to achieve a 40 per cent increase of useful power, the actual engine power may have to be increased as much as 50 per cent. Also, the additional weight of the supercharger increases the overall weight of the engine. In addition, the engine had to be designed and made strong enough to cope with the total power. It stands to reason an engine designed for 700 hp cannot be expected to stand up under 1000 hp. Yet, even with all of these factors and limitations, the power to weight factor is improved considerably by adding a supercharger instead of simply increasing the engine size.

Sea-Level Supercharging

Sea-level supercharging, as the above is called, presents one more problem—*detonation.* Compressing the air and fuel into the cylinder increases its temperature enough to prefire or cause knocking. High octane gasolines permit more latitude of working pressures than conventional gasolines, and thus are important as aviation fuels. Because of them, the supercharger can increase intake pressures which increases compression, and results in greater power.

Altitude Supercharging

Altitude supercharging is needed because the air is *thin* several miles up. Thus supercharging makes an engine deliver as much power at high altitude as on the ground.

The air at sea level is 14.7 psi and it becomes less dense as altitude is increased. For example, at 30,000 feet the pressure is about one-third as much or less than 5 psi. Therefore, an engine without a supercharger at these altitudes lacks enough air and its power drops considerably below one-third of its ground power. Planes with conventional reciprocating engines and no altitude supercharger reach a *service ceiling* (can no longer climb faster than 100 feet per minute) at an altitude of about 10,000 to 15,000 feet.

The *altitude supercharger* is used to ensure a stabilized pressure or intake of air, regardless of the altitude. Sometimes, the sea-level supercharger is also used as an altitude supercharger by increasing its operational speed. This can be done by increasing the gear ratio and providing a means by which the volume of air can be controlled.

Several disadvantages to this arrangement restrict its wide use. It takes more power to run the supercharger at such high speeds and this power is wasted at low altitudes where it is not necessary to use supercharging. The result is that an engine of 1000 sea level horsepower may have less than 800 horsepower at take off if it employs this type of altitude supercharger; although at higher altitudes, this engine would perform better than the same engine using sea level supercharging.

Multi-Stage and Turbo-Superchargers

Many methods have been tried to overcome these difficulties. One such method uses two sets of gears. One set drives the impeller at slower speeds for take-off and sea level flying and the other set is used at higher speeds for high altitude flying. Another idea is to use two superchargers, one for each extreme flying condition. This is sometimes referred to as two-stage supercharging.

A refinement or modification of the latter system uses an auxiliary supercharger powered by exhaust gases, Fig. 12-17. This turbo-

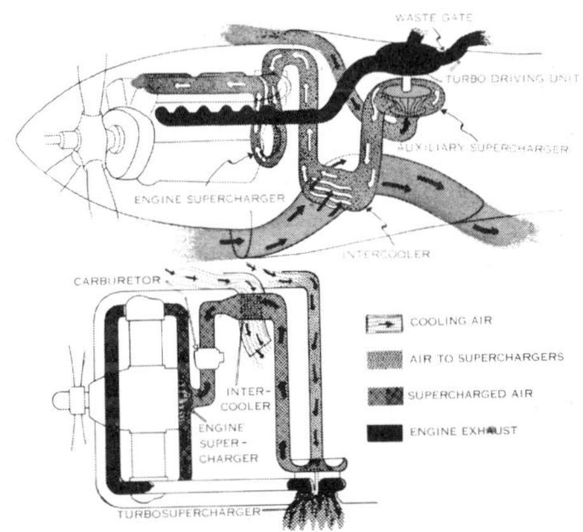

Fig. 12-17. Turbo-Superchargers, In-Line and Radial (G.M.)

supercharger permits speed control as the boost is needed. The *differential* between exhaust gas pressures and atmospheric pressure increases with the altitude. Thus the turbo-supercharger delivers the needed higher pressures at higher altitudes.

All of these arrangements yield better weight to power performance than a single-stage engine. They all, however, add weight and exhibit particular limitations. The system used depends on what the engine is specifically designed to do since the same engine must pass through low altitudes to do high stratospheric flying.

With high rates of supercharging, there is danger from the air or fuel mixture becoming too warm from being compressed. An intercooler is placed in the supercharger to reduce this temperature. See Fig. 2-17. Gauges for each engine indicate temperatures, flaps control and intercooler operation.

Fuel System

The fuel system of an aircraft engine is much like that of an automobile engine. There is a gasoline tank, a fuel pump to get the fuel to the carburetor, and a carburetor to atomize the fuel and properly mix it before it is drawn (or blown, if a supercharger is employed) into the cylinder.

The airplane engine encounters extreme and rapid variances in temperature, unusual positions in flight, and the pressure variations

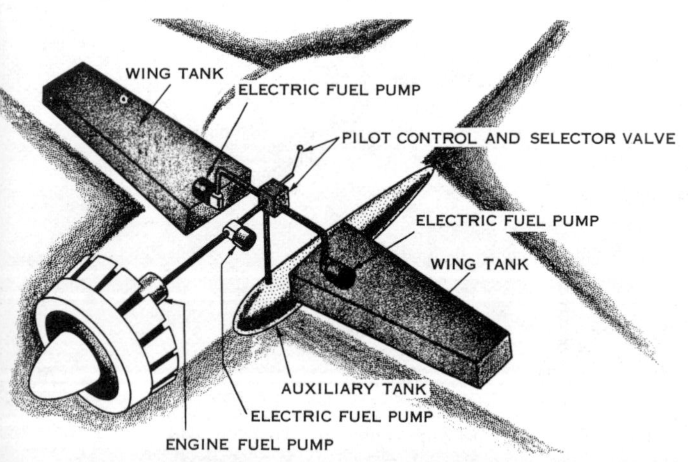

Fig. 12-18. Aircraft Fuel System (G.M.)

of low and high altitudes. Precautions must be taken to guarantee top operating efficiency and safety. Thus, fuel systems may include vapor eliminators, strainers, auxiliary electrical and/or hand pumps, and a carburetor that includes many regulating devices to compensate for the existing conditions that may exist while providing the engine with the proper air and fuel mixture.

Fuel Tanks

Most aircraft have several fuel tanks in the wings and sometimes in the fuselage. A selector control is used in monitoring the flow from one or all tanks. See Fig. 12-18. The engine fuel pump draws gasoline into the carburetor at higher pressures than in the conventional engine. Each tank, in addition, has an electrical pump that continually operates as a booster and vapor separator. The booster also serves in an emergency if the main pump goes bad. Gauges indicate fuel pressure. Other gauges indicate the approximate amount of fuel in each tank.

Injection Carburetor

The carburetor unit is attached behind the fire wall at the back of the engine with the necessary tubes and valves coming from it. The carburetor is likely to be the injection type. (This is not similar to fuel injection systems as were previously discussed.)

A simplified aircraft injection carburetor is diagramed in Fig. 12-19. The air tube has a throttle valve similar to automobile carburetors. The air is drawn down this tube by the supercharger.

In the air passage, there are two small tubes. One is located above the venturi where the pressure is normal and the other is located right at the venturi where the pressure is lower. There two tubes are connected to the opposite side of a diaphragm. The position of the diaphragm is determined by the difference in the pressure. The fuel valve located in a separate part of the carburetor is controlled by this diaphragm. The amount of air flowing through the air passage thus controls the amount of fuel to the engine.

Pressure from the engine fuel pump forces the gasoline through the valve and injects it from the nozzle right at the entrance of the supercharger below the throttle. The nozzle atomizes the fuel as it is injected under pressure into the intake system. This type carburetor is referred to as an *injection carburetor* since the fuel is not mixed within the carburetor. The amount of fuel is controlled by the flow of air through the carburetor. Air flow is controlled by the throttle valve.

The throttle valve is linked to the hand throttle in the cockpit (one for each engine). This controls the amount of fuel mixture going to the intake manifold. A *manifold pressure gauge* (for each engine) on the instrument panel indicates the throttle setting. As with most gauges, a maximum point is indicated on the face. This *red line* must not be exceeded because of the danger of engine damage.

The fuel injected through the nozzle in a fine spray is further broken up by the impeller of the supercharger. In two-stage supercharging, the carburetor may be located in front of the first stage so that both stages are handling the fuel-air mixture. Or, it may be located between the two superchargers so that the first stage is handling just air and the second stage is handling the fuel-air mixture.

Several features of aircraft carburetors are not found on automobile systems. Some of these are *mixture controls, water injection, and deicing controls.*

Fuel Mixture

Most aircraft piston engines, have mixture control levers in the cockpit. A fuel mixture which is right for sea level is too rich at 5,000 feet higher, and larger carburetors automatically make some adjustment for this. But pilots or the flight engineer also control the richness of the fuel-air mixture from the carburetor. Richer mixtures give more power, and help cool the engine, but waste fuel. Too lean a mixture runs hot, might backfire, and can damage the engine. The correct power and mixture setting vary with the load carried (amount of fuel consumed), and whether maximum performance, maximum range, or a compromise is desired at a particular time. Mixture controls are normally full rich for take-off and at landing (in case of an emergency). For cruising, mixture controls are commonly set just above the point which causes a drop in rpm.

Some engines provide for a safe momentary overloading of manifold pressure for take-off or emergencies. Detonation and overheating of cylinders is reduced by *injecting a water spray* into the intake manifold. As this is turned to steam, excess heat is absorbed and some extra power derived from the steam pressure.

Carburetor Icing

Several carburetor accessories combat the problems of icing as illustrated in Fig. 12-20.

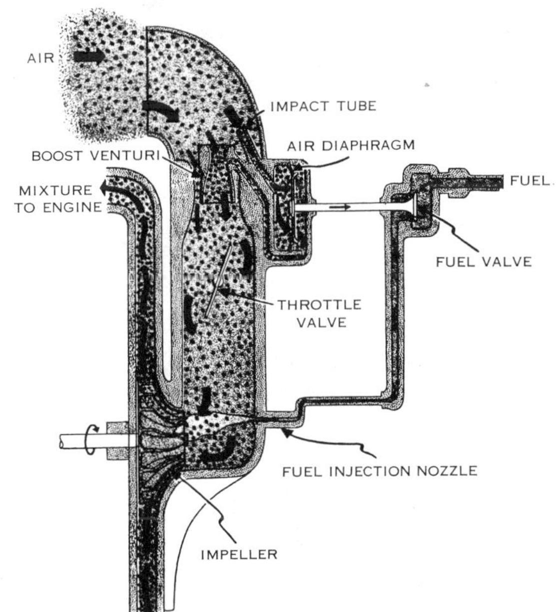

Fig. 12-19. Injection Type Carburetor (G.M.)

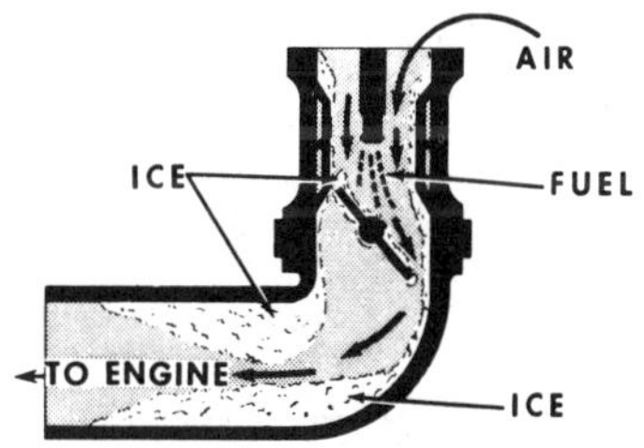

Fig. 12-20. Carburetor Icing

The vaporization of fuel combined with the expanding air in the carburetor throat causes a big drop in temperature at this point. If the air supply is moist and slightly above freezing, the cooling causes ice crystals to form. Even a slight accumulation clogging the throat reduces the fuel mixture enough to cause engine failure. With simple carburetors the only remedies are either to lean out the mixture hoping a backfire might loosen the ice, or to get out of the weather.

The *carburetor deicer* is a device to pump alcohol into the throat to prevent ice formation. The *carburetor temperature gauge* indicates throat temperature. If it is dangerously close to freezing (even though *free air temperature* may be 90°), either the deicer should be used, or the air should be warmed above freezing by the *carburetor air heater*. This device uses exhaust heat to raise the throat temperature above the danger level. Both supercharging and injection carburetors lessen the danger of icing.

Icing dangers are cumulative. At the same time carburetor ice is reducing power, ice may also form on the wings and propeller. This destroys their airfoil shape reducing lift and thrust. At the same time, the weight of the ice increases the load and further decreases speed. Wings are deiced by heaters or boots which expand and contract. Alcohol injected on the propeller helps to control its icing. Power for these ice control systems comes from the engine and its electrical system, and thus detract from power available for thrust.

Ignition

The ignition system of an aircraft engine is quite similar to those found in small gasoline engines used to operate lawn mowers and similar equipment. There is a source of low voltage stepped up by a coil and a distributor to direct the electrical impulse to the correct spark plug. See Fig. 12-21.

The low-voltage system does not depend on the battery, but uses a magneto. This electrical energy is increased many times by a coil as previously discussed. The unit may be contained in one case with the breaker points, condenser, and distributor. In each cylinder, there are two spark plugs to insure proper ignition and to provide a margin of safety. Some systems employ a dual magneto, and

Fig. 12-21. Single Magneto Dual Ignition System (G.M.)

Inset shows magneto switch for twin-engine plane. Each engine has a handle. Each handle can switch to either set of plugs, to both, or to off.

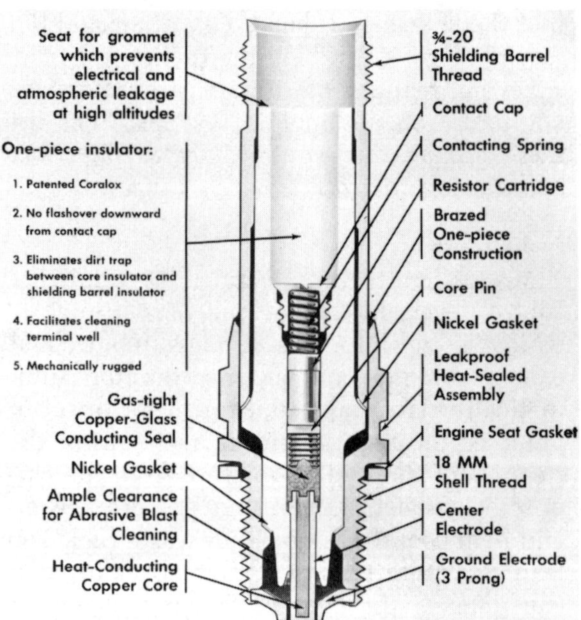

Fig. 12-22. Aircraft Spark Plug (G.M.)

some systems employ two separate ignition systems each with its own drive.

Spark plugs are similar to automobile plugs but are encased in metal to prevent radio interference, Fig. 12-22. Their job is a little more difficult because of the different temperature ranges and higher compression ratios, which require them to have better insulator properties and better electrodes.

Starting and Electrical Systems

Smaller aircraft engines are started by an electric starting motor much like automobiles are started. Larger engines require more torque than is available in such a motor, so usually have an *inertia starter,* Fig. 12-23. The electric starting motor first causes a small heavy flywheel in the motor to gradually pick up speed until it is rotating about 16,000 rpm. This stored energy is then released to the engine through reduction gearing. The starting motor also continues to crank the motor until the engine fires. Some inertia starters can be hand cranked.

Most aircraft have a 24 volt electrical system for starting, radio equipment, and other accessories. It contains batteries, a generator on each engine, and the necessary regulators. DC motors driving alternators produce AC for various users. An external *auxiliary power source* (usually an engine driven generator) can be plugged into the system to aid in starting.

Fig. 12-23. Inertia and Direct Starter (Bendix)

Terms to Understand

airstream engine
reaction engine
third dimension
lift
weight
thrust
drag
airfoil
Bernoulli
angle of attack
stall angle
pitch
power to weight
safety features
radial engine
bank
master rod
link rod
cam ring
water injection
carburetor icing
dual ignition
thermocouple
scavenger pump
cowl flaps
turbo-compound
oil cooler
supercharging
impeller
altitude supercharger
sea level supercharger
service ceiling
two speed
two stage
turbo-supercharger
intercooler
injection carburetor
diaphragm valve
manifold pressure
red line
carburetor mixture
inertia starter
auxiliary power

Study Questions

1. Analyze the demands imposed on aircraft engines.
2. What are the inherent problems that had to be overcome in designing aircraft engines?
3. How do aircraft reciprocating engines differ from landcraft engines?
4. Describe the characteristics of a radial engine.
5. Describe how the crankshaft operates on a radial engine.
6. Analyze the purpose of supercharging.
7. Describe the various techniques of supercharging.
8. How does the fuel system differ in an aircraft engine as compared to comparable stationary engines?
9. How does the ignition system differ in an aircraft engine from conventional spark ignition engines?
10. Analyze the limitations of the reciprocating internal combustion engine.
11. What is important about the weight to horsepower ratio?

Gas Turbines

The success of the steam turbine led inventors to attempt a gas turbine. The idea was to compress air, inject fuel into it, ignite the mixture, and use the pressure of expanding hot gases to turn a turbine rotor.

The word *gas* is applied to this type of engine to distinguish it from those turbines which operated by water, steam, and air. Most gas turbines do use *heated air* as the working-medium, but the term *air turbine* is usually reserved for windmills and other engines driven by compressed air. When the gas turbine is used to power an airplane it is known as a *turbojet* or *turboprop engine*. These jet engines are covered in Chapter 14.

Gas Turbine Development

The first patent covering a gas turbine was issued to John Barber of England in 1791. The patent included all the essential elements of the modern turbine except that it employed a reciprocating type of compressor. John Gimbell of England, in 1808, was granted a patent for a gas turbine which had rotating blades but no stationary or stator elements, thus missing the advantage of the multi-stage type turbines in use today. W. S. Fernihough in 1850 was granted a patent in England for a turbine that operated by both steam and gas, but because of the success of steam, the development of a true gas turbine was held back.

First Gas Turbine

The first true gas turbine engine was designed by Dr. Stolze in 1872. In his engine, the air passed into an axial compressor and then into a heating chamber which was externally heated by burning fuel. The heated air was then used to turn the turbine rotor that operated the compressor. The drawback was that the air was not heated to a high enough temperature, and all the power was needed to drive the compressor resulting in poor efficiency. Although the unit was of little practical use, it served to stimulate others to design more efficient gas turbines.

Steam Turbine Converted

In 1904, Armengaud and Lemale, two Frenchmen, converted a 25 hp DeLaval steam turbine into a gas turbine. A separate compressor was used to compress the air which then passed into a combustion chamber to the turbine nozzle. The combustion chamber was cooled by water-tubes surrounding it, and the steam generated in these tubes was mixed with the hot air in the nozzle. This engine was quite successful and generated 400 hp which was considerably more than 25 hp of the original engine. The engine was not efficient, however, since it used 2.7 pounds of gasoline per horsepower as compared to 1.6 pounds per horsepower for the 4-stroke cycle engine.

Gas Turbine in U. S.

In the United States, the first patent for a complete gas turbine was awarded to Charles G. Curtis in 1914, but for many years after little progress was made in gas turbine design. See Fig. 13-1. Many reports from 1917 to 1928

Fig. 13-1. 1920 Gas Turbine by Holzwarth, 1,000 Hp (Smithsonian Institution)

Fig. 13-2. Model of 40,000 Kw Brown-Boveri Gas Turbine Power Station in Switzerland (Science Museum, London)

Fig. 13-3. Parsons' Experimental Gas Turbine, 500 hp (1938) (© Science Museum, London)

describing the gas turbine as a means of jet propulsion for aircraft labeled the engine impractical, unsuitable, and unsafe. However, in 1928, Frank Whittle, then a flight cadet in the R.A.F., presented a thesis on the possibilities of jet propulsion for aircraft. In 1930, he patented the first design of a gas turbine aircraft engine. His engine became the basis for early work in this country which resulted in the first jet flight in 1942.

New metals and aerodynamic research led to more efficient air compressors and metals that could tolerate the high heats of these engines. In 1933, Brown-Boveri Company of Switzerland built a turbine which was used in a German steel plant. Fig. 13-2 shows another of their gas turbine plants. Success of these prompted others to be built. In this country, large gas turbines have been used to drive electric generators since 1936. See Fig. 13-3.

Gas Turbine Locomotive

Dr. Adolf Meyer designed the first gas turbine locomotives. His turbine was used to drive an electric generator which supplied current to motors connected to driving wheels. In his engine, the air enters the compressor, and after compression is heated by the exhaust gases. The air then passes to the combustion chamber where it is caused to expand by the burning fuel. These gases then act on the turbine rotor. This turbine developed approximately 8,000 horsepower, but 5,800 horsepower was needed to drive the compressor when starting. A diesel engine was used to drive the compressor until enough air was delivered to the combustion chamber. Here it mixed with the fuel, was electrically ignited, and the starter was no longer needed.

Military Developments

Prior to World War II, the United States military departments made serious investigations into the feasibility of utilizing gas turbines for aviation and marine uses. During the war they were primarily concerned with jet engines for aircraft and guided missiles. Since the end of World War II, however, advancements have thrust gas turbines into many fields.

Gas Turbines Today

Types of Gas Turbines

There are two main cycles or types of air circulation used in gas turbine engines. In one, the exhaust gases pass from the turbine and exhaust directly into the atmosphere, with a continuous fresh supply of air being drawn into the compressor. This engine is known as the *open-cycle* type, and most gas turbines operate on this principle. Fig. 13-4 shows two variations in open cycles. The lower diagram shows a *regenerator* which increases efficiency by using exhaust gases to preheat the compressed air.

The *closed-cycle* turbine is the other type, Fig. 13-5. In this engine, the air does not come in contact with the burning fuel. The turbine exhaust is cooled and then it re-enters the compressor. The compressed air is heated externally by oil, gas, or solid fuel. The heat source may also be a nuclear reactor. In some gas turbine installations, both open- and closed-cycle principles are employed.

Most gas turbine engines contain *two sections*. The first section, *the gasifier,* contains the compressor and combustion chambers. The compressor may be *turbo-driven*. In *one-shaft* units, the compressor is turned directly by the power turbine. *Independent free-turbine two-shaft* units have the compressor drive shaft mechanically free of the power output. *Free-piston engines* also can be used as gasifiers which provide hot expanding exhaust gases to the power turbine.

The second section, the *power turbine,* converts the energy of the exhaust gases emitted from the first section into mechanical energy. This energy may then be used directly or transmitted through a gear train to do work. In other words, the gasifier section provides the hot expanding gases which the power turbine converts into mechanical energy.

The main types of gas turbines classed by *use* are those for *land vehicles,* those for *reaction-propelled aircraft,* and those which satisfy industrial *stationary power* needs. *Universal or multipurpose turbines* may have both vehicular and stationary applications.

Basic Characteristics

The intrinsic advantages of gas turbines are many and generally well-known. Their *simplicity* might very well be most important. This leads to other advantages. A gas turbine may have only 20 percent as many moving parts as a comparable reciprocating engine. The size is smaller and lighter in weight, as illustrated by the 410 pound Chrysler regen-

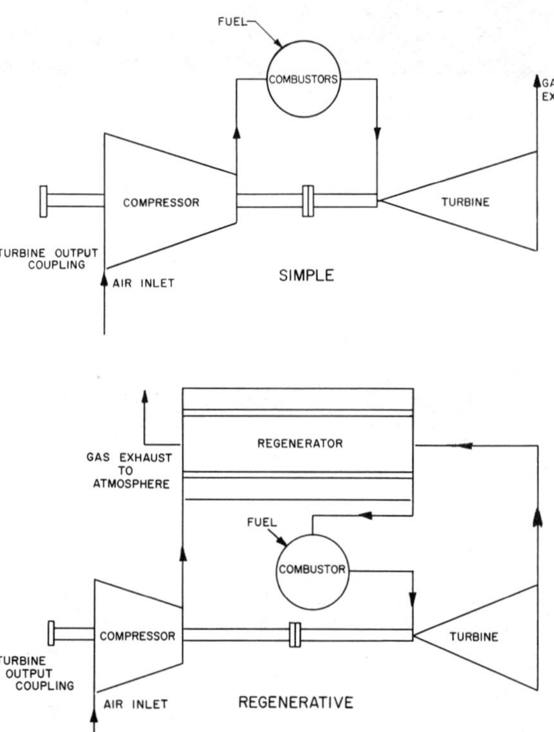

Fig. 13-4. Open-Cycle, One-Shaft Turbines—Simple and Regenerative (Westinghouse)

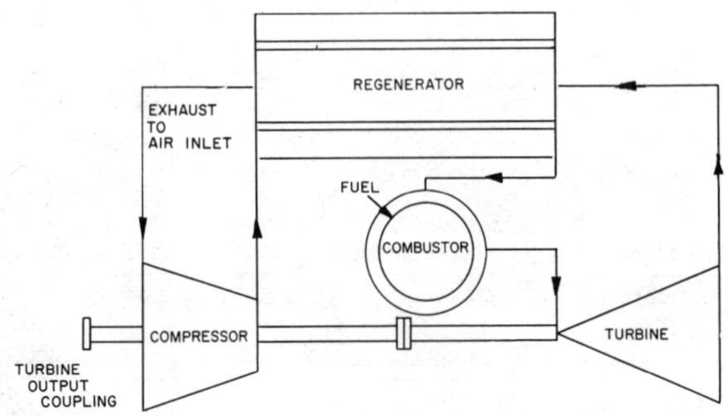

Fig. 13-5. Closed-Cycle, One-Shaft Gas Turbine (Westinghouse)

erative automotive gas turbine. Fig. 13-6. This is nearly 200 pounds lighter than a V-8 engine of comparable power.

No radiator is necessary because the power plant is air-cooled. The electrical system is extremely simple with a storage battery, starter-generator, coil, breaker, and a single spark plug which is needed only for starting. Such simplicity makes the turbine easy to build and maintain, with reliability and dependability important factors. Also, the turbine power plant is essentially vibration free because combustion is continuous and because the moving parts rotate continuously instead of reversing back and forth. Its low-temperature starting characteristics have long been proven superior to other power plants.

One of the best qualities is its *multi-fuel capability.* It will operate on practically any liquid hydrocarbon, such as unleaded gasoline, diesel fuel, kerosene, or JP4 jet fuel.

The gas turbine, like all internal combustion engines, operates on a four-phase principle: air intake, air compression, air expansion, and air exhaust. In reciprocating engines, these phases occur separately and in sequential order for each combustion chamber. However, in the gas turbine the process is continuous with each stage of the turbine, permitting each phase to occur simultaneously. The major thermodynamic difference is that the gas is heated continuously in a gas turbine engine while in a reciprocating gasoline engine heat is added at the instant of maximum compression.

Last, but not least, the gas turbine enjoys a versatility which is unique. It is adaptable to automobiles, buses, trucks, aircraft, locomotives, pumping stations, power stations, ships and even space vehicles. This prime mover is relatively unaffected by climatic conditions, and is not hindered by geographic location because it can use any readily available liquid carbohydrate as fuel.

As noted previously, the requirements of the prime mover vary with the application and so does the degree of complexity. Any engine performance, output versus fuel consumption, is the direct result of the thermodynamic characteristics of its components and the pressure and temperature limits of the operating cycle. Each of these must be kept at the best attainable levels to achieve satisfactory engine performance.

Vehicular and stationary types of gas turbine engines will be described separately here. The design of compressor, burner, and turbine units for these engines will be explained in more detail with turbojet engines (which are also gas turbines) in Chapter 14

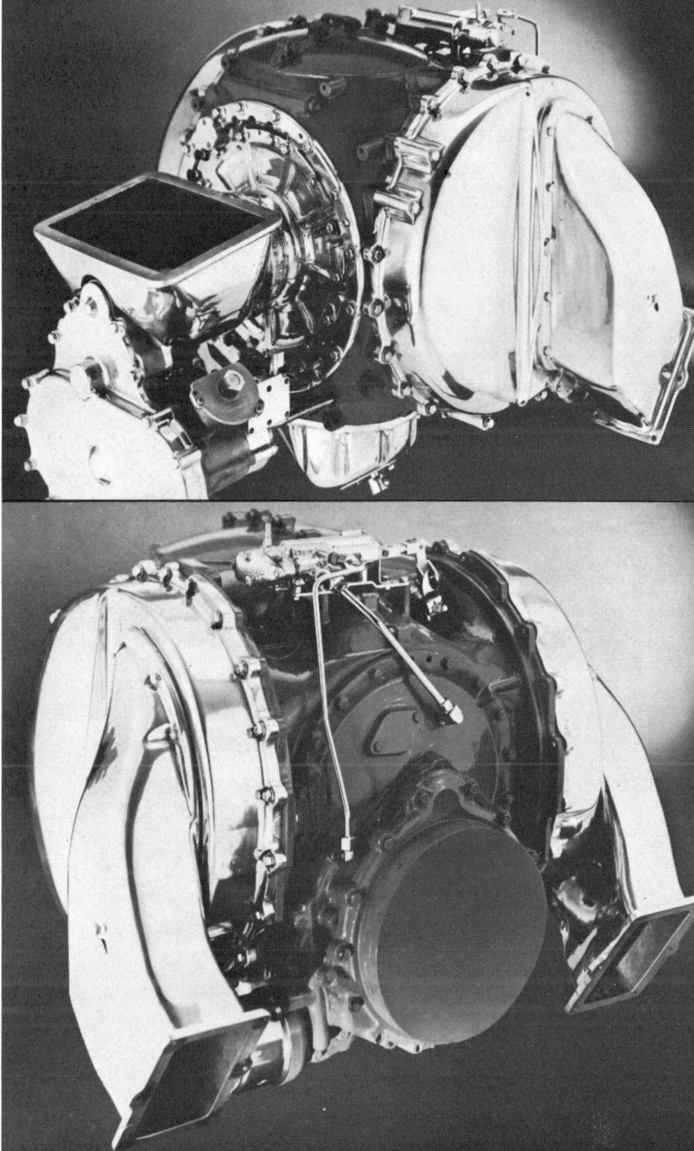

Fig. 13-6. Chrysler Gas Turbine

Vehicular Turbines

Recently, much progress has been made in reducing fuel consumption of vehicular gas turbines. There is not an automobile manufacturer that does not have an experimental gas turbine engine.

The design of a gas turbine to be used to power land vehicles presented engineers with problems of immense complexity. Many of these have been solved but there are many more to be resolved before the gas turbine can replace the reciprocating engine as the basic means of automotive propulsion. Much time and effort will continue to be spent if this newcomer is first to challenge its worthy predecessor and then to gain the advantage of which it is potentially capable.

Designers of military aircraft have not been deterred by the scarcity of strategic materials nor by noise levels. Similarly, power station engineers are not concerned with weight and size as are the automotive designers and engineers. It seems that the only limitations common to all was to develop as low cost and efficient a prime mover as possible for each application. Without a doubt, the most difficult job of all has been to design a gas turbine for *passenger cars* because of the problems imposed.

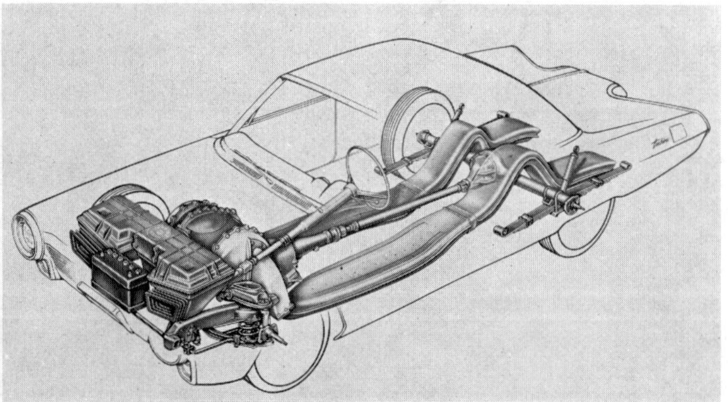

Fig. 13-7. Turbine-Powered Chrysler
View below shows engine installation in this first turbine car to achieve limited production runs.

The vehicular gas turbine engine had to be designed for high volume tooling and manufacture. This power plant, if successful, can serve the transportation needs of practically all Americans and may be counted in tens of millions. Only by using such a mass market as a production base, can the unit cost be reduced. An automotive gas turbine engine that could *not* be produced in volume would represent an engineering specialty and not a low cost power plant for all.

Details of three typical gas turbines designed for vehicular uses have been made public and will be studied here. These three engines are: the Chrysler Turbine, The General Motors Turbine 305, the Boeing 502 (and 520). The General Motors Hyprex 4-4, a free piston engine used to provide the expanding gases to operate a power turbine is also discussed.

Chrysler Gas Turbine

Chrysler Corporation was the first to achieve limited production of a turbo-car – a four-passenger luxury hardtop, completely power equipped. See Fig. 13-7. It had a regenerative gas turbine engine rated at 130 hp. This engine, now in its fourth generation, provided performance characteristics comparable to a power-equipped 200 hp V-8 engine. The engine was coupled to a modified three-speed automatic transmission.

Mechanical Details

The Chrysler gas turbine employs two independent turbine wheels. One drives the compressor and accessories while the other propels the vehicle. See Fig. 13-8. The regenerative turbine uses two *regenerators* which rotate slowly in vertical planes, one on each side of a centrally located burner.

The major components are arranged symmetrically. This arrangement using dual regenerators provides improved flow to and from the regenerator cores as compared to the single regenerator used on the previous model CR2A. The accessories are driven by a single-stage *reduction gear* at the front of the compressor intake. See Fig. 13-9.

Gas Flow

The air flow through the engine is shown in Fig. 13-8. The air enters through dual intake filters and a silencer assembly. It then passes axially into the *impeller*. Here, the air is compressed (raising its temperature to 425° F) and is radially discharged outward by the impeller into the *diffuser*. Diffuser channels direct the compressed air toward the outside of the front half of the regenerator cores. The air passes through the core absorbing heat from the regenerator. The heated air (1100° F) passes down to the *combuster* or *burner*, where air flow reverses. This reversal sets up a complex whirling pattern giving good combustion throughout the range of operating speeds.

The hot combustion gases (1700° F) are guided to the first (compressor) *turbine nozzle and wheel*. The high velocity gas leaving the wheel is guided through the *variable nozzle blades* that direct its flow to the *power turbine wheel*. The exhaust from this second stage is discharged outward through the rear half of the two regenerator cores where some of its heat is recovered for reuse.

The main components of this vehicular gas turbine will be briefly discussed and presented in order.

Compressor: The *centrifugal* compressor had to be designed specifically for the engine because none existed in the small sizes and pressure ratios needed. It has a maximum efficiency of 84 percent and the pressure ratio at designed speed is 4.25 to 1.

There are two types of compressor-flow patterns. In *centrifugal-flow*, air enters near the shaft and is thrown outward. In *axial-flow*, air moves parallel to the shaft through a series of fans much like the turbine wheels shown in Figs. 13-8 and 13-9. Air is compressed as it is moved into a progressively

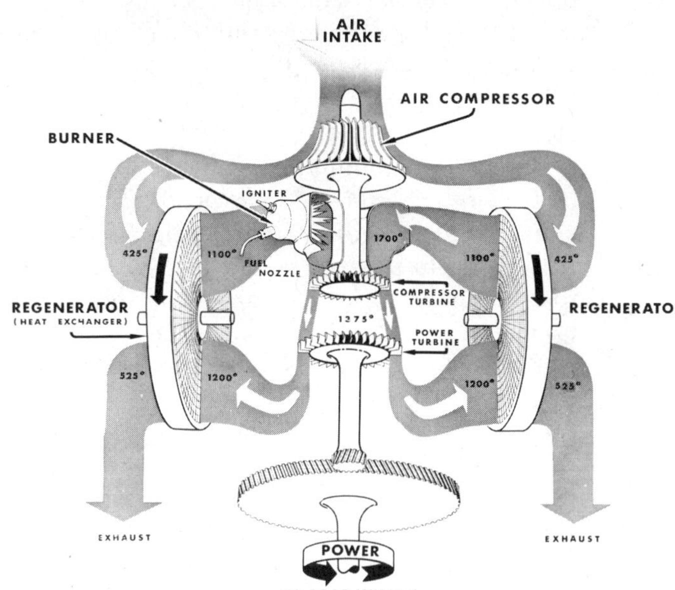

Fig. 13-8. Operation of Chrysler Gas Turbine

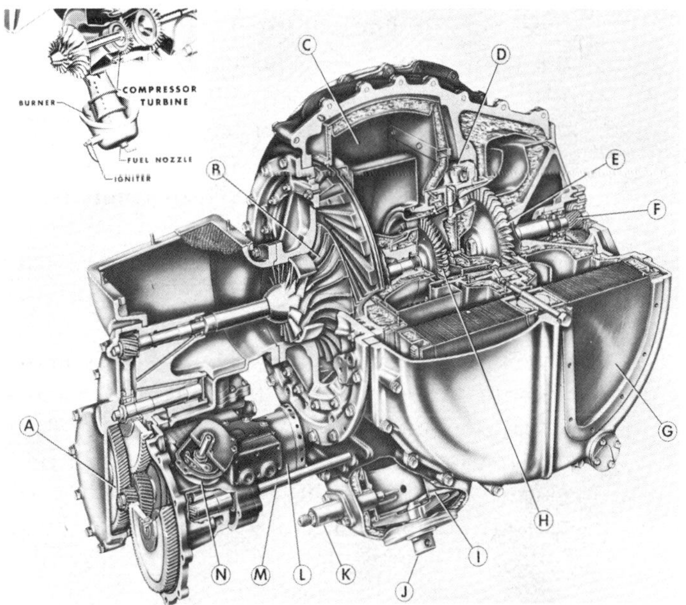

Fig. 13-9. Components of Chrysler Gas Turbine
(A) accessory drive, (B) compressor impeller, (C) right regenerator core, (D) variable nozzle unit, (E) power turbine, (F) 10 to 1 reduction gear, (G) left regenerator core, (H) first-stage turbine, (I) burner, (J) fuel nozzle, (K) igniter plug, (L) starter-generator, (M) regenerator drive, (N) ignition unit. Inset shows burner can detail.

smaller area. The centrifugal compressor was selected over an axial type because of its ruggedness, moderate rotational inertia, simplicity, shorter length, and its radial discharge — although axial ones are more efficient.

The cast aluminum *impeller* has 30 blades, half being shorter or *splitter blades.* The aerodynamic loading demanded a large blade area to prevent separation. A separate row of blades is located ahead of the main impeller.

The *diffuser* has a short vaneless region to assure *subsonic* air flow even at maximum speed. This means air flow is kept below the speed of sound. Basic shape was established through air-channel model tests. The vaned area beyond then provides a uniform flow to the throat. A large portion of the compressor losses occur in this area and major improvements in efficiency are expected.

The discharge from the compressor diffuser empties into the irregular shaped housing on its way to the regenerator.

Regenerator: The thermodynamic requirements of a heat exchanger have already been discussed for steam generators and nuclear reactors. Basically the needs are high heat transfer, design simplicity, freedom from maintenance and minimum pressure loss. In addition, the limitation of size is important for vehicular application.

The recuperative-type heat exchanger (where heat energy is transferred through a wall separating the hot fluids as in a radiator) was used in nuclear power plants because of its inherent advantages of lower leakage, higher efficiency and greater flexibility; of course, these units are necessarily large. In vehicular gas turbines the regenerative rotary-disc type of heat exchanger has found prominence because it is less complicated, more compact, simple, and basically maintenance free. It is self-cleaning because of flow reversal (inwards at front, out at rear) and cyclic fluctuation of core temperature.

Each regenerator core is 15.5 inches in diameter and 3 inches thick. The stainless steel corrugated matrix of .002 inch metal 3 inches wide is wound spirally around the hub. A pressure wall or seal is made by a thin rim and flange arrangement. Regenerator geometry was determined using mechanical considerations such as stresses, deflections due to temperature changes, and necessary sealing. The cast iron ring gear is mechanically fastened to the cooler surface flange to minimize thermal distortion and insure good tooth contact and endurance. The driving pinions operate unlubricated at temperatures over 400° F.

The seal assemblies divide the core in half. The front half passes the high-pressure air from the compressor, and the rear half the low-pressure opposite-flowing hot air from the power turbine.

Burner: The burner assembly is situated between the regenerators. The burner is a single can-type of reverse-flow configuration (see Figs. 14-27, 14-28), approximately 5 inches in diameter and 12 inches long. An extended mixing zone is provided by a transition section located between the burner tube outlet and the turbine nozzle inlet.

A single fuel nozzle atomizes the fuel into the primary zone of the combustor liner. It is of the air-atomizing type where the fuel is broken by means of an airstream.

Ignition is by a conventional spark plug made with tubular electrodes to provide for air passage from the nozzle air pump to cool and extend their life.

Compressor Turbine: The impeller is driven by the turbine located just behind the combustion chamber. The rotating part of the compressor is fastened to the same shaft as the turbine so that the two rotate together at the same speed. This turbine also drives the fuel pump, regenerators, and other accessories. The entire assembly must be dynamically balanced to prevent any vibration. The turbine revolves at 22,000 rpm at high idling speeds. Both the compressor and power turbines are a single-stage axial type.

The rotational speed of the compressor turbine is determined by the compressor and burner output. The rotor of the gas generator consists of two major parts: the compressor impeller assembly and the compressor turbine wheel. The shaft of the impeller is flash-butt welded to the turbine wheel. The blade width and rotational speed determines the size of the turbine wheel needed for a given output. A 53-blade wheel of one-half inch width was finally adopted.

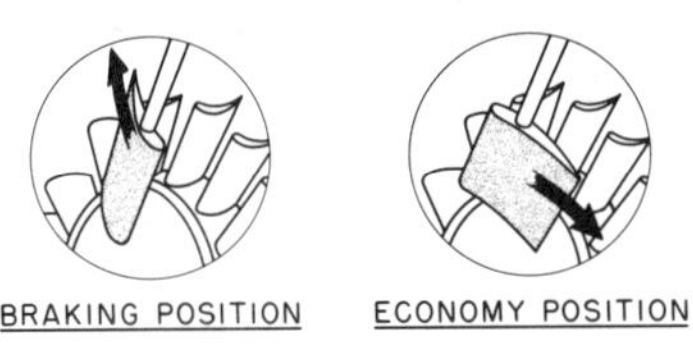

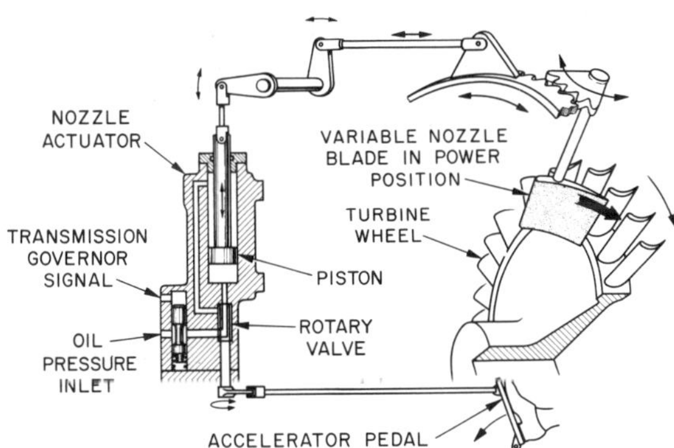

Fig. 13-10. Variable Nozzle System (Chrysler)

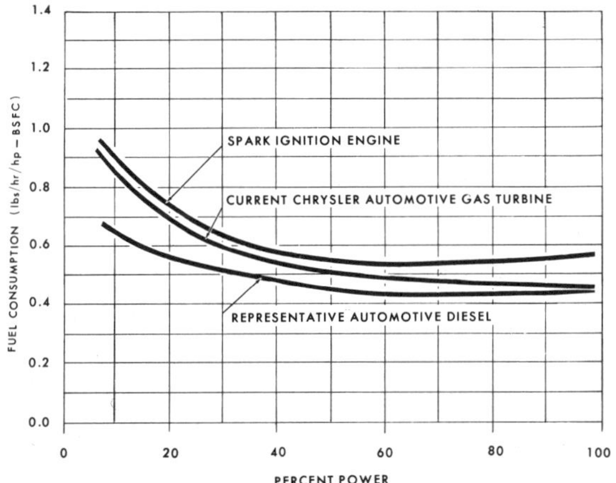

Fig. 13-11. Fuel Economy of Installed Engines (Chrysler)

Power Turbine: The power turbine requirements differ considerably from those of the compressor turbine. For example, the power turbine must operate over a wide range of speeds from stationary to maximum rpm as required by the driving needs at any particular instant.

The power turbine is bolted to its shaft and is dynamically balanced. The power turbine assembly includes the rotor, reduction gear assembly and the supporting housing. The rotor is supported by a steel-backed bushing at the front and a ball bearing at the rear. A pressurized labyrinth, much like those previously discussed for steam turbines, provide a seal.

Power Turbine Nozzle

The accelerator pedal is connected by mechanical linkage to a unit containing the *fuel control governor, transmission throttle valve,* and *nozzle actuator.* See Fig. 13-10.

The power turbine nozzle actuator is a hydraulic servo unit actuated by the lubrication pump. Nozzle blade attitude is controlled by pedal position as long as the engine performs correctly. At starting or idle speeds, the nozzle blades direct the gas flow straight back in an axial direction reducing the temperature and the tendency for the car to creep. During acceleration, the blades close directing gas flow into the cups of the turbine blades.

To provide braking, the actuator reverses the 23 nozzle blades directing the gases to strike the turbine against its rotation.

The same hydraulic system which operates the variable nozzle also is used for power steering and transmission servos. In addition it lubricates the engine, the accessory drive, reduction gears, and the transmission. The transmission oil pan is the sump for the system which uses type A transmission fluid and has an air-to-oil cooler.

Accessories

The Fuel System: The fuel system contains a fuel control assembly with fuel pump, and altitude compensator, solenoid shut-off valve, fuel nozzle, air pump, and electric booster pump. The fuel control assembly consists of fuel pump, governor, pressure regulator and a metering orifice. Fuel flow is automatically controlled during the start cycle and is not affected by accelerator pedal position until the gas generator reaches idle speed. At deceleration the governor throttles the fuel to the nozzle.

Electrical System: The starter-generator is geared directly to the impeller turbine rotor. It uses two 12-volt batteries connected in series to provide the necessary starting voltage. At self-sustaining engine speed, (about 20,000 rpm) the generator aspect takes over providing 12 volts of charging and operating voltage. Relays are employed to switch the batteries into series or parallel circuitry to provide the necessary voltages. Ignition is provided by a high-voltage vibrator and spark gap igniter plug.

Vehicle Test Program

A consumer research program was conducted by Chrysler Corporation on the fourth generation turbine engine. Typical drivers used the turbine cars under a wide variety of conditions. Each selected user drove one of the cars for a period of three months. In total, 203 motorists used the vehicles over a two-year period from October 1963 to October 1965.

Generally, the users were very enthusiastic about the turbine car. Many expressed the feeling that the gas turbine power plant would eventually replace the conventional piston engine. Three out of four users singled out the smooth, vibrationless operation of the engine as its principal advantage. They were also impressed by the reduced maintenance and the instant starting ability of the engine regardless of weather conditions. The vibrationless operation of the engine led many to describe driving the car as a gliding sensation felt at all speeds, especially on long trips. The sure ignition of the engine and the instant heat provided by the engine were noticeable assets. Also mentioned were: good engine power, quietness of operation, and nonstalling characteristics. In commenting on disadvantages, one person in three expressed some dissatisfaction with the acceleration lag, primarily when starting from a standstill. It was not as noticeable when cruising. It was felt that the car had exceptional acceleration and expressway speeds for an engine rated at 130 horsepower.

The only instrument indicating engine conditions is the *gasifier tachometer.* Conditions of *turbine over temperature, high oil temperature,* and *low oil pressure* are noted by warning lights on the instrument panel.

The 1.1 million miles accumulated during the 50-car testing program have been a valuable source of information. Chrysler Corporation has designed a fifth generation turbine engine, which is now being road-tested in a 1965 Dodge Coronet model. A sixth generation turbine engine has also been developed. Technical information on these engines has not yet been released.

The design potential of the turbine engine has by no means been fully realized, although progress in its development has been impressive. It has been determined that increasing the nozzle inlet temperature by 400°F will result in a 40% increase in specific output and an improvement in fuel economy of 20%. Design engineers are now working with materials that will be able to withstand this increased temperature.

A turbine design must be capable of being mass-produced at a suitable economic level as well as be at least the equal of piston-engine in performance, fuel economy, and reliability. When such a design is achieved, the complex process of developing tools and facilities necessary for mass production can begin. Major decisions still lie ahead, for the adoption of a new type of power plant has implications of great magnitude and far-reaching effects. Recent developments in engine technology, public concern for atmosphere quality, and federal legislation have led to massive developmental efforts on the Wankel engine (Chapter 9), electric cars, and the steam-driven vehicle.

The Allison GT 309[1]

A more recent development of the General Motors GT 305 pictured in Figs. 13-12 and 13-13 is the 309 shown in Fig. 13-12A. This engine is designed primarily for trucks, buses, farm machinery, construction equipment, generator sets, pumps, compressors, and marine use.

The series began with the GT 300, which was a nonregenerative turbine engine used to power the first turbo cruiser. GT 302, a two-burner version of this engine, was used to power the Firebird I, the first American-built gas turbine automobile. These were followed by the GT 304, which powered the Firebird II, and the first Turbo-Titan. The GT 305 was used to power the Firebird III and the Turbo-Titan II.

Both the GT 304 and GT 305 employed drum-type generators which were pioneered at General Motors. With some design changes to facilitate manufacturing, the Allison Division of General Motors built several GT 305 engines for evaluation by selected military

Fig. 13-12A. GT 309 Turbine Engine (G.M.)

Fig. 13-12. G. M. Gas Turbine

This 590 pound engine is only 32″ x 24″ x 26″, yet is rated at 225 hp. Saving is even greater as no torque converter is needed in the transmission nor a radiator other than a small oil cooler.

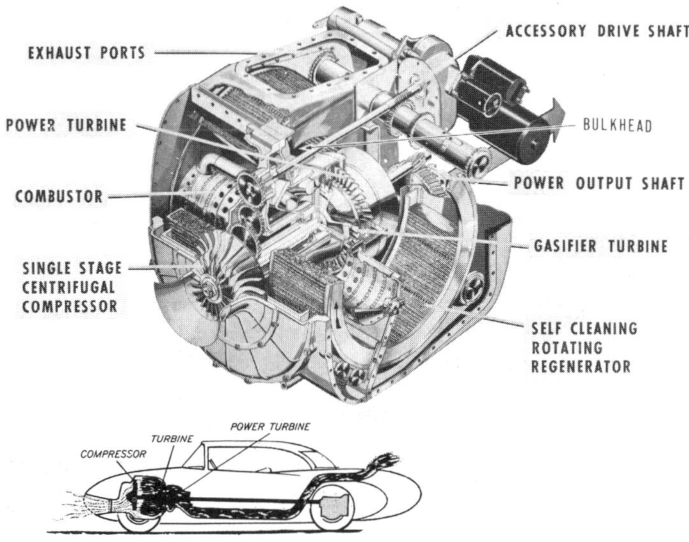

Fig. 13-13. Components of a GMT 305 (G.M.)

and commercial users, Figs. 13-14 and 13-15. Some of these engines are still in operation today and are used for test or educational purposes. The experience gained from these installations coupled with continuing economic evaluations indicated that the heavy-duty vehicle market presently dominated by the diesel engine offered the greatest potential for gas-turbo applications. Many features of the turbine worked to its advantage in the heavy vehicle field, allowing the turbine to show economic benefits to the user.

Selection of Power Level

The selection of the power level for the GT 309 was based on a survey of the vehicle power-weight spectrum. It was determined that the greatest potential was for vehicles in the 60,000 to the 76,000 lb. class. In this weight class, 260 to 280 horsepower engines will provide maximum speeds from 60-65 miles per hour on level roads, depending on load. On a 3% grade, the same power level will provide speeds which range from 27 to 35 miles per hour. These figures represent performance levels above the average of trucks selected by most of the freight operators today.

[1] Adapted from W. A. Turunen and J. S. Collman, *The General Motors Research GT 309 Gas Turbine Engine,* Research Bulletin No. 495, Research Laboratories, General Motors Corp., Warren, Michigan.

The design power level for the GT 309 was established at 280 brake horsepower on an 80° day. The engine will produce more than rated power most of the time because the 80° day is well above the average temperature in the United States. On hot days, the engine still has sufficient output to move the load with a minimum deterioration in performance. For instance, the output is reduced to 260 brake horsepower at 100°F which would result in reducing the maximum speed of a fully loaded truck trailer by only 3 mph.

General Engine Design

Several basic criteria were established at the onset of the GT 309 engine design program:

1. The engine would incorporate power transfer, a newly-developed feature that improved part-load economy and in addition provided large amounts of engine braking;
2. Since the engine was intended for heavy-duty vehicle applications, the turbine rotor design and material selection would be based on resisting long term stress before rupture;
3. Every effort to design for economy of manufacture would be considered, but compromises in the design which sacrificed efficiency for cost would be weighed very carefully;
4. The rated output of the engine would be continuous power available to the transmis-

Fig. 13-14. Locating Gas Turbine and Transmission on Truck Frame (G.M.)

Fig. 13-15. Gas Turbine Powered Truck (G.M.)

sion after deduction of essential engine accessories;

5. The size and arrangement of the engine would be compatible with vehicles now using high output diesel engines; and,

6. The output shaft speed and mounting provisions would be compatible with existing transmissions.

The general arrangement of the GT 309 is illustrated in the perspective cutaway view, Fig. 13-16. The most obvious departure from earlier models is the single, drum-type regenerator rotating in a horizontal plane (compare to Fig. 13-13). The radial flow compressor is driven by a single-stage axle turbine. The independent single-stage power turbine drives the output shaft through a single-step vehicle reduction gear unit. The combustion chamber is located vertically within the regenerator drum. A pinion on the compressor turbine shaft provides power for the gasifier driven accessories through suitable reduction gearing. A shaft paralleling the turbine shafts and driven by the accessory gears extends to the back of the engine. In addition to driving the regenerator drum and providing power to rear-mounted gasifier-driven accessories, this shaft is connected to a multiplate clutch, one of the principal elements of the power transfer system. The main structural members of the engine are cast aluminum, supporting the light gauge sheet metal ducts which contain the hot gases. A significant design improvement in the GT 309 is the extensive use of insulation to protect the structural components of the engine from heat and to minimize the inefficiency associated with heat losses from the working fluid circuit.

Power Transfer System

Power transfer is a hydromechanical system of transferring controlled amounts of power between the independent turbine shafts. One set of plates of a hydraulically actuated clutch is driven through suitable gearing by the gasifier turbine. The other set of clutch plates is geared to the power turbine. The clutch torque can be regulated by means of the hydraulic pressure. The gear ratios are chosen so that the power turbine drive plates turn more slowly than the gasifier drive plates during all normal engine operating conditions. Application of a light amount of pressure to the hydraulic clutch cylinder results in a torque reaction between the clutch elements turning at different speeds. The torque on the faster-turning gasifier turbine connected elements acts to slow this component. The gasifier governor, however, increases the fuel flow to maintain constant speed. The result is an increase in turbine inlet temperature, as well as a slight increase in engine output. By operating the engine at the maximum of allowable temperature throughout the speed-power range, significant reductions in fuel consumption are realized. With the gears, shafts, and clutch-coupling the two turbines to transfer power from the gasifier turbine to the output shaft, it is entirely practical to use the same components to transfer power in the opposite direction. This provides a means of developing engine braking by having the output shaft drive the compressor. Also, the power turbine can be coupled to the gasifier turbine whenever the power turbine speeds exceed a safe limit to provide positive overspeed protection.

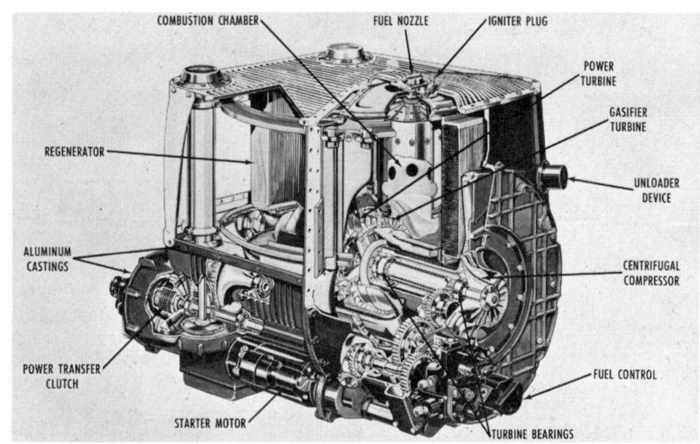

Fig. 13-16. Cutaway of GT 309 (G.M.)
Engine Horsepower – 280 @ 80°F
Gasifier Turbine Speed – 35,700 rpm
Power Turbine Speed – 33,860 rpm
Maximum Inlet Temperature – 1725°F
Compressor Pressure Ratio – 3.8:1
Weight – 950 lbs.
Size – 36″ x 30″ x 35½″

The power turbine system operates as a single-shaft engine with advantages in certain applications. When a control system for the power transfer was designed, the problem of handling variations in gasifier turbine driven accessory loads could be overcome and full-rated engine output could be either delivered entirely to the output shaft or divided between the output and accessory shafts without affecting turbine inlet temperature. Mechanical arrangement of the power transfer system components can be seen in the cutaway view (Fig. 3-16). The gasifier-driven accessory drive gear system has been increased in capacity to handle more power which reaches a maximum during braking operation. The regenerator driven shaft has been strengthened and extended rearward through the power transfer clutch. The gasifier-driven shaft is connected to the inner members of the clutch. The outer members of the clutch are geared to the main output reduction gear. During power transfer operation, the clutch slips moderately because it is lightly loaded. Since only a small part of the total output goes through the clutch and the slip ratio averages less than 15%, the power loss is negligible. When the engine is used for braking, the clutch is locked and no slip occurs.

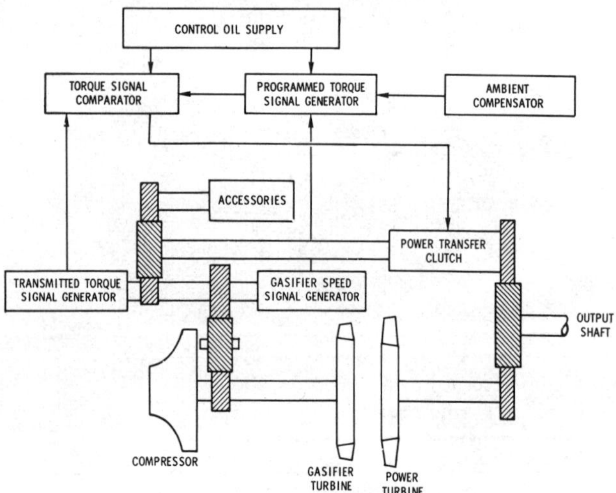

Fig. 13-17. Power Transfer Engine Control System Diagram (G.M.)

The use of the speed and torque signals to control the power transfer system is illustrated schematically in Fig. 13-17. The pressure from the speed signal generator is used to position the cam in a variable pressure regulator which is supplied with control system pressure. With the proper cam shape, the regulated output pressure is proportional to the torque which is required to maintain the desired turbine inlet temperature at any gasifier speed. This desired torque pressure signal is compared to the actual torque pressure signal from the torque sensor. The comparator regulates the flow of control system oil to the power transfer clutch cylinder, increasing or decreasing its pressure to maintain the scheduled gasifier shaft torque loading.

Ambient pressure and temperature compensators are built into the control system to maintain the desired turbine inlet temperature regardless of ambient conditions. An important feature of this system is that the torque is controlled directly so variation in clutch coefficient of friction does not affect control. Furthermore, the torque sensor is located so that it measures the combined accessory and power transfer clutch torques. As accessory load is increased, the power transfer load is automatically decreased and the turbine inlet temperature remains at a constant level. Actually, the turbines and compressor are so matched that some power transfer is required even at full power. This permits the "trimming" of each engine so it will operate at the design temperature and output in spite of slight variations in other dynamic components from engine to engine. This method of power transfer control was selected because temperature sensing devices are not noted for either their durability or their rapid response, and a more suitable control thermometer was sought.

Perhaps equal in importance to the improvement in part-load fuel consumption is the engine braking provided by the power transfer system. The same system components which transfer power from the gasifier turbines to the output shaft are used to transfer power in a reverse direction. With the fuel shut off, the output of the turbine falls off to very low level and the compressor becomes a dynamic braking device. The compressor is ideal for this purpose because the energy is dissipated directly as heat added to the air it is pumping, eliminating the need for an intermediate heat exchanger such as that required with a hydraulic retarder. The continuous braking capacity of the engine is somewhat greater than its rated output power.

When the driver wishes to decelerate or retard the vehicle by means of the power transfer system, he simply releases the accelerator pedal. When this is done, the governor shuts off the fuel supply to the engine and the gasifier turbine slows down until the gasifier-driven plates of the power transfer clutch are turning at the same speed as the power turbine driven plates. At this point, the clutch torque goes to zero and then reverses direction. The torque sensor of the power transfer control system responds to negative torque by applying full control pressure to both clutch cylinders. This connects the output shaft solidly to the gasifier turbine, which is then driven by the coasting vehicle. The gasifier governor cuts the fuel supply to the engine until the vehicle has coasted to a speed that turns the turbine at the idle speed setting, or the driver depresses the accelerator pedal.

The same features of the power transfer system which provide engine braking serve two other valuable functions. Power turbine *overspeed protection* is provided by the same control function which provides engine braking. This is accomplished by locking the power turbine to the gasifier turbine shaft through the power transfer system whenever the power turbine overruns the gasifier turbine. Another function is the ability to run the GT 309 as a single-shaft engine. In applications such as AC electric power generation, engine speed control and regulation are essential. A single shaft turbine engine is much more suited for this type of service because the rotating components run at constant speed. High inertia and load variation are accomplished by changing the turbine inlet temperature. With the power transfer unit, the GT 309 can be started as a two-shaft engine, accelerated to synchronize speed and the power transfer system locked up. The engine then operates as a single-shaft engine having the advantages of precise speed regulation and overspeed protection. In summary, the advantages gained by the application of power transfer to a vehicular gas turbine engine compare most favorably with the engines that employ variable power turbine nozzles or engines that employ a supercharged turbine engine cycle.

Structural Details

The GT 309 has two major subassemblies: the gasifier section and the power section. The regenerator seals and cover which are common to both sections are installed after the subassemblies are joined together. The combustor is then installed and the cast aluminum top cover is attached. The top cover completes the high-pressure front plenum as well as the low-pressure exhaust plenum. In addition, the cover locates and supports the upper ends of the two regenerator support shafts. Assembly of the engine is then completed with installing of the sheet metal exhaust housing, the starting motor, the fuel pump and controls, and connecting the fuel and lubrication oil lines. The completed engine weighs 950 lbs. and is 36″ long from compressor inlet flange to transmission mounting flange. It is 30″ wide and 35½″ high. The engine is conservatively rated at 280 brake horsepower with normal inlet and exhaust system losses, at an 80°F ambient temperature. Rated gasifier speed is 35,700 rpm and maximum power is delivered at power turbine speed of 30,000 rpm. Maximum rated speed of the power turbine is 33,860 rpm. The reduction gear ratio of 8.47 to 1 provides a maximum shaft speed of 4,000 rpm with maximum power development at 33,550 rpm of the power turbine.

Engine Components

Extensive component development programs were carried out for the GT 309 assembly.

Compressor: The GT 309 centrifugal compressor incorporates a 23-blade rotor which is cast in one piece. Finish machining is done on the bore, the upstream face of the hub, the shroud profile, the outer diameter, and the rear disk face. The rotor is shrunk and pinned onto a steel hub. The compressor was developed through a long series of tests. Several compressor rotor designs and a multitude of diffusers were tried before a suitable combination was determined.

Turbines: The gasifier and the power turbine for the GT 309 are single-stage designs. The two stages, which rotate in opposite directions, are closely spaced axially. The gas flow part diverges in the axial direction on both the inner and outer walls to minimize the velocity pressure in the gas leaving the power turbine.

Regenerator: The drum-type regenerator has four significant advantages:

1. It provides a straight line engine air-flow path; 2. It has a short high-pressure seal perimeter; 3. It lends itself to compact engine component arrangement; and 4. It lends itself to the use of highly efficient heat transfer surfaces.

The basic function of the regenerator is to transfer heat from the turbine exhaust gas to the compressor discharge air. Its usefulness in the cycle is a function of thermal effectiveness and resistance to fluid flow and fluid leakage. Basically the regenerator is a porous medium assembled in the form of a drum that can be rotated. Part of the drum is in the high-pressure plenum of the engine, and the remainder is in the low-pressure exhaust plenum. Exhaust gas leaving the power turbine gives up heat as it flows outward through the porous medium. Rotation of the drum transports stored heat energy from the exhaust plenum to the compressed air plenum. There the porous medium gives up its heat to the compressed air as that air flows through the drum. A close fitting seal assembly is necessary where the drum passes through the walls separating the high- and low-pressure plenums in order to minimize leakage of compressed air into the exhaust stream.

The heat exchanger drum segments are mounted between two steel rims. The brazed segments are made of .002″ corrugated stock, interspersed with slightly wider longitudinal strips in a labyrinth-like manner.

Combustion System: The combustor and the nozzle box are fabricated with sheet metal. The nozzle box is a symmetrical plenum. Special provisions are made to divert a fraction of the regenerator-heated combustion air around the combustor and onto the turbine stator and rotor blade roots. The temperature of this air does not vary over as wide a range nor at as high a rate during transients as does the combustor discharge gas. This greatly reduces the transient thermal stresses in the high-temperature turbine components. The compressor itself is a simple cast stainless steel cylinder for emission of primary and secondary air. Cooling air for the combustor is admitted axially through an annular opening between the cylinder and conical dome. Dome cooling air is emitted through the small holes and diverted onto the inner surface of contra-swirl plates. The fuel nozzle fits the central dome opening and the hole to the side of the nozzle. The fuel nozzle is a low-pressure air atomizing type using air extracted from the engine compressor by means of a ram tube in the outlet of a diffuser passage. During starting, atomizing air is drawn from the vehicle air brake reservoir or from the separate motor driven air pump. The igniter employs a cylindrical center electrode energized by a transistorized, inductance-type electrical source.

Conclusions

The early gas turbine engines were noisy, were characterized by large volume, and had a ravenous appetite for fuel. Today's gas turbine engine is extremely quiet in operation. It discharges its exhaust at temperatures less than 500°F, and has economy approaching the diesel engine. Much of this progress can be attributed to the development of the highly efficient rotating regenerator. Figure 13-18 shows the progress that has been made in the intervening years, and even makes a predic-

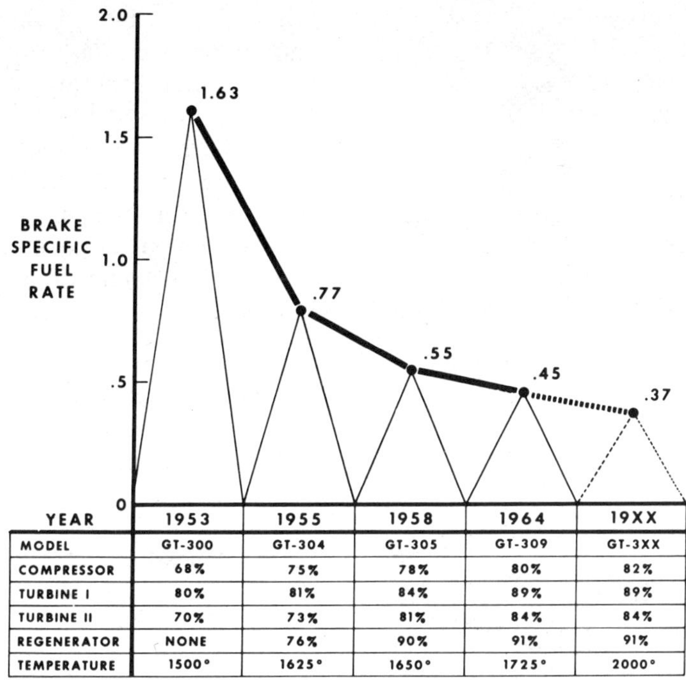

YEAR	1953	1955	1958	1964	19XX
MODEL	GT-300	GT-304	GT-305	GT-309	GT-3XX
COMPRESSOR	68%	75%	78%	80%	82%
TURBINE I	80%	81%	84%	89%	89%
TURBINE II	70%	73%	81%	84%	84%
REGENERATOR	NONE	76%	90%	91%	91%
TEMPERATURE	1500°	1625°	1650°	1725°	2000°

Fig. 13-18. Gas Turbine Progress, Past, Present, and Future (G.M.)

tion of things to come. Improved components have done their part to make the gas turbine more efficient. Without the regenerator, the vehicular turbine could not hope to compete.

The development of the power transfer does not help the full-power efficiency of the engine, but it does greatly enhance its part-load economy. In addition, power transfer overcomes one of the most significant problems in operating previous gas-turbine-powered commercial vehicles by providing larger amounts of dynamic braking. What the future will bring in the way of gas turbine development and applications cannot be predicted. The GT 309 engine is still a research project. The cost picture looks very encouraging for the turbine engine, and new developments in materials and processing techniques should improve the situation.

At present, the durability of the vehicular turbine engine can only be predicted from the experience in other applications. The aircraft turbine has established an unbelievably good record for long, trouble-free service. With its continual change in load, vehicle service will undoubtedly be more rigorous. Actual experience with many engines over long periods of time must be accumulated before this feature can be firmly established. Further advances in thermal efficiency will come from improved components and higher operating temperatures. Already pressing an upper practical limit, more efficient components will require technological improvements that result from attention to the smallest details. Current operating temperatures tax the best available materials to their practical limits and further advances will require the development of efficient means of utilizing both air and fuel for cooling the hottest engine parts. The techniques for making many of these advances are now being developed as the diesel engine provides a continually advancing target.

Free-Piston Engines

The General Motors Research Laboratory concluded its free-piston engine program several years ago. Although they developed this engine to the point where it could be installed and operated in a car, they were unable to overcome such major problems as objection-

Fig. 13-19. Hyprex 4-4 Free-Piston Automotive Engine (G.M.)

Fig. 13-20. XP-500 Free-Piston Vehicle (G.M.)

Fig. 13-21. GM-14 Free-Piston Gasifier (G.M.)
Designed for ship propulsion or power stations, this unit is one of six which power turbines for trans-Atlantic service in SS Wm. Patterson.

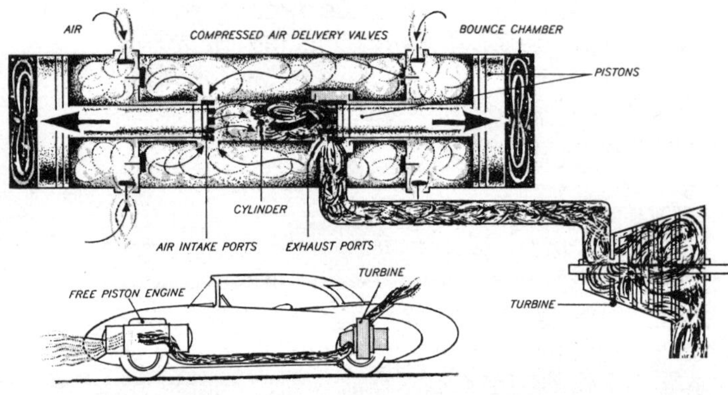

Fig. 13-22. Free-Piston Components (G.M.)

able noise, low power, and violent combustion leading to parts failure. Although the free-piston engine program has been deactivated, it will be discussed because it employs a gasifier of a free-piston engine type to provide a continuous flow of gas to operate a power-producing turbine. This is an entirely different type of vehicular gas engine exhibiting similarities to both the diesel engine and the gas turbine.

Free-Piston Applications

General Motors Research Laboratories have designed a 4-cylinder free-piston engine, the 4-4 *Hyprex*, for *automotive use*. This is shown in Fig. 13-19. To better test this experimental engine it has been installed in a car shown in Fig. 13-20 which was engineered for this purpose. Another G.M. division has built several much larger free-piston gasifiers for *ship propulsion* and *power station operation*. See Fig. 13-21. The 4-4 Hyprex is a small twin version of the larger unit.

Description

A free-piston engine, Fig. 13-22, has no connecting rod, crankshaft, or flywheel. It consists only of a *casing* and an inner *cylinder* with *pistons* located at its ends. The large outer ends of the pistons compress air; the smaller ends receive the power of combustion in the cylinder. At each end of the casing, there is an air chamber for the large piston head. Outside each head is the *air cushion* or *bounce chamber;* between them is an *air compression* space with valve that will permit suction and delivery to the combustion cylinder. The inner cylinder has *fuel injectors* at its center and a ring of *intake ports* (at the left) that open to the compressed air supply in the casing. A ring of *exhaust ports* is located at the right end of the inner cylinder. These open out into a manifold leading to a gas collector and then to the turbine. The pistons move freely forward and backward in opposite directions. They are lightly linked so as to move symmetrically in unison. See Fig. 13-23.

Operation

Fig. 13-24 illustrates the operational cycle. When the pistons move together with a quantity of compressed air between them (A), fuel injectors spray oil at such a time as to cause combustion (B). The hot expanding gases push the pistons apart with the air cushion spaces absorbing the energy (C).

When the air-compressor spaces fall below atmospheric pressure, inlet valves permit fresh air to move into the spaces (C). At the same time, one piston uncovers the exhaust ports (C), and soon the other piston also uncovers the intake or scavenger ports (D). The air pressure in the case surrounding the inner cylinder rushes in and sweeps the remaining gases out through the exhaust ports (D).

Air in the cushion spaces again drives the pistons back toward the center so that the air in the compressor spaces is compressed and forced into the space surrounding the inner cylinder (E and A). When the inner pistons cover the ports, the trapped air once again is compressed ready for fuel injection (B), and the next cycle.

Thus, we have a highly super-charged and perfectly balanced diesel engine producing exhaust gases consisting of at least 75 percent of unburned air, an excellent medium for operating a gas turbine. Where requirements of power demand a larger turbine, several gasifiers may be employed to serve one larger turbine, see Fig. 13-21.

Gas Turbine Applications

Even though we have thus far discussed mainly the *automotive* gas turbine, a broad

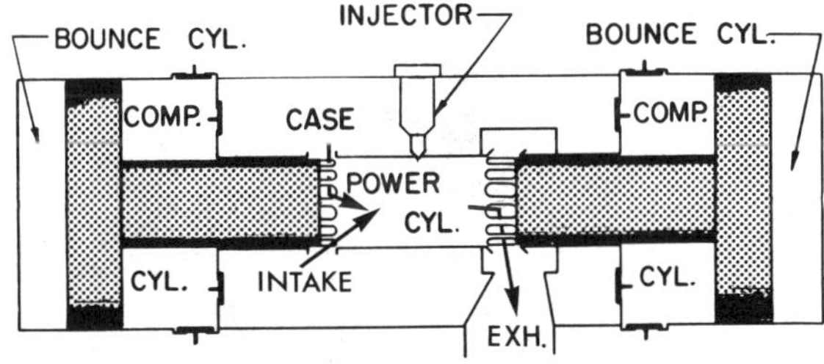

Fig. 13-23. Free-Piston Starting Position (G.M.)
Intake and exhaust ports are open, all valves closed.

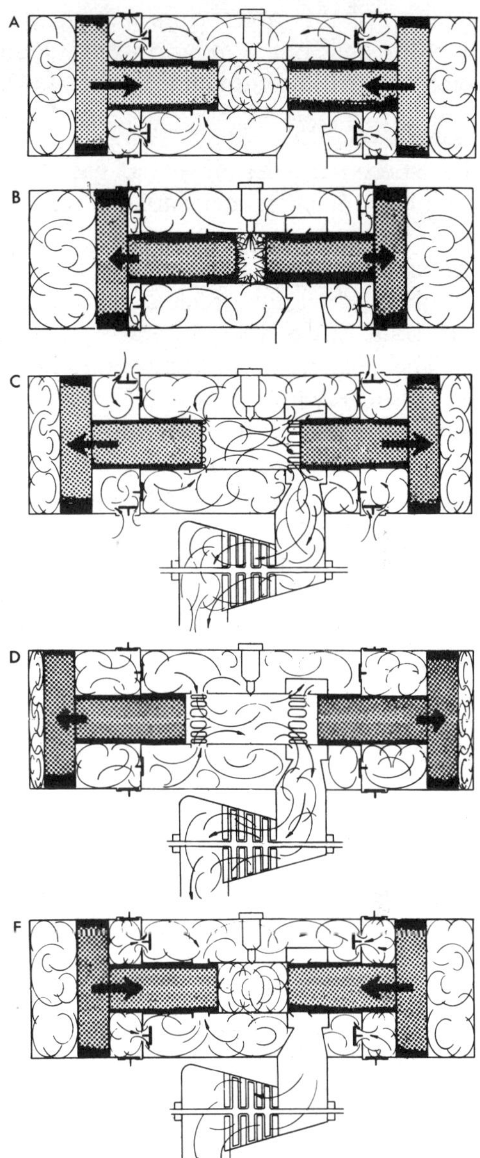

Fig. 13-24. Free-Piston Cycle (G.M.)

A. Starting air pressure admitted to bounce cylinders forces pistons inward, closing ports, compressing air in power cylinder. Air from compressor cylinder moves into case.

B. Fuel is injected and power stroke begins.

C. Air in bounce cylinders is compressed to store energy for return stroke. Compressor intake valves open, exhaust ports open and gas is admitted to turbine.

D. Completed power stroke opens intake ports. Case air scavenges power cylinder and escapes to turbine.

E. Bounce cylinder pressure moves piston inward starting next cycle.

application of this new prime mover appears most promising. Let us now consider some of the vehicular and stationary applications.

Vehicular Uses

The successful design of a gas turbine power plant for passenger cars can also serve other surface vehicles.

Trucks, buses, and off-highway equipment are readily suited for quick adaption to the gas turbine since they operate at higher loads. They also do not require the refinement of the passenger car.

The military services have expressed a keen interest in these power plants because of their ability to accept sudden overload without stalling and because of the *multi-fuel* characteristic. Also, their simplicity, ease of operation and maintenance, plus the ability to start in cold temperatures make them more desirable. There are wide applications for powering personnel transport, minesweepers, fog screen generators, portable power units, light aircraft and drones, and pneumatic starters for large jet engines.

The railroad industry has developed an interest in gas turbine power. They are conscious of superior operation characteristics of even simple cycle, non-regenerative turbines under high loads as well as for uninterrupted hauls. See Fig. 13-25.

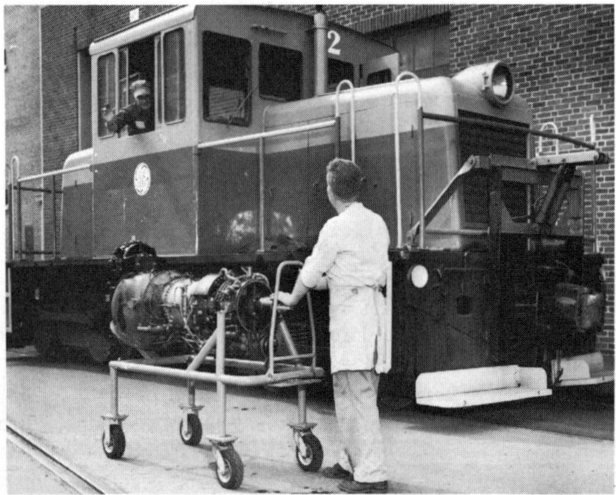

Fig. 13-25. 1000 Hp Gas Turbine on Stand Compared with 300 Hp Twin-Diesel Switch Engine (GE)

The GE LM100 weighs 350 pounds and can replace a 14,000 pound piston engine.

Marine applications of gas turbines have already been varied, ranging from high speed experimental craft, to ocean going vessels. See Figs. 13-26 and 13-27. It is anticipated that large ships will soon be fitted with turbine power plants of special design, providing high horsepower per shaft and operating under corrosive conditions with very little need for overhaul.

Should *nuclear power* spread as rapidly as expected, there is a strong possibility that gas turbines will find an ally because of the demand for a closed cycle turbine to convert this energy into a directly usable form.

Stationary Uses

Stationary gas turbines have already been employed for power generation, gas line

Fig. 13-26. Gas-Turbine Powered Hydrofoil Ship (GE)

This 90-ton experimental passenger craft uses submerged foils which produce lift like an aircraft wing, enabling it to skim over the surface.

Fig. 13-27. GE Gas Turbine

This 7500 pound engine develops up to 18,000 hp at 5500 rpm. Designed for craft above, it has a variety of uses.

pumping, oil field repressuring, oil line pumping and chemical processing. See Figs. 13-28 and 13-29. It is in these fields that gas turbines first proved their usefulness. Their versatility caused them to be installed all over the world in various shapes and sizes, as well as for a variety of applications.

It is conceivable that small stationary units will someday invade the home where they will provide heat, refrigeration, and electrical power at nominal operating cost.

Multipurpose Gas Turbines

The versatility of the gas turbine will become more evident if we note how three basic turbine power plants have been adapted or modified to satisfy various industrial demands. Even though their original design and production might have been for a single use, they can now be considered multipurpose turbines. Fig. 13-30 shows some applications for a converted aircraft turboprop jet engine.

Lycoming Gas Turbine

The Lycoming T 53 is a nonregenerative open-cycle gas turbine with two independent concentric shafts. The drive shaft revolves within the compressor shaft. This allows the drive shaft to be opposite the exhaust end.

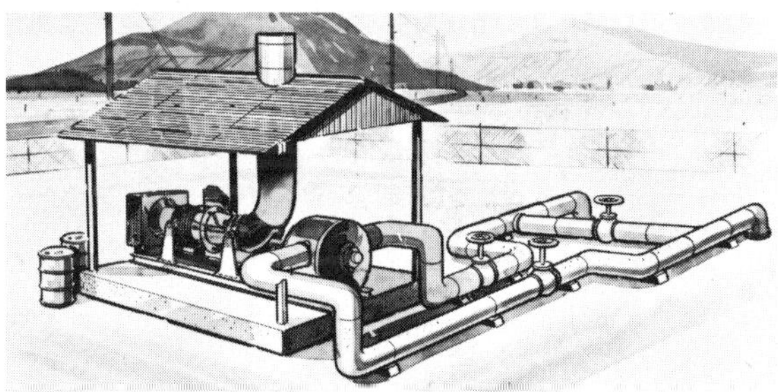

Fig. 13-28. Natural Gas Pipeline Pumping Station Uses GE 722 Gas Turbine

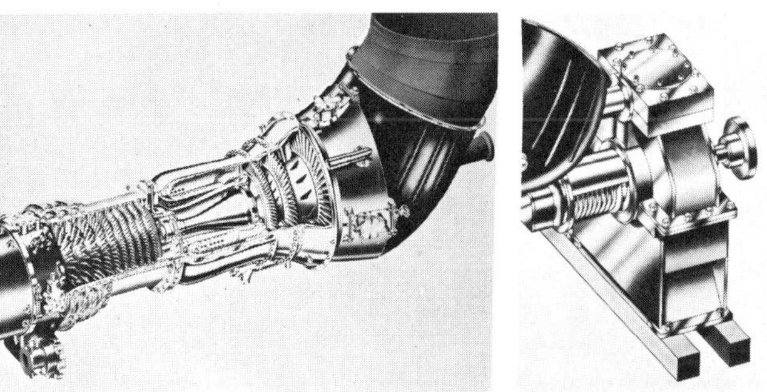

Fig. 13-29. GE 722 Gas Turbine

This industrial engine develops 900 continuous shaft hp on natural gas or liquid fuels and weighs 300 pounds. The reduction gear (right) weighs 800 pounds. Spare engine can be carried by two men or moved in a station wagon simplifying maintenance and nearly eliminating down time.

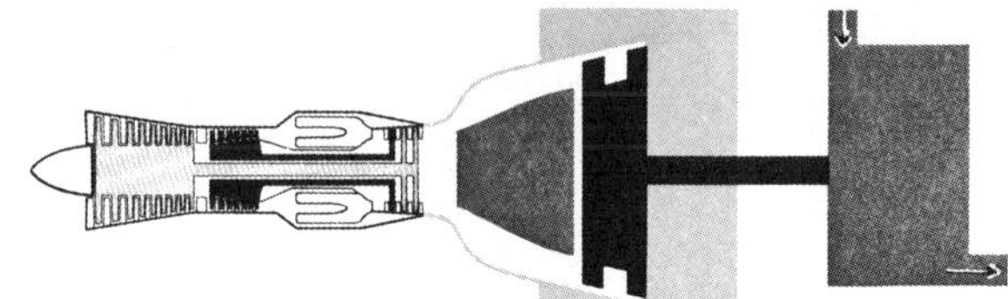

Free turbine drive for pumps, compressors and blowers

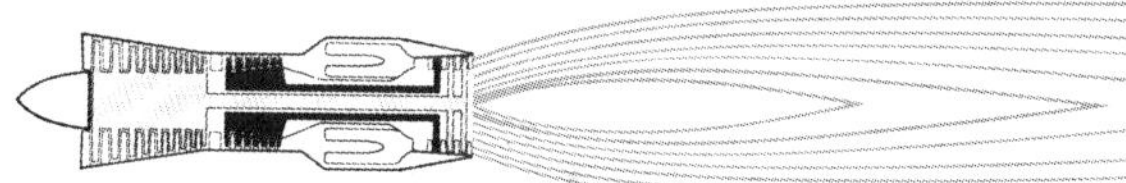

Gas generator as source of heat

Free turbine drive for electric power generation

Free turbine drive for marine and vehicular propulsion

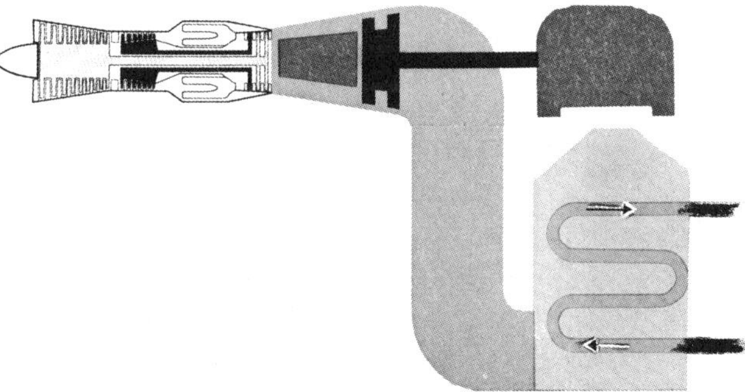

Simple combined cycle for waste heat utilization

Fig. 13-30. Gas Turbine Modifications

See Fig. 13-31. Note especially that the compressor has *axial flow,* rather than the *radial flow* previously studied. This compressor operates much like a driven multi-stage turbine. See Chapter 14 for more details.

The engine is an example of a medium powered gas turbine engine engineered specifically to provide the versatility required by the many applications for engines, larger than the automotive turbines yet smaller than the

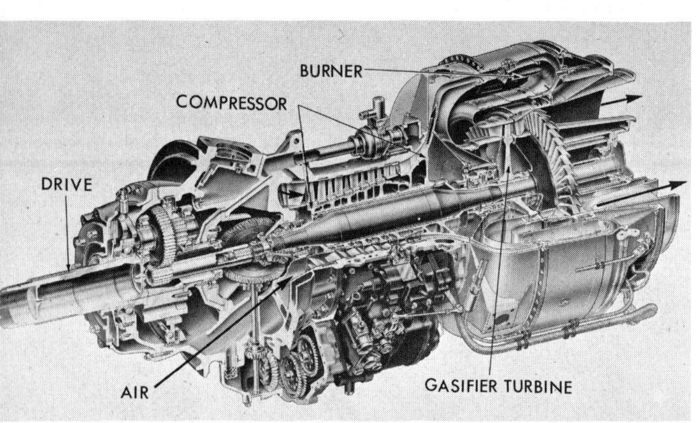

Fig. 13-31. Lycoming T53 Universal Power Unit
This basic gas turbine can be used for turboprop, helicopter, turbojet, vertical take-off and landing craft, industrial, marine, or mobile applications.

Fig. 13-32. J-57 Jet Engine Adapted for Stationary Power (Pratt & Whitney)
Jet engine is the gasifier for a turbine which produces 10,500 hp for pumping gas through a pipeline at Clementsville, Kentucky.

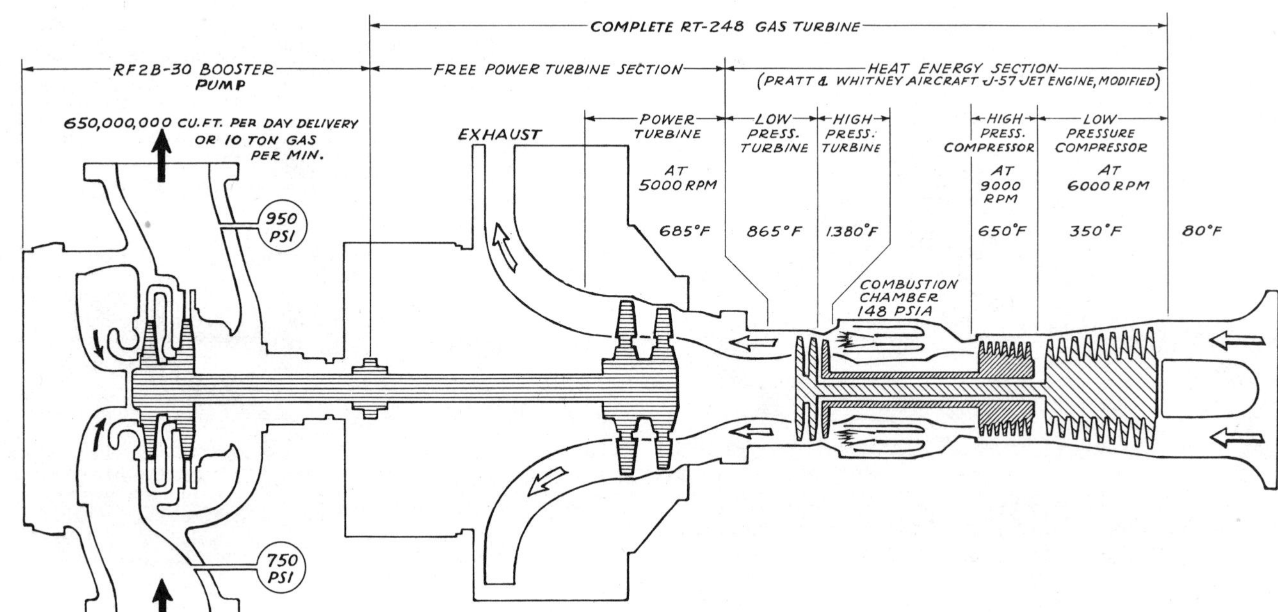

Fig. 13-33. Diagram of Pipeline Booster Station shown in Fig. 13-32

larger power plants. This engine has accumulated more hours of running time under more operational conditions than any engine in its class.

Because it is a volume produced engine, the T 53 offers low cost turbine power for a range of industrial, marine, vehicular, and aircraft applications.

Pratt & Whitney Gas Turbine

The Pratt & Whitney Aircraft J 57 turbojet engine was modified to drive the Cooper-Bessemer RT-248 Centrifugal Compressor as shown in Fig. 13-32. This engine is already in production, with more than 18,000 in aircraft service today, and offers ideal characteristics for the new power concept. The completely new RT-248 weighs less than one-fifth as much as a conventional gas turbine and provides upwards of 10,500 horsepower while weighing only 4,000 pounds. This means that the gas generator needs only a simple foundation and a light weight end-support.

Fig. 13-34. 5,000 kw Gas Turbine Powered Generators (Westinghouse)

Mechanical Details: The gas generator is of *two-spool design* as shown in Fig. 13-33. That is, it has two independently driven axial flow compressors, giving optimum combustion air pressures and a 10:1 compression ratio. These features, together with the performance of the specially designed heavy duty power turbine, result in an overall thermal efficiency of 25 percent. Since this efficiency is comparable to that of the best regenerated units, a regenerator is not desirable so there is a savings in weight.

Along with this new multipurpose concept in gas turbine power, there is also a new concept in maintenance. The light integrated design requires only 4 hours of maintenance *downtime* and this only after 8,000 operating hours.

The standard controls afford automatic protection against adverse operating conditions such as overspeed, overload, and over-temperature. Additional units with a range of 500 to 15,000 hp are now being developed for industrial use.

Westinghouse Gas Turbine

The Westinghouse 5,000 kw gas turbine generator unit makes an important new concept available to meet power generation requirements. It is shown in Fig. 13-34, 13-35,

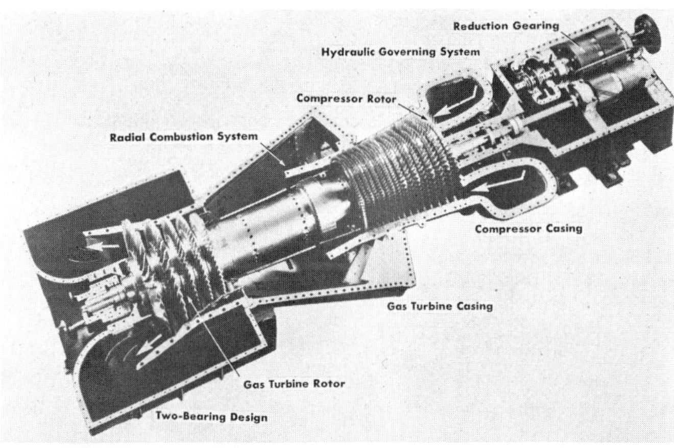

Fig. 13-35. Gas Turbine Opened (Westinghouse)

13-36. It has a one-shaft turbine with five stages, and a 16-stage axial flow compressor, Fig. 13-35. As no regenerator is used, exhaust is 760°F.

The 5,000 kw gas turbine is a complete power plant for the conversion of gaseous or liquid fuel energy into electrical energy. See Fig. 13-36. The three major gas turbine components, axial air compressor, combustion system, and gas turbine, develop rotary power from the expansion of hot gases at moderate pressure and high temperature, exhausting them at lower pressure and temperature. Reduction gears reduce 5740 rpm of turbine to 3600 rpm. This power drives the generator converting mechanical power into electrical energy. This concept minimizes the requirements of water supply, plant cost, complex buildings, installation and maintenance, and marks another milestone in power generation.

The 5,000 kw simple, open cycle, gas turbine exhausts hot gases which can be used advantageously as a by-product. This exhaust contains approximately 73,000,000 BTU per hour when operating at full load. From one-half to two-thirds of this exhaust heat can be recovered and used for such purposes as generating low-pressure process steam in a waste heat boiler, feedwater heating, direct heat supply for some process operations or for combustion air in nearby fuel-fired boilers. Naturally, the utilization of the exhaust heat makes possible very high overall thermal efficiencies when considering both the electric power and steam generation obtained with fuel input to the gas turbine.

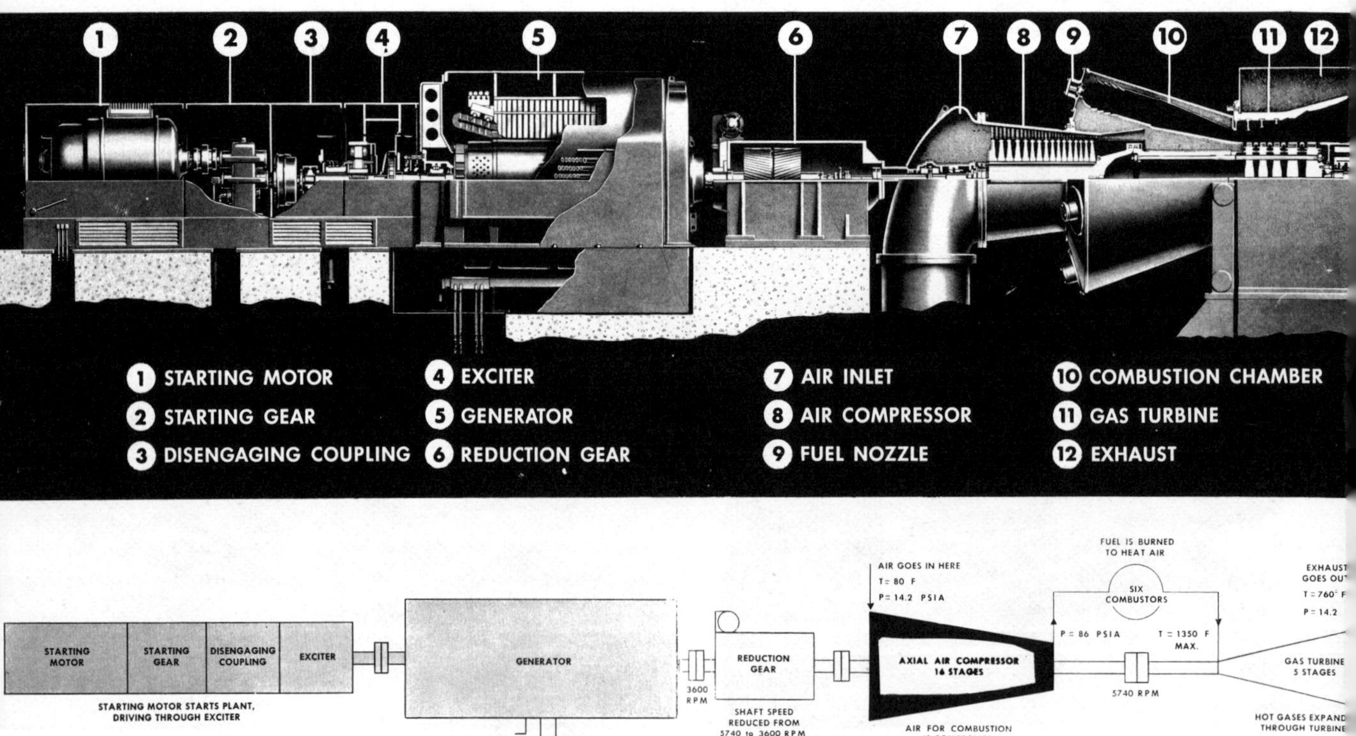

Fig. 13-36. **5,000 kw Gas Turbine Power Plant for Generating Electricity** (Westinghouse)

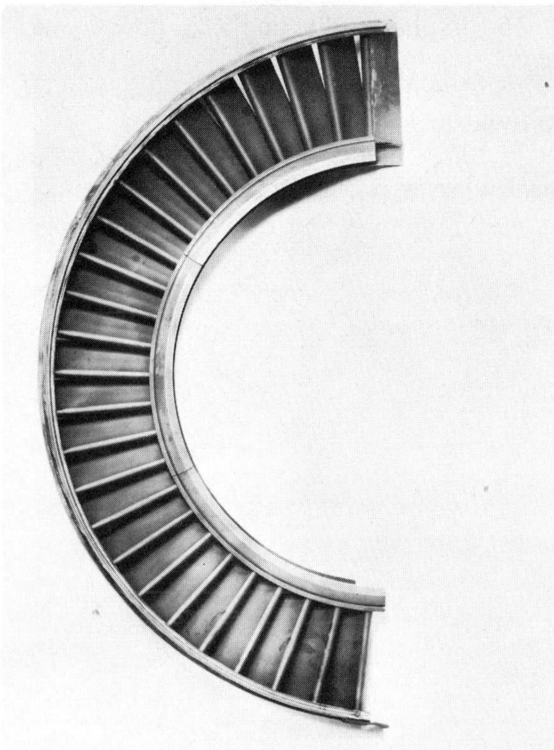

Fig. 13-37. Stationary Turbine Nozzle (Westinghouse)
These are welded into shroud rings to form half diaphragms. Cooling air from the compressor flows between the diaphragms and casing.

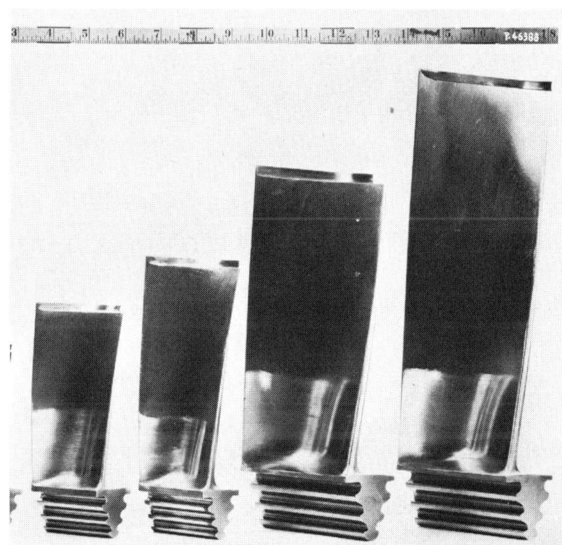

Fig. 13-38. Rotating Turbine Blades (Westinghouse)
Note side-entry roots held in axial grooves on the rotor discs.

Terms to Understand

gas turbine
John Barber
John Gimbell
W. Fernihough
Dr. Stolye
Armengaud and Lemale
Charles Curtis
Frank Whittle
open cycle
closed cycle
gasifier section
free power turbine
regenerative turbine
continuous combustion
turboprop engine
thermodynamic
vehicular turbine
aerodynamic
gas flow circuit
ambient temperature
radial compressor
starter-generator
plenum
tachometer
two-shaft turbine
power transfer system
drum-type regenerator
free-piston engine
two-spool design
multipurpose turbine
axial flow compressor
coaxial shaft

Study Questions

1. Explain the principle of operation of the gas turbine.
2. Discuss briefly the evolution of the gas turbine.
3. How is a gas turbine used to power a land vehicle?
4. What is a gasifier?
5. Analyze the characteristics of gas turbines.
6. Explain how the Chrysler automotive turbine operates.
7. What system is employed to start the gas turbine?
8. How does the G.M. gas turbine differ from the Chrysler turbine?
9. Analyze the operating principles of the G.M. turbine.
10. Does the Boeing gas turbine differ in any way from the turbines discussed?
11. What is a free-piston engine?

12. Explain the operation of a free-piston engine.

13. Analyze some of the uses for gas turbines.

14. How can the gas turbine be used in stationary power plants?

15. Explain radial and axial flow compressors.

16. What is the advantage of a two-shaft turbine in vehicles?

17. When is a regenerator an advantage and when a possible disadvantage?

CHAPTER 14

Airstream Reaction Engines

The generic term *reaction engine* includes such individual types as jet propulsion engines, thermal jet engines, rocket engines, and ionic propulsion engines. Their common defining characteristic is that they all operate on the principle of *Newton's law of interaction,* or third law of reaction, which states that *every action has an equal and opposite reaction.*

A reaction engine is easily demonstrated by blowing up a balloon and setting it free into the air, Fig. 14-1. The air rushing out the stem propells it crazily around the room, but actually, it is always travelling in a direction opposite to the jet of air rushing out of the stem. This is definitely *jet propulsion.*

In *thermal jet propulsion,* a fuel is burned in a combustion chamber. The gaseous products of the combustion escape through an opening in the rear of the device and produce the desired reaction of forward thrust. See Figs. 14-2 to 14-4. By examining the definition of an internal combustion, it can be seen that the jet engine qualifies as such an engine.

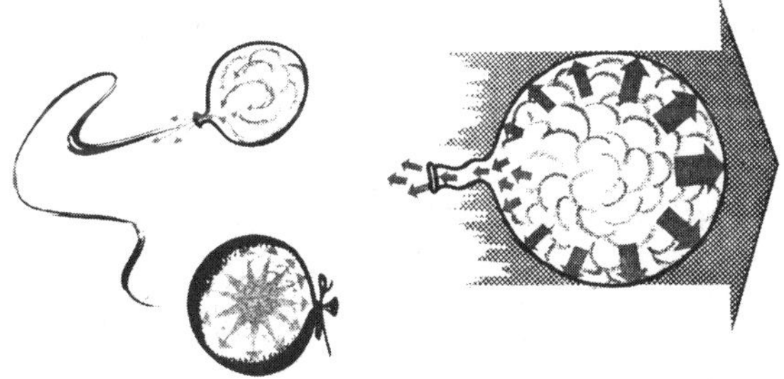

Fig. 14-1. The Reaction Principle

Fig. 14-2. B52 Stratofortress (USAF)
Range is 10,000 miles, weight 244 tons; 8 engines produce 17,000 pounds of thrust each. Sky Bolt missiles under wings fly an additional 1000 miles.

Fig. 14-3. Cockpit of B52 (USAF)
While there is a maze of instruments, there are many less than with piston engines. Jets are safer, more efficient, faster, and easier to handle.

Fig. 14-4. F8U2N Fighter with Armament
(Chance-Vought)

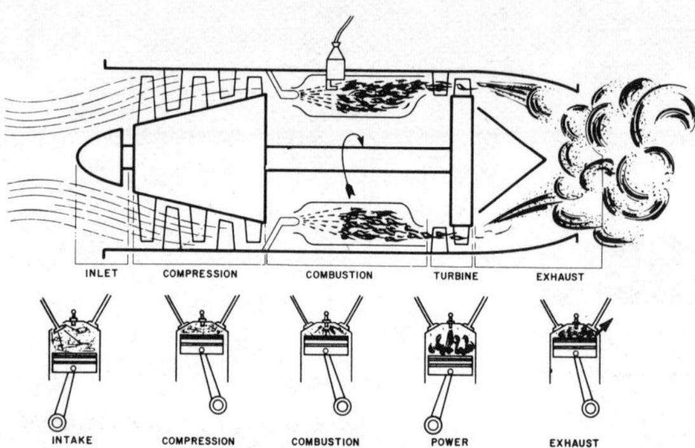

Fig. 14-5. Turbojet Continuous Cycle Compared with Four Stroke Cycle

Fig. 14-6. Ramjet Engine (GE)

Fig. 14-7. Bomarc, Pilotless Interceptor, with Twin Ramjet Engines (USAF)

Jets are just as much heat engines as are the types discussed previously, since they convert heat energy of a fuel into mechanical energy. Fig. 14-5 compares their *continuous cycle* to the familiar *four-stroke cycle.* Continuous power is a major reason that jets have attained the highest efficiencies of any heat engine, 50 percent to 75 percent, in the conversion of heat to work.

The two principle types of reaction engines defined in terms of the source of oxygen used for combustion are *airstream engines* and *rockets.* The airstream engine uses the oxygen in the air to accomplish combustion of the fuel. They are limited to an operational environment where adequate oxygen occurs. Rockets, on the other hand, are not so limited because they carry their own fuel and oxidizing agent. Consequently, rockets can function beyond our atmosphere.

Ionic propulsion directly uses the small forces exerted by ions—charged particles of matter. It is one form of *electrical propulsion* to be explained with rockets in Chapter 15.

Jet Engines

Fig. 14-5 has shown that jet engines resemble reciprocating piston engines in their fundamental pattern of operation. Air and fuel are introduced into a combustion chamber, compressed, caused to combust, and the resulting expansion is used to produce motion. They differ from reciprocating engines in how these functions are accomplished. Airstream engines have fewer moving parts. It is in these parts that they differ from one another, but each has a horizontal cylinder in which the fuel is burned. It is against the front of this cylinder that the thrust is exerted as the hot expanding gases leave out the rear.

Ramjet

The simplest of all airstream reaction engines is the *ramjet,* Fig. 14-6. It consists of nothing more than the combustion cylinder opened at both ends, an igniter, and a fuel nozzle that extends into the chamber. The engine burns either gasoline or kerosene mixed with air. It must be launched by a rocket booster to ram or compress air into the combustion chamber where it can be ignited after it is mixed with the fuel. The hot expanding gases drive the jet forward with enough forward speed to provide the compression needed for operation.

The *ramjet cylinder* is of interesting aerothermodynamic design. The necessary ram effect is assured because the diffuser is designed to decrease the air velocity while increasing its pressure. This is accomplished by the small inlet diameter leading to a larger combustion chamber and nozzle. The air pressure is increased to a point where the combustion of fuel and air within the chamber will not overcome the ram effect of air.

The *fuel injectors* continuously supply fuel to provide constant firing. The initial ignition is by *spark plug;* the operation is continuous because the incoming air and fuel mixture is ignited by hot combustion gases. A *flame holder* is located just before the nozzle to prevent the flame from moving too far to the rear or out the nozzle.

The ramjet is an excellent high altitude jet. It has application today as an auxiliary power plant for some high speed jet aircraft, and is used on some missiles. See Fig. 14-7.

Pulse Jet

The pulse-jet is another simple engine—consisting of a pipe open at both ends but larger at the intake end. About one-fourth the way back from the large end, a series of diaphragms permits air to flow inward only, Fig. 14-8. Air is forced into the large end at high speed, past the diaphragms, into the combustion chamber, where it mixes with fuel and the mixture is ignited. The expanding hot gases can not escape past the diaphragm so they go only out the long pipe-like end. As the gases escape, the pressure drops sufficiently to permit more air to enter, atomize the fuel, ignite, expand, and blow out the pipe end. This action is not steady, but in rapid pulses, about 45 explosions per second, depending on length of the pipe. The reaction of the escaping gases push the engine forward fast enough to cause the air to enter under pressure, continuing the cycle.

This is a comparatively inefficient engine, very wasteful on fuel consumption and difficult to start. However, like other internal combustion engines, it takes in air, compresses the fuel and air mixture, ignites the mixture, uses the energy found in the expanding gases, and then exhausts the gases.

The pulse-jet was developed in Germany during the early 30's. It was used against England during the World War II. The Buzz Bomb, as the V-1 was called, maintained an altitude of two miles because of a pre-set gyroscopic system. It traveled about 400 miles per hour toward the target area. Upon reaching this area, the fuel supply was cut and momentum hurled it into oblivion.

Today, the pulse-jet has little application. It is used on drones or test vehicles.

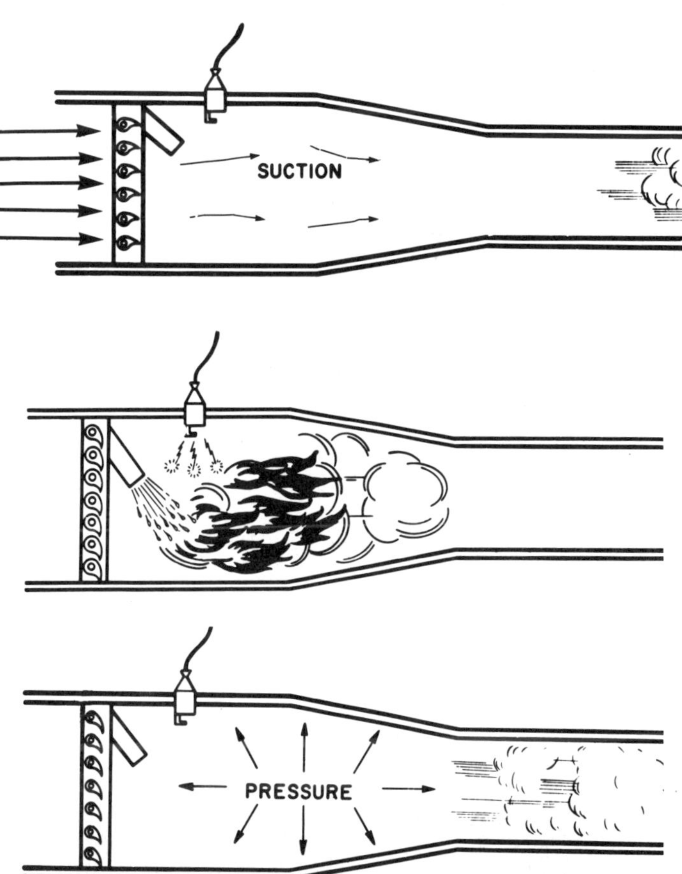

Fig. 14-8. Pulse-Jet Cycle—Suction, Ignition, Pressure (GE)

Jets with Turbines

The most important airstream engines for both military and commercial use are the *turboprop* and *turbojet* engines. These are compared in Fig. 14-9. The most distinguishing characteristics of these types from the more simple airstream engines is the addition of a compressor powered by a gas turbine which is turned by the exhaust.

It may benefit us to reflect a moment on the development of these turbojet and turboprop engines.

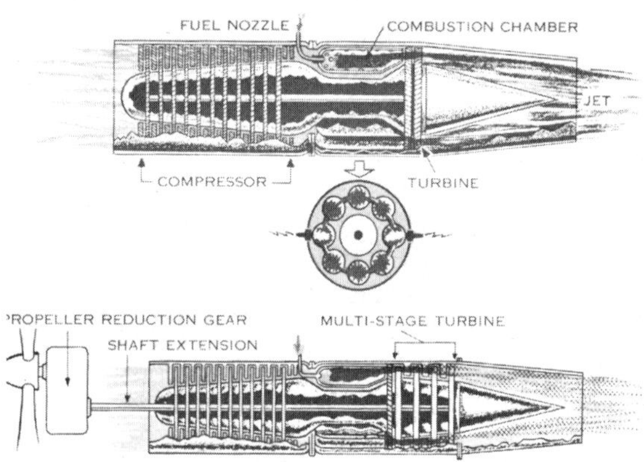

Fig. 14-9. Turboprop and Turbojet compared (G.M.)

Fig. 14-10. Orville Wright and Type A Plane, Ft. Myer, Virginia, Sept. 9, 1908 (USAF)

Weight-to-Power Trends

From the very beginning of powered flight, the need for a light, high-powered engine challenged man to design, experiment, and develop new power plants. The first Wright brothers' engine was a 4-cylinder engine that weighed 152 pounds and developed 16 horsepower as it carried man on his first epic flight in 1903. See Fig. 14-10. A later engine produced 35 horsepower and weighed 180 pounds, reducing the weight-to-power factor from nearly *10 to 1* to just over *5 to 1*. Bit by bit, the weight-to-power ratio was reduced until, by the start of World War I, a *3-to-1* ratio was achieved.

Piston Engines Achieve 1-to-1 Ratio

During World War I, the famous Liberty Engine, rated at 400 hp and weighing 1,000 pounds for a 2.5-to-1 ratio was developed. Between the two world wars, engine development continued with efforts concentrated largely on radial air-cooled engines and in-line water-cooled engines. Just prior to the Second World War, the long sought goal of 1,000 hp was achieved. During the war, another hard sought objective was realized when engines were developed with a weight-to-power ratio of 1 to 1. By the end of the war, 3,000 hp engines had a ratio a little less than 1 to 1.

Development to this point was devoted to a single type of reciprocating engine with varying cylinder arrangements in many shapes and sizes. One engine had 28 cylinders. The continuing need for more power and less weight was creating complexities in engine structure which brought about the end for further development of this type power plant.

Turbojet Development

Attempts to design a practical turbojet as far back as 1902 were not very rewarding, but the modern form began to take shape as newer materials and deepened understandings were developed. This new form was seen in 1937 when, under the direction of Air Commodore Frank Whittle, the first model turbojet engine was built and tested in England.

See Figs. 14-11 and 14-12. Encouraged by the test, despite obvious deficiencies, the British Air Ministry became interested and constructed a like model. A third model was built in 1938 and was tested in 1941. Then it became apparent that a successful turbojet engine was a practical certainty and could solve many problems confronting aviation at that time.

The United States and Great Britain had an agreement to share their technical wealth, and in October, 1941, the Whittle engine was brought to this country. The first American-made airplane with an American-made jet engine was flown in 1942. By the time the problems or "bugs" were removed, the war was over. However, progress did not stop, and by 1947, American factories were producing large quantities of these dependable turbojet engines.

For turbojet engines, the horsepower-to-weight factor is not directly measurable because their power output is measured in *pounds of thrust*. If you recall, horsepower is a measure of the rate of work performed, and it is defined as equal to lifting 33,000 pounds one foot per minute.

Thrust

Net thrust is the result of the change in momentum of the masses of air and fuel which pass through the engine, plus the additional force created at the engine's nozzle represented by the difference in static pressure and ambient static pressure. Engines installed in aircraft must operate under varied and extreme conditions of air speed and altitude which radically affect (1) the temperature and pressure of the air entering the engine, (2) the amount flowing through the engine, and (3) the exhaust velocity at the nozzle. This means that the pilot must be continually compensating for these varying conditions to maintain a given thrust setting. This is accomplished by varying engine speed, inlet and exhaust gas areas, and/or the operating temperature of the engine.

Horsepower and Thrust

With jet propulsion, there is no work being done until the engine is made to move. At 375 mph one pound of thrust is said to equal one horsepower. Early jet engines developed about 5,000 pounds of thrust, so by propelling an engine at 375 mph, they produced 5,000 hp.

Since reaction horsepower increases with the speed produced, an engine with 5,000 pounds of thrust develops more than 7,000 hp. at 550 mph, a speed earlier engines were not capable of. Therefore, in one step from piston to the jet, horsepower doubled. The early jet engines weighed about 1750 pounds

Fig. 14-11. Early Turbojet Engine — Front
(Smithsonian Institution)

Fig. 14-12. Early Turbojet Engine — Rear
(Smithsonian Institution)

so they were producing *four horsepower per pound of weight.* Remember, it had taken 40 years to develop piston engines to a point where a 1-to-1 ratio was operational. Today, some of our turbojet engines weighing nearly 7,000 pounds, are in the 20,000 pound thrust class with operational speeds of 1500 mph—thus producing 80,000 horsepower for 1/12-to-1 weight-to-hp ratio. With a thrust engine this can be reversed and expressed as a 12-to-1 *hp-to-weight ratio.*

Modern Turbine Engines

Today, "turbofan" jet engines have become the operational standard for military and commercial aircraft in less than a generation after their invention. Let us consider the function of the different kinds of engines.

Turbojet Engine

Turbojet engines as we have already mentioned are more dependable and durable than piston engines. Basically, they are less complex and easier to maintain. Within a few years, it is expected that turbojet engines will set operational standards impossible with piston engines.

For maximum engine power and speed with high dependability, the turbojet engine has no equal today. However, this overlooks another major objective—acquiring the most power from a given quantity of fuel. The turbojet engine has an enormous appetite for fuel at low altitudes and low speeds. Fuel consumption is an important factor in engine and aircraft performance. This is very important to commercial airlines where survival is dependent upon competitive economy and requires careful evaluation of each item of cost. In addition to the destination cost, the quantity of fuel consumed determines the distance that an airplane can fly or the payload it can carry. Jet aircraft may carry more than 100,000 pounds of fuel to fly non-stop across the ocean or across the continent. Each pound of fuel lessens the payload. This enormous fuel supply is still not enough and the big jet aircraft must fly at top speed and at high altitudes of 35,000 to 40,000 feet or nearly 8 miles.

Because the efficiency of the turbojet is sustained at high speeds and at high altitudes, engines of this type are best suited for long range flight. See Fig. 14-13.

However, there are many requirements for an airplane to fly shorter distances and, consequently, at lower altitudes—so, another challenge faced designers and engineers. They designed the turbo-prop engine to meet these needs.

Fig. 14-13. B70 (North American)
This supersonic, intercontinental manned aircraft is designed to cruise at Mach 3, faster than 2,000 mph. It uses 6 GE YJ93 turbojet engines, derived from the J79. Such planes help to make Mach 3 commercial craft available within a decade.

Turboprop Jet Engine

The turboprop, (prop-jet or turboprop-jet) is propelled by a combined action of a propeller at the front and thrust produced by the exhaust gases as they escape through the rear of the engine. See Fig. 14-14. The gas turbine in this instance is designed to absorb the maximum possible energy from the expanding gases within the engine to provide maximum thrust after providing the power necessary to run the accessories as well as to deliver maximum torque to the propeller shaft.

The turboprop combines the advantages of the propeller-driven piston-engine aircraft at low speeds and altitudes with those of the turbojet. The high rpm of the turbine, to develop top efficiency, must be reduced about

9 to 1 through a gear train. This is in contrast to the typical 2- or 3-to-1 speed reduction of large reciprocating engines. Most of the turboprop power results from propeller thrust with only a small amount of jet thrust from hot gases escaping out of the rear nozzles.

The turboprop engine, as we have already noted, drives a propeller which is of the controllable pitch type. The power is transmitted through gear reduction as shown in Fig. 14-15. In this type of turboprop engine, the turbine drives a compressor and a propeller, with all units mechanically connected. The propulsive effect is caused by the combined action of the propeller (a *wind screw*) and the jet effect of the exhaust gases.

The *free-turbine* turboprop employs two turbines. See Fig. 14-16 and 14-14. This engine was studied as a multipurpose unit in the previous chapter. The forward unit drives the compressor by means of a hollow shaft. The exhaust gases pass to the rear turbine and drive the propeller. The propeller gearing is driven by a second shaft located within the compressor shaft.

Many commercial and military aircraft use *prop-jet* engines as their power plant because they were designed for medium-distanced flights. Many aircraft with these engines cruise at speeds in excess of 400 mph and frequently clock shorter running time than turbojet engines for the same flight. Some prop-jet engines develop a 2.2-to-1 horsepower-to-weight ratio with horsepower ratings beyond 3750 hp.

Many aircraft operators are converting their out-dated conventional type reciprocating engine powered aircraft to turboprop powered aircraft. These planes serve many more cities with shorter hops than the big jets because they can use the airport runways and facilities presently available. They are also smoother flying at moderate high speeds and capable of carrying more payload.

Present day turboprops are generally in sizes of 600 horsepower and less, and are primarily being used in intermediate size aircraft. Power requirements above this level are being met by turbofan engines.

Turbofan Jets

Some of the newer jet engines use a large broad-bladed fan to nearly double airflow of the engine. Turbofans can provide up to 40 percent more thrust and better specific fuel consumption than straight turbojet engines. Reduced take-off and landing requirements and improved performance encourage use of fan-jets for short and intermediate flights.

Fig. 14-16A shows the fan in the inlet section. Output of the fan can be used both to

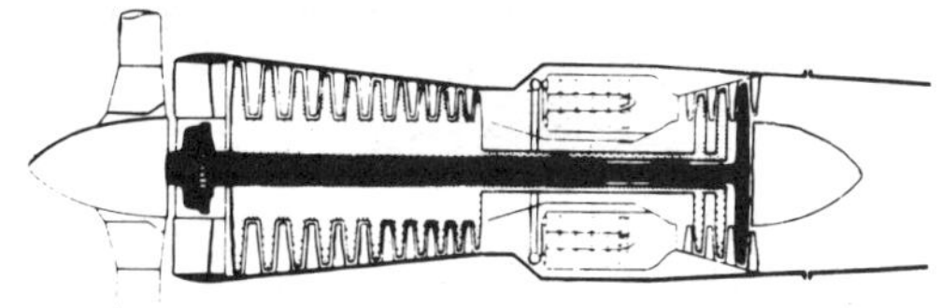

Fig. 14-14. Free-Turbine Turboprop Engine

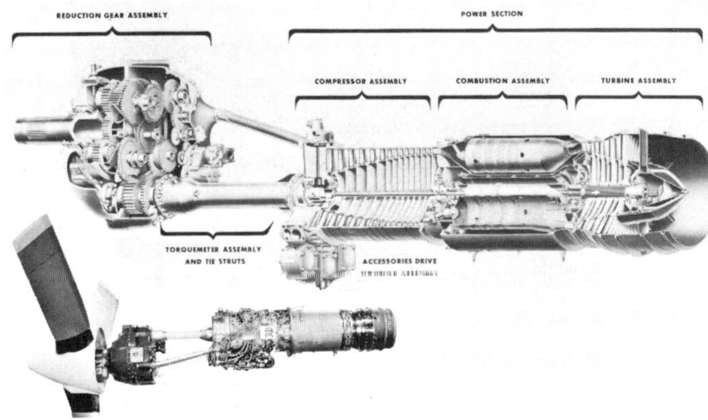

Fig. 14-15. Allison Turboprop Engine (G.M.)
The 501-D-13 or T56-A-1A turboprop shown uses a basic T56 turbojet military engine for power. Reduction gear can be installed either up or down.

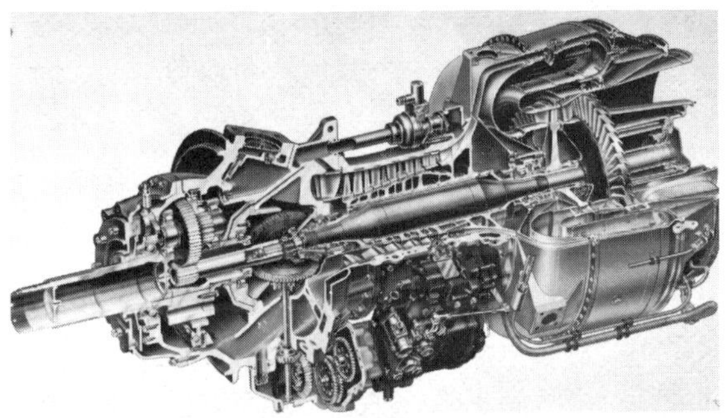

Fig. 14-16. Lycoming T53 Turboprop Engine
This is the turboprop version of the gas turbine shown in Fig. 13-31.

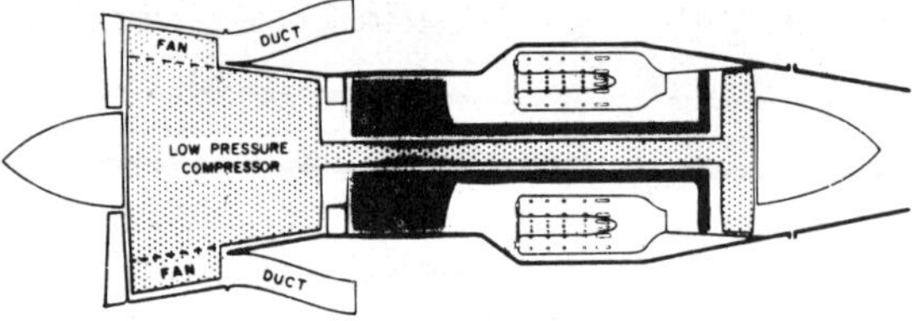

Fig. 14-16A. P&W JT3D (TF33) Turbofan Engine

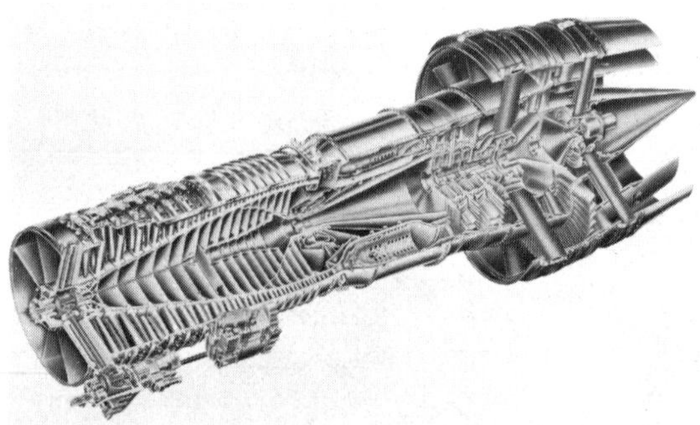

Fig. 14-16B. GE CJ-805-23 Aft-Fan Engine
This is used on the 640 mph Corvair 990.

Fig. 14-16C. Testing Side-Mounted GE Aft-Fan Jet for Caravelle 10A

increase airflow through the engine as well as bypassing part directly to the exhaust. Thus, this is a combination turbofan and bypass system.

Fig. 14-16B shows an aft-fan. The inner portion of the blades is turned by exhaust gases. The tips of the blades pull outside air through an outer duct around the exhaust duct. This added airflow is about equal to that flowing through the engine. This arrangement uses no more fuel than the straight turbojet because the addition of the aft-fan does not change any operational characteristics. It does greatly increase engine thrust. It both improves slow-speed low-altitude characteristics and provides nearly sonic speeds. It might be likened to a many-bladed rear-mounted turboprop operating in a confined and controlled airstream. An exterior view of an aft-fan engine is given in Fig. 14-16C.

Jets Today

Development from the 16 hp Wright brothers engine to the modern 80,000 hp engines has taken place during a single life span or less than sixty years. In conjunction with this development we have developed a variety of engines designed to satisfy specific needs, such as, turbojets, turboprop, ramjets, radial engines, and others.

One factor should be remembered: true jet propulsion is suitable only for high speed travel. At low speeds, the fuel is wasted as the potential of the engine is not being fully used. *At low speeds* of 100 to 200 mph, the conventional reciprocating propeller-driven craft are more efficient. *At high speeds* of 500 to 600 mph, the turbojet is more efficient, since at high speeds the conventional propeller has to turn so fast that it loses much energy in simply stiring up the air. In addition, the turbojet's relatively low weight and few moving parts make it particularly useful as an aircraft engine. The turboprop engine combines these advantages with those of propeller-driven craft to meet needs of *middle speeds*, moderate altitudes, and shorter hops. Today, most military and commercial aircraft are being powered by turbojet or turboprop

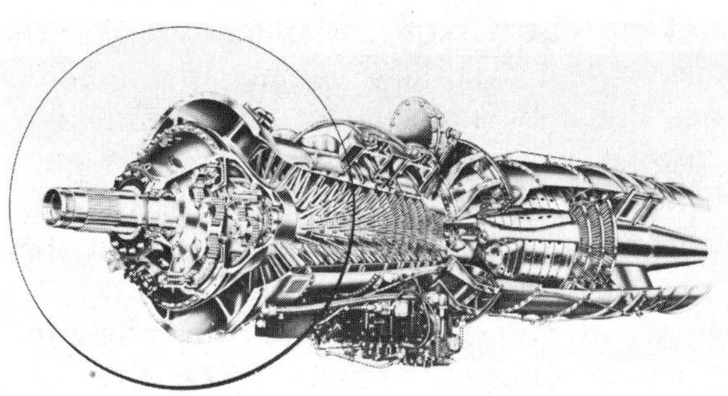

Fig. 14-17. P&W T34 Turboprop Engine
Note hot air intake around gear box. Commercial version is called PT2.

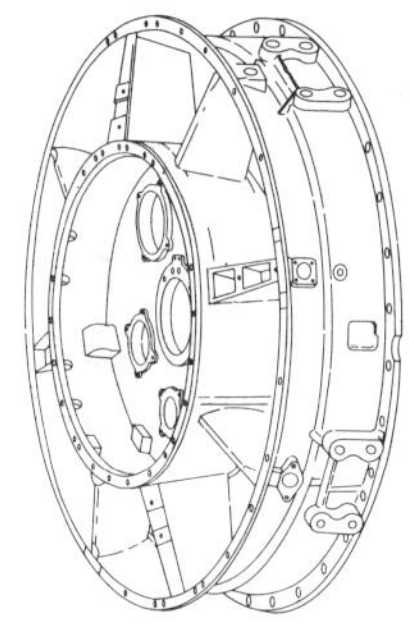

Fig. 14-18. Compressor Front Frame (GE)

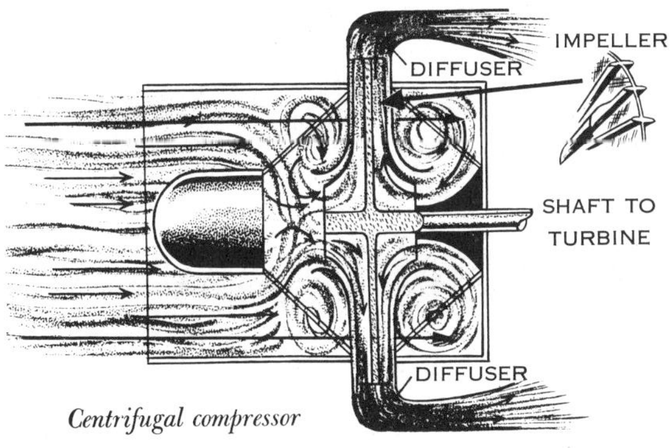

Fig. 14-19. Centrifugal Compressor (G.M.)

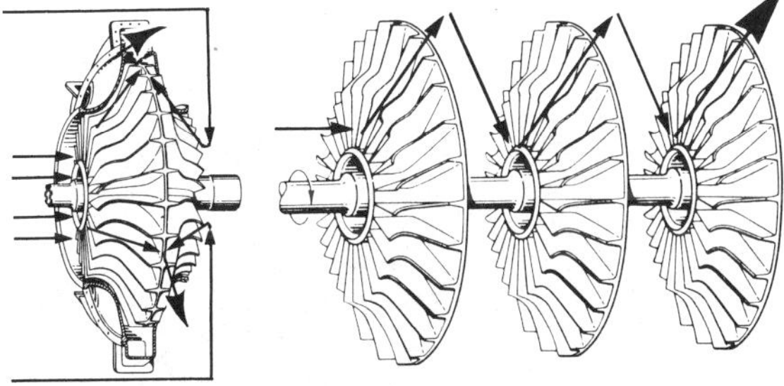

Fig. 14-20. Double-Faced (left) and Tandem Centrifugal Impellers (P&W)

engines. Most small private aircraft continue to use reciprocating engines.

Jet Fuels: When jet engines were first introduced, they used kerosene as fuel. In some cases, high octane gasoline was used, particularly if it was available for the reciprocating engine. The military specifications for jet fuel are very stringent in kindling range, viscosity, safe storage and shipment requirements. The BTU output is particularly important because it is the heat from combustion that furnishes the energy to propel the craft. Detonation (as measured by octane ratings of gasoline) or ignition speed (as measured by cetane ratings of diesel fuels) are less important. Today jet fuel is essentially a special blend of kerosene. Military jets use nearly 150 million barrels (42 gal.) per year. Civil aircraft use about 50 million barrels. By comparison, civil aircraft use less than 15 million barrels of aviation gasoline per year for reciprocating engines.

Jet Engine Sections

The remainder of this chapter will emphasize operational details of the *turbojet engine.* Most of the basic principles also apply to the *turboprop engine* except some having to do with thrust augmentation. The added power turbine, drive shaft, and gear reduction units peculiar to the turboprop engine have been noted earlier in this chapter as well as in Chapter 13.

All airstream combustion engines depend on oxygen from the air for their operation. Providing this air supply is more of a problem than any other one requirement. For example, a typical jet will consume about 1,000,000 cubic feet of air for every 10 minutes of peak operation. Only about one quarter of this air is consumed with the fuel, the other three-fourths has other uses. All must pass progressively through the inlet section, the compressor section, the burner section, the turbine section, and the exhaust section. These will be covered in order.

Inlet Section

The inlet section of a jet engine can be located at the front, rear, or side of the compressor, and can be fixed or variable depending on the type of the engine and the design of the compressor. Fig. 14-17 shows how the nose section of a turboprop engine is designed so air can flow around the reduction gearing to the axial flow compressor.

The air inlet section is formed by the structural support members located forward of the compressor and has the purpose of admitting air to the compressor. The major engine component in this area is the *compressor front frame*, Fig. 14-18. It is imperative that this particular section of the engine be as cleanly designed (aerodynamically) as possible, insuring a smooth evenly distributed air flow into the engine. The compressor front frame serves as the structural support member for the forward end of the engine. The struts extending inward from the outer shell support the bearing for the forward end of the compressor rotor and nose gear case section. These struts are usually anti-iced with internal flow of hot air or oil.

Inlets and Air Flow: The air inlet section of the *centrifugal-flow* engine is located behind the compressor as well as in front, Fig. 14-19. This is because some centrifugal impellers are double faced and some use several single-faced impellers in tandem. Air flow for these are indicated in Fig. 14-20. In jet engines with centrifugal compressors, the compression ratios are sufficiently low so that the air admitted can be controlled by a fixed inlet.

The design of the *axial-flow engine* is such that the air inlet section is located at the front of the compressor. A set of blades known as inlet guide vanes control the inlet area, Fig. 14-21. These vanes direct the air flow into the first compressor at the proper angle.

Metered Inlet: Metering of air to the compressor in the axial-flow engine is sometimes necessary because at low engine speed, it is quite possible that the forward stages of compression could deliver more air than could be effectively handled by the rear stages of compression. When this condition is evident, the engine could possibly encounter engine stall, a phenomena discussed later.

Compression ratios have increased in the more recent axial-flow engines to the extent that the inlet area cannot be controlled by one size orifice or a single set of inlet guide vanes. The high compression ratios of the forward stages inevitably deliver more air than the rear stages can handle. To control the mass of air entering the engine, the inlet guide vanes and some of the first stages of the stator vanes are varied, depending upon the engine operating conditions.

Compressor Section

As has already been discussed, the compressor supplies large masses of air under pressure to the combustion chamber. Two different types of compressors are utilized, *centrifugal flow* and *axial flow*.

Centrifugal flow: The centrifugal-flow compressor must rotate at extremely high speeds. Air is admitted to the compressor through the front and rear sides near the eye (or hub) of the impeller, Fig. 14-22. The air is then spun outward due to the centrifugal force. The air

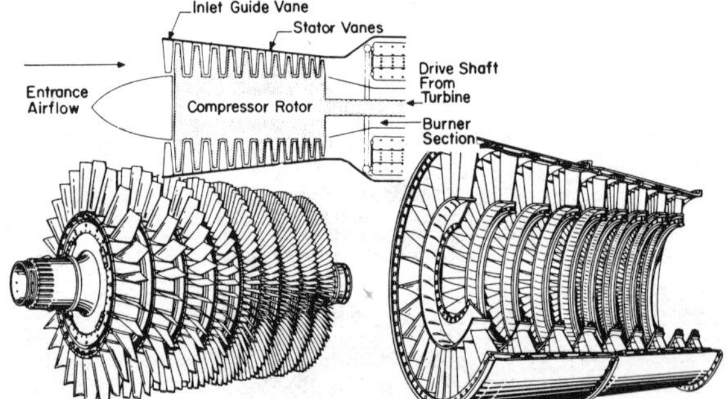

Fig. 14-21. Components of Axial-Flow Compressor (P&W)

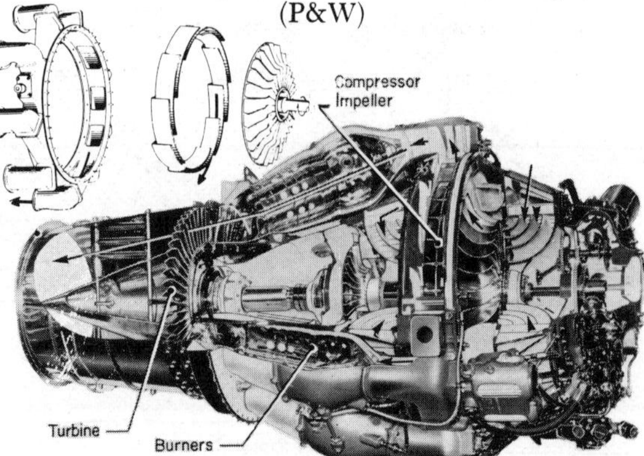

Fig. 14-22. J48 Turbojet with Centrifugal-Flow Compressor (P&W)

discharged from a centrifugal compressor is traveling at high velocities but at low pressures. The maximum effective compression ratio is approximately 4 or 5 to 1. As the air leaves the compressor it is permitted to expand in the diffuser passage thereby decreasing its velocity and increasing its pressure.

Axial Flow: The axial-flow compressor operates quite differently from the centrifugal flow compressor in that the compression takes place horizontally to the drive or axis of the compressor. The axial-flow compressor rotor is constructed of several vanes or blades which are driven as a unit by the shaft. See Fig. 14-23.

A compressor stator is also required to make up the whole unit. The stator unit is a casing with vanes or blades extend inwardly from the casing. A stator stage is placed between each of the stages of the rotor as was shown in Fig. 14-21. One rotor and one set of stator blades make up a stage of compression and there is an increase in pressure across each stage.

The compressor rotor imparts motion to the air, thus supplying the force necessary to compress it. The inner channel between the rotor discs and the stator case is a ring like structure (annulus) which gradually gets smaller toward the rear of the compressor. As the air is forced toward the rear of the compressor, a pressure rise occurs across each stage, resulting in the highest pressure being attained at the discharge of the compressor. In addition, the stator vanes direct the airflow onto the next stage or rotor blades at the correct angle to provide a smooth even flow to prevent any compressor disturbances, see Fig. 14-24. Like the air foil of a wing or a propeller, air must flow smoothly past the blades to prevent *stalling*. Compressor stalls result from incorrect flow angle, a sudden change in rpm-pressure-volume relationships or from excessive rpm, air pressure or air volume.

Dual-Spool Units: Axial-flow compressors may be *single- or dual-spool*. Thus far, the description describes a single-spool unit. A dual-spool unit is actually two compressors

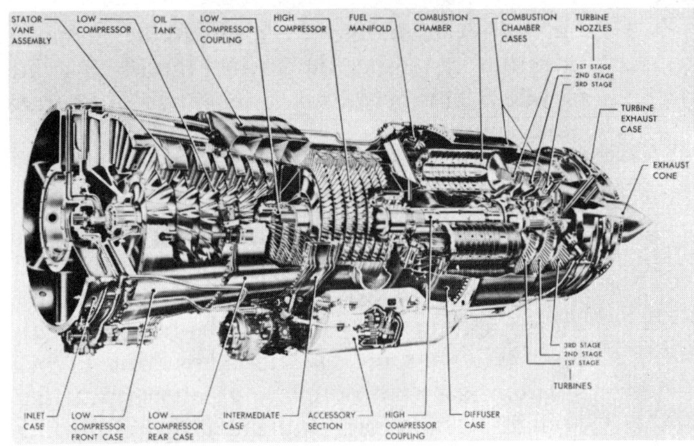

Fig. 14-23. Turbojet with Dual Axial-Flow Compressors (P&W)

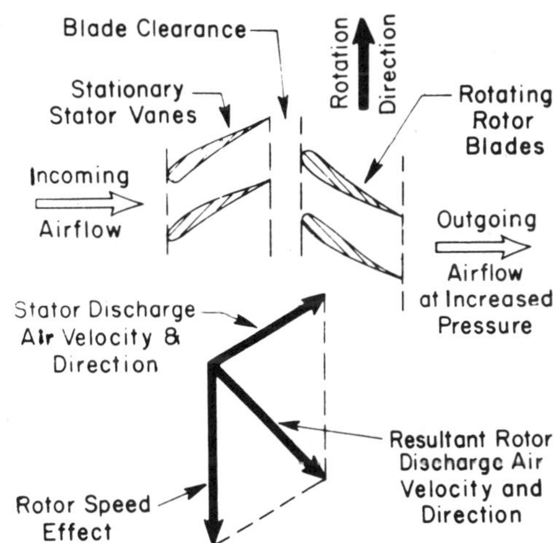

Fig. 14-24. Air Flow in Axial Compressor

Stator vanes align air flow at best angle to meet rotor. Rotor blades discharge air at increased velocity in direction of center arrow. The decreasing size of the air flow area, the diffusing effect of the blades, the vanes and their airfoil shape all combine to partially resist this velocity, thus resulting in an increase in pressure.

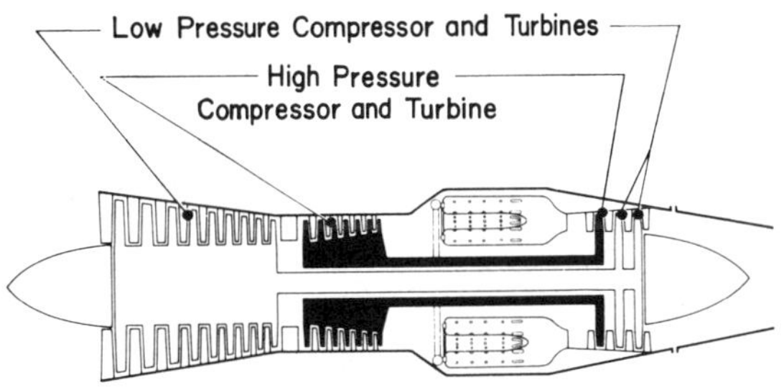

Fig. 14-25. Twin-Spool System (P&W)

mounted in tandem to supply air to the combustion system as shown in Fig. 14-25 (and 14-23). This permits a wider range of operating conditions.

Usually, there are one or two turbine wheels acting as a unit to drive the single compressor section the single-spool system. In dual-spool compressor systems, there are 2 or 3 turbine wheels driving one or more compressors together or separately. The *two-compressor or dual-spool system* allows for higher compressor ratios over greater operating ranges. This is accomplished by permitting the forward or *low-pressure compressor* to regulate the amount of air flow to reach the rear or *high-pressure compressor*, thus preventing air flows that cannot be handled effectively. Dual compressors also usually have smaller diameter rotors in the high pressure compressor. This greatly reduces the rim speed of the rotor. In addition the narrower

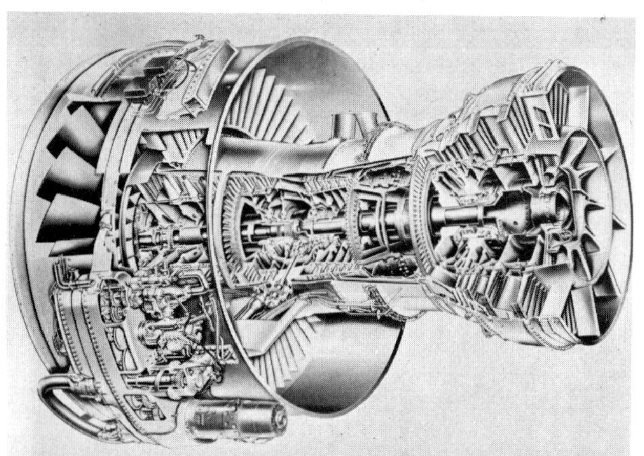

Fig. 14-25A. The Rolls-Royce RB-211 Turbofan Engine (Rolls-Royce Aero Engines, Inc.)

Fig. 14-25B. Rolls-Royce RB-211 Engine on Test Stand—Note Comparative Size of Man (Rolls-Royce Aero Engines, Inc.)

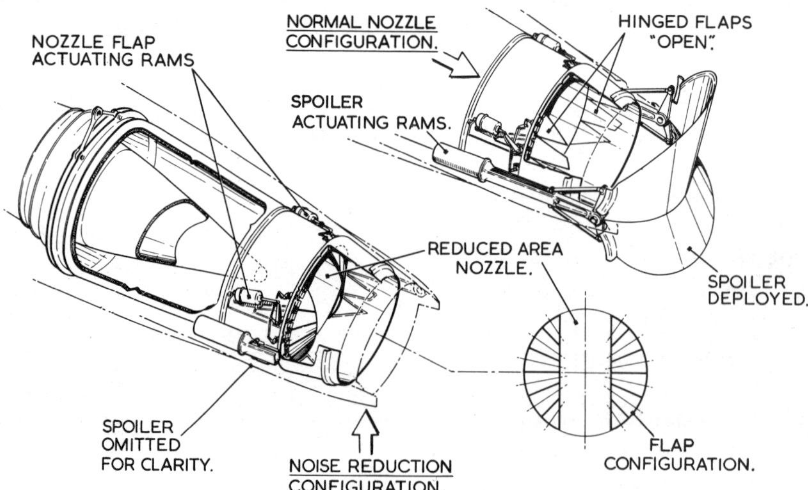

Fig. 14-25C. Noise Reduction Nozzle in Rolls-Royce RB-211 Engine (Rolls-Royce Aero Engines, Inc.)

waist provides space for a more compact arrangement of accessories such as the starter and fuel control unit.

Axial-flow compressor engines now have as many as three separate compressor or fan and turbine assemblies, Figs. 14-25A and 14-25B. The Rolls Royce RB-211 engine has an independent fan and turbine assembly as well as two independent compressor turbine assemblies. The three-shaft concept permits a fan speed reduction and therefore noise reduction. The design of a single two-position nozzle further reduces noise, and additional reduction is achieved by the use of acoustical linings in the by-pass duct. In past years there has been a steady increase in engine pressure ratios giving improved fuel consumption, but this has tended to produce high smoke and atmospheric pollution levels with certain of the most recent turbofans. In order to correct this situation and bring the smoke content to a very low level, a new design of air spray fuel injection nozzle was conceived, Fig. 14-25C.

Variable-Stator Blades: Thus far, all the axial-flow compressors described contain fixed blades in the stator and rotor. This means that a compressor must be operated at its designed operating range to yield best performance. To overcome this limitation, variable-stator blades have been introduced in the higher compression engines. This mechanism can be seen in Fig. 14-26. The amount of air flow passing through the early stages of compression can thus be controlled in much the same manner as inlet guide vanes control the air flow in the dual spool compressor. This will permit effective compressor operation throughout the entire operating range regardless of the particular design point of the compressor.

Compressor Rear Frame: The rear frame serves as a structural support of the engine between the compressor and the combustion sections. In some cases, the compressor rear frame also houses the compressor exit guide vanes. These vanes are used to straighten the air flow leaving the compressor. The construction of the compressor rear frame contains an outer shell with struts extending inward to provide support for the bearing area. The bearing in this area supports the aft end of the compressor rotor and the forward end of the turbine shaft. Fuel nozzles are usually installed through holes in the frame and are bolted to a flange on the rear casting.

Burner Section

The combustion section is immediately after the compressor section. It provides the necessary space in which the compressed air is expanded and accelerated by the addition of fuel and the combustion process. There are two major combustion system designs, *reverse flow* and *through flow*. These are compared in Fig. 14-27.

Reverse Flow: In the reverse-flow system the air abruptly changes direction, setting up a turbulence designed to aid combustion. It is presently used in some vehicular gas turbine engines. It was used in early centrifugal-flow jet engines, but is not now used in reaction engines.

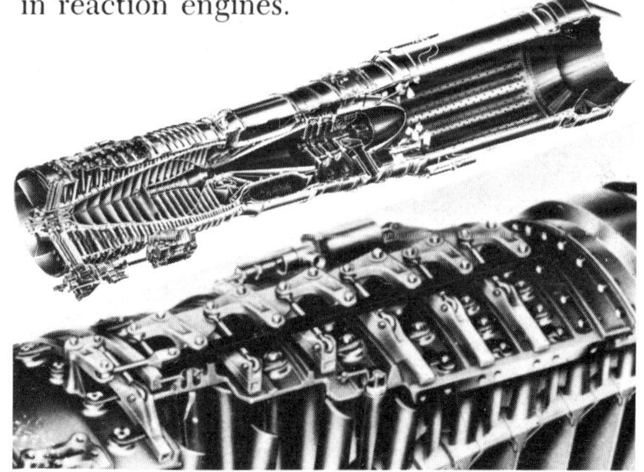

Fig. 14-26. GE J79 Turbojet
Insert shows variable stator action. It also has an afterburner to aid in producing 17,000 pounds of thrust. CJ 805 series are commercial versions.

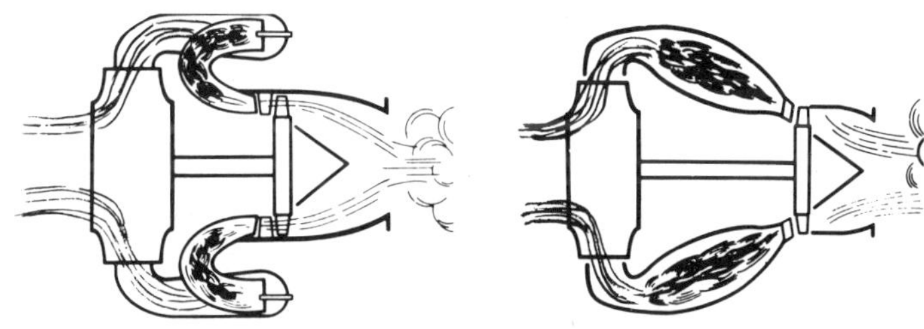

Fig. 14-27. Reverse Flow (left), and Through-Flow Centrifugal Compressor (GE)

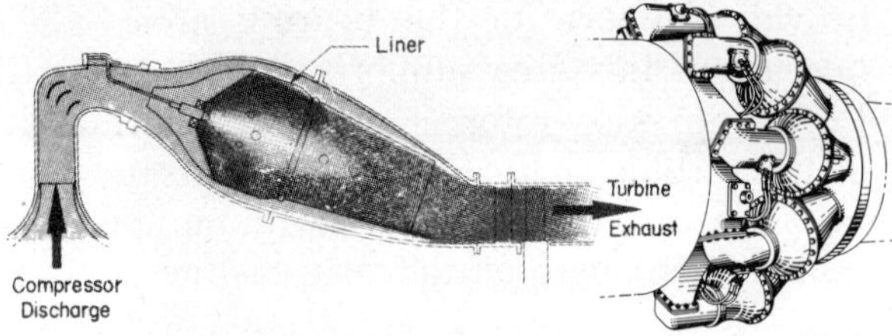

Fig. 14-28. Cellular Burner (P&W)
Left view shows cross section of a cell. Sometimes called *multiple-can* combustion chamber.

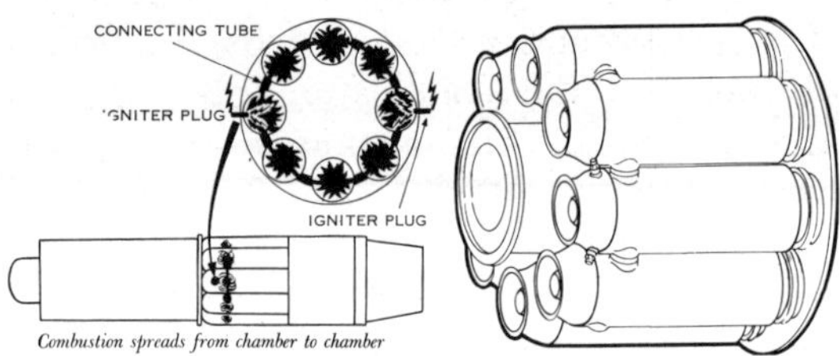

Fig. 14-29. Another Type of Cellular Burner (G.M.-GE)

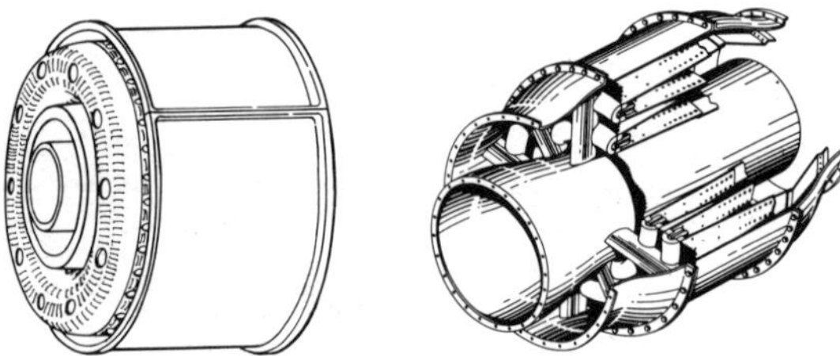

Fig. 14-30. Annular Burner Variations (GE-P&W)

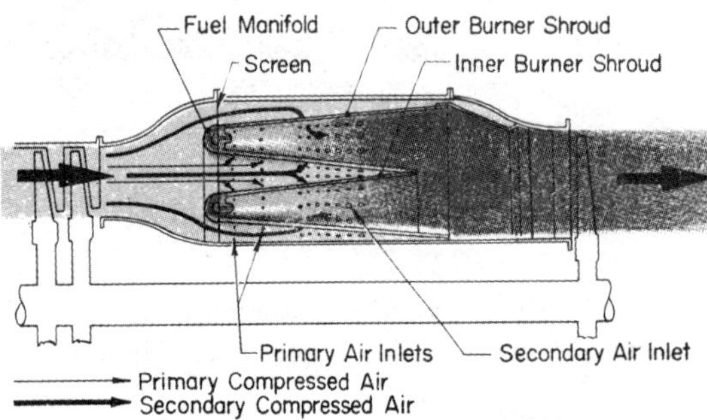

Fig. 14-31. Section of Annular Chamber (P&W)

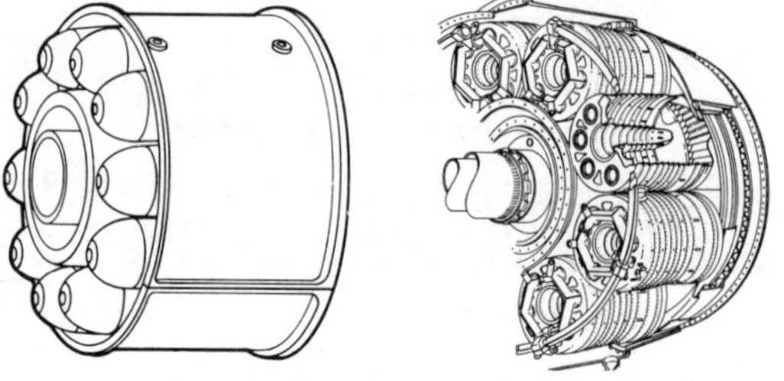

Fig. 14-32. Cannular Burner Variations (GE-P&W)

Through Flow: *The through-flow system* is used today on most production jet engines in the United States. This system is located behind the compressor in a radius or diameter equal to the compressor. Air enters this system in the front of the combustion section, travels back and out the rear into the turbine section.

The through-flow combustion systems may be divided into three categories—cellular, annular, and cannular systems.

The cellular system consists of a number of outer combustion chambers plus inner liners. See Fig. 14-28. There are 6 to 14 of these chambers on most engines depending upon the air flow required for the combustion system and the amount of expansion possible. Each combustion chamber is a combustion system in itself. These cellular units may be connected today by crossover tubes located near the forward end of the combustion cells as shown in Fig. 14-29. The tubes provide a path for flame propagation from one cell to the other. In this case, ignition is supplied to only one or two of the chambers.

The annular system is a ring-like chamber composed of outer and inner casings and outer and inner shrouds or liners, making it the simplest of the combustion systems, see Fig. 14-30. The perforated liners form an efficient circular burner basket within the chamber around the drive shaft, Fig. 14-31. Fuel is sprayed from a series of nozzles at head of the basket. Small perforations near the nozzles allow enough compressed air to enter from the surrounding outer case for initial burning of fuel. Larger holes in the basket downstream of the flame allow secondary cooling air to enter the burner for more complete combustion. All types of burners are short lived in comparison to other engine parts so require frequent inspections and sometimes replacement. While the annular system is compact, simple and efficient, the engine must be removed to inspect and service the combustion section surrounding its middle.

The cannular system, Fig. 14-32, is a combination of the annular and cellular systems. It consists of outer and inner annular casings enclosing a number of cellular perforated liners. Each cell unit is a ring like burner basket, Fig. 14-33. Each of the inner baskets is connected by a cross-fire tube to spread the initial flame. Smaller baskets are more resistant to buckling. Casing arrangement and unit burners permits easy access and maintenance. Thus, the cannular system combines the merits of both cellular and annular type combustion systems and eliminates most disadvantages.

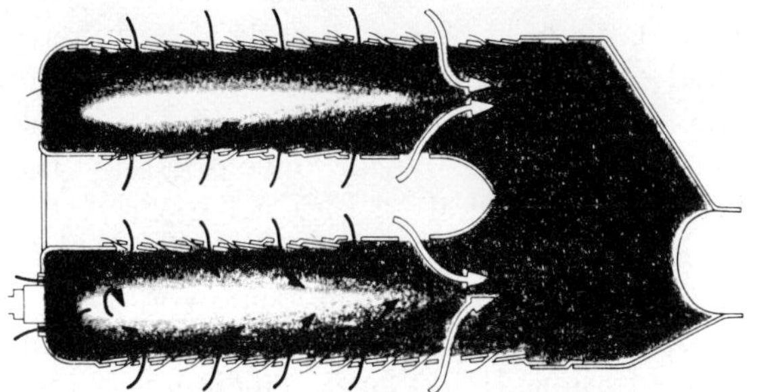

Fig. 14-33. **Section of Cannular Burner Unit** (P&W)

Turbine Section

The turbine section converts the energy of expanding gases into shaft horsepower to drive the compressor. This consumes nearly three-fourths of all engine power. The other fourth is available for thrust. In the case of the *turboprop* or shaft-type engine, the power turbine extracts all energy possible. These turbines are so efficient that the propeller provides 90 per cent of the thrust, leaving only 10 per cent from jet thrust.

The turbine section of either type of engine has these parts: *nozzle* (blades, guide vanes, diaphragm, or rings), *rotor* (wheel, blades or buckets, shrouds), and if more than one wheel, *stators* (intermediate vanes or nozzles) before each additional wheel. See Fig. 14-34. A complete turbine section (except for bearing details) is shown in Fig. 14-35.

The turbine nozzle is constructed of several blades or guide vanes, the length of which is determined by the discharge area of the combustion system. See Fig. 14-36. The spaces between vanes form a series of small nozzles around the ring. Their purpose is to direct air onto the turbine rotor blades at the proper angle. These blades may have an airfoil shape which increases the velocity of the gases directed onto the turbine wheel buckets.

Turbine buckets are mounted around the periphery of the wheel and are shaped in such a way that the gases impart a rotational effect on them as they leave the turbine nozzle. See Fig. 14-37. There is just a small rotational force on each bucket, but tremendous power is developed since there are many buckets rotating at high speeds. Some turbines rotate

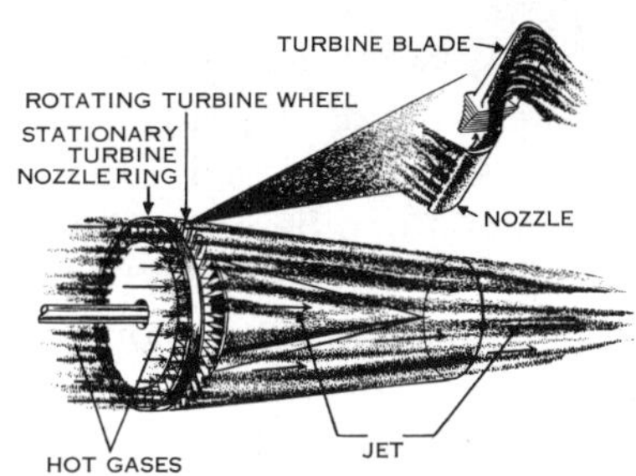

Fig. 14-34. **Turbine Section** (G.M.)

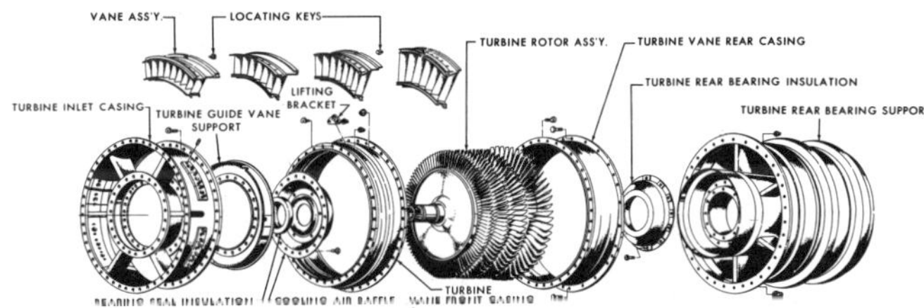

Fig. 14-35. **Turbine Assembly Exploded** (G.M.)

Fig. 14-36. **Turbine Nozzle** (GE)

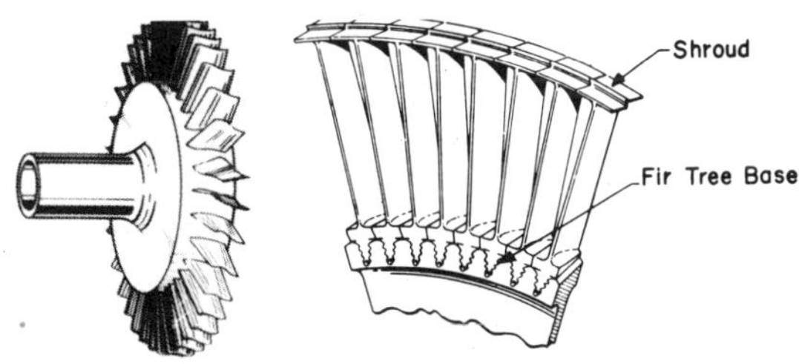

Fig. 14-37. **Turbine Rotor Variations** (GE-P&W)

at more than 11,000 rpm with a peripheral speed of more than 900 mph. This is done under brutal temperature conditions of well over 1500°F. The power developed by the turbine rotor is shafted forward to drive the compressor rotor, and sometimes develop as much as 5,000 to 15,000 horsepower.

The turbine-nozzle section is critical in engine design. If too large, efficiency is lost; if too small, the nozzle tends to choke in maximum performance.

Number of Wheels: Depending upon the design requirements of the engine any number of turbines can be used in an engine. The most common numbers of turbine wheels in use on engines today are one, two or three. These may be impulse or reaction types.

A single-stage wheel is the simplest type used in a jet engine. A single-stage turbine was utilized in most of the older jet engines because it extracted a sufficient amount of energy from the gases to drive the compressor. However, as the amount of work required to drive the compressor increased due to higher compression ratios and greater air volume through the engine, it became necessary to add turbine wheels. Of course, the wheel could be enlarged to handle the demands, but would be so large that it would be impractical for use in a jet engine.

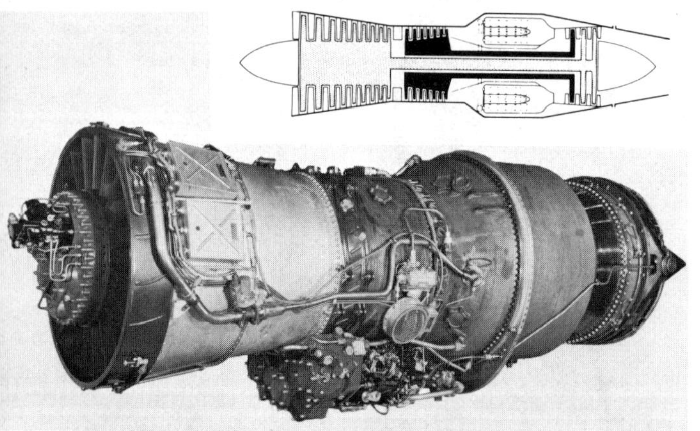

Fig. 14-38. P&W J57 (or JT3C-6 Commercial) Turbojet

This two-spool engine is rated at 12,000 pounds of thrust. The 9-stage low compressor is driven by the second and third turbine. The 7-stage high compressor is driven by its first turbine stage.

A dual- or triple-stage wheel is nothing more than 2 or 3 single stages working together in tandem with a turbine nozzle or stator located between. There is also a turbine nozzle located in front of the first stage wheel.

When a dual-spool compressor is used in a jet engine, the turbine section must have at least two turbine wheels which operate independently of each other. The forward turbine wheel is connected to the rear (high pressure) compressor unit and drives this portion of the compressor only. The second (and if necessary a third) turbine wheel drives the front compressor section. The shaft for the additional turbine is located inside the shaft of the first turbine wheel. The rear compressor requires more energy so is driven by the first stage turbine wheel which receives the high energy gases directly from the burner. See Fig. 14-38.

Impulse and Reaction Types: As previously stated, the turbine may operate on either the impulse or the reaction principle or a combination of the two. We have discussed these previously in the study of steam and water turbines, but it would be well to review the principles in this situation. The moving air mass pushes on the turbine buckets which in turn rotate the turbine rotor.

In the impulse turbine, the necessary temperature and pressure drop required for the extraction of energy is accomplished in the turbine nozzle. The turbine nozzle has a larger inlet area than exit area causing an increase of pressure upstream of the nozzle, see Fig. 14-39. However, when the exhaust gases leave the turbine nozzle, they are expanded and thus accelerated, causing cooling and a pressure drop. The accelerated air mass leaving the nozzle then pushes against the turbine buckets driving the turbine wheel.

In the reaction turbine, the passage through the turbine nozzle is a constant size, Fig. 14-40. Thus there will be no pressure or temperature drop or increase in velocity through the nozzle as in the impulse type. The turbine buckets in the reaction type turbine are arranged similar to the nozzle diaphragm of the impulse-type turbine. That is, the inlet area between the buckets is larger than the exit area. This means the temperature and pressure drop which accompanies power extraction occur in the turbine wheel and the gases are actually moving faster leaving the turbine wheel than upon entering. In this situation, the acceleration of the air mass through the turbine wheel creates a reaction which rotates the turbine wheel. This is the same action-reaction principle that is utilized in the overall air mass acceleration through the engine to produce thrust.

Turbine Design: The gas turbine is usually a balanced combination of impulse and reaction types and is thus known as a reaction-impulse turbine. The design must achieve both a small diameter and a proper match for the compressor-burner output. Variables to consider include shaft rpm, gas flow rate, turbine inlet temperature, outlet temperature, inlet pressure, outlet pressure, exhaust velocity, and required power output. To be efficient, gases must have a high expansion ratio in the turbine section which results in a large temperature drop and a cool exhaust. Fig. 14-41 shows variation in temperature, pressure, and velocity at different points through a jet engine at a given throttle setting.

Turbines encounter extremely high speeds and high temperatures and must operate close to the endurance limits of the materials. Blades and vanes tend to *flatten out* toward a low pitch. Rotor blades also tend to *creep*—to elongate or stretch. These conditions are cumulative and result from overloading the turbine. Much research is being conducted on new heat-resistant metals, ceramic, and combination materials, as well as fabrication.

Exhaust Section

The exhaust section of the jet engine is located at its rear extremity, Fig. 14-42. The *exhaust duct* collects, straightens the flow and directs the exhaust gases through the *exhaust nozzle* at the increased velocity needed to produce maximum thrust. This stainless steel section also contains several sensors for instruments indicating pressures and exhaust temperatures at several points.

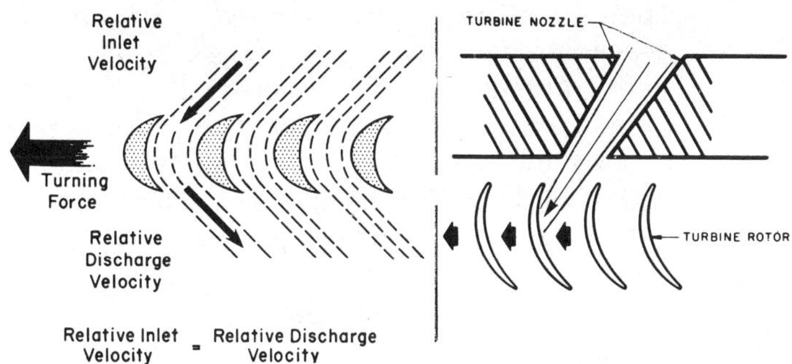

Fig. 14-39. Impulse Turbine Action (P&W-GE)

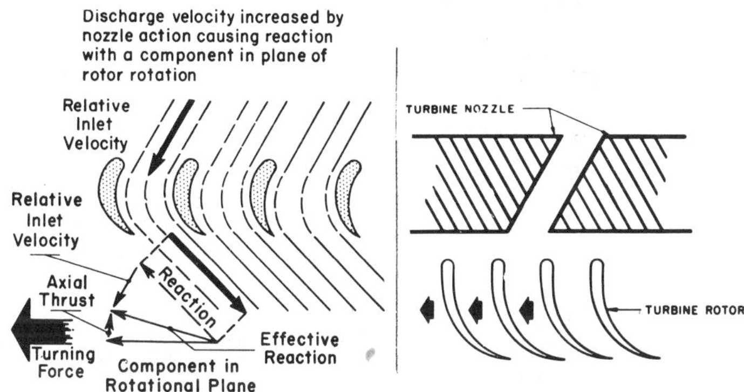

Fig. 14-40. Reaction Turbine Action (P&W-GE)

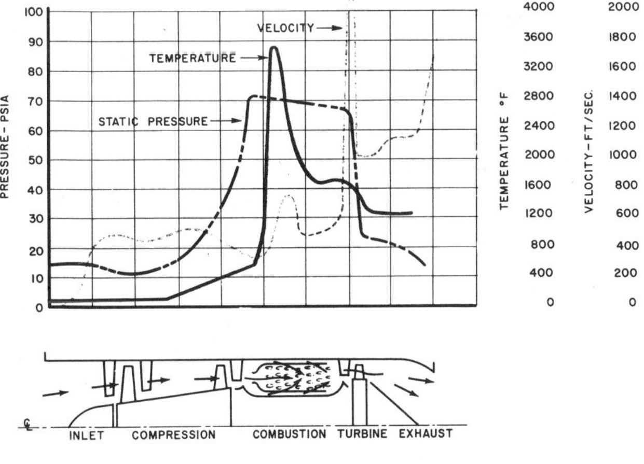

Fig. 14-41. Pressure, Temperature, and Velocity Through a Jet Engine

The broken line shows pressure building up through the compressor. The solid line shows temperature reaching a sudden peak of nearly 3500° during combustion but dropping to 1200° in tail pipe. The dotted line shows velocity has a sudden peak of over 2,000 ft/sec in the turbine nozzle, drops suddenly but again builds up in being exhausted. Pressure and velocity move in opposite directions.

The exhaust nozzle may be *fixed* or *variable* depending upon the engine design.

The *fixed area nozzle* is generally in the form of a portion of a circular cone consisting of an outer and inner skin and layer supported by four struts, Fig. 14-43. The diameter at the forward end of the exhaust duct is the same as the exit area of the turbine. The inner tail cone is designed so that the inlet area to the cone is approximately the same as the outlet area, preventing the exhaust gases from expanding too rapidly and thus losing velocity.

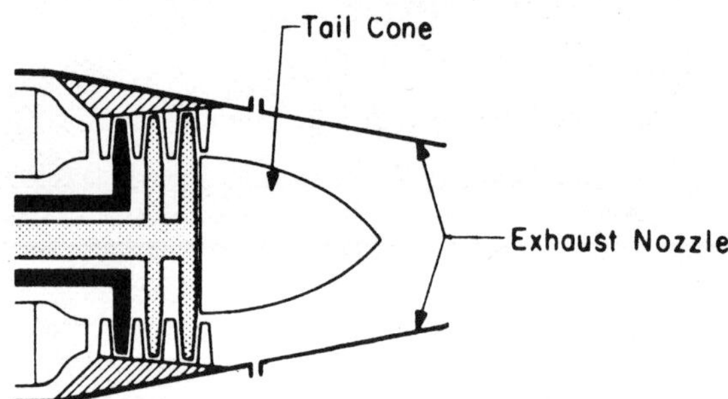

Fig. 14-42. Exhaust Section (P&W)

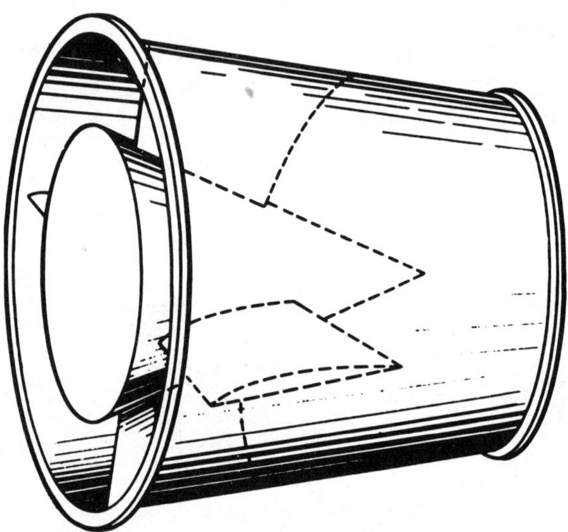

Fig. 14-43. Fixed Area Nozzle

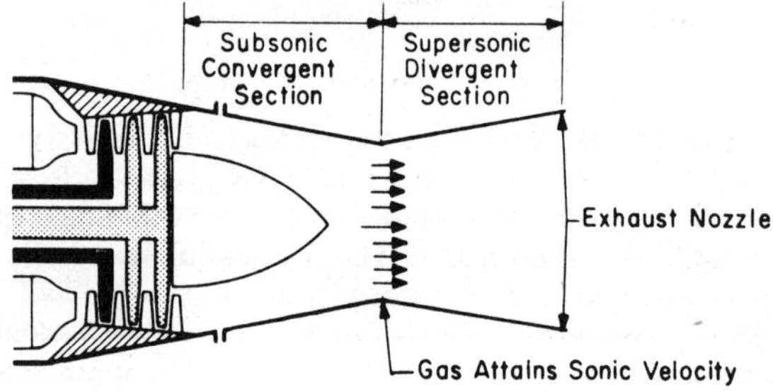

Fig. 14-44. Convergent-Divergent Exhaust Nozzle (P&W)

Exhaust velocities may exceed the speed of sound. This point is known as the *sound barrier* because air builds up shock waves at *supersonic* speeds. Aerodynamic behavior is much different at speeds faster than sound. The speed of sound in air varies with the temperature and altitude. It is about 1088 ft. per second or 742 mph at sea level at 32°F. In jet and rocket propulsion, speed is designated by Mach (pronounced mock) numbers. These give the ratio of the speed of the craft to the speed of sound at that point. Thus Mach 2 is twice the speed of sound, Mach .5 is half the speed of sound (1484 mph and 371 mph at sea level freezing). A craft must also register air pressure and temperature to determine the Mach number.

When the pressure at an exhaust nozzle is high enough to create Mach 1 velocities, shock waves can be correctly handled and thus thrust gained by using a *convergent-divergent* nozzle. This is true if the extra thrust from the larger duct is not cancelled by its additional weight. Such a C-D exhaust nozzle is shown in Fig. 14-44. The convergent section is designed to bring the gases up to a sonic speed (for their temperature) and then increased to more than Mach 1 in the spreading tail section. The C-D nozzle is more efficient than the conventional convergent nozzle, especially at higher speeds. However, it is most effective only at the speed, power, and altitude for which it was designed. It needs a means of varying the nozzle shape and area for other conditions when they are encountered.

Generally, most engines with fixed nozzle areas have little or no means of thrust augmentation, and are referred to as *dry engines*. The afterburner, a common means of thrust augmentation located behind the turbine section will be covered later rather than with exhaust components.

The *variable exhaust nozzle* is generally used on engines fitted with some sort of thrust augmentation such as an afterburner or pre-turbine injection.

In the variable area nozzle, the size of the exhaust area may be changed to provide a wider range of operating conditions. These conditions may result from the addition of fuel in the form of afterburning or pre-turbine injection. This additional fuel will raise the temperature of the exhaust gases beyond tolerable limits if the nozzle area is kept constant. Opening the nozzle will reduce the temperature of the exhaust gases, maintaining them within limits.

There are several different types of variable area nozzles. They can be actuated electrically, hydraulically, or pneumatically. One type is shown in Fig. 14-45. This one has two *clamshell-like lids* that pivot 180° apart, operating much like eyelids, to control the exit area. Another type is shown in Fig. 14-46. It has a number of *segments* which are varied in their angle to produce a larger or smaller exit area.

Thrust Reverser: In large propeller-driven aircraft, the prop pitch or blade angle, can be reversed so that engine power can be used to shorten the landing roll. This same function is served by the *thrust reverser* in some turbojet engines. The normal rearward flow of exhaust gases is diverted outward and through forward-facing deflectors located around the exhaust or afterburner cowling. This is shown in Figs. 14-47 and 14-48. Note also the daisy sound suppressors which are an important part of the exhaust section in commercial aircraft.

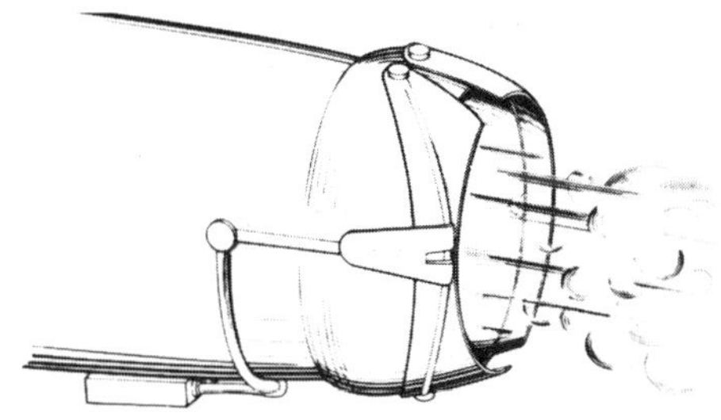

Fig. 14-45. Clam-Shell Variable-Exit Nozzle (P&W)

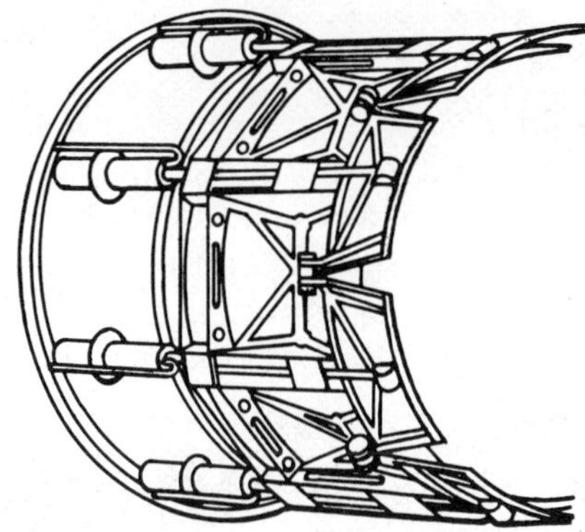

Fig. 14-46. Flap-Type Variable-Exit Nozzle (P&W)

Fig. 14-47. GE CJ-805-3 Turbojet on Convair 880 Airliner

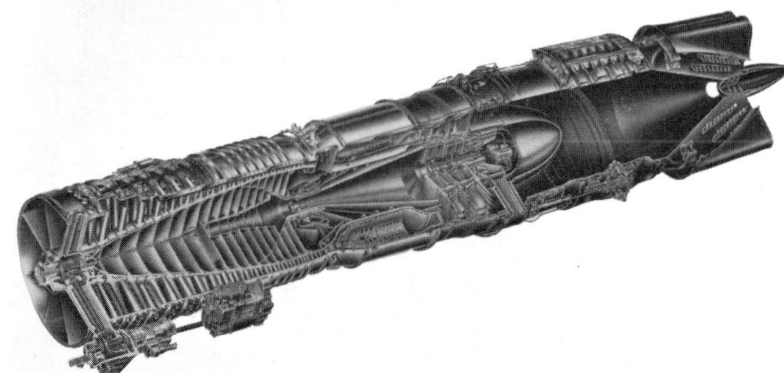

Fig. 14-48. Details of GE CJ-805-3 Turbojet

Engine develops 11,200 pounds of forward thrust. 1 or 2 section blocker doors at exhaust nozzle close, deflecting exhaust through side louvers and developing 5,000 pounds reverse thrust. This will slow a 75 ton plane from 100 knots to 40 knots without brakes on 3,000 feet of runway.

Accessory Systems

Accessory Drive

The power take-off portion of the engine is used to drive the many accessories necessary for the aircraft as well as to operate the engine. Such devices as fuel pumps, lubrication pumps, generators, alternators, fuel controllers, tachometer, and generator are accessories. The accessory or power take-off section may be located at the front of the engine on the compressor front frame as shown in Figs. 14-22, 14-38, 14-48. This often is covered by a nose cone. Some engines which require larger inlet areas may have the units on the bottom of the engine as shown in Fig. 14-49. In this case, the gear trains are driven by shafts through the compressor rear frame or front frame.

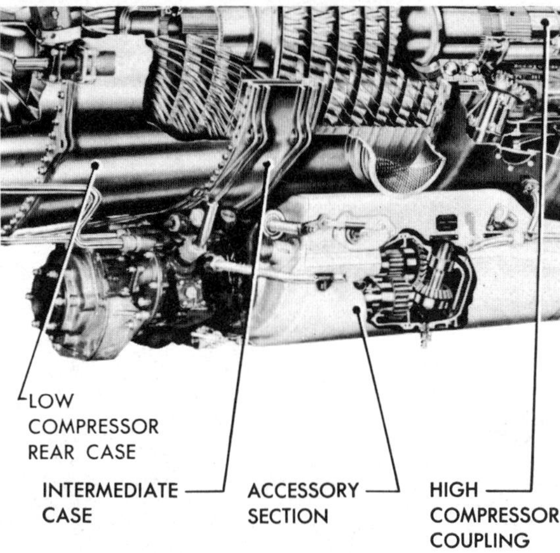

Fig. 14-49. Midsection Power Take-Off (P&W)

Lube System

The lubrication system of a jet engine is much less complex than those found in a reciprocating aircraft engine. See Fig. 14-50. Turbojets have fewer moving parts and very little sliding friction. Therefore, they have fewer lubrication points. Oil systems in reciprocating engines must dissipate heat, but in jet engines this is needed less. Since the oil picks up less heat, less oil is required in jet engines. Also oil consumption is low so the problem of oil storage is less complex.

Most oils used in jets are of lower viscosity than those used in reciprocating engines.

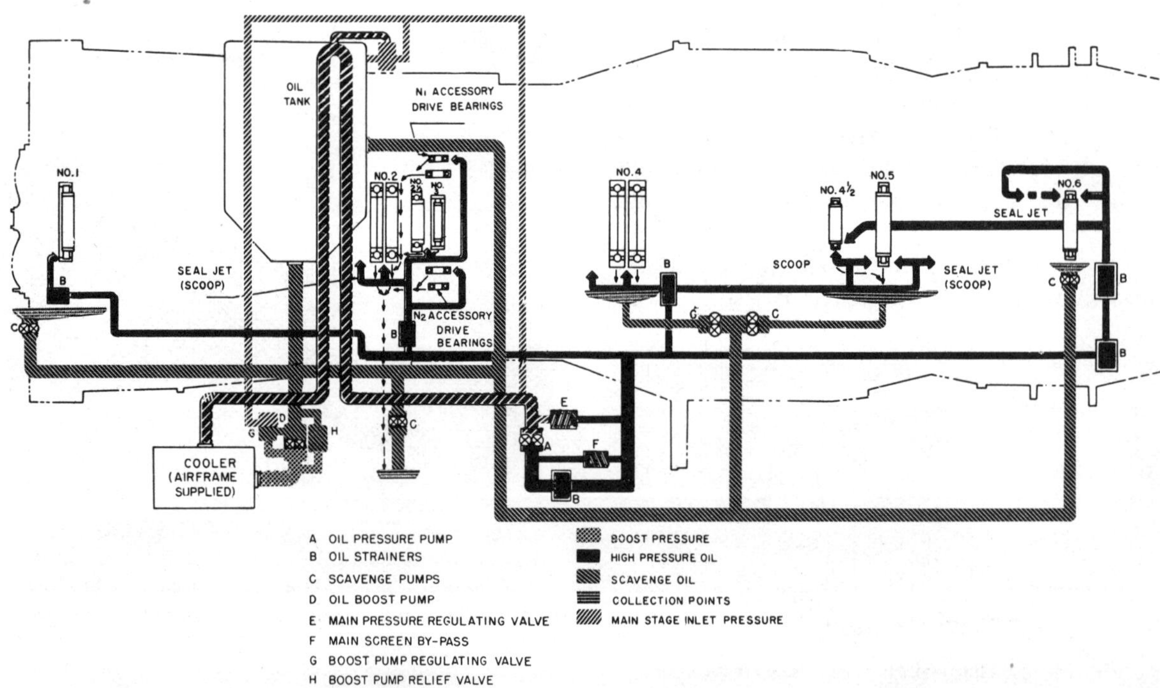

Fig. 14-50. Lubrication System for a Dual-Compressor Engine (P&W)

Many times, the oils used are synthetic types which are much more resistant to the effects of heat. In the case of the typical jet engine there are only 3 or 4 main bearings which require lubrication other than the power take off unit.

Two main lube systems are employed, the *wet sump* and *dry sump* systems. *The wet sump system* has the oil carried internally in the engine while the dry sump type has the oil carried in a separate tank externally. In this country, the dry sump type system is more widely used than the wet sump type.

The major components of a dry sump lube system are supply and scavenge pumps, an oil filter and cooler, oil jets, and the necessary oil lines. These are shown in Fig. 14-50. The pumps supply oil under pressure to the areas which require lubrication and then return the oil to the tank. Oil temperature is reduced in an oil cooler by transmitting heat to another fluid, in most cases, the fuel. Fuel on its way to the combustion system enters and passes through the oil cooler in small tubes surrounded by oil. See Fig. 14-51. Since the fuel flow is much greater than the oil flow, the fuel is able to absorb considerable heat from the oil. The purpose of the cooler is to cool the oil and not heat the fuel. A filter located in the supply or scavenge line removes any foreign material in the oil. In the operation of a typical system, oil is gravity fed from the tank to the supply pump. This pump supplies the oil under pressure through a filter to the number 2 and number 3 bearings. The number 1 bearing receives its oil from a separate line to the pump. It can be supplied from a line behind the filter. The oil collects in the sumps and gravity drains into the scavenge pumps which return the oil to the tank.

The lube pump is usually an internal gear-type positive-displacement pump, Fig. 14-52. The construction of the internal-gear type pump permits the combination of several pumps in a single housing, mounted on a single pad and driven along a single shaft. There are only two moving parts in this pump—the inner tooth element meshing with an outer tooth element. The inner element has one less tooth than the outer element and it is the *missing tooth* that provides the chamber which moves the fluid from intake to discharge. Both elements are mounted eccentric to each other on the same shaft. This structure permits stacking a number of sets of pumping elements along the same shaft in a common housing. If each set is provided with its own compartment, the inlet and discharge ports will permit several systems to be served simultaneously. By varying the diameter and thickness of the gears the capacities of the pumps can be varied.

Fuel System

The main purpose of the fuel system is to provide a metered fuel flow to the engine for all operating conditions. In those engines having an *afterburner*, a second and similar fuel system is employed. The fuel system of the turbojet will sense a number of engine and atmospheric conditions and compare these

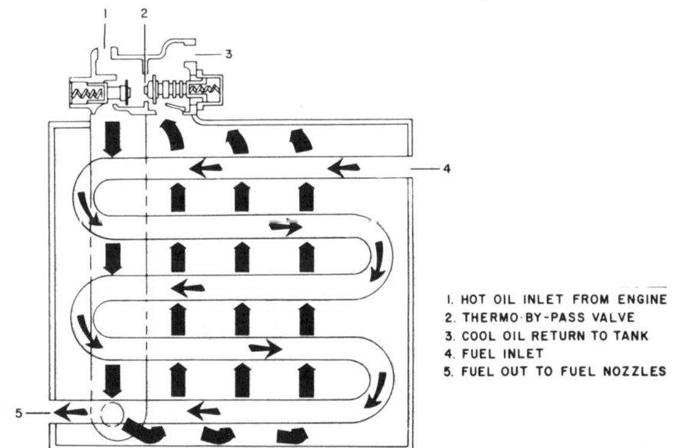

Fig. 14-51. Oil Cooler Diagram (GE)

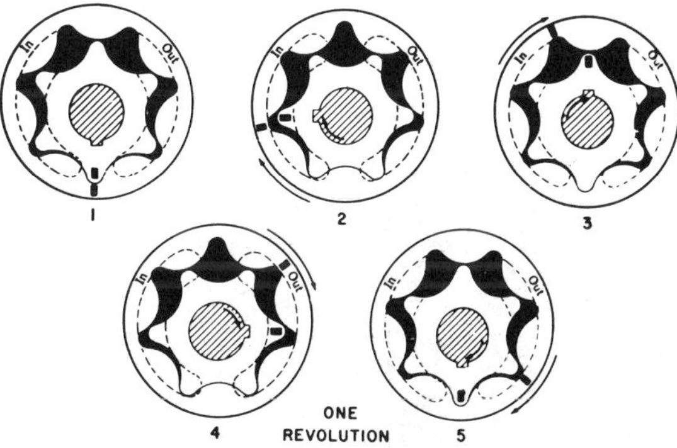

Fig. 14-52. Internal Gear-Type Pump (GE)

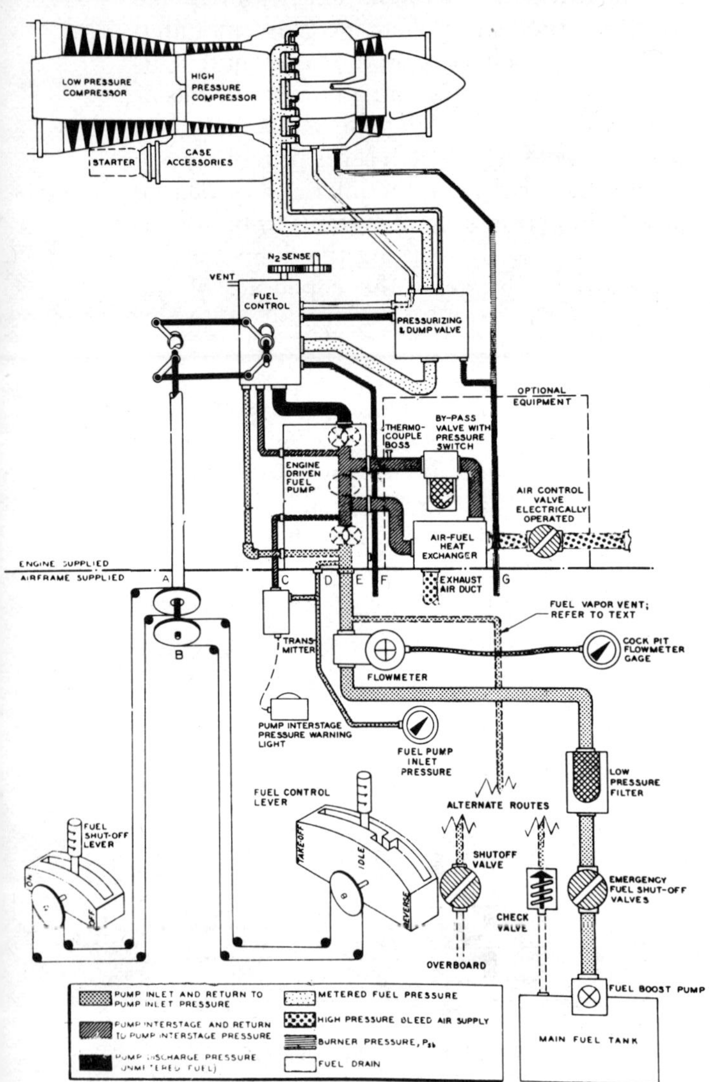

Fig. 14-53. Fuel System Diagram (P&W)

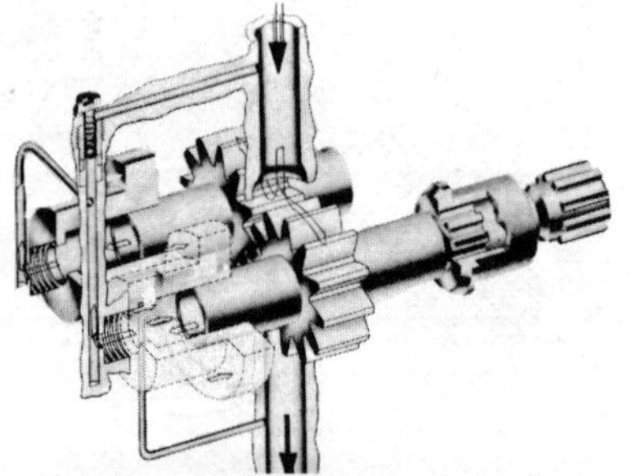

Fig. 14-54. Fuel Pump (GE)

to the desired conditions before metering the required fuel. This makes it rather complex and sophisticated. Some of the main conditions (operational variables or *parameters*) sensed are throttle position, compressor rpm (N2), compressor inlet temperature, compressor inlet pressure, and burner pressure, and exhaust temperature.

The main fuel system is composed of many components mounted in the air frame and on the engine. The common air frame components are the fuel cells, booster pumps, aircraft fuel shut-off valve and the low-pressure fuel filter. The engine-mounted components are the main fuel pump, fuel filter, fuel control unit, stopcock, oil-cooler, flow-divider and fuel nozzles. These are shown in Fig. 14-53.

The fuel supply is always carried in the air frame and usually contains more than one fuel tank or cell. Regardless of the number of cells used, the fuel is fed to the engine primarily from one main fuel pump. Aircraft booster pumps of the centrifugal or impeller type, electrically operated, maintain a constant fuel pressure in the line between the tank and the engine driven fuel pump.

An electrically-operated aircraft mounted fuel shut-off is installed between the tank and the engine to allow fuel lines to be disconnected at the engine without danger of spoilage. The most common type of supply pump used in jets is the *spur-gear* type, Fig. 14-54. This is a positive displacement type pump which may contain more than one pumping element, depending on the fuel requirement of the engine. This pump will supply a constant flow (in gallons per minute, gpm) at a given rotational speed. A high-pressure relief valve is often incorporated in the housing to prevent damage to the pump in the event of a line restriction downstream of the pump.

From the engine driven fuel pump, the fuel is pumped to a high-pressure fuel filter. This filter is usually a fine mesh screen disc-type, and in case the filter should become clogged, a relief valve is provided to bypass the fuel flow around the filter to continue the engine with the normal supply flow. These components are diagramed in Fig. 14-55.

Fuel Control

The fuel next encounters the control components. There are two aspects of fuel control systems to discuss. The first is the method of control, and the second concerns the factors which must be sensed to control flow. There are two general methods employed, *bypass control and flow-control.* The flow-control method is most accurate and most widely used and can be accomplished in one of three ways. Each of the three considers the *metering area* and the *fuel pressure drop* across the metering area. If the *area is held constant* the fuel flow can be metered by regulating the pressure. Secondly, the *pressure can be held at a constant* value with the fuel metered by controlling the size of the opening. The third method regulates both the pressure and the metering opening.

The other aspect to be discussed are the *operational parameters* which must be sensed to control flow. These vary with the needs of a particular engine design. Some parameters which have been sensed by various fuel control units are throttle position, engine rpm, compressor discharge pressure, compressor inlet pressure, fuel pressure, fuel temperature, and exhaust gas temperature. No fuel control unit used today senses all of these parameters but use only those which are necessary for satisfactory metering in a particular engine design. The fuel control unit illustrated in Fig. 14-56 is sensitive to throttle position, engine speed (N_2), compressor discharge pressure at burner (Pb), and compressor inlet pressure, (P_2) and temperature (T_2). By checking movement of throttle, and control components the effect of various functions can be seen. Note that the throttle valve varies the metering area in this simplified drawing.

The metered fuel may pass through a *stop-cock* operated by the throttle and arranged to provide an engine-mounted positive fuel shut-off. It operates when the throttle is cut-off.

The typical fuel system may have an oil cooler. This unit is actually a lube system component and represents only a restriction in the fuel system. It was discussed with the lube system.

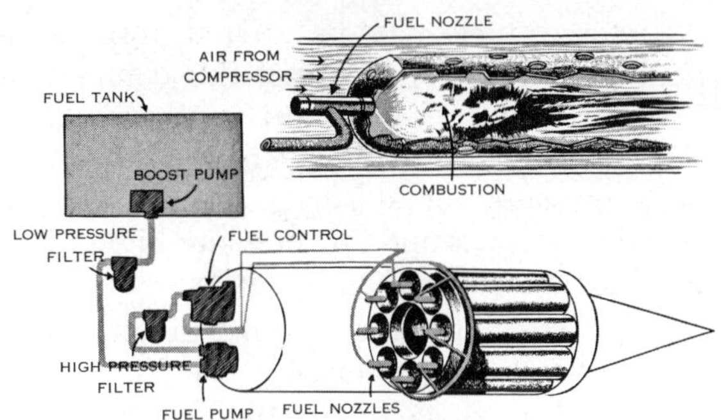

Fig. 14-55. Fuel System (G.M.)

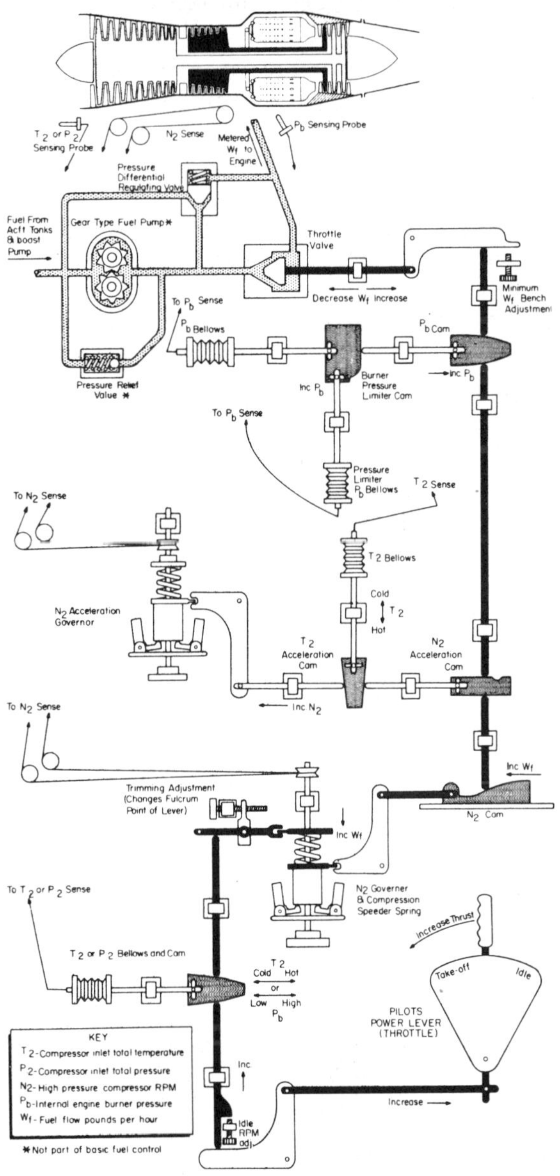

Fig. 14-56. Basic Fuel Control Functions (P&W)

Metered fuel may be routed through a *flow-divider*. The purpose of this component is to separate fuel flow into small and large slot manifolds, providing small flows under high pressure for starting and low engine speed conditions and low pressure higher fuel flow demanded by high engine speeds.

The last component carrying metered fuel are the several *fuel nozzles*. See Fig. 14-57. Each fuel nozzle combines fuel flow from the large and small slot manifolds providing a single pattern to the combustion chamber. During starting, the spray pattern will be wide and fine to provide easier initial combustion, and once started, the fuel flow increases with a decrease in the spray pattern.

Electrical System

The jet engine electrical system is, relatively simple. It provides for the operation of igniter plugs, starter, generator, and engine control systems, as well as engine instruments such as a tachometer or thermo-couples to sense exhaust gas temperature. Fig. 14-58 shows such a system.

Ignition: Jet engines generally employ one of two types of ignition systems, the *opposite-polarity* ignition system or a *capacitor-discharge* system.

The *opposite-polarity system* is quite similar to the ignition system of an automobile engine or a reciprocating engine in that the sparks are very high voltage, approximately 25 to 30 thousand volts, with relatively low amperage or current flow, approximately 0.5 amperes. Generally, there is a set of ignition coils and a vibrator to supply the high voltage. With this system, there are also two igniter plugs required, one positive and the other negative. When the spark jumps between the two igniter plugs, ignition occurs. Fig. 14-59 compares circuits of this and the capacitor-discharge system.

In the *capacitor-discharge system*, there is only one ignition plug similar to the reciprocating engine plug and the ignition unit. The capacitor discharge unit is generally composed of a vibrator, transformer, rectifier, and storage capacitor. The DC voltage input is changed to pulsating DC to increase the voltage so that it may be stored by the capacitor. When the storage capacitor becomes sufficiently charged, it will discharge and fire a spark across the igniter plug. A typical plug is shown in Fig. 14-60. This system is quite unique in that the current may reach several amperes while the voltage remains relatively low, approximately 2500 volts.

Instruments and Controls: The jet engine electrical system also provides power for the electronic engine controls that record engine speed, compressor discharge pressure, compressor inlet temperature, exhaust gas temperature, nozzle area and other factors that are necessary to operate the engine. Here the various signals are measured and analyzed electronically, and the correct amount of fuel is metered to the engine by setting the fuel metering valve. Some engine components

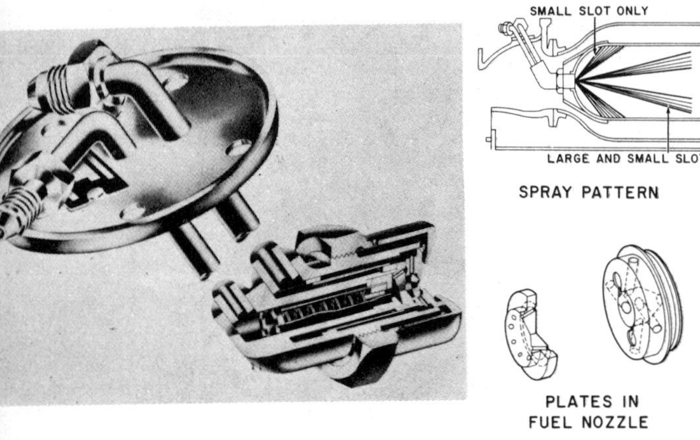

Fig. 14-57. Fuel Nozzles and Spray Pattern (GE)

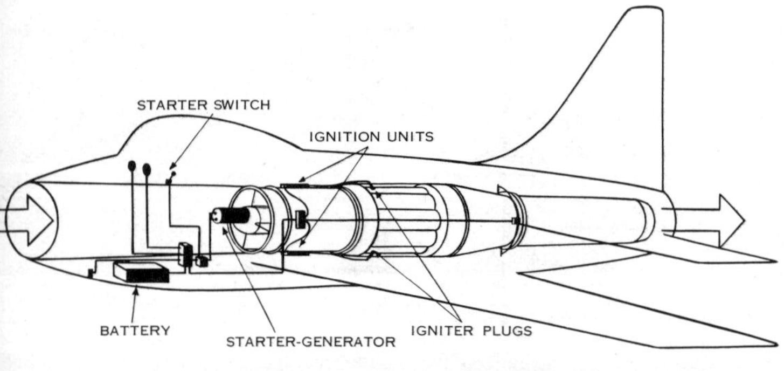

Fig. 14-58. Jet Airplane Electrical System (G.M.)

such as nozzle actuators or inlet guide vane actuators, may be actuated either electrically or hydraulically.

Some engine instruments have independent electrical circuits. A set of thermocouples downstream of the turbine section generates current used to record the *exhaust gas temperature. Tachometers* record turbine speed by means of an electrical signal-generator turned by the turbine.

Hydraulic System

Hydraulic pressure may be used to actuate a variable area nozzle, variable inlet-guide vanes, or a number of other components such as landing gear retractors. A common source of such pressure is a *hydraulic system pump* specifically designed to supply high pressure hydraulic oil to the system. This pump is generally a piston type pump with a variable displacement, but a constant pressure output. Another source of hydraulic pressure is a *pump combined with the fuel pump.* When used, this eliminates one component. A third source of hydraulic pressure may be a *pump combined with the lube oil pump.* All such hydraulic systems are essentially the same as actuation systems which have been perfected in previous aircraft. Fig. 14-61 shows a typical hydraulic piston operating a clamshell two position afterburner nozzle.

Thrust Augmentation Methods

Thrust augmentation systems were developed to overcome inadequacies of the turbojet engine. It is found in a given airplane that while thrust is ample for high altitude high speed cruising, it is not adequate for short take-off runs usually associated with propeller driven aircraft. In this airplane, if attempts were made to improve the take-off characteristics, a compromise would have to effect pay load or range. A heavier engine could provide higher thrust, but during cruising, more engine would be carried than is required. The solution for this problem is *thrust augmentation*. These methods exhibit a high thrust-to-weight ratio, but because of their prohibitive appetities for fuel, they can only be used for short periods of time.

Water Injection

One method of thrust augmentation injects water or a water-alcohol mixture to increase the weight of the fluid passing through the engine. Simultaneously this increases the tailpipe pressure. Fig. 14-62 shows a typical system for injecting water both ahead and behind the compressors.

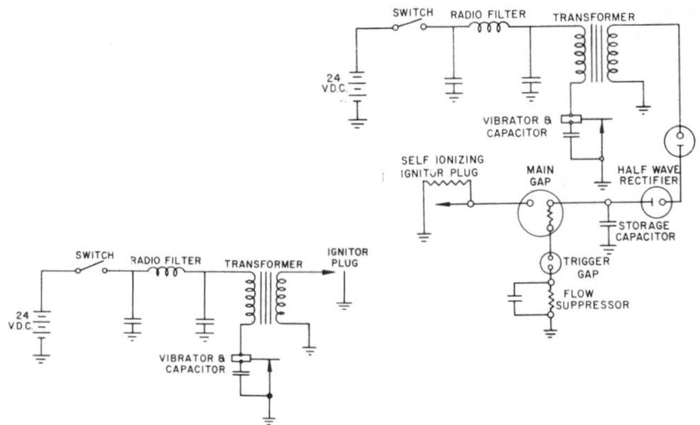

Fig. 14-59. Opposite Polarity (left) and Capacitor Discharge Ignition Systems (GE)

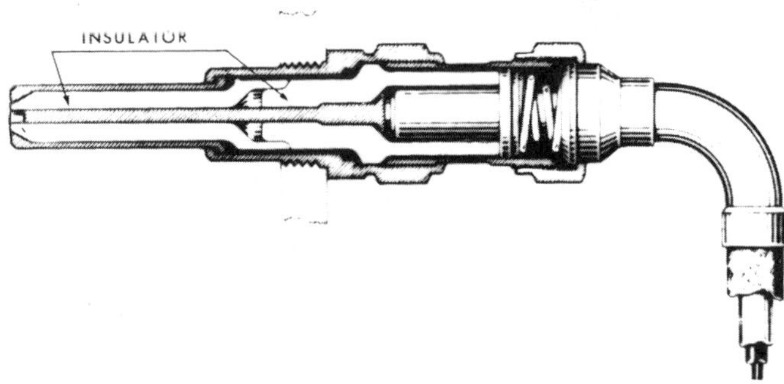

Fig. 14-60. Constrained-Gap Igniter Plug (P&W)

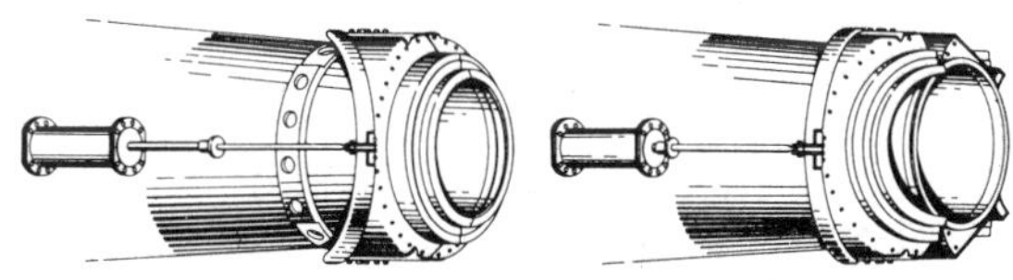

Fig. 14-61. Hydraulic Cylinder Operates Two-Position Afterburner Nozzle (P&W)

Test results have indicated that approximately half of the increase in thrust is due to increased weight of fluid passing through the engine. The remainder is due to the increased pressure at the exhaust. In operation, the water turns into steam when it is pumped into the combustion system and passes through the turbine wheel. Of course, the tailpipe temperature decreases when a fixed area nozzle is used because of the heat energy used in the transformation. A variable thrust nozzle must be used to maintain thrust and temperature during periods of injection.

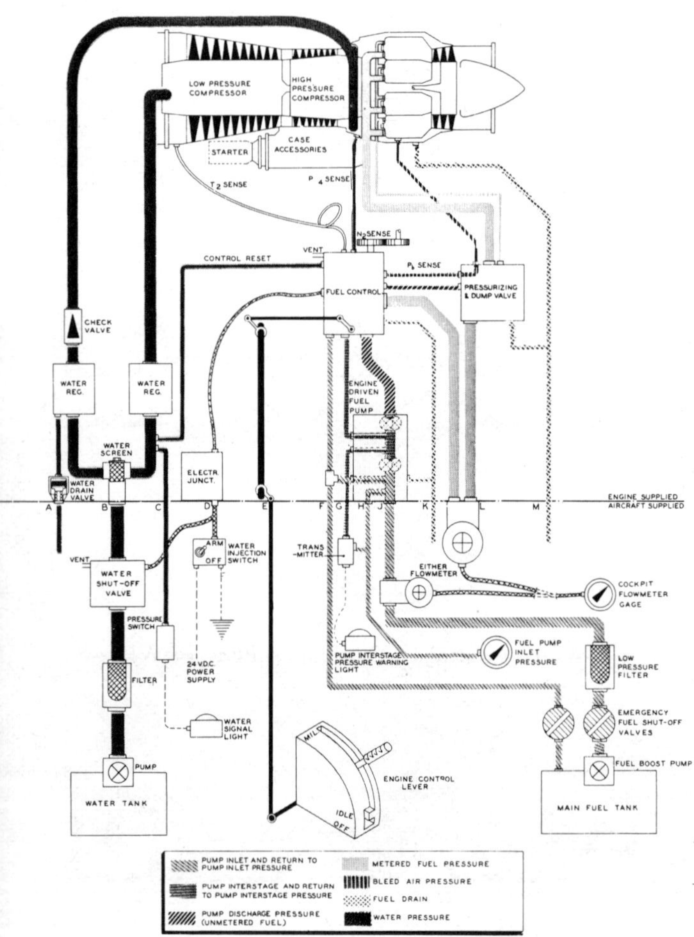

Fig. 14-62. Water Injection Before and After Compressor (P&W)

Usually, for every pound of fuel consumed, 5 pounds of water-alcohol mixture are used. There are limits to the amount of thrust augmentation because of the increase in the compressor discharge. At a given compressor speed, there is a maximum compressor discharge pressure that the compressor can support. Attempts to surpass this point will result in compressor stall, leading to breakdown of airflow and overheating of the critical engine parts. Therefore, a limit must be set below the stall point.

Alcohol is added to furnish water with the necessary heat for vaporization. Therefore it keeps the temperature constant and causes the least disturbance to the main engine fuel and control systems. If a greater proportion of alcohol is used, less thrust augmentation will result. This is because less fuel is required from the main engine fuel system since the extra alcohol replaces a portion of the fuel and heats the air as well as the water. The proportions of water to alcohol will vary with the engine, but a 1 to 3 ratio of alcohol to water by weight is common. At the completion of a take-off run the unused mixture may be jettisoned.

Engine Overspeed

Another recent augmentation method achieves greater air flow or weight of air simply by increasing the compressor speed above its maximum normal speed. This is an extremely desirable means of thrust augmentation because the power-to-weight factor is not affected. The *engine overspeed* must be carefully controlled and used for only short periods of time.

Afterburner

The afterburner (sometimes shortened to A-B) is a widely used method of thrust aug-

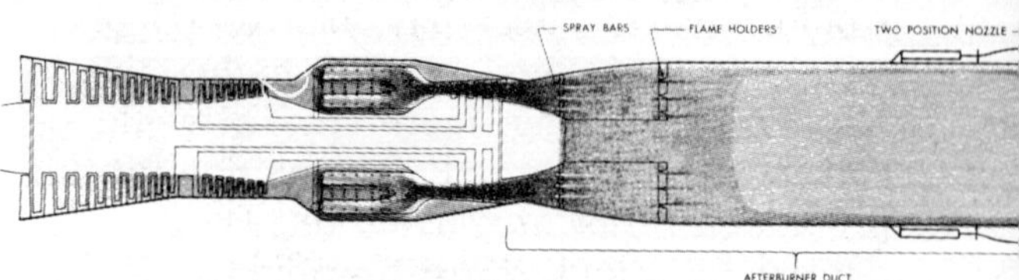

Fig. 14-63. Afterburner (P&W)

mentation in which thrust is increased by increasing fuel flow. The afterburner portion of the engine is immediately behind the turbine section and has no effect on normal (or cold) operation. It operates on a ramjet principle and has no moving parts. Afterburner components include a fuel manifold with spray bars, ignition system, flame holder, a special exhaust duct which must have a variable nozzle. Fig. 14-63 shows this arrangement.

The manifold and spray bar system provides the means for injecting the fuel and air mixture, often by shooting a jet of burning fuel from a burner of the basic engine. A flame holder is installed to prevent the flame

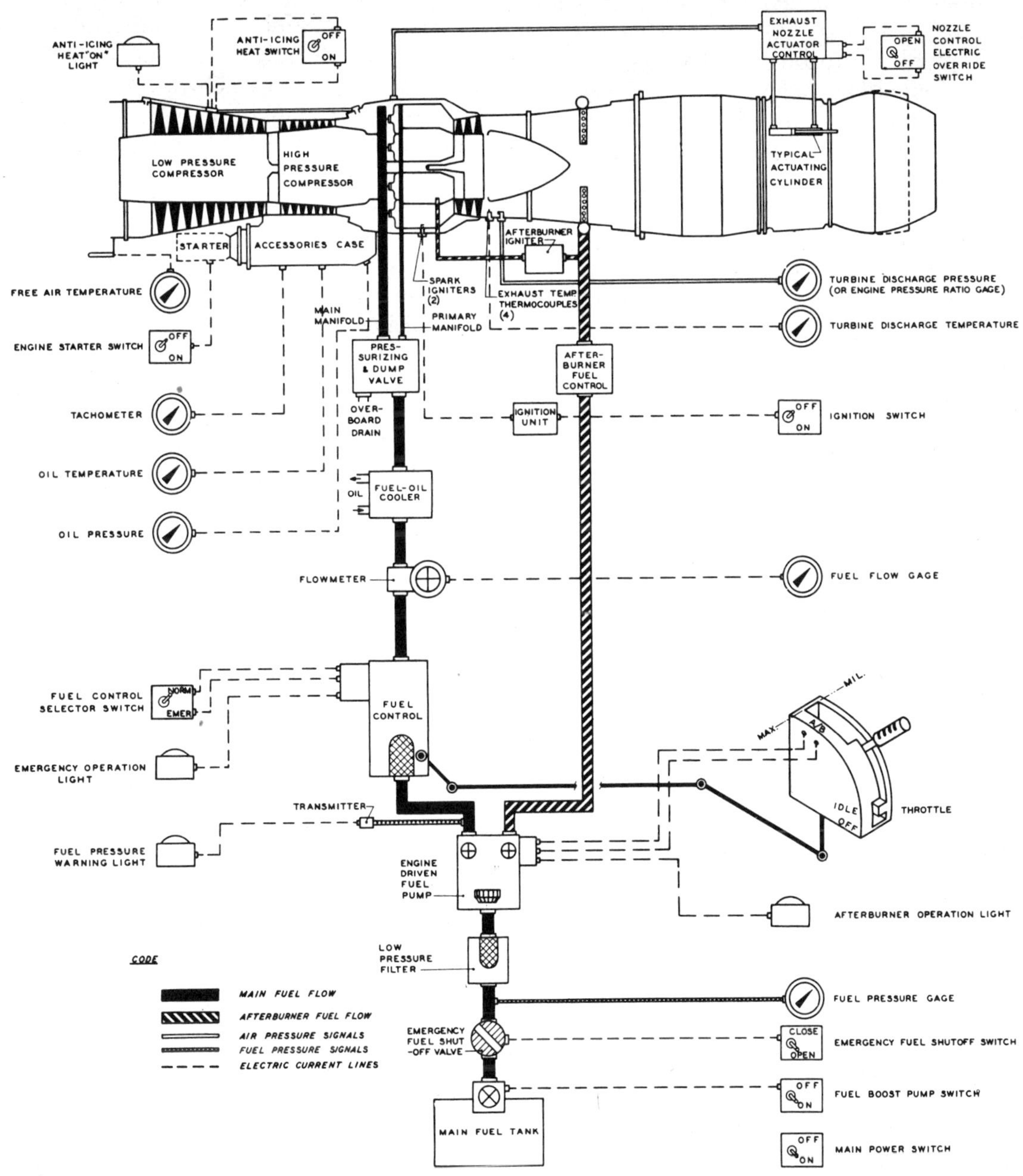

Fig. 14-64. Fuel and Control System for Afterburning Engine (P&W)

from being blown out by the fast-moving exhaust gases. The flame holder creates enough turbulance and reduced speed that the fuel-air mixture will burn.

The air necessary for combustion comes from the normal exhaust. Remember that only about 25 percent of the intake air is burned in the basic engine. This leaves 75 percent that is not needed for combustion and is used for cooling. Once the exhaust gases pass through the turbine section, this air is no longer needed for cooling.

At this time, some may be mixed with fuel, ignited and burned in the tailpipe. This combustion will re-accelerate (at a higher velocity) the gases as they leave the afterburner section, thus increasing temperature and thrust considerably. A variable-area jet nozzle is desirable to produce optimum exhaust velocity either with or without tailpipe burning. It is *imperative* that nozzle area be increased for tailpipe burning. Otherwise the back pressure would increase, and eventually raise the temperature beyond safe limits.

A separate fuel control system is used for afterburner operation. Fig. 14-64 gives an excellent overview of the entire fuel and control system of an afterburner engine. Afterburner operation is labeled *emergency operation*. In some countries the British term *reheater* is used rather than *afterburner*. In jet slang the use of the A-B is said to be "hot" operation.

An afterburner will *double* the thrust of an engine traveling at 600 mph at an altitude of 35,000 feet, while increasing fuel consumption *threefold*. Thrust is increased 50 percent for a sea level take-off. It is no wonder that afterburner augmentation is so highly regarded. If another engine were added to achieve this doubled thrust the extra weight and nacelle drag would reduce maximum usable thrust to considerably less than double, besides detracting from available power when maximum thrust is not needed.

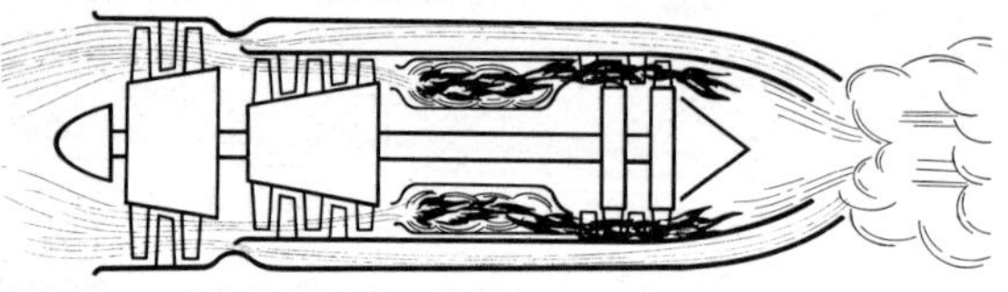

Fig. 14-65. Bypass Turbojet

Pre-Turbine Ignition

Another means of increasing thrust by adding fuel flow is pre-turbine ignition (PTI). PTI augmentation was originally developed to provide engines with substantial thrust increase at altitudes of 20,000 to 50,000 feet for fast-climb rates. This system employs a shut-off valve, a metering valve, a drain valve, and fuel nozzles. Fuel is usually provided by the regular fuel system.

In operation, the variable-area exhaust nozzle is closed slightly, increasing the operating temperature at the discharge of the turbine and in the combustion system. This establishes a higher temperature level in the tailpipe to permit tailpipe burning. Extra fuel is injected just forward of the turbine nozzle, and vaporizes in the turbine nozzle and the turbine buckets. This mixture of fuel and air burns in the exhaust cone and tailpipe. The exhaust nozzle then opens to maintain the required turbine-discharge temperature.

The thrust increase realized from PTI is a result of increased temperature and fuel flow which causes an increase in velocity of the exhaust gases. This method of thrust augmentation is relatively light weight, adding only 150 pounds or so to the engine and air frame weight. However, the engine is caused to operate at an overtemperature reducing the life of various engine parts.

Air Flow Bypass

The bypass system is also a means of thrust augmentation. It uses an outer skin to form an air duct around the jet engine as shown in Fig. 14-65. Note that a certain amount of front compressor air can bypass the engine and be exhausted with the gas stream at the rear. This arrangement increases the mass of the air flow without any appreciable increase of engine weight or fuel flow. The resulting bypass air flow through such a engine may be mixed with additional fuel and burned as an afterburner system.

Operational Controls

The relative simplicity of the basic jet engine is reflected through the entire plane, particularly the instrument panel. As we have discussed, the engine has only one revolving shaft, and two essential moving elements, the turbine and the compressor. The combustion chambers have no moving parts and the thrust is delivered to the plane is an extremely simply manner by fast-moving gases expelled through a fixed opening.

Instruments

Gone from the instrument panel are many of the conventional engine instruments. Aside from the standard instruments such as fuel gauges, instruments are retained for engine rpm (tachometer), pressure gauges for oil, fuel, exhaust, temperature gauges for free air, oil, and exhaust.

Of course there is a full complement of flight instruments: altimeter, air speed, rate of climb, needle-ball turn indicator, artificial horizon, compasses and radio direction finding equipment. Instruments or signal lights, show position or use of landing gear, flaps, exhaust nozzle, anti-icers, and afterburner.

Manual Controls

Manual controls are more simplified too. Gone are the levers for propeller pitch, fuel mixtures, and cowl flaps. The entire range of jet power output is throttle controlled.

Other Advantages

Gone also is most of the vibration and the dampening devices necessary for minimizing vibration at critical speeds in planes with reciprocating engines. This vibration was caused by revolving an eccentric crankshaft and the intermittent firing of cylinders. Replacing this is the smooth spinning of the dynamically balanced main shaft and rotors of the jet with its steady, continuous burning in all combustion chambers.

Of course, with this simplicity comes greater dependability. There is also no need for a supercharger, distributor, complex ignition wiring, valves, pistons, crankshaft and other devices. It is no wonder that the jet engine has revolutionized air travel.

There are many advantages over conventional piston aircraft which are experienced in actual flying or handling. There are also some differences in performance. Service of the engine and the entire plane is simpler because the absence of the propeller permits a low slung aircraft easily accessible from the ground. There is relatively no warm-up. As soon as the engine is brought up to full rpm, the plane is ready for take-off—usually about 30 seconds. Preparation for take-off is equally simple. Wheel brakes are locked while the pilot makes a rapid check of rpm, exhaust temperature, fuel and oil pressure. Then, when set for take-off, he releases the brakes and starts to roll with maximum thrust.

Starting

Electric starters are used on small gas turbine engine installations and can be powered by the aircraft battery, or from an external power source when available or necessary. Jet engines are most frequently provided with pneumatic starters, although they sometimes have combustion (cartridge) starters and occasionally hydraulic starters. Combustion starters will also act as pneumatic starters when sufficient air pressure is available. The pilot pushes a start button and advances the throttle to idle position. The engine controls and electrical system do the rest. When the engine reaches idle, the generator output is sufficient that external power source may be removed. Start, acceleration, and idle speeds are controlled by the simple throttle controls. All the information needed to schedule the fuel is *sense integrated* and transmitted electrically. The pilot monitors the controls and engine speed.

Water Reaction Propelled Craft[1]

A hydrofoil reaction-propelled craft capable of traveling more than 40 knots has been developed, Figs. 14-66, 14-67, and 14-68. This hydrofoil craft uses a water jet propulsion system. Water is drawn through an aft strut into a centrifugal pump and discharged at

[1] Public Affairs Statement, Public Affairs Staff, Brentwood, Essex, England.

Fig. 14-66. **Hydrofoil Craft** (Boeing Company)

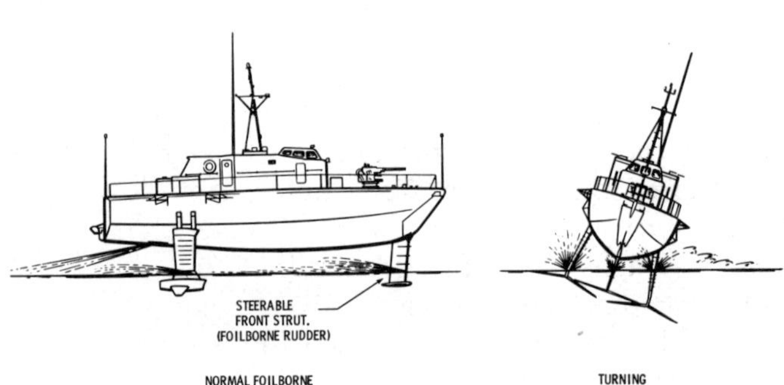

Fig. 14-67. **U.S. Navy Tucumcari Foilborne Operation** (Boeing Company)

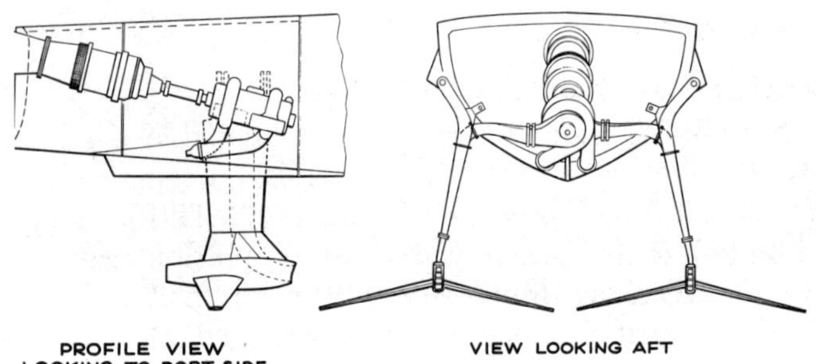

Fig. 14-68. **Main Propulsion System of Hydrofoil Craft** (Boeing Company)

very high speed through stern nozzles which are above the water line. Water jet propulsion has the advantage of mechanical simplicity and ease of maintenance. The foils on this unit are fully retractable. The craft is highly maneuverable and may be the forerunner of a new class of special marine craft. The Boeing Company is working in hydrodynamics as well as in aerodynamics. The relationship is logical, however, because aircraft and hydrocraft design problems of fluid dynamics, stability, control, structures, electronics, hydraulics, propulsion are similar. In fact, hydrofoil language is a *mixture* of nautical and aeronautical terminology.

Safety Precautions

To those new to jet engines, there are two main areas which require precaution, *inlet* and *exhaust* areas.

Inlet area precautions are necessary because of the tremendous volume of air being drawn into the engine. It is entirely possible for human beings to be drawn into the inlet of an operating engine. Too, any foreign matter drawn into the engine may damage or completely destroy the engine. Nuts, bolts, and birds have been known to make engines in-operative. Therefore, it is imperative that the inlet area be kept clean and clear of all objects which could be drawn in.

The exhaust area also is dangerous. The large volume of hot exhaust gases moving at several hundred miles per hour extends the area of precaution a considerable distance behind the aircraft.

Sometimes people speak of using turbojet engines to drive land vehicles. This probably will never happen except for laboratory study, because of their prohibitive noise and their potential hazard caused by the hot exhaust gases. Also, the seemingly low speeds at which such vehicles may safely operate would cause these engines to consume many times the fuel of comparable power piston-type engines, and the newer gas turbines.

Aircraft Engines of the Future[2]

Any speculation on the future development of prime movers must begin with the present state of the art. At this time the Pratt and Whitney JT9 (Fig. 14-69), the General Electric TF-39, and the Rolls Royce RB-211 are the leaders in engine technology. In fact, these engines may well still be in operation in the 1980's.

Development Requirements

An almost unlimited number of power plants are technically feasible to build and develop.

[2] Sends, William H. and Meyer, Robert M., SAE Paper, Pratt and Whitney Aircraft Corporation, April, 1968.

Fig. 14-69. Two Views of the JT9 Engine
(Pratt and Whitney)

However, only a few power plants will actually be fully developed and used. In order to justify development, the power plant has to be not only technically feasible but also must satisfy other fundamental requirements.

1. There must be a substantial potential market.

2. The power plant must be superior to current existing power plants in satisfying this market.

3. There must be money available to support its development, which cannot be assured without requirements *1* and *2* being met.

Potential Markets

The world's commercial aircraft market grew rapidly in the 1960's. Future needs may be several times larger than exist today. The trend in military engine procurement is not clear.

Advanced Technology

The second requirement is to have a sufficient advance in technology to justify the development cost of a new generation engine. In the past, new technology has received its impetus from military requirements. This will remain the rule in areas of specialized demand. The rate and direction of these efforts will depend on the interest and evolving requirements of the military as expressed through research and development programs. The growing importance of commercial aircraft has already stimulated both private and government financed propulsion research and development. These efforts may be expected to increase with a growing market.

In the past 15 years the development of titanium technology, consistent improvement in component aerodynamics, fabrication techniques, turbine cooling, and high temperature alloys have approximately doubled the thrust output per pound of power plant weight. The development of fiber and composite materials, continued improvement in component aerodynamics and high temperature alloys, and the development of cooling techniques promise a continued improvement in the future.

Noise abatement requirements and advancing technology insure that engines now under development will not be any noisier than the engines now flying, although several times larger. This is being accomplished by eliminating inlet guide veins, adjusting the number of fan and compressor blades and veins, lowering tip speeds, increasing by-pass ratio, and acoustic treatment of the fan duct. Public pressure to reduce noise will continue. The research for designing smokeless burners is being carried on and will be applied in new engines. By the 80's smoke should no longer be a problem. Another market for power plants is special purpose airplanes. Examples are VTOL (vertical take-off and landing) and VSTOL (very short) airplanes requiring lift turbofans, compound helicopters requiring convertible engines, and military multipurpose airplanes requiring variable cycle engines. The need for special purpose airplanes will very likely increase as our civilization and our weapons systems become more complex. The trend to improve the specific fuel consumption and the thrust/weight ratio of new engines, along with noise reduction and smoke abatement systems, indicates that the advances can and will be achieved.

Subsonic Transports

Commercial transport planes tend to be larger as each major design achievement matures, as shown with piston engines, turboprops, and jets. This trend is likely to continue for two good reasons: direct operating costs decrease as gross weight increases, and fewer aircraft minimize traffic congestion. The development cycle of a broad class of aircraft tends to be 11 years, and this is also the approximate manufacturing life of a given model of aircraft. This would indicate that in the 1980's there is a good possibility of a new class of aircraft with gross weights approaching two million pounds. This would call for engines with a total combined take-off thrust of approximately one-half million pounds, requiring power plants in the 80,000- to 150,000-lb. thrust range, depending on the size of the aircraft and whether four, five, or six engines were used.

Fuel Consumption

Fuel costs, engine maintenance, and engine depreciation are 40% of the direct operating costs of an aircraft. Specific fuel consumption is by far the most significant of these factors. Turbine temperature levels increase steadily with increasing by-pass ratio; however, it is likely that the technology will be available by 1980 to permit long-time operation at the turbine temperature required for the very high by-pass engines. Thus, a 15% improvement in total fuel consumption appears technically possible with present JP fuels as they will be modified for next generation engines. Noise and pollution abatement programs will be a major factor in engine improvement. Further improvement in noise can be made only by better understanding and control of the engine noise generation process or by the application and refinement of noise absorbent liners. Future aircraft engines will be essentially smokeless. Since buyers must pay $100 to $150 additional for an automobile reciprocating engine to cover the cost of smoke and air pollution eliminating devices, they will not tolerate a show of dense smoke emanating from an aircraft taking off. Analysis of engine aircraft exhaust gases has shown that the compounds normally considered to be toxic such as carbon monoxide, oxides of nitrogen and sulfur, hydrogen sulfide, and hexane are found at insignificant levels. Although the contribution of turbine aircraft exhaust smoke to the overall pollution problem is relatively small, engine manufacturers must eliminate smoke as a problem in future aircraft.

Engine Maintenance

The engine maintenance cost per revenue mile has been decreasing dramatically and steadily with time. This has been one of the most significant contributions of the gas turbine engine. Several major airlines have been testing the use air-integrated data systems which include programs for engine-condition monitoring. Experience with these programs indicates that conventional types of schedule maintenance, based on certified time between overhauls, can be replaced with parts maintenance as required. Economic benefits of this new maintenance approach include: reduction in the number of inflight shutdowns, reduction of the required spare parts and engine inventory, and reduction in fuel expenditures resulting from early detection and correction of deficiencies.

Supersonic Transports

In 1971 Congress failed to approve a budget for the continued development of supersonic passenger aircraft. The legislators apparently were influenced by the environmentalists' concern regarding air pollution and noise, by the economics of passenger load/operating costs, and by conflicting statements of experts in the new science. Since the termination of the supersonic development program, Japan has expressed an interest in purchasing the research from Boeing, the prime contractor. There is continued speculation that it is only a matter of time before the travelling public will demand supersonic transportation. Travel in an aircraft or any conveyance for any length of time is considered by some to be a boring experience at best, in spite of the movies, reading, and music that is provided as entertainment. Many people want to arrive at their destination in the quickest way possible so that they can engage in business or pleasure.

It is felt in some circles that the demise of the SST program in our country represents a serious default of aerospace technological leadership. The design teams, experimental groups, and other researchers had contributed immensely to the advancement of a whole new facet of aerodynamic experimentation at considerable cost in money and time. The discarding of the evolved research may well be an irretrievable loss. Perhaps, in the future, a new start will be made toward the development of a U.S. supersonic transport. At present, the France-England combination and Russia are flying supersonic passenger aircraft, while military aircraft have been supersonic for many years.

The proposed Boeing supersonic transport aircraft was to have used General Electric engines. These engines utilized methane as a fuel which offered a 15% improvement over present JP fuels. The cryogenic properties of this fuel were used to cool the engine so that higher turbine inlet temperatures were avoided, extending engine life. Methane also was expected to increase the range of the aircraft by 20 to 25% over similar aircraft powered by JP fuel. Methane is clean burning with a low luminosity, is reasonable in cost, safe to handle on the ground and in the air, and is available in large quantities. Using methane, however, required a new fuel logistics system and fuel handling techniques. Static tests of engines powered with this fuel established a world's record for power.

To abate the noise in takeoff, the engine was redesigned and instead of using afterburners, an afterfan was employed. These propulsion systems were expected to provide the SST with speeds of from Mach 2 to 3.5 with no greater pollution than that found in conventional jet aircraft and certainly far below that of a diesel bus.

Terms to Understand

reaction engine
Newton's third law of interaction
jet propulsion
airstream engines
rocket engines
oxidizing agent
ramjet
pulse-jet
weight-to-power ratio
turbojet engine
turboprop engine
inlet section
compressor section
turbine section
dual spool
combustion section
axial flow compressor engine
reverse flow
through flow
cellular chamber
annular chamber
cannular chamber
nozzle
variable exhaust nozzle
subsonic
supersonic
power take off
wet sump lube system
dry sump lube system
gear-type positive displacement pump
operational parameters
opposite polarity ignition system
capacitor discharge ignition system
hydraulic
thrust augmentation
afterburner
water injection
PTI, pre-turbine ignition
bypass augmentation
A-B with a C-D nozzle
dry engine
hot, cold operation
turbofan
water reaction
hydrofoil
hydrodynamics
supersonic transport
methane fuel
cryogenic

Study Questions

1. How does the gas turbine differ when it is used as a reaction engine as compared to its application as stationary prime mover?

2. Describe the operation and stages of an airstream jet engine.

3. What are the differences between centrifugal and axial flow compressors?

4. Explain how the thrust of a jet engine is increased or augmented.

5. Explain the principle of Newton's Third Law of Motion.

6. The gas turbine engine is considered to be more dependable, durable, and simple than any modern day prime mover. Explain.

7. Explain the starting and ignition principles employed in a jet engine.

8. How is the horsepower of a reaction engine figured?

9. Explain the effect of gas turbines with regard to increasing the weight to power ratio.

10. Explain the principle of operation for the ramjet, pulse jet.

11. How does the jet engine resemble the gasoline and diesel engines?

12. Explain the differences and principles of operation between a turbojet and turboprop engine; the advantages and disadvantages.

13. Turbojet engines do not lend themselves for powering land vehicles. Explain.

14. Describe the principles of thrust augmentation using at least two different popular systems.

15. List and describe the various stages of a turbojet.

16. Compare hydrodynamics and aerodynamics.

17. What aircraft power plant developments may likely come about by 1985?

CHAPTER 15

Rocket Engines and Space

This chapter is devoted to prime movers capable of operating beyond our atmosphere. It also describes some of man's attempts to conquer space. Engines to be studied include the various solid and liquid fuel rockets (chemical propulsion), as well as nuclear propulsion, electrical propulsion, and solar propulsion. Three types of electrical reaction engines are: 1. the arc jet (electro-*thermal* power), 2. the plasma accelerator (MHD or *magneto*-hydro-dynamic power), and 3. the ion engine (electro-*static* power).

The reason that fuel burning rockets are independent of an air supply is that they carry an *oxidizer* rather than using atmospheric oxygen for combustion. The typical chemical rocket engine is an internal combustion heat engine which burns a mixture of fuel and oxidizer. Together, the fuel and oxidizer are known as *propellants.* A rocket engine provides the necessary means of handling the propellants, provides a combustion chamber for them, and exhausts the gases of combustion through a nozzle yielding thrust like other reaction engines.

As a rocket travels upward through our atmosphere (through the stratosphere and ionosphere) and finally beyond about 50 miles to the void of outer space, it needs less and less thrust. This is because of the reduced air resistance and because of less gravitational pull. Unlike air-burning engines the efficiency of a rocket engine does not decrease with the altitude. With other reaction engines, they attain the highest efficiency (50 to 70 percent) yet developed in the conversion of heat to work.

In airless space the normal airfoil control surfaces of aircraft—fins, tail surfaces, wings, ailerons, flaps—will not function. Steering and changing the attitude of the craft must be accomplished by small *guidance rocket jets* aimed in various directions, or by changing the direction of reaction of the main engine.

Basic Developments

The exploration of space is anything but new to human endeavors. Men have always yearned for knowledge of what it would be like to fly so high as to reach the stars, Fig. 15-1.

Greek Ideas of Space

One of the most famous Greek myths is the story of Daeldalus and his son, Icarus, who escaped from King Minos of Crete by flying on wings made of feathers and wax. Although Daeldalus escaped, his son perished because he flew too close to the sun and melted the wax adhesive.

Fig. 15-1. Leonardo da Vinci's Idea of a Flying Machine

A tale has also been told by the Greeks of how Alexander the Great flew to the moon in a basket harnessed to a pair of *griffons.* These poor birds were tricked into flying upward by dangling a sheep's carcus above them.

Although these stories seem primitive today, the Greeks did produce some sober ideas of unquestioned importance to astronomy. These included the belief that the earth was a sphere afloat in space with the sun as the center of the solar system. Also, more than two hundred years B.C., Eratosthenes calculated the diameter of the earth quite accurately: Yet, while some important astronomical ideas were advanced, some beliefs also caused stagnation. It was thought that the earth was at the center of the solar system, and another error was Aristotle's dogmatic opinion that there was only one solar system.

Sky Rocket

The exact time and origin of the sky rocket has been buried in legend. However, it is generally accepted that it was a Chinese invention. Some records indicate that the Chinese employed fireworks more than 5,000 years ago. While these records may not have any basis for such a claim, the *T-hung-lian-kang-mu,* an old Chinese historical document, establishes the use of rocketry in China in 1232 A.D., during the Mongol siege of the city of Kaifeng. During this siege, two new weapons were used by the defending Chinese. The first was called *chin-t'ien-lei* (heaven shaking thunder) and the other, *fei-i-ho-chien* (the arrow of flying fire). Most likely, gunpowder, in the form used today, was used in these weapons. If saltpeter was used, then it is certain that the thunder came from bombs which were exploded and the flying arrow was propelled by rocket power instead of being shot from bows. These weapons set fire to the enemy's wooden installations and created psychological havoc. By the close of the 13th Century, their use traveled to Europe and Asia. But, as the cannon was developed, the use of rockets declined, putting them in the simple task of decorating the sky during firework displays or for rocket signalling.

Fig. 15-2. Rocket Propelled Wan Hoo (GE)

According to tradition, a Chinese named Wan Hoo tried to ride a rocket vehicle about 1500 A.D. The story describes how he attached two large kites to a framework. He then placed 47 large gunpowder rockets to this for propulsion, and fastened a saddle to the center for comfort. After he had become seated, he directed a ground crew of 47 torch bearers to light one rocket apiece. The resulting blast and cloud of smoke propelled Wan Hoo from history, Fig. 15-2.

Modern Astronomy

In the 17th Century, Galileo was imprisoned by the Inquisition until he recanted his *heresy* that the earth was in orbit around the sun. This was heresy since it was contrary to the Ptolemaic view that the *earth* was the center of the solar system. Giordano Bruno, only a little earlier, had been burned at the stake for heresies that included a vehement rejection of the Aristotlelian dogma of the solar system.

The birth of *modern astronomy* during the Renaissance did much to awaken man's interest in conquering space and exploring other worlds. Many fantasies were written and illustrated about the exploration of the moon, and later, the planets. Strange creatures and strange societies with even stranger propulsion systems were described from the imagination. One suggestion used giant swans forever bent on flying upward. Another used bottles of dew that vanished upward toward the sun at dawn. Another was to be propelled upward by the attraction of lodestones thrown above a metal chariot.

Rocket Propulsion on Land

Some early experimenters were concerned with using rockets for other than space travel. An Italian, Joanes DeFontana, described in 1405 a military vehicle that was rocket-propelled in his book on war instruments.

Sir Isaac Newton has been given credit for designing a steam wagon in the latter half of the 17th century, Fig. 15-3. It was made to move forward as a reaction to steam that shot out the back. At about the same time, a Dutch professor, Willen Jakob Gravesande designed a reaction steam car in Holland. Some have questioned whether both of these designs were original. High-pressured steam issued out the tailpipe caused the Gravesande car to move. The fire pot under the boiler was mounted between the wheels, and the driver regulated the speed by a rod that controlled a valve in the tailpipe.

Fritz Von Opel, the noted car manufacturer, in the late 1920's permitted his friend, Max Valier, of the German Rocket Society, to experiment in his shop. There, Valier built several rocket cars using two types of solid fuel engines. Some of these early cars went 108 mph with 45 to 400 pound thrust provided for 3 to 30 seconds. Unfortunately, Valier was killed by an explosion while developing a liquid fuel rocket engine in 1930.

Military Rockets

During the latter part of the 18th Century, the British Forces in India were defeated by an Indian Rocket Corps of 5,000 men. The Indians learned their rocket *know-how* from the Chinese. After this defeat, British scientists began to develop rockets for their own army and by 1805 William Congrese designed a rocket with a range of 2,000 yards.

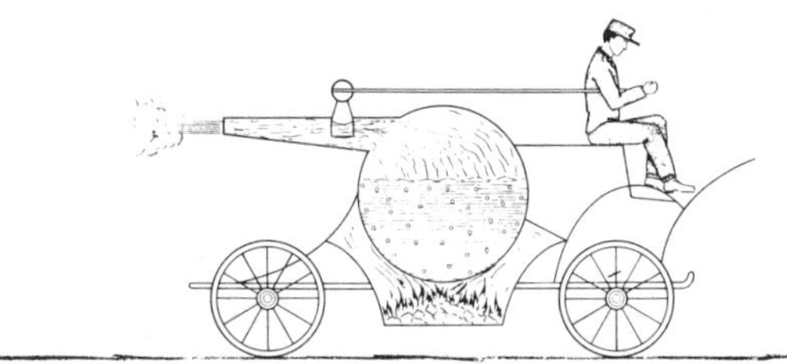

Fig. 15-3. Newton Steam Carriage

It consisted of a heavy sheet iron casing, 40.5 inches long and 3.5 inches in diameter, to contain the propellant and a 16 foot stick was attached to the rocket casing to act as a stabilizer. Congrese rockets were used successfully against France and Denmark.

During the War of 1812, the American militamen were demoralized and beaten by the flanking British rocket brigade at the Battle of Bladensburg. This led to the fall of Washington, D.C. As a result of this defeat, the British fleet was able to launch a rocket attack on Fort McHenry in Baltimore Harbor. It was during this attack that Francis Scott Key stood on the deck of a British ship and watched amid "the rockets red glare." He was inspired to write our national anthem, *The Star Spangled Banner,* when he saw the American flag over the fort still flying the following morning.

In 1846, almost 20 years after Congrese died, an American, William Hale designed a three-curved-vane stabilizer to improve rocket guidance. Two thousand of these rockets were made and used in 1847 during the Mexican War.

Conquest of Space

Also, during this time scientists were beginning to believe that other planets might be inhabited. In the middle of the 1800's, science fiction flourished with many of these books describing space travel and living conditions in other planets. Among the most impressive were those of Jules Verne.

The dawn of the 20th Century saw three pioneers, a Russian, an American, and a German spearhead enthusiasm and thought on rocket potential. Konstantin Ziolkowski wrote several papers indicating the possibility of space flight and the necessities of a space ship. He also published the important finding that liquid propellants were more efficient than solid propellants. The German Professor Herman Oberth wrote extensively on space rocketry, and in 1930, he did experiments with the German Rocket Society in Berlin. Aiding him were Wernher Von Braun and Willy Ley. Oberth is often regarded as the "Father of Practical Astronautics." The American, Dr. Goddard, made tremendous progress in practical rocket development and is considered the "Father of Modern Rocketry."

The New York Times, in 1920, reported on Professor Robert H. Goddard's belief that a rocket was capable of soaring from the earth to the moon. Professor Goddard attracted a great deal of attention by describing how this could be achieved and how the rocket's arrival could be made visible with a flash of powder. Although the suitability of the rocket for use in a vacuum was established by Newton, it remained Goddard's province to experimentally prove this theory. Ahead of his time in 1926, he developed a rocket engine that used liquid propellants. The Germans used the same idea 20 years later to power their V-2 rocket. The Germans subscribed and translated all of Goddard's writings because they saw the potential of this *new source of power.* Goddard was also the first man to perform mathematical analysis of multistage rockets or rockets mounted one on top of the other, establishing the basis for our multistage missles such as the *Vanguard, Titan,* and *Atlas.* See Figs. 15-4 to 15-6. His contributions during almost four decades of rocket research were as astounding as numerous, resulting in more than 150 patents. He died in Maryland in 1945.

Rockets Become Operational

Gen. Walter Dornberger and Dr. Wernher Von Braun, two German scientists in 1945, were instrumental in setting up the German rocket testing station at Peenemunde on the Baltic Sea. They developed and tested the V-1 buzz bomb, and later they developed the V-2 during World War II. This monster of a weapon rained terror on England, but it came too late to be decisive in the war.

The V-1 was not exactly a rocket because it used the air from the atmosphere to burn its fuel. The larger V-2, however, was definitely a rocket. It carried its own oxidizer, *liquid oxygen. Lox,* as it is called, must be kept at 297°F below zero, and is most dif-

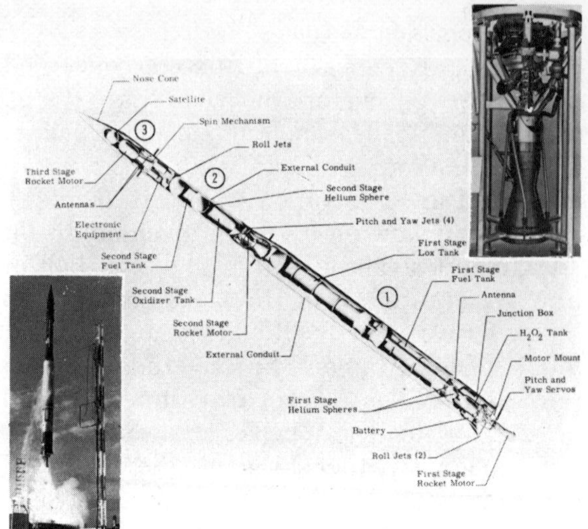

Fig. 15-4. Vanguard Three-Stage Rocket—Inset Shows First Stage Engine (Martin)

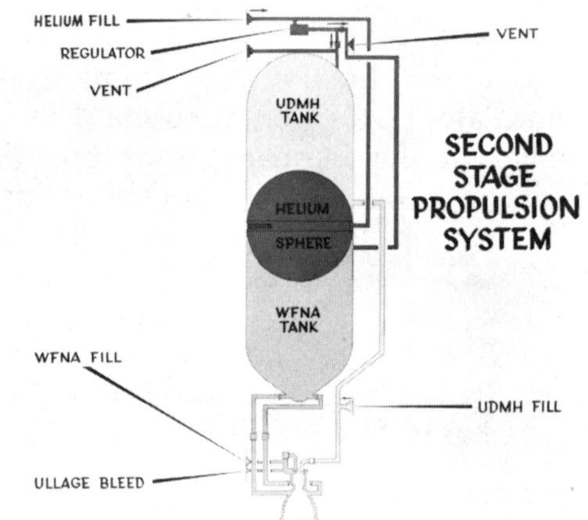

Fig. 15-5. Vanguard Second Stage (Martin)

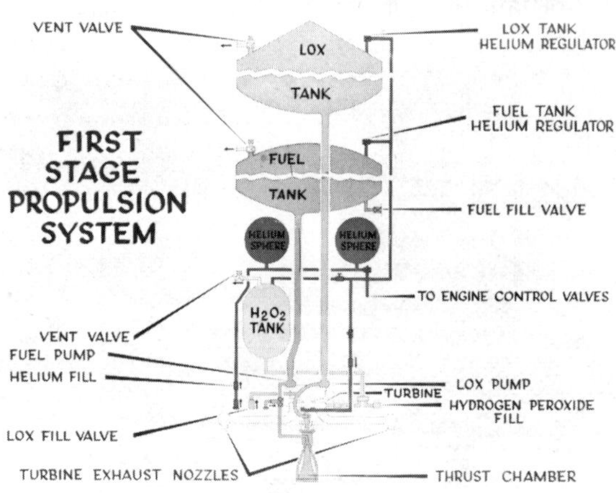

Fig. 15-6. Vanguard First Stage (Martin)

Fig. 15-7. Titan Two-Stage ICBM and Engines

This is an Intercontinental Ballistic Missile with a range of 6,300 miles at 18,000 mph. It burns kerosene (RP-1) and liquid oxygen (Lox). It is 98 feet tall, 10 feet diameter (at base), weighs 110 tons. First stage thrust is 300,000 pounds, second stage is 80,000 pounds at altitude. It rises vertically for 20 seconds, arches for another 100 seconds, then the first stage separates. Second stage has *vernier guidance nozzles* for steering, and takes over to high point at an altitude of 500 miles. Then re-entry vehicle separates and falls to target.

ficult to handle, requiring special valve and fittings because of the extreme cold and the resulting condensation and brittleness of the materials used. A series of "A" vehicles was produced using alcohol for fuel. The A-1 experimental model developed 660 lb. of thrust where as the A-4 model, the infamous V-2, developed 56,000 lbs. of thrust. It could climb 22 miles in one minute and developed a speed of 3,600 mph.

Produced by the hundreds in underground plants at Nordhausen and elsewhere, in spite of shortages of materials and technicians, they were fired at London and Antwerp in such numbers as to cause great concern to the Allies. Many historians claim that if the Germans would have had 6 months more production time, they could have turned the tide.

American Rockets

One of the first large liquid-fuel rockets to be launched from Cape Kennedy (then Canaveral), Florida, after World War II, was the *Bumper WAC*. This was two rockets, a captured German V-2 and the U. S. Army *WAC* liquid rocket as the second stage. It set an altitude record then of 252 miles and a speed of 5,150 mph. Since that record firing, many rockets have been developed, declared obsolete, and further refined. The Atlas, Vanguard, Corporal, Honest John, Jupiter, Redstone, Thor, Viking, Explorer, and Titan are just a few. See Figs. 15-7 and 15-8.

Fig. 15-8. Titan Assembly Line (Martin)

Note workers (circle) and difference between first and second stages.

The X-15 Rocket Ship

Man's first trip into space beyond the 20 miles atmospheric belt above the earth was accomplished in 1959 in a strange craft that is half rocket and half airplane, the X-15. This craft has stubby wings 22 feet from tip to tip with a body 50 feet long. It looks more like a missile with fins. It is painted black, so that frictional heat due to the earth's atmosphere will radiate from its shell as quickly as possible. It is made of *Iconel-X*, a new alloy of stainless steel and titanium which can withstand temperatures of 1200°F. Most of the test flights have begun higher than 40,000 feet after being launched from underneath the wing of a B-52. See Figs. 15-9 to 15-14.

Jet nozzles, which squirt steam (made from concentrated hydrogen peroxide) from the nose and tips of the wings, help the pilot sitting up front to guide the craft. Most of the lower part of the thick vertical tail is blown off before the X-15 begins to land. It employs a replaceable tail skid instead of a wheeled landing gear because of its fast 275 mph landing speed.

X-15 Performance

Major Robert White flew the rocket ship at a record speed of 4,535 mph, and attained on another occasion a record breaking altitude of 354,200 feet or more than 67 miles high. He was the first man to pilot his way out of the earth's atmosphere. The speed attained was twice that of a 30.06 rifle bullet, and swift enough to fly from New York to Los Angeles in 30 minutes or around the world in less than seven hours, if the speed could be sustained. Actually, the fuel supply is consumed in a little over 80 seconds at full throttle.

Fig. 15-9. X-15 Moved Under B-52 Mother Ship (USAF)

Fig. 15-10. Preparing X-15 for High Altitude Research Mission (USAF)

Fig. 15-11. Testing Fuel System before Drop from B-52 (USAF)

Fig. 15-12. X-15, Piloted Rocket Ship Under Power (North American)

XLR-99 Engine

The XLR-99 engine of the X-15 in its present form develops more than 50,000 pounds of thrust and has been shown to give a service life of better than two hours without overhaul. The pilot's *throttle* electrically activates a governored *metering valve* which controls the flow of *hydrogen peroxide* (H_2O_2) into the *gas generator*. The peroxide decomposes into steam (H_2O) and free oxygen (O_2) to drive a *turbine*. The turbine drives two propellant *pumps*, one for liquid *ammonia* (NH_3) and one for liquid *oxygen* (Lox). *Propellant valves* give a positive cutoff on flow from each tank into the *main* stage, the *second* stage, and the *first* stage. The cold liquid ammonia is circulated through the walls of the engine chamber for cooling during operation.

In starting, the *first stage ignition propellant valves* are opened and the NH_3 plus the O_2 are ignited by an electric spark, yielding an immensely hot blast of steam (H_2O), and nitrogen gas (N_2, which forms 78 percent of our atmosphere). This combustion signals the opening of the *second stage propellant valves,* and second stage operation opens the *main propellant valves.* In full operation now, power output can be throttled as needed by the pilot from a possible low of 11,700 pounds to over 50,000 pounds of thrust. When the pilot closes the main propellant valves, *helium* (a light nonburning gas) automatically purges the injectors and burners of fuel and oxidizer so as to remove all residual propellants. The ignitors are the last to be shut down and purged. This entire process can be repeated as long as the fuel lasts.

X-15 Research

The X-15 program has been a research project for manned space travel. Findings show the present craft has a potential far above present power. An increase in the capacity of the fuel tanks will increase burning time enough to permit a vehicle in this weight class to achieve orbital velocity. High energy fuels offer another approach to increased power. Such fuels could double the thrust to allow orbital velocity with the present fuel capacity. The only major engine modification necessary would be an increase in the throat diameter.

The X-15 has already been attributed many firsts. It was the first with a cryogenic (very low temperature) cooling and pressurizing system for both cockpit and equipment. It used the evaporation of extremely cold liquid nitrogen rather than the usual compressor system. It was the first aircraft to use high energy propellants such as hydrogen peroxide for accessory power units. It was the first engine developing 57,000 pounds of power which can be throttle controlled. It was the first rocket to use a positive expulsion bladder which will expell the propellant in any flight attitude. It was the first to use cold

Fig. 15-13. X-15 Engine—the XLR-99 (USAF)

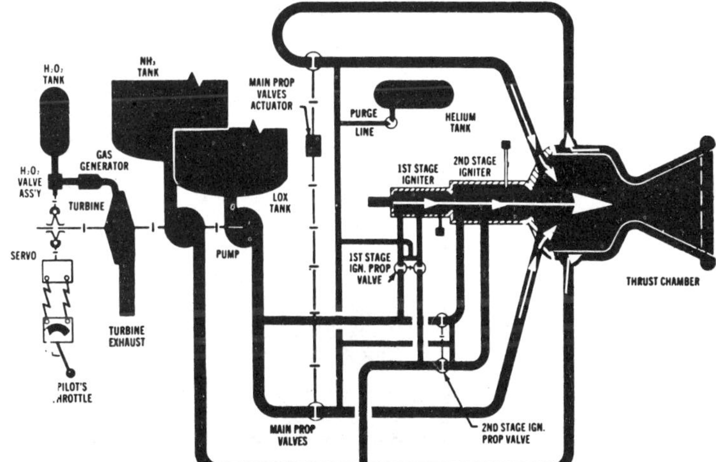

Fig. 15-14. Diagram of XLR-99 Engine (Revell)

regulators to control −300° to −400°F helium gas. It was the first craft for a full-scale study of controlled space flight.

Fig. 15-15. Dyna-Soar on Titan III Rocket (USAF)

X-15's Retirement

In 1969 NASA indicated that the X-15's 12-year, $300,000,000 research program was to come to an end. The rocket plane's last chores as a research workhorse: to test atmospheric re-entry conditions that satellite-to-ground ferries will encounter. The last flight of the X-15 ends an era in aviation design. All United States experimental rocket planes, starting with the X-7, which broke the sound barrier back in 1947, have been launched at altitude by larger aircraft. There is no designated successor to the X-15. Plans now call for a craft capable of taking off from the

Fig. 15-16. Dyna-Soar Space Sled, Orbital Glider (USAF)

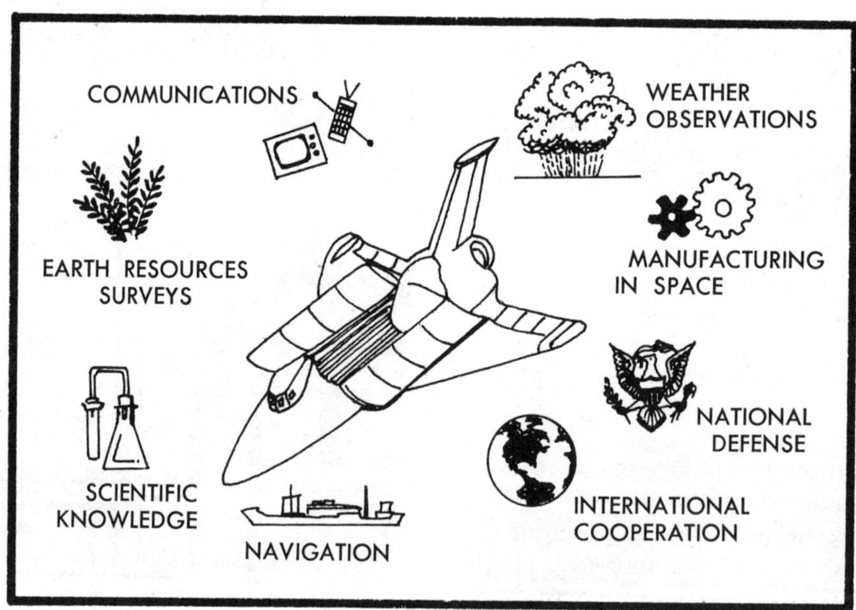

Fig. 15-16A. Space Shuttle Missions

The space shuttle will be used to launch unmanned space craft into orbit for many types of missions.

ground under its own power, reaching orbit, and landing at a point virtually any place on the globe. It is presumed at least one of the X-15 aircraft will eventually be placed in the Smithsonian Institution along with the Wright Brothers' first heavier-than-air craft and other historic planes.

Piloted Rocket Flight

In piloted rocket flight, gliding back to earth was also an objective of the *Dyna-Soar* space program, Figs. 15-15 and 15-16. The objective of this program was to launch a space craft similar to the one shown into orbit atop a *Titan III* rocket. The Dyna-Soar program was dropped in a government economy move, but such piloted rockets continue to be a part of our research.

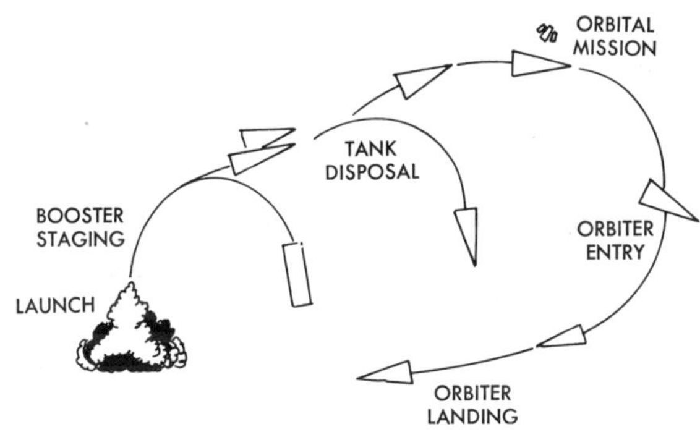

Fig. 15-16B. Schematic Profile of the Space Shuttle Mission

Space Shuttle[1]

In 1972 Congress and the President approved and appropriated monies for the Space Shuttle Program. This program can really be thought of as an extension of the Dyna-Soar program, in that the space shuttle program will provide a space transportation system designed to carry out various missions in earth orbit employing a reusable airplane-like manned orbiter. See Fig. 15-16A. It will consist of two stages: the first stage will boost the shuttle into an orbital mission and the second stage, the shuttle, will then separate from its booster, going into orbit under its own power. When it accomplishes its mission, the shuttle's pilots will fire rockets to slow the vehicle down, flying it through the atmosphere and landing it as they would a conventional aircraft on a jet-sized airstrip. See Fig. 15-16B, 15-16C.

[1] *Space Shuttle* EP-77, U. S. Government Printing Office, Washington, D. C.; and "Space Shuttle—Investment in the Future" by Representative Olin Teague, *Aerospace Magazine*, published by The Aerospace Industries of America, Inc., Washington, D. C.

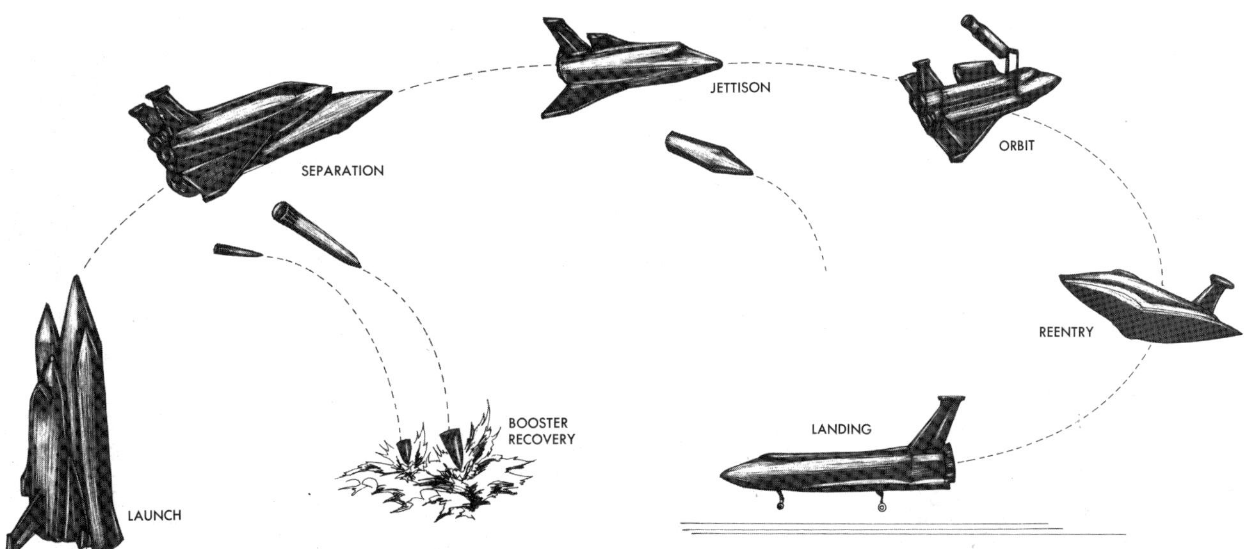

Fig. 15-16C. Pictorial Profile of the Space Shuttle Mission

The Delta-winged orbiter will be about the size of a DC9 airplane with a cargo compartment of 15 feet (4½ meters) in diameter and 60 feet (18 meters) long, Fig. 15-16D. The orbiter will be able to carry cargo and/or passengers weighing in total approximately 65,000 pounds (29,500 kilograms).

The crew of the shuttle will consist of two pilots and two flight engineers. Each orbiter will be designed for reuse up to 100 times and is expected to be able to take its major role in space by the end of this decade. It will then be used to launch all but the very smallest and very largest payloads.

The space shuttle program will bring about major reductions in the cost of space research because it will be designed to replace all present expendable launch vehicles. It will carry space craft into orbit for the U.S. Weather Bureau, the communications industry, the NASA Space Science and Applications Program, and the Department of Defense. It will take care of the future needs of commercial users, other government agencies, and foreign governments. It is projected that it will carry passengers and cargo between the earth and other orbiting space stations or laboratories.

NASA recently announced that it would abandon its traditional use of liquid fueled rockets in manned space flights and switch to solid fuel in its space shuttle program. It is expected that the shuttle will go into operation by 1980 and will be the first reusable manned spacecraft. The decision to switch to solid fuel rockets will cut development costs considerably, although the change will raise operational costs per mission. Liquid fuel rockets have been used for all American and Russian man-in-space ventures so far. Solid fuel rockets have been used for intercontinental ballistic missiles, as strap-on boosters to increase the thrust of liquid fuel launchers and to launch small unmanned payloads into space.

Chemical Propulsion

As has been indicated, there are two basic types of chemical rocket engines. Those burning *liquid fuel* and those burning *solid fuel*. The Vanguard shown in Figs. 15-4 to 15-6 uses liquid fuels in its first and second stages, and a solid fuel in its smaller third stage. Solid fuel engines are much simpler as the propellant is burned directly in its storage casing as shown in Fig. 15-17. The *hybrid* rocket combining both of these types uses a liquid oxidizer with a solid fuel or vice versa. It is shown in Fig. 15-18, but is not widely acclaimed. By burning fuel, any of these engines change potential chemical energy into useful kenetic energy in the form of thrust. The fuel is ignited, burning is continu-

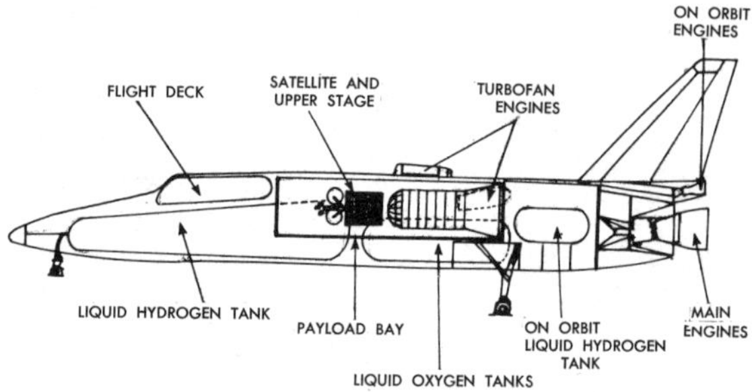

Fig. 15-16D. Cutaway View of the Orbiter Element

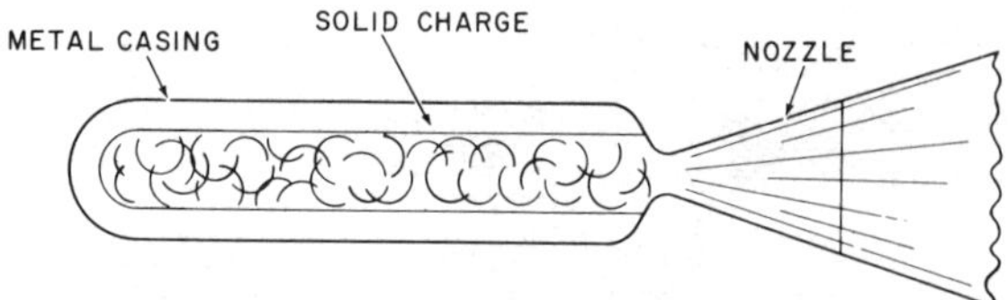

Fig. 15-17. Solid-Propellant Engine (GE)

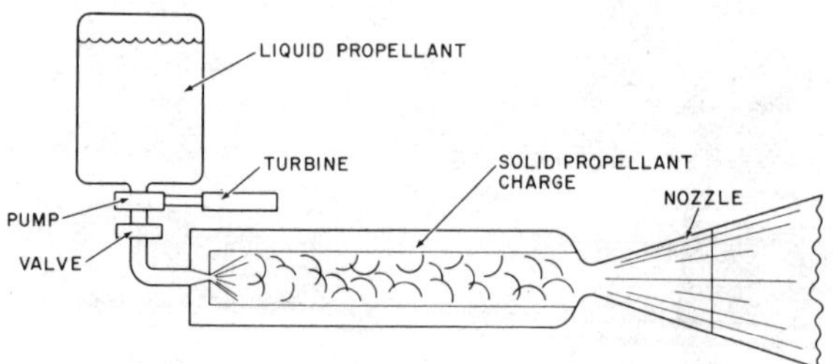

Fig. 15-18. Hybrid Engine, Liquid and Solid Propellant (GE)

ous, and hot gases are forced out through the nozzle.

A controversy among missile scientists and engineers exists as to whether the liquid propellants or the solid propellants possess the greater development potential. But neither liquid or solid propellants are likely to be the ultimate means of propulsion as they presently exist and both systems have their place in a wide variety of uses. Neither is expected to usurp the field.

Most rocket engines employ a *convergent-divergent* (C-D) nozzle for accelerating the gases to produce thrust. The burning gases attain a speed of about 4,000 feet per second in the *convergent* section. The nozzle constriction or throat increases velocity of the gas to Mach 1, the speed of sound corresponding to local temperature.

In the *divergent* section, the gases continue to expand increasing the velocity to 8,000 feet per second and thereby increasing the thrust produced. With solid fuels especially, nozzle shape is very important. As burning rate and pressures are fixed values, exhaust velocity is controlled largely by the nozzle.[1]

Solid-Fuel Engines

The ordinary 4th of July skyrocket is probably the best known rocket engine of the solid-fuel type. The propellant, usually black powder, is mixed with something that will retard its rapid burning, and is packed into a paper cylinder. The rear of this tube is shaped to form a nozzle, and the rear surface of the propellant is shaped like a hollow cone. The fuse is made to run from the tip of the cone to outside the tube's nozzle.

When combustion begins, the hollow cone acts as a combustion chamber, and the reaction to the rush of gases out the nozzle sends the rocket on its way. Although rocket engines vary somewhat in such details as exact nozzle shape, fuel composition, and texture, even the largest and most powerful operate in exactly the same manner described.

[1] See page 288 for listing of publications by NASA, the National Aeronautics and Space Administration. They give many accurate details.

Solid propellants have generally lower ratings of specific impulse although they combust at higher temperatures. Many of the compounds used as propellants are extremely dangerous to mix and many contain explosives known for many years. In their final state, they may be perfectly stable and insensitive to shock, friction, and heat. The process of mixing and compounding them can be fraught with danger. More often than not they must be mixed in a molten state and cast into the rocket chamber or compacted under tons of pressure in order to achieve the required density.

Solid Fuel Advantages

Solid propellant rockets possess definite advantages which make them well suited for applications requiring immediate dependable launchings. Some of these advantages follow.

Low toxicity—reducing handling problems and hazards to personnel, eliminating the need for much protective clothing and equipment.

High density—less bulk resulting in less space and weight in missile airframe.

Ease of handling—the propellant and rocket can be shipped as one unit, eliminating time-consuming fueling and elaborate count down procedures.

Economy—pound for pound, lower cost is a major factor.

Dependability—eliminates more complicated and temperamental ignition systems.

Solid Fuel Disadvantages

Although solid fuel rockets have these desirable characteristics, they also have the following disadvantages and limitations:

Lower Thrust—pound for pound solids are generally 20 percent to 50 percent less efficient

Decomposition—aging during storage changes the chemical structure of the fuel due to such factors as heat and humidity.

Cracking—Cast grains may break through aging or mishandling. Sometimes thermal cracks caused by the burning process increases the burning surface, and consequent temperatures and pressures created may cause faster burning or even an explosion.

Hot casing—entire case is subjected to the full pressure of the combustion chamber.

Inability to vary burning rate once ignited—this and the *rapid decrease in mass* as the propellant is consumed affects flight stability.

Solid Charges

Most solid propellants are molded or cast into a solid bar the shape and size of the combustion chamber of the motor in which they are to be used. The mixture of fuel and oxidizer is referred to as *grain* or *charge.* In some instances, the charge in a molten state is poured into the combustion chamber and allowed to harden under conditions which permit it to adhere to the chamber walls. This is a *bonded charge.*

In other cases, the mixture is cast, or formed under pressure, to the exact dimension of the combustion chamber and inserted into the motor. In still other cases, the charge is cast into cylinders the approximate size of the chamber and then *machined* to fit any one of a variety of motors by sawing, turning, grinding, or milling. Naturally, such propellants must not be sensitive to shock, friction or pressure.

Controlling Burning

The thrust provided by solid-fuel engines can be made constant or can be made to increase or decrease during the burning time. Constant-thrust rockets are those characterized by *neutral* burning, while in *regressive* burning and *progressive* burning, the thrust decreases and increases respectively during the operating time. Neutral and regressive burning are by far the most widely used.

Neutral burning charges permit the area of the burning surface to remain nearly constant throughout the burning process. The rate at which the propellant is consumed remains constant as does the burning pressure.

Regressive burning charges are those in which the area of the burning surfaces decreases during the burning process, with a consequent drop in pressure and in the amount of propellant burned in a given time.

Progressive burning charges cause the exposed burning surfaces to increase in area during combustion. This increases the propellant burned per period of time with a resulting pressure increase.

Restricted burning—the burning characteristics of any propellant charge may be altered by the grain design and by the use of *inhibitors.* Inhibitors are noncombustible or slow burning substances which are applied to portions of the grain surface in order to retard or prevent burning of that surface. Charges so treated are referred to as *restricted burning* grains. The heavy black borders on various charges shown in Fig. 15-19 indicate the location of such inhibitors.

Note that the end-burning type of grain has a layer of inhibitor on every surface except the end which it is desired to have burn. In the case of bonded charges the inhibitor is the bonding material, thus requiring no coating of the grain. By studying the grain designs you will be able to determine the type of burning. Note the surfaces which are permitted to burn and the direction burning progresses. Note that some grains burn inside out, others outside in, and still others burn in both directions, simultaneously.

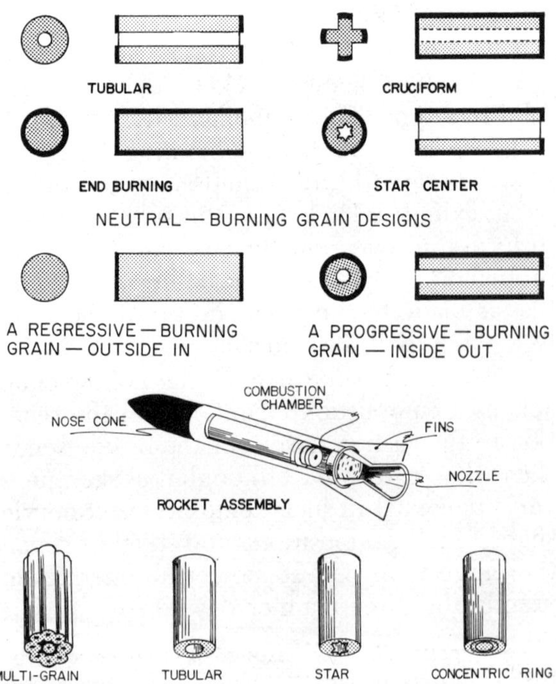

Fig. 15-19. Solid Propellant Designs

Burning Rate

The *burning rate* of a propellant is the *number of inches consumed per second.* It is determined empirically and is a figure which remains constant for that particular propellant at a given pressure, regardless of grain design or surface exposed to burning. (However, we will see that differences in chamber pressure caused by grain configuration can affect the rate of burning.)

The direction of burning is perpendicular to the burning surface. As long as the pressure remains constant, it progresses at the same number of inches per second regardless of the area of the burning surface.

To illustrate the difference between burning rate and the amount of propellant consumed, assume that a rectangular block of fuel, 1 inch square and 12 inches long, is ignited on its end. One square inch of fuel is exposed to burn and if the burning rate is one linear inch per second, the fuel will be consumed in 12 seconds.

Fig. 15-20. Minuteman ICBM, First Stage Inverted Test Firing, and (below) Third Stage

Each stage has four nozzles which have adjustable vector control for steering. This is an operational three-stage solid-fuel military missile.

If, on the other hand, the side is ignited, there will be 12 square inches exposed to burning and since burning proceeds in a direction perpendicular to the burning surface, the entire block would be consumed in one second. In the first instance, the amount of fuel consumed per second is one cubic inch whereas the second case, the 12 cubic inches is consumed per second. In both cases, the burning rate is the same, one linear inch per second.

In an enclosure, larger burning surfaces do cause faster burning rates because of the *higher pressures* generated in the rocket chamber. For this reason, it is desirable for fuel to be quite insensitive to pressure changes. If it is too sensitive to pressure changes, the burning rate may increase enough to explode.

Another factor affecting the burning rate of a propellant is the combustion temperature. Usually high temperatures cause faster burning rates.

Solid Propellants

Solid propellants contain both fuel and an oxidizer. It is usually a hydrocarbon mixed with a compound containing a large amount of oxygen by weight. For example, the oldest propellant, black powder, has carbon and sulphur as fuels and potassium nitrate (KNO_3) for an oxidizer. These are mixed with a *binder* and molded in various *grain* shapes.

Common *oxidizers* include potassium perchlorate, ($KClO_4$), ammonium perchlorate (NH_4ClO_4), and ammonium nitrate (NH_4NO_3). *Ballistite,* a very popular propellant, is composed largely of plasticized nitrocellulose and nitroglycerine. *Galcit* uses petroleum solids for fuel and potassium perchlorate for an oxidizer.

The *specific impulse* of a propellant is the pounds of thrust per second given by each pound of fuel. This is a measure of its efficiency. Modern solid propellants operate in the specific impulse class of 210 to 240 pounds of thrust a second per pound of fuel (lb-sec/lb). Experts see no way of exceeding 265 lb-sec/lb in the immediate future, and 300 lb-sec/lb is considered maximum. *Stable* chemical systems contain just so much energy and no more. Higher values may be forthcoming, but at the expense of being *unstable.* Information about common solid propellants is given in Table II.

Starting

All solid propellants must be ignited by a *pyrotechnic* or flare-like device that provides enough heat to ignite the propellant. At the same time it must provide enough hot gas to raise the chamber pressure to a value where steady operation can be initiated.

Table II
Solid-Propellant Combinations[1]

Oxidizer/Fuel (percent by weight)	Combustion Temp. F°	Specific Impulse
Zinc (Powdered) Zn (50–80%) Sulfur S (50–20%)	2600	20–50
Ammonium Picrate (70–40%) Potassium Nitrate KNO_3 (20–50%) Ethylene Oxide C_2H_4O (10–10%)	3500	150–200
Potassium Perchlorate $KClO_4$ (50–80%) Ethylene Oxide C_2H_4O (50–20%)	2800–5000	155–210
Asphalt (22–30%) Potassium Perchlorate $KClO_4$ (78–70%)	3800–5300	180–195
Ammonium Perchlorate NH_4ClO_4 (50–80%) Ethylene Oxide C_2H_4O (50–20%)	2800–4500	175–240
Ammonium Nitrate NH_4NO_3 (80%) Ethylene Oxide C_2H_4O (18%) Catalyst (2%)	2700	195

[1] From: Brinley, Bertrand R., *Rocket Manual for Amateurs,* (New York: Ballantine Book Co. 1960)

Applications

There are common commercially-made solid-fuel rockets that assist planes to take off quickly. These are known as *Jato, jet-assisted take-off* units. Among the larger solid-fuel rockets, are the Nike, Dart, Honest John, Sergeant, Polaris, and Minuteman, Fig. 15-20. We depend on many of these for anti-missile protection. Such rockets have been fired from airplanes, ship installations, and from below water by submarines. The trend is toward solid fuel for military missiles. The liquid-fueled Corporal has been replaced by the solid-fueled Sergeant. The liquid-fueled Redstone is being replaced by the solid-fueled Pershing.

Recently the Air Force test fired a 250 ton solid-fuel rocket motor. The ten foot diameter device developed one million pounds of thrust for about two minutes. Two such motors, the largest solid motors known to have been ignited, are used in the Titan III-C space vehicle.

The solid-propellant boosters would push the Titan III to a height of one hundred miles. Here the standard Titan II liquid rocket system will take the payload further.

The entire Titan system will stand 110 feet high and is expected to throw a 25,000 pound payload into orbit. The heaviest known payload of the Soviet Union, Sputnik VII, is believed to have weighed less than 15,000 pounds.

The test motor was made of five segments separated by a few inches and held together by clevis type joints. The propellant, bound by synthetic rubber was fueled by aluminum and other metal additives, with ammonium perchlorate as oxidizer. The motor was ignited in a fraction of a second by a series of three small engines, started by one using sensitive pellets that sprayed hot gases to full length of the rocket core.

Whatever their advantages and disadvantages, solid-fuel rockets will find many uses. Solid-fuel rockets are less expensive, are simple and reliable. They can readily be stored because the combustion chamber is also the propellant container.

Liquid-Fuel Engines

Liquid-fuel engines are more complex but operate on the same principles as the solid-fuel type. Obviously, however, combustion cannot take place in the cavity containing the fuel. Instead, the burning takes place in a metal combustion chamber into which the fuel and oxidizer are injected. This requires metering valves, pumps, nozzles, and fuel lines to move the liquids from their storage tanks to where they are to be burned.

Liquid propellants have special problems which are in various stages of solution. Gaseous propellants (oxygen, helium, hydrogen and ammonia have been mentioned) are liquified by greatly reducing their temperature and are called *cryogenic* propellants. Temperatures are so low that the Rankine (°R) or absolute scale is used. This is the Farenheit reading plus 460° to eliminate all minus temperatures. Absolute zero (0°R) is the coldest possible temperature. Lox must be maintained at about 163°R (−297°F), liquid hydrogen at about 37°R (−423°F), depending on the pressure and system. Materials become brittle at these temperatures and standard parts will not operate. Problem areas are the storage tanks, internal baffles, insulation, pressurization system, plumbing, control system, and heat exchangers. At the other extreme, combustion heat may be 8000°F or hotter and also requires consideration.

Cryogenic propellants must be shielded from internal system heat and external solar heat. The empty space in supply tanks is known as *ullage*. Heat transferred to ullage gas causes increased pressures and must be controlled. Another problem is the sloshing of the liquids—corrected by baffles, collapsing bags, or stiffer fluids. In addition, the effects of zero gravity must be dealt with in all systems.

The major considerations of this section are: 1. the various *feed systems*, pressure devices, pumps, and turbines; 2. the *liquid propellants* and their characteristics; 3. *combustion*, thrust chambers, and nozzles; and 4. *specific impulse*, a measure of effective thrust.

Feed Systems

There are two popular feed systems employed to get the fuels and oxidizer into the combustion chamber, the *pressure feed system* and the *pump feed system*.

The *pressure feed system*, Fig. 15-21, uses a gas under pressure to displace the fuel and oxidizers out of their respective tanks.

The *pump feed system*, Fig. 15-22, uses a centrifugal pump to propel the fuel and oxidizer to the combustion chamber. A turbine drives the pump so the system is often called *turbopump* feed system.

The turbine may be driven by some of the exhaust gases which are tapped from the main combustion chamber. These gases must be cooled because their high temperature would melt the turbine. This is known as a *bootstrap* or *bleeding* turbopump system.

Another turbopump system has a *gas generator* to produce a pressurized gas. It may use the main fuel supply or a separate one as shown in Fig. 15-22. The combustion is separate from the rocket's and at a much lower temperature.

Sources of pressure for either pressure feeding or for turbopumps include: 1. stored

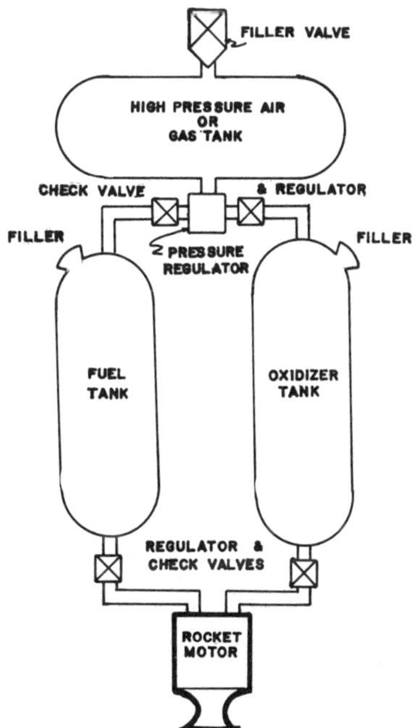

Fig. 15-21. Pressurized-Gas Feed System

pressurized gas (helium is typical), 2. evaporated propellants (using combustion heat), 3. evaporated nonpropellants (untested), and 4. products of chemical reaction (has future potential). About a third of rocket engine development is devoted to feed systems.

Applications

The major advantages of these fuels are that they produce more than 20 to 25 percent more thrust than their solid counterparts, and the combustion can be controlled by regulating the flow of the liquid and the size of the orifice. Furthermore, they can be shut down and started again with no problem. These engines are preferred where flights are to be controlled, and where greater payloads and longer distances are desired.

The Russian engine that propelled the first and second man into space was a liquid-fuel type. Three large ballistic missiles, the T1, T2, and T3 are liquid fueled.

The United States Mercury-Friendship 7 Orbital flight depended on liquid-fuel systems in its Atlas booster. See Figs. 15-23 to 15-29. The Atlas is one of America's largest and dependable operational missiles. It is

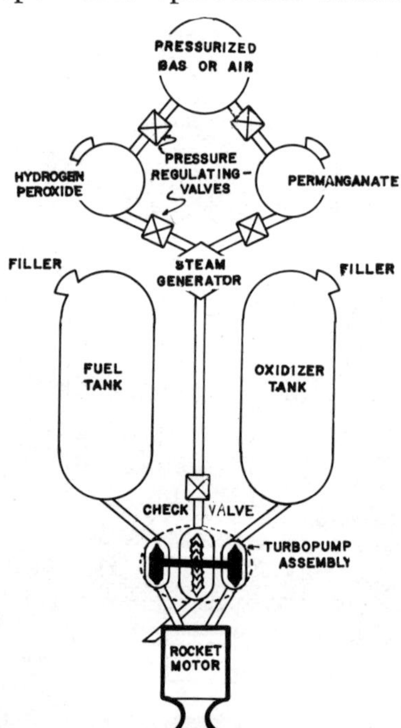

Fig. 15-22. Gas-Generator Turbopump Feed System

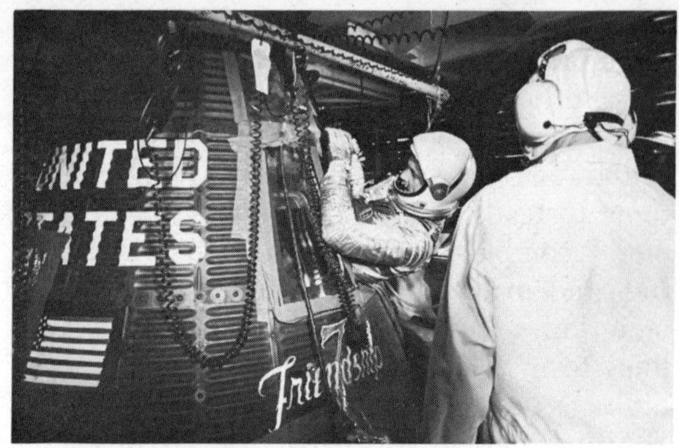

Fig. 15-23. Astronaut Glenn Boards Mercury Spacecraft, February 20, 1962. (NASA)

Fig. 15-24. Readying for Launch (NASA)

Fig. 15-25. Mercury Capsule Blast-Off for Three-Orbit Mission (NASA)

Fig. 15-26. Florida Coast Seen from 100 Miles up at 17,500 mph. (NASA)

Fig. 15-27. Cape Kennedy Mercury Control—Spacecraft Leaving Australia (NASA)

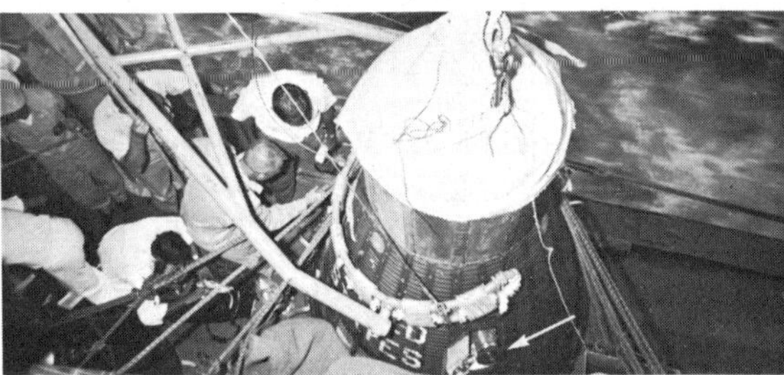

Fig. 15-28. Recovery of Spacecraft (NASA)

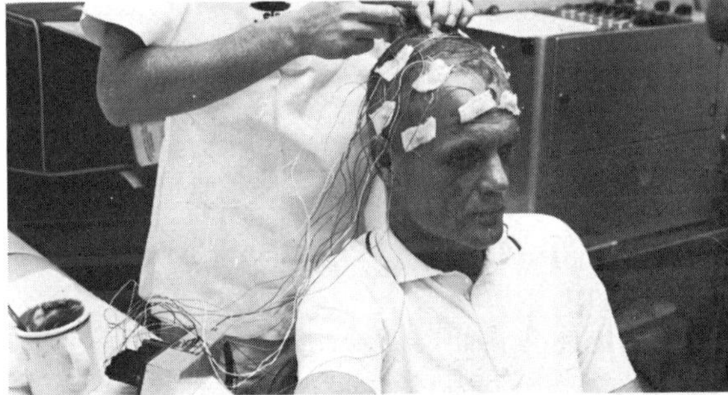

Fig. 15-29. Glenn Undergoes Medical Debriefing (NASA)

powered by a sustainer engine and two boosters, developing a total of 360,000 pounds of thrust. It weighs 243,000 pounds and is radar controlled. The Mercury program, now completed, had the objective of one-man orbital flights.

The new Saturn space booster also uses a liquid system. Most of the early liquid-fuel systems and many present ones use kerosene (RP-1) and liquid oxygen as propellants, along with hydrogen/oxygen.

Liquid Propellants

Two classes of propellants are used: *mono-propellants* and *bi-propellants.*

Mono-propellants are fluids which contain both fuel and oxidizing agent. See Fig. 15-30. They may be a *single chemical* such as nitromethane or 80 percent hydrogen peroxide, or a *mixture* such as ammonia and nitrous oxide. Mono-propellants are generally unstable and deliver energy through their own decomposition. This is usually induced by a catalyst such as potasium permanganate. These propellants are stored and fed into the combustion chamber as a single fluid, thus eliminating the need for an additional tank, extra plumbing and storage equipment as well as extra mixing valves and complex injectors. Although these systems are less complicated and less costly, they yield low specific impulse compared with other liquid propellants, and are less used.

Bi-propellants consist of a fuel and an oxidizer which are stored separately within the missile. They are fed independently to the combustion chamber where they are mixed at the instant combustion is to take place. See Fig. 15-31. This timing is necessary because some combinations of fuel and oxidizer (such as aniline and nitric acid) are self-igniting when mixed, and cannot be brought together advantageously until the moment that combustion is desired. Some combinations such as alcohol and liquid oxygen, while they do not ignite spontaneously, nevertheless form highly unstable compounds that can explode without warning.

Table III
Liquid-Propellant Combinations

Fuel	Oxidizer to Fuel Ratio	Combustion Temp. F°	Specific Impulse
(Chlorine Trifluoride as Oxidizer:)			
Ammonia*	3.93	4980	240
Hydrazine[1]*	0.677	5840	251
Methyl Alcohol*	2.88	5150	218
(Fluorine as Oxidizer:)			
Ammonia*	2.90	75.2	295.5
Hydrazine[1]*	1.98	7692	300
Hydrogen	9.42	8072	371
Lithium	2.19	7000	335.5
Methyl Alcohol	2.37	7472	298
(Hydrogen Peroxide as Oxidizer:)			
Alum. Borohydride*	3.0	5772	200
Hydrazine[1]*	1.69	4200	240
Methyl Alcohol, Hydrazine, and Water (57–32–11%)	2.54	3934	224
Nitromethane	0.42	4719	232
n-Octane	5.10	4095	230
(Liquid Oxygen as Oxidizer:)			
Acetylene	1.23	6012	266
Alum. Borohydride	1.32	6000	276
Ammonia	1.25	4834	250
Ethane	2.30	5308	254
75% Ethyl Alcohol	1.31	4887	234
Ethyl Methyl Alcohol (95–5%)	0.84	5338	240
Ethylene	1.86	5538	264
Gasoline	2.26	5660	252
Hydrazine[1]	0.83	5382	263
Hydrogen	2.89	3886	345
Isopropyl Alcohol	1.85	5553	241.1
Kerosene	2.28	5702	249
Lithium*	1.15	13000	318
Borohydride*	1.47	8300	306
Hydride*	1.34	6400	268
Methane	2.33	4874	263
Methyl Alcohol	1.15	5076	237
80% Methyl Alcohol	1.50	4881	228
Nitromethane	0.076	4703	228
n-Octane	2.20	5498	248
(Ozone as Oxidizer:)			
Ammonia	1.13	5175	267
Hydrazine[1]	0.63	5418	277
Hydrogen	2.65	4280	373
(RFNA[3]–6.5% NO_2–as Oxidizer:)			
Aniline-Furfuryl Alcohol (80–20%)*	3.35		228
Hydrazine[1]*	1.00	4437	240.6
Isopropyl Alcohol	3.33	4797	218.1
(RFNA[3]–16% NO_2–as Oxidizer:)			
Aniline*	3.00	5067	221
Ethyl Alcohol	2.50	4555	219
Hydrazine[1]*	1.16	4728	242
(WFNA[2] as Oxidizer:)			
Aniline*	3.00	4942	222
Purfuryl Alcohol	2.65	4885	210
Gasoline	4.60	4941	223
Hydrazine[1]*	1.22	4681	246
Hydrogen	12.6	5360	298
JP-4	4.7	5000	229
Methyl Alcohol	2.36	4480	219
Octane	4.00	4744	229

Table II shows the more common types of propellants. You will note that virtually all combinations consist of some type of oxidizing agent and a hydrocarbon fuel. The table gives the specific impulse for many combinations, the flame temperature produced during combustion, as well as the fuel to oxidizer ratio.

Specific impulse will be discussed later in the chapter. It will suffice to know that it is a measurement of the ability of a propellant to produce thrust and is expressed in seconds. The higher the value of specific impulse the more powerful is the propellant. In the case of liquid propellants, the term *specific thrust* rather than *specific impulse* is often used, because the measurements mean something slightly different in reference to liquids. It takes into account the rate of flow of the pro-

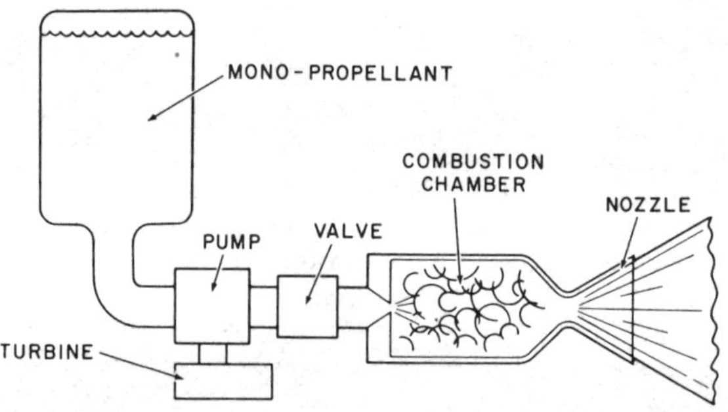

Fig. 15-30. Liquid Mono-Propellant Engine (GE)

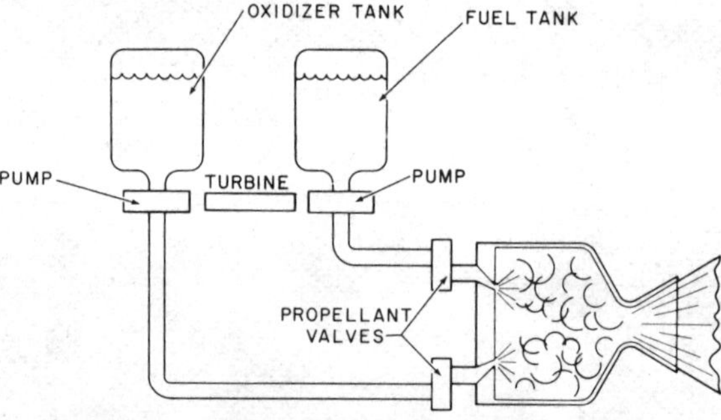

Fig. 15-31. Liquid Bi-Propellant Engine (GE)

* Self igniting mixture (*hypergolic*).

[1] Full name of hydrazine is *unsymmetrical dimethyl hydrazine*, abbreviated UDMH. See Fig. 15-5.

[2] White fuming nitric acid is abbreviated, WFNA.

[3] Red fuming nitric acid is abbreviated RFNA.

pellant into the combustion chamber. Both terms are equivalent in all respects except the method of calculation, and specific impulse has come to be more widely used regardless of the type of propellant.

Liquid Fuel Advantages

Liquid propellants possess certain definite advantages as compared to solids, but also pose certain design problems, storage and handling problems which must be considered.

Liquid fuels are approximately 20 percent to 50 percent more powerful than solid fuels. Their advantages are chiefly:

They are *readily available* and often can be produced in large quantities.

Temperature of combustion and combustion pressures are generally lower permitting lighter motor wall construction.

Rate of fuel flow can be controlled directly, permitting a wide range of performance for a given propellant.

Liquids are relatively unaffected by changes in temperature, humidity and pressure, and can be stored for indefinite periods of time without detrimental affects.

Liquid Fuel Disadvantages

Their main disadvantages are:

The elaborate plumbing systems necessary are weighty and offset the advantage of light weight motor construction.

The *necessary intricate systems* of valving and plumbing make for a highly temperamental contrivance.

The *chemicals used are usually highly corrosive,* requiring the use of expensive hard-to-obtain materials for storage tanks, valves, seals, fitting, tubing, and so on.

The *fuels are usually toxic, demanding rigorous safe handling* and storage procedures that are necessarily costly.

Fueling time and the logistics involved in their transportation and storage render them almost useless for many defense applications.

Their low density creates a bulk displacement problem which is reflected in size of storage and transportation facilities as well as the size and weight of the missile airframe in which they are used.

Liquid and Solid Fuels Compared

It would appear that after all things are considered, the big advantage of liquid fuels is their higher energy yield or specific impulse. However, considerable progress has been made toward reducing this advantage by the newer more powerful solid propellants.

It must be considered that the advantage of the liquid propellants in terms of specific impulse is not a true measure of comparative performance of the two types of propellants in their ultimate use with the missile. Specific impulse is a measure of performance in terms of pounds of propellant used. In light of the lower density of fluids, and consequently greater bulk, greater size and weight of the airframe of the missile must be considered. This factor reduces appreciably the advantage of superior thrust since a greater number of pounds of liquid propellant must lift a greater weight of airframe as compared to solid propellant. This means that even if solid fuels never achieve the high energy yield of liquid propellants, they may reach the point where they outperform them in terms of payload delivered.

Satellite launching vehicles currently in use in this country have already abandoned liquid motors except for the initial or booster stage. In the medium and long range artillery missiles of the U.S. Army, the liquid fuel Corporal and Redstones are being replaced by the smaller, lighter solid rockets such as the Sergeant and Pershing. In both cases, the newer rockets are roughly two thirds the size and weight of their predecessors, but will deliver the same size payload, the same distance, with lower impulse propellant, simply because of the weight saved in the missile airframe. Solid fuel rockets have other advantages particularly to the military, such as zero fueling time, simplified handling, and firing procedures, less complicated supporting apparatus and a significant reduction in size and training of a launching crew.

Liquid Fuel Combustion

Generally, the liquid propellant is sprayed around the walls of the combustion chamber in a helical pattern. This serves to cool the chamber wall and also increases the chances of complete combustion by creating a fine spray of fuel and oxidizer. Ignition, as has been previously mentioned, must be almost instantaneous or it is dangerous, because of the formation of highly explosive propellants.

What happens from ignition until the moment the hot gases exhaust is a matter of conjecture. Much research is being conducted to provide enlightenment on how the many compounds are formed, broken, reformed before eventually being exhausted in some form of exhaust product; and how the various shock waves develop contributing to what is termed *combustion instability*. This condition inhibits the smooth exhausting of the gases. Simply, the hot exhaust gases under high pressure and temperature, rush to get out through the opening provided by the nozzle. When these produce a high enough gas velocity, thrust is developed and the rocket is propelled forward.

How much thrust is developed is dependent upon the inter-relationship of a combination of factors involving the design of the combustion chamber, injection system, the properties of the propellant and the nozzle configuration. The nozzle has the function of accelerating the exhaust gases to optimum velocity.

As for the propellant the most important factor affecting thrust is the relationship between flame temperature and the molecular weight of the exhaust products. The higher the temperature within the chamber and the lower the molecular weight of the ejected gases through the nozzle, the higher the exhaust velocity of the burned gases or the higher the thrust.

The ejected exhaust products may consist of a variety of combinations of the basic elements making up the fuel and oxidizer. In many cases, they cannot be isolated and analyzed before they are converted to other compounds by changes in temperature and pressure. For this reason, it is impossible at the present stage of technological progress in rocketry for researchers to make a complete chemical analysis of the products of combustion that are formed in the combustion chamber and flow out through the nozzle. However, many exhaust gases can be identified after exiting. These products represent matter with measurable mass, weight and chemical composition.

Whenever low molecular weight and high flame temperature are evident, the resulting specific impulse is high. Whenever high molecular weight and low flame temperature are evident, the resulting specific impulse is correspondingly low. A definite correlation exists between flame temperature, molecular weight of the propellant and the resulting specific impulse. It is important to mention that the molecular weight of the exhaust products and not that of the original propellants is considered.

Specific Impulse

The *specific impulse* or *specific thrust* of a propellant is probably the most important and most frequently used index of its efficiency. There are a number of ways of computing it, depending on the performance of a propellant in a particular rocket motor. In other words, a propellant combination is entirely dependent on the motor system for its actual specific impulse because combustion chamber pressure and nozzle exit pressure and velocity will vary with each motor design. The values given for specific impulse in Table II are the highest obtainable for each combination in a motor of optimum design.

There are several ways of defining what is meant by specific impulse because it represents a relationship involving many factors which are under constant change during combustion through ejection. One way is to say that it represents the rate of change of momentum of the gases through the nozzle. This definition is fairly good but not quite complete because we are also concerned with the rate the gases expand as they leave the nozzle. These two factors are interrelated with one following the other.

The ability of the gas to expand is due mostly to the property of the gas itself, whereas its acceleration depends on the design of the nozzle and combustion chamber. There exists a simple and direct relationship between specific impulse and the exhaust velocity and if any one factor is known the other can be easily determined. Thrust is not a matter of gas exhaust velocity but the rapidity with which it reaches that velocity.

Thrust is accounted for by the fact that gases in the combustion chamber have zero velocity and are made to reach a very high velocity on their way to the nozzle exit. Thrust takes place between the combustion chamber and the nozzle exit, not at the nozzle exit, and by the time the expanding gases reach the exit they have done their work. Regardless of their velocity at that point, they cannot any longer have effect on the rocket's movement. Beyond the nozzle, it is important only to permit the gases to dissipate themselves rapidly as possible, quickly reaching atmospheric pressure in order to provide room for the gases that are to follow out the nozzle. Failure of the gases to reach atmospheric pressure rapidly after they exit from the nozzle would create a *back pressure* which would slow down the movement of succeeding gases.

Selecting Propellants

Ideally, propellants should have great propulsive efficiency. They should also be stable, easy to handle, to transport and to utilize. They should be nontoxic, noncorrosive, and exhibit low vapor pressures. Freezing points, boiling points, viscosity, ignition characteristics, availability, logistics, and cost are a few other factors that must be taken into account before a propellant is chosen. The ideal, unfortunately, has not been achieved, and the engineer must choose the combination exhibiting the least number of evils.

Liquids are like solids in that thermodynamic calculation indicates that there have definite performance limits. These limits are not too much higher than the specific-impulse value of those now being used. We realize that a 400 lb-sec/lb specific-impulse is maximum and that many rocket systems now give a specific-impulse of 250 to 300 lb-sec/lb. To assess properly any system reaction product, it is necessary to consider stability, heat content, vapor pressure, molecular weight, and chamber conditions. It is never possible to extract all of the energy since combustion losses, heat losses through the walls, residual kinetic energy, and unavailable thermal jet energy are all present.

Rocket engineers know that by lowering the propellant molecular weight, the specific impulse will increase. They also know that lowering the ratio of specific heats and increasing temperatures and pressures will help. To improve fuels, light metals such as lithium, boron, beryllium, are being added.

Despite energy and controllability advantages, there are many built-in problems which have discouraged military uses especially. Long, tedious fuelings and readying periods before launching are required. Toxic fumes, acid burns, and accidental combustion of the chemical elements are always bothersome and dangerous.

Intensive research is being carried on to develop highly energetic liquid and solid fuels. New metallic alloys better able to withstand the extreme temperatures attained during firing are needed. More efficient methods of control are also needed. Rocketry of the future will probably include solid and liquid fuel engines as well as engines of total different design—such as nuclear, electrical, and solar engines.

At no time in history has man had at his disposal a greater variety of prime movers that could be used to do work. Yet, he is still not content because he realizes that better and more efficient engines are his destiny to conceive.

Rocket Engine Development

Our National Aeronautics and Space Agency has developed and is constantly refining a family of reliable launch vehicles of various sizes, shapes, and capabilities. The aim is to develop the smallest number of launch vehicles consistent with the full scope of the space missions now contemplated. This policy is first, economical and second, flexible with experience providing a high incidence of reliability. Presently there are four general categories of flight missions requiring a variety of launch vehicles:

A *sounding mission* investigates the upper atmosphere outward from the earth to 4,000 miles into space.

A *space probe mission* extends beyond 4,000 miles.

An *orbital mission* remains within the earth's gravitational influence and orbits around the earth. The flight usually reaches a velocity of at least 5 miles per second or 17,500 miles per hour and upward to 7 miles per second or 24,600 miles per hour.

A *deep space probe* is a trajectoral flight to another celestial body – our moon or another planet. The launch vehicle must attain speeds beyond 7 miles per second in order to escape the earth's gravitational influence and enter a solar orbit onto its target.

Most rockets today are built in stages so that as the propellants are consumed the empty stages can be *jettisoned* or dropped away. The remainder of the launch vehicle after stage separation is therefore much lighter and continues on its course using smaller engines and less fuel. The earth's gravitational pull is greatest at ground level and, of course, the launch vehicle and its payload at launch time has zero momentum. In addition, the total weight of the vehicle at launch is greatest because the vehicle propellant tanks are fully loaded. To overcome these gravitational forces the first stage must produce the greatest amount of total thrust. The thrust then is usually less in the second, third and fourth stages.

Fig. 15-31A. Scout Launch Vehicle (NASA)

NASA launch vehicles include the Scout, Delta, Thor Agena, Atlas Agena, Atlas Centaur, Uprated Saturn I, and Saturn V. The famous Mercury Atlas Launch Vehicle of Project Mercury and the Project Gemini Launch Vehicle, the Titan II, have completed their missions.

Scout

Scout, Fig. 15-31A, the smallest of the basic launch vehicles, is a reliable and relatively inexpensive launch vehicle for payloads ranging up to 240 lbs. It is mainly used for unmanned, small satellite missions, high altitude probes, and re-entry experiments. The Scout has four stages, is 68 feet high less the spacecraft, and has a diameter of four feet at its widest cross section. Guidance is provided by a strapped-down gyro system, and the vehicle is controlled by a combination of aerodynamic surfaces, jet vanes, and hydrogen peroxide jets. The Scout is the only United States launch vehicle with solid propellants exclusively. The first-stage thrust is 88,000 lbs. which can put a 400 lb. payload into lower levels of space, 240 lbs. into a 300 nautical mile orbit, or carry 100 lb. scientific probe about 7,000 miles away from the earth.

Delta

Delta has two liquid fuel stages topped by a solid fuel stage. It is 98 feet high and 8 feet in diameter at the base, excluding fins. It can boost 550 lbs. into a 500 nautical mile earth orbit. Its gross weight is 114,200 lbs., and the total thrust of its first stage is 170,000 lbs. The Delta is the workhorse for a wide variety of small payload satellite missions and space probes. It launched the first orbiting solar observatory, some of the Taurus weather satellites, and has been used on communications satellites Echo I, Telstar, Relay, and Syncom Programs. Its first stage is a modified Thor; second a modified and improved stage from the Vanguard and Thor Able Programs; and its third stage is the Spin Stabilized Solid Propellant Altair. The Altair is also derived from the earlier Vanguard and Thor Able vehicles.

Thor Agena

Thor Agena is a two-stage vehicle that can send 1,150 lbs. into an earth orbit of 100 nautical miles, or 600 lbs. into a 1,200 mile orbit. Both stages burn liquid propellants, and the total thrust is 186,000 lbs. The vehicle is 76 feet high without spacecraft and 8 feet wide without the fins. The second stage is the restartable Agena, which permits great precision in selecting an orbit. Agena was developed by the Air Force as a second stage for use in its own programs. Early in the 60's NASA decided to use it in combination with Thor and Atlas rather than develop a similar vehicle. The NASA version of Agena, developing 16,000 lbs. thrust, is modified so that various types of payloads can be appended to its front end. Thor Agena is used by NASA for meteorological communications and scientific satellites including the Orbiting Geophysical Observatory, Nimbus Cert 2, and the Pageos Programs.

Atlas Agena

The Atlas Agena, Fig. 15-31B, is a two-stage, liquid propellant space vehicle capable of putting 5,950 lbs. in a 100 nautical mile earth orbit and of sending instrument payloads of 950 lbs. to the moon. It is 88.3 feet high (less the spacecraft) and 10 feet in diameter. The total thrust is 404,000 lbs. The Atlas was developed from the Air Force Intercontinental Ballistic Missile and weighs approximately 260,000 lbs. A typical lunar application has the Atlas 5 engines burn for about two and one-half minutes before the outer engines cut off and are jettisoned. The smaller center engine and vernier engines continue firing for another two minutes, taking the vehicle to an altitude of 80 miles. One thousand pound thrust vernier engines continue firing after the center engine cutoff in order to trim the velocity. After the vernier is cut off, the Atlas Agena coasts for a few seconds; then a spring loaded aerodynamic shroud protecting the payload is discarded. Explosive charges separate the Agena from the Atlas first stage. The Agena then goes through a pitch maneuver to bring it into horizontal alignment with the earth's surface, the timer signals the propulsion system, and Agena ignition occurs.

The Atlas Centaur

The Atlas Centaur with an Atlas first stage and a Centaur second stage is the most advanced of the Atlas A Series of launch vehicles. It is 100 feet long, weighs 300,000 lbs. and is capable of sending approximately 8,500 lbs. into a low earth orbit, 2,150 lbs. to the moon, and 1,300 lbs. to Venus and Mars. The

Fig. 15-31B. Atlas Agena Launch Vehicle (NASA)

two-stage, liquid-fueled vehicle develops a total thrust of more than 400,000 lbs. Atlas develops 388,000 lb. thrust and the Centaur 30,000 lb. thrust. The Atlas Centaur combination is a high-performance, general-purpose vehicle. The Centaur Program has pioneered research to develop a rocket vehicle that can utilize high energy liquid hydrogen as fuel. It has provided much of the basic high-energy knowledge required for the design of the upper stage of the Saturn Vehicles and Propulsion Systems, which use the same fuel.

The Gemini Titan

The powerful Gemini Titan was selected as the launch vehicle to boost the Gemini II manned spacecraft into orbit. It was chosen for this mission because of its payload capability and most importantly because its propellants are nonexplosive, a feature permitting use of an ejection seat escape system instead of the rocket escape tower of Mercury. All engines operate on a mixture in which the fuel is a blend of unsymmetrical dimethylhydrazine (commonly referred to as UDMH) and hydrazine, and the oxidizer is nitrogen tetroxide. The mixture is hypergolic and can be stored for some time in the Titan's fuel tank. Titan II has a 430,000 lb. thrust first stage and 100,000 lb. thrust second stage. It is 90 feet high (less payload) and 10 feet in diameter at the base.

Fig. 15-31C. Uprated Saturn I Launch Vehicle (NASA)

The Uprated Saturn I

The original Saturn launch vehicle was conceived in 1948 to provide early capability for large payloads. The decision to arrange the engines and tanks in clusters allowed the use of equipment already developed for earlier rockets as well as the machine tools that produced them. Thus, the first stage of the two-stage Saturn I was a cluster of eight H-1 engines, each capable of generating 18,800 lbs. of thrust. The second stage of the earlier version had six liquid oxygen, liquid hydrogen engines each generating 15,000 lbs. of thrust. The first ten vehicles, called Saturn I, were launched for research and developmental purposes and placed into earth orbits engineering test models of the command and service modules of the Apollo Spacecraft. The last three Saturn I's placed meteroid technology satellites into earth orbit to examine the size and distribution of particles in space near the earth. Beginning with the 11th flight, a new, more powerful second stage was used on the Saturn I. This new second stage has a single 200,000 lbs. thrust engine utilizing liquid hydrogen and liquid oxygen and replaces the six-engine stage used in the earlier vehicles. The first stage of the Uprated Saturn I, Fig. 15-31C, has the same eight liquid oxygen kerosene engines previously used, but with thrust uprated to 1.6 million pounds. The Uprated Saturn I mated to the Apollo Spacecraft and its launch escape system stands 225 feet high. It can orbit 40,000 lbs. and was used to launch manned and unmanned modules of the Apollo Spacecraft.

The Saturn V

The ultimate in space launch technology is the three-stage Saturn V, Fig. 15-31D, which stands 363 feet high with its Apollo Spacecraft in place. It has a liftoff weight of more than 6.1 million pounds. The first stage is powered by five F1 engines which burn kerosene and liquid oxygen. See Fig. 15-31E. The five engines consume 15,000 tons of propellant a second and produce 7.5 million pounds of thrust.

On a trip to the moon, the first-stage engines burn for two and one-half minutes, boosting the Apollo astronauts to an altitude of 36 miles and a velocity of about 6,000 miles per hour. See Fig. 15-31F. The first stage then drops away and the second stage ignites. The second stage is powered by five J2 engines, each producing 200,000 lbs. of thrust. These hydrogen-oxygen engines burn for six and one-half minutes, push the spacecraft into an altitude of 100 miles and near orbital velocity. The third stage of the Saturn V, (the same as the second stage of the Uprated Saturn I) has a single J2 engine which develops 200,000 lbs.

Fig. 15-31D. Saturn V Launch Vehicle (NASA)

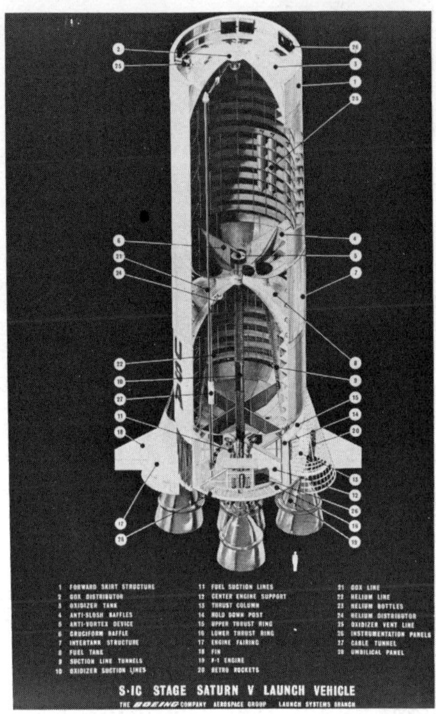

Fig. 15-31E. First Stage of Saturn V (Boeing)

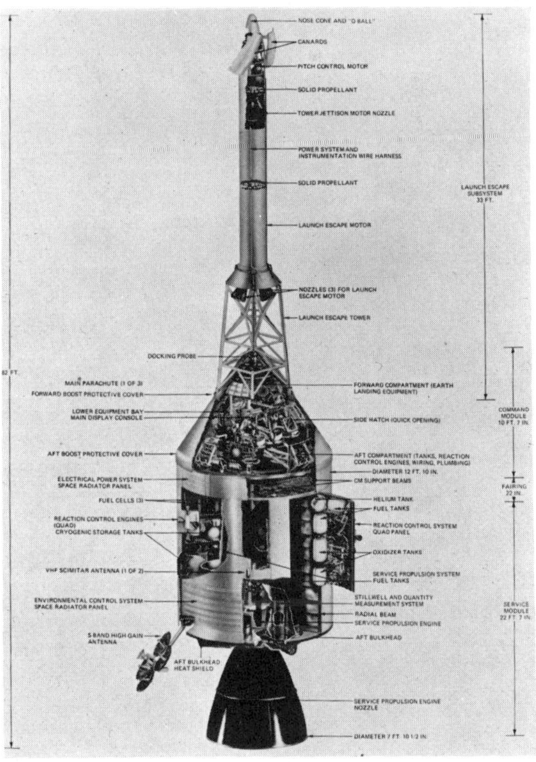

Fig. 15-31F. Apollo Command/Service Module (NASA)

of thrust. See Figs. 15-31G and 15-31H. This stage gives the Apollo Spacecraft the final shove to place it into earth orbit at an altitude of about 115 miles, then the engine shuts down while the spacecraft is checked out. At the proper moment the third stage engine is reignited. It burns for approximately six and one-half minutes, accelerating the spacecraft from its orbital speed of 17,400 miles an hour to about 24,600 miles an hour to overcome earth's gravity. The Saturn V can place a payload of 285,000 lbs. into earth orbit or send 98,000 lbs. to the moon. The Apollo Saturn V space vehicle employs a total of 91 different engines using a variety of liquid and solid fuels.[2]

Emerging Propulsion Systems

As was listed earlier, the best material to discharge from a rocket is *hydrogen*. This is likely to remain so for the forseeable future because it has the lowest molecular weight of any element. The basic problem of hydrogen propulsion is getting the hydrogen as hot as possible. Thus far, we have mentioned only that hydrogen is an element within the fuel,

[2] *NASA Facts,* "Space Launch Vehicles," Educational Publication, U. S. Government Printing Office.

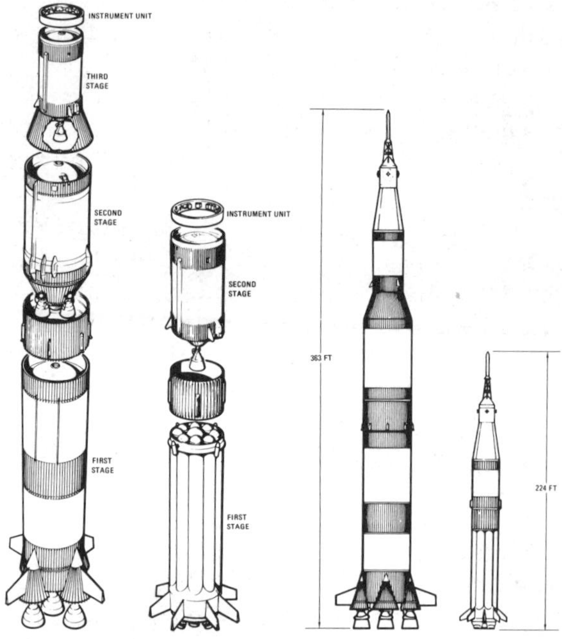

Fig. 15-31H. Saturn V and Saturn I (NASA)

Fig. 15-31G. Saturn Rocket Engines (NASA)
The H1 engine is shown at left, the F1 at center, and the J2 at right.

so is exhausted with the products of combustion. There are also other ways. The hydrogen can be heated by any of several means, or a combination of them. Some of these methods are the use of chemical fuels as already discussed, as well as the use of solar energy, electrical energy, or nuclear energy.

Nuclear Propulsion

We are familiar with two large-scale applications of nuclear energy—the nuclear bomb and the nuclear reactor for steam generation giving mechanical power. The first is almost instantaneous and in all directions. It is a burst of uncontrolled energy. The other is both controlled and continuous and is therefore adaptable to propulsion systems.

The continuous nuclear power plant, however, is beset by the extremely severe problem of weight. See Figs. 15-32 and 15-33. The actual reactor weight is not so critical, but the necessary shielding is. Many proposals have been made to lessen this difficulty. A frequent one is to locate the crew as far as possible from the reactor and to shield them separately. The servicing and handling problems of an atomic device are also extraordinarily acute. Nevertheless, nuclear propulsion for space exploration is very important because of the high specific impulse. For example, the Titan has a specific impulse of 300, whereas the specific impulse of a nuclear rocket could be about 900.

Nuclear Power Plants in Space

General Electric's concept of a nuclear turbo-generator space power system is shown in Fig. 15-34. It is a nose cone ahead of a shadow shield which protects the following systems against radiation. Components include circulating pumps, heat exchanger boilers, the turbo-generator with its associated control valve, and the condensers.

A conical shell radiator extends for some distance aft of the turbo-machinery space. Two sub-cooler radiators, also conical in shape, are located forward of the main radiator and partially enclose the turbo-machinery. All components are symmetrical for balance.

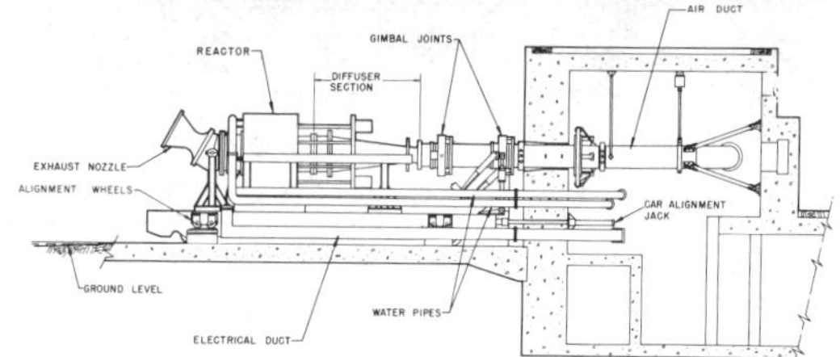

Fig. 15-32. The Tory II-A Experimental Nuclear Ramjet (Livermore)

Fig. 15-33. Kiwi A-Prime, Studying Nuclear Rocket Propulsion (Los Alamos)

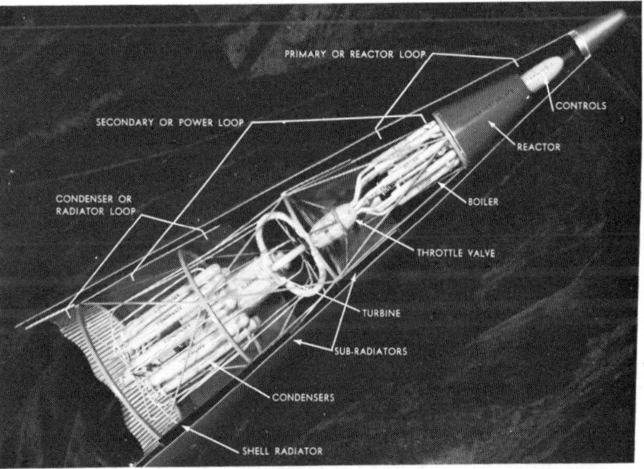

Fig. 15-34. Model of Nuclear Space Power Plant (GE)

The system consists of three major flow loops. Pressurized liquid metal reactor coolant at about 1800°-2000°F. is circulated in the *primary loop*. In the boiler, heat is transferred to the *power loop*, which contains the wet vapor turbine, the heat exchanger condenser, and the condensate pump. The condenser is cooled by pressurized liquid metal which is circulated by a motor driven pump through the complex armored tube network of the *radiator loop*. Heat is radiated from the fin surfaces at the rate of about 2.5 kw per square foot at temperatures in the range of 1200°F.

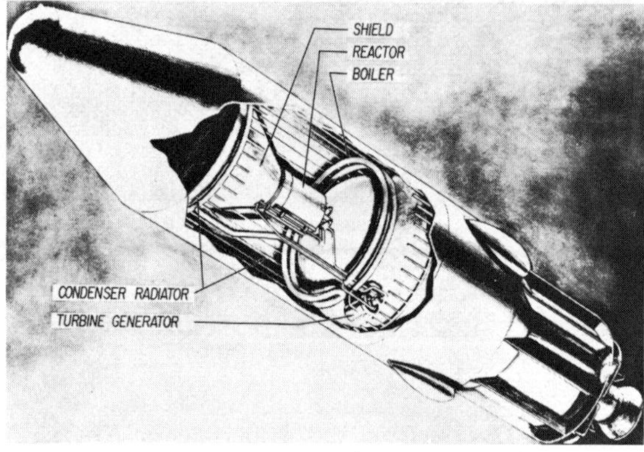

Fig. 15-35. SNAP-2 Reactor in Spaceship (Atomics International)

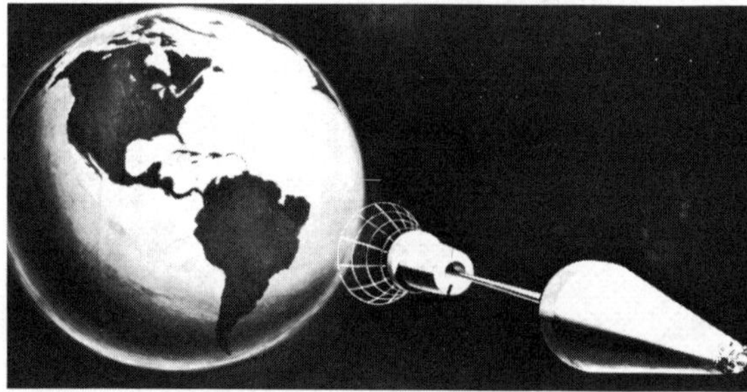

Fig. 15-36. SNAP Television Relay Station

Because of zero gravity, the sub-loops perform the functions of pump inlet pressurization and also for the circulation of motor and generator coolant and bearing lubricant. A centrifugal separator and a jet pump pressurize the inlet of the power loop condensate pump. In the reactor and radiator loops, small pumps and whirl chamber are used.

This design of a nuclear turbo-generator was developed by the GE's flight propulsion laboratory. Heat energy from a nuclear reactor would be converted into electrical energy by the turbo-generator and associated equipment to provide power for electrical propulsion systems, electronic equipment and life support functions.

Nuclear Rocket Power

The nuclear-powered *rocket* then, must have some form of nuclear power plant. One has just been described, and Fig. 15-35 illustrates another. In these, the high heat resulting from the nuclear reaction could be transferred to hydrogen gas, and the hot gas expelled rearward. The hydrogen would

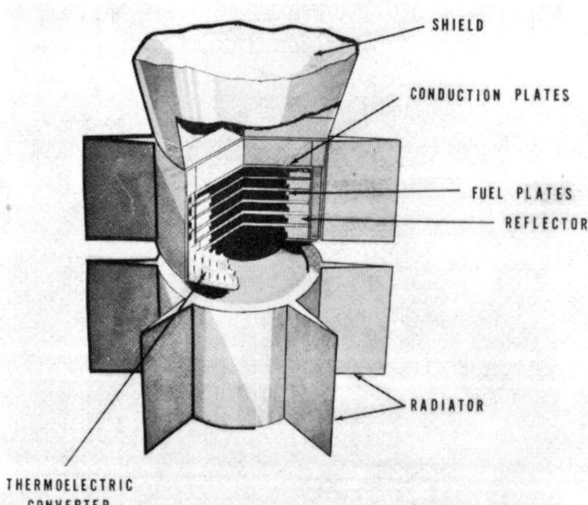

Fig. 15-37. SNAP-10 Nuclear Thermoelectric System

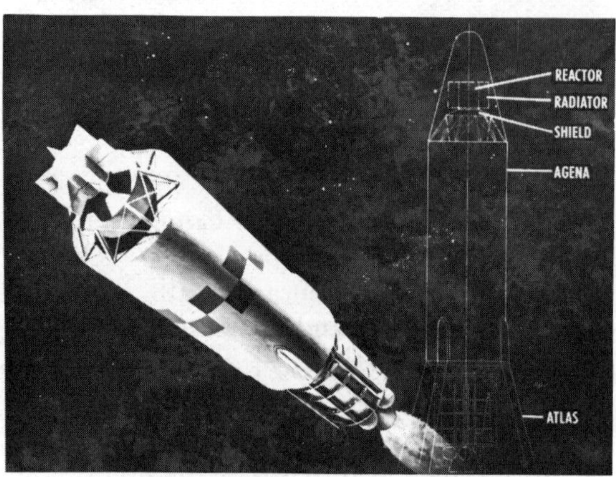

Fig. 15-38. SNAP-10 System on Agena-Atlas Rocket (Atomics International)

have to be stored on board in liquid form, which could also be used as general coolant for the reactor system. Nuclear power can also be used to generate electrical power (as was shown in Fig. 15-34) to operate one of the electrical propulsion systems described in the next section.

Because of heavy shielding, and the relatively large size of our present nuclear components, it follows that nuclear-powered rockets will be large, heavy, and expensive. They do, however, represent one of the potentially most valuable long-term heavy-duty power sources for space applications. See Fig. 15-36 for a possible use as a high powered TV repeater station 22,600 miles above the earth. Three such relays would give world wide television. Figs. 15-37 and 15-38 show another System for Auxiliary Nuclear Power (SNAP) producing 300 watts of power and weighing 620 pounds exclusive of the booster rocket.

Electrical Propulsion

In many respects the electrical propulsion systems are the direct opposite of the nuclear ones. Very small forces are produced, in electrical propulsion, in terms of the weight of the equipment required. For example a one pound thrust may require an electrical propulsion engine weighing two tons. At first this seems ridiculous, but on further examination, this device has much merit for missions to planets or other long distance exploration.

By way of illustration, if you could push on a two ton object with no friction, using a force of one pound, the object would achieve a speed of about one-quarter mph in the first minute. At the end of the first hour it would reach 15 mph and at the end of the first day it would travel well over 380 mph. In a month it would attain speeds in excess of 11,000 mph, and in two months it would attain escape velocity. When you lift an electrically powered vehicle out of the atmosphere at perhaps 15,000 mph and continue to add an additional 11,000 mph every month, it soon becomes apparent that idea of electrical space propulsion has merit.

The very high weight of powerplants which appear to be necessary for electrical propulsion is acceptable because the consumption of hydrogen turns but to be extremely small due to the high specific impulse of this system. This is in the range of 5,000 to 10,000. On very long missions (such as round trips to Mars, Venus and other planets) which may involve two or three years, electrical propulsion is a very promising method. It is competitive with *solar-heated rocket engines* and *solar sails,* which will be explained later. These too are low-force continuously acting systems.

Presently there are three major kinds of electrical propulsion engines: electrothermal (arc jet), magnetohydrodynamic – MHD (plasma accelerator); and electrostatic (ion engine). Each has its best own range of operation. Space missions, not yet defined, could require specific impulses which cover the range of all three engine types.

Electrothermal Arc Jet

The simplest electric rocket is the so-called *arc jet.* An electric arc struck between two electrodes provides the energy input. A propellant, helium for example, is introduced into the arc chamber, where it is heated to extremely high temperatures, and then exhausted out through a nozzle to produce thrust.

Fig. 15-39 shows a small *arc-jet test unit.* This tiny one-killowatt arc jet produces .02 lb. of thrust. The engine has demonstrated in tests the ability to run continuously for several hundred hours. Such engines would be suitable for controlling the attitudes and orbital paths of satellites.

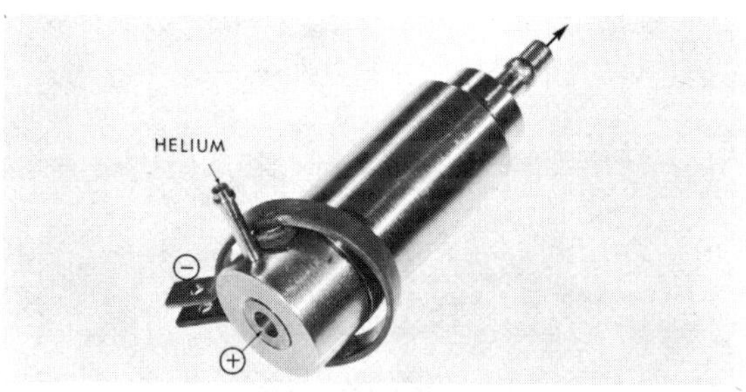

Fig. 15-39. Arc Jet (GE)

Electrostatic Ion Engine

Today one of the most promising electrical propulsion systems in the *ion engine.* In the electron-ion engine, a reactor heats cesium vapor from which electrical power is generated. It operates on a principle quite advanced in propulsion devices. This engine could send a manned craft to Mars at speeds of 2,000,000 miles per day. Plans call for it to be space tested enough that a complete ion system with nuclear-electric power can be tested soon.

These engines use electrostatic fields to accelerate charged particles of matter (called *ions*) enough to produce thrust.

Ion Engine Operation: Cessium is heated and vaporized then allowed to strike on a heated *grid or emitter,* Fig. 15-40. Cessium becomes ionized easily (gives up an electron from the neutral cessium atom) so that a cloud of ions is formed at the emitter. These ions are positively charged particles. Two strips of metal in the center of the engine form a set of accelerating electrodes. A voltage, impressed between the emitter and the electrode, draws the ion cloud off the emitter. The voltage accelerates and focuses it into a beam, which shoots off at very high velocities.

Since the ion beam is positively charged, it must be made electrically neutral. If this were not done, a negative charge would build up on the vehicle. This would draw the ions back to the engine, reducing the thrust to zero. To neutralize the beam, filamets are placed on the engine exhaust. These filaments emit electrons (those that were stripped off the atoms) which neutralize the ion beam.

Ion Engine Applications: Ion engines are suitable for controlling orbits of satellites (by overcoming atmospheric drag at fringes of space), for changing altitude, and for propelling space vehicles from planet to planet. A small amount of thrust is all that is needed in space. This thrust may be provided over long periods of time with little propellant consumption. This is the main advantage such an electrical propulsion system offers.

MHD Plasma Pinch Engine

The plasma pinch engine, Fig. 15-41, completely self-contained, including the electrical power supply and propellant fuel supply, and as well as the engine.

Plasma Pinch Principles: A complete operating plasma propulsion system consists first of a basic *energy source* which may be solar, chemical or nuclear. Second, is needed a *conversion system* to electrical energy such as solar cells, a fuel cell, turbogenerator or thermionics. The third component is the *engine system* itself. This includes a high-voltage converter, a charging circuit, capacitors, electrodes, a propellant, pressure regulators, valves and a pulse control circuit.

Fig. 15-40. Ion Engine (GE)

Fig. 15-41. Battery-Powered Plasma Engine (Republic)

The propellant for this engine is a relatively inert gas. This operating fluid is *pinched* or accelerated electromagnetically until it reaches a very high velocity, thus the term *magnetohydrodynamic* (or MHD) propulsion. This high velocity gas is then directed out a nozzle and produces an impulse which is applied to the engine in a direction opposite the exhaust velocity. This pinch process is repeated at a rate which will sustain the required level of thrust. Thrust is very low compared to the weight of the engine, but the exhaust velocity is very high and the specific impulse is also high.

In addition to the high specific impulse, this engine has other advantages. The temperature of operation is low, the thrust level is variable and controlled by changing the pulse rate. Specific impulse is variable by changing the fuel flow rate to the engine. Since each pinch is a separate operation dependent only upon the charged condition of the capacitors, the engine may be started and stopped instantly regardless of the time between successive operations.

Operation of Plasma Pinch XE-1 Engine: The shape of the hollow electrodes are important and many shapes have been tested. The two types used on the XE-1 engine are the *radially dominant* and the *quarter circle* electrodes shown in Fig. 15-42. The pair of electrodes contain an evenly distributed low pressure gas and are connected through a switch to a fully charged capacitor bank, Fig. 15-43. The electromagnetic "pinch" is started by throwing a switch. The closed switch applies the voltage to the capacitors across the electrodes. The charged capacitor ionizes the gas.

As the gas becomes ionized, a current starts to flow discharging the capacitor. The current growth is extremely rapid and is accompanied by a growing, self-induced magnetic field. The magnetic field is outside the skin current or current sheath with no field within it. The interaction of this magnetic field and the current sheath is such as to produce a force or pressure on the gas directed inward toward the axis of the cylinder, Fig. 15-44.

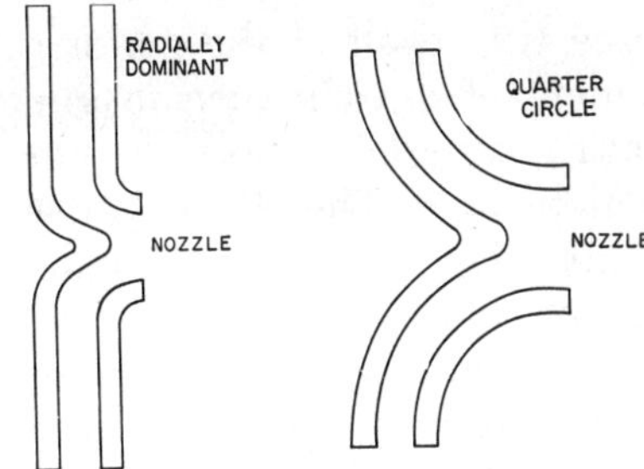

Fig. 15-42. MHD Engine Electrodes (Republic)

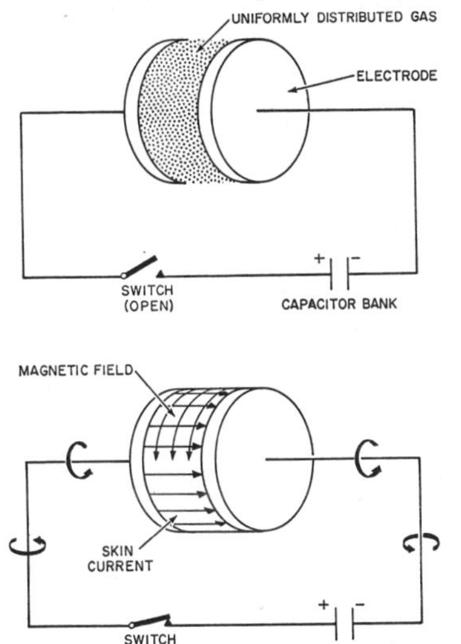

Fig. 15-43. Electromagnetic Pinch Between Flat-Disk Electrodes (Republic)

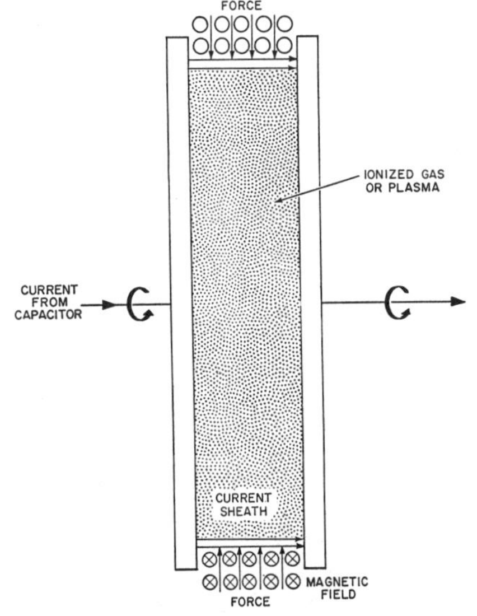

Fig. 15-44. Cross Section of Disk Electrodes During the Pinch (Republic)

This force is a result of the motor action by any element of current in a magnetic field, and is at right angles to both the current and the magnetic field. The effect is as if the current sheath were heavily stressed elastic band compressing and accelerating the plasma inward. This sheath is sometimes called a *magnetic piston.* It acts like a mechanical piston pushing the plasma before it.

In order to make use of the kinetic energy of the plasma available during the first stages of the pinch, the electrodes must be so shaped as to provide a means of exhausting the plasma to the surrounding atmosphere, Fig. 15-45. The current, magnetic field, and forces are all developed as previously described. Radial kinetic energy is transformed into axial kinetic energy geometrically, and the plasma is forced out the nozzle providing thrust.

Fig. 15-46 shows a simple schematic of the XE-1 electrical system. Battery voltage is converted to high level DC and a constant current charging technique is employed, charging the capacitors to the required voltage.

The propellant fuel system is mounted on the engine. The fuel tank contains dry nitrogen at pressures in excess of 2000 psi. A control valve is pulsed at a rate determined by a transistorized timer. This may be many times per second, resulting in a high level of thrust. A plenum chamber is used as an accumulator so that the pressure remains fairly constant during each pulse. See Fig. 15-47 for a rear view of the engine.

Solar Propulsion

On the drawing boards, scientists and engineers are designing a solar-powered space ship. This engine would use the cheapest and oldest form of energy—heat and light from the sun. (This prime source of energy is symbolized by the orange ball on the cover of this book.)

The power of the sun can be harnessed either by absorption or by reflection. Either can be applied in many schemes for space flight. Two proposed systems designed to use solar power are the *sun-heated chemical rocket engine* and the *sun-powered sail.*

The solar heated rocket engine will have large ball-like mirrors which will gather and aim the sun rays at boilers carrying the engine fuel. The resulting heat will convert the fuel to high pressure gas or steam. The steam will be directed out the exhaust with the resulting reaction propelling the vehicle. To

Fig. 15-45. Cross Section of Curved Electrodes During the Pinch (Republic)

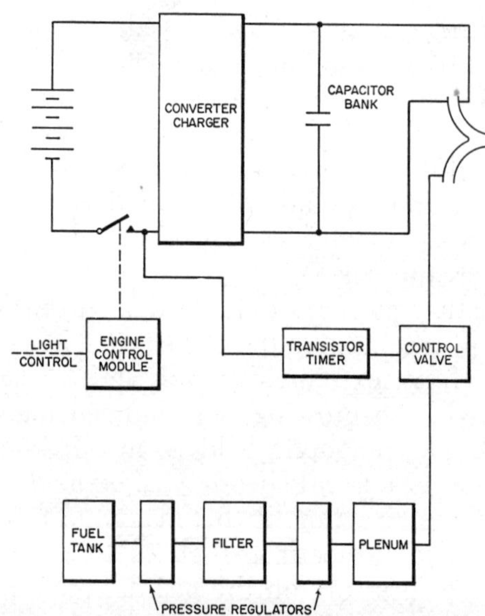

Fig. 15-46. Ion Engine Schematic (Republic)

Fig. 15-47. Adjusting Gas Pressure During Test of Plasma Engine (Republic)

accumulate enough power to propel a space ship very large mirrors will have to be used to collect the sun rays. In fact, one design has mirrors 125 feet in diameter.

The sun-powered sail, on the other hand, will not use heat from the sun, but the pressure caused by its light. Of necessity its sails will also be very large. It would probably be made of a large plastic sheet covered with a very thin coating of aluminum. The propulsive power will be obtained in much the same way a *radiometer* is made to rotate when it is brought into the light.

These two designs do pose problems, but they can be made of available materials, inexpensively, and rather quickly. They should be tested in the not too distant future.

Terms to Understand

chemical propulsion
oxidizer
propellant
fuel
guidance jet
modern astronomy
Newton steam wagon
Fritz Von Opel
German Rocket Society
solid-fuel engine
liquid-fuel engine
William Hale
Ziolkowski
Herman Oberth
Robert Goddard
V-2
electrostatic
Polaris
Titan
Gemini
Apollo
LEM
ion
black powder
Ballistite
neutral burning
regressive burning
progressive burning
grain figure
inhibitor
pyrotechnic
mono-propellant
bi-propellant
nuclear propulsion
electrical propulsion
ion engine
X-15
X-152A
hybrid engine
specific impulse
MHD
Jato
Scout
Delta
Thor Agena
Atlas Agena
Atlas Centaur
Gemini Titan
Saturn I
Saturn V
electrothermal
magnetohydrodynamic
arc jet
pinch plasma engine
solar space ship
sun-powered sail
magnetic piston
pressure feed
turbopump feed
bootstrap system
gas generator system
pressurized gas system
WFNA
UDMH
H_2O_2
Lox
NH_3
helium
hydrogen
nitrogen
cessium

Study Questions

1. Explain the difference between a rocket and an airstream reaction engine.
2. Describe the types and the principles of operation for chemical fuel rocket engines.
3. What are the criteria that must be considered in selecting the fuels for a rocket?
4. Explain why a solid fuel rocket is never packed solid with fuel.
5. What are the advantages and disadvantages of a liquid and solid fuel rocket?
6. Analyze Goddard's contribution to rocket development.
7. What is meant by a convergent divergent nozzle?
8. Analyze the popular feed systems employed in liquid rocketry.
9. What does the future hold for airstream and rocket reaction engines?
10. Why must new reaction engines be developed for space flight?
11. Discuss the principles of the ion, solar and pinch plasma engines.

Selected Readings for Part III
Internal Combustion Converters

Adams, Carsbie C., *Space Flight,* (New York: McGraw-Hill Book Co., 1958)

Adventures in Jet Power, (Schenectady, New York: Educational Relations, General Electric Co., Free.) Development and use of jet propulsion explained in illustrated booklet. Upper grades.

Armstrong, Lloyd, and Hartman, James, *Diesel Engine,* (New York: Macmillan Co., 1960)

Barnard, P. N., *Engines for Small Crafts,* (Hollywood-by-the-Sea, Florida: Transatlantic Arts, Inc., 1959)

Bricker, Frederick E., *Automobile Guide (3rd Edition),* (Indianapolis, Indiana: Theodore Audel & Co., Div. Howard W. Sams Co., Inc., 1972)

Brinley, Bertrand R., *Rocket Manual for Amateurs,* (New York: Ballentine Book Co., 1960)

Bronley, Frank M., *Experiments in the Principles of Space Travel,* (New York: Thomas Y. Crowell Co., 1955)

Chapel, Charles Edward, *Jet Aircraft,* (California: Aero Publishing Inc., 1954). A detailed account of how jet propulsion works.

Coombs, Charles, *Lift-off, The Story of Rocket Power,* (New York: Wm. Morrow & Co., 1963)

Dean, Frederick, *Turbines,* (London: Frederick Muller Limited, 1959)

John Deere Service Publications, *Fundamentals of Service – Engines,* (Moline, Ill., 1971)

Diesel, Eugene, and others, *From Engines to Autos,* (Chicago: Henry Regnery Co., 1960)

Diesel, The Modern Power, (Detroit: General Motors, 1959). Pamphlet, 31 pp.

Dietz, David, *Atomic Science, Bombs and Power,* (New York: Dodd, Mead & Co., 1954)

Gill, Paul W., *Gas Turbines and Jet Propulsion,* (Annapolis: U. S. Naval Institute, 1952)

Graham, Kennard C., *Understanding and Servicing Fractional Horsepower Motors,* (Chicago: American Technical Society)

Green, William, and Cross, Roy, *The Jet Aircraft of the World,* (New York: Hanover House, 1956). Complete and authoritative history of world progress in jet propulsion.

Haley, Andrew, *Rocketry and Space Exploration,* (Princeton: D. Van Nostrand & Co., Inc., 1958)

Hellman, Hal, *Transportation in the World of the Future,* (World of the Future Ser., Gr. 7-9: M. Evans & Co., Inc., 1968)

Hobbs, Marvin, *Fundamentals of Rockets, Missiles and Spacecraft,* (New York: John F. Rider, 1962)

Hoess, Joseph A., (Columbus Laboratories, Technical Planning Div., Battelle Memorial Institute)

Jet Facts, (Cincinnati: Aircraft Gas Turbine Division, General Electric Co.)

Kates, Edgar J., A.B.M.E., *Diesel and High-compression Gas Engines – Fundamentals,* Second Edition, (Chicago: American Technical Society, 1970)

NASA, *Chemical Rocket Propulsion, SP-19,* (Washington: U. S. Govt. Printing Office, 1962). Excellent survey.

NASA, *Electric Propulsion for Spacecraft, SP-22,* (Washington: U. S. Govt. Printing Office, 1962)

NASA, *Nuclear Rocket Propulsion, SP-20,* (Washington: U. S. Govt. Printing Office, 1962)

Northrop Institute of Technology, *Power Plants for Aerospace Vehicles,* 3rd Edition, (New York: McGraw-Hill Book Co.)

Outboard Motor Service Manual, 5th Edition, 2-Volume Set: Vol. I, Motors Under 30 HP; Vol. II, Motors 30 HP and Above, (Kansas City: Technical Publications, Div. Intertec Publishing Corp., 1970)

A Power Primer, (Detroit: General Motors, 1955). Pamphlet, 101 pp.

Power Goes to Work, (Detroit: General Motors, 1955). Pamphlet on transmissions, 136 pp.

Purday, H. F. P., *Diesel Engine Designing,* (New York: Van Nostrand, 1963)

Purvis, Jed, *All About Small Gas Engines,* (Chicago: Goodheart Willcox Co., 1960)

Roeing, Richard S., *Auto Engine Tune-Up,* (Indianapolis, Indiana: Theodore Audel & Co., Div. Howard W. Sams & Co., Inc., 1970)

Schultz, Morton, *All About Transistorized Ignition, Popular Mechanics,* Sept., 1963, p. 172-180.

Small Engines Service Manual, Ninth Edition, (Kansas City, Mo.: Technical Publications, Div. Intertec Publishing Corp., 1969)

Space Shuttle EP-77, (Washington, D. C.: U. S. Government Printing Office)

"Space Shuttle–Investment in the Future" by Representative Olin Teague, *Aerospace Magazine,* (Washington, D. C.: The Aerospace Industries of America, Inc.)

Stahman, Ralph C., (National Air Pollution Control Administration, Dept. of HEW), *Unconventional Thermal, Mechanical, and Nuclear Low-Pollution-Potential Power Sources for Urban Vehicles,* (New York: Society of Automotive Engineers, Inc., 1969)

Stin, Harry, *Rocket Power and Space Flight,* (New York: Henry Holt & Co., 1957)

Stockel, Martin W., *Auto Mechanics Fundamentals,* (South Holland, Ill., Goodheart-Willcox Co., 1969)

The Story of Power, (Detroit: General Motors, 1956). Pamphlet, 51 pp.

Toboldt, Wm. K., and Purvis, Jud, *Motor Service's Automotive Encyclopedia,* (Homewood, Ill.: Goodheart-Willcox Co., 1962)

Uskali, George, *Outboard Motors and Boating,* (Indianapolis, Indiana: Theodore W. Audel & Co., Div. Howard W. Sams & Co., Inc., 1969)

Venk, Ernest A., and Spicer, Edward D., *Automotive Maintenance and Troubleshooting,* (Chicago: American Technical Society, 1964)

Woodbury, David, *Outward Bound for Space,* (New York: Atlantic Press, 1961)

IV PART

CONVENTIONAL ELECTRICAL CONVERTERS

Potential energy is first converted to *mechanical power* by:

1) direct conversion (as a water turbine)
2) external combustion (as a steam turbine)
3) internal combustion (as a gas turbine)

This mechanical power is then converted to *electrical energy* by a generator. This energy is transmitted over power lines to motors and other devices converting it to *mechanical power, heat, light or electronic uses.*

1. 1892 DeLaval Steam-Turbine Generator (Smithsonian), **2. Substation Steps up Voltage for Transmission** (Niagara-Mohawk), **3. Pole Transformer Reduces Voltage for Use** (Niagara-Mohawk), **4. Even "Hand Tools" Use Electrical Power** (Porter-Cable)

Operating Center for the Shippingport, Pennsylvania Atomic-Electric Generating Plant (Westinghouse)

This first full-scale civilian nuclear power plant began operations in 1957. The control console shows the energy conversion stages in this modern form of the conventional generation of electricity.

The operator in the background controls the reactor which releases energy by nuclear fission and uses it for steam generation. The center operator controls the turbine-generator section which converts steam energy to electricity. The third operator controls the high-tension distribution system.

The Nature of Electricity

Today, we are living in a great electrical and nuclear age—the fifth stage of man's technological development, and an age in which the power potential has been barely realized. New uses are constantly being developed to provide us with conveniences that will relieve the toils of manual labor.

Electricity has become such a common part of our everyday life that it is scarcely thought of as anything less than a necessity. It is difficult to realize that a generation ago, we did without the marvels of electrical heat, incandescent and fluorescent light, heating and cooking elements, refrigerators, air conditioners, radio, and television. It seems that no matter what we do, electricity is there, available as our servant. It certainly must be studied as an area of power.

Developing Concepts of Electricity

Electricity has been in existence since the beginning of time. Primitive man was terrified by lightning which he interpreted as being a punishment for past sins or a warning against committing future ones. Thales of Miletus in about 600 B.C. amused his friends by demonstrating that amber beads which he rubbed vigorously against his garments were able to cause dust and other light particles to jump through space as if overcome by some inexplicable attraction.

William Gilbert

These effects were observed by man 26 centuries ago, but not until William Gilbert's work early in the 17th Century was man's knowledge of electricity increased. Gilbert's experiments concerned the generation of electrical charges by friction. He tested many substances to see if, upon being rubbed, they would react with light bodies. He discovered the effect could be produced with many substances including amber, diamond, sapphire, glass, sulfur, sealing wax, and hard resins. These he labeled electrics, and the phenomenon itself electricity, after the Greek word for amber, *elektron*.

Otto Von Guericke

The first machine using friction to generate electricity was devised by a German lawyer, philosopher, and scientist, Otto Von Guericke, during the latter part of the 17th Century. His machine was a sulphur sphere which was made to rotate while he held his hand on it, Fig. 16-1. He created a greater electrical charge than did Gilbert and discovered that under certain conditions charged objects repelled rather than attracted each other.

Fig. 16-1. Von Guericke Static Generator Sulphur Ball

Stephen Gray

In the early part of the 18th Century, Stephen Gray learned to conduct electrical charges from one place to another. He differentiated between those that conducted and those that did not conduct electricity.

Charles Dufay

A French scientist, Charles Dufay, at about the same time experimented with various materials and learned that there were two kinds of electricity. He called one *vitreous* and the other *resinous* electricity. He found that each attracted the other although they repelled like charges. He found that both could be conducted and that most materials contained both kinds of these electrical charges if they were uncharged.

Benjamin Franklin

Benjamin Franklin's lightning experiment proved that the electrical charge of a storm cloud was identical to that which was produced from an ordinary electric machine. His work marked about the last that was done with what may be termed pure static phenomena. Development since has involved a combination of both (static and current) manifestations of electricity.

Luigi Galvani

Current electricity dates from a chance discovery by Galvani in 1786 when he observed that the leg of a recently killed frog contracted under the influence of the discharge of an electric machine. He observed a similar contraction when the muscle was placed between two dissimilar metals. He attributed this to what was then called *animal electricity*.

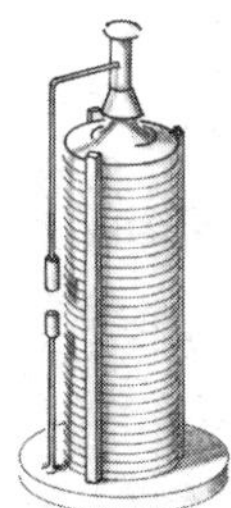

Fig. 16-2. Voltaic Pile

Alessandro Volta

Volta, another Italian, showed that the phenomenon had no connection with animal tissue. In the early 1800's, he constructed a pile of alternate disks of zinc and copper that were separated by paper moistened with a solution of salt. This is shown in Fig. 16-2. When he connected a conductor to the ends of this pile he observed the presence of an electric charge.

Since the time of Volta, many different kinds of cells have been made. This can easily be realized if we note that the only requirements for a cell are two dissimilar metals with an electrolytic solution that will react with one of them. For example, iron and zinc or carbon and zinc with such solutions as diluted sulfuric acid, hydrochloric acid, or sodium hydroxide will produce electricity. In fact, zinc and copper wire thrust into a lemon will provide some electrical current. In popular *primary cells* today, we use carbon and zinc with a paste solution of ammonium chloride. The most common primary cell is the *dry cell* as used in flashlights. Several individual cells can be interconnected to form a *battery*.

Thomas Edison

Thomas Edison inventor of the incandescent light, Fig. 16-3, phonograph, and the motion picture also invented the *secondary* or *storage battery*, Fig. 16-4. The storage battery differs from the primary cell in that it can be recharged over and over again after it becomes discharged. The primary cell depends

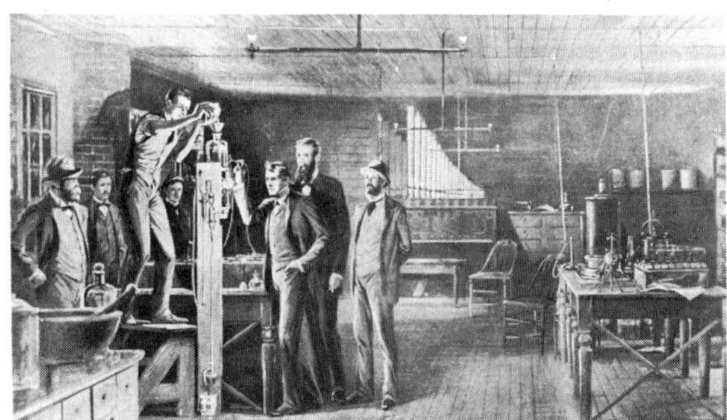

Fig. 16-3. First Successful Incandescent Lamp
Edison is shown testing the lamp after 40 hours operation at Menlo Park, N.J., October 21, 1879.

on one element being acted upon by the electrolyte, and after much use, the terminal is consumed, rendering the cell useless. Also, the resistance of the secondary cell is so small that very large currents may be obtained from such storage cells.

In the Edison nickel-iron-alkaline cell, the *positive plate* was made of nickel-plated perforated iron sheets filled with hydrated nickel oxide. The *negative plate* was made of nickel plated perforated sheets filled with iron oxide. The electrolyte used was caustic potash (potassium hydroxide, KOH). This Edison cell was quite an improvement over the primary cell. In fact, it is lighter than the common automotive lead-acid cell of equal capacity. However, its efficiency is somewhat less than 75 percent of the lead cell. But it can withstand repeated rapid discharging and recharging—a punishment the lead-acid cell is not capable of tolerating. Also, the lead cell may be discharged so completely, that over-sulfation may occur, damaging the cell permanently. The Edison alkaline cell is not thus damaged, and is best stored discharged.

Maximum output of the Edison cell is 1.25 volts, an amount that would require 5 cells to approximately attain the voltage output of 3 lead cells. The charge of a lead-acid cell is determined by its specific gravity as read on a hydrometer, Fig. 16-6. A fully charged cell will read better than 1260 (1.260) and about 1100 when discharged. The electrolyte in alkaline cells does not vary in density with its charge and thus cannot be tested with a hydrometer. It also will not freeze when discharged.

Today, Edison's nickel-*iron*-alkaline storage battery has been replaced for most uses by the Nicad or nickel-*cadmium*-alkaline cell. Construction is similar except the negative plates contain cadmium oxide, CaO, and the positive plates are nickelic hydroxide, Ni(OH), treated with graphite to increase conductivity. Both sets of Nicad plates have a similar improved structure and use polystyrene separators. Nickel-cadmium batteries have a long life (about 15 years), a voltage

Fig. 16-4. Semi-Portable Edison Primary Battery

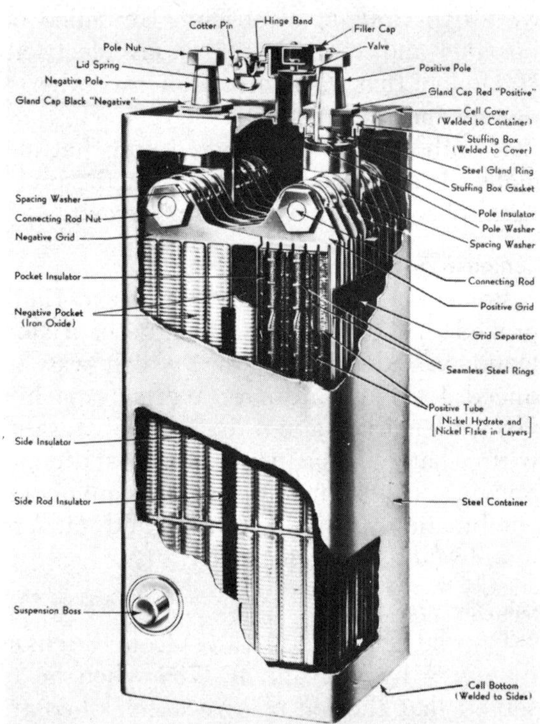

Fig. 16-5. Edison Nickel-Iron-Alkaline Cell

Fig. 16-6. Testing a Lead-Acid Battery

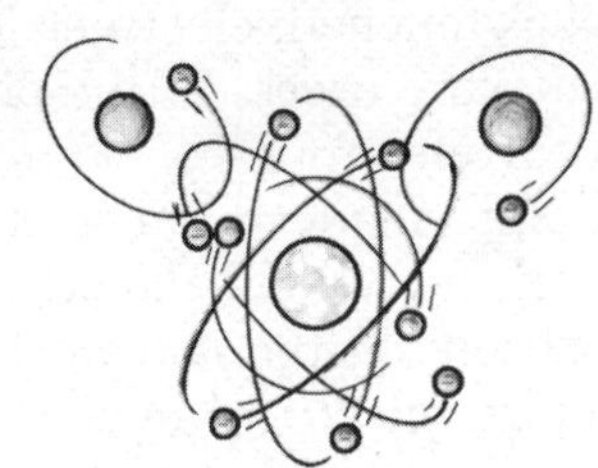

Fig. 16-7. Water Molecules, H_2O

DEUTERIUM
ONE ELECTRON
ONE PROTON AND ONE NEUTRON

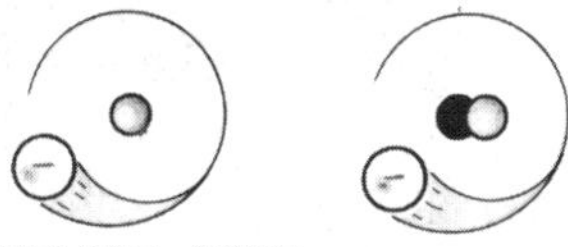

HYDROGEN ATOM
ONE ELECTRON – ONE PROTON

Fig. 16-8. Hydrogen Atoms

Note that atom on the right is the rare *heavy hydrogen* atom with a supplemental neutron in the nucleus.

OXYGEN ATOM
EIGHT PROTONS
HT NEUTRONS—EIGHT ELECTRONS

Fig. 16-9. Oxygen Atom

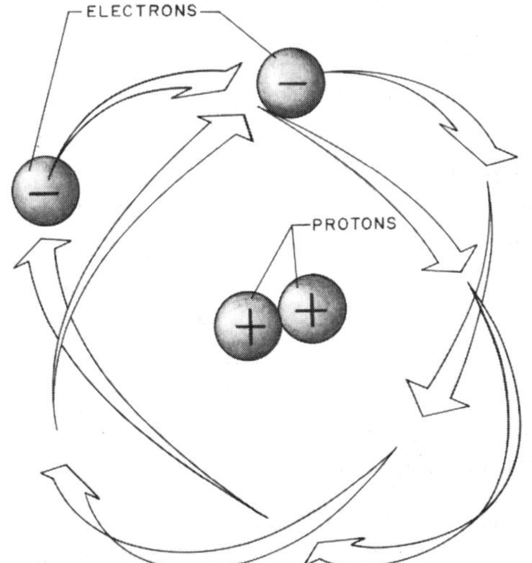

Fig. 16-10. The Atom

of 1.3 and operate over a larger temperature range than other batteries.

Friction to Electrical Energy

A discussion of how electricity is created by friction will provide a more complete understanding of this important source of energy. To do this, we must reflect a moment on the composition of matter.

Composition of Matter

While the atomic structure of matter has been briefly discussed earlier, more details are needed to understand electrical theory. Any substance is made up of minute particles called *molecules* which are combinations of smaller particles called *atoms.* In other words, if we were to keep dividing a substance into parts, we would eventually reach a point (the molecule) where no further division would be possible without changing the identity or property of the substance. The atoms that compose that molecule are the smallest divisions or parts of an element. Elements do not usually exist in a pure state, so we generalize by saying that matter is made up of molecules or combinations of atoms.

We are aware that water is made up of two parts hydrogen to one part oxygen. If we were to keep subdividing water, we would arrive at a point where we would have one last H_2O molecule left, Fig. 16-7. If we were to divide that molecule, we would no longer have water, but the elements that compose water. These elements are two hydrogen atoms, Fig. 16-8, and one oxygen atom, Fig. 16-9. These atoms would have their own properties and if they are further divided, tremendous energy would be given off, proportional to the energy that keeps them together. This tremendous emission of energy can be controlled as in an atomic reactor or spontaneous as in an atomic explosion.

For many years it was believed that nothing smaller than the atom existed. Recently, physicists have explored the structure of the atom to find that it is composed of particles 50,000 times smaller. These tiny bits of matter are nothing more than charges of electricity. They have discovered that the core of the atom, the *nucleus*, contains most of the weight (or mass) of the atom and is made up of *protons* (positive particles of electricity) and *neutrons* (neutral particles of electricity). Orbiting the nucleus are tiny negative particles of electricity called *electrons*. See Fig. 16-10. These electrons are considered to be alike in kind, size, and shape, and possess the same amount of negative electricity. Less is known about the protons, although they are believed to be alike and possess a like amount of positive electricity. These electrons and protons cannot be destroyed, but seem to exist as a fundamental substance, constituting the *structural particles* of the universe, where matter and energy are united. Under ordinary conditions, the number of electrons orbiting around the nucleus of an atom is equal to the number of protons located in its nucleus. Such atoms are electrically *in balance* or *neutral*.

Frictional Electron Unbalance

If this condition becomes unbalanced by the atom gaining or losing electrons, the atom is *ionized*. If the atom gains more electrons, it is said to be negatively charged (a *negative ion*) and if it made to lose electrons, it is said to be positively charged (a *positive ion*) because of its greater number of protons.

This explains how an electric charge is generated by friction. We have witnessed this phenomenon many times when we comb our hair with a hard rubber comb. Electrostatic charges can be heard crackling and even seen if the room is dark. Sometimes, entering or leaving a car generates an unpleasant study of electrostatics as we slide along the seat and then touch some metal. There are times as we shuffle our feet across the floor, especially if it is heavily carpeted, that we are shocked as we touch a door knob or another person not moving about.

In all of these situations, and they are only representative of many, an electrical unbalance was created by friction. Once another object with a larger accumulation of electrons on its surface is touched, electrons jump from the object with the excess to the object with a deficiency of electrons.

Electrons were made to *move* in order to balance the electrical unbalance caused by friction. Electricity is the *movement* of electrons. Therefore, *electrical energy* was generated by friction when the electrons were made to move from one object to another.

Electrostatic Charges

Charles Dufay, as already mentioned, discovered that there were two types of electrostatic charges. He also indicated that these charges behaved in certain ways with respect to one another. The unlike charges attracted one another, and the like charges repelled. The reason for these forces of attraction and repulsion is not known, but it can be shown that they are extremely powerful.

Someone calculated that if it were possible to place two masses of electrons about the size of small marbles one foot apart, they would repel one another with the enormous force of 350 trillion tons. Two similar proton masses would repel with equal force, but two unlike masses of electrons and protons would attract one another, with equally tremendous force. This is the basis of the tremendous potential of electrical energy. Electrons in motion constitute electrical current, and it is these tremendous forces that cause electric current to flow giving it the ability to transmit great amounts of energy.

The forces of attraction of unlike charges and the repulsion of like charges was explored by the famous French scientist, Charles Coulomb. Because it would be difficult and impossible to estimate or describe the difference of potential between a body with one electron or two electrons more than the other, a more practical unit of measurement containing larger quantities of electrons, known as the coulomb, must be employed. A *coulomb* represents 6.28×10^{18} electrons or: 6,280,000,000,000,000,000 electrons.

Conducting Electron Flow

Protons are located within the nucleus of the atom, and they are considered to be permanently fixed. This makes it difficult to change or move them about. Altering their position results in *tearing* the nucleus and therefore the atom, completely apart.

Electrons, however, are constantly orbiting the nucleus at tremendous speeds. In some materials, these electrons can be driven about from place to place quite easily in large numbers. Such a material would be considered a good electrical conductor because only a small *electromotive force* is necessary to cause them to give up electrons. Electrical energy is transferred by the movement of free electrons from one atom to the next through a conductor, Fig. 16-11. As electrons enter one end of the conductor, displaced electrons become available at the other end. This transfer of electrons is commonly referred to as *flowing* or *current electricity.* Actually a single electron moves only a very short distance as electrons displace one another throughout the length of the conductor, Fig. 16-12. This displacement takes place at the speed of light, 186,000 *miles per second.*

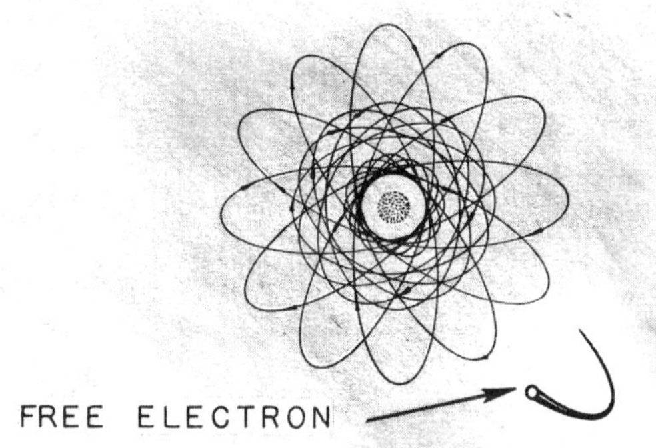

Fig. 16-11. Atom from an Electrical Conductor

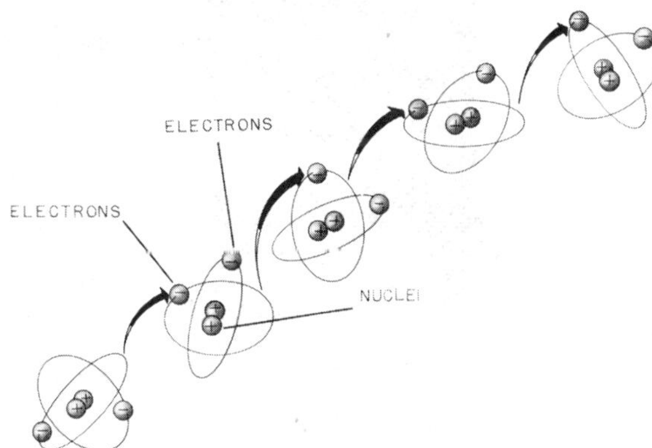

Fig. 16-12. Flow of Electrons in a Conductor

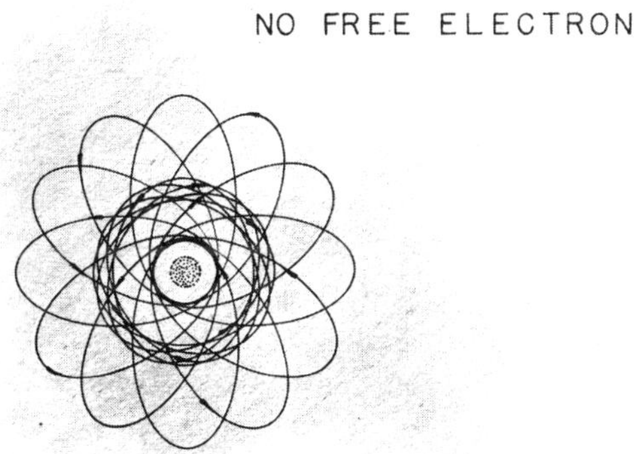

Fig. 16-13. Atom from an Electrical Nonconductor

On the other hand, if a material does not permit the electrons to move freely, it is considered a poor conductor or an *insulator.* See Fig. 16-13. Opposition to electron movement is called *resistance.* Poor conductors will have *high resistance* to electron movement whereas good conductors will have *little resistance.*

The larger the diameter of the conductor, the greater is its capacity to pass electrons. Large diameter conductors are used for high current loads and small diameter conductors are used for light current loads. If a light conductor is used to carry a high current, its resistance to current flow causes it to overheat. This overheating can prove dangerous since the heat created will further increase the resistance of the wire. Resistance is proportionate to the *temperature* of the conductor.

Electricity, is caused by a movement of electrons. Electrons may be caused to move by *friction, chemical action, magnetism, heat, light,* or *pressure.* We will be studying energy converters using each of these methods. In each case electrons receive a form of energy, work is done upon them, results in an electrical pressure (*electromotive force, emf,* or *voltage*). When this pressure is permitted to cause *electrons to flow* around a circuit (*current* or *amperage*) and thus create electrical balance, *energy is released* which can be used to do *work.*

Chemical to Electrical Energy

In a cell, an unbalance or a difference of potential is created by *chemical* action. The basic cell may be made by using two different kinds of metals as *electrodes*. An *electrolyte* is a diluted acid or salt solution in a paste or liquid form surrounding the electrodes, and which reacts with one of the metals more than it does with the other. If the electrolyte is in the form of a paste, it is a *dry cell*, Fig. 16-14. The *wet cell*, Fig. 16-15, employs a liquid electrolyte in an identical manner. In any case, each of these primary cells produce up to 1.5 volts.

Primary Cell

The primary cell in Fig. 16-15 can be easily explained using the electron theory. Here, *carbon* and *zinc* are used as electrodes and dilute sal ammoniac solution (ammonium chloride, NH_4Cl) as the electrolyte. When the ammonium chloride is dissolved in water, the millions of molecules are caused to break apart into positive ammonia ions (NH_4) and negative chloride ions (Cl). An ion, as you recall, is a charged particle. The ammonia (NH_4) ion is attracted to the carbon electrode giving it a positive charge. At the same time, the zinc electrode attracts the negative (Cl) ions, giving it a negative charge. Here, it is seen that the current in a liquid consists of charges moving in both directions.

When the chloride ions move to the zinc plate, they combine and form a new substance, zinc chloride (ZnCl); and in doing so, each atom of zinc leaves two electrons on the zinc electrode. This is the important chemical reaction that sets up the needed difference of potential. The zinc plate accumulates an abundance of electrons and exhibits a negative potential. If a conductor were connected from the zinc to the carbon electrode, the electrons, due to their strong repulsion for each other, would be forced to move in large numbers to the wire. Here they flow as current to the carbon electrode attracted by the excess protons collected there.

The electron flow seeks to equalize the unbalanced condition, but the chemical action continues as long as the circuit remains intact, electrically and chemically. Thus *cell action*, the surplus of electrons caused at the *cathode* or negative terminal and the deficiency of electrons caused at the *anode* or positive terminal, sets up a voltage that makes current flow. All cells work on this same general principle.

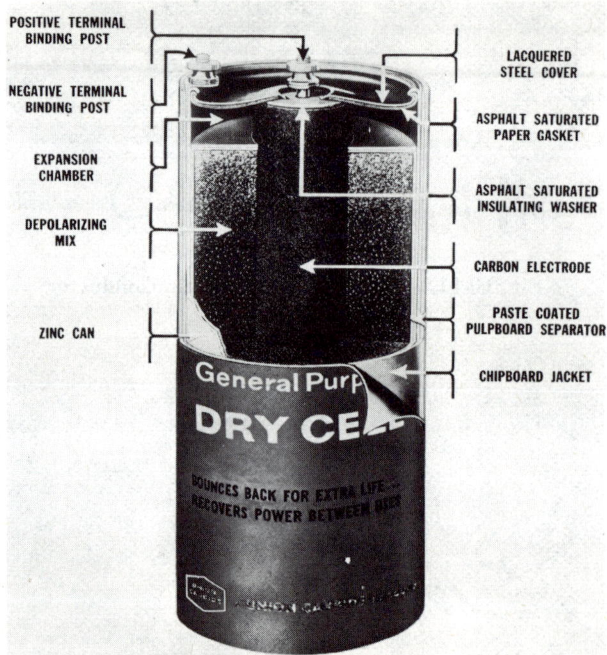

Fig. 16-14. Dry Cell Construction
(Union Carbide)

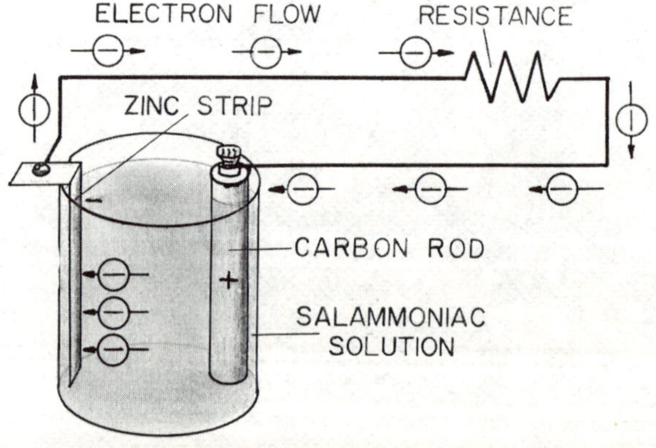

Fig. 16-15. Wet Cell Electron Movement

Storage Cell

Unlike the primary cell, the storage cell must be charged first by passing a *direct current* through it. This brings about a chemical condition that can later be reversed to yield a flow of electrons. There are three popular secondary cells in use today—*the lead-acid cell, the nickel-iron cell,* and *the nickel-cadmium cell.*

The storage battery does not store electricity, but merely charges the electrical energy received during charging to chemical energy. The chemical energy is changed back

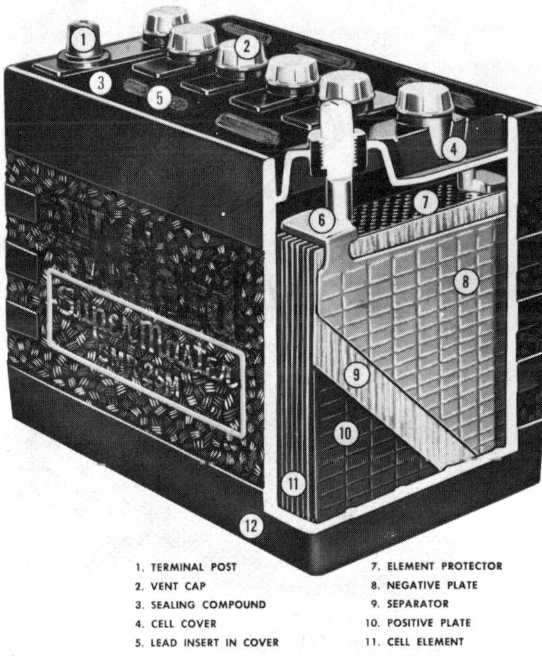

Fig. 16-16. Lead-Acid Cell (Willard)

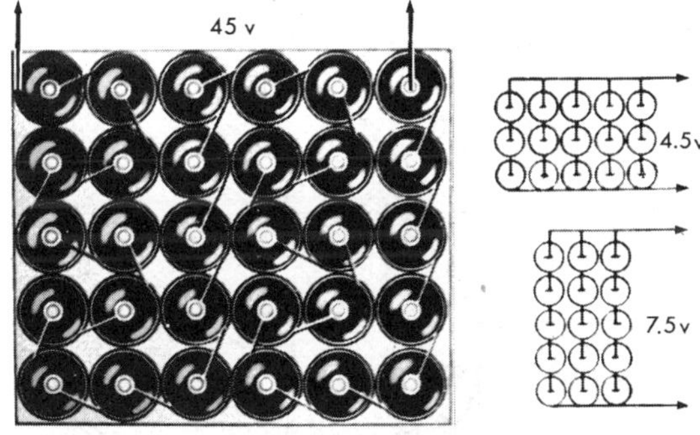

Fig. 16-17. Dry Cell Connections in a Battery

to electrical energy when the cell is discharging. The *lead-acid* cell, Fig. 16-16, is by far the most popular storage cell today. It consists of lead plates in a solution of sulphuric acid (H_2SO_4) and water (H_2O). The positive plate, when charged, consists of lead peroxide (PbO_2) while the negative plate is pure lead (Pb). When discharged, the lead peroxide has largely disappeared from the positive plate with lead sulphate ($PbSO_4$) taking its place. Also, lead sulphate has formed on the negative plate; thus, the plates are quite similar in the discharged condition. They are, however, quite unlike when charged. These unlike plates fulfill the original requirements of a cell. In this instance, the chemical action is reversible, permitting charging and discharging.

Because the sulphur ions of the acid merely pass into and away from the plates during charge and discharge, there is no loss of them in the cell. Therefore, there is no need to add acid to the cell because the acid is not consumed. However, water must be added at times as its oxygen combines with the lead to form lead peroxide (PbO_2) at the positive plate while emitting hydrogen during the charging period. The output of this type storage cell is usually 2 volts.

Battery condition is checked with a hydrometer which measures the density of the solution. When the cell is fully charged, it contains a maximum of sulfuric acid (a relatively dense liquid) and reads about 1.260 specific gravity. On many battery hydrometers this is read as 1260. During discharge, the percentage of acid present decreases and that of water (a less dense substance with a specific gravity of 1.000) increases, thus progressively reducing the density of the solution to a low of about 1.100.

Cell Output

The physical *size of a cell has no effect on pressure* or voltage. Large cells contain more chemical matter and therefore can operate for a *longer period of time* under similar service. As the supply of electrons is greater in a *large* cell, it takes longer for all to be transferred from one plate to the other. If the potential (voltage) of the cell is not sufficient, a battery may be made of many cells, Fig. 16-17. If these cells are connected in *series* as shown at the left, the voltage of the battery would be the sum of the voltages from each cell. The current output, however, will remain constant. If the cells were connected in *parallel,* the current output will be the sum of each cell with the voltage output remaining constant. Current and voltage output of a battery can be controlled by connecting cells in parallel or in series as necessary. Diagrams at the right of Fig. 16-17 show two series-parallel combinations for 15 cells. The hookup at the top has three cells in series and five such combinations in parallel. This produces three times the voltage and five times the current of the single cell. Below this is a hookup producing five times the voltage and three times the current of the single cell. Modern dry batteries often use flat cells to eliminate wasted space between cells.

Units of Electrical Energy

We must now better define the meanings of *voltage, current* and *resistance* and show their interrelationships. These are basic to any study of electricity and electromotive force.

Voltage

Voltage is the electromotive force or pressure which causes electrons to flow in a circuit. It is caused by the natural repulsion and attraction which electrons and protons exert on each other. Other means of generating an electromotive force besides those already mentioned—friction and chemical action—will be described later.

One volt is the electrical pressure necessary to drive one ampere of current through one ohm of resistance. Voltages vary from one to two volts as produced by a cell to the very high voltages in power transmission lines.

Voltmeters such as shown in Fig. 16-18, are used to measure voltage. They operate on the magnetic principle as found in the galvonometer. Special meters are needed to measure current flow which is constantly alternating its direction of flow (AC). Meters for direct current (DC), such as the output of a cell, use a *permanent* magnet. AC meters require an *electro*magnet or a means of changing alternations to DC.

A voltmeter must be connected *across* the line, or *across* the terminals where the voltage drop is desired to be known. The range of a voltmeter can be increased by using multiplier resistors in series with the meter, Fig. 16-19. These resistors drop the voltage so it can be read on the basic scale of the meter,

Fig. 16-18. DC Voltmeter (Weston)

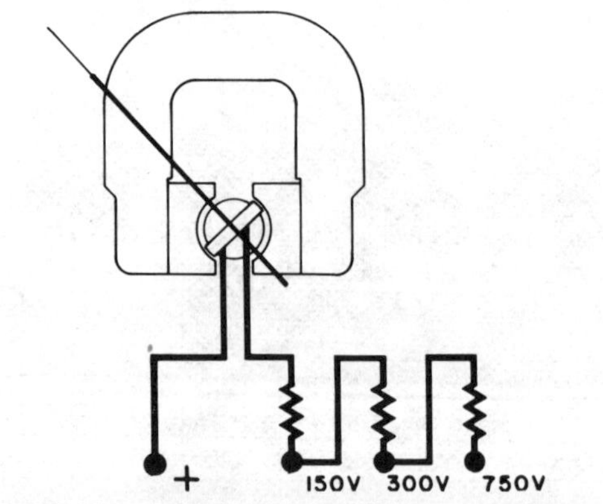

Fig. 16-19. Multipliers in Multi-range Voltmeter

and the reading must be adjusted or read from another scale. Caution must be exercised in obtaining a voltage scale that will adequately handle the voltage to be measured. *The meter can be ruined if a low range is used for a higher voltage.*

Some voltmeters have a self contained battery. If a resistance is placed in series with the battery and the meter, a reduced voltage is noted on the meter. Such a *volt-ohmmeter* has a separate scale for determining resistances, Fig. 16-20.

Fig. 16-20. Volt-Ohmmeter (Weston)

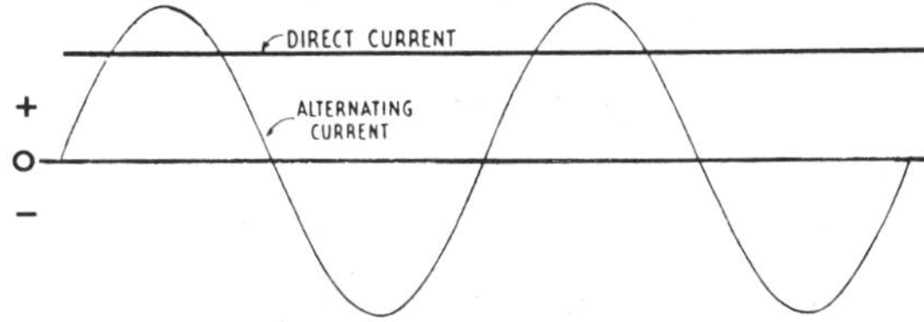

Fig. 16-21. DC and AC of Same Effective•Value
Note that AC peak voltage is higher than steady DC to offset periods of minimum current flow. Effective value of AC is .707 of its maximum value and is known as rms value (root mean square). Unless otherwise specified AC measurements are rms.

The voltage of a circuit is able to do work. The device which *generates* electrical pressure does work by moving electrons, separating them from their protons against the forces of attraction and repulsion already mentioned. This separation then increases their difference in potential. They then want to flow back, to balance the created difference of potential. This electromotive force is capable of doing work as the electrons move back to their plates. The movement of electrons causes a voltage drop as electrons move through a resistance. Work done is proportional to the voltage consumed in each part of a circuit.

Current

Current is the *flow* of electrons. These tiny negative charges move through a conductor by the billions even when the current is relatively small. When the movement of electrons is in one direction only, it is called *direct current* or *DC*. When the movement of electrons is constantly alternating or moving in one direction and then reversing to build up in the other direction, we refer to the flow as *alternating current* or *AC*. These are graphed in Fig. 16-21. The difference between the two types of current is so great that we study them separately and use them for different purposes. *Pulsating direct current* or *PDC,* flows in one direction, but because of its rising and falling surges of current, exhibits alternating current characteristics. PDC was shown in Figs. 10-11 and 10-12.

Direct current has use today in battery charging, electroplating, distilling, and operating direct current motors. Some early automobiles and trucks used alkaline-type storage batteries for vehicular power, Fig. 16-22. However, problems of weight, limited operational time, and problems of recharging permitted the gasoline engine to gain favor for general vehicular use. Today stock trucks and fork-lift trucks operating indoors are often battery powered to eliminate noise and fumes.

Small electric-lighting systems for rural homes, automobiles, aircraft, small marine craft, and certain electronic circuits found in radio, television, telephone, and telegraph also operate best on direct current.

A New Electric Car

An electric car for city or shopping use was recently shown in prototype form by Ford of Britain, Fig. 16-22A. The experimental car is only 6′ 8″ long (less than half the length of a conventional car) and has been designed so that three can be parked in a normal parking space. It has a turning circle of 18 feet, no clutch, no gears, and therefore offers automatic driving. The car has been designed to carry two adults and two children.

Unveiling the new car, the Assistant Managing Director of Ford of Britain said, "We expect electric cars to be commercially feasible within the next ten years, although we believe that their uses will be primarily as city-center delivery vans and suburban shopping cars. The internal combustion engine will probably continue to be the most practical form of power for long distance driving, but we are sure that electric cars will have a part to play in meeting some future transportation needs." This statement becomes more significant as we become more conscious of the air pollution dilemma.

Many technical problems are still to be overcome. This particular little car has a range of 40 miles at a steady speed of 25 miles per

Fig. 16-22A. An Experimental Electric Car (Ford)

Exterior View

Cutaway View

hour and is powered by conventional batteries. As more effort is put into battery technology and new batteries are developed, this range will be increased.

Alternating Current

Alternating current, on the other hand, is used in over 90 per cent of the electrical circuits in the United States. Hundreds of appliances and machines found in industry, and in the home use alternating current. Power, heat, light, radio, television, and hundreds of other devices, operate best on alternating current. Most electrical power is *mechanically generated* as AC.

The flow of electrons produces a number of useful effects. These effects are used for the transmission of power, the production of heat, light, magnetism, and chemical action.

Heat energy is produced when current flows through a resistance. If the resistance is slight, no appreciable heat is caused. But if the resistance is high, such as those found in tungsten and nichrome conductors, much heat will be emitted. In some situations, the heat is so great that the conductor is caused to glow and give off light, Fig. 16-23.

Chemical energy is produced as current flows through a liquid. This chemical action charges batteries, electroplates metals, separates metals from their ores, and breaks down certain molecular combinations into their individual elements.

Today, mental and physical diseases are being treated as a result of the chemical effects produced in the body by the flow of electrons.

Energy is silently, instantly, and efficiently carried from the power generating station to the consumer when current flows through transmission lines. This is the most economical method of transmitting power that has ever been devised, especially over long distances and in large amounts.

Current is measured by a definite quantity of electrons passing any given point in a conductor. We already mentioned that the unit of quantity of electrons is known as the coulomb, a very large number of electrons. A coulomb is also defined as that amount of electricity which will deposit .000329 grams of copper. *If one coulomb of electrons passes a fixed point in a conductor per second, a current of one ampere is said to flow.*

Current is measured with an *ammeter*, Fig. 16-24. Since it would be quite difficult to count directly the enormous number of electrons flowing, these meters operate on one of the several effects caused by electron flow: magnetism, heat and chemical action. Most meters work on the magnetic principle.

Fig. 16-22. Lansden Battery-Powered Automobile

Fig. 16-23. First Successful Lamp

Fig. 16-24. AC Ammeter (Weston)

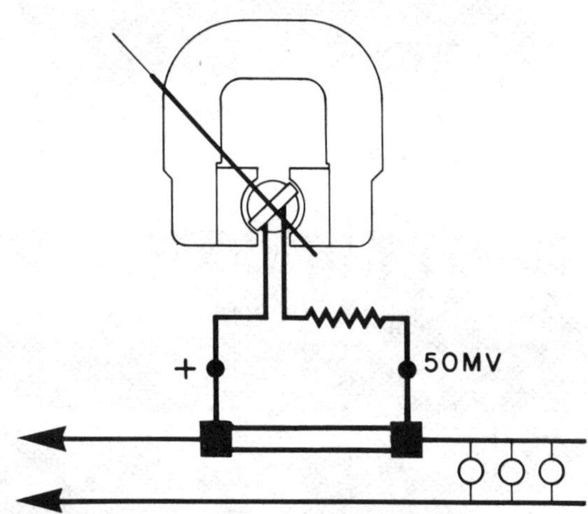

Fig. 16-25. Ammeter Circuit

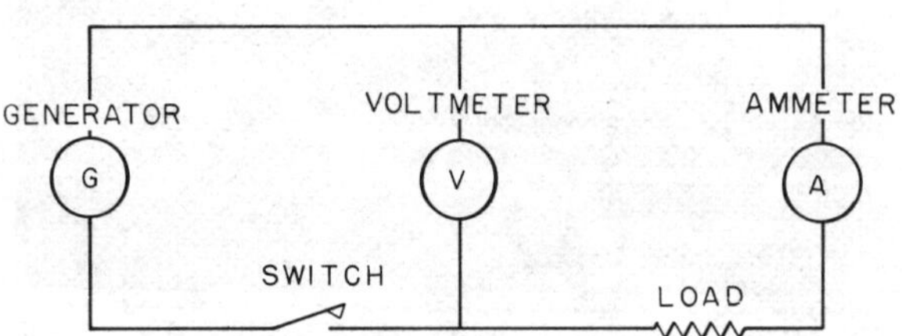

Fig. 16-26. Voltmeter and Ammeter Connected in Circuit

Ammeters are connected in the circuit so that the circuit current flows through it, Fig. 16-25. An ammeter is a low resistance device which would draw excessive current if placed across the line. An ammeter is inserted in series with the resistances—*never in parallel.* Particular attention must be given the current range of the meter, making sure it is adequate to cover the amperage flowing in the circuit. It is best to insert a meter with too large a range than one with a limited range. Change the meter or meter range until the needle deflects enough to give a proper reading.

Fig. 16-26 contrasts the manner of connecting an ammeter and a voltmeter.

Resistance

Resistance is the opposition to the flow of electrons. This opposition may be due to various kinds of electrical *friction*—that caused by the conductor, the current characteristics, and the temperature, to mention a few factors.

Resistance in a circuit causes several useful and necessary effects—such as the ability to produce heat, control current flow, and consume voltage. As was already mentioned, a resistance of one ohm requires a pressure of one volt to force one ampere of current through it.

Resistance is that element of a circuit which consumes power. Resistance can be measured by an *ohmmeter*. Each component must be measured separately as it is taken out of the circuit. In practice, a simple method used for finding the resistance of a component or a whole circuit is by calculation. Here we measure or determine the voltage and the current consumed, and divide the voltage by the current to determine the resistance or ohms. We call this relationship of voltage to current and resistance, *Ohm's Law.*

Ohm's Law

Ohm's Law is one of the most useful laws concerning electricity because it is used for almost all electric circuits. The law was discovered in the early 19th century by Georg Simon Ohm, a German scientist.

Ohm's Law states that *in any electrical circuit the current flowing in amperes is equal to the electromotive force in volts divided by the resistance in ohms.* It is usually written:

$$\text{Amperage (I)} = \frac{\text{Electromotive Force (E)}}{\text{Resistance (R)}}$$

$$I = \frac{E}{R} \quad \text{so } R = \frac{E}{I} \quad \text{and } E = IR$$

Circuits

Electricity can be made to flow if there is an uninterrupted path from the source through the consuming device and back to the source. If no such path exists, the circuit is said to be open.

Two types of circuits are commonly used, *series* and *parallel.* See Fig. 16-27. In the series circuit, the current leaving the source passes through all the consuming devices before returning to the source. In the parallel circuit, there are several paths for the current leaving the source to flow through before returning.

In the *series circuit,* because there is only one path for the electricity, the total resistance is simply the sum of each resistance. The sum of the voltage drops across each resistance equals the input voltage. Because there is only one path, any opening in the circuit will interrupt the current flow. Current is constant throughout the completed circuit.

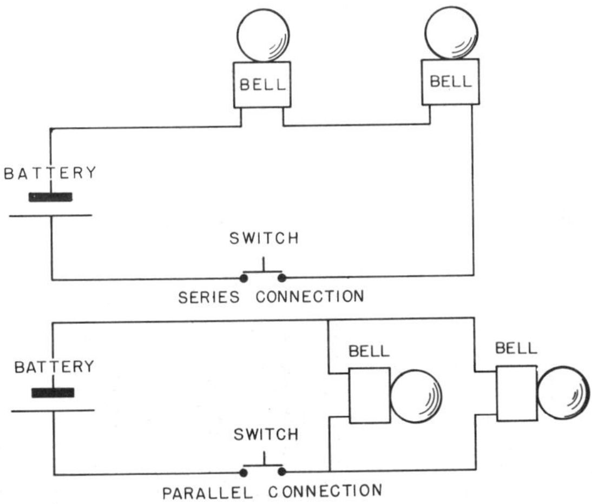

Fig. 16-27. Series and Parallel Circuits

The formula for finding total resistance in series is:

$$R_T = R_1 + R_2 + R_3 + \ldots$$

Thus, if resistance of 1, 2, 4, and 8 ohms were in *series,* the total effect would be a resistance of 15 ohms.

In the *parallel circuit,* because of the individual paths for the current, total resistance of the circuit is *less than the smallest* resistance. The pressure or voltage throughout the circuit is constant, but the current varies depending upon the resistance for each individual path. The formula for finding total resistance is:

$$\frac{1}{R_T} = \frac{1}{R_1} + \frac{1}{R_2} + \frac{1}{R_3} + \ldots$$

Thus if resistances of 1, 2, 4, and 8 ohms were in *parallel,* the total effect would be

$$\frac{1}{R_T} = \frac{1}{1} + \frac{1}{2} + \frac{1}{4} + \frac{1}{8}$$

$$= \frac{8}{8} + \frac{4}{8} + \frac{2}{8} + \frac{1}{8}$$

$$= \frac{15}{8}. \text{ So } R_T = \frac{8}{15} \text{ ohms or just}$$

over half of smallest resistance.

Electrical Power

Power is the rate at which work is done. The unit of *electrical power* is the *watt. One watt is the power delivered by one ampere under the pressure of one volt.* The wattage of an appliance indicates how fast electrical energy is being transformed into some other form such as heat, light, or motive power.

Power can be found by multiplying the amperage by the voltage flowing in the circuit or appliance:

$$\text{WATTS} = I \times E \text{ or } P = I \times E$$

As $E = IR$, IR can be substituted for E, so P also $= I \times IR = I^2R$. Power loss or heat loss in transmission systems is sometimes called I^2R loss. Because the *amperage is squared* in this formula it can be seen that reducing current flow to $\frac{1}{10}$th reduces power loss to $\frac{1}{100}$th, a considerable increase in efficiency.

A *wattmeter* measures wattage by combining an ammeter coil and a voltmeter coil in the same instrument. This automatically finds their product, and records it on a scale calibrated in watts. Fig. 16-28 shows one type of wattmeter.

Electric motors are rated in horsepower instead of watts. The number or fraction of horsepower stamped on the name plate indicates its mechanical output; the electrical input equals the output plus frictional losses. One horsepower equals 746 watts. Using this figure we can determine the watts output of any motor at full load.

A *kilowatt* (KW) is 1000 watts, and is the common unit for commercial power. Thus, a 6000 kw generator produces 6,000,000 watts. At 120 volts this would produce a current flow of 50,000 amperes. With AC units, power is sometimes given in *kilovolt-amperes* (KVA) which is only the *apparent AC power.* Because voltage and amperage flow do not always alternate precisely together in AC, the *true power* must be read with a wattmeter. The ratio between true power and apparent power is known as the *power factor.* For most efficient operation, the power factor should be close to 100 percent, but it is often closer to 90 percent.

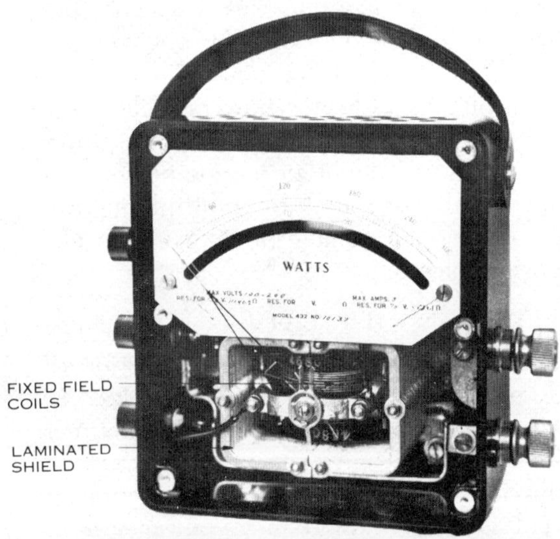

Fig. 16-28. Dynamometer-Type Wattmeter

A *kilowatt hour* (KWH) is the unit of quantity in which electrical power is bought and sold. Fig. 16-29 shows the mechanism of a watt-hour meter.

$$\begin{aligned} P &= I \times E \\ \text{(Watts)} &= \text{(Amperes)} \times \text{(Voltage)} \end{aligned}$$

$$\text{Kilowatt Hours} = \frac{\text{Watts} \times \text{Hours}}{1000}$$

or

$$\text{Kilowatt Hours} = \frac{\text{Amperes} \times \text{Volts} \times \text{Hours}}{1000}$$

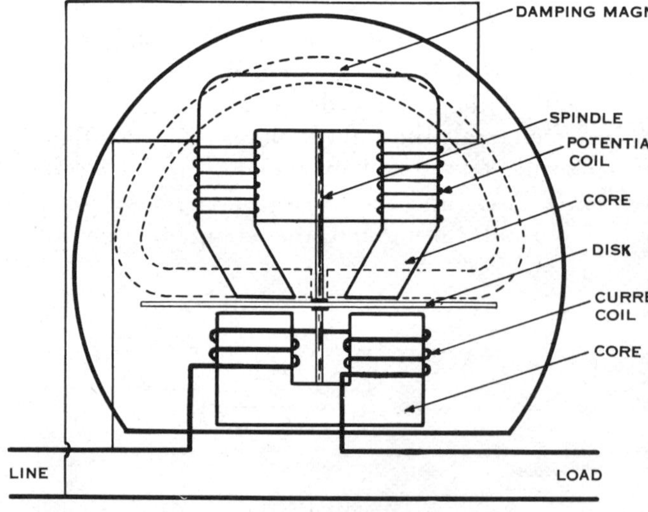

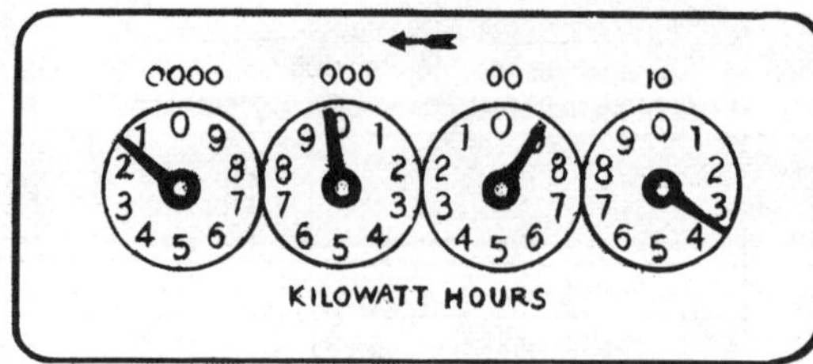

Fig. 16-29. Watt-Hour Meter and Dial
Dials alternate directions. Reading is 19933KWH.

By using these equations, we can determine the cost of operating any appliance, by first determining the kwh consumed and by multiplying this by the cost of electricity per kwh.

Terms to Understand

electrostatic charge	electron
electrical energy	neutron
Luigi Galvani	ionize
Alessandro Volta	electrical current
Charles Coulomb	6.28×10^{18}
Thomas Edison	1.86×10^{5}
galvanometer	conductor
one volt	insulator
one coulomb	hydrometer
one ampere	series circuit
one ohm	parallel circuit
primary cell	voltage
secondary cell	amperage
dry cell	resistance
wet cell	Ohm's law
battery	AC, DC, PDC
Edison cell	voltmeter
Nicad cell	ohm-voltmeter
lead-acid cell	ammeter
cell outputs	watt
molecule	Hp to watts
atom	kilowatt
nucleus	KWH
proton	KVA

Study Questions

1. Today we are living in a great electrical age. Explain.
2. What is electricity? Explain how it may be generated.
3. What is the difference between the two types of electricity?
4. Identify Gilbert, Von Guericke, Dufay, and Franklin.
5. Explain Galvani's contribution to the development of electrical knowledge.
6. Explain how Volta disproved that electricity had anything to do with animal tissue.
7. Explain how a primary cell operates.
8. Explain how a secondary cell operates.
9. Explain the operation of the Edison cell.
10. What are the advantages and disadvantages of the primary and secondary cell?
11. Analyze the composition of matter.
12. Describe the composition of an atom.
13. Explain how an electrical charge may be caused by friction.
14. What are some conductors, non-conductors? Explain what makes them behave as they do.
15. Explain how voltage or amperage may be increased by employing a combination of cells.
16. What is voltage, current, and resistance? How are they interrelated?
17. What is a coulomb?
18. The size of the cell does not effect its voltage output. Explain.
19. Analyze the voltage and current outputs when cells are connected in series and in parallel.
20. What are the two basic circuits? Explain the characteristics of each.
21. What is electrical power? How is it used to measure the cost of electricity consumed by a user?

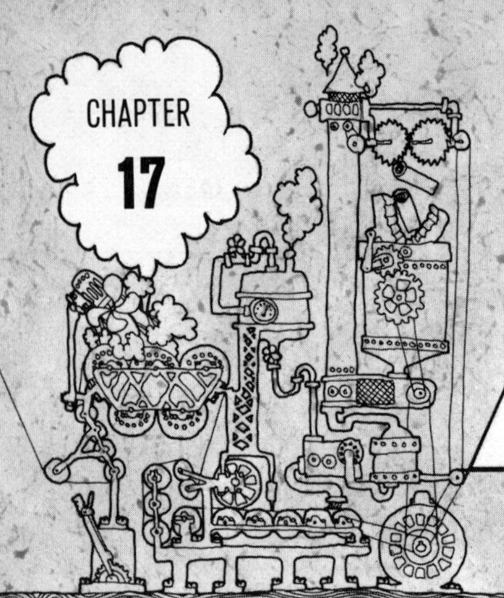

The Nature of Magnetism

A major portion of the world's power supply is converted into electrical energy for easy transmission and control. Most of it is again reconverted into mechanical energy before being used. This transformation involves many kinds of electrical apparatus, such as generators, transformers, motors, meters, safety-controls, and switching devices. Most of these devices use some principle of magnetism, and include some type of magnet.

Developing Concepts of Magnetism

The exact nature of magnetism is unknown. But, as with the study of electricity or moving electrons, man has learned to use magnetism and to formulate theories upon its nature.

Magnetism and Energy

Magnetism is related to energy because it involves forces; and whenever forces act, there exists the capacity for doing work. Magnetism is closely related to electricity since it is the vehicle through which mechanical energy is converted into electrical energy by the generator. Magnetism is also used to convert electrical energy back to mechanical energy in the motor.

Magnetism will pass through any known substance—there is no insulator for it. Materials vary greatly in permeability, however. *Permeability* is the ability of a material to carry magnetism. Iron has a permeability 7,000 times that of air, and a special magnetic alloy, Permalloy, is about 10 times more permeable than iron.

Magnetism will exert its forces of attraction and repulsion in any direction. The explanation of this mysterious force and its exact nature remains a challenge for the future.

Early Beliefs

No one can say when, where, or by whom the phenomenon of magnetism was discovered. It is known that magnetism was discovered a long time ago as evidenced by some of the legends that have grown up about it. According to one legend, a shepard named Magnus, who lived on the island of Crete, was said to have experienced great difficulty one day in lifting his feet or his shepard's staff from the ground. Immediately, his curiosity prompted him to dig into the earth and he dug up a rock that was attracting the nails of his shoes and the tip of his metal staff. According to this legend, the word *magnetism* is derived from his name. A much more likely theory of the origin of the word is that large deposits of the ore were found in Magnesia, a city of Asia Minor.

Another legend is told in the Arabian Nights. It concerns a costal mountain that contained so much magnetic ore that it was not unusual for all the nails of a passing ship to be drawn out of the hull, sending it to the bottom. Although this story cannot be true because the forces of magnetism are comparatively small, it does indicate the existence of early knowledge of the phenomenon.

One of the earliest verified references is made by Socrates where he refers to iron rings suspended one below the other, the top ring being held by a magnet. There is also some evidence to support the theory that the Chinese as early as 100 or 200 A.D. had learned the direction-finding property of magnetic ore. They suspended it or caused it to float on water with a wooden support so it would point in the direction of north. This was the earliest form of the compass and these stones became known as lodestones, or *leading* stones. The first use of compasses by the Chinese to guide them on the sea, seems to have occurred around 1100 A.D. They had learned by that time that long thin pieces of metal could be made magnetic if they were stroked with natural magnets. By the latter part of the 12th century, European ships used the compass to navigate the seas.

Many weird and superstitious beliefs cluttered the study of magnetism in early times. It was believed that garlic would remove the magnetic properties of a compass, and elaborate precautions were taken to ensure this never happening. Power to cure all diseases, toothaches, and even the mending of broken marriages, was attributed to magnetism.

Gilbert's Study of Magnetism

The modern study of magnetism may be said to have been published in 1600 A.D. by Sir William Gilbert, court physician to Queen Elizabeth and James I of England. As a physician, he first was interested in disproving or verifying the curative effects of magnetism. He was also interested in trying to find what kept the planets in their orbits because he supported the Copernican theory based on magnetism and he desired to substantiate his belief. His greatest contribution to the knowledge of magnetism was his conclusion that the earth was a huge magnet.

Properties of Magnetism

Magnets are objects which possess the peculiar properties of polarity, repulsion, and attraction. There are three kinds of magnets, *natural* (magnetic or lodestone), *permanent*, and *electromagnets.*

The permanent magnet holds its magnetism indefinitely. Only three pure substances can be permanently magnetized; these are, iron, nickel, and cobalt. These elements, however, are found in many compounds and impart their ability to become magnetized to the compounds. If any of these compounds, such as hard steel, is stroked with a magnet, it will hold permanently some of the magnetism imparted to it. Why this is true, no one really knows.

Magnetic Structure

For many years, it was believed that in these magnetic substances, the molecules themselves were tiny magnets, very much disarranged, pointing in all directions. In the process of being magnetized, the molecules were caused to move about the line-up with their North poles facing in one direction, and their South poles in the other, Fig. 17-1. These tiny forces combined to appear externally as a magnet. In a natural unmagnetized state their jumbled condition neutralized each other completely. Hardened metal could retain its magnetic properties whereas the soft metals permit the molecules to return to their jumbled positions thus losing their magnetism. Also by this theory, it was believed some molecules were unaffected by magnetism and could not be lined up.

These beliefs have recently been disproved. Experimental evidence now shows that magnetism is caused by unbalanced electron orbital movement within the atoms of magnetic substances, Fig. 17-2. The exact details have

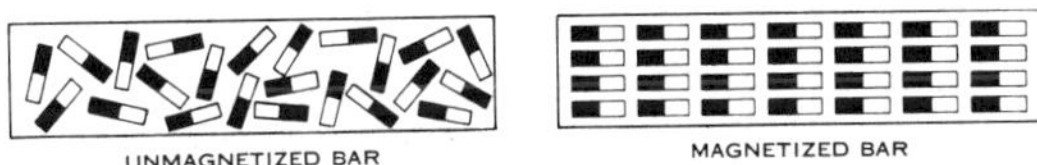

Fig. 17-1. Molecular Theory of Magnetism

Fig. 17-2. Electron Theory of Magnetism

not been formulated because of the difficult nature of the investigation. Further study is being continued.

Whatever the theory, working magnets are made in a variety of shapes and sizes, such as bar, horseshoe, and disc. Magnets range in size from microscopic to several pounds.

Law of Magnetism

All magnets tend to behave in a predictable fashion. For instance, they all will exhibit a polarity of north and south, which will attract the unlike poles of another magnet, or they will repel like poles of another magnet. These poles also exhibit the greatest concentration of magnetic force.

From what has been said, we now may state the *basic law of magnetism: Opposite poles of magnets attract and like poles repel.* See Fig. 17-3.

Often, iron fillings are sprinkled on a piece of glass or paper, placed over a strong magnet to exhibit the forces of the magnet. Their lining up end to end along numerous lines from pole to pole have been referred to as *lines of force.* However, such lines probably do not exist and are caused by each iron particle lining up one behind the other with its north attracted to another's south pole. It repels the particle along side of it because it too is lined up in the same manner. The force that causes this behavior is referred to as *magnetic flux,* and the space that encompasses this flux is called the *magnetic field.*

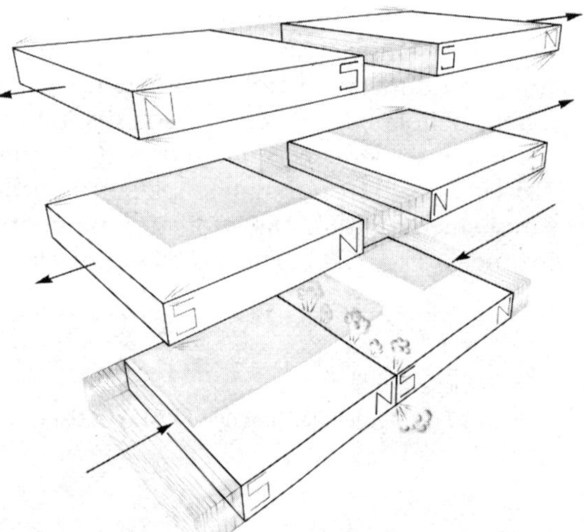

Fig. 17-3. Magnetic Attraction and Repulsion

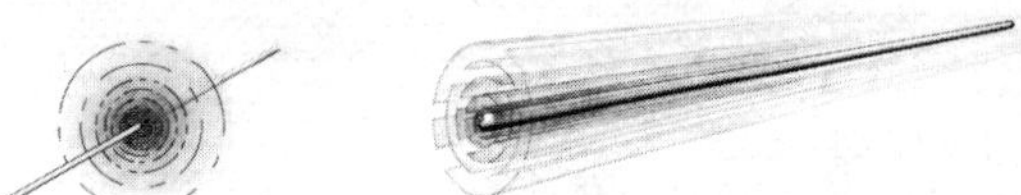

Fig. 17-4. Field Around Electrical Conductor

Flux of Conductors and Coils

A conductor that carries current has a magnetic field surrounding it as shown in Fig. 17-4. No one can explain why the magnetic field is there, but it is used in electromagnets. This magnetic field is built up when current flows and disappears when it stops. This was discovered by Hans Christian Oerstead, in 1819. This Danish physicist was the first to understand and experiment with the relationship between electricity and magnetism.

The magnetic flux that surrounds the conductor can be of considerable strength. If the wire is insulated and coiled and the current is again passed through it, the field becomes concentrated. The magnetic flux becomes much greater in, throughout, and around the coil, Fig. 17-5. This coil of wire will possess the same physical properties as a permanent bar magnet, with north and south poles and with the same forces of attraction and repulsion.

Magnetic flux can be increased several hundred times if a soft iron core is placed within the coil. This makes an electromagnet, Fig. 17-6. The increase in flux is achieved because

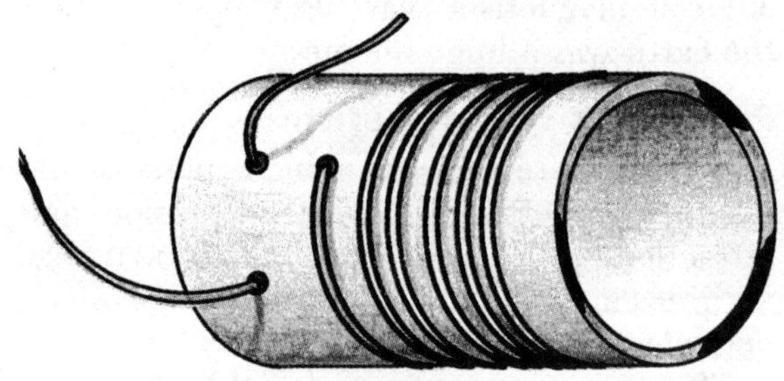

Fig. 17-5. Coil

the iron is more permeable than air and so concentrates the flux. The core of an electromagnet (or of a transformer) is usually laminated of layers of a special mild steel rather than being solid. Silicon alloys are common. Laminating and alloying are means of reducing the magnetic resistance called *reluctance,* as well as reducing hysteresis. *Hysteresis* is the lag in flux returning to zero after the magnetizing force is removed. It is especially important to minimize reluctance and hysteresis losses in AC electromagnetic transformer circuits. When the actuating current alternates, the magnetic field must rapidly build up, collapse, and reverse polarity many times a second.

If a steel plunger is positioned so it can enter a coil, it will be *drawn* into the coil by the magnetism formed when current flows through the coil, Fig. 17-7. This is called a *solenoid* or *"sucking coil."* It is widely used in electrical circuits which control mechanical functions. Examples are remote controlled switches (or *relays*) or devices to remotely operate valves, clutches or gears.

It is interesting to note that the electrical-to-mechanical action of a solenoid can be reversed to a mechanical-to-electrical action. If the plunger is replaced by a magnet and is *pushed* in and out of the coil, current is generated within the coil. This current can be measured by connecting a meter across the two leads of the coil. This comparison shows the essential similarity of a motor and a generator.

The strength of an electromagnet is determined by the number of *turns* of wire in the

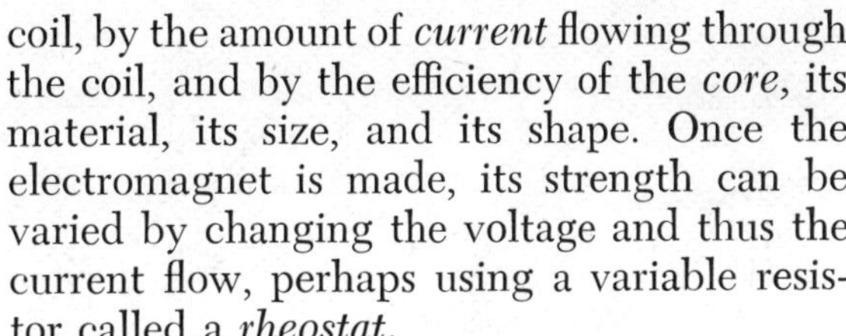

coil, by the amount of *current* flowing through the coil, and by the efficiency of the *core,* its material, its size, and its shape. Once the electromagnet is made, its strength can be varied by changing the voltage and thus the current flow, perhaps using a variable resistor called a *rheostat.*

Magnetic Circuits

Flux travels in a path (from N to S) called a *magnetic circuit* which can be compared to an electrical circuit. *Magnetomotive force* (mmf) is the pressure which sets up the flow of flux, and is represented by the letter F. It is comparable to electromotive force (emf) or voltage represented by the letter E. *Magnetic flux,* represented by the Greek letter Φ (capital phi), is comparable to current or amperage (I) in electrical circuits. Magnetic resistance is called *reluctance* and is represented by a script $\mathcal{R}$. It is comparable to electrical resistance R or ohms. Ohm's law applies to both circuits:

$$\underset{\text{(amperage)}}{I} = \frac{\text{E (emf or voltage)}}{\text{R (resistance)}}$$

$$\underset{\text{(flux)}}{\Phi} = \frac{\text{F (mmf or ampere turns)}}{\mathcal{R}\text{ (reluctance)}}$$

The practical unit of magnetomotive force is the ampere-turn. This unit is found by multiplying the number of turns in a coil by the amperage flowing through it. Thus a 100-turn coil carrying 5 amperes develops the same mmf as a 500-turn coil carrying 1 ampere, but the latter uses only one-fifth as much current. When an increase in ampere-

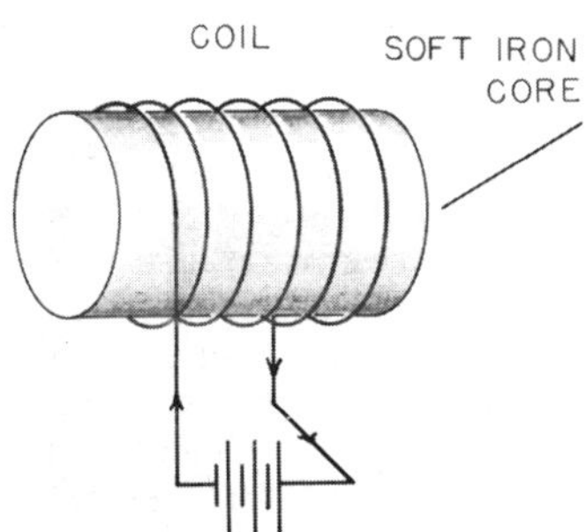

Fig. 17-6. Electromagnet.

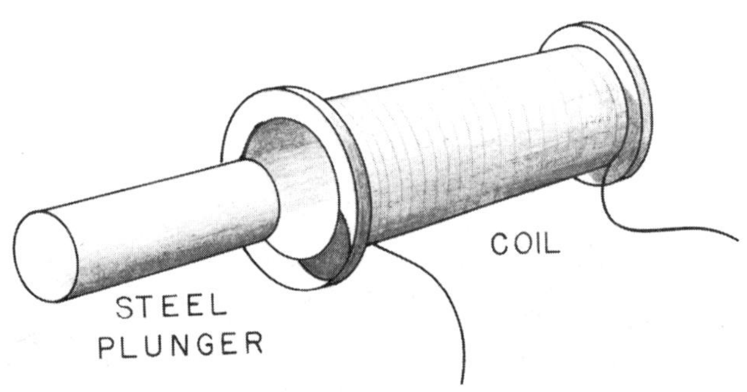

Fig. 17-7. Solenoid

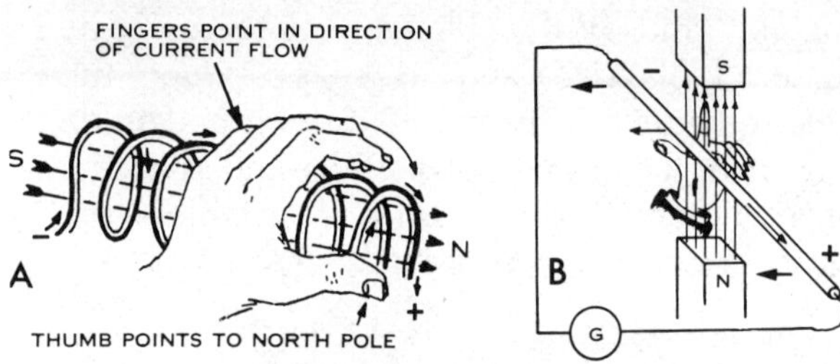

Fig. 17-8. Left-Hand Rules for (A) Determining Polarity of a Coil, and (B) Determining Direction of Induced Current

At (B) the left thumb, forefinger and middle finger are held at right angles to each other. Point the thumb in the direction the conductor is moving, and the forefinger in the direction of the magnetic flux circuit (N to S across the gap). The middle finger current flow. For more practice apply the left hand rule to Figs. 10-8 and 10-11.

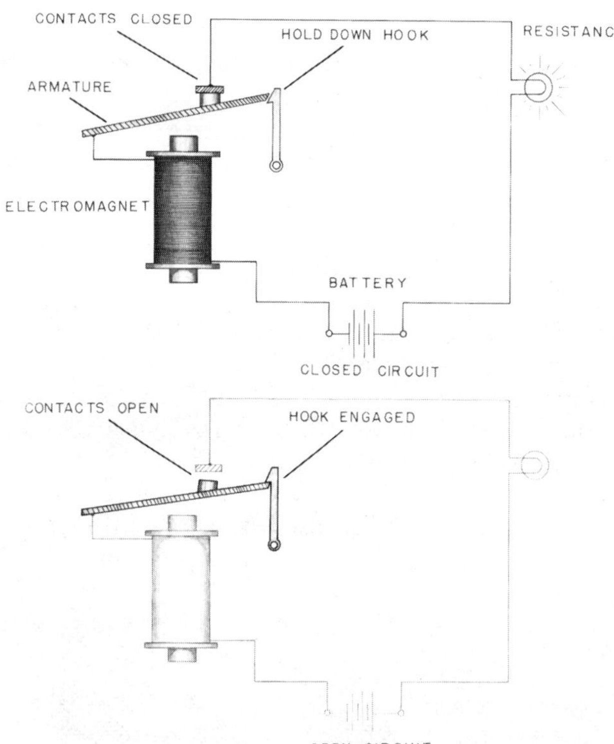

Fig. 17-9. Magnetic Circuit Breaker

The electromagnet and its armature with contact points are in series with the external load. If excess current flows, the increased magnetism of the coil will open the contact points. After the overload has been eliminated, the hold down can be reset thus restoring operation.

turns does not give the expected increase in mmf, the *saturation point* has been reached.

To determine the polarity of magnets, a compass can be used. The pole of the electromagnet which attracts the north-seeking pole of the compass is by definition the south pole, and visa versa. It is important that all electromagnets used for relays, circuit breakers, meters, generators, and motors exhibit a north and south pole. This can be assured if the winding of the coils of wire is done in one direction only.

Two *left-hand rules* are also useful in determining polarity and current flow. They are sometimes called *Fleming's rules* (who stated them as right-hand rules when current was thought to flow from positive to negative). One is for determining the polarity of a coil or electromagnet. The other is for determining the direction of induced current as in a generator. Both are illustrated and described in Fig. 17-8.

Uses of Electromagnets

As we have learned about magnetic force, its behavior with magnetic materials and other magnets, it is quite easy to understand

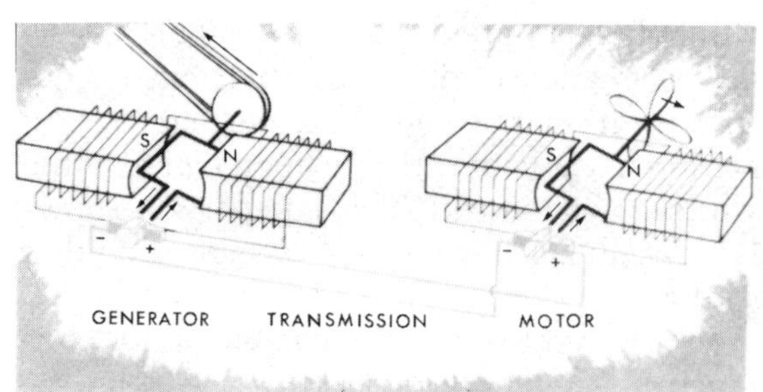

Fig. 17-10. Energy Conversion: Mechanical to Electrical to Mechanical (GM)

Use the left hand rule shown in Fig. 17-8 (A) to check the polarity of each electromagnetic field. Then use the rule from Fig. 17-8 (B) to check the direction of current induced in the generator.

To determine the direction of rotation of a motor, use the same rule (B) but with the *right* hand. Point the forefinger in the direction of the flux circuit (N to S) and the second finger in the direction of current flow (to +). The thumb will point in the direction the conductor will move. Try this for each side of the armature in the motor above. This is known as the *right-hand motor rule.*

how this device is used to convert electrical energy to mechanical energy. The process is a three-step conversion: electrical energy to magnetism to mechanical energy.

In the case of circuit breakers, relays, meters, and other such devices, Fig. 17-9, it is simple magnetic attraction alone that transforms electrical energy into mechanical. In motors, Fig. 17-10, the alternating repulsion and attraction of the magnet's poles that operate to generate mechanical energy will require a more detailed explanation. Fig. 17-11 shows a vehicle run by one of the first electric motors.

Principles of DC Motors

In the direct current motors, an *armature* (a permanent magnet or an electromagnet) is caused to rotate within a magnetic *field* by alternately changing the polarity of either armature or field so as to cause an attraction and then repulsion of the rotating member.

The field of the motor is usually non-changing. In small motors, it may be a permanent horseshoe-shaped magnet. In larger motors, it is usually an electromagnet so as to produce the greater force. Usually, within this field is an electromagnet, the armature, fixed so that it can rotate. A switching device, the *commutator* (or changer), is used to change the polarity of the armature. This commutator is mounted on the same shaft as the armature so that both will rotate together. For each coil of the armature, there are two segments; two coils would have four segments, three coils would have six segments, and so on. These segments are completely insulated from each other, and connected to the ends of the armature coils. These parts are shown in a simplified manner in the motor in Fig. 17-10 and in Fig. 17-12.

The commutator rotates between brushes that conduct electricity into one segment through an armature coil and travels out the other segment back to the source to make the necessary circuit. The rotative motion is caused by each armature pole being first attracted and then repelled by the field poles, their polarity being alternated by the commutator segments. As they make contact with the opposite current-carrying brushes it causes a reversal of current through the armature field at the proper moment. Thus, the cycle is repeated and the armature made to continually rotate.

Fig. 17-11. One of the First Applications of an Electric Motor (Edison Lab. National Museum)
A "Long-waisted Mary Ann" generator (See Figs. 18-1, 18-2) was wired as a motor by Edison and powered the first electric rail car.

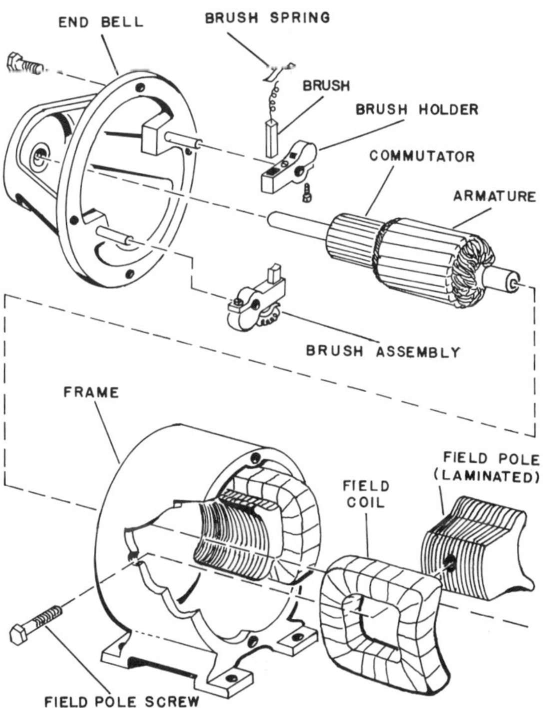

Fig. 17-12. Disassembled DC Motor

The rotative armature of a DC motor is cutting the flux of the field, thus self generating a voltage of its own. This is called *counter emf* or *back emf*, as internal current flow from this opposes the driving current. Back emf increases with field strength and with armature rpm. An added load slows the armature and decreases the back emf. This allows the armature to draw more current and produce more torque, maintaining speed.

The current flowing in the motor through the brushes is always in the same direction. To reverse the direction of rotation, all that must be done is to reverse the current going through the brushes, and this reverses the polarity of the armature. Another way is to reverse the polarity of the field by switching the field connections if an electromagnet is used. The field can be physically reversed if a permanent magnet is used.

Types of DC Motors

There are three major types of direct current electric motors. The difference is in the field windings. The same armature may be used for all types.

The series-wound motor, Fig. 17-13, has a field coil which is made of only a few turns of large wire, and which is connected in series with the armature. The result is that the field carries most of the current received. Since any motor draws current proportional to the load—light current for a light load and heavy current for a heavy load—the field flux of a series motor varies in strength with change in load which causes its speed to change. Such a motor is used where variable speed is allowable and where the motor must be able to start under heavy load, as in electric railcars, cranes, automobile starters, and diesel locomotives. Small series motors are sometimes used as universal motors, operating on alternating as well as direct current.

The shunt-wound motor, Fig. 17-14, has a field made of many turns of light gage wire providing high resistance. The field coil is connected across the main line. In this way, the field receives full voltage that is fairly constant, providing a fairly constant flux which serves to keep the speed from varying much with changes in load. This motor is used where constant speed is desirable, and where load does not vary much. Speed can be controlled by a rheostat in series with the field. More resistance will lower the field flux, causing the armature to develop less back emf, allowing the armature current to increase, producing more torque and speed.

The compound-type motor, Fig. 17-15, is a combination of series and shunt types. It has two sets of field coils, one in series with the armature and the other in parallel with the armature. Series winding may either oppose (*differential compound*) or aid (*cumulative compound*) the shunt windings. The cumu-

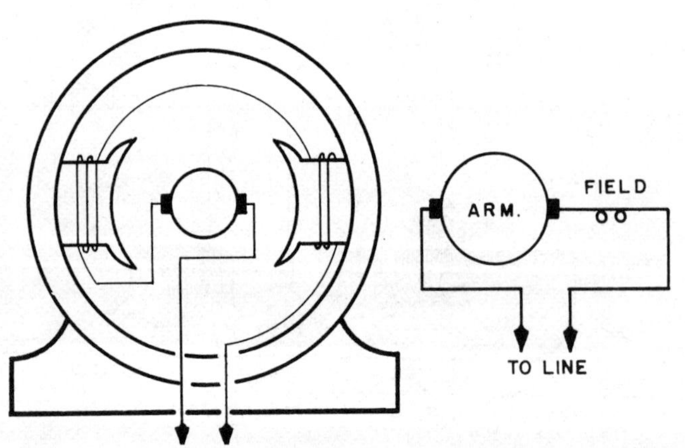

Fig. 17-13. DC Series Motor

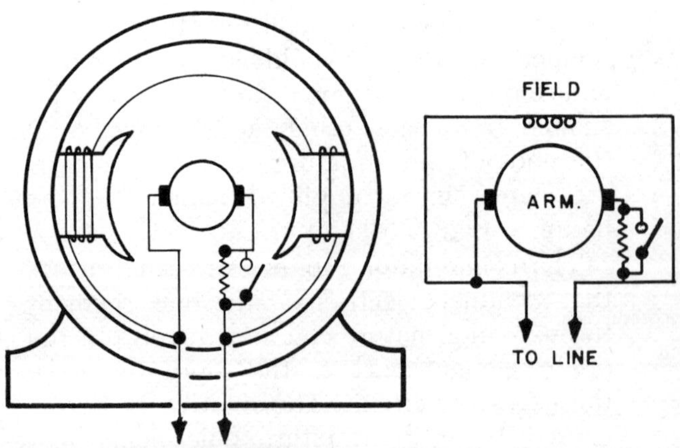

Fig. 17-14. DC Shunt Motor

lative type handles extreme load ranges. The differential type has even more constant speeds than shunt motors but is rarely used because of low starting torque. The compound motor operates in the same way as each of the types that were previously described. The cumulative compound type has a fairly high starting torque, much more than shunt motors, but less than series motors. These combined features give it a wide variety of uses making it the most popular DC motor.

Starting a DC Motor

Care must be exercised in starting a DC motor under load so as not to send the full line voltage to the motor all at once. This would draw a large current through the line and probably blow the fuses, as well as overload the windings of the motor and damage the motor enough to cause repair. To avoid this damage, a starting box is used, which contains resistances in series with the armature circuit to cut down in the initial surge of current. The resistance is gradually cut out as the motor speed increases. See Fig. 17-16.

Care of DC Motors

The maintenance and care of motors and generators is important to guarantee their proper operation. The spring tension of the brushes must be enough to allow good contact with the commutator, and they must not be allowed to wear too short. Arcing at the brushes is avoided by keeping the commutator clean and the brushes properly shaped. New brushes should be ordered to fit the motor and shaped to the commutator. This can easily be done by drawing fine abrasive paper under the brush after it has been formed around the commutator. If the commutator becomes pitted, scored, or burned, it can be turned down on a lathe and then sanded lightly. Bearings must be kept lubricated, and the lubricant kept free of the electrical contacts. The machine should be kept free of dirt to prevent undue wear on the moving parts.

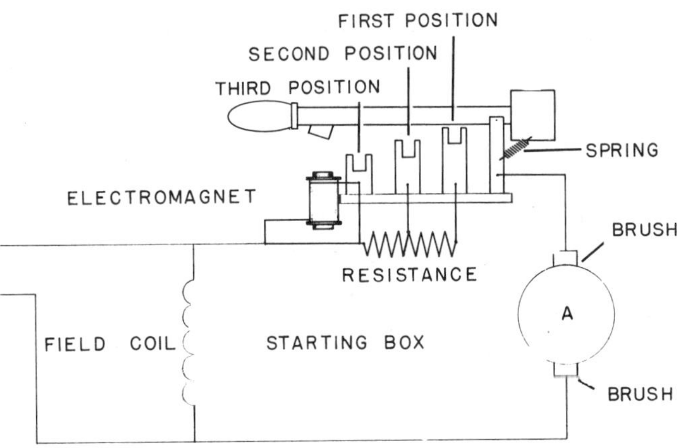

Fig. 17-16. DC Motor Starting Box

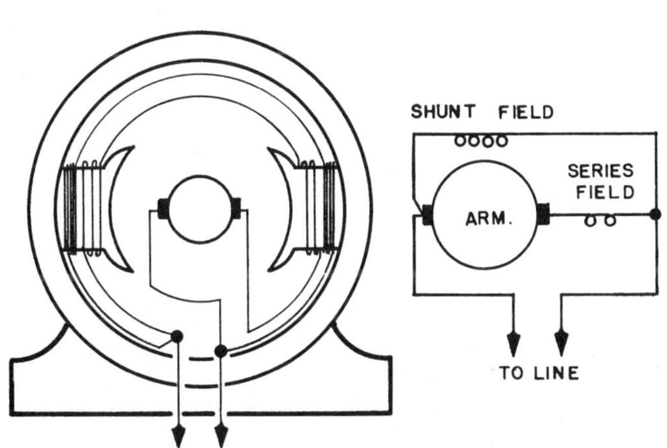

Fig. 17-15. DC Compound Motor

Fig. 17-17. Modern DC Motor (Westinghouse)
This shunt-wound motor develops 3 hp. at 400 to 1600 rpm using 11 amps at 240 volts.

Terms to Understand

magnetism
Magnus legend
Magnesia
lodestone
William Gilbert
three types of magnets
law of magnets
lines of force
flux
Christian Oerstead
solenoid
relay
reluctance
hysteresis
mmf
emf
Ohm's magnetic law
ampere-turn
circuit breaker
armature
field
commutator
brushes
back emf
series wound
shunt wound
compound motor
permeability

Study Questions

1. A major portion of the world's power supply is converted into electrical energy. Explain.

2. What is magnetism?

3. What are magnets and magnetic materials?

4. What is the law of magnetism?

5. What is meant by magnetic permeability? How is this property used?

6. How is the phenomenon of magnetic force surrounding an electricity carrying conductor used?

7. What is a solenoid and electromagnet? Explain the characteristics of each.

8. How may the strength of an electromagnet be controlled?

9. Analyze how an electric motor converts electrical energy to mechanical energy.

10. What is the purpose of brushes and commutator in a DC motor?

11. How may the direction of rotation be changed in a DC motor?

12. Describe the various types of DC motors.

13. Analyze the characteristics of each kind.

14. What is direct current and alternating current? Explain the advantages and disadvantages of each.

Energy Interchange and Alternating Current

A motor converts electrical energy into mechanical energy by using the magnetic field surrounding a current-carrying conductor. But how can the magnetic field be used for the reverse—to convert mechanical to electrical energy?

Michael Faraday, early in the 19th century, learned that a conductor which carries current creates a surrounding magnetic field. This was the discovery which led to the development of the electric motor, and other electromagnetic devices. He also reasoned that it should be possible to use magnetism to *produce* an electric current. This great physicist in England's Royal Institute experimented over a period of ten years to try to establish this reverse effect. However, not until he discovered the need for quickly *moving* the conductor across the magnetic field did he prove his reasoning. Thus he revealed the phenomenon that underlies the operation of the electric current generator.

Edison made one of the first practical generators. He developed his "Z" type dynamo (the "long-waisted Mary-Ann") in 1879, Fig. 18-1. This had an efficiency of 90 percent at a time when theoretical scientists believed no more than 50 percent efficiency was possible. *Dynamo* was the early name for both DC generators and motors. Often the same machine was used for either purpose. See Figs. 17-11, and 18-2.

Inside the generator, a coil of wire is mechanically rotated within a surrounding magnetic field. This coil cuts the magnetic field, and a flow of electrons is induced within this conductor according to the left-hand rule (*B* in Fig. 17-8). The induced current can be picked off by a commutator and brush arrangement like that found in the motor. The electron flow can then be converted to heat, light, chemical energy or mechanical energy.

Fig. 18-1. Edison Dynamo, 1879

Fig. 18-2. Edison Electric Generators, 1879

Fig. 18-3. Edison "Jumbo" Steam Dynamo No. 1, 1881

DC Generators

As we have learned in the last chapter, the segmented commutator is necessary in the DC motor to change the polarity of the armature. In the generator (as was shown in Chapter 10, Figs. 10-8 to 10-12), this type of commutator generates a pulsating current flowing in one direction even though the coil is rotated first past the north pole and then past the south pole of the field magnet. Fig. 18-4 reviews the current collecting arrangement on DC and AC generators.

Small generators may have a permanent magnet as the field. In this case, they usually are called magnetos. Large generators must use electromagnets because of the greater force possible. These electromagnetic fields are self-excited by using a small amount of the current generated.

No one can explain what causes the necessary unbalance to create a flow of electrons. This is one more unsolved mystery which remains a challenge. We do know that when a conductor cuts across a magnetic field, the electrons in the conductor are pushed sideways by the force of the field. Electrons are drawn away from one end of the wire, leaving it relatively positive and are crowded onto the other end, making it negative. If a complete circuit is made, the electrons will flow with a potential for doing work.

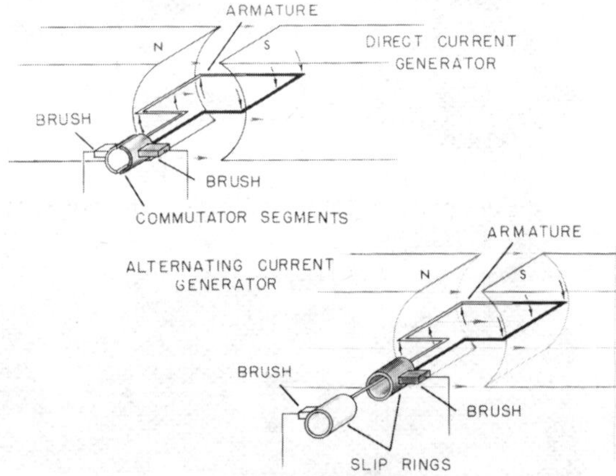

Fig. 18-4. Current Collecting Arrangement on AC and DC Generators

What is the polarity of the darker brush in each case? What will each be after a half turn?

AC Generators

Fig. 18-4 shows that if a generator is made with two full rings contacting the brushes in place of the segmented commutator, the current flow alternates. As the coil rotates between the fields, each side cuts the flow of flux upward near one pole, and downward at the next. Since there is no split commutator to reverse the current direction, flow changes each half revolution. This machine is called an alternating current generator, or alternator. As we learned with automobile alternators, this arrangement of a *revolving armature* generator is becoming less popular.

Revolving-Field Generators

The *field-poles* of most modern AC generators are made to revolve with the shaft and thus are called *rotors.* The armature conductors, in which the emf is induced, are held stationary to the frame, and are called *stators.* This arrangement provides safer handling of high currents as well as being more efficient and durable. The alternating current is taken off the stationary armature by heavy bus bars or well-insulated wires running directly to the switchboard. This arrangement can be seen in Fig. 18-5 as well as Fig. 1-13.

Fig. 18-5. Three-Phase Revolving-Field Alternator (Fairbanks, Morse)

A direct current generator, the *exciter*, is used to provide the relatively low-voltage direct current for the rotor field coils through slip rings. The voltage of this exciter is controlled by rheostats to regulate the current generated by the main AC generator.

It should be noted that the rotor of a generator may be either the field or the armature depending upon its function. The *field* coils set up a magnetic flux; the *armature* receives the induced current flow. Either one may move.

Sine Wave

A graph of alternating current flow is a *sine wave,* Fig. 18-6. Note that the horizontal or time scale is divided into degrees: emf builds up to 90°, reverses at 180° and completes the cycle at 360°. The number of these cycles per second determines the *frequency* of the AC. In this country, 60-cycle AC is standard. In fact, care is exercised at power stations to keep this frequency very exact in order to insure proper operating conditions. Most appliances are designed to operate at that frequency. Motors, for example, will not operate properly except at the designed frequency. Electric clocks have motors which depend on the exactness of the frequency to maintain their split-second accuracy.

Phase

In AC systems, we often hear the word *phase.* Phase refers to the timing of the beginning of the cycle of voltage and current in various circuits of an AC system. A single-phase system has only one path for current flow. A two-phase system has two paths so that the cycle of the current in one is at its peak when the second has minimum flow, Fig. 18-7. Note the spacing of the cycles is 90° apart. A three-phase system has three paths, and the current in each is spaced one-third cycle (120°) apart, Fig. 18-8.

A single-phase generator or motor has only one set of windings, regardless of the number of poles, and requires only two conductors, Fig. 18-9. This single circuit gives a single-phase motor a simple alternating field that does not revolve, as is the case of the two-phase and three-phase systems, unless an auxiliary winding is added.

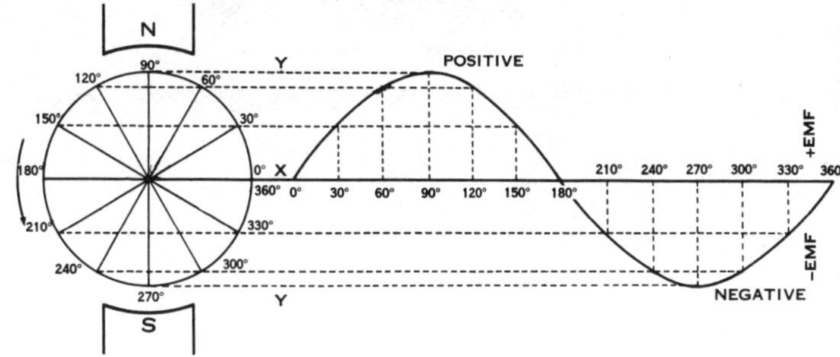

Fig. 18-6. Constructing a Sine Curve

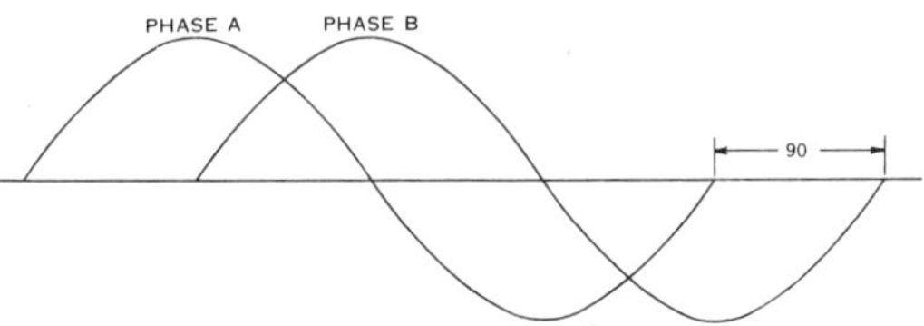

Fig. 18-7. Sine Curves of a Two-Phase Current

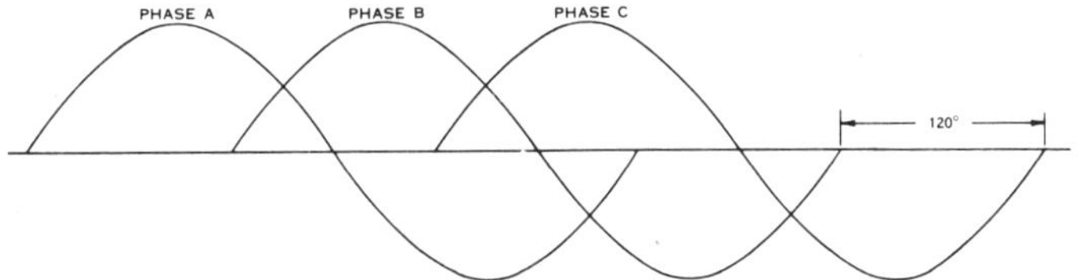

Fig. 18-8. Sine Curves of a Three-Phase Current

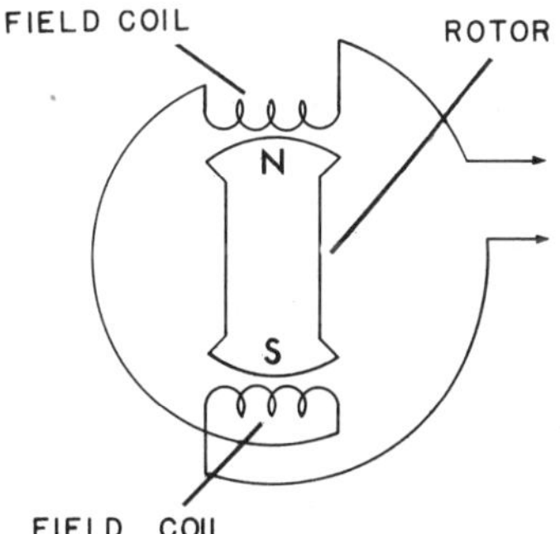

Fig. 18-9. Single Phase Generator

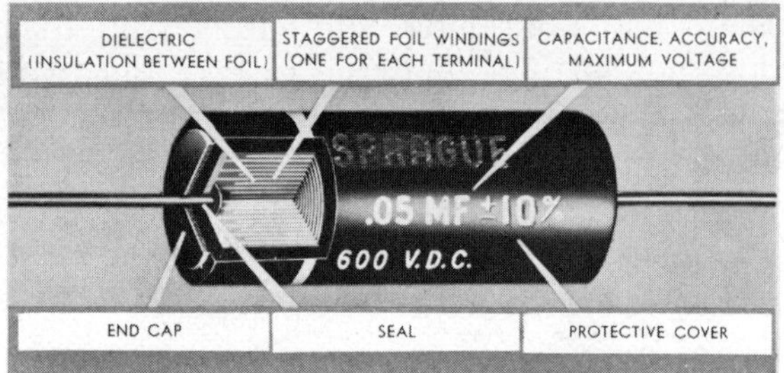

Fig. 18-10. Capacitor (Sprague)

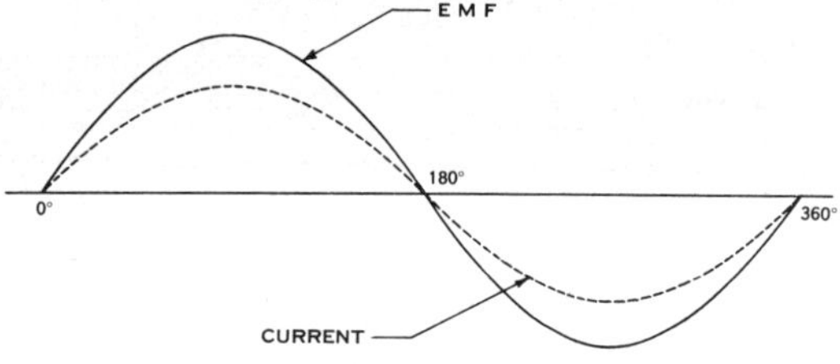

Fig. 18-11. Current and Emf in Phase

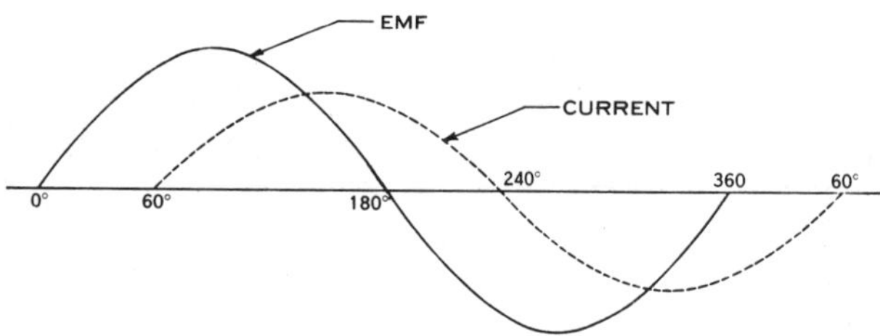

Fig. 18-12. Lagging Current Due to Inductive Reactance

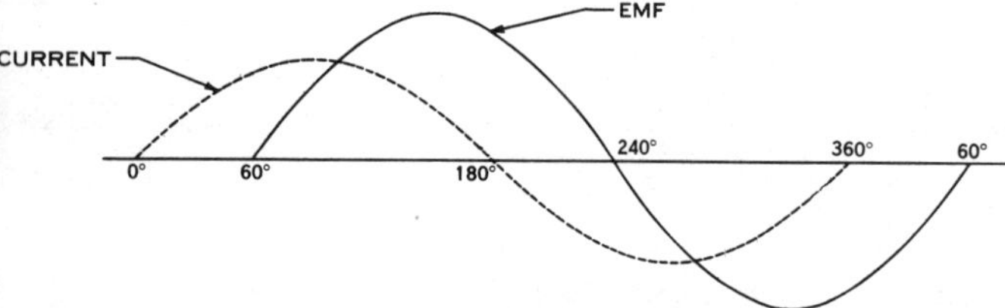

Fig. 18-13. Leading Current Due to Capacitive Reactance

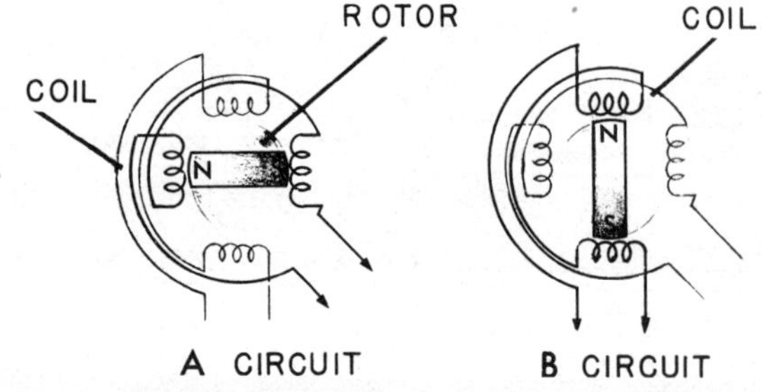

Fig. 18-14. Two-Phase Electric Generator

Reactance and Phase

Resistors, coils, and capacitors have different effects on current alternations. If the circuit contains resistance only, the voltage and the resultant current-flow reach their peak together and are said to be *in phase*, Fig. 18-11. A coil (especially one with many turns on an iron core) offers a different kind of opposition to alternating current flow called *inductive reactance*. Inductance can cause *current-flow* peaks *to lag* behind *voltage* peaks by as much as 90°. The greater the inductive reactance, the more the current flow is *out of phase* with the emf which caused it. See Fig. 18-12. Inductive reactance is much different on DC. A high inductance coil may draw so much current on DC that it will burn out. So never connect a transformer or AC motor to DC.

A capacitor is a pair of conducting surfaces (metal plates or foil) separated by an insulator (air or waxed paper), Fig. 18-10. A capacitor stores electrons (voltage) for later discharge. This is *capacitive reactance*, and with AC, it has an effect just opposite to inductive reactance. Remember that inductance opposes a change in *current* and causes it to *lag* voltage. Capacitance opposes change in *voltage* and causes *current to lead* voltage. See Fig. 18-13. Capacitors often are used to neutralize the inductance of a coil. Later we will see their use in motors.

Two Phase

In a two-phase system, both generators and motors have two complete sets of windings, Fig. 18-14. There are two sets of stator coils, one set for each phase. The system may have four conductors, two for each phase. As the north and south poles of the generator revolve past phase A and then phase B, two separate currents flow, one for each phase.

The two-phase *motor* receives these currents in the same A-B order, causing its field to build up first in one phase, and then in the other. This action moves the magnetism across the faces of the poles, setting up a revolving field which drags the rotor with it, causing rotation.

The two-phase system is much better than the single-phase system, and was used until about 50 years ago. It was then replaced by the still popular and better three-phase system.

Three Phase

In the three-phase generator, there are three sets of stator coils—one set for each phase, see Fig. 18-15. As the north and south poles of the generator field revolve, they pass these stator windings in an A, B, C order, sending out three currents that flow into the motor in the same order.

This action, as in the two-phase motor, sets up a moving or revolving field that drags the rotor along. Because AC current flows in one line at a time, any two wires may carry one of the currents and three wires serve for all three currents. So with three-phase current three wires serve the function of six by carrying three circuits.

From any two wires of a three-phase line, a single-phase current may be taken off, and since single-phase and two-phase generators are rarely used, this is the way single-phase current is now obtained.

AC Motors

Today, with the increasing application of electricity, there has been a continued growth in the number of small motors used in household appliances and in industry. Many of these small motors employ single-phase, 60-cycle alternating current obtained from any standard 120-volt receptacle. Such motors are one horsepower or smaller, and most fall into three general classes: universal motors, induction motors (split-phase, capacitor, shaded pole, or repulsion starting), and synchronous motors.

Universal Motors

Universal motors can be used with either alternating or direct current. Essentially, these are series-wound DC motors with laminations which permit them to be used also with AC. When current is alternating the magnetic poles reverse in both field and armature at the same time, maintaining the same effective relationship throughout the cycle. Being series wound, these motors have excellent starting torque. The speed of the motor can be varied by a rheostat in series with the line. Shaft rotation can be reversed by switching the leads to the brushes. (On AC however, brushes may have to be repositioned slightly to prevent arcing if motor is run backward.)

Universal motors are used in vacuum cleaners and powered, small, hand tools because of the good starting torque, and in sewing machines, food mixers, toy trains, and similar uses where variable speed is desired.

Induction Motors

Induction motors operate only on AC, and with all of their variations are our most common source of localized stationary power. They are widely used in homes, farms, buildings, and industry. Yet many people, even those technically educated, have only a vague idea of what makes a typical AC motor operate, and most explanations are inadequate. While this book is not intended to give a complete course in electricity, the following generalized explanation should develop at least a working knowledge of this common AC motor.

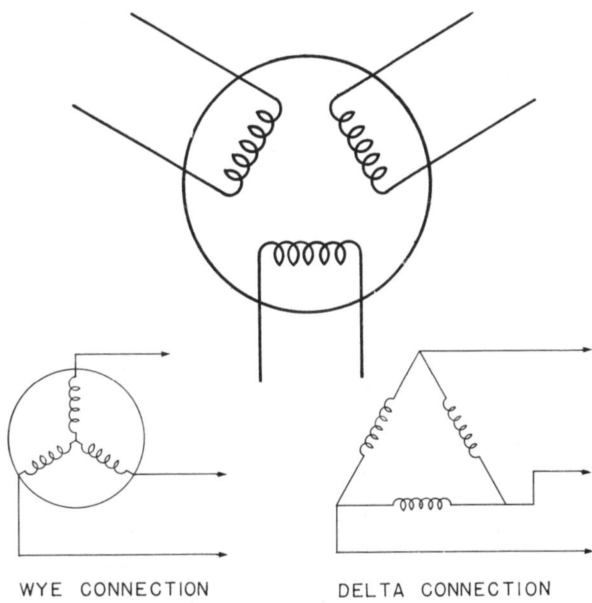

Fig. 18-15. Three-Phase Electric Generator

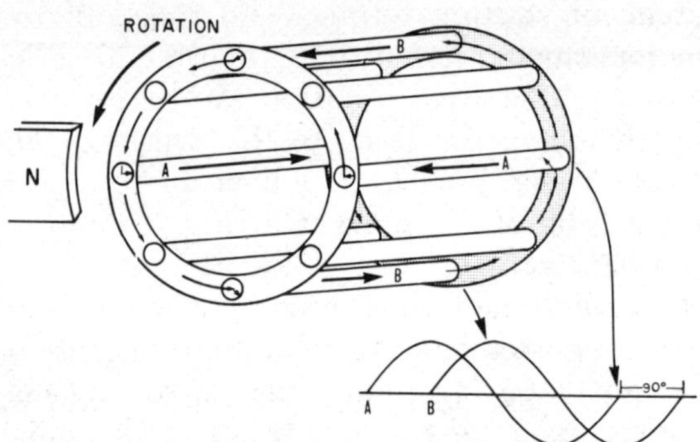

Fig. 18-16. Squirrel-Cage Rotor and its Induced Currents

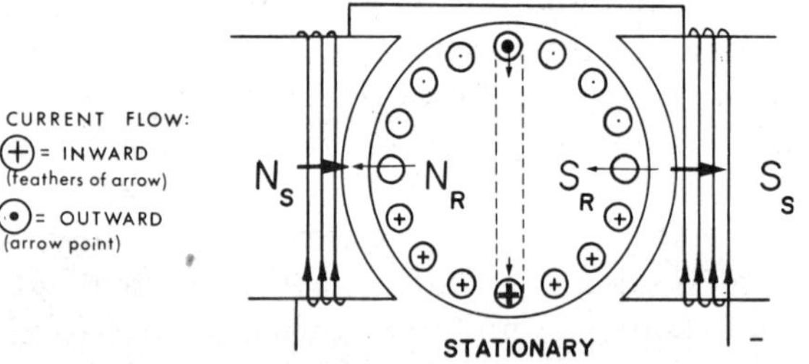

Fig. 18-17. B Current Induces a Flux which Opposes Stator Poles

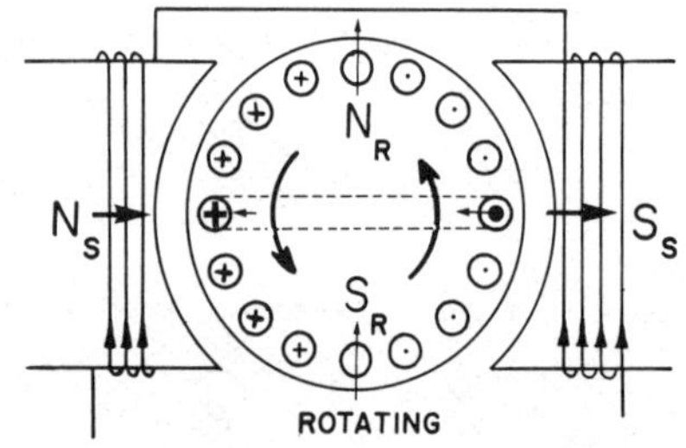

Fig. 18-18. A Current Induces a Flux Perpendicular to Stator Poles

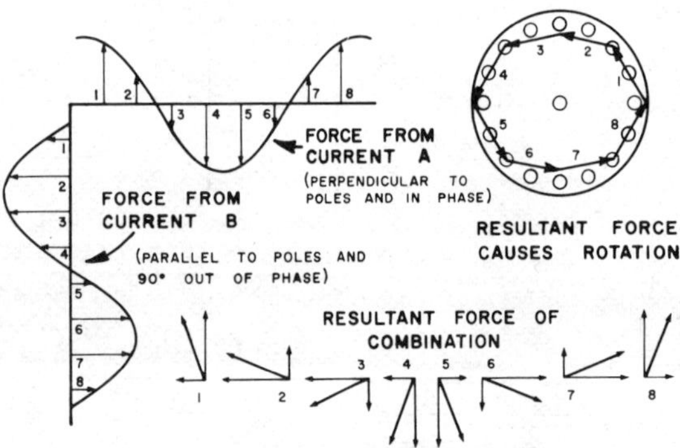

Fig. 18-19. Resultant of A and B Flux Is Rotational Force

Induction motors can usually be identified by the *squirrel-cage rotor*. The rotor body is laminated of soft iron. Around the circumference it is slotted or drilled lengthwise. Each opening is filled with a heavy copper or aluminum conductor. All of these bars are connected to a heavy conducting ring at each end. This current-carrying structure, if removed from the iron core, would look much like the exercise wheel of a squirrel cage. The stator poles induce two separate out-of-phase currents flowing within this cage. Fig. 18-16 shows these currents labeled as *A* and *B*. Conductors on opposite sides being connected by the end rings form what functions as a single-loop coil. Circuit *A* is shown in the horizontal loop, and circuit *B* is in the vertical loop 90° out of phase with each other. Loops on either side of these main loops carry similar but weaker currents; some carry a composite of the two phases.

The heavy conductors in this cage have almost no resistance and can carry enough amperage to produce a usable magnetic flux. As voltages induced in these coils are not large, and resistance of the iron core is much greater, no insulation is used on the conductors of the rotor cage. Essentially, the squirrel-cage rotor is a self-contained two-phase generator which uses its current directly in developing a revolving magnetic flux to produce torque more efficiently than most motors. Let us now consider how each of these two current flows is induced in the rotor.

Fig. 18-17 shows what we have labeled *B current flow*. This current is induced whenever flux flows between stator poles—even when the rotor is stationary. Current is induced from the stator coils to the rotor coils just as it would be from the primary to the secondary windings of a transformer. This current flow is greatest in whichever loop is midway between stator poles—the loop parallel to stator windings. As the flux *builds up* between stator poles at the beginning of a cycle or as it *collapses* during an alternation, the moving lines of force of the flux cut the conductors of this loop inducing an emf in the conductor. As this resulting current flow is greatest when the stator current flow is least, the two are 90° out of phase.

This *B* current flow creates a *B magnetic flux* which opposes that of the stator poles which created it—rotor north is at the stator north and the rotor south is at the stator south. This flux flow is always parallel with the stator poles (to the left as shown in Fig. 18-17, or to the right depending upon the point in the cycle). The force of this flux is always equally balanced between poles, so by itself it produces no torque to start or maintain rotation. A single-phase induction motor requires any of several types of supplementary starting systems. These starters will be explained later.

Once the rotor is set in motion, however, the second or *A current flow* is induced because loops of the rotor are *cutting through* the flux between field poles. This current flow is strongest in the loop passing the center of the stator poles. Also, as the current flow is caused by mechanically cutting through the field (and not by its electrical movement) the current is *in phase* with that in the stator windings.

As shown in Fig. 18-18, this rotationally induced current creates an *A magnetic flux*, flowing crosswise to the field poles (either up or down depending upon the point in the cycle). Again this field alone would not cause rotation. These two alternating magnetic fields, A and *B*, act at right angles to each other and their peak strengths occur 90° out of phase. Fig 18-19 shows that the combination of these two magnetic fields produces a resultant field which rotates once each cycle. As A and B currents are seldom equal, the rotational force is usually unbalanced (not perfectly round). This causes some vibration, and is characteristic of single-phase induction motors. This is usually dampened by rubber mountings.

However, the rotor will cut no flux if it rotates exactly in time with the resultant rotating field. The speed of the rotating field is called the *synchronous speed*. The rotor must *slip*, or lag slightly behind the synchronous speed of the rotating resultant field so that its conductors may actually cut across lines of force. In practice, the rotor rotates about 4 or 5 percent slower than the synchronous speed in order to provide enough torque to balance the load. An increased load causes an increased slip cutting more stator flux, which in turn produces the increased torque needed to almost maintain the original speed. Thus, a single-phase induction motor sometimes is used for a constant speed motor, especially if the load is constant or quite light.

The speed of an induction motor is determined by the number of stator poles (for each phase when the line current is polyphase), and the frequency of the current. Doubling the number of poles would cut the rpm in half. For example, with 60 cycle current and two stator poles, the synchronous speed would be 3600 rpm, but slip reduces this to about 3450. Four-pole motors run at about 1725 rpm and six-pole motors at about 1150 rpm. Stator windings on some motors have leads brought out so the effective number of poles can be changed giving two speeds. Some polyphase induction motors use wound coils on the rotor with leads brought out to slip rings. This allows a rheostat to be placed in series with the rotor coils to reduce current flow and thus vary the speed.

Three-phase induction motors have separate stator poles for each phase. Three-phase motors are self starting because the phase of adjacent stator fields is different and they rotate electrically. This causes the rotor loops to cut a revolving field even when the rotor has not begun to rotate. This causes the rotor to begin revolving and to speed up to where it almost locks into the synchronous speed. The squirrel-cage rotor does not develop as high a starting torque as do various wound armatures, however. To reverse a three-phase induction motor, interchange phase connections of any two sets of poles (that is ABC to *CBA*, to *ACB*, or to *BAC*).

Induction Starting Arrangements

Single-phase induction motors, however, have no revolving field in the stator poles, and so will not start without supplementary windings. There are several ways to incorporate such starting windings.

Split-phase induction motors have an auxiliary or starting winding either on poles between those of the main windings, or on top of the main windings. During the starting cycle, the split-phase motor operates much like a two-phase motor because it has a field which is moving electrically. The starting winding is made of fewer turns of small diameter wire. The main or running winding is made of many turns of heavier wire. Fig. 18-20 shows the wiring diagram of a split-phase motor. Both windings are across the power line. The high resistance and low reactance of the auxiliary winding has minimum effect on the phase. Remember that *resistance* does not cause current lag, but *reactance* does. The main winding carrying more current, has little resistance and high reactance so the phase of this current lags. An extra reactor (a heavy coil with an iron core) may be in series with the main winding of older motors to provide additional reactance. An automatic centrifugal switch opens when about 75 percent of running speed has been reached. This switch cuts out the starting coil, shorts across any extra reactor, and shunts the main field coil across the line. Reversing rotation is accomplished by reversing the connections to either the starting or the main winding.

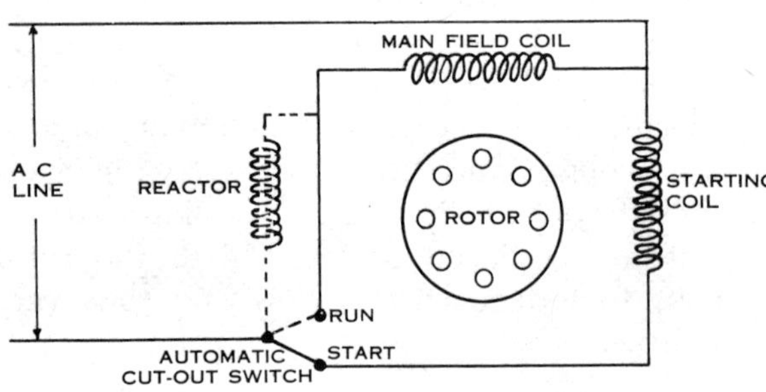

Fig. 18-20. Split-Phase Motor

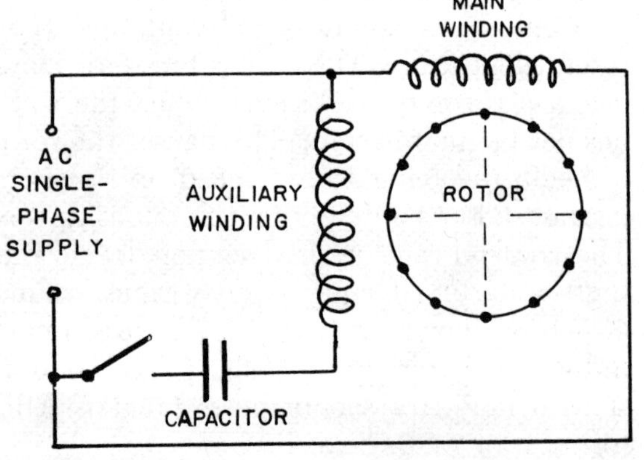

Fig. 18-21. Capacitor-Start Motor

Split-phase induction motors are used to power many home appliances such as washers, dryers, and light machine tools which do not require high starting torque.

Capacitor-starting motors are also single-phase induction motors which split the phase for starting. They are used where heavy starting loads are needed, such as in refrigerators, pumps, stokers, and compressors. Capacitor motors can usually be recognized by the extra container which contains a large capacitor located on the outside of the motor. Fig. 18-21 shows the wiring diagram. During starting, current flow leads the emf in the auxiliary winding because of a capacitor in series with this winding. Current in the main winding lags because of its high reactance. The combined phase difference is greater than in the simple split-phase, so it gives a higher starting torque. The automatic centrifugal switch, stator poles, and the squirrel cage rotor, are all similar to the plain split-phase motor.

Shaded-pole motors have one side of the stator pole encircled by a loop of copper. Current induced in this loop opposes the flux on that side of the stator pole, Fig. 18-22. The loop retards the flux on this one side when it is building up, and later in the cycle when the main flux is decreasing, the shaded portion is building up. This imbalance of the poles gives just enough starting torque to overcome light friction and inertia. The loop does not open after the motor is running so it continues to oppose the main winding. Thus it is used only in small sizes in fans, clocks, and phonograph turntables.

Permanent-split capacitor motors are similar to capacitor-start motors except the capacitor and auxiliary windings remain in operation. This means the auxiliary circuit must not be designed for just starting torque but for continuous operation so as not to oppose the main winding. Starting torque is poor—even less than split phase motors. But simplicity and efficiency make it popular for powering fans. It is both more powerful and more efficient under load than the cheaper shaded pole motor which is commonly used for this purpose.

Repulsion-induction motors are not popular today although some may still be found in such old household appliances as refrigerators. See Fig. 18-23. These motors have brushes, commutators, and armatures similar to direct current motors, but run only on alternating current. The brush holders are so arranged for running that the armature generates its own voltage by induction from the flux of the stator the same as a squirrel-cage rotor. For starting, however, the brushes carry line voltage to energize armature windings so as to repel stator poles. The windings are usually in two circuits, which may be connected in series for 240 volts or in parallel for 120 volts. The performance and power consumption in any case will be identical, but amperage is doubled at the lower voltage. These motors start by repulsion, and at about 75 percent of full speed, a centrifugal device within the rotor changes the connections to those of an induction motor. At the same time, the brushes are pulled away from the commutator. The advantage of this motor is its high initial torque at low current intake. Its chief disadvantages are its initial higher price and costly repair characteristics.

Synchronous Motors

Synchronous motors have the ability to lock into exact step with the alternations in current, but they must be brought up to this speed by various starting arrangements. This may be done manually as on older electric clocks which had to be restarted by twisting or moving a knob after each power interruption. It can also be done by an extra starting motor, or by any of the phase splitting arrangements used for starting induction motors. The speed is determined by the frequency of the current and the number of poles. They are used on instruments where an absolutely constant speed is necessary. They are also used in connection with small AC generators so that generator and motor always revolve in unison for speed indicating devices, and synchronized controls. Each time the generator (or transmitter) turns, the motor turns a like amount.

Synchronous motors are used on clocks and some record players. These motors frequently used shaded-poles to produce starting torque. Large synchronous motors are used to drive generators at exact speeds. Most use direct current to energize constant N and S rotor poles, and have a separate motor for starting.

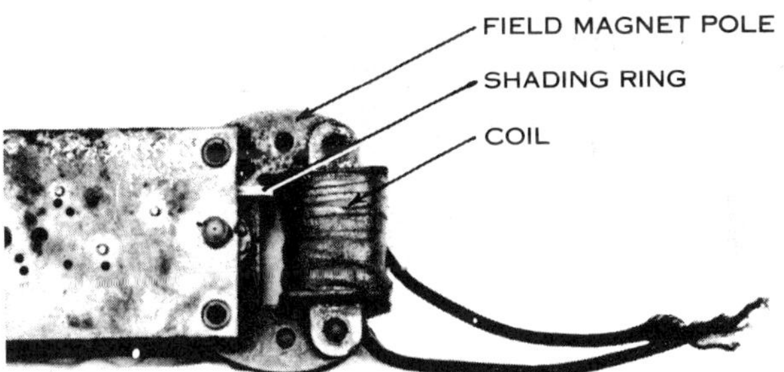

Fig. 18-22. Shaded-Pole Motor

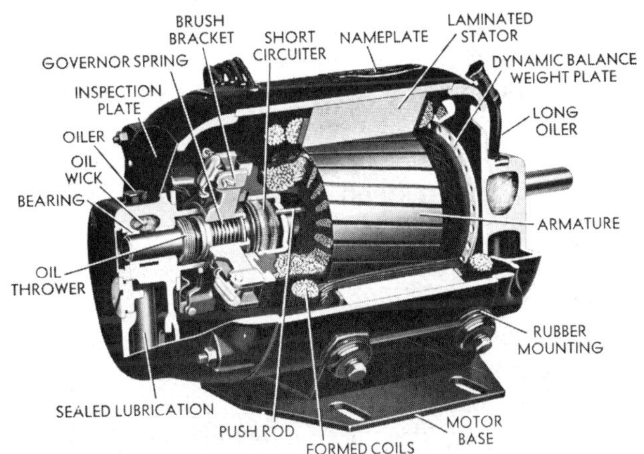

Fig. 18-23. Repulsion-Start Induction Motor
(Delco)

Selecting a Motor

Common types of small motors, their wiring diagrams, characteristics, and uses are shown in Fig. 18-24. There are two types of torque described. *Starting torque* (locked rotor torque) is the maximum turning effect produced at the instant of start. *Breakdown torque* is the maximum load the motor will carry without an abrupt drop in speed. Torque characteristics are described in general terms such as *high* or *very low*. These terms can be defined more accurately in percentages of the rated running torque (100%) as follows:

Description	Starting Torque	Breakdown Torque
Very low	Below 85%	
Low	85 to 175%	Below 175%
Medium	175 to 250%	175 to 220%
High	250 to 400%	220 to 270%
Extra high	Above 400%	Above 270%

Considerations for selecting a motor for a particular job would include: 1. The available power supply—voltage, phases, AC or DC, frequency. 2. The horsepower required, momentary overloads, possible overheating, and whether continuous or intermittent duty. 3. Starting torque required, directly connected or pulley driven, speed requirements, and possibility of no load periods (see graphs at bottom of Fig. 18-24). 4. Starting current limitations, and maximum current draw (split-phase sometimes objectionable here). 5. Starting control and safety cut-out type of fuse, circuit breaker, or high temperature protection. 6. Considerations of mounting, bearings, sealing against moisture or explosive vapors, method of oiling, price limitations, number needed.

Motor Care

To insure proper operation of any motor, a program of maintenance must be followed. A clean, carefully-lubricated motor will outlast a dirty, dry, or neglected one. If dirt and dust are permitted to collect around the vent holes, the necessary air cooling is cut off and the motor will overheat. This may break down the insulation around the coil windings. Naturally, dirt on the bearing surface of any machine will tend to wear these parts rapidly.

Motors should be periodically cleaned and lubricated as part of a preventive maintenance program, and thereby, increase its operational life. Sealed bearings are almost standard. They are sealed with a permanent lubricant to guard against dust and to guarantee a full life time of service. Some motors use an oil ring, rolling on the shaft, carrying the oil from a reservoir situated below. Such systems require periodic draining, cleaning, and refilling. Motors which have oil or grease cups can always be easily lubricated by keeping these cups full. Be careful of over oiling motor bearings.

If the motor is taken apart for any reason, care must be taken to remove any brushes first. Brush position should be noted so they can be replaced in their original holders, right side up, assuring a good fit with the commutator.

Small parts should be cleaned and stored in a container to prevent their being lost. A small paint brush can be used to dust the insides. If a visual inspection indicates insulation wear, a good grade of insulation varnish can be used to recoat the coils.

If any parts must be replaced, it is a good practice to order them from the manufacturer of the motor. A full description of the part, including the necessary information found on the name plate of the motor, should accompany the order.

Transformers

One of the most important characteristics of alternating current is its ability to induce an electron flow into an adjoining conductor. We noted how this phenomenon operates when explaining the induction of the B current of the induction motor. It is this same inducing of current by a growing or collapsing flux that permits the transformer to transfer power from one circuit to another.

Class	Type of Motor	Wiring Diagram	Ⓦ Type	HP. Range	Speed Data: Rated Speed	Speed Data: Speed Characteristics	Speed Data: Speed Control	Approximate Torque (4-Pole Motors): Starting	Approximate Torque (4-Pole Motors): Break-down	Built-in Starting Mecha-nism	Reversibility: At Rest	Reversibility: In Motion	Radio Inter-ference	Approxi-mate Compar-ative Price	Application Data
Alternating Current, Single Phase, Split Phase	General Purpose (Rigid Mounting)		FH	1/20 to 1/3	3450 1725 1140 860	Constant	None	Medium to Low	Medium	Centrif-ugal Switch	Yes—Change Connec-tions	No—Except with Special Design and Relay	None	85%	For oil burners, office appliances, fans, blowers, low locked-rotor current minimizes light flicker making motor suitable for frequent starting. For applications up to 1/3 hp. where medium starting and breakdown torques are sufficient. Thermoguard available for ratings from 1/12 hp. up.
Alternating Current, Single Phase, Split Phase	High Torque		FHT	1/4 and 1/3	1725	Constant	None	Medium	High	Centrif-ugal Switch	Yes—Change Connec-tions	No—Except with Special Design and Relay	None	65%	Ideal for washing machines, ironers, sump pumps, home workshops. For continuous and intermittent duty where operation is infrequent and locked-rotor current in excess of N.E.M.A. values is not objectionable. May cause light flicker on underwired or overloaded lighting circuits.
Alternating Current, Single Phase, Split Phase	Two-Speed (Two Windings) (Resilient Mounting)		FH	1/8 to 1/4	1725/1140 1725/860	Two-Speed	1-Pole Double-Throw Switch	Medium	Medium	Centrif-ugal Switch	Yes—Change Connec-tions	No	None	165%	For belted furnace blowers, attic ventilating fans, similar belted medium-torque jobs. Simplicity permits operation with any 1-pole, double-throw switch or relay. Starts well on either speed—thus used with thermostatic or other automatic control. Thermoguard recommended, as tight belt or incorrect pulley ratio may overload motor.
Alternating Current, Single Phase, Capacitor	General Purpose Capacitor-Start		FJ	1/6 to 3/4	3450 1725 1140 860	Constant	None	High	High	Centrif-ugal Switch	Yes—Change Connec-tions	No—Except with Special Design and Relay	None	100%	Ideal for all heavy-duty drives, such as compressors, pumps, stokers, refrigerators, air conditioning. All purpose motor for high starting torque, low starting current. Quiet, economical. High efficiency and power factor. Single voltage in 1/6, 1/4 hp., 1725 rpm. ratings—dual voltage in others. All sizes obtainable with thermoguard.
Alternating Current, Single Phase, Capacitor	Two-Speed Capacitor-Start (Two Windings)		FJ	1/6 to 3/4	1725/1140 1725/860	Two-Speed	1-Pole Double-Throw Switch	Medium	Medium	Centrif-ugal Switch	Yes—Change Connec-tions	No	None	200%	Supplements line of 2-speed split-phase motors (see Type FH, 2-speed). Used on identical applications requiring horsepower ratings from 1/3 to 3/4 hp.
Alternating Current, Single Phase, Capacitor	Permanent Split (Single Value)		FL	1/20 to 3/4	1620 1080 820	Constant or Adjustable Varying	Two-Speed Switch or Autotrans-former	Very Low	Low	None	Yes—Change Connec-tions	Yes	None	155%	For direct connected fan drives . . . particularly unit heaters. Not for belt drives. Same motor adaptable for 115 or 230 volts for 1-speed, 2-speed, or multi-speed service by use of 1-pole, single-throw switch, 2-pole, double-throw switch, or speed controller, respectively. Fan load must be accurately matched to motor output for proper speed control. All ratings dual voltage and dual rotation.
Alternating Current, Single Phase, Capacitor	Permanent Split Capacitor		FLL	1/25 to 1/4	1625 to 1075	Varying or Adjustable Varying	Tapped Winding or Choke Coil	Low	Low	None	Yes	Yes	None	—	Companion to type FE shaded-pole motor. Their higher efficiency and power factor make this type motor ideal for driving fans in room air conditioners and window fans.
Alternating Current, Single Phase, Shaded Pole	Shaded Pole		FE	1/30 to 1/8	1550 1050	Constant or Adjustable Varying	Tapped Winding or Choke Coil	Very Low	Low	None	No	No	None	—	Constant speed, switchless motor for low-power applications. Used for fans, small blowers, unit heaters, hair driers. With fan load accurately matched to motor output, proper speed control can be obtained by means of series choke or resistance.
Alternating Current, 1, 2, 3 Phase, Synchronous	Split-Phase	Refer to FH	FBH	1/250 to 1/3	3600 1800 1200 900	Absolutely Constant	None	Low	Medium (See Note)	Centrif-ugal Switch	See FH	See FH	None	375%	Used mostly on instruments, sound recording and reproducing apparatus, teleprinters, facsimile printers. Definitely constant speed. Type selected depends largely on starting torque. Type FBL recommended where low watts input desirable and low starting torque sufficient. Type FBH or FBJ recommended where higher starting torque needed. Pull-in torque on all types affected by inertia of connected load. Note: The "breakdown" torque refers to torque at point where motor speed drops below synchronous speed.
Alternating Current, 1, 2, 3 Phase, Synchronous	Capacitor-Start	Refer to FJ	FBJ					Medium	Medium (See Note)	Centrif-ugal Switch	See FJ	See FJ			
Alternating Current, 1, 2, 3 Phase, Synchronous	Permanent Split Capacitor	Refer to FL	FBL					Very Low	Medium (See Note)	None	See FL	See FL			
Alternating Current, 1, 2, 3 Phase, Synchronous	Polyphase	Refer to FS	FBS					Medium	Medium (See Note)	None	See FS	See FS			
Alternating Current, Polyphase, 2 or 3 Phase	Squirrel Cage		FS	1/4 to 3/4	3450 1725 1140 860	Constant	None	High to Medium	Extra High	None	Yes—Change Connec-tions	Yes—Change Connec-tions	None	110%	For all applications where polyphase circuits are available. Special designs with extra high starting torque for hoists, door operators, tool traverse and clamp devices. High frequency motors are used for high speed applications such as rayon spinning machines and portable tools.
D-C	Shunt Wound and Compound Wound	Compound Wdg.	FK	1/12 to 3/4	3450 1725 1140 860	Constant or Adjustable Varying	Armature Resistance	Extra High	—	None	Yes—Change Connec-tions	No—Except with Special Design	Yes	195%	For all applications operated from D-C circuits. Companion D-C motor to single phase and polyphase A-C motors. Ratings of 1/12 hp., 1725 rpm. and smaller shunt-wound. Larger ratings compound wound. Starting rheostats recommended for ratings 1/2 hp. and up.
A-C or D-C, Universal	Non-Compensated (Salient Pole Winding)		ADS	1/150 to 3/4	1500 to 15000	Varying	Voltage Control Using Resistance or Transformer	Extra High	—	None	No—Except with Special Design	No—Except with Special Design	Yes	—	Especially suitable for sewing machines, portable tools, vacuum cleaners, motion picture projectors, and mixers. Operates on A-C or D-C circuits. Inherent characteristics are high-starting torque, high speed, varying speed regulation and small size and light weight for given hp. output. Type ADS sold as parts and complete motors.
A-C or D-C, Universal	Compensated (Distributed Winding)	Two Field Type; Single Field Type	AD	1/40 to 2 1/2	2500 to 15000	Varying		Extra High	—	None	No—Except with Special Design	No—Except with Special Design	Yes	—	Type AD compensated parts recommended when higher power at lower speeds required as for larger commercial type vacuum cleaners, large portable tools. Wide variety of electrical characteristics and housing designs available.
A-C or D-C, Universal	Governor Controlled		ADS	1/50 to 1/8	2000 to 7500	Adjustable Constant	Adjustable Governor	Extra High	—	None	No—Except with Special Design	No—Except with Special Design	Yes	—	Governor permits utilizing light-weight, high-speed, universal motor for constant speed applications. Two types governors supplied. One permits adjustment while running—used on electric typewriters, motion picture projectors, cameras. Other type adjustable at standstill only—used for adding machines, calculating machines, other constant speed office machines.

FH GENERAL PURPOSE SPLIT PHASE — Switch Operating Speed; Running Winding Only; Combined Winding for Starting

FJ CAPACITOR-START INDUCTION RUN — Switch Operating Speed; Running Winding Only; Combined Winding for Starting

FL PERMANENT-SPLIT CAPACITOR

FE SHADED POLE

FS POLYPHASE

FK DIRECT-CURRENT

ADS UNIVERSAL — DC; 60 CYCLE AC

(Vertical axes: PER CENT SYNCHRONOUS SPEED, 10–100; ADS: PER CENT 60 CYCLE FULL LOAD SPEED. Horizontal axes: 0 100 200 300 400 500)

(Curves are percent of full-load torque, 1725 rpm) **Fig. 18-24. Small-Motor Guide** (Westinghouse)

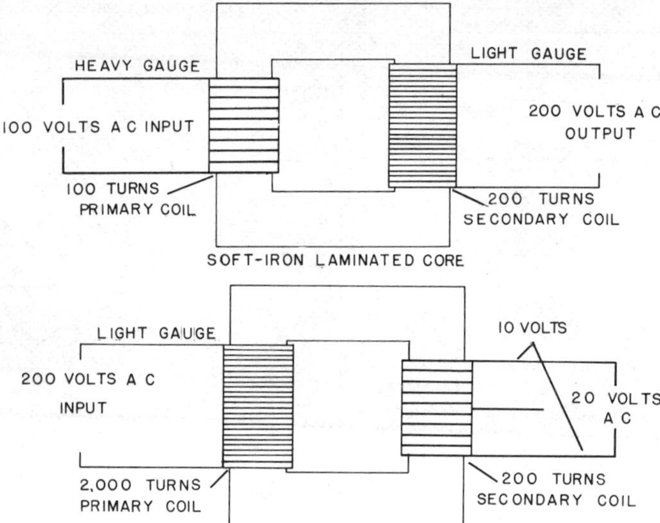

Figs. 18-25. Step-Up Transformer (above) **and Step-Down Transformer**

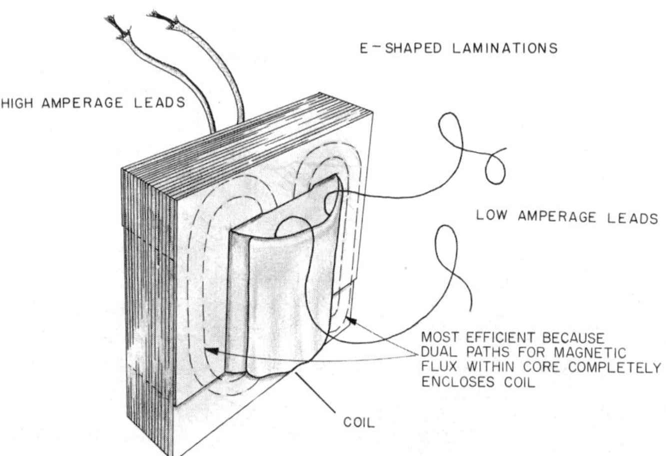

Fig. 18-26 Shell-Type Transformer

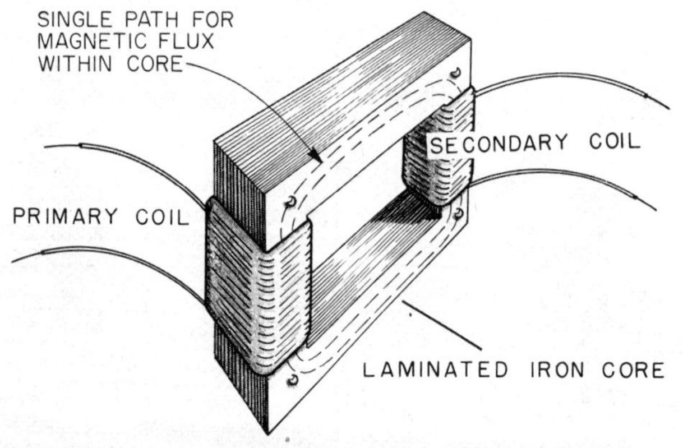

Fig. 18-27. Ring-Type Closed-Core Transformer

Description

The transformer is made with two separate circuit windings. One is called the *primary* winding and carries the AC line voltage, and the other, the *secondary* winding, carries the induced voltage of the same AC frequency and almost the same power as the primary.

We have discovered that power is a product of voltage and current and in a transformer the power input is almost equal to power output although the voltage and current ratios may be different. This ratio of current to voltage depends upon the ratio of primary windings to secondary windings. If the secondary winding has more turns than the primary, the voltage will be greater, and if the secondary has fewer turns than the primary, the voltage would be less than the voltage in the primary. Power in the secondary remains almost equal to that received by the primary. Therefore, as the voltage increases the current decreases, or as the voltage decreases the current increases proportionately.

Turns Ratio

If the ratio of the primary winding to the secondary winding is 1 to 1, the magnetic flux cuts across both windings and induces a voltage in the secondary winding that is almost the same as the voltage input in the primary. Such a transformer is called an *isolation* transformer, and finds application where a physical separation is desired between the line circuit and the secondary circuit. Servicemen sometimes employ this device as a protection against electric shocks and for the protection of the test equipment. We have also learned that such an induced current will be 90° out of phase with the original current.

If there were twice as many turns in the secondary as in the primary, then the magnetic flux of each primary turn cuts two secondary windings, inducing twice the voltage in the secondary. Thus the output voltage would be twice the input or a ratio of 1:2. See Fig. 18-25. However, because the power output is equal to power input, the current is always proportionately less. In other words, the ratio of current in the primary winding and secondary winding is the reverse of the ratio of voltages, or 2:1.

It is important to realize that when a current flows and a magnetic field is produced in the primary, the induced current flow in the secondary will be in the opposite direction. The magnetic field created will be of opposite polarity to the primary. The induced magnetic field opposes the primary magnetic field, a fact known as *Lenz's Law.*

Efficiency

The modern transformer is one of the most efficient devices of man. Copper losses caused by the resistance found in the copper windings is small. Losses due to *eddy currents* of magnetism in the core are reduced by using insulated laminations for the core, instead of a solid core. Special silicon steel has minimized the *hysteresis* loss due to molecular friction in the core. Other considerations to minimum loss is the shape of the core, and the placement of windings on the core.

Types of Transformers

Transformers may have cores of either air or iron. *Air cores* are used for ratio frequencies, never for power uses. There are three basic types of *iron-core transformers,* classified by the flux flow.

The *shell-type,* Fig. 18-26, is the most efficient. The secondary is wound over the primary and the core surrounds the coil. The *ring-shaped closed-core,* Fig. 18-27, has separated windings and a single flux path around the ring, so is less efficient. The *open-core* type has a straight iron-core such as in the ignition coils shown in Figs. 9-34 and 9-35. Flux must return through the open air around the poles, so it is very inefficient for power use.

There are many variations of these types. The *auto-transformer* has a single winding connected to the high voltage. Taps taken off along this winding give lower voltages. It is inexpensive, but the output is not isolated from the source, giving a shock hazard.

Importance of AC

Almost all of the electrical energy used in our modern civilization comes from generators. Household and commercial applications use alternating current almost exclusively. One reason is that AC generators, requiring no commutators, are much simpler to operate, maintain, and build.

Line Loss

Such an advantage is of minor significance compared to those inherent in AC when it comes to transmitting electrical energy from one place to another. Sometimes, electricity is transmitted over hundreds of miles from where it is generated. Although the power lines are made of low-resistance material, they still offer enough resistance to the flow of current to cause an appreciable *line loss.* This line loss results in the emission of heat from the conductor, and is called I^2R loss. Thus this heating effect is proportional to the square of the current. A 2-ampere current produces 2^2 or 4 times the heating loss of one ampere, 4 amperes of current produces 4^2 or 16 times that of a one-ampere current. To minimize heat loss, it is desirable to transmit the electrical energy at as low an amperage as possible.

Advantages of High Voltage

Power, if you recall, is the product of voltage and amperage. This indicates that if we were to increase or *step up* the voltage, the current would be decreased proportionately, keeping the power the same. For example, a current of 5 amperes at 100 volts would have the same wattage as a current of one ampere at 500 volts. The heating loss would be 25 times as great (5^2) with the 5 amperes as with one ampere.

In transmitting electrical energy over long distances it is desirable, therefore, to step the voltage up (within limits) in order to cut down on the line losses. Then at the point of consumption, the voltage can be stepped down, increasing the amperage proportionately. Electric railways using DC find an advantage in transmitting AC and rectifying it for use.

Transformer Applications

These changes in voltage and current are achieved with a transformer. A transformer that steps up the voltage is referred to as a *step up* transformer and has proportionately more windings in the secondary than in the primary. This establishes a desired ratio of input to output. A transformer that has fewer windings in the secondary than in the primary is called a *step down* transformer.

High Voltage Transmission

Typical voltages employed in the transmission of electrical energy are the following: the power-plant generator produces 13,800 volts. See Fig. 18-28. For reasons already cited, this is stepped up to as high as 700,000 volts for transmission. Higher voltages than these are not practical because of the inherent insulation and spacing problems. At the outskirts of the receiving city, a sub-station transformer steps down the voltage to 13,800 volts (Fig. 18-29); and at a few other places, transformers step down the voltage to 2,200 to 2,300 volts. Then, near the place of consumption, further reduction occurs to the usual 120, 240, or 480 volts.

Appliance Uses

Transformers find many applications in addition to those already cited in connection with power transmission. In television receivers, voltages are stepped up in excess of 550 volts, whereas model railroading and house bell-circuit voltages are stepped down to 10 to 16 volts. Electric arc welders step the voltages down considerably in order to increase the heat-producing current needed to fuse two metals together.

New Techniques Improve Power Transformers[1]

Traditionally, progress in power transformer design has been evolutionary with many

[1] Duboc, W. T., Westinghouse Technical Paper, Westinghouse Power Transformer Department, Muncie, Indiana.

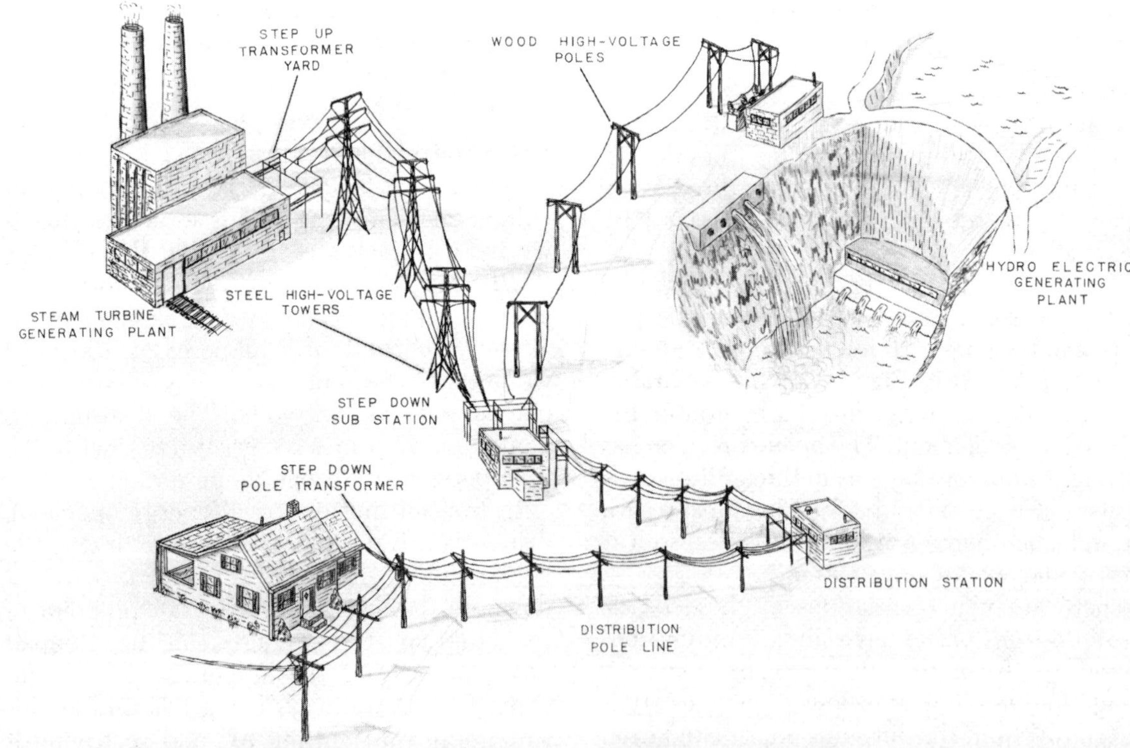

Fig. 18-28. Commercial Power Generation and Distribution

individual developments as contributing factors. During the last 40 years there has been a sixfold increase in the power output of a constant weight of transformer. The same techniques and materials utilized to improve efficiencies of high-voltage transformers are of benefit to most power transformers, Fig. 18-28A. This is especially important because 99% of all power transformers are for voltages below 230 KV. The developments now taking place in power transformers are largely evolutionary, but they have been accelerated by demands for higher voltage transformers. For example, the rise in maximum line voltage from 287 KV to 345 KV took about two decades. In contrast, the first commercial 555 KV lines were energized in 1964; and the first 700 KV lines were energized six months later. Development is now proceeding toward the possible use of 1,000 KV lines.

Insulation Improvements

Many of the more significant improvements in reliability and size reduction have been brought about through developments in insulation, either in the nature of improved materials or better design. The net result of this is that it is now possible to use smaller clearances. This work is continuing at an accelerated pace because of the present and future requirements for higher voltages and higher load capacities.

Windings

As the load requirements of power transmission have increased, the size and the assembly of the core and the windings have also been made larger and more complex. The design of transformers in this range of core-formed construction employs computer techniques because it is otherwise impossible to optimize designs with a degree of sophistication. In fact, the design and configuration of some units would have been out of the question as recently as ten years ago. The computer programs for power transformers were automated to simulate a trial-and-error approach for the design engineer. A theoretical transformer then could be built and tested in a computer prior to a model being constructed. Once the feasibility of the unit has been determined, then a prototype is built, tried, and tested. See Fig. 18-28B. This whole approach has shortened the development time considerably.

Aluminum Windings

Developments in the joining of metals have made it possible to build transformers with aluminum windings that are at least as reliable as those made with copper. Price stability and ready availability have always made aluminum attractive, but until recently these advantages were offset by the difficulty in making reliable joints. The development of MIG (metallic inert gas) and TIG (tungsten inert gas) welding as a substitute for brazing

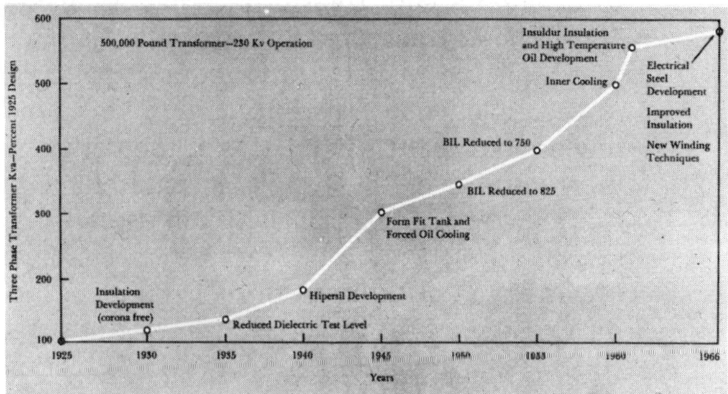

Fig. 18-28A. The Trend in Development of Shell-Form Transformers Illustrated by a Curve for One Weight and KV Capacity (Westinghouse)

Fig. 18-28B. Scale Model Used to Determine Voltage Differences Between Points (Westinghouse)

and the new mechanical crimping techniques have solved the joining problems to the degree that it is at least as easy, and in some cases more economical to join aluminum that it is to join an equivalent amount of copper. One of the most interesting developments along this line is the resistance welding of copper braid to aluminum strap.

Manufacturing Techniques

In addition to the utilization of different materials and different transformer designs, improved manufacturing practices have produced a more consistent and uniformly reliable transformer, Figs. 18-28C and 18-28D. The tolerances are tighter, and assembly techniques much more precise. The technology of adhesives and fastening provides opportunity to develop a core transformer that is smaller and more compact and yet consistently much more reliable than those heretofore possible.

Technology today permits coils to be wound much more tightly than those in the past, and the tightness of these coils is maintained to the life of the transformer by the use of high density pressboard and by the mechanical pre-stressing of the coils during the manufacturing process. Still another example of a recent development has been the introduction of a new insulating oil which has three times the oxidation stability of oils used previously. Epoxy materials have largely replaced the porcelain bushing, particularly for indoor applications, Fig. 18-28E. The epoxy materials have the advantage of flexibility. One of their earliest applications, for instance, was the molding of buss bar bushings for furnace transformer applications which permitted the first thoroughly effective and reliable gas-type bushing in this type transformer. Therefore, it made possible the use of an effective oil preservation system. The state of the art in power transformers is progressing at an accelerated rate with the advent of new materials, techniques, and concepts, Fig. 18-28F.

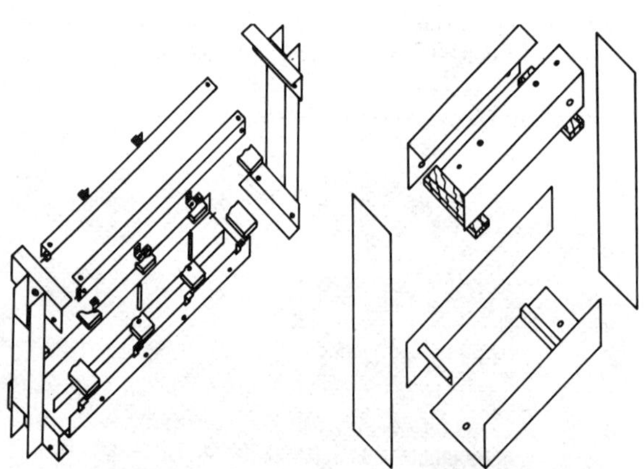

Fig. 18-28C. Improvements in Design of Parts Required to Hold Together the Core of a 2500-Kva Transformer (Westinghouse)

Left—Old Design, Composed of 53 Parts

Right—New Design, Composed of 14 Parts (Smaller, More Compact and Reliable)

Fig. 18-28D. This Automatic Core-Stacking Machine Cuts and Stacks Punchings for a Three-Phase, Core-Form Transformer (Westinghouse)

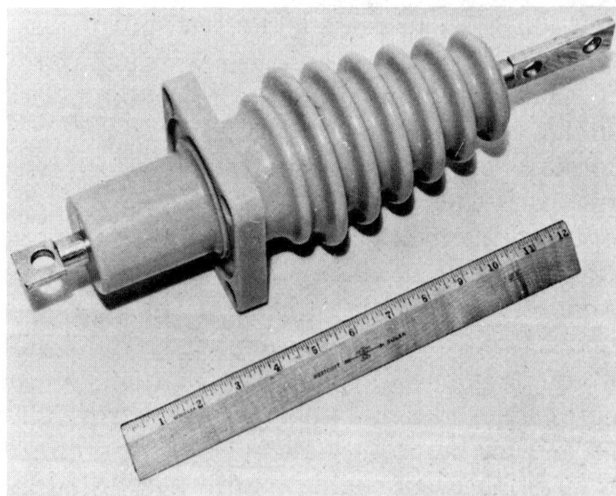

Fig. 18-28E. Cast Epoxy Bushing (Westinghouse)

Uses of Direct Current

Direct current, in spite of all the advantages found in alternating current, is needed for some applications. DC is required for operations which employ electrical energy to produce chemical change such as metal plating, metal refining, and battery charging. Direct current is also used where steady magnetic fields are needed, such as in electromagnetic cranes found in junk yards. Direct current motors, as we have already learned, have certain advantages for specific purposes. They find no equal where high initial torque is needed, as in railcars and elevators. The diesel-electric locomotive and marine engine use a diesel engine to generate a direct current which energizes the motor used for locomotion.

Stepping Up DC

Since the transformer requires alternating current for operation, it cannot be used to step up DC voltages. In its place, a less satisfactory induction coil is used. This device operates on the induction principle. A switching device breaks the primary circuit. This causes the magnetic field to build up and collapse. The moving flux cuts the many windings of the secondary and induces a high voltage. Potentials of hundreds of thousands of volts can be produced in this fashion. The ignition coil of an automobile, which generates the high voltages necessary to cause ignition is such a device.

Fig. 18-28F. 100 MVAR Single-Phase Shunt Reactor (Left) and 765 KV, 500 MVA Transformer (Right) (Westinghouse)

Rectification

Devices which are designed to operate only on direct current and need to be operated from a source supplying only alternating current require a rectifier to convert AC to DC. Rectifiers are of several types: electronic, mechanical, and chemical.

Superconductivity

Although the idea of superconductivity is not new, having been discovered at the University of Leyden in 1911 by Dr. Onnes, research was at a relative standstill until the improvement of techniques in cryogenic technology. As liquid helium, once a laboratory curiosity, was made commercially available, further research into the principles of superconductivity became feasible.

At temperatures near absolute zero, certain metals and metallic compounds have electrical resistance too small to be measured: zero as nearly as can be determined. Dr. Onnes first observed this phenomena in a specimen of mercury, which was held at a temperature of about 4.2° Kelvin. On the Kelvin Absolute Zero Scale, zero represents the complete absence of heat or —459.7°F. Therefore, the specimen of mercury was slightly more than 4° above absolute zero, the boiling point of liquid helium. His observation remained somewhat of a puzzle or oddity for decades, and was inexplicable at that time. We now know that an ideal metal, a large perfect single crystal, has zero resistance at exactly absolute zero. A superconducting actual metal has a small finite resistance at 0° Kelvin. Superconductors, however, attain zero resistance at a transition temperature somewhere above 0° Kelvin. Transition temperatures range from a fraction of a degree to 18° Kelvin, the highest recorded temperature where this phenomenon has occurred. Superconductor research has led to the discovery of superconducting magnets. It was conceived that a magnet constructed with superconducting windings and operated below the transition temperature would have no resistance to the flow of current, and thus no heat would be developed in generating the magnetic field. Power consumption would be limited to a negligible amount, only that needed to generate the field of magnetic power required.

There has been continued and increased enthusiasm in developing a superconducting magnet in order to supply the increased needs for high field magnets in physical research. At present, research indicates that superconductors have both the magnetic and thermal properties necessary to establish without doubt that a bulk effect is being realized.

Energy and the Environment

Our environment is composed of air, water, land. Our plant life ranges from bacteria to forests, our animal life from protozoa to fish and mammals. They are all interdependent; if any essential component is removed or modified, the total environment is affected.

Man has affected his environment adversely. For example, he has cut the trees and improperly cultivated the soil which has resulted in soil erosion. Just as these activities were executed by people of another generation not wholly conscious of long-term environmental effects, so has modern man innocently employed chemicals as fertilizers and pesticides and caused some undesirable environmental effects.

Sources of Energy - Review

The sun is the major source of natural energy. It continuously pours thermal energy on to the earth at the rate of 177 trillion kilowatts. Fortunately for us, the earth constantly reflects most of this heat back into space.

It is estimated that the natural energy about us is 10,000 times as great as what man creates for himself. There are two important points to remember about natural energy. The first is that there are severe limitations on the conversion of natural energy to electricity. Solar heat and wind energy, for example, are precluded because they are not constant and electricity is difficult to store in large amounts. Water energy is more dependable but is limited in amount, and often is in an inaccessible location. Normally the energy we use for conversion is "stored" energy which can be released or converted as man wants it.

The second important consideration of natural energy is that stored energy originated as solar energy. The process of storage was through photosynthesis and took place over millions of years. All of the fossil fuels such as coal, oil, and natural gas represent absorbed solar heat, and by their combustion this energy is released. It took millions of years, under proper conditions, to store this energy. Therefore, we can rightly say that these fossil fuels are not reproducible resources.

There is, of course, one other known source of stored energy—"nuclear energy." This could properly be referred to as stored "cosmic energy" that may be released through nuclear fission or fusion, and is one of the great technological achievements of the 20th century. The original process converted nuclear energy to electricity by consuming the natural resource uranium much in the same manner as fossil fuels were consumed. That is, when the energy was released, the fuel was burned up and there was nothing left.

The new generation of reactors, called "breeder reactors," will create a new fuel as they convert energy to electricity and come close to making nuclear fuel that will be fully reproducible.

Enviromental Concerns

Within the last 10 years much concern has been expressed about the ways man is polluting and damaging his environment. There are several reasons for this increasing concern.

First, increased population and increased industrial activity have proportionately increased pollutants, in some instances beyond the self-cleaning ability of nature. In earlier days, raw sewage could be dumped into the lakes and streams without permanent damage, but population increases and increasing urbanization have produced a quantity of sewage that has exceeded the cleansing action of nature in some areas.

Second, many of these environmental effects are cumulative. For example, ten small communities could utilize a stream for sewage disposal, but as each community doubles in size the stream is overtaxed and the accumulation in a downstream lake rapidly approaches a critical life-or-death condition.

Third, many of the problems of our environment have been only recently recognized; for example, the effects a generating station has on the aquatic life in the lakes and streams.

Fourth, our affluent society can afford to consider the relative expense of purchasing remedial systems to protect the environment, particularly in the United States. In earlier, less prosperous times, the long-range protective measures suggested by conservationists could not even be discussed.

An Industrialized Society

In primitive societies man changed his environment and frequently did so in a damaging manner. As Glenn Seaborg, Chairman of the Atomic Energy Commission, observed, "We could return to the horse, but most people forget that at the height of the horse-and-buggy days, even the old gray mare created a pollution problem." However, a highly industrialized society represents a greater potential threat to the environment than an agricultural society.

Donald Straus, former Chairman of the Board of Planned Parenthood-World Population, was quoted in the *New York Times,* November 2, 1969, page 58: "Every child born in the United States consumes eight times as much of our natural resources as a child born in an underdeveloped country."

A highly industrialized society engages in tremendous heat energy conversion. Large amounts of natural resources are consumed, and a tremendous amount of combustion pollutants are released into the environment. Much of this combustion is for the purpose of providing heat, and much is for energy conversion to electrical power and automotive power.

The technology that is accused of polluting society must be able to find ways and means of curbing and controlling pollution. Mechanical cleaners, electrostatic precipitators, cooling towers, and anti-pollution devices must be continued in development and refined. Technology may lead to the conservation of natural resources as with the breeder reactor, but on the other hand these advances result in an increased standard of living and an increased alteration of the environment. Technology is the tool of man, and man alone is responsible for its results, useful or harmful.

Electricity and Technology

The problems involving energy conversion, technology and industrialization, population, and the adverse effects to the environment come together in an intricate inter-relationship in the study of electricity. Electricity exhibits advantages superior to other sources of energy. The consumption of electricity is reflective of the degree of industrialization. Since most electricity is produced by the use of heat, increases in the production of electricity usually mean increases in adverse environmental effects. Electricity usually is the result of a heat energy conversion, and although electrical energy is used as an energy source to heat homes and buildings, this decrease in pollution from coal, oil and gas space-heating plants is reflected in an increase of pollutants from power generating stations.

There are many projections of electrical power needs for the next two or three decades. The installed capacity by the end of 1969 was 300,000 megawatts. If the capacity is to double (a conservative estimate) in the next decade, 250 to 300 new power plants will have to be built, all of a size larger than the largest plants that are now in operation. The magnitude of this projection can be realized in several ways. Two decades of new power plants will cost more than 100 billion dollars, and these plants will have to be located on sites that range in size from 100 to 1,200 acres. Unless the plant recirculates cooling water, each plant will require 7.9 billion to 12 billion gallons of water per day. It has been estimated that by 1980 the electrical power generating system for this country will require about one-sixth of the available fresh water supply.

If all these power plants were coal fired, they would consume approximately 800 million tons of coal per year by 1980. If these new plants were oil fired, by 1980 there would be 3.4 billion barrels of oil required. If the new plants used natural gas, by 1980 they would require 19,200 billion cubic feet of gas.

Now, for comparison, the coal production for the United States for all purposes in 1967 was 565 million tons; oil production was 3.2 billion barrels and gas production was 18,171 billion cubic feet. Of course, the projected power plants will not use any one energy source. Some will use coal, others oil, still others gas and some will use nuclear fuels. A minute number will be hydro plants. Nevertheless any combination will provide staggering environmental problems for society.

For constructive planning over the next two decades, two environmental considerations are: (1) the significant consumption of unrenewable natural resources, and (2) the adverse effects on the environment of fossil fuel converters.

Of the three fossil fuels, the one that is most plentiful is coal. Ironically, it is the one that pollutes the atmosphere most when burned. Gas pollutes the environment the least but is also the least plentiful of the natural fuels. These fossil fuels are also employed to satisfy other needs of man. Natural gas is a source of hydrogen and ammonia, and coal and oil are sources of dyes and some plastics.

Since the first chain reaction in Chicago in 1942, nuclear fuels have produced heat with relatively little adverse effect on the environment except for a small amount of radioactive gases and some increase in water temperature and air temperature depending on the type of coolant the system employs. Economically and environmentally, the life cycle of the nuclear fuel is such that it may be the sole support of electrical generation in the next 25 to 50 years.

As noted earlier in the production of electricity by the use of heat, not all of the heat is "consumed" and the excess is dissipated into the air or water. The only distinction between fossil fuel plants and nuclear power plants in regard to excess heat is that nuclear power plants are less efficient today. By 1980 it is likely that nuclear powered generation will be as efficient as fossil fuel systems.

The problem of heat dissipation is common to all steam-electric power plants. It is significant because of the great size of these plants and the increasing demands of the future. The addition of heat to the environment is obviously not pollution as such. The entire dynamic environment constantly involves heat transfers and any problem of heat dissipation in a power plant is one of the manner of dissipation and the degree of concentration. These thermal effects, where undesirable, have been ameliorated by technological ingenuity.

Nuclear power plants involve an element of water "pollution" because isotopes do show up in the water discharged from nuclear plants. The contamination from isotopes, how-

Fig. 18-29. Inner-Cooled Transformer at Substation (Westinghouse)

ever, will be markedly decreased as the state of the art is improved.

In summary, it is evident that fossil fuels are in sufficient supply to satisfy the world's power requirements for about three centuries. Water power and geothermal power are useful, but of small magnitude, leaving only nuclear energy as a source of sufficient magnitude to supply the world's long-range power requirement.[2]

Terms to Understand

Michael Faraday	sine wave
DC generator	phase
self-excited	two phase
AC generator	three phase
alternator	out of phase
split commutator	inductive reactance
ring commutator	capacitive reactance
rotor	leading current
stator	lagging current
exciter	induction motor
field	universal motors
armature	split phase motors
capacitor starting	starting winding
shaded pole motors	transformers
repulsion-induction	primary
synchronous motors	secondary
squirrel cage rotor	induced voltage
rotor currents	line loss
resultant force	I^2R
slip	superconductivity
synchronous speed	cryogenic technology
centrifugal switch	environmental pollution
step up transformer	high voltage transmission
step down transformer	aluminum windings
shell transformer	epoxy insulation

[2] Braden, G. D., and Brown, D. H., *Energy and the Environment in Perspective,* Paper included in Manual for Instructors, Northeast Utilities, March 26, 1970.

Study Questions

1. What happens when a conductor is made to move within a magnetic field?
2. Analyze Faraday's contribution to the field of power.
3. Explain the operation of a DC generator.
4. How does an AC generator differ from a DC generator? Explain the principles of operation.
5. What is AC?
6. Analyze the term "phase" in AC circuitry.
7. Describe the operation of an induction motor.
8. How do AC motors differ from DC motors?
9. Describe types of AC motors and where they are used.
10. What is meant by single, double, and three-phase AC systems?
11. What is transformer action? Explain how transformers operate.
12. What is meant by *step-up* and *step-down* transformers? Explain.
13. Explain how electricity is transmitted.
14. Describe the various types of transformers.
15. Describe superconductivity.
16. What is likely to be the predominant fuel of the future?

Selected Readings for Part IV
Conventional Electrical Converters

Anderson, Edwin P., *Electric Motors,* (Indianapolis, Indiana: Theodore Audel & Co., Div. of Howard W. Sams & Co., Inc., 1968)

Fuchs, J. David, and Garstang, S. W., *Electrical Motor Controls and Circuits,* (Indianapolis, Indiana: Howard W. Sams Co., Inc., 1968)

Fundamentals of Service – Electrical Systems, (Moline, Illinois: John Deere Service Publications, 1971)

Graham, Kenvard C., *Understanding and Servicing Fractional Horsepower Motors,* (Chicago: American Technical Society, 1961)

Jones, E. W., *Fundamentals of Applied Electricity,* (Milwaukee: Bruce Publishing Co., 1956)

Lytel, Allen, *ABC's of Electric Motors and Generators,* (Indianapolis, Indiana: Howard W. Sams Co., Inc., 1964)

McIntyre, R. L., *AC Motor Control Fundamentals,* (New York: McGraw-Hill Book Co., 1960)

Miller, Rex, and Culpepper, Fred, *Energy, Electricity and Electronics,* (Bloomington, Illinois: McKnight & McKnight Publishing Co., 1964)

Nesbitt, E. A., *Ferromagnetic Domains,* (New York: Bell Telephone Laboratories, 1962)

Schweitzer, Gerald, *Basics of Fractional Horsepower Motors and Repair,* (New York: John F. Rider, Publisher, 1960)

Sears, Francis, and Zomansky, Mark, *College Physics, Mechanics, Heat, and Sound,* (Addison Wesley Publishing Co., 1956)

Smeaton, Robert W., *Motor Application and Maintenance Handbook,* (New York: McGraw-Hill Book Co., 1968)

Steinberg, William S., and Ford, Walter B., *Electricity and Electronics,* (Chicago: American Technical Society, 1962)

Suffern, M. G., *Basic Electrical and Electronic Principles,* (New York: McGraw-Hill Book Co., 1962)

Tinnell, Richard W., *Electronics – Electricity:* Electromechanical Technology Series. TERC EMT STAFF, (Albany, New York: Delmar Publishers, 1971)

Van Valkenburgh, Nooger and Neville, *Basic Electricity,* (New York: John F. Rider, Publisher, 1959)

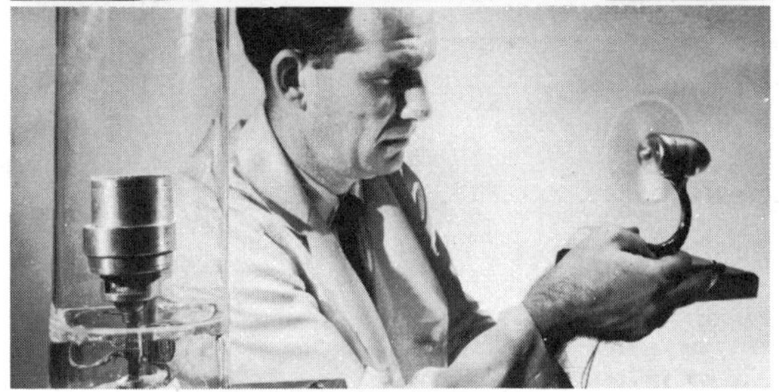

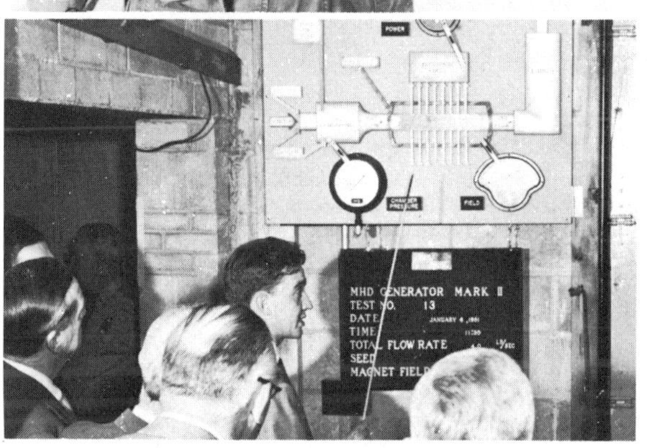

1. Testing Solar Cell Output (RCA), 2. Motor Run by Small Semiconductors Heated to 1800°F (RCA), 3. $H_2 + O_2 = H_2O$ and 200 watts in Military Fuel-Cell Pack (GE), 4. Power Company Executives Study MHD Generator Designed for 500,000 watts.

PART **V**

DIRECT ELECTRICAL CONVERTERS

The potential energy of heat, light, or fuel is *converted directly* to usable electrical power.

Chapter

Exotic Generators as Power Sources, **19**

Exotic Generators as Power Sources

The development of modern civilization can be traced through the study of the energy converters used by man. Today, our society is characterized by an abundant and rapidly expanding use of power. Fig. 19-1. This can be noted especially in the relationship between per capita energy consumption and per capita productivity in several countries which are presently at different levels of development. This is shown in Fig. 19-2. The types of power which could be commanded at different points of historical development and their application provide interesting material for study. These observations indicate that the use of energy is rapidly accelerating. Per capita energy consumption indicates that a present-day middle aged man has consumed more energy than was used by all generations of individuals before him back to the early part of the 17th Century.[1]

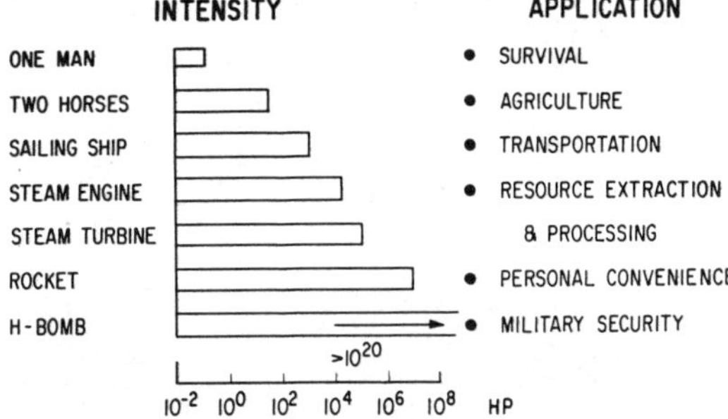

Fig. 19-1. Historical Growth of Power (GE)

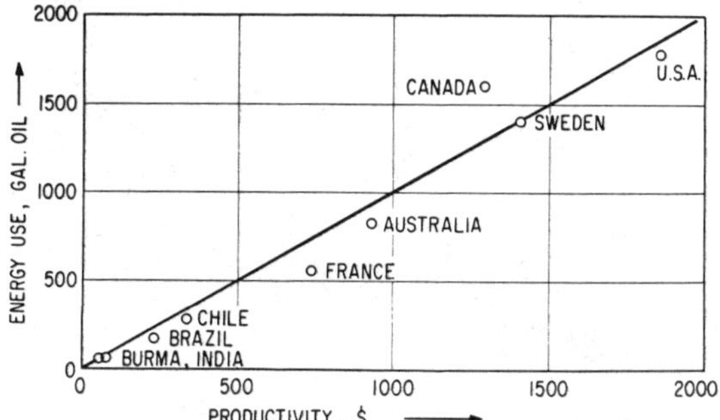

Fig. 19-2. Per Capita Energy Use vs. Productivity (GE)

Direct Converters

Dynamic changes in the technology of energy conversion is to be expected with such rapid increases in consumption. More activity has taken place in the recent past than in any other time during the history of man. Fig. 19-3 lists five new sources of power developed since 1950. These are the several kinds of *direct conversion processes,* known

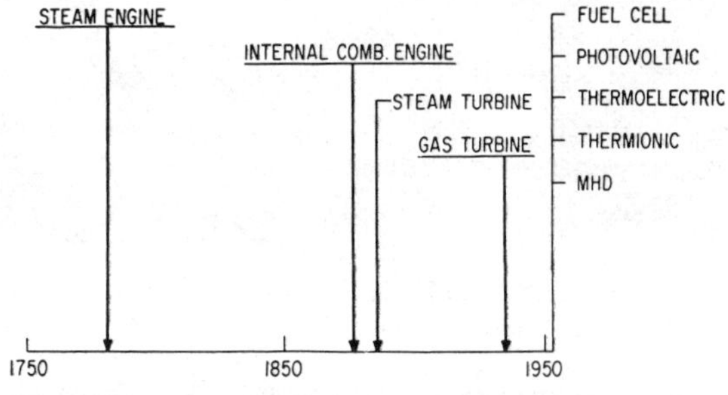

Fig. 19-3. Introduction of Power Generators (GE)

[1] D. H. Marques, "A Survey of Direct Energy Conversion", presented at the 69th Annual Meeting of the American Society for Engineering Education, Lexington, Kentucky, (June, 1961).

as *exotic power sources.* They represent a complete departure from the conventional energy conversion processes and have characteristics which may bypass some of the limitations of conventional converters.

Developmental Factors

Some of the factors prompting direct converters provide an interesting study of modern man's needs. Obviously, the new needs of the missile and space programs have provided a powerful impetus. Coupling new technology with unique needs is bound to produce innovations. For example, thermoelectric converters were being studied as far back as 1947. However, they did not command widespread attention until the development of semiconductors. Semiconductors have interesting physical properties which make them suitable for such use. Similarly, MHD power generators were experimented with more than fifteen years ago, Fig. 19-4. Their potential was never fully realized until the development of high temperature materials and a better understanding of the behavior of hot ionized gases called *plasmas.* Plasmas are a by-product of our missile nuclear program.

Even though none of the exotic energy conversion processes developed so far suggest any serious competition for the big job of producing electricity in quantity for home and industry, they are earning serious attention. This is because turbine generators have reached an efficiency plateau as shown in Fig. 19-5. Inasmuch as present turbine generators are relatively mature, the opportunity for further improvement is limited to increasing the maximum temperature at which power is extracted. Hotter temperatures will require costly austentic steels in turbines and boilers. The best application of such large power stations presently lies in situations where the 40 percent efficiency of steam-turbine generators is not important. The new direct power sources seem especially suitable to specialized military applications where portability, noise-free operation, and low fuel needs are desirable. However, pressures do exist for more economical generation of central station electrical power. Since the cost of efficient and accessible fossil fuels is gradually increasing this is becoming more and more pressing. Pressure will continue to soar as the demand for power in this country steadily doubles every ten years and the problems of air, land, and water pollution become more acute.

Efficiency

Direct-conversion processes offer interesting possibilities for improvement in efficiency. The *fuel cell,* for instance, has efficiencies close to 100 per cent. *Magnetohydrodynamic* and *thermionic converters* may extend the upper limit of temperature used by conventional steam and gas turbines and extract energy not available to them. This is seen if one compares the 1050°F temperature plateau of the steam turbine to the 5000°F temperature required for hot gas plasma conductivity in the MHD generator shown in

Fig. 19-4. Experimental MHD Power Generator (Westinghouse)

This unit blasts hot ionized gas from an oil-oxygen flame through a magnetic field at 1,800 miles per hour. Designed for 10 kw., unit has produced 2.5 kw. A current gathering electrode is in the man's hand.

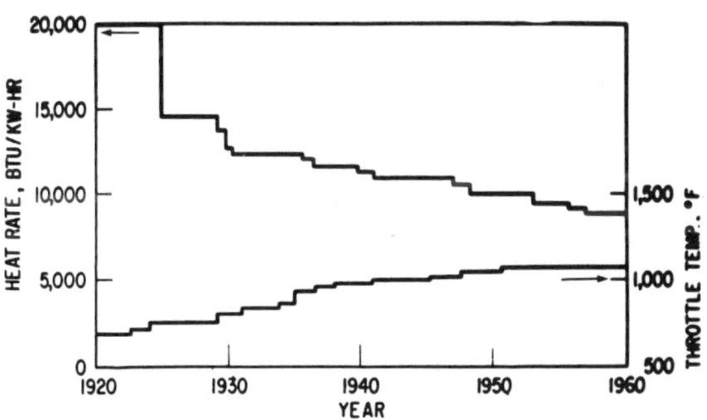

Fig. 19-5. Typical Best Power Stations

Fig. 19-6. Harris[2] has suggested the possibility of adding MHD converters to the steam cycle of turbine generators to increase their potential efficiency from 40 per cent to better than 50 per cent. This idea of using the MHD converters would have merit especially in nuclear reactors because fission releases tremendous heat. This heat typically is not used until it has cooled to about 600°F. If the MHD converter is placed so that the heat flows from the reactor through it then to the turbine, this may provide man with the possibility of extracting energy from the extreme heat that is now wasted. One of several methods of adding an MHD converter to a steam turbo-generator system is shown in Fig. 19-7.

[2] L. P. Harris, *MHD Power Generator: An Application of Magneto-hydrodynamics.* Proceedings of the National Electronics Conference, Vol. 16, 1960, p. 356-368.

Fig. 19-6. One-Watt Experimental MHD Generator (Westinghouse)

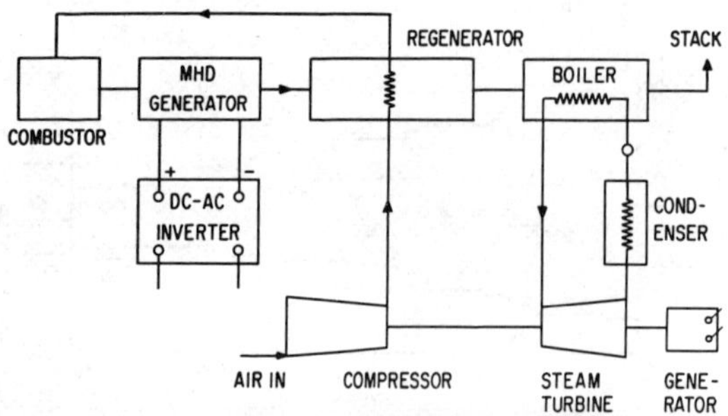

Fig. 19-7. MHD Unit Topping a Steam System

Needs for New Power

Of course, the true purpose for all this power advance is to be able to provide the world's underdeveloped areas with a source of power which can be utilized for industrial growth and generate the necessary capital for further development. The major part of the world's population uses less than one-tenth the per capita power of that used in this country. Noticeable differences exist in productivity between the U.S. and other countries with less per capita power. Electrical power must be made available for productive uses in order to change the historical trends that have seemingly created this unbalance in living standards. Lack of money restricts power development and creates a need for small generating equipment suitable for isolated communities.

Primitive transportation systems place another obstacle in the development of power stations. Exotic power converters offer the possibility of generating electricity from locally available energy sources. For example, photovoltaic converters change sunlight to electricity, and solar thermoelectric converters change the heat of the sun to current.

Variety of Direct Converters

A better look at direct conversion processes reveals a variety of techniques. They can generally be classified by the energy source, the transfer mechanism, and the converter which produces electrical power with waste heat. Some of the main types are MHD generators, fuel cells, photovoltaic converters, thermionic converters, and thermoelectric converters.

Magnetohydrodynamic Generator

Magnetohydrodynamics, abbreviated MHD, is that branch of physics which includes both electromagnetic and fluid dynamic phenoma. MHD *power generation* is somewhat the reverse of the MHD plasma pinch propulsion studied earlier. For *propulsion,* an electromagnetic field causes a gas, the plasma, to flow. For *power generation,* a fast-flowing plasma is forced through a magnetic field to create an emf. Similar electromagnetic comparisons are made of mechanical motors and generators.

Present MHD generators use a conducting stream of ionized gas for the *plasma*. For the gas to be conducting, it must be partly ionized and must be made to contain a certain number of free electrons. The main body, however, must remain mostly un-ionized. This quality of partially ionizing a gas and thereby making it a conductor can be directly achieved by *heating* it sufficiently. Presently, the necessary temperatures are beyond the limits of even the most modern materials.

To lower the required temperatures to about 5000°F the gas is *seeded* with potassium or cesium salts. MHD generation, as currently conceived, is made possible by the small region of tolerance between the temperature requirement and the temperatures that present-day materials are able to withstand.

Operation of MHD Generator

In the MHD generator, Fig. 19-8, the hot plasma is generated and seeded in a burner similar to a rocket engine. It then travels through a magnetic field which is applied at right angles to the flow and past electrodes which are exposed to this stream of gas. Electrons in the gas are deflected by the field, and between collisions with the particles in the gas, they make their way to one of the electrodes. Electricity is caused to flow as the electrons move from the cathode through the load to the anode and back again to the gas stream.

The generated voltage is directly proportional to the intensity of the magnetic field, the velocity of the gas, and the distance between the electrodes. The overall thermal efficiency of a plant utilizing an MHD generator might be as high as 60 per cent, as compared with 40 to 45 percent for conventional power generating systems.

Closed Cycle

A possible cycle arrangement is shown in Fig. 19-9. This *closed-cycle* system uses helium seeded with 1 per cent cesium for its plasma. This plant could produce 380 megawatts of AC power. An inverter must be employed to produce AC because MHD generators produce only DC. Although the initial cost would be appreciably greater, it would not be prohibitive since the greater efficiency of the total system would cut the cost per kilowatt.

The MHD generator for this system would be 30 to 40 feet long with an operating temperature of 4000°F. The reactor used as the heating device would not be possible until newer materials are developed. The boiler or heat exchanger also presents serious developmental problems.

In this system, a boiler picks up some heat to generate steam. This is used to drive a 38 megawatt turbine which powers the gas compressor. A motor can be used to supplement the turbine, receiving its energy from the MHD generator.

To circumvent burner developmental problems, there are two possible approaches. The first uses a combustion-fired external heater (as diagramed in Fig. 19-7) while retaining

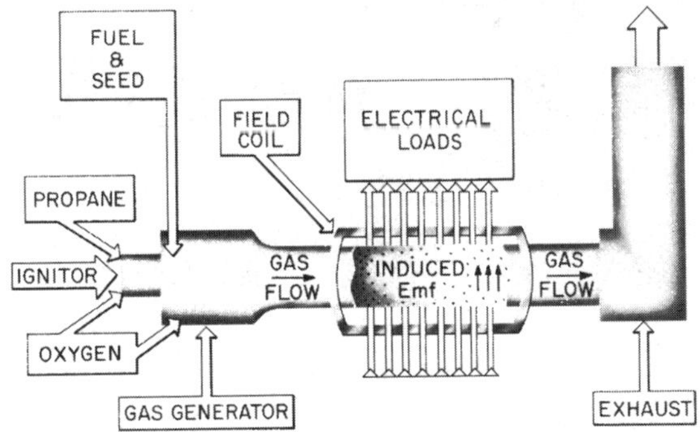

Fig. 19-8. Mark II MHD Power Generator (Avco)

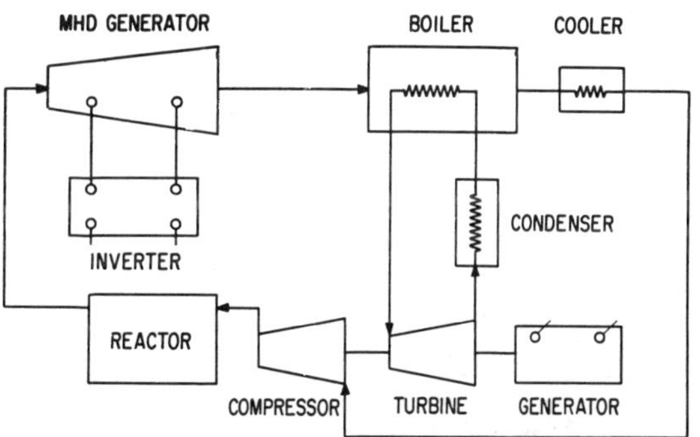

Fig. 19-9. Closed-Cycle MHD System

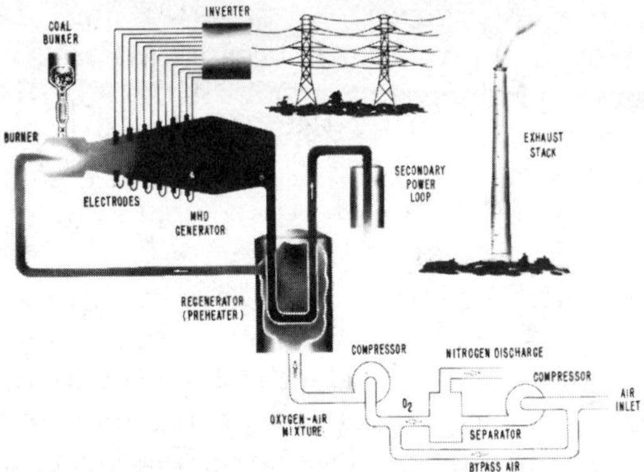

Fig. 19-10. Proposed Commercial Power MHD Generator (Avco)

By using oxygen-enriched air rather than air itself the preheater can be constructed of conventional materials available today. Steam generated in the secondary power loop turns turbines giving power for the compressors and conventional generators. This is being studied by 12 leading power companies.

Fig. 19-11. Large Scale Research MHD Generator

This is probably the largest most advanced MHD generator—designed for 500 kw. It has iron pole pieces with copper plates connected to form a coil. A gas burner like a rocket engine (out of view to the right) produces 5000°F plasma which is exhausted at left. Electric cables are at top left.

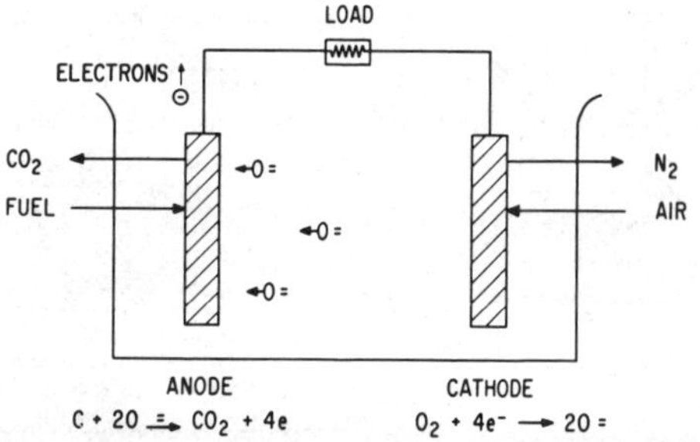

Fig. 19-12. Carbon-Oxygen Fuel Cell (GE)

the closed-loop helium system. The second uses an open system in which the combustion gases pass directly through the generator as in Fig. 19-10. The temperatures of operation here must be higher because of the lower mobility of electrons in the combustion gases than in helium. Potassium is used to seed the gas because cesium is too expensive to discharge. Also, precautions must be taken to avoid air pollution.

Future Possibilities

The MHD generator has tremendous potential, but its worth will never be fully realized until some problems of plasma physics, materials, and engineering technology are solved. General Electric, Westinghouse, and Avco are only some of the com-

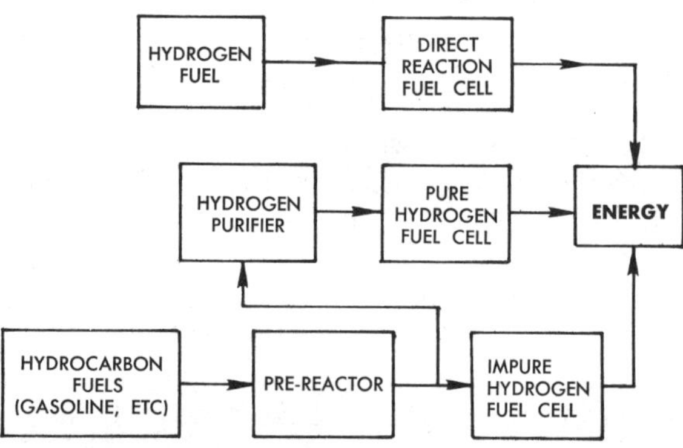

Fig. 19-12A. How Fuel Is Reacted (Pratt-Whitney)

Top: If the fuel is sufficiently reactive, it can be oxidized directly in the fuel cell.

Bottom: An alternate approach is to prereact the fuel to produce hydrogen plus impurities consisting of carbon dioxide or nitrogen (depending on the fuel). This impure hydrogen can be sent directly to a fuel cell which can tolerate the impure hydrogen.

Center: The impure hydrogen can be put through a purifier to separate the impurities and then sent to a conventional hydrogen-oxygen fuel cell.

The simplest and most desirable method is to oxidize the fuel directly into the fuel cell. However, most fuels react at lower rates than hydrogen, even at elevated temperatures and in the presence of catalysts. The weight and volume of a fuel cell increase rapidly with decreasing reaction rates, tending to make such a power plant less competitive with the combustion engine because of its size. The alternate approach — to prereact the fuel in compact appropriate equipment — can make use of less reactive fuels. The techniques depend upon the fuel.

panies that are doing research in this field of power generation. See Fig. 19-11. It is interesting to note that in three or four years, this generator has been developed to produce continuously, hundreds of kilowatts in combustion plasmas as compared to watts for milliseconds in shock tubes of yesterday. The future may see this generator extended to produce megawatts at an attractive cost.

Fuel Cells

A *fuel cell* is an electrochemical device which converts the *free energy* of a chemical reaction directly to electrical energy. It differs from conventional batteries in that it consumes a low cost fuel and an oxidant which are continuously fed into the system.

Oxygen-Concentration Cell

Fig. 19-12 is a diagram of one of the simplest fuel cells. This cell is called an *oxygen-concentration cell,* and it consists of an electrolyte which conducts an electric charge in the form of oxygen ions, but acts as an insulator to electrons. The electrolyte is located between the two electrodes and when the oxygen is at different concentrations at the two electrodes, a voltage exists.

In operation, an oxygen molecule moves through the porous cathode to the junction with the electrolyte. The molecule picks up four electrons creating separate oxygen ions. These move into the electrolyte leaving a positive charge on the cathode. The ions continue to move through the electrolyte to the anode where they release their electrons and combine again to form an oxygen molecule. The cathode receives the released electrons and becomes negatively charged. The oxygen continues on into the chamber where it combines with a fuel or is exhausted from the system. If the two electrodes are connected externally through a load, a current will be caused to flow. As long as there exists at the anode a fuel to react with the oxygen, there is a difference in oxygen concentration between the two electrodes and a current will continue to flow in the circuit.[3]

[3] R. Ruka, *High Temperature Fuel Cells,* Westinghouse Electric Corp., Pittsburgh, Pa.

Hydrox Cell

The *hydrogen-oxygen fuel cell* reverses the well-known process of electrolysis. See Fig. 19-13. Instead of separating water into its components by passing an electrical charge through it, water is created in a controlled reaction that liberates electrical energy.

In this fuel cell, an acid electrolyte is used. At the anode, hydrogen gives up an electron (e–) to the load while simultaneously releasing hydrogen (h+) to the electrolyte. At the cathode, these hydrogen ions combine with oxygen and the electrons from the load circuit to produce water. Balance of material and electrical charges is maintained by the movement of electrons through the circuit and ions through the electrolyte. Water is formed at the anode. Interrupting current flow in the external circuit or ion flow internally interrupts the power.

Presently, there are four major types of fuel cells: *hydrox cells, redox cells, hydrocarbon cells,* and *ion-exchange membrane cells.*

We have already discussed the oxygen concentration and the hydrox (hydrogen and oxygen) cells. These moderate temperature

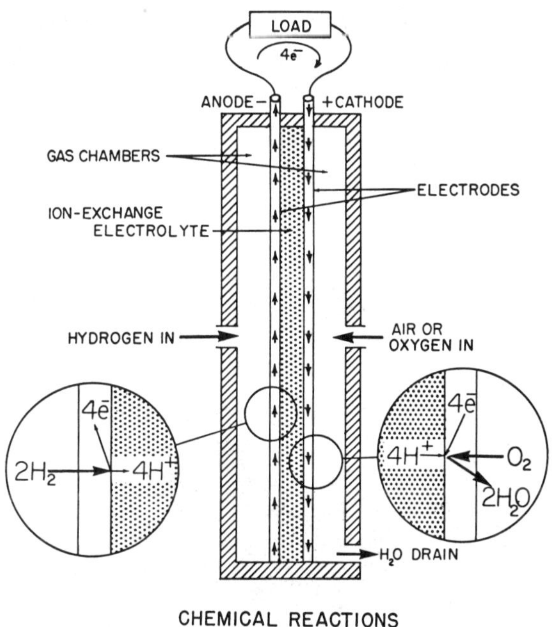

Fig. 19-13. Hydrogen-Oxygen Fuel Cell (GE)

cells use either acid or alkaline electrolysis and depend upon nickel or carbon electrodes of controlled porosity to acquire a large reaction area.

The reaction of these cells is limited but can be increased by raising cell temperature. However, to insure adequate partial pressures of fuel and oxidant, the cell must be pressurized. One factor that limits the utility of this type cell is that the theoretical maximum efficiency decreases as the temperature is increased.

Fig. 19-14. Experimental High-Temperature Carbon-Oxygen Fuel Cell (Westinghouse)

Fig. 19-15. Ion-Exchange Membrane Fuel Cell (GE)

Redox Cell

The redox fuel fuel cell is a hydrogen and oxygen cell, but it differs from the previous approach in that the fuel and oxidant consumed in the overall reaction are not reacted to at the electrodes. It is a two-step process. The separating membrane, located between the electrodes, separates two electrolyte solutions. On each side, intermediate reactions take place between the gasified fuel and liquid electrolyte on one side (reduction) and between air and a liquid electrolyte on the other (oxidation). The liquid electrolyte contacts both the solid electrode and the membrane. Electrical and material balance is maintained by the migration of hydrogen ions across the separating membrane.

Hydrocarbon Cell

A hydrocarbon fuel cell, Fig. 19-14, operates at temperatures above 500°C and uses molten carbohydrates as its electrolytes. This electrolyte is usually held in a sponge-like matrix of magnesium oxide, and the metallic electrodes are kept in direct contact with the solid electrolyte matrix.

The usual fuel for this cell is a hydrocarbon such as gasoline which is cracked inside the cell to produce hydrogen and carbon monoxide. This combination is diffused at one electrode into the cell. This reacts with ions in the carbonate to form water and carbon dioxide while releasing electrons to the electrode. Oxygen or air at the other electrode picks up the electrons to produce ions which move through the electrolyte to make the circuit complete.

Current research indicates that molten salt cells may have a higher efficiency potential than any other method, dependent upon chemical energy of fuel reactions. However, these cells have not yet reached the stage of practical application because of the size of the furnace and the limitations of present materials.

Ion-Exchange Membrane Cell

The ion-exchange membrane cell Fig. 19-15, is like the hydrox cell of Fig. 19-13 but it eliminates the liquid phase entirely. The reaction is localized by the use of a solid electrolyte and a plastic membrane. The plastic membrane permits hydrogen ions to migrate from one electrode to the other.

Here again, hydrogen and air enter chambers on opposite sides of the ion-permeable membrane and penetrate the porous electrodes to contact the surfaces of the membrane. On the hydrogen side the electrons are given up, collected by the electrode, and conducted to the load. The hydrogen ions travel through the solid electrolyte to the other surface of the membrane where they combine with the returning electrons in the presence of oxygen from the air. The formation of water and electrical energy is the total end result.

Fuel Cell Application

The unique characteristic of the fuel cell offers many advantages for electric power generation. For example, a fuel cell contains no moving parts and can operate silently. This makes maintenance almost a thing of the past. Fuel cells do not operate on a heat cycle which limits the more conventional heat engine generators. Fuel cell efficiency is independent of the size of the cell over a wide range of power output as compared to the efficiency drop of conventional generators at low output. Fuel cells are low-voltage direct-current devices which makes them particularly useful in the electrochemical industries.

In order to compare the fuel cell with heat engines directly, the efficiency of fuel cells is usually defined as the ratio of electrical energy output to heat of combustion of the fuel. *Efficiency = electrical energy output — heat of combustion fuel.* On this basis, fuel cells can theoretically operate at efficiencies close to 100 percent. Practical fuel cells can convert 70 to 90 percent of their chemical energy directly into electrical energy, compared with a maximum of 42 percent for today's most modern generating plant.

Fuel cells are not new. The first successful cell was made by Sir William Grove in 1839. Their need and development have reached the threshold of economic significance only recently. Of all the exotic generators, fuel cells are the most developed and are now being readied for military and industrial use. Fig. 19-15 shows a military unit weighing 30 pounds. It produces 200 watts at 24 volts DC. The suitcase-size unit runs 14 hours silently and unattended as a power source for radar. The efficiency, energy cost and energy content of fuel cells are shown in Figs. 19-15A and 19-15B.

WHY ARE FUEL CELLS ATTRACTIVE ?

High Efficiency — No moving parts
Easy maintenance — Reliable operation
Permits the first truly all-gas home
Clean exhaust — Silent operation
Adaptable to high volume production
Low heat rejection — Independent of environment

SIZE EFFICIENCY RELATIONSHIP

EFFICIENCY
FUEL CELL SYSTEMS
DIESEL-ELECTRIC SYSTEMS
STEAM TURBINE SYSTEMS
POWER OUTPUT – KILOWATTS

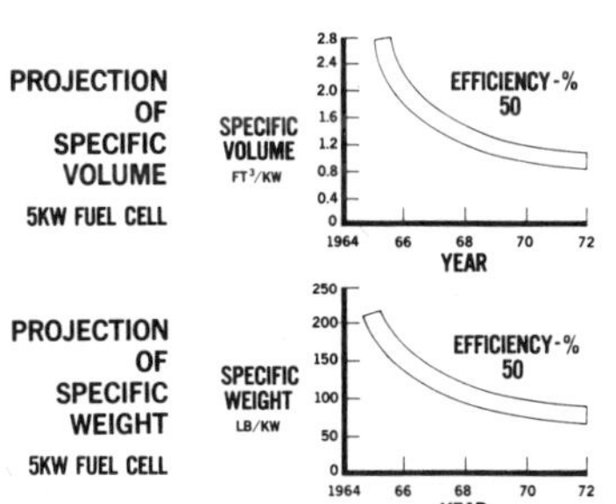

COMPETITIVE POWER SYSTEM EFFICIENCY

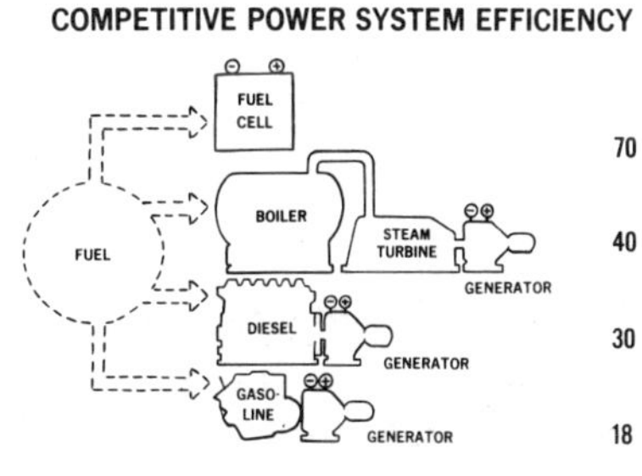

Fig. 19-15A. Projected Efficiency of Fuel Cells (Pratt & Whitney Aircraft)

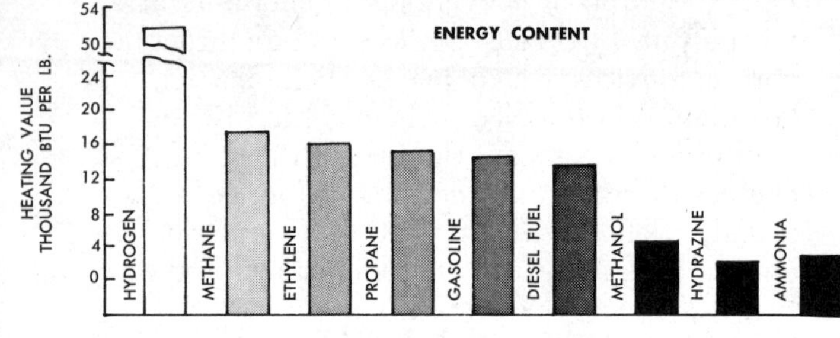

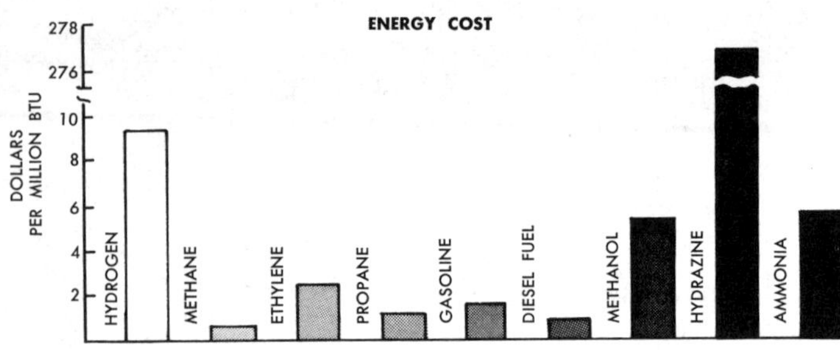

Fig. 19-15B. Comparison of Energy Content and Energy Cost

Photovoltaic Converters

The sun is the ultimate source of all the power which man has at his disposal. The conversion of solar radiation directly into electrical power by some cheap and efficient means has been sought for several decades. Many different methods have been tried for the purpose, but none of these can compete in cost with conventional fossil fuel or hydroelectric power plants. Until recently, the efficiency figures were very discouraging. Within the past few years, however, a major improvement in efficiency by one particular method has been achieved. This again lead to extensive research in this field.

The three most successful devices for converting solar radiation directly into electrical power are the *thermopile, photogalvanic cell,* and *barrier-layer photovoltaic cell.*

Development of Solar Conversion

In 1832, T. J. Seebeck's investigations lead to growth of the *thermopile.* He found that an electromotive force (emf) is developed in a circuit containing two dissimilar conducting materials when the junctions are held at different temperatures. In a solar-energy converter, it is heated by the solar radiation. A converter of this sort is only about one per cent efficient.

In 1839, A. E. Becquerel wrote an article, "Electrical Effects Under the Influence of Solar Radiation", in which he described the first *photogalvanic* cell. This cell consists of two electrodes immersed in an electrolyte. It produces an emf when light falls on one of the two electrodes. The highest efficiency ob-

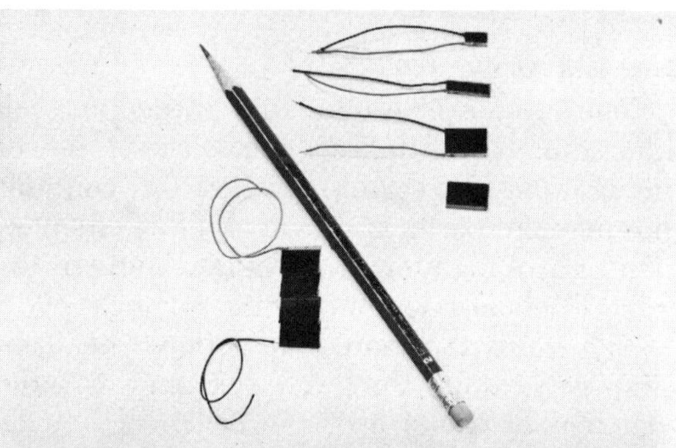

Fig. 19-16. Variety of Selenium Photovoltaic Cells
These convert as much as 12% of the radiant energy falling on them to electrical energy. The cells are used in meters for measuring light intensity, and various photoelectric controls. They can also be used as a power source when connected in series-parallel combinations to provide the needed voltage and amperage.

Fig. 19-17. 58-Watt Solar Cell Combination for Tiros Satellite (RCA)

Fig. 19-18. 200-Watt Solar Cell Collector Panel (International Rectifier)

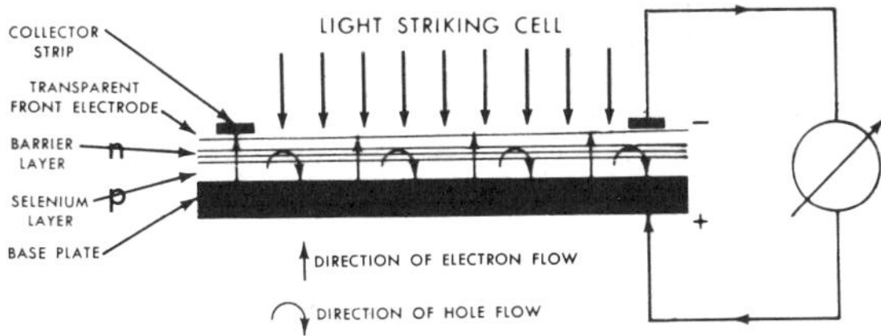

Fig. 19-19. Selenium Photovoltaic Cell (International Rectifier)

The p-type selenium layer is about .003 inch thick on a metal base plate. This is covered by a very thin n-type barrier layer and a transparent coating. Light energy causes selenium electrons to flow through the barrier but the positive holes can not, thus setting up an emf potential. When the terminals are connected to an external circuit, a current flows. The barrier action of the p-n junction is explained in the next figure.

tained from this type of cell is somewhat less than one per cent.

The *barrier-layer photovoltaic cell* is a true solid-state device and was first developed in 1876 by using selenium as a light sensitive material. Selenium photocells are widely used today for such devices as photographic exposure meters, photoswitches, and photoelectric eyes. They have an overall conversion efficiency of about .06 percent when operated in direct sunlight. See Figs. 19-16 to 19-18 for forms and uses of the photovoltaic cell.

In 1954, Bell Telephone Laboratories announced they had raised the efficiency of the photovoltaic cell to 6 percent by using a specially prepared silicon. This chemical element, our second most common, is that found in clear crystals of sand. Since then, the efficiency of photovoltaic cells has been improved to as high as 12 percent. This is much better than the best previous devices

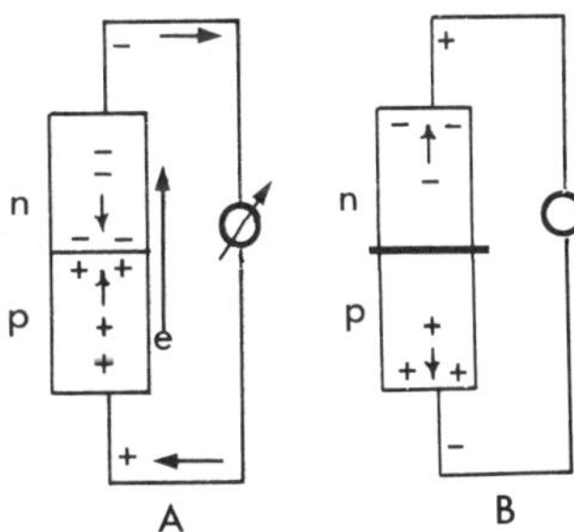

Fig. 19-20. Barrier Action of a p-n Junction

When electron flow is from the p-type layer to the n-type layer (A), the junction between layers offers very little resistance to electron flow. This is because the excess electrons of the n-type layer are repelled away from the negative terminal (toward the junction) because of their like polarity. At the same time, the holes in the p-type layer are attracted away from the positive pole (also toward the junction). This accumulation of available electron-hole pairs at the junction between layers allows light-generated electrons to flow readily across the junction.

If, however, electron flow were to reverse, or if a positive hole were to attempt to cross the barrier, the polarity of the terminals instantly reverse as in (B). Electrons of the *n* layer and the holes of the *p* layer would be attracted away from the junction toward the temporary opposite polarity of their terminals. This forms a barrier at the junction so almost no current will actually flow in this direction. Thus the electrical potential remains constantly in one direction.

and makes this type of solar energy converter a distinct practical possibility. For example, the solar energy falling on a square yard of the earth's surface in Phoenix, Arizona, on a clear day, is more than 1000 watts, so a silicon photovoltaic cell of this area could have an electrical output of more than 120 watts.

Principles of Semiconductors

Silicon solar cells are one of several types of *semiconductors* which electrically are a combination of conductor and insulator. They are able to conduct current flow in one direction or in one situation while resisting it in another. *Transistors* as well as the *p-n junction diodes* used in rectifiers are other semiconductors.

Silicon at room temperature is an insulator if it is chemically pure. This is because the outer ring of a silicon atom has *four* electrons available for combining, and needs *four more* to become stable. Normally two silicon atoms mutually share their electrons and become so stable no free electrons are available for conducting electricity.

However, if a trace of an element such as phosphorus or arsenic (which have *five* free electrons) is added to silicon as an impurity, excess electrons will be available to carry a *negative electrical charge.* Such a material is an *n-type* semiconductor. It has only electrons or negative charges free to move about.

If a trace of an element such as boron or gallium (which have only *three* free electrons) is added to the silicon, there will be missing electrons or *holes.* These can be thought of as carrying a *positive electrical charge.* Such a material is called a *p-type* semiconductor. It has only positive charges or *holes* free to move about.

Other elements besides silicon can also be used as the basis for solar cells. Fig. 19-19 explains a photovoltaic cell which uses multiple coats of *selenium* compounds and precious metals deposited on a metal base plate. The function of the *n* and *p* layers is much the same. The barrier action of the junction between any *n* and *p* layer is explained in Fig. 19-20. This same barrier action can be used in other types of semiconductors to rectify AC to DC, to invert DC to AC, or to amplify and control electronic signals. Transistors and Trinistors have a third element

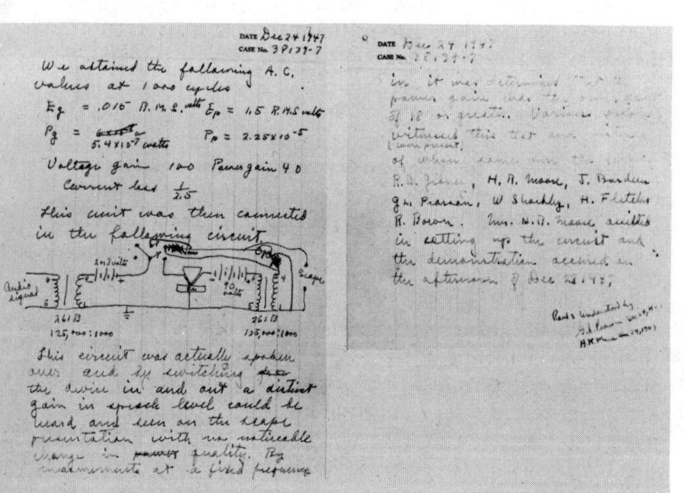

DATE Dec 24 1947
CASE No. 38139-7

We obtained the following A.C. values at 1000 cycles.

Eg = .015 R.M.S. volts Ep = 1.5 R.M.S volts

Pg = 5.4x10-7 watts Pp = 2.25x10-5

Voltage gain 100 Power gain 40

Current loss 1/2.5

This unit was then connected in the following circuit.

Audio signal
90 volts
scope
261B 125,000:1000
261B 125,000:1000

This circuit was actually spoken over and by switching the device in and out a distinct gain in speech level could be heard and seen on the scope presentation with no noticeable change in quality. By measurements at a fixed frequency

DATE Dec 24 1947
CASE No. 38139-7

in it was determined that the power gain was [illegible] of 18 or greater. Various people witnessed this test [illegible] (were present) of whom [illegible]

R. B. Gibney, H. R. Moore, J. Bardeen, G. L. Pearson, W. Shockley, H. Fletcher, R. Bown. Mr. H. R. Moore assisted in setting up the circuit and the demonstration occurred in the afternoon of Dec 23 1947.

Read & understood by G. L. Pearson Dec 24, 47
H R Moore Dec 24, 1947

Fig. 19-20A. Laboratory Entry Following Discovery of the Transistor (Bell Telephone)

Fig. 19-20B. Vacuum Tube (Left), Transistor (Center), Integrated Circuit (Right)
(Bell Telephone)

The IC includes 22 transistors and other components and is used in the Touch-Tone telephone. It has a protective coating and does not need the physical shield of a can.

which acts as an electronic switch controlling the barrier action.

Transistor Has Come of Age[4]

The transistor was invented in Bell Telephone Laboratories Research and Development Unit on December 23, 1947, by Bell Lab scientists Bardeen, Brattain, and Shockley. A small piece of the element germanium amplified a voice signal noticeably and showed a power gain of about 40 times. See Fig. 19-20A. In 1956 the trio was given the Nobel prize for the discovery of the transistor effect.

Transistors are everywhere – homes, banks, automobiles, factories, even on the ocean floor and in outer space. They function in radios, TV sets, hearing aids, telephones, industrial equipment, wrist watches, power tools, and in the complex circuitry of the giant computers and telemetry equipment for today's space age. Transistors play a vital role in communications and information processing. They perform all the functions of vacuum tubes: amplify electrical signals, act as oscillators, or control and combine pulses of current. For practically every application they are less expensive, more reliable, smaller, and consume less power than vacuum tubes.

The transistor is considered to be one of the greatest inventions of the 20th Century. It has led to advances in various scientific fields. Increased interest in the properties of solids has led to such other devices as lasers, light amplifiers, and light modulators. Recently, applied transistor technology has achieved integrated circuitry (IC). These are complete electronic circuits fabricated on paper-thin wafers of material. An integrated circuit of 50-100 transistors and other components can fit on the head of a tack, Fig. 19-20B. Miniaturization is important for compact equipment such as the telephone and in many space applications. An integrated circuit can perform a function at one percent of the cost and with 100,000 times the reliability of vacuum tubes. The invention of the transistor and its resulting development have affected the future of our society profoundly. Better world-wide communications, automatic control equipment, and the ability to process large amounts of information are vital in today's industrial world.

[4] Raymond, D. L., "Transistor Is Twenty Years Old," *News*, Bell Telephone Laboratories, 1967.

Silicon Cell Construction

In manufacturing a *silicon* photovoltaic cell, a trace amount of arsenic is melted with the silicon just before it crystalizes. The ratio is about one part of arsenic per million parts of silicon. This mixture is formed into a large single-crystal ingot. The ingot is *n-type* because of the arsenic impurity. The electrical resistivity is about 0.5 ohm per centimeter. The crystal is then cut into thin wafers with a diamond cutting wheel. The thickness of this piece is about one twenty-fifth of an inch.

A *p-type* silicon can be formed over the entire surface of the *n-type* wafer. This is accomplished by placing the wafer in a quartz tube containing vapors of boron compounds and then heating them at 1000 to 12000°C. During this treatment, boron atoms are deposited on the silicon surface and diffused inside to make a thin *p-type* silicon skin covering the *n-type* wafer. The thickness of this covering is controlled by the amount of heat applied for a given length of time. This *p-type* skin is about .0001 inch thick. After cooling, the *p* layer is removed from the back of the silicon wafer.

The point at which the *p* and *n* layers meet form what is known as the *p-n* junction. This is the heart of the solar cell.

Photon Energy

Light is the transmission of *photons*. These photons are transmitted at different *frequencies* which we see as different colors. Each varies in the intensity of energy carried. Higher frequencies have shorter *wavelengths*—the distance occupied by one cycle. The amount of energy in a photon is inversely proportional to its wavelength. Bright sunlight is a combination of all wavelengths, and carries about 130 watts of energy per square foot, Fig. 19-21. When light is absorbed in a silicon crystal those photons having sufficient energy liberate a free-to-move negative charge and a free-to-move positive charge, or, they expand their energy in creating a hole-electron pair. In a solid ingot of silicon where there is no electric field present, these hole-electron pairs re-combine in a matter of a few *microseconds* before they can be made to do any useful work. If an electric field is applied to the ingot, a force is exerted on the charged carriers and the free ones move. This force moves holes in one direction and electrons in the opposite direction. Once separated, the charged carriers can be made to do useful work.

In a *p-n* junction as previously mentioned, there is a permanent, built-in electric field which keeps the electrons on the *n-side* and the holes on the *p-side*. When light is absorbed in this region, electron-hole pairs are produced, and the built-in electric field forces the *holes* to the *p-side* and the *electrons* to the *n-side*. This displacement of the freed charges causes a voltage difference between the ends of the crystal.

In full sunlight, each cell in a solar battery produces an open circuit voltage of about 0.6 volt. When a circuit is connected to the terminals this potential difference causes an electric current to flow and thus light energy is converted into electrical energy.

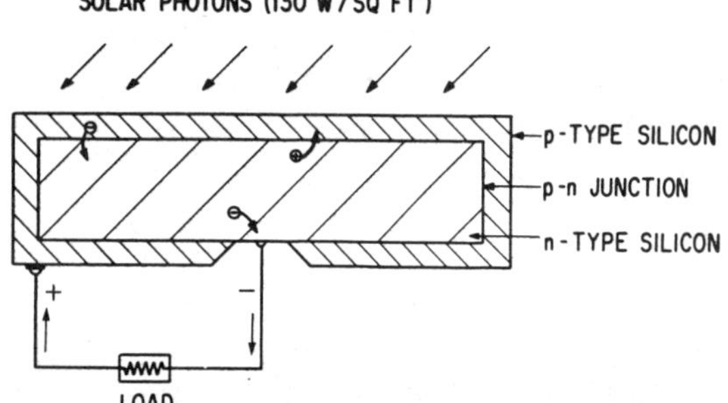

Fig. 19-21. Silicon Photovoltaic Converter

Solar Cell Application

Silicon solar cells in their present form are still too inefficient to replace the conventional power generators now supplying most of our electricity. These cells are, however, being used in special cases such as in our rockets and satellites and other such places where weight and space are critical factors and the voltage required is low. See Figs. 19-22 and 19-23. As soon as the technique of applying the necessary thin films of photovoltaic material on large surfaces are improved, costs would probably be made more competitive for commercial applications.

Fig. 19-22. Thin Slices of Sapphire Protect Cells from Space Radiation (Bell Telephone)

Fig. 19-23. 4,000 to 12,000 Sapphire-Covered Solar Cells Power Satellites for Years (Bell Telephone)

Thermionic Converters

Thermionic converters are usable with many heat generating systems. Such a converter requires that the temperature of a metal be increased until its electrons become energetic enough to leave the surface—the higher the elevation of temperature, the greater the number of electrons emitted and the greater their energy. See Fig. 19-24. If two such thermionic emitters are placed close together, each having different temperatures and each externally connected by an electrical conductor to a load, a flow of electrons from the *hotter* to the *cooler* electrode will be caused to flow, Fig. 19-25. The energy with which the electrons are emitted is dependent upon the material and the temperature of the electrode, Fig. 19-26. The effect can be enhanced by selecting the anode(+) to have a lower work function than the cathode(−).

An initial efficiency of 8 percent that was attained in 1957 by using a converter which employed cesium vapor to neutralize the space charge located between the two electrodes. This converter has been improved and has reached operational efficiencies as high as 17 percent.

Fig. 19-24. Thermionic Tube a New Source of Power (Westinghouse)

Experimental tube has glowing wire emitting electrons causing current flow in ionized cesium gas. Finger points out cesium capsule. Heat could be supplied by nuclear power.

Heat Problems

Thermionic converters operate at relatively high temperatures upwards of 800°F at the cathode and 300° at the anode. The temperature difference between the two electrodes creates the necessary unbalance to cause electrons to flow from the cathode to the anode, Fig. 19-27. Further reduction of

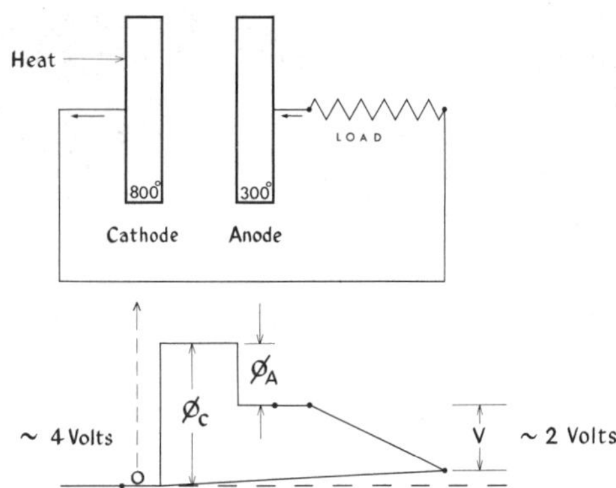

Fig. 19-25. Schematic Diagram of Thermionic Generator

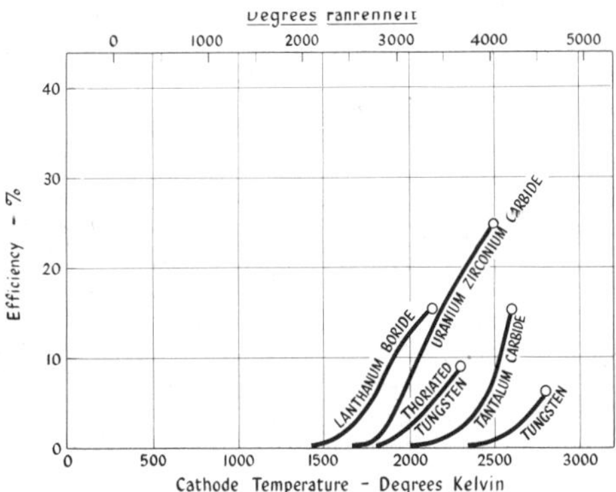

Fig. 19-26. Efficiency Curves of Thermionic Materials

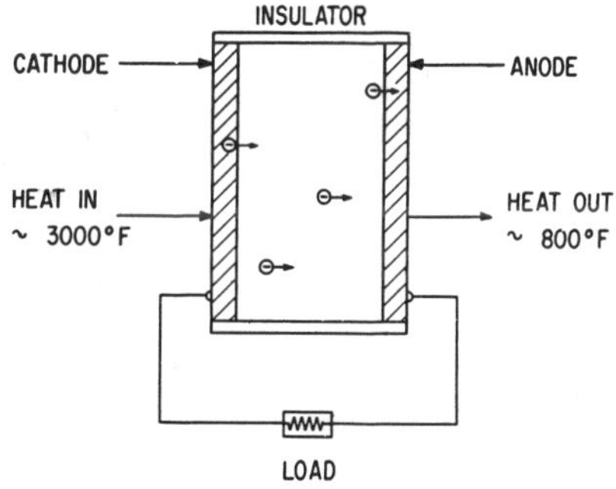

Fig. 19-27. Thermionic Converter

the anode temperature does not cause appreciably more electrons to flow, but it does increase the heat transmitted through the converter, an undesirable effect. Also, the elevated anode temperature is a distinct advantage for space power generation where heat must be rejected by radiation. For space power, high cathode temperature and heat flux combine conveniently with a focusing solar collector as a heat generator. These characteristics also operate from heat supplied by nuclear fission. Thermionic converters might be built into the fuel elements of a boiling water reactor where the anode may be caused to reject heat to the reactor coolant. Although thermionic converters are already in production, research continues to improve efficiency and find other applications.

Fig. 19-28. Pyrometer with its Thermocouple

Fig. 19-29. 5, 10, 50 and 100 Watt Thermoelectric Generators (Westinghouse)

Thermoelectric Generators

Almost 150 years ago, the German physicist Thomas Seebeck discovered that the flow of heat through a metal segment could produce a difference of electrical potential between its hot and cold ends. Such a *thermocouple* has been used for many years in heat sensing instruments such as pyrometers, Fig. 19-28. The amount of current generated in a twisted-wire thermocouple by some external heat (such as in a smelting furnace) deflects a galvanometer needle calibrated in degrees or activates a control device.

Recently, the development of new thermoelectric materials has enabled us to raise both the power output and the efficiency of thermoelectric devices to levels suitable for the practical generation of power. In 1959, the thermoelectric device's output was slightly over 1 watt. We now have generators rated at 100 watts with some being built rated at 5,000 watts. See Fig. 19-29.

The qualities of thermoelectric devices that have encouraged these developments include ruggedness, compactness, the lack of moving parts, and lack of maintenance. The military realizes this quality because heat could be converted to electricity easily without noise. In space vehicles, the absence of rotating parts would eliminate the gyroscopic forces that occur in rotating machines and simplify guidance and stability.

Thermoelectric Operation

In any uniformly heated thermoelectric material, its positive and negative electrical charges are uniformly distributed, but when heat is applied to one surface, this distribution is no longer uniform. Usually, the positively charged ions remain virtually fired within the crystal, but the negative ions tend to move to the cooler end. This results in a potential difference between the hot and cold ends which can cause current to flow through an external circuit. A p-type semiconductor has this same movement of negative ions from hot to cold, but an n-type has a reverse action. This allows a compact series-stacking at a central heat source, Fig. 19-30.

Because of each device's very limited output, connecting many thermocouples in series is necessary to achieve an adequate voltage. It is through pre-determined arranging or stacking that working voltages and currents are achieved. See Figs. 19-31 and 19-32.

One of the most important factors in the growth of the thermoelectric technology is the ability to adjust the number of free electrons in such semiconductor materials. The importance of this is due to: (1) the output *voltage* of any thermoelectric material is *inversely proportional* to the number of free electrons in that material; and (2) the *conductivity* of the material is *directly proportional* to the number of free electrons.

Increasing Efficiency

To obtain maximum power output or best efficiency, we must adjust the electron density for an acceptable compromise value between high voltage and high electrical conductivity. This is important in the production of useful power since a combination of high voltage and low current, or low voltage and high current, results in lost power. The best compromise is shown by efficiency curves. Such graphs indicate the best electron density to be 10^{19} free electrons per cubic centimeter, a value well within the range of good conducting semiconductors. This value will yield about 175 microvolts per degree C. Some materials that demonstrate these desirable traits are zinc, antimony, lead telluride, bismuth telluride, and germanium telluride.

It is desirable to use a number of different thermoelectric materials in practical applications. In this way, each material can be used at its best operating temperature. This con-

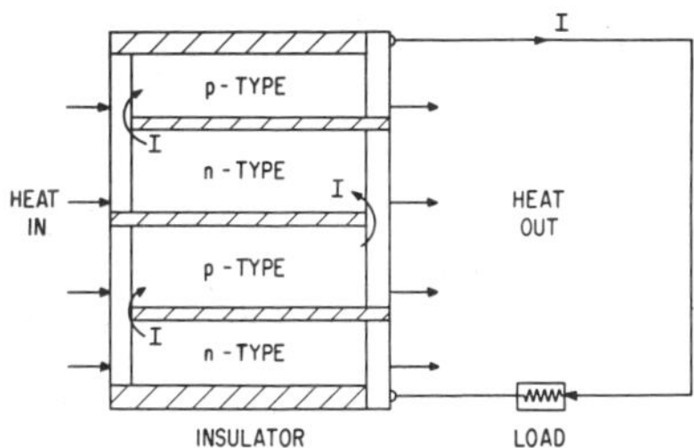

Fig. 19-30. Thermoelectric Converter

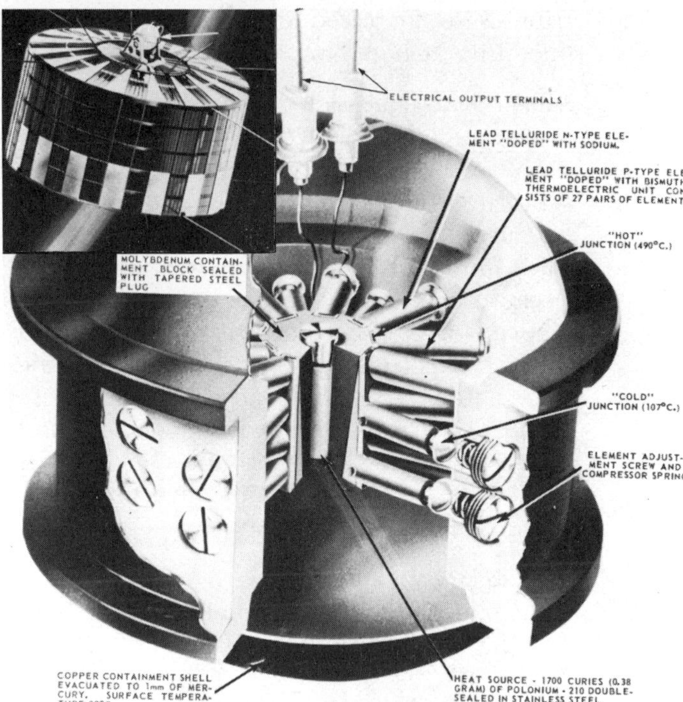

Fig. 19-31. SNAP-III Atomic-Powered Generator

This grapefruit-sized 2.5w thermoelectric converter powers instrumentation on a Transit satellite.

Fig. 19-32. 125 Watt SNAP-1A has Hundreds of Thermocouples Heated by Cerium 144.

Fig. 19-33. Spring-Loaded Thermocouples

tributes to increased efficiency allowed by operating at high temperatures.

Manufacturing Problems

Despite these developments, there are problems of manufacture. Materials must be fabricated as thermocouples and then be assembled in finished devices. Such assemblies must not have high contact resistance because this would reduce their efficiency. Above 300°C, it becomes necessary to shield all materials from the corrosive effects of the air. Another aspect is the need to mount these devices so that they will withstand shock and expansion. Some thermocouples are spring loaded by applying compressive forces to them. See Figs. 19-31 and 19-33.

Applications

In one of the first generators to be built for the Air Development Center at Rome, New York, the output was 100 watts from a 50 lb. unit. The unit was cooled by free convection for a power-to-weight index of 2-1 or 2 watts for each pound. Since performance can be improved considerably by using forced movement of air or water, it is believed that generators with forced cooling will produce 15 watts per pound of weight for a power-to-weight index that is comparable to a typical 500 watt gasoline powered generator.

Applications of such direct converters are numerous. One of these is the thermoelectric power supply for communication and instrumentation equipment at locations along natural gas transmission lines. Another is for power generation along oil or fuel lines for pipeline equipment. These power requirements are well within the capacity of available direct converters.

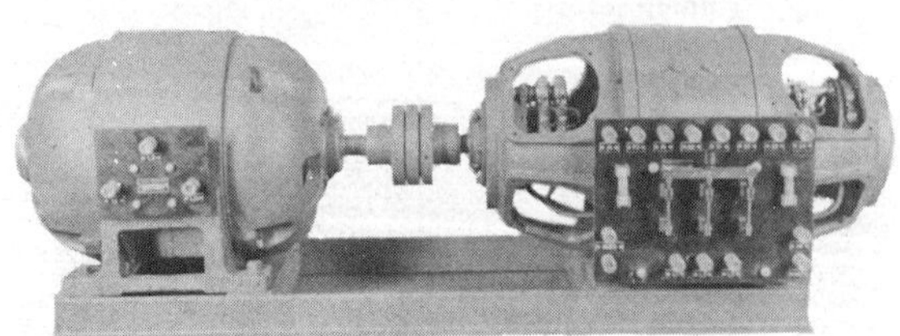

Fig. 19-34. Motor-Generator Set (GE)

It is possible to visualize thermoelectric power generators as a device using the high heat of nuclear reactors. In this way, the heat of fusion will not be partially wasted as it currently is, but will be used to generate 20 percent more electricity, increasing overall efficiency.[4]

AC from Direct Converters

All of the new exotic generators produce direct current. While DC is used in some applications, the majority, particularly where large amounts of power are involved, demand alternating current. This means that we must have efficient, economical and maintenance-free methods of converting DC to AC. Devices that accomplish this are called *inverters*. Inverters have the opposite function of rectifiers (which change AC to DC). In general, inverters use the same rectifier components but in a reverse manner.

Several types of inverters are now available: 1. motor-generator sets, 2. gas tube inverters using mercury-arc rectifiers or similar tubes, and 3. the new semiconductor power inverters. Of the three, the motor-generator system is the only one that requires mechanical motion for operation. The others are static units having no movement.

Motor-Generator Sets

Let us consider these three inverters in terms of their present and potential capabilities. The *motor-generator* sets as shown in Fig. 19-34 have developed over a period of many years. The DC motor drives an AC generator. They represent a reliable method for converting DC to AC. However, since they are rotating devices, a number of disadvantages become apparent. For example, bearings require lubrication, carbon brushes need to be periodically replaced, commutators must be maintained, and because of their weight and size, they are not very adaptable to compact equipment. Therefore, it is difficult, or often impossible, to rearrange

[4] Stephen J. Angelo, *Thermoelectricity: Applying the Seebeck Effect to Power Generation*, Westinghouse Electric Corp., Pittsburgh, Pa.

elements to make the most economical or effective use of available space.

Unless the motor-generator is kept rotating constantly, there is no output. The distinct advantage of this system is its ability to withstand overloads for a time.

Gas Tube Inverters

The *gas tube inverter system* is a static unit, and because of this, maintenance is less than for most dynamic systems. The cost of such a system varies with the operating voltage. For example, a 600 volt unit will cost $60 per kilowatt, whereas a 2500 volt unit may cost as little as $50 per kilowatt.

The system uses *ignitron or thyratron* electron tubes having control elements activated by an auxiliary circuit. This outside circuit triggers the reversal of current direction at intervals thus causing the alternations.

Since the system is static, it is quiet operating, and because there are no brushes and commutators (and hence no arcing) the device is suitable for areas in which explosive gases may be present. The operating efficiency of the ignitron system is good, and efficiency improves at higher voltages.

Semiconductor Inverters

The newest inverter systems uses semiconductor elements. As noted earlier, semiconductors perform many basic electrical functions. The silicon diode and the transistor have become extremely familiar, but even more recent semiconductor developments such as the *Dynistor* and the *Trinistor* (controlled rectifier elements), offer new possibilities in the electrical power field. Both transistor and Trinistor semiconductors have been used in power inverters, but the Trinistor appears to have the greatest potential for very high power operation.

The *Trinistor rectifier,* is shown in Fig. 19-35. It consists of a silicon wafer arranged so that a control element (small wire) can cause the device to change from a high impedence state to a low impedence state to serve as an electronically controlled switch. It can function either as a rectifier or an inverter. This fundamentally is similar to the thyratron or ignitron gas tubes in electrical characteristics. However, it is free of maintenance and does not require heated filaments as do the electron tubes.

Semiconductor Inverter Operation

A study of the semiconductor unit shows that energy losses are extremely low when the device is at minimum or maximum conduction conditions. High losses occur only under operating conditions in which the unit is not operated fully turned on or off. It is, therefore, essential that the switching time from one state to the other be made as rapidly as possible for highest efficiency and for a minimum of dissipated energy. Since the *all-on* or *all-off* operation is essentially the behavior of a switch, this operation is identified as the *switching mode.* All of the semiconductor power conversion equipment has been designed with this instantaneous switching action as a basic part of their circuitry. The semiconductor performs this function at a high speed with no deterioration.

The transistor and Trinistor can be used effectively as inverters as shown in Fig. 19-36.

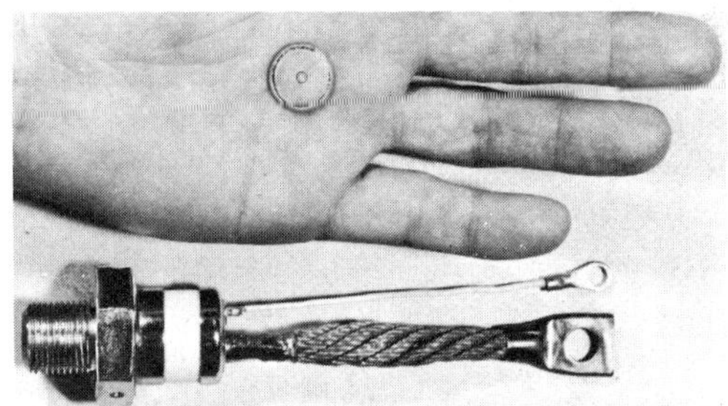

Fig. 19-35. Silicon Wafer, the Semiconductor Element of the Rectifier-Inverter (below it)

Fig. 19-36. Eight Transistors in 15 KVA Inverter (Westinghouse)

Transistor inverters have been constructed up to the 10 kilowatt level and have performed at frequencies as high as 20,000 cycles per second. Above the 10 kilowatt level, the Trinistor appears to be more suitable since the technical considerations indicate that extremely high powers can be obtained in single units. Presently there is much research and developmental activity in this area.

The Trinistor switch is a 3-terminal device in which the control element is capable of turning on the unit, but the turning off of a circuit can be accomplished only when zero current is reached. This characteristic makes it necessary to carefully design the electrical circuitry so that the proper control of the unit can be maintained at all times.

An inverter requires a pair of Trinistor units. One of which supplies the positive half cycle of the alternating current wave, and the other the negative half. So far the inverters constructed have been operated to approximately 60 kilowatts of power with a frequency as high as 20,000 cycles per second. The small size of the Trinistor requires that a heat dissipating element be used to keep the operating temperature at a reasonable level.

The circuitry developed thus far permit parallel or series combinations of the Trinistor rectifiers. The output waveforms can be made sine or square wave as desired (either gradual or instantaneous alternations).

Advantages

The semiconductor power inverter has all the advantages generally associated with static units, such as high reliability, low maintenance, and minimum operational noise. In addition, weight and volume of the semiconductor inverter can be much less than a comparable motor generator set. The Trinistor probably will be designed in the near future to handle much greater power than present units. If the operating voltage

Fig. 19-37. 6000 KW Motor-Generator Rectifier (left) **and Equivalent Semiconductor Units.** (Alcoa) Panel (right) contains the 312 silicon-rectifier cells in pile at left and handles 10,000 amps at 600 volts.

is increased, the efficiency of the inverter will be increased.

The functional element of the Trinistor is the specially prepared silicon wafer; thin and smaller in diameter than a dime. Yet, this wafer is capable of controlling 100 amperes at 200 volts. This power handling capacity has been developed in the past few years with greater capacities possible in the future. Possibly wafers of the same size will be capable of handling 1000 kilowatts.

The power handling capabilities of the individual semiconductor devices for a single device have been increased ten times in several years. In a few more, they may increase as much as 30 times our present day limits.

Limitations

One of the limitations of the static inverter occurs when it is overloaded. A static inverter has little or no thermal energy storage. Damage results when elements of the semiconductor fails. Thus, it is necessary to add protective circuitry increasing circuit complexity.

Other problems involve training personnel to understand new type apparatus. Building in factors of safety to allow inverters to run at maximum outputs without being overloaded is another problem. The potential of static inverters has not been fully realized. As they become widely used, the cost per kilowatt is expected to drop much below the cost of a motor-generator system. In fact, for lower power applications, the semiconductor power inverter is already the most economical.

Applications

These new inverters are now being used for a large number of military applications. In missiles, in submarines, and in emergency power systems, the low volume, low noise, low weight, and improved reliability under adverse conditions have established the value of the semiconductor inverter.

Commercial and industrial use of the new inverters are just beginning to evolve, and these applications are expected to skyrocket the device to unexpected achievements. One of the most important applications is expected to come as an outgrowth of changing alternating current from one frequency to another. This gives the electrical engineer a new dimension in equipment design. With frequency change, we can expect high frequency panel-lighting, new motor designs and power supplies, and new concepts in speed control.

Recently, a three year joint effort by Alcoa and Westinghouse resulted in a compact AC to DC converter rated for 10,000 amperes at 600 volts. This capability far exceeds any previous large silicon rectifying equipment. The unit requires about one-third the floor space of other types of rectifiers having similar ratings. It has an efficiency better than 97 percent. The unit has been installed at Alcoa's Badin, North Carolina smelter, where it is supplying power for aluminum smelting. See Fig. 19-37.[5]

In addition to its being a new tool for the aluminum industry, the new converter represents comprehensive use of aluminum. Approximately 60 percent of the entire assembled converter is aluminum. It uses aluminum for conductors, heat sinks, hardware, and the cubicle enclosure.

Terms to Understand

direct converters
exotic generators
thermoelectric converters
MHD generator
seeding
fuel cell
thermionic converters
hot plasma
hydrox cell
redox cell
hydrocarbon cell
ion-exchange membrane cells
solar cell
T. J. Seebeck
n-type layer
p-type layer
photons
inverters
semiconductors
transistor
Trinistor
integrated circuit
rectifiers
photovoltaic cells
thermocouple

[5] E. J. Duckett, *Conversion of Direct Current to Alternating Current,* New Products Laboratory, Westinghouse Electric Corp., Cheswick, Pa.

Study Questions

1. What are exotic generators?
2. Outline the needs of man that are prompting their development.
3. Describe the principles of operation of the MHD generator.
4. Contrast plasma generators and plasma propulsion engines.
5. Explain how the MHD generator can increase the output of present day power generators.
6. What is a fuel cell? Explain its operation.
7. Why can a p-n junction control electrical circuits?
8. Explain the function and potential of the solar cell.
9. Explain the principles of thermionic generators.
10. What is an inverter? Why are they used?
11. What are the various types of inverters and how do they operate?
12. What is a rectifier? Why are they used?
13. Explain the operation of a silicon rectifier.

Selected Readings for Part V
Direct Electrical Converters

Angelo, Stephen J., *Thermoelectricity: Applying the Seebeck Effect to Power Generation*, Westinghouse Electric Corp., Pittsburgh, Pa.

Duckett, E. J., *Conversion of Direct Current to Alternating Current*, New Products Laboratory, Westinghouse Electric Corp., Cheswick, Pa.

General Electric Co., *Some Plain Talk About Fuel Cells*

Harris, L. P., *MHD Power Generator: An Application of Magnetohydrodynamics*, Proceeding of the National Electronics Conference, Vol. 16, 1960.

Marques, D. H., "A Survey of Direct Energy Conversion", presented at the 69th Annual Meeting of the American Society for Engineering Education, Lexington, Kentucky, June, 1961.

Ruka, R., *High Temperature Fuel Cells*, Research Laboratories of Westinghouse Electric Corp., Pittsburgh, Pa.

Telkes, M., *The Efficiency of Thermoelectric Generators*, Journal of Applied Physics, Vol. 18, 1947.

United Nations, *New Sources of Energy and Energy Development*, (New York, U.N., 1962)

Way, Steward, "MHD", Research Laboratories Technical Paper, Westinghouse Electric Corp., Pittsburgh, Pa.

Opposite—
1. (top) Anchor Post (Racine Hydraulics & Machinery Inc.) This machine applies rail anchors to the ties by snapping them to the base of the rail and can develop up to 50,000 pounds of thrust.
2. Telescopic Crane (Racine Hydraulics & Machinery Inc.)
3. Aerial Work Platform (Racine Hydraulics & Machinery Inc.)
In each application identified above, fluid power provides high compact mechanical advantage, smooth operation, precise operator control, and relatively safe, portable operation.

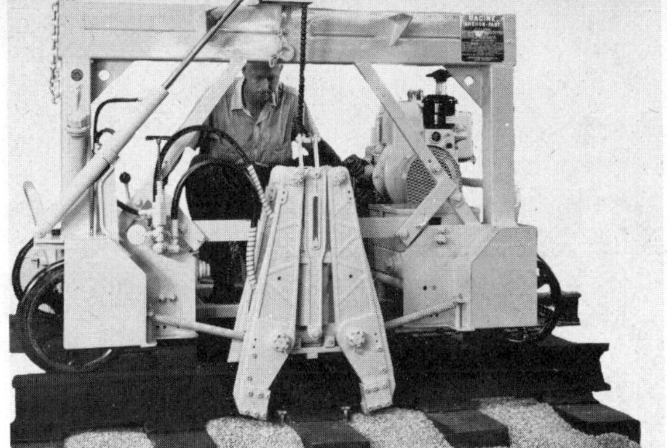

PART **VI**

TRANS-ACTIONAL SYSTEMS

Trans-actional systems apply energy to do work. Control of energy transmission is a key to its application. Trans-actional systems are categorized by the means and principles of application employed, such as mechanical, fluid, and electrical systems. The underlying theme is the utilization of energy to increase its value.

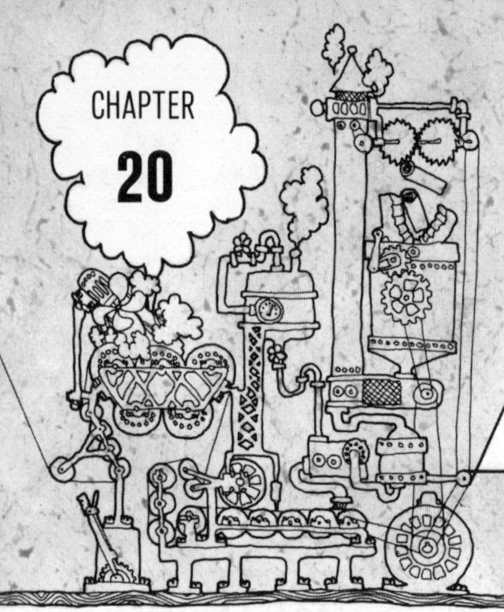

Mechanical Power

Mechanical systems may be defined as those systems that exclusively use the principles of the six simple machines to transmit and control energy to do work.

The system designer has wide latitude in developing the solution to a given power need: most often the choice is dependent upon initial and operating costs.

Mechanical trans-actional systems consist of straightforward, rather fundamental transmission and control components. They are reliable, flexible in application, easily maintained, and are relatively low in cost.

Mechanical energy transmission utilizes shafts, belts, chains, gears and wheels, Fig. 20-1. Application of the variable pitch principle provides the necessary control of output force and speed relative to the power input.

Mechanical energy control most often is dependent upon clutches and brakes. The control function, because of the nature of the system, is continuous, providing a spectrum of energy transmission from minimum to maximum. Discontinuous control, on or off energy transmission, is difficult except at very slow operational speeds.

Fig. 20-1. Components of Mechanical Energy Transmission Systems (Woods)

Mechanical Transmission Components

Shaft Design and Selection

Most transmission systems ultimately provide mechanical energy in the form of linear or rotating motion. Delivery of the required mechanical energy is dependent on proper shaft selection.

In selecting the shaft material, one must consider the following: torque; load requirements; compression and tensile limits; and contraction, bowing, or distension limitations. Hollow shafts are lighter, place less load on supporting bearings, distend less, but usually are more expensive and require balancing. Solid shafting is usually employed for moderate size energy transmissions where bearing load, distension, and expansion of the material can be tolerated.

Usually the smallest shaft capable of transmitting the required motion and energy is selected. Larger shaft sizes require more energy to overcome inertia and expose a greater surface area to the bearings, causing higher frictional losses. A shaft size that is too small has a tendency to vibrate, bow, twist, and also presents problems of coupling.

Shaft materials must not be hard or brittle but tough, capable of absorbing shocks, and able to resist becoming work hardened or crystallized. Mild steel is the most popular shaft material. Nickel, chrome-nickel, and vanadium steel are preferred for rough service applications.

Whenever possible, standard shaft sizes should be selected. Manufacturers' catalogues or machinists, handbooks should be consulted.

Shaft Couplings

Sometimes it becomes necessary to lengthen or to connect shafts. There are three basic types of couplings: rigid, flexible, and the universal joint. The selection of the type of coupling is dependent upon the driving element, alignment angle, load, relative stability, type of bearings, and operating environment (space, temperature and possible contamination).

Rigid Couplings

Rigid couplings are used where it is necessary to provide a joint that is rigid and strong, where torsional flexibility is not required, and where perfect shaft alignment can be maintained. The two most popular types of rigid couplings are the sleeve coupling and the flanged coupling. Sleeve couplings are used where the shaft diameter is the same. Flange couplings are provided with male and female members to accommodate shafts of different diameters.

Flexible Couplings

Flexible couplings are the most popular coupling devices because they are able to compensate for a degree of shaft misalignment.

There are many types of flexible couplings. Generally speaking, all flexible shaft couplings fall into one of three classifications: (1) those which provide flexibility using resilient materials; (2) those which provide flexibility using mechanical components and connections; and, (3) those that combine mechanical as well as material flexibility.

Resilient Material Coupling: Some resilient material couplings employ a rubber flexible synthetic material permanently fastened to the metal coupling components. When failure occurs, the entire coupling must be replaced.

Spoked and wedge rubber couplings use a replaceable element that is located between the metal coupling components. These elements are made in a variety of styles.

Mechanical Flexible Couplings: These coupling devices are not as popular as the resilient material couplers for fractional horsepower installation because they require lubrication and are more costly. One such coupling uses two standard *chain* sprockets and a connecting double width strand of roller chain as a coupler, Fig. 20-2. Another uses two shaft-mounted gears and a sleeve-like internal mating *gear* serving as the coupler.

The *slider* coupling consists of two flange hubs that are machined so as to allow a square sliding member to interlock them. All of these coupling devices depend on the looseness of fit between components, and are known by the device that serves as the coupling agent.

Combined Mechanical and Resilient Couplers: There are three popular types of couplers in this category. One uses internal splines in a flexible sleeve, usually rubber or neoprene, which mate with external splines on the hub. Another uses a rubber insert with externally molded gear teeth that engage the internal mating teeth of the two hubs. Some-

Fig. 20-2. Roller Chain Couplings (Morse)

times the insert is split, and a lock ring of steel is used to keep the two pieces together, Fig. 20-3. The third uses two metal flanges that are machined so as to allow a piece of resilient material to serve as an interlock, Fig. 20-4. The design of this coupler varies with each manufacturer. All of these couplers exhibit good torsional characteristics, may be repaired easily, and require no lubrication.

Floating Shaft Couplings

Where two shafts are not close enough to be coupled with standard couplers, a floating shaft coupling is often used. The floating shaft is supported between two special couplings on the driver and driven shafts. The length of the floating shaft determines whether it will be made hollow or solid. This coupling eliminates the need for intermediate supporting bearings. Generally speaking, the allowable misalignment is double that of a single coupling.

Fig. 20-3. Coupling with Rubber Gear-Toothed Insert (Woods)

Brake Drum Couplings

This design is employed where shaft length is at a premium and external braking is required. The brake drum is fastened to the flange of the coupling hub.

Torque Limiting Couplings

A variety of couplings are used to limit the transmitted torque and thereby provide protection from overload and jamming. In addition to styles which employ spring-loading faces or plates that permit intermittent slips when precalculated overload occurs, shear pin couplers are used. The connecting pin is broken (sheared) at a predetermined limit, and the shaft is disengaged.

Universal Joints

Flexible shaft couplings provide for relatively limited misalignment in transmission systems. Where high torque is to be transmitted and severe misalignment may occur, a universal joint must be used. The principle of

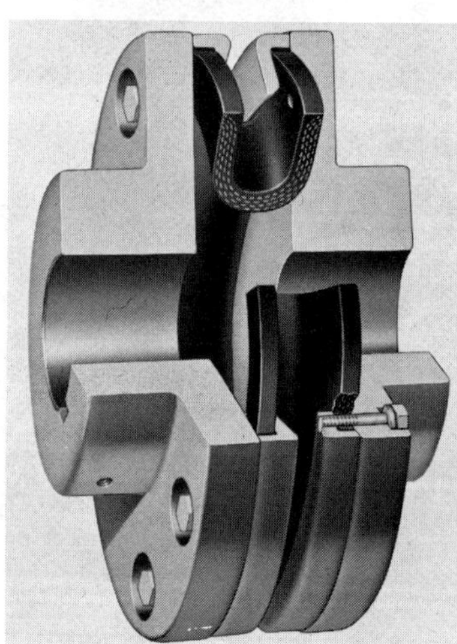

Fig. 20-4. Coupling with Interlocking Insert (Falk Corp.)

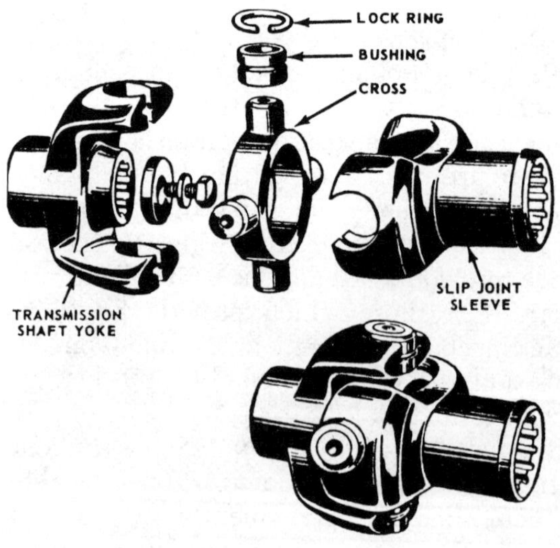

Fig. 20-5. Universal Joint (Brake and Steering Div., Bendix Corp.)

the universal joint was conceived by Leonardo da Vinci and later refined by Robert Hook in the late 1600's. The single and double universal joint are the two most common, although many variations exist.

The Single Joint: The single joint may be described as two shafts, shaped and drilled to provide a free interlock and drilled so that a cross member fitting can be secured through holes provided in each, Fig. 20-5. The power is transmitted from one shaft to the other through the yoke. A double joint is simply a center member or body connected on each end with single universal joints. The single universal joint will handle angular misalignment. It will not compensate for offset or parallel misalignment. The double joint will handle both types of misalignments.

Friction

Throughout the study of energy conversion, friction has been a major concern. It complicates the simple formulas applicable to the six basic machines. It is the cause of machines not operating to 100% efficiency. It is the one phenomenon that prevents man from developing a perpetual motion machine. Yet friction is indispensible in technological development. Without friction, machines could not operate. In fact, man could not move in a wheeled vehicle or even by walking.

The dual role of friction has been one of the classic studies of science. Simply, friction is the resistance opposing any effort to slide or roll one thing on another. Resistance is inherent whether the two surfaces are solid or fluid. Friction slows the progress of a ship in water, of a plane in flight, of a space vehicle in re-entering the earth's atmosphere.

Causes of Friction

There are three causes of friction between two bodies that are moved while in contact. One is the intermeshing of the small irregularities on the surfaces. This microscopic roughness is inherent in most surfaces even though they appear smooth. A second cause is adhesion due to the molecular attraction between two surfaces. The more highly polished the surfaces, the more prone they are to stick together. Precision gauge blocks can be wrung together easily. The third cause of friction is due to the indention of a hard body into a soft body. The hard body then has to move out of the indentation. There may be a fourth cause of friction – electrostatic attraction. This still has not been proven completely. Lubricating oil provides a film between two moving surfaces so that the surfaces ride on oil and do not touch each other. Many other lubricants do the same thing: graphite, wax, soap, and the new dry silicone lubricants, to give some examples.

Mechanical Friction

There are three kinds of mechanical friction.

1. *Static friction* is resistance to movement between two bodies that are in contact and at rest.

2. *Sliding friction* is the resistance to continued movement after the body has been set in motion. Sliding friction is always less than static friction.

3. If the two sliding bodies were separated by rollers, *rolling friction* would exist and this has the least resistance of all.

To overcome friction, energy must be expended. The amount of friction is dependent upon the force pressing the two surfaces together and the coefficient of friction for those particular materials. Coefficients of friction are usually stated for both dry and lubricated surfaces and for static and sliding conditions.

Selected Coefficients of Friction

MATERIALS	STATIC	SLIDING
Hard steel on hard steel	0.78 (dry)	0.42 (dry)
Steel on graphite	0.21 (dry) 0.09 (lubricated)	
Aluminum on mild steel	0.61 (dry)	0.47 (dry)
Brass on cast iron		0.30 (dry)
Glass on glass	0.94 (dry) 0.35 (lubricated)	0.40 (dry) 0.09 (lubricated)
Cast iron on cast iron	1.1 (dry) 0.2 (lubricated)	0.15 (dry) 0.07 (lubricated)
Bronze on cast iron		0.22 (dry) 0.077 (lubricated)
Steel on babbitt	0.42 (dry) 0.17 (lubricated)	0.35 (dry) 0.14 (lubricated)
Teflon on teflon or teflon on steel	0.04	0.04

Rolling Friction

Rolling friction is much less than sliding friction, and it is normally utilized in systems that require bodies to move over other bodies. Hard rollers over hard surfaces are most efficient. Anti-friction bearings employ this concept.

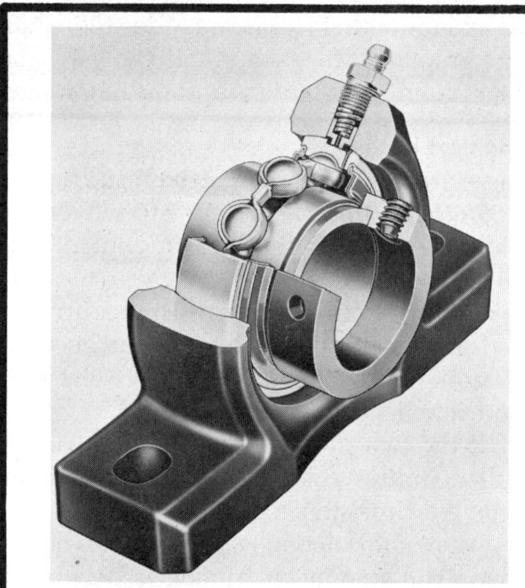

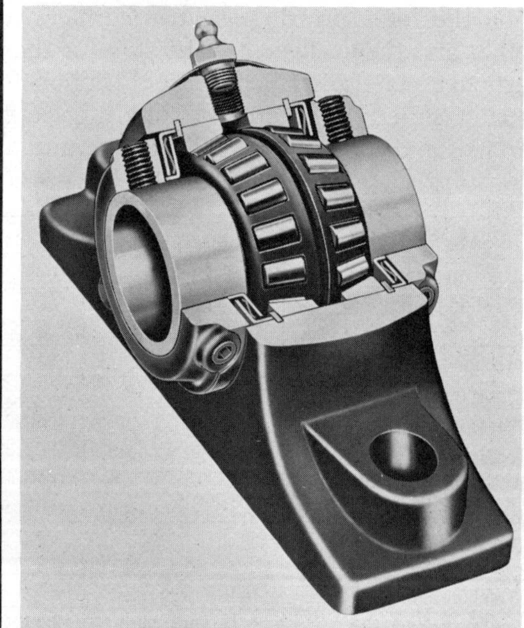

Fig. 20-6. Two Types of Anti-Friction Bearings in Pillow Blocks (Dodge)

Work and Friction

Friction is a fundamental need in mechanical transmission systems that involve pulleys and belts, flat wheels and flat surfaces, etc. It is the basis upon which mechanical energy is controlled. Clutching systems and braking systems depend upon friction to convert one form of energy to another.

Shaft Bearings

Sleeve Bearings

To lessen the friction of a rotating shaft, bearings are employed. Bearings provide support and allow free rotation of shafts or other moving parts. Their selection is usually made after consideration of the load characteristics and operating conditions, which may include temperature extremes, shock, vibration, contamination, malalignment, space restriction, and shaft rigidity. As discussed in Chapter 8, each type of bearing finds specific applications.

The two general classifications of bearings are journal and anti-friction bearings. *Journal bearings* are plain or sleeved bearings used for shaft rotation and support. They are most often machined or cast of a relatively soft material and contained in a suitable housing. *Anti-friction bearings* have rolling rather than sliding contact points. They have less surface contact area and require less lubrication. Types include ball, roller, and needle bearings, Fig. 20-6. Industrial bearings are similar to the bearings used in automotive, marine, aircraft and power generating applications.

A sleeve or insert bearing is a housing lined with sintered bronze, nylon, teflon, wood, graphite, or some other material which is usually softer than the shaft in order to mini-

Fig. 20-7. Bearing Block (Woods)

mize shaft wear, Fig. 20-7. These bearings are low in cost and are available in pillow blocks and flanged units which are usually mounted flush, vertically, or horizontally. Insert bearings have high radial load-bearing capacity and low thrust capacity. The lubrication of these bearings is most important, and an oil cup, wick, or grease fitting should be provided. Seals are an integral part of the bearing design to keep lubrication in the bearing and to protect it from contamination.

The success of any bearing surface depends upon the light film of oil lubricating and separating the two operating surfaces. Without this film the hard metal journal riding within the softer metal bearing would wear it rapidly. Sintered bearings, impregnated wood, nylon, and graphite-lined sleeve bearings may be self-lubricating. Plain and sleeve bearings are used for food processing equipment where they can be applied with little or no lubricant, for marine or wet applications where they may be exposed to water or moisture, and in combustion engines where they operate under oil pressure.

Housings

Pillow Blocks: Most often used where the shaft is to be mounted parallel to the base, pillow blocks can also be used for vertical or inclined mounting, and are usually made of cast metal with a hole bored to receive the actual bearing, Fig. 20-6. They are available in two-bolt and four-bolt varieties.

Fig. 20-8. Flanged Block (Dodge)

Flanged Blocks: Designed for thin wall mounting, flanged blocks provide a large clearance hole for the collar and the necessary bolt holes for mounting in the framework. Flanged blocks are usually mounted vertically, Fig. 20-8.

Flanged Cartridge Blocks: Similar to flanged blocks, cartridge blocks are used in machines where the cartridge housing is located within the structural member. The flanged cartridge block is supported entirely on the cartridge with the mounting holes serving to stabilize the shaft in a lateral position. The mounting base should be perpendicular to the shaft.

Cartridge Units: Any type of equipment with a thin wall support member can utilize a cartridge unit, eliminating the cost of housings. A fabricated base cut to the desired shape is simply bored to size, with the cartridge added to this assembly. To prevent lateral movement, a locking device is provided.

Shaft and Housing Fits

Bearings should have a snug fit on the shaft. For severe conditions, or where dynamic balance is necessary, a press fit is usually provided. The desired fits are obtained by controlling the dimensions and tolerances for the shaft and housing. The selection of fit is determined by the character of the load, physical design, housing material, bearing dimensions, temperature conditions of the bearing in operation, heat expansion of shaft and other parts, and requirements for running accuracy.

Sealing System

Bearings are seldom made with seals as an integral part. However, when installed in a housing, some type of sealing system is required to retain lubrication and prevent entry of contaminants. Seals vary from a baffle or labyrinth type similar to Fig. 3-12 (Chapter 3) which employ metal or synthetic discs, to a material such as rubber, fiber, or felt which directly contacts the rotating members.

Lubrication

As an aspect of reciprocating engine design, lubrication of ball and roller bearings was discussed in Chapter 8. Omitted from this discussion was grease lubrication. Grease lubrication is restricted to low-speed applications within temperature limits of the grease. Grease lubrication is confined in the bearing housing and is an important consideration in food, textile, and chemical applications. A bearing grease should have the following properties: freedom from chemically active ingredients such as lime, iron oxide, and similar mineral or solid substances; even consistency with a wide range of operating temperature; a melting point considerably higher than the operating temperature of the lubricated journal, and free of abrasive contaminants.

Many grease-lubricated bearings are pre-greased by the manufacturer and are normally regreaseable. If a grease fitting is not provided to facilitate this operation, the seals of the bearing must be disassembled, packed with grease, and then reassembled. Some bearings do not have such a provision and are marked "Sealed for Life." The two most popular grease fittings are the Zerk and the Alemite fittings.

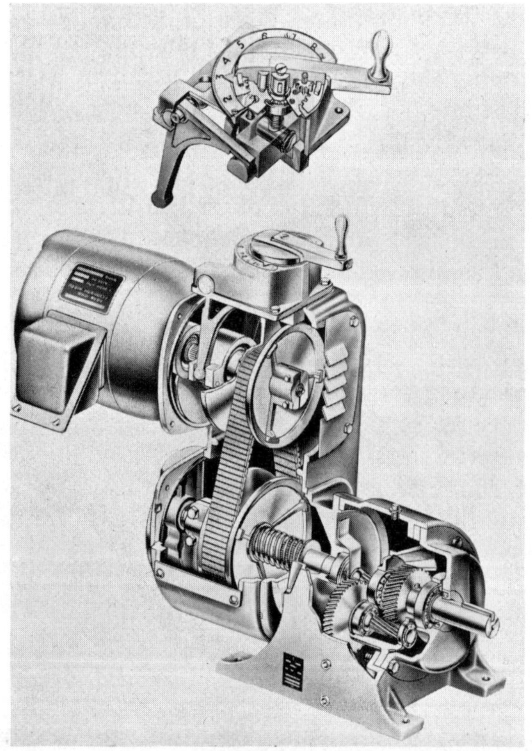

Fig. 20-9. Transmission System (G.E.)

Oil lubrication is better for high-speed and high-temperature applications because oil can be cooled to help reduce the bearing temperature. Oil is also easier to handle and allows better control of the amount of lubricant reaching the bearing. In applications where contamination is a problem, oil can be filtered. Silicone lubricants are recommended for very high temperatures or wet applications. For operation in very low temperatures and at very slow speeds, special lubricants are required.

Transmission Systems

Gearing describes systems that consist of wheels, gears, pulleys, belts, and chains, Fig. 20-9. This term does not include associated components such as clutches, ratchets, etc.

Gears act as levers of the first order and may be considered as combinations of spinning levers. Varying the diameters of the driver gear compared to the driven gear will vary the mechanical advantage of the system and proportionately affect the speed of the driven assembly.

If the driver and driven shafts are located close to each other, a wheel or gear system may be used to transmit power. If the shafts are separated widely, belts or a chain transmission system would be a logical choice.

Principles of Belt Drives

In most belt systems the coefficient of friction between the belting and the pulleys provides for the energy transfer. The force pulling the belt and pressing the belt against the pulley must be regulated and is commonly referred to as *tension*. Too much tension will cause undue bearing wear and belt fatigue. Too little tension will cause undue slipping and reduced energy transfer. Belt systems, because of the natural give of the belt material and inherent slippage, are able to absorb initial shock and vibration.

Tension

In all belt transmission systems, proper tension between driver and driven pulley must be provided to compensate for normal belt stretch. Often the engine or motor mounting provides for tension adjustment. In other systems, an idler pulley is used.

When a system is provided initial tension, the tension extends throughout the belt and provides the necessary pressure to create friction between the belt and the pulley. However, as the driving pulley turns, friction causes the belt to move, creating a pulling force within the belt. Because the driven pulley is at rest, it resists the pulling force and tensions build up within the belt strand. At the same time, the other strand of the belt loses some of its initial tension and becomes slack. The difference between the tension of the two strands of belt is essential to the belt's performing work, and is known as the *tension ratio.* When the belt and pulley system is at rest, there is no tension difference between the strands. This condition changes immediately as one pulley is caused to turn. The belt then automatically seeks its working tension ratio. Tension will increase on the tight side and decrease on the slack side until the difference in tension is equal to the force required to transmit power.

Belt Wrap

The arc of wrap for two pulleys in any belt system will total 360°. Systems with pulleys of the same size will have a wrap of 180° per pulley, and a speed ratio of 1. In systems with pulleys of different sizes, the larger pulley will always have greater wrap. High-speed ratios require pulleys so different in size that the distance between centers must be increased, or an idler used, in order to insure good wrap. Most belt systems never exceed a six-to-one speed ratio.

Optimum Speed

There is a speed at which a belt system reaches optimum efficiency. Beyond this speed efficiency decreases because centrifugal force throws the belt away from the pulleys and causes excess slippage.

Material Flexing

Consideration must be given the flexing ability of the belt. Exceeding the limits for a given belt results in abbreviated belt life, increased operating temperature, and low system efficiency.

Flat Belts

In the past, the flat belt and pulley system was frequently used to transmit power from a prime mover such as a steam or gasoline engine to the drive shaft, both on the farm and in factories. Pairs of pulleys (one fixed to the shaft and one idler) were suitably placed along the drive or *line shaft* to convey power to small countershafts. By means of a forked device, the belts were moved sideways from one pulley to the other. When the belt was on the fixed pulley, the shaft revolved. When the belt was on the adjacent loose or idler pulley, the shaft would stop. This simple means was used for stopping and starting the various machines without stopping the common drive shaft.

Flat belting was one of the earliest, and at one time, one of the most widely used means for transmitting power, for increasing and for reducing the speed of an operating shaft. Industrial plants and textile mills in particular were literally covered with flat-belt drives and running line shafts suspended from the ceiling. Flat belting is used on some power take-off equipment for farm machinery, for material handling, and moving sidewalks.

Flat belts may be employed to transmit power when there is a moderate distance between the prime mover or the driving shaft and the driven shaft. No guiding arrangement is required to maintain them on the pulleys as long as the shafts are parallel. If necessary the belt may be crossed to reverse the rotation of the driven shaft. With adequate distance, they also may serve to transmit power between shafts that are at right angles to each other.

Flat Belt Principles

In flat belt systems, the coefficient of friction between the belting material and pulley, the belt's width, thickness, grade of product, number of plies, flexibility, and the tension determine the amount of power transmitted.

Common Belt Types and Construction

The most popular belting materials include leather, impregnated leather, rubber, cotton duck, canvas, composition belts of cotton duck impregnated with rubber or vegetable gum, nylon, and camel's hair belts that may or may not be rubber impregnated.

Leather because of its long history and general use is considered the standard to which other belting materials are compared. Leather provides a good medium for power transmission. It has good service life, excellent flexibility, and good fastener-holding ability.

Rubber belting exhibits a lower coefficient of friction than leather and therefore requires greater tension.

Solid woven cotton belting is available in multiple plies and used for low-power transmission as well as for conveyor applications.

Combinations of cotton, nylon, cotton and rayon, and cotton and polyester have greatly reduced the overall thickness of belting with no sacrifice of strength. These belts are impregnated with rubber through a calendering process which rolls the rubber or gum into the cloth. The plies of impregnated fabric are then combined with layers of rubber and vulcanized. The rubber between the plies allows for bending around pulleys without separation.

Fig. 20-10. Pulley Used with Flat Belting (Woods)

Belt Fasteners

Wherever possible, endless belts should be used, insuring that the belt is uniform in strength throughout. When fasteners must be used to provide a belt of proper length, care should be taken to select the right fastener for a given belt. The three most common styles of belt fastener are lacing, hinges, and plates. Generally lacing and hinges are used for light to medium loads. Plates are used on heavier, slower speed and larger pulley installations.

Flat Belt Pulleys

Flat belt pulleys are available in a variety of materials and in a variety of styles: solid or spoked wheel made of cast iron; steel; combination steel and cast iron; wood and paper composition; plastic or aluminum, Fig. 20-10.

V-Belt Systems

A V-belt drive system may be defined as consisting of a belt and two or more V-grooved pulleys or sheaves used to transmit or receive power from a motor or engine. V-belt drives are popular because they are less expensive than most other forms of power transmission equipment, require no lubrication, and operate noiselessly with a minimum of maintenance. They operate over a wide spectrum of speed ratios and horsepower requirements. They can be used in abbreviated center distances providing system compactness and simplified belt guard design. They cushion bearings, shafting, motors, and connected equipment against load fluctuations and operate with a minimum of vibration. Belts are easy to install and easy to replace when worn. They are virtually unaffected by moisture, abrasives, dust, or extreme variations in temperature.

The V-belt drive system, like the flat belt system, depends upon frictional contact between the belt and the sheaves to transmit power from the driver to the driven shaft. In a V-belt drive the belt tension and the resistance of the driven sheave forces the belt into the sheaves. If the belt is so loose over the sheaves that it hangs freely above them, frictional contact between the belt and sheaves will not exist because there is no force to create it.

Mechanical Advantage of the Wedge

The coefficient of friction between the belt fabric and pulley is identical with flat belts and V-belts. The V-belt derives its greater pulling power chiefly from the fact that tension wedges it into the sheave, thereby employing a mechanical principle to multiply the friction, Fig. 20-11. V-belts are able to operate satisfactorily with only moderate tension, subjecting bearing, shafting, and connecting equipment to a minimum of strain. The wedging principle also enables V-belts to operate on short centers and at high speed ratios.

V-Belt Construction

V-belts are made of the three basic materials: rubber compounds, fabric, and cording. Rubber compounds are mixtures of natural and synthetic rubber; some belts must be resistant to oil and grease or to high operating temperatures.

The fabric is a cross woven material like cloth and is most commonly used as the cover stock. Most often it is cotton or some synthetic fiber impregnated with rubber. The cords provide tensile or load-carrying capability. In most belts, they are of synthetic material called polyester, although rayon and nylon are used to some extent as well as steel cable, wire, and fiberglass. There are two types of V-belt designs employing textile fiber cords — *single* and *multiple ply* belts.

The single ply cord consists of hundreds of individual filaments of fiber spun into a single continuous cord or cable, quite similar in appearance to commercially available twine. Multiple ply cords consist of numerous strands of cord which are held together in sheet-like form by a single filament, like the fabric material previously described. This cord stock is impregnated with rubber so that it will adhere to the other elements of the belt.

Belt Standards and Types

Standard V-belts meet dimensional tolerances and horsepower ratings and are indentified with a common numbering system. Standard belts are made of oil and heat resistant materials that withstand temperatures up to 180°F. When a belt is made to withstand higher temperatures, the manufacturer notes the operating temperature of that belt on the belt label. Additionally, some manufacturers produce a line of "super belts." The premium quality of workmanship and the materials used are noted on the belt label and the manufacturer certifies them to be oil- and/or heat-resistant, or static dissipating.

Notched Belts: V-belts with single ply construction have maximum flexibility, yet resist bending around a small radius. This is chiefly caused by the incompressible rubber resisting compression caused by the bending stresses. In order to relieve this strain, many manufacturers cut notches in the base section of short belts or belts which are likely to be used in drives involving small diameter sheaves. These notches are machine cut into standard belting.

Carved or Cog Belts: Although the carved belt is similar in appearance to the notched belt, the design is molded into the uncured belt during vulcanization. The design of the

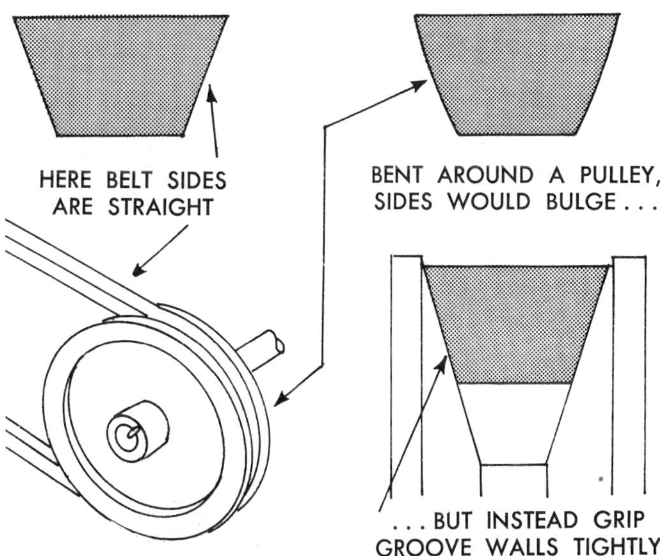

Fig. 20-11. The Grip of a V-Belt

belt makes it extremely flexible, Fig. 20-12. One of the noticeable differences between a carved belt and a notched belt is that the carved belt has no cover. It is usually described as a raw-edge belt. Carved belts exhibit a horsepower rating 50% higher than standard V-belts. They are priced proportionately higher than standard belts.

Steel Cable Belts employ a cord of brass-coated steel as the tensile member and are made in the same way as standard single-ply V-belts. These belts are only made in single-ply construction and are notched in all sizes. They exhibit a horsepower rating 50% higher than standard and are priced accordingly. Steel belts are usually made to be oil- and heat-resistant, as well as static-dissipating. They may be purchased in standard construction.

Glass Cord Belts are identical to other single-ply, wrap-molded belts except that the tensile material is made of normally more than 50,000 microscopically thin filaments of fiberglass. As a consequence the cord has a high flexibility. They have the same horsepower rating as standard belts. They are also heat- and oil-resistant and static-dissipating.

Fig. 20-12. Carved or Cog Belts (Woods)

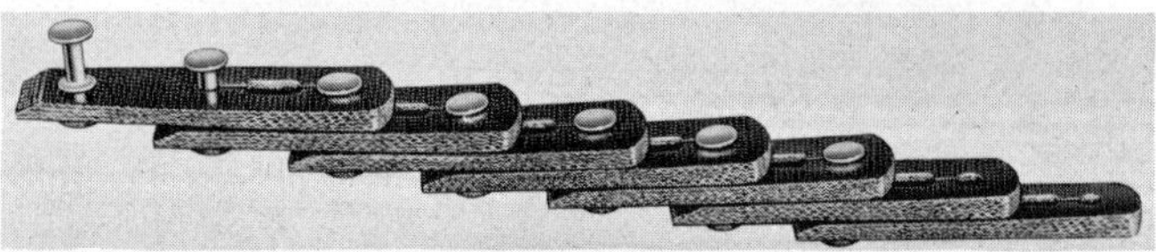

Fig. 20-13. Link Belt (Dodge)

Connected Belts are most commonly used for emergency replacement of a broken endless belt because they can be cut to any required length and easily installed. A connected belt operates at 75% of the rating of a standard V-belt. They are capable of withstanding up to 180° operating temperature. They are not oil-resistant and are not static-dissipating. Another belt that can easily be connected by mechanical fasteners is the open-end belt.

Link Belts are another style of open-end belting, consisting of small, precision-shaped pieces die-cut from rubber reinforced fabric. These belt pieces are linked together with metal rivets which can be easily inserted or removed with simple hand tools, Fig. 20-13.

Double Angle V-Belts are used where power must be transmitted from the top and bottom of the belt to shafts that are not all to turn in the same direction. The double-angle V-belt was developed to provide for the serpentine drives that are common in cotton gins and textile mills.

Banded V-Belts consist of several V-belts joined together at their tops by a single ply of rubber-covered cord stock. They are built in exactly the same manner as ordinary single- or multiple-ply V-belts. After they have been built they are placed in molds and covered with a sheet of multiple-ply cord material and vulcanized.

V-Belt Industrial Standards

Most of the belts listed above are "industrial V-belts" as distinguished from other categories such as automotive, agricultural, and fractional horsepower belts. V-belts are offered under more than 20 brand names, produced by eight manufacturers. The Rubber Manufacturer's Association, the Mechanical Power Transmission Association, and the Belt and Sheave Manufacturers have agreed upon standards of nomenclature, dimension, tolerances, horsepower ratings, and sheave-groove dimensions for the convenience of the user.

Cross Section Standards: An A-section belt has a nominal top width of ½″ and is 11/32″

thick. The included angle of all belt cross sections is 40°. The various belt sections match corresponding grooves or sheaves of a pulley. Figure 20-14 shows standard sizes and typical designs of belts.

Length Standards: V-belt size is specified by total length although the belt is endless. The industry terminology defines length and circumference synonymously. A V-belt has thickness and therefore both an inside and an outside length. Each is measurable. Somewhere between the inside and outside measurement is a dimension called *pitch length.* Every manufacturer of V-belts lists inside, outside, and pitch lengths.

Nomenclature: The number of the belt indicates the approximate length of the belt in inches. The letter that precedes this number is the section designation. Therefore, an A 36 belt designates a belt 36″ long with an A section configuration. An E 150 belt designates a belt 150″ long with an E configuration.

Matching Standards: Belt dimensions vary when made by the same manufacturer, with the same materials, by the same personnel, and on the same equipment. The chemicals, rubber, and textiles from which the belts are fabricated do not lend themselves to exact precision manufacture. In order to achieve a higher degree of uniformity, each belt manufactured in the United States is measured on an inspection fixture. A code number known as a "sag" or "matching" number is given the belt to indicate its actual size. This permits the selection of matched sets of belts. This is significant in a multiple-drive system to insure that each belt carries its share of the transmission load.

The belt is marked with a "matching" number *50* if the belt size is equivalent to the standard pitch length specified by the RMA for its size number. If the belt measures one-tenth inch longer than the standard pitch length, it is marked *51,* if two-tenths longer *52.* When a belt is measured one-tenth inch shorter than its standard pitched length, it is stamped with a matching number *49,* two-tenths shorter *48,* etc. It is not necessary for belts to have matching numbers to be con-

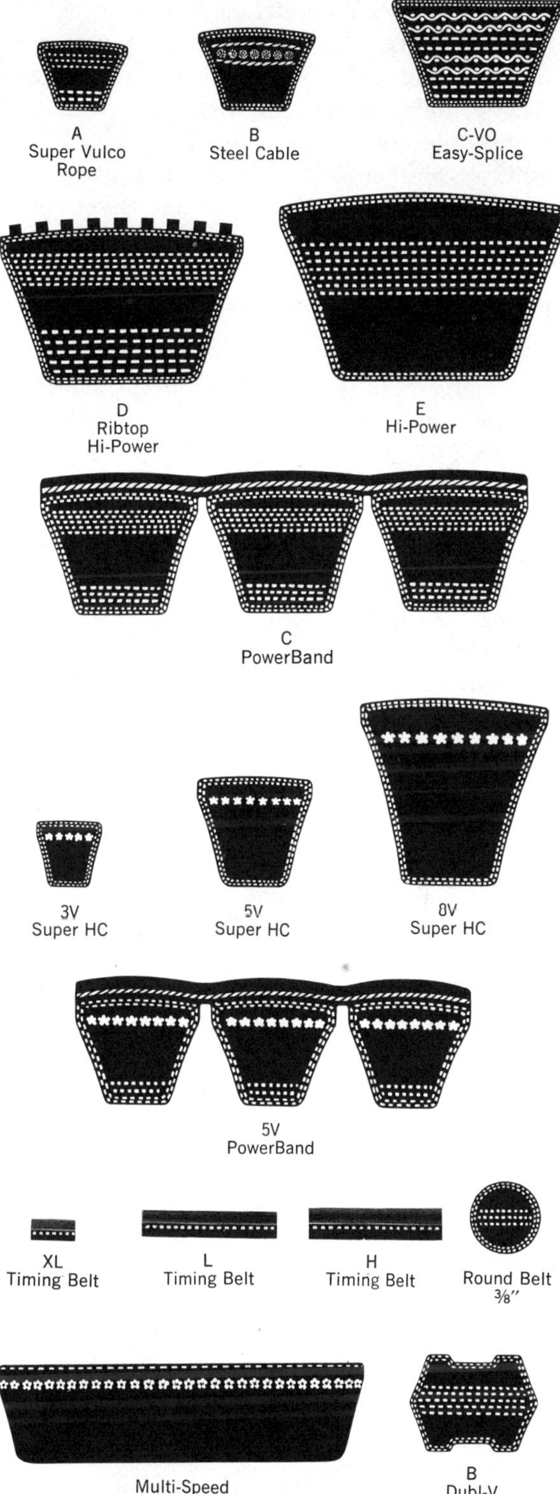

Fig. 20-14. Belt Standards (Actual Size)
(Gates Rubber)

sidered acceptably matched except in the case of short belts. These are the RMA matching limits permissible between the shortest and longest belts in one set: belt sizes from 26″ to 59″ plus or minus one-tenth inch; 60″ to 79″ two-tenths; 80″ to 104″ three-tenths; 105″ to 172″ four-tenths; 173″ to 299″ five-tenths; 300″ to 389″ six tenths; and 390″ to 660″ seven-tenths of an inch. These tolerances are presently being reviewed.

Narrow V-Belts

V-belts of an entirely different cross-section dimension, designated as narrow V-belts, are referred to as 3-V, 5-V, and 8-V V-belts. These numbers are derived from the top width dimension in eighths of an inch. A 3-V belt has a top dimension of ⅜″, a 5-V belt ⅝″, and an 8-V belt 8/8″ or 1″. The size designation of narrow V-belts is simplified. 3-V 1400 belt identifies the belt as a 3-V cross-section belt with an effective pitch length of 140.0″. Since these belts are customarily used in multiple sets, they usually must be matched, and the digit following the decimal point is used for that purpose.

Fractional Horsepower Belts

These belts are commonly used in home laundry equipment, small fans and blowers, lawnmowers, garden tractors, cultivators and small home-shop equipment. By RMA specifications there are three standard cross sections of fractional horsepower belts identified as 3L, 4L and 5L. The numerals describe the widths of the cross section in eighths of an inch. The L indicates light duty, or fractional horsepower.

Numerals following the cross-section designations define the lengths of the belts in tenths of an inch. Thus, a 3L 360 identifies a FHP belt with a top width of ⅜″ and a length of 36″; a 5L 235 belt will have a top width of ⅝″ and a length of 23½″.

Fig. 20-15. The Ribbed or Poly V-Belt (Browning)

Sheave Standards

The MPTA and RMA have established dimensional standards for standard and FHP sheaves. Manufacturers cast most sheaves of gray iron or mild steel. Usually those sheaves which are used for high-speed drives are made of ductile iron.

There is no completely uniform numbering system because of the variety of constructions. However, the first digit in the size designation signifies the number of grooves in the sheave. This number is followed by a letter, A, B, C, D, or 3V, 5V or 8V which identifies the belt cross section to be used with the sheave. The final part of the size designation consists of two or three numerals which define the sheave pitch diameter in tenths of an inch. It is the line on the sheave groove side wall which contacts the pitch line of the belt. In purchasing sheaves, it is also necessary to state the required bore size, i.e., the diameter of the shaft upon which the sheave is to be mounted.

There are two major styles of sheaves available: bored-to-size and bushed. In the bored-to-size, the sheave hub is bored to the exact size required. Since this is a custom operation, such sheaves are economical only when ordered in large production runs. Bushed sheaves are especially advantageous to a distributor because an assortment of inexpensive bushings may be stocked, enabling him to supply sheaves in a variety of bore sizes with a minimum of inventory investment.

Ribbed Belts

The ribbed or poly V-belt is manufactured by several companies and is basically a guided flat belt with many small V ribs molded lengthwise on the underside of the belt below the tension section, Fig. 20-15. The ribs may be made of soft rubber and are totally confined in compatible sheave grooves.

Unlike standard V-belts which wedge into the sheave grooves and consequently require clearance at the bottom of the groove, the poly-V's do not operate on this wedge principle, but use the incompressibility and fluid characteristics of the rubber to apply radial pressure in all directions. One advantage of poly-V's is that there is no need to match belts because of the unified construction of each drive. The manufacturers of this rubber belt provide three basic cross sections covering a wide range of transmission applications. See Fig. 20-14.

Gear Systems

Gear drives were among the earliest forms of energy transmission, and their popularity has not waned. At the dawn of energy transmission, two cogged wheels were cut or made of wood by hand. Gears provide a direct non-slip energy transmission device. They can be employed in a myriad of ways: to reverse direction of rotation, to change speeds, to change shaft direction, to allow shaft location in other than the same plane, and complex combinations of these functions.

Gear Material

Gears may be made of cast iron, ductile iron, many grades and hardnesses of steel, bronze, brass, aluminum, plastic materials, and a wide selection of sintered metals. Gear hardness and surface finish is determined by the operational speed and the torque to be transmitted. Manufacturer's catalogs will identify the material furnished in their gear stocks. Usually low speed, low torque and light load applications will permit non-metallic and non-ferrous materials to be used. High speed, high torque, and high load applications, along with heavy shock conditions, will require gears of alloy steels. Alloy steels with special heat treatment have a wide range of application.

Gear Terminology

The pitch circle is an imaginary circle which passes through the center of each tooth on the gear. The pitch diameter is the distance from a point on the pitch circle through the center of the gear to another point on the pitch circle. Figure 20-16 identifies other features of gears.

Pitch

Pitch refers to *diametral pitch (DP)*. It is the ratio of the number of teeth to the pitch diameter expressed in a whole number. It is also a measure of the size of the tooth. *Circular pitch* is the distance in inches from a point on one tooth to a corresponding point on an adjacent tooth measured along the pitch circle. As previously mentioned, diametral pitch is not a measurement and is expressed as a whole number. It is the relationship between the pitch diameter and the number of teeth. Circular pitch, however, is a distance measurement and is expressed in inches. The circular pitch of a bevel gear is measured at the larger end of the tapered tooth. These parts apply to all gears with possibly some modification depending on the gear type. *Gear ratio* is usually determined by dividing the number of teeth of the pinion gear into the number of teeth of the mating gear, except in worm gears where the ratio is determined by dividing the number of teeth on the worm gear by the number of starts or threads on the worm.

One other important factor to consider is that gears are usually furnished with two pressure angles, 14½° or 20°. The *pressure angle* is the angle formed by a line through the line of action of two mating gears and the line perpendicular to the center line of the gears. Manufacturers identify the pressure angle of gears. To mesh properly, mating gears must have the same pressure angle.

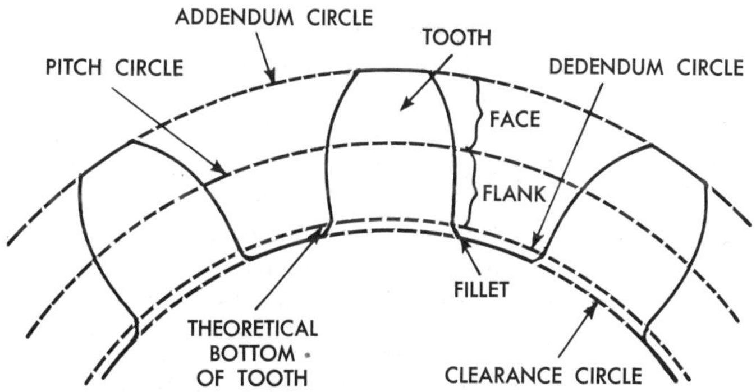

Fig. 20-16. Pitch Diameter of a Gear

Gear Body Design

The body design of a gear, as other power transmission devices, is furnished in several styles. Pinions can be furnished with or without hubs, and gears are available in solid, webbed, or spoked bodies. Some of the standard styles include the plain, plain with hub, webbed, webbed with hub, spoked, and spoked with hub.

Backlash

Backlash is necessary to insure proper gear operation. Insufficient backlash will generate early breakdown because of overloading, overheating, fatigue of tooth surface, and undue wear. Backlash clearances provide for proper lubrication, permit a degree of misalignment tolerance, allow for thermal expansion, and prevent binding.

Gear Maintenance

Proper gear maintenance and gear lubrication are extremely important in gear life, especially in open gearing because of the exposure to contaminants and environmental conditions that may cause excessive wear.

Fig. 20-17. Spur Gears (Woods)
Spur gears have teeth cut parallel to the axis of the shaft. They are economical in cost. They are noisy because they have only one tooth in mesh at any one time, requiring an abrupt contact and disengagement. The amount of power transmitted is dependent upon the strength of one tooth.

When a gear is purchased, the diametral pitch, size of the tooth, the pitch diameter, the size of the gear, the pressure angle, and the shape of the tooth must be designated. Two gears will not engage properly unless the diametral pitch and pressure angle are the same.

Helical Gears

As with spur gears (Fig. 20-17), helical gears are used with shafts in the same plane and parallel. Their teeth, however, are cut on an angle to the center line of the shaft. This results in an increased length of contact between the engaging teeth. Usually several teeth are in mesh at any one time, insuring uniform transfer of energy from one tooth to another. They run much more quietly and have greater strength and capacity to operate at higher speeds. Normally, helical gears are cut at an angle of 45° to the shaft center line. Helical gears are cut left or right hand so that one gear serves as the driver and the other the driven in parallel shaft installations. If both gears are cut the same hand, they can be employed in nonintercepting 90° shaft installations (thrust bearings must sometimes be employed because of side thrust).

Crossed-Axis Helical Gears

Crossed-axis helical gears are a special worm gear type with the ratio of 1-to-1. They are generally employed in light load applications, Fig. 20-18.

Fig. 20-18. Crossed-Axis Helical Gears (Morse)

Herringbone Gears

Helical gears that are double cut (with left- and right-hand teeth at right angles to each other) are referred to as herringbone gears. They are used for heavy loads at medium to high speeds and for continuous service. As one would expect, there is no side thrust to herringbone gears because the reaction of one gear is counterbalanced by the action of the other. Herringbone gears handle shock and vibration well. They have high capacity and are used in installations where a high single reduction is required.

Internal Gears

Internal gears may be cut as spur or helical gears to provide a drive that is compact, smooth running, and capable of high reduction ratios. Internal gears have shafts that are parallel and in the same plane. A planetary gear system depends on internal gears. In this system the sun or center gear, sometimes referred to as the pinion gear, turns in one direction causing the planet or idler gears to turn counter to it. The fixed internal ring gear then causes the planet gears to travel as a group in the same direction as the sun gear, but at a lower speed. This system can also be devised to have the planet gears fixed with the ring gear free to move and drive an output shaft.

Enclosed Gear Drives

Enclosed gear drives are usually employed for efficient, positive transmission of power, Fig. 20-19. Most often they are employed to step down the running speed of a prime mover and step up the force or torque applied to the operating equipment. Ordinarily, the enclosures are made of cast iron or fabricated steel, although formed metal, fiberglass, and epoxy enclosures are also employed. Typically the case supports the gears in a rigid housing and lubrication is provided by an oil bath.

Enclosed gear drives are self-contained, have positive lubrication, are quiet and clean, require a small space, have close shaft centers adaptable to a wide range of shaft replacement and mounting combinations, have extremely long life, and maintain the alignment of bearing and gears.

Basic considerations in selecting or designing a gear reduction system are: (1) the degree of reduction required; (2) the shaft centers and the direction of rotation; (3) the output power required as compared to the power input; (4) the type of service whether it be continuous or intermittent; (5) the source of power; (6) input speed and output speed; and, (7) the environment in which it is going to operate.

The two basic enclosed gear drives are the parallel shaft gear drive and the nonparallel shaft gear drive.

Parallel Shaft Gears

Spur gears may be used when the operating shafts are maintained in the same plane and parallel. Their teeth are cut straight and parallel to the axis of the shaft. When spur gears are in mesh, the contact is by a combined sliding and rolling motion. Because a sliding motion induces wear, proper lubrication is necessary to reduce friction. With spur gears no more than two sets of teeth are in mesh at any one time so the load is transferred from tooth to tooth rapidly. Spur gears are more often used for low-speed applica

Fig. 20-19. Enclosed Gear Drives (Falk)

tions. High-speed employment causes excessive noise and wear. Gear trains or multiple gear installations employ spur gearing for speed control and to bridge large center distances between the driver and the driven gear.

Parallel shaft drives may contain three basic types of gears: spur, helical and herringbone. Spur gears are less expensive; however, they are noisier and will transmit less torque in the same gear width than helical or herringbone drives.

Helical or herringbone drives are well suited to extremely high speeds with resulting high gear ratios. These drives employ sleeve bearings or anti-friction roller bearings, which also contributes to high efficiency, long life, and low maintenance cost. A single reduction unit can provide up to a 10-to-1 ratio. A double reduction unit can easily give a range of 40-to-1. Parallel shaft drives have one advantage in that shafts can be extended on either side of the reducer with the load shared equally by each of the bearings. The efficiency of these drives is high, better than 95%; therefore, little allowance need be made for frictional loss when the prime mover is selected.

Shaft Mounted Reducers: One of the most popular parallel shaft drives is the shaft mounted unit. It is small in size, very adaptable, and very economical. Many times this unit is employed with a V-belt and sheave transmitting the energy. The torque arm with a simple turnbuckle is employed as a tensioner for the V-belt, as well as to prevent rotation of the unit. In some cases an overload release is incorporated in the torque arm. In the event of overload, it automatically releases the tension of the belt. This overload release in conjunction with an electro-mechanical switch can shut off the driving motor or give a warning signal.

Fig. 20-20. Spiral Bevel Gears (Falk)

Nonparallel Shaft Gears

Plain bevel gears transmit power between shafts that are intersecting. They are cone-shaped with teeth that are tapered, narrow on the inside and wider to the outside portion of the gear. They can be provided to accommodate shafts intersecting at an angle other than 90°. When two bevel gears are in a 1-to-1 ratio, they are commonly referred to as *mitered gears.* These gears are always provided to accommodate shafting that intersects at 90°. As in all gearing, the smaller gear is commonly referred to as the pinion gear, and the larger is simply referred to as the gear. Bevel gears are most commonly used for shafts that intersect at right angles; therefore, the sum of the extended pitch lines meet at a point called the *apex.* It is important to remember that in bevel sets, the pitch angle of the pinion is determined by the number of teeth in the pinion. It is important to remember, also, that each bevel gear or pinion gear is designed to run with a specific mating gear. Beveled gears are ordinarily designed to operate at low speeds and with low ratios.

Spiral bevel gears are essentially the same as plain bevel gears, Fig. 20-20. Their teeth, however, are cut in a spiral arrangement. They afford the same advantages as helical cut gears provide over spur gears. They, too, combine rolling and sliding action when the teeth are meshing. They are quieter running and capable of running at higher speeds, although generally at low ratios.

Hypoid gears are designed so that the pinion is not in the same plane, usually being positioned lower on the gear. They are practically the same as spiral gears. Refer to Fig. 20-18. Because of its design, the pinion gear is usually larger than a similar spiral bevel gear. The prime use of hypoid gearing is to allow clearance for any piece of equipment that conflicts with the drive shaft location. Hypoid gearing provides high speed and medium ratio application. A common application of hypoid gearing is for automotive differential drives where it is desirable to lower the drive shaft position in relation to the rear end assembly.

Worm gears allow a high-speed single reduction application in a relatively compact space. They are used on non-intersecting shafts at 90°. The driving member gear is commonly referred to as the worm, and the driven gear, the worm gear. The worm gear is essentially the same as other gears although the teeth are cut differently. The worm is not a gear, but rather is a screw which drives the worm gear in a sliding fashion. Worms can be made in right- or left-hand cut for use with companion right- and left-hand worm gears. They are made with one or more than one start or lead thread. The number of starts of a worm can be determined by looking at the end of the worm. Because of the friction of the sliding action of the worm to the worm gear, it is the least efficient of all gearing. As in other gears, the helix angle must be the same for both the worm and the worm gear in order that they mesh properly.

Rack and pinion gears transfer rotary to linear motion. It usually consists of a spur gear and a bar with straight-sided teeth cut into its surface of matching pitch. Refer to Fig. 20-41. Many feed tables, such as those found on etching and proof presses, and some automobile steering systems use rack and pinion gears.

Nonparallel Shaft Reducers

The *worm gear speed reducer* is capable of providing reduction at as high as a 60-to-1 ratio, or in a double reduction system 3500-to-1 or higher. This type of drive generally is not as efficient as parallel shaft reducers. In many cases, though, it is the only economical way of acquiring a high reduction ratio with no sacrifice of quality and in a restricted space. These drives are known for their quietness of operation and their long life. As a self-contained, fully enclosed unit, they exhibit many of the advantages of the parallel shaft drives, Fig. 20-21.

In some instances right angle *bevel gear drives* are used to change shaft direction and rotation. They normally vary in ratio from 1-to-1 to 3-to-1. Some engine manufacturers employ a gear drive system as an integral part of their prime mover.

Shock and Overload Protection

Because all gear drives are positive drives, it is customary to employ a belt, flexible coupling, or some type of clutching system to reduce shock load. A slip clutch is used in some instances to protect against overloading.

NUMBER	PITCH
25	¼
35	⅜
40	½
50	⅝
60	¾
80	1
100	1¼
120	1½
140	1¾
160	2
200	2½
240	3

Fig. 20-21. Worm Gear Speed Reducer
(Eaton Yale & Towne, Inc.)

Chain Drives

Another popular means of positive transmission of energy is the chain drive. These drives may be used in a variety of ways and permit a wide latitude of design. They can serve components that are physically separated from each other. See Fig. 20-22. They are moderate in cost and used to drive bicycles, motor bikes, elevating machinery, conveyors, and timing devices. Basically a chain drive consists of many links which can be readily joined together. The center distance from one chain link or hinged point to the next is known as the pitch of the chain and is the primary identifier of any chain.

The construction design, the material used in the links, and the specific types of joints differentiate the style or the type or chain. An important consideration in selecting a chain drive is the power transmission requirement. In general, as the chain pitch increases, power transmission capability increases because larger pitches have larger pins, more bearing area between the pin and the hole, and heavier side bars.

The material used also affects transmission capabilities. Alloy steel or hardened pins fitted into heat-treated side bars with close tolerances make a stronger chain than carbon steel pins fitted into cast malleable side bars. Also, the open joint design will not transmit as much power as the pin-cast barrel types.

Speed of Operation

The maximum speed of a chain is determined by its joint design. At the slow end of the speed spectrum is the open joint with speed capabilities increasing through to precision roller chains with closely controlled tolerances. Obviously, as the pitch of a chain increases, the weight of the chain also increases. This affects the centrifugal force operating on the chain, decreasing its maximum operating speed. The materials used also affect maximum speeds; steel chains have greater strength than malleable chains, permitting higher speeds.

Fig. 20-22. Double Strand Roller Chain Assembly (Morse)

Environmental Conditions

The operating environment will determine the type of chain selected. The open joint, for instance, makes the detachable chain desirable for agricultural applications where dust, stalks, leaves, and moisture are prevalent. The steel pin, cast barrel joint of the pintle and mill chain, is ideal for general duty work, providing moderate resistance to abrasion, moisture, and corrosion. The pin and bushed barrel form of intermediate carrier chains provide excellent corrosion resistance, especially when they are made with stainless steel pins and bushings. Standard precision roller chains generally require a dust-free and dry environment to insure optimum service life. The larger pitched chains, on the other hand, withstand heat better but take longer to cool because they retain the heat longer. They also yield longer service life in conditions of extreme moisture and abrasion because of their size.

Lubrication

Lubrication depends upon joint material and joint tolerances. The open joint chain requires less lubrication than the precision roller chain with its close tolerances. The lubrication requirements for a given type chain are generally the same regardless of pitch and depend on link design and materials used. Open link types with higher tolerances have better ability to withstand the lack of lubrication than links made with close overall tolerances. Some chain designs incorporate special lubrication reservoirs or holes. As a rule, chains made of identical metals require more lubrication and attention than those made of different metals. Sintered bushed chains may contain their own lubricant.

Pitch Selection

The proper selection of chain depends, too, upon the sprocket and pitch requirements. In general, the smaller sprocket should have at least 16 teeth. Low ratio, larger sprockets will produce less chain pull, lower bearing loads, and even less joint wear. When ratios are high, a small speed sprocket may be required. When speeds are below 100 rpm, it is often practical to use 9 or 10 teeth which may provide ratios of 12-to-1. At higher speeds the ratio should be limited to a maximum of 7-to-1.

Speed of operation is also a lubrication factor. Slower speed units usually employ a manual lubrication system or a drip system. High speed applications demand oil bath lubrication or forced oil lubrication at the maximum speed range. Oil bath lubrication requires an enclosure or an oil-tight chain case. Forced lubrication systems demand circulating pumps. Consequently, chain drives in these speed ranges are relatively high in cost.

Chordal Action

One of the limiting factors in chain drives is chordal action. The chain link is a straight line segment trying to follow the circular path of the sprocket pitch diameter. Experimentation has shown that for a given horsepower ratio and speed the best drive will be one that utilizes the smallest pitch chain of the least number of strands.

General Purpose Chains-Standard ASA Series

The most commonly used chain for general power transmission is the Standard ASA chain, available in a variety of pitch sizes. Each series is available in single, double, triple, and quad strands, with several sizes available in bronze, stainless steel, and a variety of plated finishes.

There are two basic components of this chain – the roller link and the pin link. The roller link consists of two roller link plates with two bushings pressed into them with rollers placed over these bushings, Fig. 20-23. The pin link consists of two pins pressed into one pin link plate, with the other pin link plate placed over the ends of the pins and fastened by upsetting or employing some type of spring fastener. Since it is all steel with all surfaces highly finished and all tolerances closely controlled, this chain is highly efficient. It is economically produced by automated equipment. The standard industry numbering system designates the series of the chain as follows:

Chain Designation: The pitch number is given first, followed by a dash and the number of strands; for example, 1″ pitch triple strand chain is indicated as 80-3, Fig. 20-23A.

Heavy series is similar to the standard series except: the pin link plates of the heavy series are thicker than those of the standard series. Generally speaking, the thickness of the pin link plates in the heavy series is the same as the next larger pitch in the standard series. The heavy series is widely used in oil field equipment, Fig. 20-23.

The *double pitch series* is similar to the standard chain series except that the pitch is double that of the standard series.

The *power transmission series* provides an efficient, economical drive for lower horsepowers and lower speeds with longer center-distance capability than standard pitch chains.

The *conveyor series* is suited for applications where the chain will drag along a surface. This series comes with larger rollers designed to eliminate sliding friction.

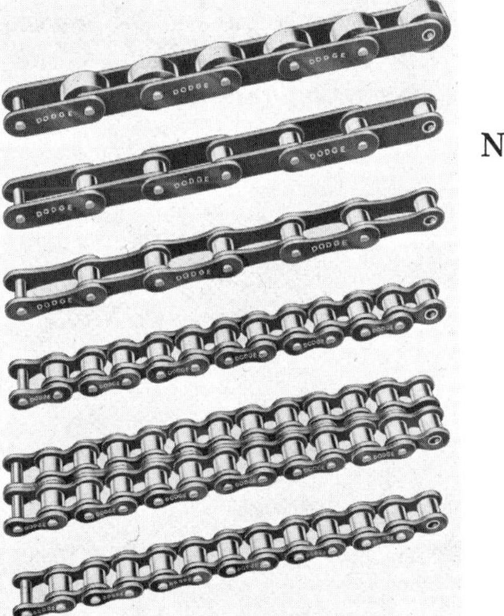

Fig. 20-23. Heavy Series Roller Chains (Dodge)

Number	Pitch
25	1/4″
35	3/8″
40	1/2″
50	5/8″
60	3/4″
80	1 ″
100	1 1/4″
120	1 1/2″
140	1 3/4″
160	2 ″
200	2 1/2″
240	3 ″

Fig. 20-23A. Chain Designation

Sintered bush chains are similar to the standard chain series but instead of a bushing or roller, sintered bush chains have an oversize bushing pressed into the link plates of the roller or block link. The bushing is of sintered steel impregnated with special lubricants. The bushing pivoting around the link pin forms the hinge that is virtually self-lubricating. While this chain does not have the capability of the standard series it is very useful where lubrication is impossible or impractical.

Leaf chain consists of a series of interlaced plates held together by pins that are upset at the ends. The hinges of this chain are formed from the plate and pivot around the rivet or pin. It is popular for hydraulic lift trucks and for various tension linkages.

Flat top chain is basically a standard roller chain with a flat top appended to provide a carrying surface, as a conveyor system. This surface plate is made to interlock the pin and form the hinge joint. The entire assembly is generally available in carbon steel, stainless steel, or plastic. If the plate is a separate attachment, a selection of chain materials, plate materials, a combination of material and attachment techniques is usually available. The flat top chain is widely used in the brewing and bottling industry as well as for general conveying service, Fig. 20-24.

There are many general and special purpose chains. Each type may be made of a variety of materials. They all operate using the same principles.

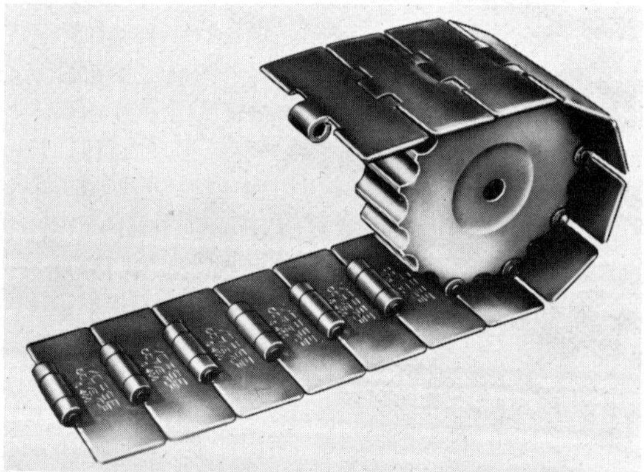

Fig. 20-24. Leaf Chain (Morse)

Chain Sprockets

The sprocket must engage the chain with the proper clearance between the slide bars and with the proper pitch to insure the mesh of the tooth with the pin or roller. These two dimensions determine the size or pattern number of the sprocket. For any given diameter of sprocket there will be variations based on the number of teeth, material of construction, body design, hub design, and diameter of the sprocket wheel.

Number of Teeth

Each size group is available in a range of tooth sizes. Cast iron and steel are used for both standard and roller chain sprockets. For engineering class chains the teeth are usually cast and for roller chain the teeth are cut and

Fig. 20-25. Sprockets (Dodge)
A. Plain Sprocket – Type A
B. Single Hub Projection – Type B
C. Detachable Bushing – Type C
D. Split Sprocket

machined to matching tolerances. More expensive sprocket wheels are heat-treated to increase abrasion resistance and service life. Sometimes steel sprockets will be machined from solid bar stock. Larger sizes may be cut from plate steel and used plain or with the desired hub arrangement welded to the plate.

Body Design

As with gears, the body of the sprocket may be solid, webbed, or spoked. As a rule, smaller diameter sprockets will be solid. Medium sizes will be webbed, and the larger diameters will be spoked.

Hub Design

The hub is one of the most distinguishing characteristics of a sprocket, Fig. 20-25. The three basic types are noted as *A*, *B*, or *C* type sprockets. The *A* sprocket is plain with no projection. This sprocket is used mainly when the sprocket is bolted or mated to a flange such as the flywheel. The *B* sprocket has a hub projection on one side. It is most widely used for general service and in small to medium diameter sprockets. The *C* sprocket has hub projections on both sides of the face and is standard for all steel sprockets, especially in the larger sizes. *B* and *C* hubs are generally supplied with a finished bore, a keyway, and one or two set screws. Lately manufacturers supply sprockets with various detachable bushings either straight or tapered. When a sprocket is to be mounted between pillow blocks which have already been installed and are difficult to remove, a split sprocket is often used. See Fig. 20-25. This sprocket can be installed around the shaft without disturbing the shaft. The halves are bolted together.

Sectional Rim Sprockets

Sectional rim sprockets are also split sprocket. However, the sections can be removed independently and permit a part of the unit to be replaced without dismantling the drive chain. This is particularly advantageous in bucket applications as well as in some conveyor applications where there would be difficulty in dismantling the unit. This type of installation also cuts the out-of-service time of these units.

Traction Wheels

In elevator and conveyor applications, traction wheels are often used as idlers, as the chain may sag undesirably. The traction wheel is a wheel that is smooth on the outside. It permits the chain to contact the periphery of the wheel between the end plates of the chain, eliminating wear on the chain barrels. Traction wheels can be obtained in segmented or solid styles.

Double Pitch Chain Sprockets

Double pitch chain sprockets resemble the standard roller chain sprocket with the pitch approximately one-half the pitch of the chain. Single cut sprockets must be used for chains with carrier rollers.

Shear Pin Hub

This arrangement is available on almost any sprocket and is used on the drive sprocket to protect the drive train from being overloaded or broken from a shock load. The hub is keyed to the shaft, and the sprocket is free to rotate on the shaft or hub when the pin or key breaks. The pin is designed to shear under a specified load. In the event of breakage, the shear pin is easily removed and replaced with another pin, making the unit again operable.

Silent Chains

Silent chains are popular for high-speed transmission systems. They are available for almost any load requirement. They normally consist of a series of two steel link plates assembled on a hinged component in such a fashion that movement occurs between the adjoining pitches. Design of the unit may vary, but generally it will be a round pin with bushing, or a round pin and segmented bushing, or a rocker pin joint design. The action of the silent chain is such that the teeth of the link plates engage mating teeth of the sprocket, which looks similar to a spur gear. The action is quieter, smoother, and higher speeds may be used than with comparable chain drives.

Silent chains are bought or identified with the letter designation *SC* followed by numerical digits indicating pitch and width. For example, SC 404 designates a silent chain 4/8″ or 1/2″ pitch and a 4/4″ or 1″ width. The pitch is noted in eighths and the width is given in quarters of an inch. In addition to the standard link plates, the silent chain requires that a guide link be provided in the center of the chain. These serve to keep the chain aligned with the sprockets. Some units have their guide links located on the outside of the chain. A guide groove is cut into the sprocket tooth to allow clearance for the guide plates, except where side guides are used. Silent chains may be made with teeth projecting from both sides, thus permitting the chain to be used or flexed in two directions. This is known as a duplex silent chain. The joint construction is basically the same as for the standard type. A reversible chain is manufactured for use where the sprockets must contact both sides of the chain.

Silent chain sprockets are basically the same as standard chain sprockets, the only difference being the shape of the teeth and the groove that is cut in the periphery of the sprocket for the center guide.

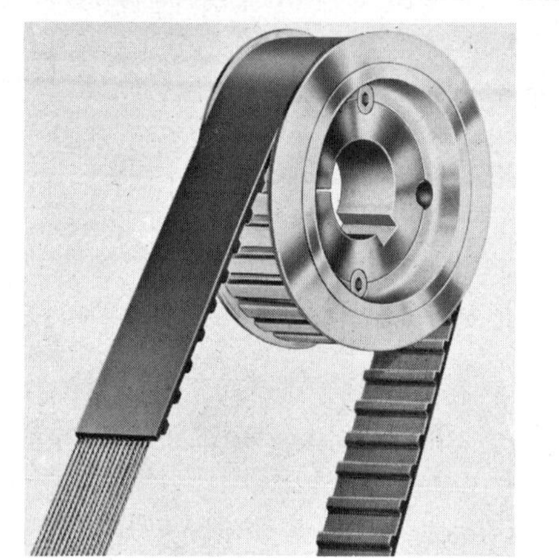

A. Cutaway Construction of Timing Belt (Dodge)

B. Typical Timing Belt Application (Gates)

Fig. 20-26. Timing Belt Drives

Toothed Belt Drives

Gear drives usually depend on a metal-to-metal contact and belt drives depend upon a metal-to-belt contact. Noise is often a problem with gears and the inherent stretch of belts is often undesirable. Many attempts have been made to develop a drive that overcomes these limitations and still combines the advantages of both these systems.

Synchronous or Timing Belts

The timing belt drive uses steel-cabled tension sections to prevent belt stretch, Fig. 20-26. The root of each belt tooth lies on the pitch line of the tension member. The pitch line was made to retain its length dimension during flexing; therefore, the roof of each tooth was located on or near as possible to the pitch line to maintain constant spacing. The design of the belt presented one problem; the design of the pulley was another. Timing belts are generally molded, endless black belts with regularly spaced teeth. Although construction varies with each manufacturer, the tooth shear strength always exceeds the tensile strength of the belt provided that six or more teeth are in mesh.

Timing belts may be considered a means of positive transmission because they have no slippage or creep, thus no speed variation from the driver to the driven pulley. There is also a minimum of elongation of the tooth, eliminating the need for belt take-up. Since the drive does not depend on friction, little tension is required. There is no need for lubrication. Speeds up to 16,000 feet per minute are permissible. It is applicable to drives ranging from a fraction to 600 or more horsepower. The absence of backlash permits a precise synchronization from one wheel to the other, yet the flexibility of the belt allows a very small wheel to be used. The timing belt operates quietly and with little heat.

Nomenclature

Two terms must be defined: *pitch* and *pitch line*. The pitch line is the area between the tension and compression sections that remains constant in length during the belt's flexing. The pitch of the pulley, or circular pitch, is the spacing between the teeth as measured along the pitch line of the belt. Therefore, the pulley pitch diameter is always greater than the outside diameter of the pulley.

Belt Design

Most stock belts have helically-wound carbon steel or fiberglass cables imbedded in a neoprene belt backing. These materials are used because they exhibit high resistance to elongation. On special order, stainless steel or synthetic cords may be employed. The belt teeth are molded with a nylon fabric cover provided to protect the teeth. The backing which houses the tension cable is made of neoprene in stock belts; but on a made-to-order basis, other compounds may be obtained that will tolerate higher temperature extremes, provide for static electricity dissipation, or permit constant oil contact.

Belt Classifications

Belts are classified into five cross sections according to their capacity for load. Each belt is identified by its pitch code, as shown below. Refer also to Fig. 20-14.

PITCH IN INCHES	CODE DESIGNATION
1/5	XL Extra Light
3/8	L Light
1/2	H Heavy
7/8	XH Extra Heavy
1¼	XXH Double Extra Heavy

A belt is ordered by giving the pitch length, letter code designation for pitch, and then the belt width in inches. For example, a 460 XL 100 belt would have a pitch length of 46″, a pitch of 1/5″ and a width of 1″. A timing pulley will be identified in much the same way, with the first number giving the number of grooves followed by the letter and width of the pulley. Timing belt pulleys are designed and manufactured to maintain a precision fit between the pulley groove and the belt tooth, minimizing runout and backlash. As in V-belt sheaves, most pulleys are supplied with detachable hubs or bushings offering the advantage of minimum stock inventory while providing for a broad range of application. Most timing pulleys are made of cast iron and are statically balanced. If the operating speed is to exceed 6,000 feet per minute, other materials such as ductile iron, steel, or aluminum are preferred. The small or driving pulley is flanged to counteract the gentle side thrust created by the spiral blade of the continuous tension member. Tension and bearing load are a minor design consideration of these transmission systems. However, minimum pulley diameters are critical because flexing affects belt life.

Clutches

Clutches are transmission devices that provide for and control energy transfer from driver to driven shaft. They can be actuated by centrifugal, rotational, mechanical, electrical, pneumatic, or hydraulic forces. The selection of a clutch should be given a great deal of consideration because it is a much-used component in the power train. The most popular clutches are the positive, friction, centrifugal, overrunning, and the electric clutch.

Clutch Selection

When a smooth start from zero to operating rpm is desired, the clutches must usually depend on slippage to dissipate energy. The loss of transmitted energy due to friction is transformed into *heat and wear,* and these are main considerations in clutch selection. Sometimes the power train application of the clutch requires an *immediate start* to full rpm. Such clutches usually operate at extremely low rpm, and it is necessary to provide a clutch of sufficient size to be able to absorb the shock of immediate acceleration.

The *load factor* of any power train is an important consideration in selecting individual components. Certainly such is the case in selecting the proper clutch. The load frequently controls acceleration time and the amount of heat and wear that the clutch will be called to withstand, or the degree of shock that the clutch will be required to absorb.

A *shielded clutch* is preferred if the clutch is to be operated in an *environment* of high particle contamination. In high-temperatures, such as in ovens, steel mills, or steam generating plants, the components of the clutch and the clutch design itself must be capable of operating under these conditions. If necessary, the clutch may be cooled by air or hyraulic oil.

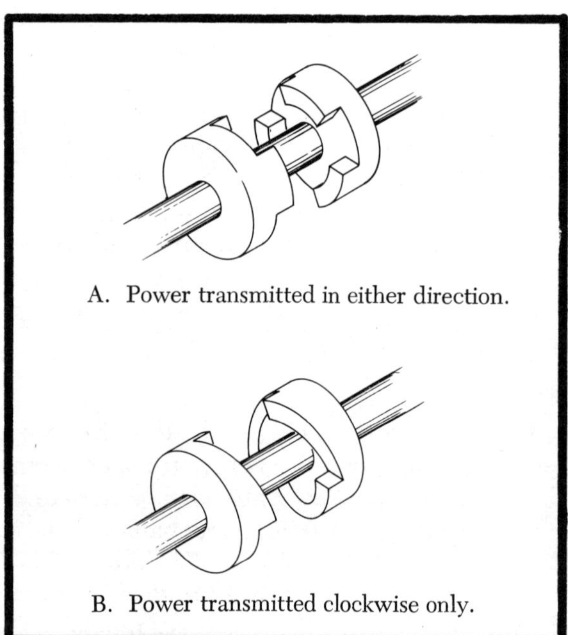
A. Power transmitted in either direction.

B. Power transmitted clockwise only.

Fig. 20-27. Positive Drive Clutches

The number of starts and stops – *the cyclic demand* – within a given period is an important consideration in selecting a clutch. The greater the frequency of engagement, the greater is the heat energy that must be dissipated, and the greater the fatigue resistance and shock absorbing capability the clutch must possess.

Usually the greater the *torque* requirement, the larger the clutch. Most manufacturers rate their clutches in terms of horsepower to be transmitted.

Clutches are made to accommodate any *shaft size.* In existing applications, a clutch must be chosen to fit the driver and the driven shaft. This may result in the selection of a clutch that is oversize, if the manufacturer's torque recommendations are not referred to, and shaft size is the only consideration.

In the design of a transmission train, the clutch should be placed in an *accessible position* because it generally requires the most service and attention.

The manufacturer's catalog will list the *limits of clutch application.* This catalog should be studied before any final decision is made, to be sure that this component in the power train will have long operable life.

Positive Clutches

Positive clutches are non-slip clutches that engage the prime mover directly with the driven shaft. The operation of this clutch depends on the shafts being at rest or turning at a very low rpm.

A *square jaw clutch* is the simplest mechanical clutch – a pair of interlocking square jaws. One member slides along a splined shaft to mate with the other clutch member. Energy is transmitted from one shaft to the other, positively, with no slip. The transfer of energy is made in either direction of rotation, Fig. 20-27.

The *spiral jaw clutch* drives a shaft in one direction only and disconnects it in the opposite direction. It is similar to the square jaw clutch except that there is a bevel cutback of the square shoulder that engages the two components of the clutch. When rotation is reversed, the bevels disengage. The Bendix starter is a classic application of the spiral jaw clutch. This type of clutch is not as popular today as it once was, as the overrunning clutch is subject to less wear.

Overrunning Clutches

Automatic automobile transmission systems employ an overrunning clutch. It is also used in industrial applications that require one shaft to rotate freely after the other shaft is stopped, such as in an indexing application or stock-feeding device for a press, Fig. 20-28. There are several types of overrunning clutches.

The *ratchet and pawl* overrunning clutch is popularly used in industry and for some hand tools such as the hand brace and wrench.

The *roller overrunning clutch* employs a spring-loaded roller and ramp. The roller is permitted to turn freely when the clutch is operated in one direction. When it is reversed, the roller moves up the ramp and binds with the outer member of the clutch to engage the load.

The *Sprague clutch* employs cams located between an inner race and an outer race. When the clutch operates in one direction, the low point of the cam is presented to the races, allowing them to slip. When the direction of rotation is reversed, the high point of the cam is presented to the races locking them to drive the system. These clutches by their very nature are suitable for applications that require a minimum of control.

Friction Disk Clutches

Friction clutches are used to transmit energy from driver to the driven machine in a smooth, gradual manner. These clutches can be engaged or disengaged with the energy source in continuous operation. Two mated surfaces are brought together under pressure to transmit power. Early clutches employed a wooden block and one of steel. The heat generated caused rapid deterioration if they were engaged often, or if they were only partially engaged to bring the unit up to optimum speed gradually. Frictional materials made from asbestos exhibited the facility of being able to withstand heat and frictional wear. These asbestos materials are popular today.

The clutch can be made in two ways: (1) the frictional or mating surfaces are the faces of two plates or (2) the mating surfaces may be the inside and outside of a drum or cylinder.

The frequency of application and the degree of slippage caused by the gradual application of clutch will determine the amount of heat and frictional wear of the driver and the driven members. Some method of external cooling must be made available if the clutch is to be used continually or if it is to operate with constant slippage. A typical use of a constant slippage clutch is winding material on a spool or mandrel. As the material is wound on the spool, there is a change in the linear speed; therefore, the roll must compensate by rotating at a slower speed. Motion picture projectors, tape playback equipment, record-

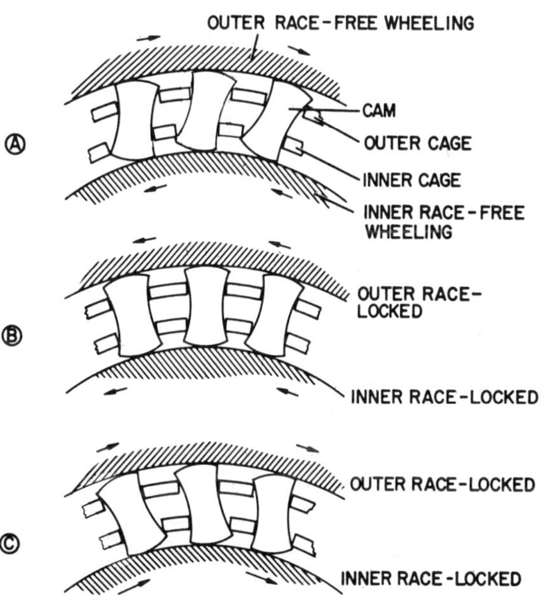

Fig. 20-28. Operation of an Overrunning or Freewheeling Clutch

ing equipment, wire drawing machines, wire wrapping machines, roll presses, etc. employ constant slippage friction clutches. Forced air cooling is frequently used to dissipate heat.

The torque transmitted by the clutch is proportional to the frictional surface area. In order to increase the surface area to provide for increased torque transmission, several disks or multiple plates may be employed. These are made to engage simultaneously. In order to bring and hold the frictional surfaces together, an external force is required. This force is proportional to the amount of torque that is to be transmitted and can be applied by mechanical, hydraulic, air, or electrical means. Modern day clutches engage and disengage rapidly. When fluids, air, or hydraulics are used in the transmission media, they also serve as the clutch coolant. If fluids are used, a piston or diaphragm arrangement is employed to transmit energy to the plates. The amount of pressure determines the amount of torque transmitted. If continual slippage is to be provided, or if a specific torque is desired, the fluid pressure is regulated so that a predetermined overload at the driven side will release the driver. Clutches are usually mounted between the prime mover and the driven machine, as in the case of machine tools or automobile transmission systems, Fig. 20-29. They are usually designed so that the greater mass is the constantly rotating member. The lesser mass is usually connected to serve as the driver.

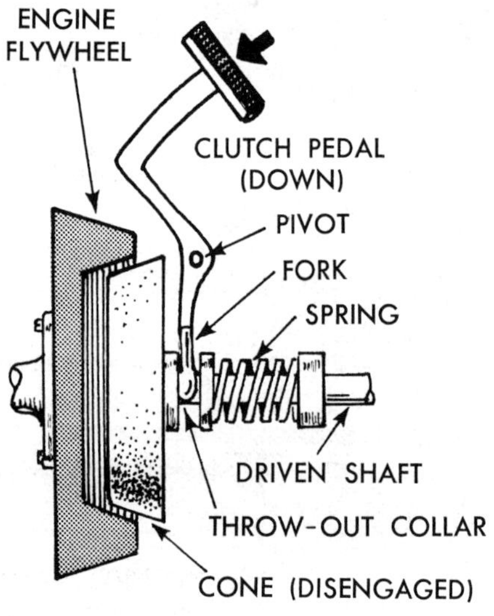

Fig. 20-29. Cone Clutch Used on Early Automobiles

Internal combustion engines cannot be started under load. Therefore, a clutching system must be used to separate the engine from the power train until the engine becomes operational. The clutch is engaged to gradually apply the load to the engine.

Automobile Friction Clutches

The automobile friction clutch contains a driven plate called the friction disk, splined to the clutch or transmission input shaft. The spline arrangement permits the disk to move back and forth on the shaft while causing the shaft to rotate with it. The friction disk is located concentrically behind the flywheel which has a polished surface of the same diameter as the friction plate. These are the mating surfaces of the friction clutch.

A spring-loaded pressure plate forces the friction plate to engage the polished surface of the flywheel, transmitting energy from the flywheel to the transmission shaft. If the clutch pedal is depressed, the pressure plate is separated from the friction plate, uncoupling the engine from the transmission shaft.

The frictional disk consists of a plate and a hub assembly to which pads of facing material are attached. The disk also contains cushioning and dampening devices. The cushioning device is a series of waved cushion springs to which the friction facings are attached. These will compress slightly as the clutch is engaged, reducing the tendency of the clutch to grab. The dampening device employs a series of heavy coil springs to absorb part of the rotary vibration that occurs as normal part of the reciprocating engine operation.

Usually power can be transmitted in either direction through the application of the friction clutch, Fig. 20-30. The engine drives the power train to propel the car or, as is sometimes necessary, the power train drives an inoperative engine. The friction clutch has a limited capacity for transmitting power. If too heavy a load is applied, or if the clutch is not fully engaged, the excess slippage will generate considerable heat. This clutch can be engaged or disengaged while the prime mover is in continual operation. It also provides a high degree of torque control, permitting the operator to accelerate the load gradually from zero rpm to operating speed.

Magnetic Frictional Clutches

This frictional clutch employs an electromagnet to attract one plate to the other, creating a non-slip bond at normal speed. These clutches require direct current. Electromagnetic disk clutches are very popular and lend themselves well to a packaged concept of clutch and brake, Fig. 20-31. Automobile air conditioner compressors are a typical application.

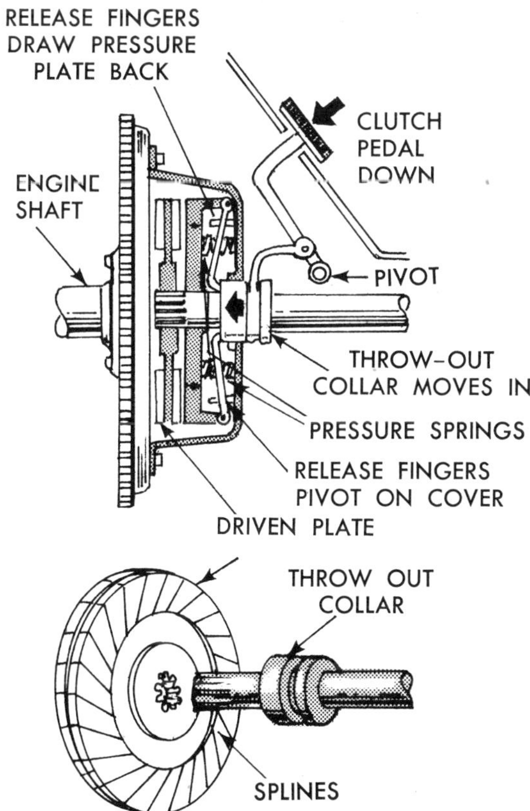

Fig. 20-30. Automobile Friction Clutch

V-Belt-Idler Friction Clutches

In a V-belt transmission system, a simple friction clutch can be arranged, Fig. 20-32. An idler sheave or pulley is located between the driver and driven sheaves and is designed to maintain the proper operating tension on the belt. When the spring-loaded idler is caused to move away from the belt, the belt slips or the driver spins freely. This simple clutch arrangement is used on many small tractors as well as on small belt-driven machinery.

Fig. 20-31. Magnetic Frictional Clutch (Bendix)

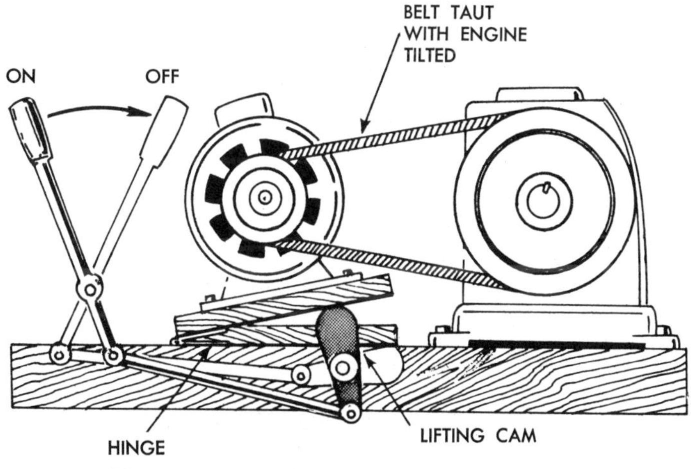

Fig. 20-32. Simple V-Belt Clutch Rig

Centrifugal Clutches

Centrifugal clutches make it possible to use normal torque motors for heavy loads rather than select a high torque motor to overcome the initial starting load. Using a centrifugal clutch reduces sharply the current requirements for an electric motor. This reduces the heat losses inherent in direct starting and means reduced power requirements, greater efficiency, and greater economy in motor drives. When used with a heat engine, the centrifugal clutch allows the engine to warm up before the starting load is applied or allows the engine to stand by at idling speed.

A centrifugal clutch is used to great advantage in such applications as dual drives, engine-driven pumping systems, equipment where the engine is started by a pull cord, mini-bikes, go-carts, etc. It can also be used to advantage with turbines where a warm-up period may be necessary. The centrifugal clutch on any drive provides protection against shock loads which occur in starting a rigidly coupled drive. Many times these loadings are capable of seriously damaging components of the drive and expensive safety devices may otherwise have to be designed into the transmission system.

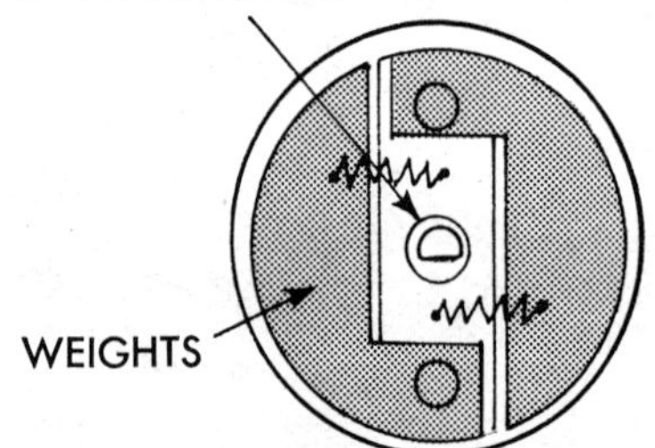

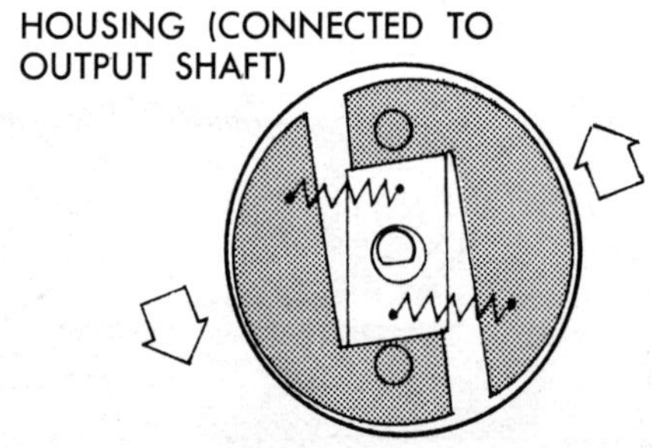

Fig. 20-32A. Centrifugal Clutch

A centrifugal clutch has an overload protection built into it. If the driven machinery develops an overloaded condition, the clutch will slip, protecting the drive machinery. A centrifugal clutch gives the designer of a transmission system complete flexibility in clutch selection. The size of the friction shoe will determine the torque capacity of the clutch, and the tension of the spring will determine the engagement or disengagement speed of the clutch.

Centrifugal clutches employ two basic force principles in their operation: centrifugal force and friction. *Centrifugal force* is that force which tends to pull a rotating body away from its center of rotation. *Friction* exists between any two bodies in contact where one of the bodies is trying to move relative to the other body. The centrifugal clutch consists of two basic components. The driver half, or spider, is mounted to the engine or motor shaft, and the driven half is connected to the load, either directly or by an indirect drive arrangement. The friction shoes are the connective element between the drive and the driven components.

When the drive is set in motion, the spider and the shoe start to rotate. The spider imposes a driving force on the friction shoe. The centrifugal force developed by the rotary motion of the friction shoe presses it against the drum, creating a frictional force between the shoe and the drum. As the drive increases in speed, the centrifugal force increases and the frictional force proportionately increases. When the frictional force reaches sufficient magnitude, it overcomes the resistance of the load. At full speed, the shoe is locked firmly against the drum and no slippage occurs.

In engine and turbine applications where it is necessary to warm-up before attempting to drive a load, a spring-controlled clutch is utilized. See Fig. 20-32A. A flat spring is placed over pins which run through the base of the shoe. This spring is retained in slots milled in the spider, and applies a restraining force to the friction shoes. The tension of the spring determines the speed at which the particular drive may idle while warming up. At this idling speed, the centrifugal force developed by the rotation is not of sufficient magnitude to overcome the spring force acting in the opposite direction on the friction shoe. As the speed of the drive increases, the shoe is forced against the drum.

Overload Control

It is often desirable to incorporate a safety device as part of the transmission system to operate in the event of an overload condition. A centrifugal switch, set to trip below a certain critical rpm determined by the application, can actuate a signal or shut down the drive. The most common method employs a centrifugal switch in conjunction with a centrifugal clutch. For example, a drive arrangement is designed to turn at 1750 rpm. It is determined that the minimum allowable output speed is 1500 rpm. The centrifugal switch is then set up on the driven member so that it will trip at 1750 rpm. When an overload condition occurs in the driven machinery, dropping the speed to 1500 rpm, an alarm is sounded.

Overload Release Clutches

An overload release clutch provides positive protection against damage from overloads. The instantaneous trigger action disconnects the load the instant an overload occurs, for there is no time lag in its action. Moreover, when the overload condition is corrected and the clutch is reset, the machine resumes operation at the exact cycle point at which it was released.

The overload release clutch consists essentially of two units: the rotor and the housing with its release mechanism. The drive shaft enters the side of the clutch housing and is keyed to the clutch rotor. The release mechanism, consisting of drive pawl and a reset pawl, is pivoted within the clutch housing. The clutch pawl is held engaged in the rotor notch by the combined pressure of the drive and reset springs. The combined pressure of these two springs determines the maximum torque to be transmitted without overload. Within the operational limits, the rotor and housing are held together and the entire unit rotates with the drive shaft and at the same speed.

The instant an overload occurs with *automatic reset,* the pressure of the drive and reset spring is overcome by the extra force applied to them from the rotor. The drive pawl slides out of the rotor notch. The reset pawl then applies pressure to the top of the drive pawl, holding it in contact with the rotor. After one revolution, the drive pawl automatically will fall back into the rotor notch. If the condition still exists, the overload will again function.

When an overload occurs, with *manual reset,* the pressure of the reset spring is overcome by the extra force applied from the rotor. The drive pawl slides out of the rotor notch, the reset pawl then engages the notch in the drive pawl and locks it out of contact with the rotor. When the overload condition has been corrected, the clutch must be reset with a wrench. When the drive pawl is positioned in the rotor notch, the reset screw must be backed out to its original stop position. This is essential to restore the torque to its original setting.

Dry Fluid Clutches

Dry fluid clutches are not as popular as shoe clutches. They must be used in transmission systems that engage the driver to the driven member quickly, because continuous slippage causes the clutch to heat rapidly. In this clutch, the dry fluid is steel pellets or "shot." As the rotational speed of the clutch increases, the particles are thrown against each other by centrifugal force, wedging them against the drum which is fluted in such a way as to make a solid connection between the driver and the driven member of the clutch. An excessive load over a long period of time will cause the particles to rub against one another and wear down, ultimately reducing the efficiency of the clutch.

Wet Fluid Clutches

The wet fluid clutch is unique in that it does not actually disengage. The wet fluid clutch is similar to the dry fluid clutch in that it begins to pick up its load gradually after the driver has started. However, it cannot completely disconnect its load until the driver has stopped. The driving component of this clutch is veined and is encased in a housing with a rotor which has opposing veins and serves as the driven member of the clutch. The entire housing is filled with oil. Seals prevent the oil from flowing out along the shaft. The driver is usually referred to as "impeller," Fig. 20-33. Instead of direct centrifugal action, the impeller pushes fluid against the opposing veins, with force and torque proportional to rotational speed. The driver and the driven members will run at about the same speed with approximately 2% to 6% loss of rpm. They are never mechanically connected at any time, as in the clutches previously mentioned. These clutches are most often used to start heavy loads, such as conveyors, pulverizers and rolling mill applications. They are most often used in conjunction with an electric motor, because electric motors usually do not build up their peak torque until they are at approximately 65% of their running speed. This type of clutch permits the motor to attain its peak torque quickly without imposing an excessive load.

Electric Clutches

There are basically three types of electric clutches: electromagnetic, metal particle, and Eddy current.

The *electromagnetic disk clutch* is basically a friction clutch which is energized by electric current, Fig. 20-34. Also see Fig. 20-31. The electromagnet is affixed to one plate, forming a nonslip bond at its rated operating speed. The electromagnetic clutch requires direct current; therefore some type of rectifier must be employed if alternating current is used in the controlling system. This is a very popular

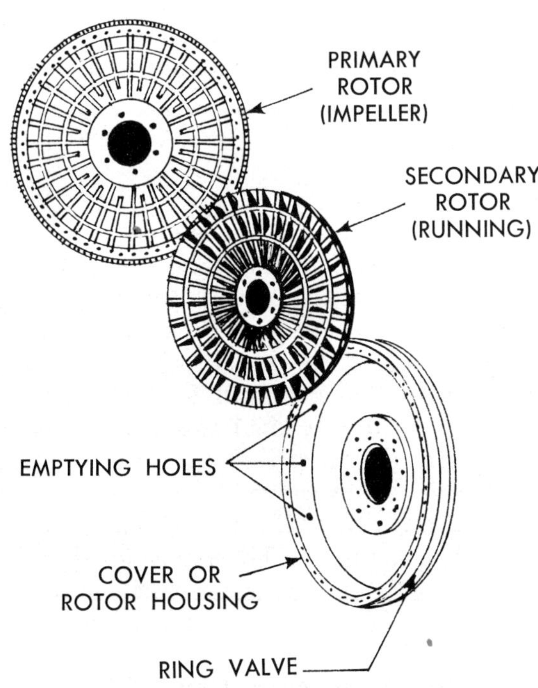

Fig. 20-33. Wet Fluid (Hydraulic) Clutch

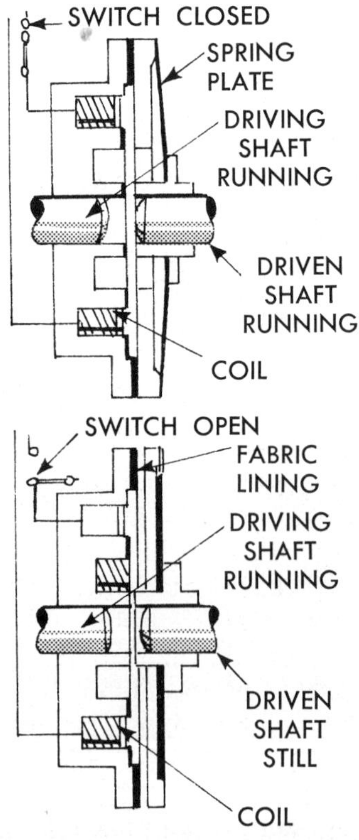

Fig. 20-34. Electromagnetic Clutch

clutch and is adaptable to a single package concept of clutch and brake.

Air and hydraulic (oil) clutches may operate with the same basic concepts. These clutches employ air or fluid pressure to engage the friction plate of the driver against the driven member of the clutch, as well as to cool the clutch.

The *metal particle clutch* operates on pure electrical principles and employs only two moving parts. The inner rotating member and outer rotating member do not touch; therefore, no wear is experienced. The space between the inner and outer rotating members is called the "working gap," and is filled with fine dry metal particles. There is a second gap between the outer rotating member and the frame. Around this gap is a coil of wire. When a current passes through this coil, an electromagnetic field is created, causing the particles to form a link between the outer and inner rotating members. The torque transmitted is proportional to the magnetic field strength and is independent of operational speed.

The *Eddy current clutch* employs a magnetic field to connect the driver to the driven components. There is no mechanical connection and the strength of the electromagnetic field determines the torque transmitted between the driver and driven components. Because there is a constant loss in rpm somewhat similar to that experienced in fluid coupling, the energy loss is transformed into heat. This heat cannot be tolerated in all applications, but is an inherent by-product of this clutch operation.

Brakes

Brakes are considered transmission control devices because they can (1) stop a moving load, and (2) regulate movement by (a) slowing it down, (b) holding the speed constant, or (c) holding it at rest. Brakes transform mechanical energy into heat energy, as they employ friction to control movement. There are many types of brakes. The two most popular are the drum brake and the disk brake.

Block Drum Brake

The most simple drum brake is the block brake. It consists of a piece of a friction material bonded to a block cut to fit a moving drum. The frictional material is commonly referred to as the "brake band." The block and brake band is attached to a lever in such a way that great pressure can be exerted on the drum. Brake capacity can be very readily calculated in terms of torque.

Brakes must be designed to dissipate large amounts of heat to the atmosphere quickly. As they are applied, considerable heat is generated. For proper operation it is necessary that this heat never increase the temperature of the lining beyond its operational limit. The surface finish of the drum, the material used for the brake lining, the operating temperature and rubbing velocity, as well as the pressure between the drum and lining, determine the coefficient of friction for the brake. The presence and distribution of foreign matter and moisture also affect the coefficient of friction and are factors to be considered in brake design. The total contact area between the drum and the brake lining will determine the braking torque of any given brake design.

The Band Brake

The band brake is also an extremely simple and inexpensive drum braking system. A belt-like device is lined with a frictional material. When force is applied to the belt, the belt tightens on the drum, increasing its friction and slowing down or stopping the drum, Fig. 20-35.

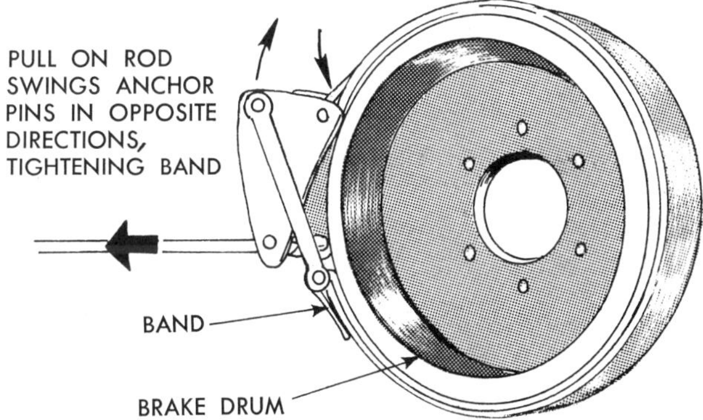

Fig. 20-35. Band Brake

Differential Band Brake

The differential band brake is sometimes referred to as a self-energizing brake. Under certain conditions it may be self-acting. As the name implies, the tension on one end of the brake band differs from that on the other and aids in applying the brake.

A brake band is connected to a lever arm, the fulcrum of which is located between two connections of the brake band. However, the fulcrum is not located in the center of this connection but to one side, resulting in different pressures being applied to the ends of the brake band.

Great care must be exercised in designing this type of brake because under certain conditions of leverage, too much self-action may result in the brake grabbing or locking. This

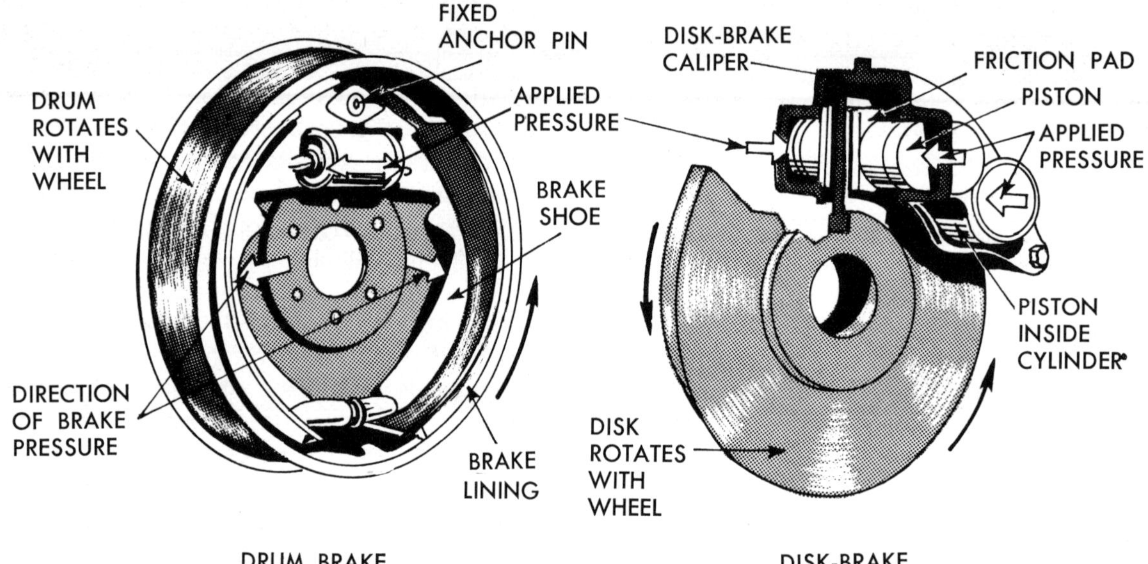

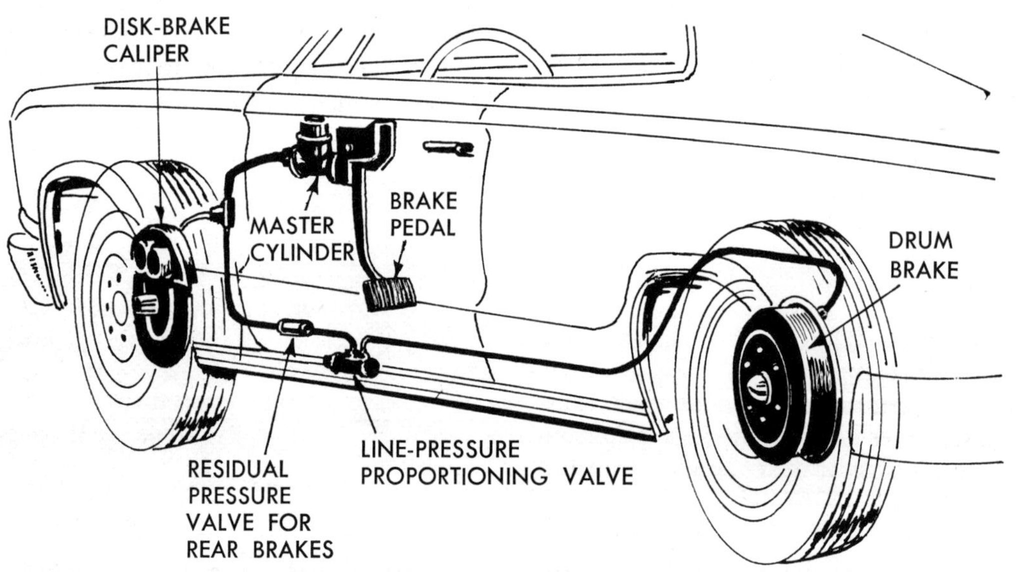

Fig. 20-36. Drum and Disk Brakes

type of brake is frequently used on conveyor head shafts. Once the braking torque needed is determined, the correct leverage arm and the force necessary for the desired braking action can be calculated.

External Drum Brake

The external drum brake is quite similar to the block brake. Two blocks are diametrically located around the drum, and their braking forces tend to balance the thrust on the axle. The increased surface area also results in an increase in braking torque. Railroad cars employ this type of braking system. The cast iron brake blocks are located on opposite sides of the train wheels. Of necessity, these blocks are made to wear in relation to the wheel and therefore are easily replaced.

Internal Drum Brake

The brake shoes are located on the inside of the brake drum. They work against the drum by moving outward engaging the inside wall of the brake drum. This is typical of the automobile brake. Usually the movement is provided by a cam, an arm and lever arrangement, or a hydraulic piston.

In the automotive brake, the operator applies pressure on the brake pedal; this pressure is transmitted by linkage to a master cylinder piston which pushes hydraulic fluid out the cylinder through connecting tubing to the wheel cylinders. See Fig. 20-36. This hydraulic pressure then forces two pistons out the wheel cylinder ends and pushes the brake shoes against the brake drum. The brake shoes are lined with an asbestos brake lining material that exhibits a high coefficient of friction with a high tolerance to heat and resistance to wear.

Disk Brakes

The disk brake contains two pressure plates on which lining segments are bonded, Fig. 20-36. The disk rotates between these pressure plates, which are kept apart by spring tension. When braking is desired, force is applied to the pressure plate, overcoming the spring tension that maintains the air gap. As long as the pressure is maintained on the actuating device, the two plates will remain engaged, applying frictional load. Once the pressure is released, the spring disengages the pressure plate from the disk and it is free to turn.

Some modern day automobiles employ disk brakes because they respond more quickly than drum brakes, and they do not exhibit fade over prolonged braking action.

Variable Speed Drives

Variable speed drives are employed where the operating speed of the driven member must vary over a wide range and the driver provides a limited range. Variable speed drives are categorized by their means of operation: (1) mechanical, (2) hydraulic, or (3) electrical.

Mechanical Variable Speed Drives

Mechanical variable speed drives employ the principle of changing the relationship of the diameters between the drivers and the driven pulley or sheave.

The simplest variable speed drive uses a V-belt and two cone-shaped sheaves. The sheaves are placed on the driver and driven shaft so that the large diameter on one sheave is opposite the small diameter on the other, Fig. 20-37. The V-belt connects the two sheaves. It must be changed manually while the system is stopped. With this variable speed

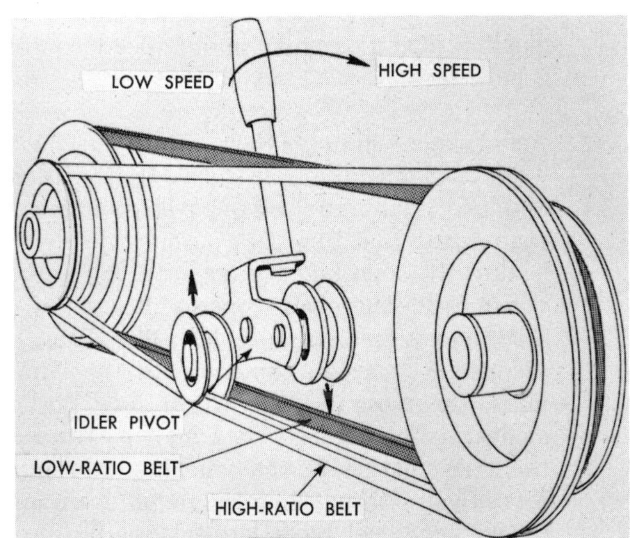

Fig. 20-37. Two-Belt, Two-Speed Clutch and Transmission

drive, the speeds are stepped and not infinitely variable from slow to fast.

A variable pitch pulley system can provide an infinitely variable speed control. It consists of a spring-loaded variable pitch pulley, a V-belt, and an adjustable base that can be moved by manual, mechanical, electrical or hydraulic means. Refer to Fig. 20-9. This drive can be classified as a constant torque device with the horsepower capacity decreasing as the driven shaft speed decreases. In this system, a speed variation of three-to-one is common. Speed change is accomplished by moving the motor on the adjustable base. This changes the centers of the drive. The spring-loaded variable pitch pulley is mounted on the motor shaft, and increasing or decreasing the distance between the motor shaft and the driven shaft varies the speed of the driven shaft. This is due to the belt riding at varying diameters on the pulley. Decreasing the center distance between the sheaves causes the belt to operate at a larger pitch diameter, thereby increasing the speed of the driven pulley and shaft. Speed change may be accomplished by turning a hand wheel or energizing a pilot motor with forward and reverse push-button control. The hand wheel is most popular because of its simplicity of operation. The push-button method is used primarily when the motor is located some distance from the machine operator and remote speed control is necessary.

Metal Chain Adjustable Sheave Transmissions

Metal chain adjustable sheave transmissions employ radially grooved sheaves mounted in such a way that the tooth on one wheel face is directly opposing a groove on its mating wheel face. The chain consists of a series of slats, and is free to move laterally. Thus, as the chain comes in contact with the wheel faces, the tooth on one wheel face pushes against a number of slats equal in width to the groove in the opposite wheel face, forming a positive mesh between the metal chain and the metal wheel faces located on the input shaft and the driven shaft. This type of transmission is positive. No slip can occur between the input and output shafts. As with any adjustable speed belt transmission, speed regulation does occur as output load changes. These transmissions are available in power sizes from one horsepower to 22 horsepower. They may include input and output gearing and integral mounted motors. Often they are used on constant torque applications, but the torque of the transmission actually increases as output speed decreases by a factor which is the square root of the overall speed range.

Roller Chain Adjustable Sheave Transmission

The roller chain adjustable sheave transmission consists of hardened roller disks which make contact with the smooth faces of the metal sheave. This system employs two chains. They are interlaced between three wheel faces or sheaves on both the input and output shafts and loaded through a cam arrangement. As a greater torque load is transmitted through the input and output shaft, a greater force pushes in on the sheaves. This, in turn, affects the amount of torque which can be transmitted to the chains. By changing the cam arrangement, the forces acting on the wheel faces may be modified to match the requirements for constant torque or constant horsepower. These transmission systems are available in sizes of 35-50 horsepower with speed ranges to five-to-one. They are available with integral input and output gear drive motors.

Metal chain transmission systems are also available with a beveled gear track differential, so that the differential expands the speed range from six-to-one to infinitely wide. The infinitely wide speed range is adjustable from the maximum design speed down to and including zero rpm. The major advantage of these transmission systems is the inherent operating accuracy with no-load to full-load regulation approaching the rigidity of fixed gearing. For example, a transmission with 5% adjustment range will not vary more than .070%.

Friction Transmission

Friction or traction drives are nonpositive drives and transmit torque through metal, wood, plastic, or rubber contact points. The contact points are considered line contact although deformation occurs resulting in area contact. Some of these drives are variable ratio systems that provide a stepless ratio; therefore the output speed can be controlled over a spectrum of speeds.

One of the most common applications of the friction drive is the phonograph and tape recorder drive system, Fig. 20-38. The motor has a cone or stepped pulley attached to it. An idler wheel under spring tension is made to contact the cone pulley and the internal rim of the turntable to transmit torque. The speed of the turntable is dependent upon the step of the cone pulley with which the idler is in contact.

All industrial units employ metal-to-metal transmission and are splash-lubricated. In some instances, torque is actually transmitted through a film of oil and the principle of operation is the resistance of the oil film to sheer. These transmission systems require special oils to insure proper and adequate torque transmission.

Ring Roller Transmission

The ring roller transmission is similar to the planctary gear differential. A hardened ring replaces the internal gear, which in the planetary differential is held motionless. Replacing the sun gears are hardened tapered rollers. These three tapered rollers are arranged in a cluster and are driven by the input shaft. The tapered rollers are mounted in such a way that their outer edge is parallel to the center line of the input shaft and the inner surface of the control ring. Pinions mounted on the end of the tapered rollers translate the rotational speed of the rollers to the output sun gear, which is also a ring gear. The speed of the output planet pinions is a function of the input speed and the speed of the rollers, as determined by the position of the ring on the tapered rollers. When this control ring is at the large end of the tapered rollers, maximum output speed is transmitted. When this ring is located at the small end of the tapered rollers, zero output speed is transmitted.

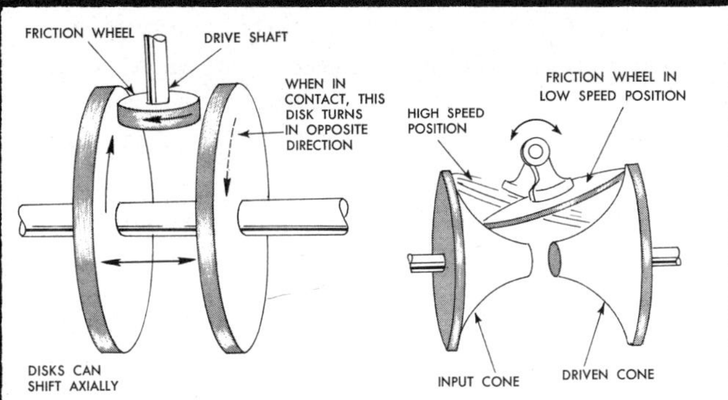

A. Friction drives with stepless ratio change, allowing output speed to be controlled within small limits.

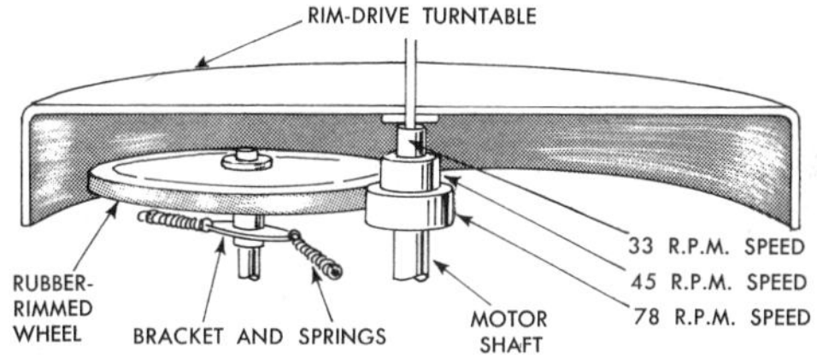

B. Friction drive commonly used in phonograph turntables.

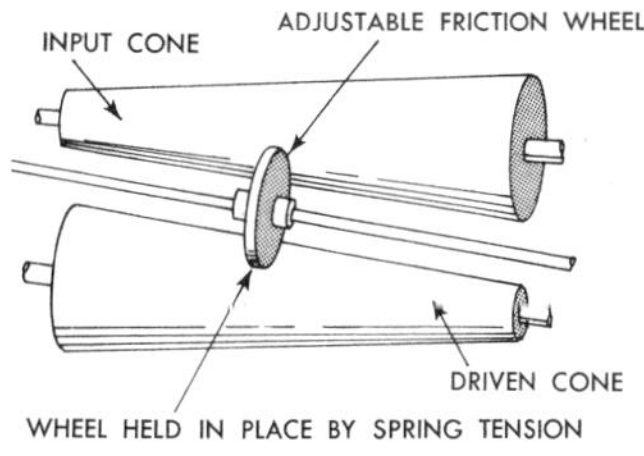

C. Turntable mechanism using variable-speed cone drive.

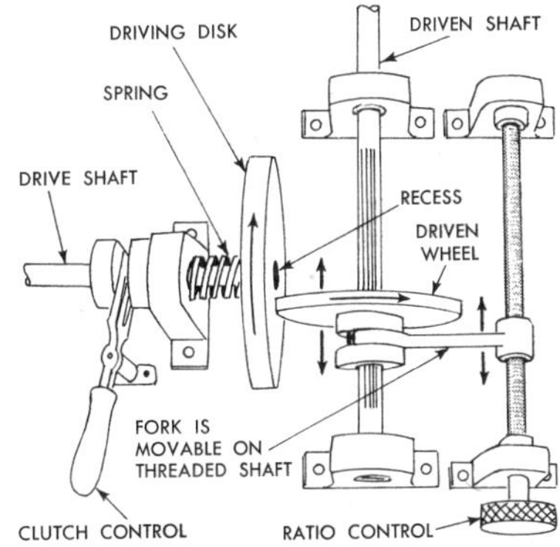

D. Narrow wheel on this friction drive can be adjusted on threaded shaft to make contact with any radius of drive disk.

Fig. 20-38. Friction or Traction Drives

The inherent characteristics of the unit limit the maximum output speed to one-third of the input speed. Generally, these units have increasing torque capacity with decreasing speed. By changing the ratios between the output pinion and ring gear, the inherent torque characteristics are altered. It is possible to acquire a torque capacity which increases as output speed increases. This is just the opposite from the basic transmission characteristic. These transmission systems can also be provided as mechanically reversing units; that is, with the input running in one direction, the output is adjustable from maximum rated speed in one direction to maximum rated speed in the other direction. This characteristic is achieved by further changing the gear ratio between the roller output pinions and the main output gear. These transmission systems are available with power capacities up to three horsepower. Integral output gearing is also available and thus rated output speeds as high as 8,000 rpm are possible. One particular advantage of this transmission system is that the input ratio adjustment can be made while the transmission is at rest, as well as while the unit is running.

Ball-Disk Transmission

One of the oldest variable speed transmission systems employs input and output disks separated by caged balls. The center lines of the input and output disk are offset from each other by approximately the radius of each disk. A ring of balls is located between them. The input-output ratio adjustment is made by moving the contact point of the ring of balls. The input-output ratio is a function of the effective diameter of the ring of balls on the input and output disks. The unit's output speed is adjustable from 50% above input speed down to zero rpm. Its torque capacity increases as output speed decreases.

Ball Transmission

In this transmission system, shaft-mounted balls ride against the chamfered edge of input and output disks. Input and output ratio of one-to-one is obtained when the ball axis is parallel to the input and output shafts, and the contact circle between the balls and the input disks and output disks is the same. Changing the axis on which the balls are mounted affects the contact circle ratio which changes the output speed. The maximum ratio possible is a three-to-one speed increase from the input speed.

Output speed adjustment is determined by the control screw, which turns a plate slotted to accept the ball shafts. Both the input and output disks are connected to their respective shafts through a ball-cam arrangement. As the torque load increases, the input and output disks are forced inward, thus increasing the pressure between the disks and the balls. Therefore the loading on the balls is a direct function of torque load being transmitted through the system. Efficiency of this unit is as high as 90% at the one-to-one input-output ratio. At maximum output speed, efficiency drops to approximately 75%. The inherent torque capacity of this transmission increases as output speed is reduced such that it can be essentially rated at a constant horsepower throughout a nine-to-one speed range. The ball-type variable speed drive can only be adjusted while it is running. Unit sizes are available from one-quarter horsepower to 16 horsepower, with separate or integral input and output gearing as well as with integral motors.

Cone Transmission

The cone transmission system employs a double-cone roller between offset input and output disks, in a manner similar to the ball-disk transmission. Maximum output speed is acquired when the cone roller is near the center of the output disk, and near the outside diameter of the input disk. See A, Fig. 20-38. If the cone roller is adjusted to the other extreme so that it is positioned near the center of the input disk and near the outside diameter of the output disk, there is infinite output speed adjustment between the design limits of transmission. The output shaft is spring-loaded and is torque-sensitive. This increases the forces holding the input and output disks together, providing better torque transmitting capacity.

An improved version of this transmission system utilizes four rollers instead of a single roll. Twin input disks have a roller driving against opposite double-output disks, providing greater torque transmitting capacity than the single disk. These transmission drives are adjustable over a six-to-one speed range and are available in power sizes of one-half horsepower to 80 horsepower. The efficiency varies between 75% and 90%. The transmission has increased torque capacity with output speed reduction and the single roll units are rated at constant horsepower over the upper 50% of their speed range. As with most traction transmission drives, the unit should only be adjusted while it is in operation.

Disk and Ring Transmission

The disk and ring transmission uses a planetary differential that employs rings and disks in place of gears. A pair of spring-loaded rings replace the sun gear. The planet disks are contained between these rings and orbit about on a carrier. The gap between the two outer rings is adjustable and their movement affects the contact diameters between the input and output rings. When the gap between the outer rings is narrow and the planet gears are orbiting on a small diameter, maximum output speed is obtained.

The speed range of this system is six-to-one with the output 60% of the input speed. Usually these systems are capable of transmitting up to 10 horsepower.

Change Gear Transmission

The "gear box" provides a stepped range of gear ratios. Although it does not provide an infinitely adjustable speed range from minimum to maximum, they are usually categorized as adjustable speed transmission systems.

Simple systems use a sliding gear that is engaged to effect a speed ratio change while the system is at rest. More sophisticated transmission systems employ a mechanical, electric, or hydraulic clutch which can isolate the unit from the power source for gear selection.

Automobile Manual Gear Transmission

The conventional automobile transmission system uses helical-cut gears and splines for silent operation. Most often the transmission system is mounted as a unit to the power plant, Fig. 20-39. A bell housing is cast or bolted onto the gear box, and serves as a mounting or aligning member and houses the flywheel and clutch.

The clutch shaft has the driven clutch plates on its front end and transmits power from the engine to the gears in the gear box. The gear on this shaft is the key in the transmission design. It is the point at which the line of power from the engine is directed into the various speed options. This shaft is known as the *main shaft* and also as the *sliding-gear shaft*. See Fig. 20-40.

The driving gear is located on the clutch shaft and engages with and drives the large gear on the countershaft. All of these gears are fixed and all are driving gears except the largest one. The small gear continually drives the reverse gear. This turns the reverse sliding gear when it is made to mesh with it. The second smallest gear transmits the power when the shift lever is in low. The second largest engages the drive train when the selector is in second. The jackshaft or countershaft continually turns when the car is in motion.

The shifting fork engages the sliding gears and moves them to engage the various speed options. Shifting the smaller sliding gear gives second and high speeds. Shifting the larger sliding gear gives reverse and low speeds.

The difficulty that is usually encountered in shifting gears is due to the varying speeds of

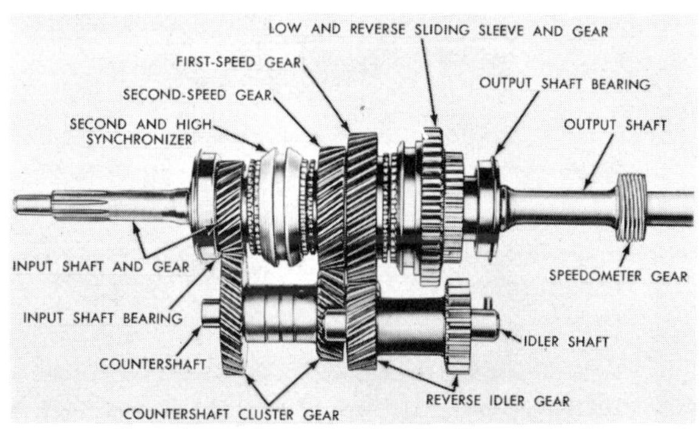

Fig. 20-39. Automobile Transmission
(Ford-Mercury)

A. Neutral Position

B. Low-Speed Forward Position

C. Second or Intermediate Position

Fig. 20-40. Automobile Sliding-Gear Shaft

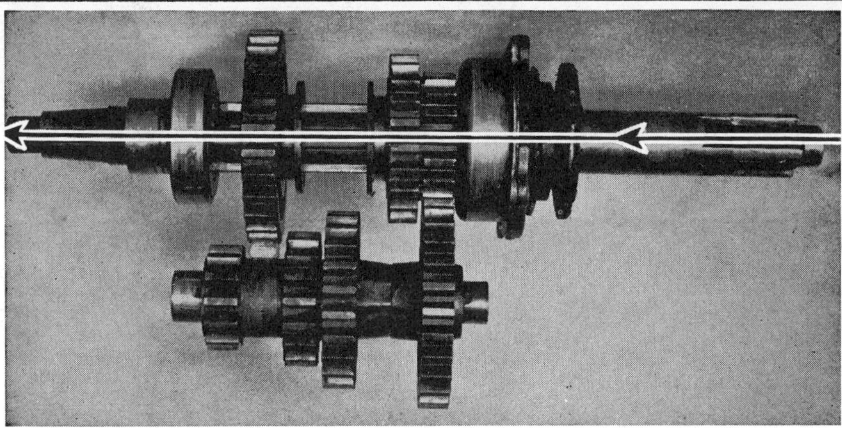

D. High-Speed or Direct-Drive Position

E. Reverse Position

the gears which cause them to clash when they are engaged. In the synchromesh transmission, the speeds of the revolving gears are synchronized so that the gears can be meshed without clashing. This transmission system depends on a cone and dog clutch which is used when the gears are shifted between third and high. Movement of this unit causes the internal cone of the shifting dog to engage the external cone of the gear that is to be meshed. The spring-controlled override contacts the gear before the gears mesh, and with further movement of the gearshaft lever, the dog clutch moves over the cone as the gears mesh.

Application Systems

Mechanical transmission and control components can be applied to do work in many systems and subsystems. Wheels may be made to turn at controlled speeds and with varying torque. Mechanical energy is applied to propel vehicles on land, sea, or in the air, and to operate machines that change raw materials to increase their value as well as transport material from place to place. Rotational force

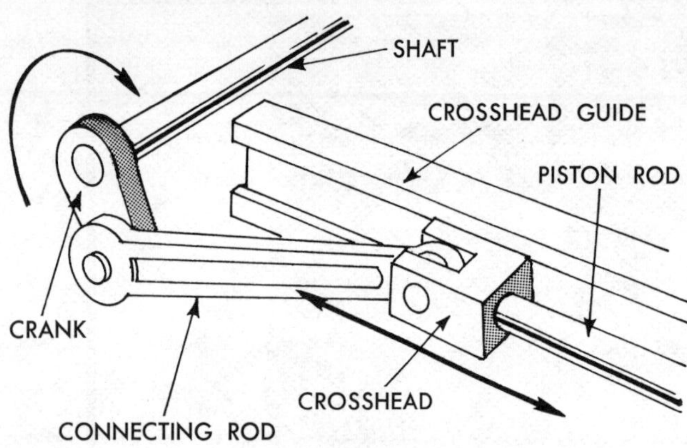

A. This device in the steam engine converted reciprocating motion to rotary motion.

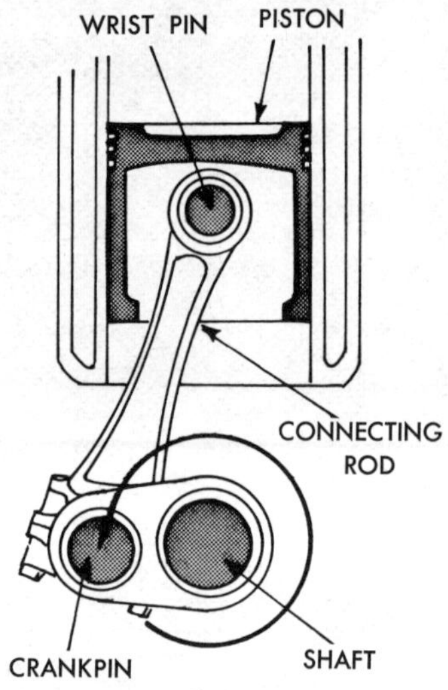

B. Modern automobile engine converts reciprocating power of the pistons into rotary power by means of a connecting rod attached to a crankshaft.

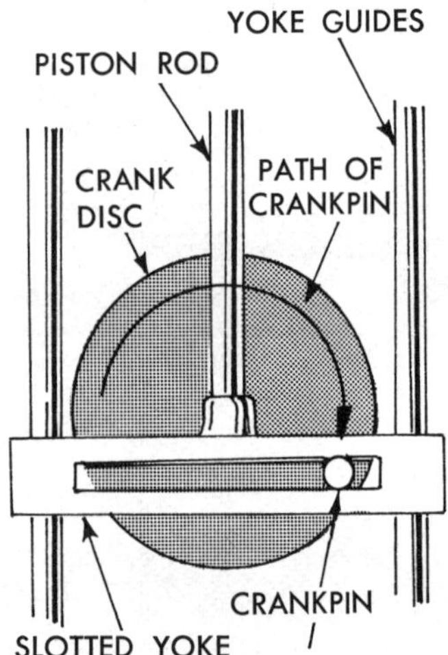

C. Scotch yoke action in steam engines dispenses with connecting rod of automobile engines and gains compactness.

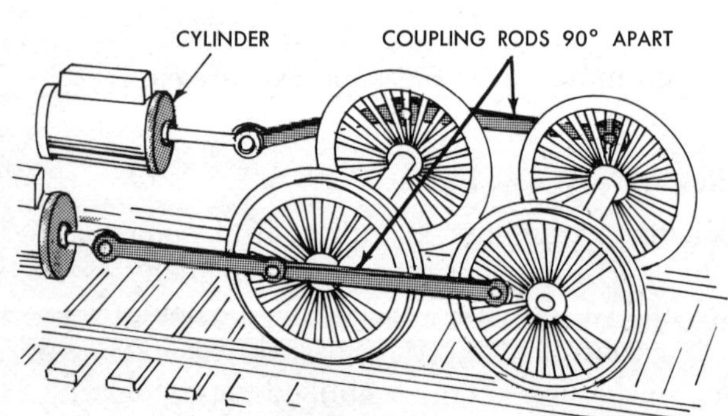

D. Two-cylinder steam engine with couplings 90° apart designed to overcome "dead center" problem.

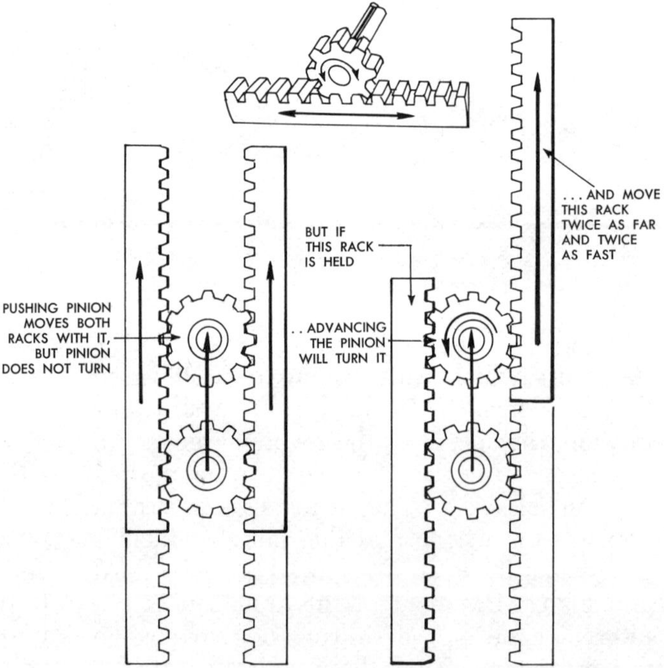

E. Rack and pinion mechanism converts rotational force to linear movement.

Fig. 20-41. Application Systems

is converted to reciprocating or linear movement by employing cams, split nut, lead screw, crank and connecting rod, scotch yoke, etc. Fig. 20-41 illustrates some application systems.

Cams

A cam is used to obtain an accelerated, continuous, or harmonic linear motion from a rotating motion. Cams are manufactured in a variety of forms such as plate, disc, cylindrical and end cams, Fig. 20-42. Cams were discussed in explaining the operation of valves in steam and gasoline engines. See Figs. 2-35 and 8-55. A plate cam is flat with an irregularly cut edge. A cylindrical cam is a cylinder with a groove cut around it. An end cam is

A. Drum or Barrel Cam B. Edge Cam

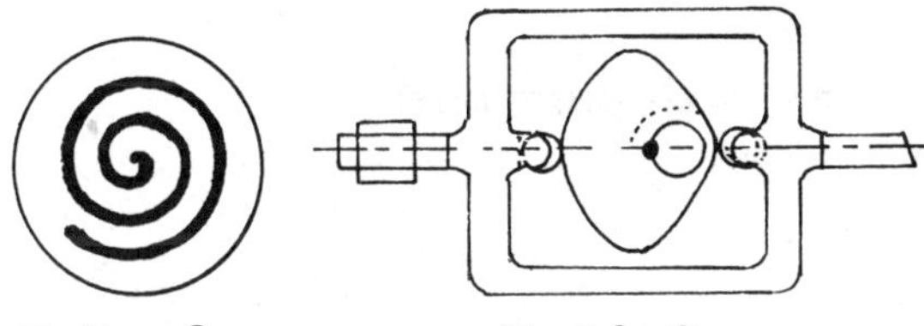

C. Face Cam D. Yoke Cam

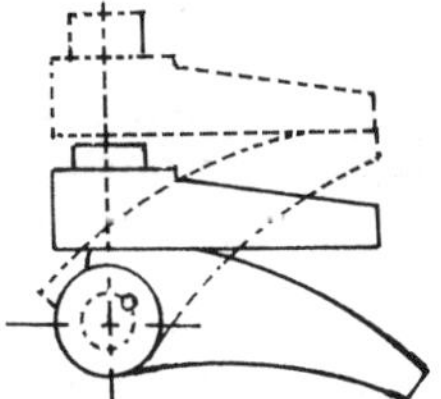

E. Toe and Wiper Cam

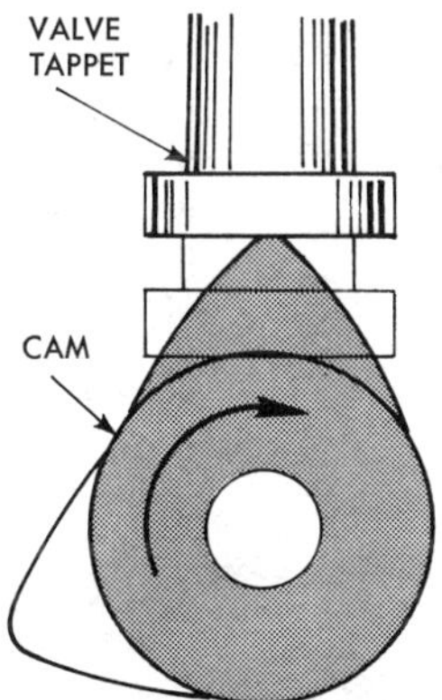

F. Mushroom Cam
This cam is used to raise and lower the valves in gasoline engines.

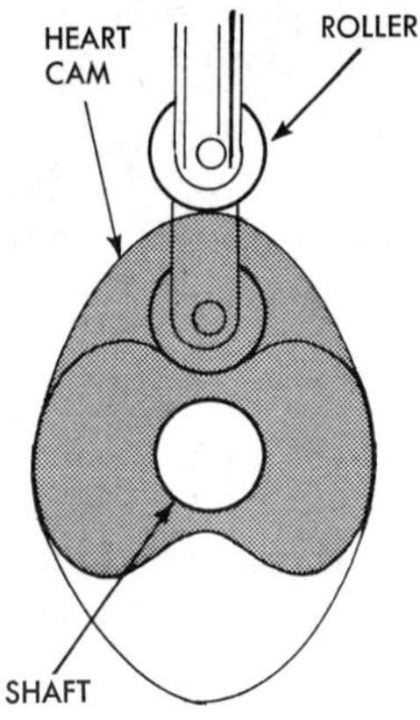

G. Heart Cam
This cam is used to lay threads evenly on sewing machine bobbins.

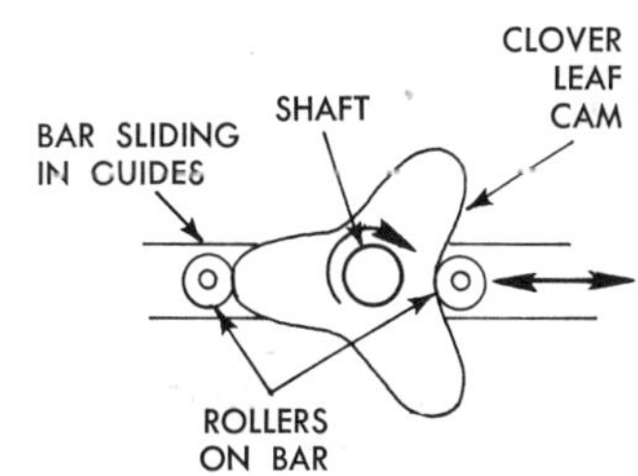

H. Cloverleaf Cam
This cam imparts reciprocating motion to the bar by means of the two rollers which are in constant contact with the cam.

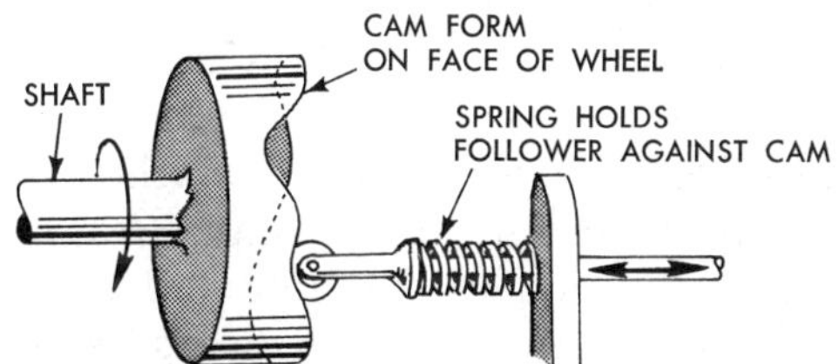

I. Contoured Face Cam
This cam imparts motion to the spring-held follower.

Fig. 20-42. Cams

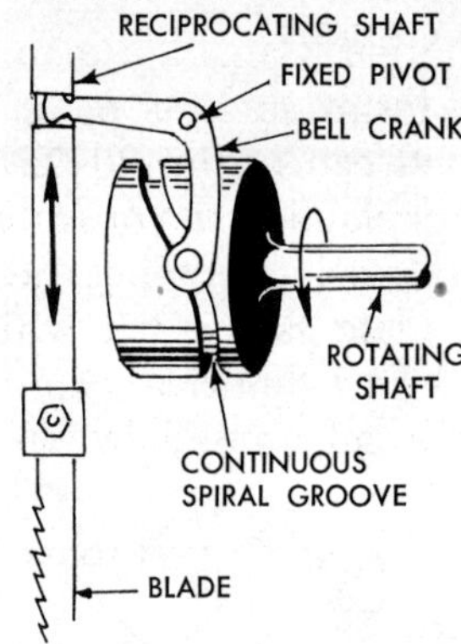

J. Cylindrical Cam
This cam imparts reciprocating action in a saber saw.

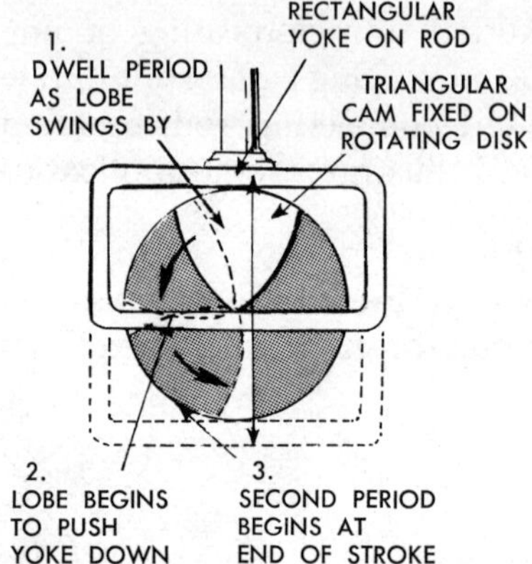

K. Triangular Cam
This cam was used inside a rectangular yoke in French railroad engines.

Fig. 20-42 (cont.)

a cylinder with an irregularly shaped end. The cam is made to rotate on a shaft, and a follower is caused to move along the irregular edge or within the groove. This follower is held to the cam by either spring tension or gravity. Cams are designed to provide for a variety of motion. Cams are usually machined individually with all surfaces finished to reduce frictional wear and energy losses due to friction.

Lead Screw

Screw threads wind around a shaft in a curve called a helix. The *lead of the screw* is the distance from one point of the helix to a corresponding point on the next turn, parallel to the axis. The *pitch of the thread* is defined in the same way. If the cylinder circumference could be laid out flat, the helix would form a diagonal line. In other words, the helix acts as an inclined plane. When a nut is turned onto a bolt, one revolution of the nut advances it proportionate to the pitch of the thread. Some machines use this principle to transmit energy; for example, the lathe and the automatic screw machine employ a lead screw to advance the carriage that holds the cutting tool. In place of the common nut, a split nut or ball nut is designed to follow the grooves of the lead screw with minimum frictional loss.

Terms to Understand

trans-actional systems
shafts
couplings
rigid coupling
resilient material coupling
slider coupling
universal joint
brake drum coupling
torque limiting coupling
mechanical friction
static friction
rolling friction
coefficient of friction
sleeve bearings
journal bearings
anti-friction bearings
pillow blocks
flanged blocks
cartridge blocks
press fits
bearing seals
lubrication
gears
belt drive
tension
driving pulley
driven pulley
idler
V-belts
sheaves
pitch circle
pitch diameter
circular pitch
gear ratio
pressure angle
backlash
spur gears
helical gears
herringbone gears
internal gears
planetary gear system
bevel gears
spiral bevel gears
hypoid gears
worm gears
rack and pinion gears
chain drives
pitch of chain
sprockets
shear pin
timing belts
positive clutch
overrunning clutch
friction disk clutch
magnetic clutch
idler pulley clutch
centrifugal clutch
overload control
fluid clutch
electric clutch
drum brake
band brake
disk brake
variable speed drive
adjustable sheave transmission
friction transmission
change-gear transmission
automobile transmission
cam
lead screw

Study Questions

1. Explain the relationship of the prime mover to the trans-actional system.
2. Explain the classification of trans-actional systems.
3. Analyze the similarities between the energy conversion and trans-actional systems.
4. What is meant by mechanical energy?
5. Cite the advantages and disadvantages of two mechanical trans-actional systems.
6. List some of the major components of a mechanical trans-actional system and describe their functions.
7. A trans-actional system must provide a high mechanical advantage and be capable of withstanding high shock loads. What mechanical system and specific components would you suggest? Explain your choice.
8. Describe the choices of components that are available in mechanical power systems to prevent reversal of direction.
9. Explain the operation of those components that would permit the gradual transfer of energy from driver to driven shaft.
10. Explain the advantages and limitations of positive and non-positive drives.
11. List those components that provide continuous and discontinuous control.
12. Reduction systems provide high operating torque at the expense of speed. Explain.
13. Why are V-belt power systems so popular?
14. Gear drive systems seem to have few disadvantages. What are they?
15. List the mechanical systems that can provide variable torque and speed, and describe their principle of operation.
16. List some applications of mechanical trans-actional systems.

Fluid Power

Fluid systems use fluids under pressure to transmit and control energy. *Fluid power* includes the generation, control, and application of smooth, effective power by means of pumped or compressed fluids (liquids or gases). Rotational and linear movement is the typical work output. Hydraulics utilize liquids and pneumatics use gases as the vehicle for transmission. Liquids and gases are similar in many respects.

The advantages of fluid power are:

1. The amount of power that can be handled is almost unlimited.
2. Easy, quick, speed adjustment is possible over a wide range while the prime mover (energy source) is operating at constant speed.
3. There is smooth, rapid acceleration and deceleration of power.
4. There is complete control over torque and power.
5. There is a natural cushioning effect to reduce shock loads.
6. There is a smooth reverse mode.

Hydraulics

The word *hydraulics* is derived from the Greek "hydro" meaning water and "aulis" meaning tube or pipe. The study of hydraulics was originally only the physical behavior of water at rest or in motion. The meaning has been broadened today to include the physical behavior of all liquids.

The science of hydraulics includes, for example, the manner in which liquids act in tanks and pipes, deals with their properties and the ways of utilizing these properties. Included in this study are the laws of floating bodies and the behavior of liquids on submerged surfaces. Hydraulics treats the flow of liquids under various conditions and the ways of directing this flow to useful ends, as well as many other related subjects.

Development

Ancient civilizations were familiar with many hydraulic principles and their applications. The Egyptians and the ancient peoples of Persia, India, and China conveyed water along channels for irrigation and domestic purposes using dams and sluice gates to control the flow. The ancient Cretans had an elaborate plumbing system and Archimedes studied the laws of floating and submerged bodies.

Beginning not more than three or four hundred years ago, the physical sciences began to flourish, leading to the discovery of fundamental principles common to almost all mechanical and fluid devices. The fundamental law underlying the entire science of hydraulics was discovered in the seventeenth century by a French scientist, Blaise Pascal. It was many years later before any real progress was made in the field of hydraulics. Pascal's theorem was as follows: "If a vessel full of water closed on all sides has two openings, the one a hundred times as large as the other, and if each is supplied with a piston that fits it exactly, then a man pushing the small piston will exert a force that will equilibrate that of one hundred men pushing the large piston, and will overcome that of ninety-nine men." For Pascal's law to be effective for practical applications, it was necessary to have a piston that fit exactly. It was not until 1795 that Joseph Brahmah invented cup packing and developed the first workable hydraulic press. The next significant step came in 1850 when W. C. Armstrong invented a hydraulic accumulator, and then in 1873 Hastie developed a variable stroke pump and motor unit.

Technological progress depended upon the invention of machines which could cut and shape the necessary closely-fitted parts, and particularly by the development of seals and packings. The refinements and development of such components as valves, pumps, and motors have served to make hydraulics one of the leading methods of transmitting and controlling power.

Applications

Today hydraulic power is used to operate many different tools and mechanisms. A mechanic raises an automobile with a hydraulic jack. Hydraulic power is used by the dentist and the barber to lift their chairs. Hydraulic door stops are used to check door operations. Hydraulic brakes are standard equipment on all modern day automobiles. Many of these automobiles are equipped with automatic transmissions, power brakes, and power steering which are hydraulically operated. See Fig. 21-1. Hydraulic power is used in the construction field to operate large earthmovers, and in the Navy and Maritime service hydraulic systems are employed for navigation equipment as well as to operate power cranes, steering gear, and other remote control devices. Most modern aircraft contain a network of hydraulic lines and components, Fig. 21-2. Hydraulic power is used to operate such units as wheel brakes, landing flaps, air brakes, control surfaces, and for the retraction and extension of the landing gear.

Pneumatics

Pneumatics deals with the properties of gases, such as pressure, density, conversion, compression and expansion, etc. The word *pneumatics* is derived from the Greek "pneuma" which means air, wind and breath.

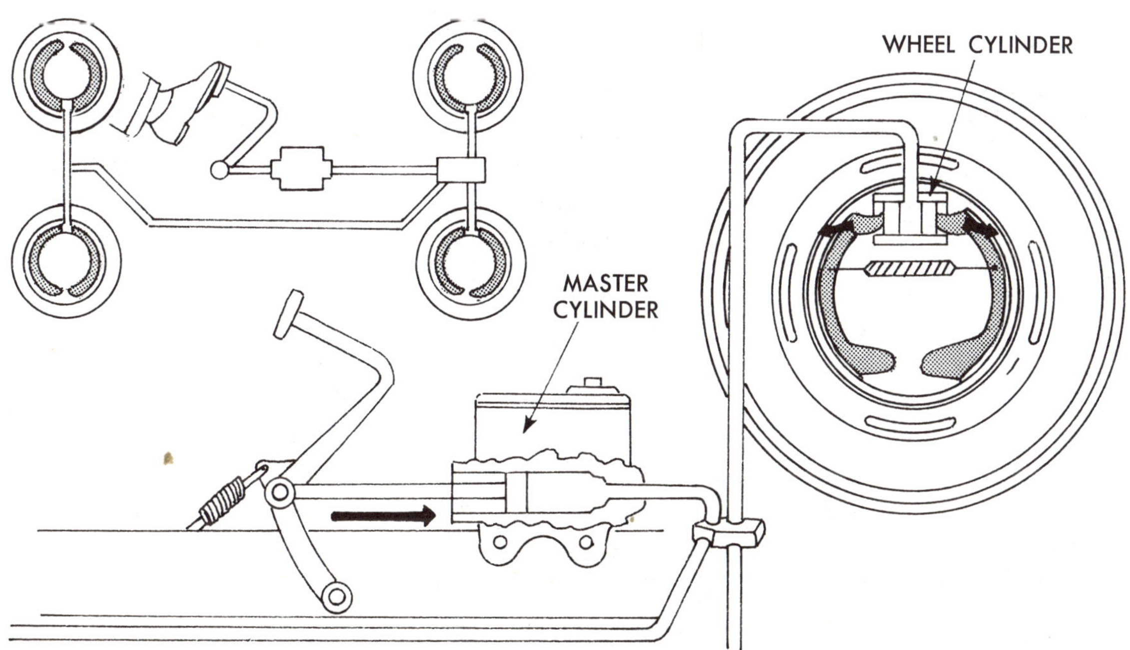

Fig. 21-1. An Automobile Brake System

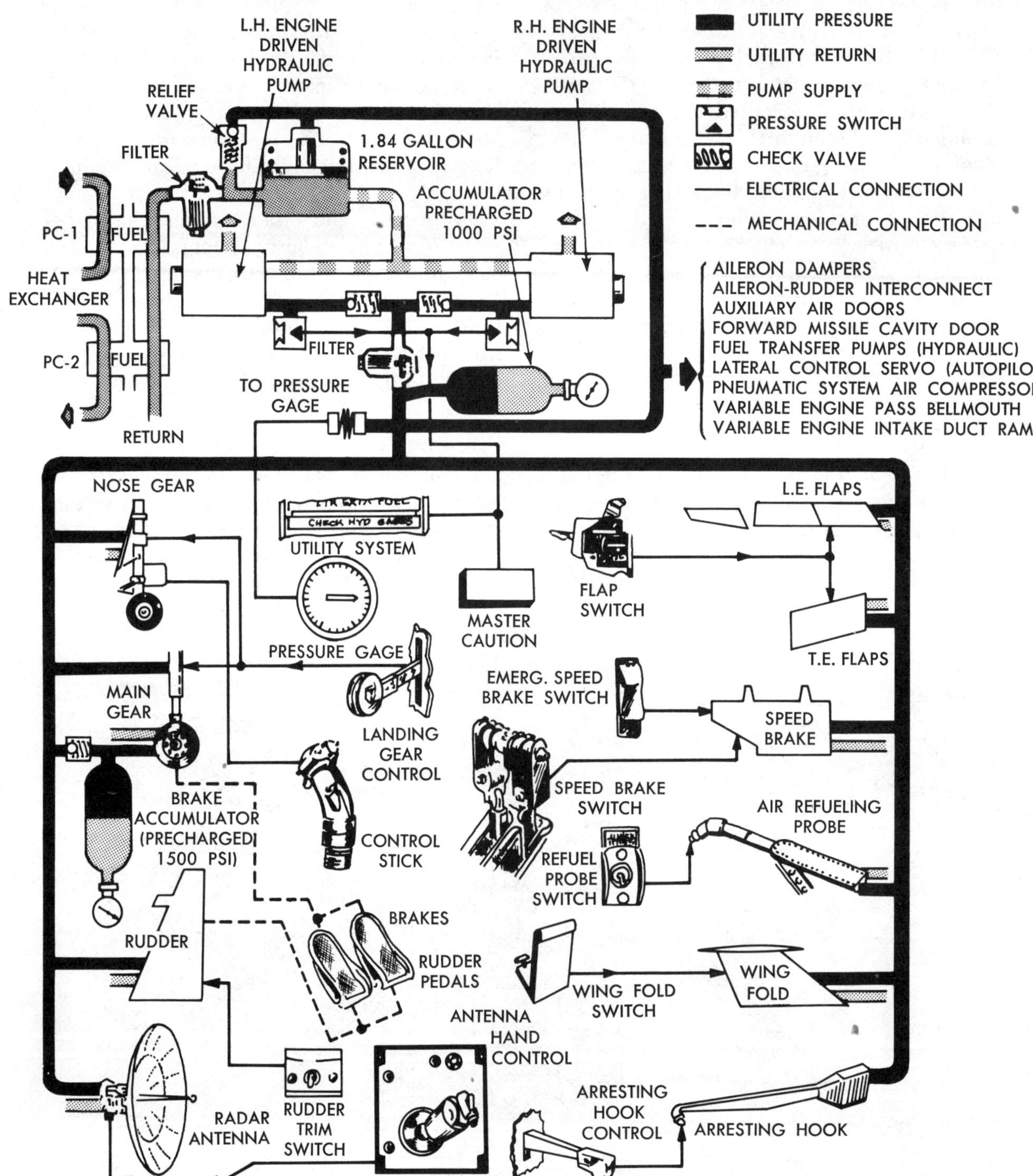

Fig. 21-2. Aircraft Hydraulic System

Development

Primitive man used one of the first pneumatic devices in the form of a blow-gun. In Indonesia a device is used to start a fire which is made from a water buffalo horn into which a small hole is drilled. A small wooden piston is made to fit into this hole. Small tinder is placed into the horn, the piston is struck, and the heat energy released is used to ignite tinder to start a fire. It seems every age of man has witnessed the development of devices to utilize air to do work. The practical application of air preceded the science of pneumatics by many years.

Many of the principles of hydraulics apply to pneumatics. For example, Pascal's law applies to gases as well as liquids. The development of pneumatics, like the development of hydraulics, required closely-fitted parts and the development of seals and packings. The invention of the air compressor has promoted pneumatics as a reliable means for the transmission of power.

Applications

One of the most popular uses of pneumatic power is in the operation of various tools such as air drills, screwdrivers, nut setters, riveting guns, chipping hammers, and punches. Trains, buses, and large trucks are often equipped with pneumatically-operated brakes, Fig. 21-3.

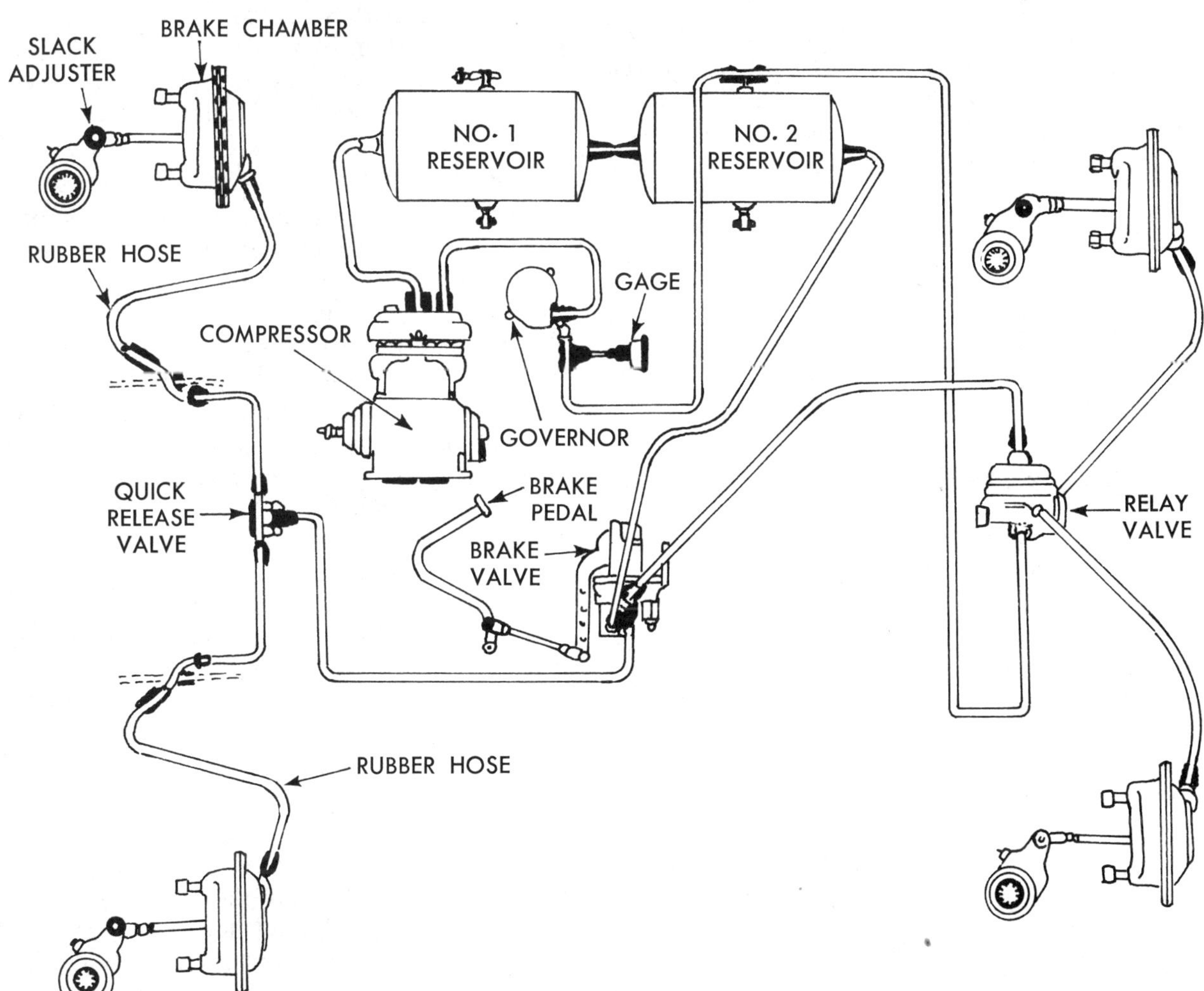

Fig. 21-3. Typical Pneumatic Brake System

Many modern day aircraft contain pneumatic back-up systems for hydraulically-operated systems. Many rocket systems utilize compressed gas as a power source for electric generators and hydraulic pumps, as well as to operate flight control components. Many times hydraulics and pneumatics are combined in an application, such as the lift in garages and service stations where air pressure is applied to the surface of hydraulic fluid in a reservoir, Fig. 21-4. The air pressure forces the hydraulic fluid to raise the lift. This system is known as an *air-over-oil system.*

Advantages of Fluid Power

Fluid power systems possess a number of favorable characteristics. Motion can be transmitted without the slack inherent in the use of some solid machine parts. Fluids are not subject to breakage as are mechanical parts, and the mechanisms have a long life expectancy. The components of fluid-powered systems can be located conveniently at separated points, and forces are rapidly transmitted over considerable distances with relatively small loss. These forces can be conveyed in any direction with little loss in efficiency and with no complicated transfer mechanisms. Often very large forces can be controlled by much smaller ones, and the forces can be transmitted through a network of comparatively small dimensions. If the system is designed well and adapted to the work it is required to perform, it can provide smooth, flexible, uniform action without vibration and unaffected by variation of load. The system can be designed to stop in the case of overload, thereby guaranteeing the life of the system and the components. Fluid power systems can provide a wide variety of rotary and linear motions. All of these advantages can be provided in a system that is economical to operate. In fact, it is difficult to find an industry today that does not utilize fluid power.

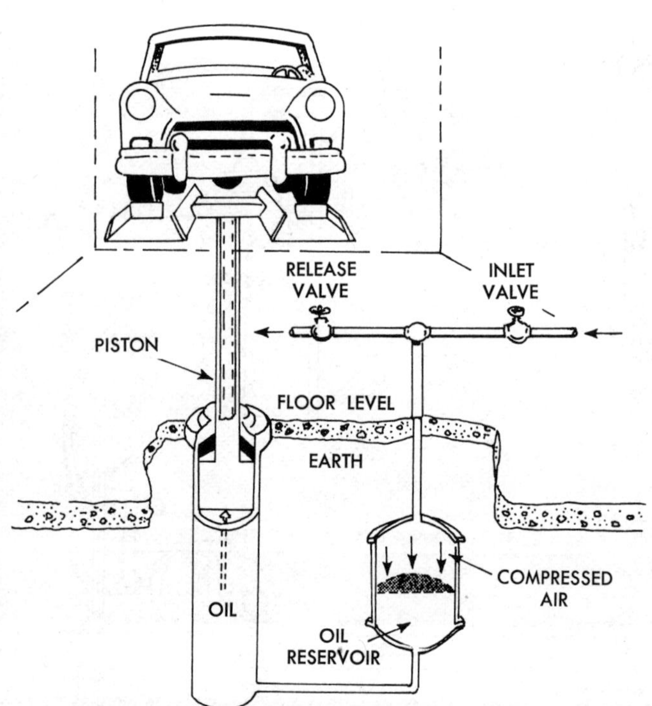

Fig. 21-4. Hydraulic Lift

Principles of Fluids

Fluid power presents some special problems. Since fluids have no shape of their own, they must be confined positively throughout the system. Consideration must be given to the system structure and the relation of parts of a fluid power system: conducting pipes and containers must be strong; and leaks must be prevented. These problems become more acute as higher operating pressures are needed to provide the necessary forces for mechanical action.

Fluid power systems require that pressures be controlled and that the movement of the component fluid be controlled. Movement causes friction within the fluid and system components which, if excessive, can lead to serious losses in efficiency. Particle accumulation must not be allowed in the system, for it may clog small passages or abrade closely fitted parts. Chemical action may cause corrosion and parts deterioration.

In order to apply fluid power properly, it is necessary to know how a fluid power system works, in terms of general application and scientific principles and the function and operation of specific components in the system.

Mechanical Advantage

A knowledge of mechanical advantage as developed with levers can serve as a basis for understanding the application of fluids.

A lever arm nine feet from the fulcrum can equalize a force three times larger that is three feet from the fulcrum. A fluid system consisting of a one square inch piston connected to a three square inch piston will be in equilibrium when the force at the larger piston is three times that of the smaller piston. The concept of mechanical advantage (input force times distance equals output force times distance; work input = work output less frictional losses) explains the operation of the lever and the simple hydraulic system.

States of Matter

Matter is defined as any substance that occupies space and has weight. Matter exists in three states: solids, liquids, and gases. Molecular movement in a solid of a substance is less than in liquid form, and in liquid it is less than that as a gas. Solid matter has a definite volume and a definite shape. Liquids have a definite volume but take the shape of the container. Cases have indefinite volume and indefinite shape. Gases not only take the shape of the container, but they expand to fill the container, no matter what its volume.

If the molecular movement in a solid is increased, the solid may change to a liquid; and if the molecular movement for energy is further increased, the liquid may change to a gas. One way of increasing molecular energy is by adding heat. For example, water at a low temperature with low molecular movement is ice; as heat is introduced, the ice melts and a liquid is formed.With still more heat, the molecular movement increases to the level that the water changes to steam or gas. In this example, *temperature* was the dominant factor in determining the state of matter. Another important factor is pressure. The boiling point of water at sea level is 212°F. At higher elevations, air pressure is less and the boiling point is correspondingly lower.

Fluids

Both liquid and gases flow freely. Each conforms to the shape of its container, and each readily transmits pressure.

Gases always fill a container completely while liquids do not; gases are lighter than liquids of equal volume; and gases are highly compressible while liquids are only slightly so.

Density and Specific Gravity

The density of a substance is its weight per unit volume. The volume may be given in cubic feet or cubic centimeters and the density is expressed in pounds per cubic foot or grams per cubic centimeter. Density is always expressed for a given temperature, as the volume of most materials varies with temperature. It is necessary to consider pressure when the density of gases is determined. Temperature is more critical when the density of gases is measured than it is for other substances. The density of a gas increases in direct proportion to its temperature and pressure. Standards for the measurement of the densities of gases have been established at 0° Centigrade and 76 centimeters of mercury (average sea-level pressure). Water is the standard with which the density of all liquids and solids is compared. For gases, air is most commonly used.

Buoyancy — Archimedes' Principle

A body submerged in a liquid or gas weighs less than when weighed in free space. This is due to the weight of the fluid displaced by its volume. This principle was stated by Archimedes (287-212 B.C.) and is known or referred to as the "Archimedes' Principle." It applies to all fluids, gases and liquids. If the volume displaced is more than its own weight, it floats or becomes buoyant.

Pressure

Pressure is defined as *force per unit area.* Pressure is usually measured in pounds per square inch (PSI). Sometimes it is measured in inches of mercury, or if very low pressure, inches of water.

Compression and Expansion of Liquids

Liquids can be compressed only slightly; for example, if a pressure of a hundred pounds per square inch (PSI) is applied to a liquid, its volume will decrease only three ten-thousandths of its volume with no pressure. It would take a pressure of 32 tons to reduce the volume by 10%. Liquids, therefore, are considered to be incompressible for practical purposes. Where extremely close tolerances are required, the compressibility of liquids may be considered in the design of a system. Liquids expand when heated, and this action is referred to as *thermal expansion.*

Fluid Flow — Bernoulli's Principle

Daniel Bernoulli found that when fluids flow steadily through pipes or tubes at high velocity, the pressure decreases; with lowered velocity, the pressure increases. The operation of the carburetor utilizes Bernoulli's principle. Refer to Fig. 9-8. Bernoulli's principle explains the relationship of the static and dynamic factors concerning fluids, while Pascal's law states the manner in which the static factors behave when taken by themselves. Steady state flow means that the energy contained by the liquid remains constant throughout the system.

Fluid Friction

Fluid power equipment is designed to reduce losses due to friction to the lowest possible level. Volume and velocity of flow are given careful study. Clean, smooth piping of optimum dimensions is used and installed to provide the most direct route possible. Sharp bends and sudden changes in cross-sectional areas are avoided. All necessary valves, gauges, and other components are designed so that they interrupt the fluid flow as little as possible, with thought given to the size and shapes of all openings. The fluid system is also designed so that it can be kept internally clean and variations from normal operation can be easily detected and remedied. The components of a fluid power system are designed to accommodate the fluid selected and provide optimum operational efficiency.

Kinetic Theory of Liquids

Liquids expand when heated because of increased molecular movement in the fluid. This action is referred to as "thermal expansion." All liquids, however, do not expand at the same rate. Alcohol expands much more than water for the same rise in temperature and most oils expand more than water. Hydraulic systems must compensate for this increase in volume in order to prevent breakage of the equipment.

Kinetic Theory of Gases

Kinetic molecular theory assumes that a body of gas is composed of identical molecules that are constantly in motion and spaced relatively far apart. The degree of molecular activity depends (in part) upon the temperature of the gas. An increase in temperature will result in an increase in molecular movement which results in the molecules striking one another in greater frequency. The increase in collisions results in an increase in pressure if the gas is within a container. If it is unconfined, it results in an increase in volume. After a car is driven at high speeds for some time, the pressure in the tires will increase due to the increased temperature from the friction with the road and the flexing of the tire walls.

Compression of Gases—Boyle's Law

Robert Boyle, an English scientist, studied the compressibility of gas. He called it the "springiness of air." By direct measurement, he discovered that when the temperature of an enclosed gas was kept constant and the pressure doubled, the volume was reduced by half. If the applied pressure were decreased, the volume increased. He concluded that for a constant temperature, the *product of the volume and pressure* of an enclosed gas remains constant. Boyle's law is normally stated, "The volume of an enclosed dry gas varies inversely with its pressure, provided the temperature remains constant."

A gas which conforms to Boyle's law is termed an "ideal gas." When pressure is increased upon such a gas, its volume decreases proportionately and its density increases. The density of a gas varies directly with the pressure if the temperature remains constant. Density also varies with temperature, since gases expand when heated and contract when cooled.

Temperature of Gases—Charles' Law

Jacques Charles, a French scientist, determined that all gases expand and contract in direct proportion to the change in the absolute temperature, provided the pressure is held constant. In other words, in an ideal gas with a constant volume, the absolute pressure of the gas will vary directly with its absolute temperature.

General Gas Law

When Boyle's Law and Charles' Law are combined, a single expression states all information contained in both laws. This is the General Gas Law. The General Gas Law applies with exactness only to ideal gases in which the gases are assumed to be perfectly elastic. It is used, however, to describe the behavior of actual gases with sufficient accuracy for most purposes.

Transmission of Forces through Fluids

When a solid in the form of a bar is struck, the force of the blow is carried straight through the bar to the other end, Fig. 21-5. This is because the bar is rigid. The direction of the blow determines the direction of the transmitted force. When force is applied to the end of a column of confined liquid, the force is transmitted straight through to the other end and *also equally and undiminished in every direction* throughout the column. Literally, the vessel is filled with force (pressure). If a gas is used instead of a liquid, the force is transmitted as with a liquid, but diminished in amount due to the fact that gas is compressible.

Fluid Pressure and Force — Pascal's Law

Pascal's Law was the foundation of fluid power development. Pascal discovered that *pressure applied to a confined fluid acts equally in all directions and at right angles to its container surfaces.* The shape of the container in no way affects pressure relationships. Remember that *force* is a push or pull against the total area of a particular surface and is usually expressed in pounds. *Pressure* is the amount of force on a unit area. Pressure is usually expressed in pounds per square inch. An equation similar to those used in conjunction with Ohm's Law in electricity is used in computing force, pressure, and area in fluid power systems: *force is equal to the product of pressure and area.*

Any force applied to a confined fluid is transmitted equally in all directions throughout the fluid, regardless of the shape of the container. It is not necessary that a tube connecting two pistons be of the same area of the pistons. A connection may be of any shape, size or length – so long as there is no obstruction to the passage of the fluid from one piston to the other.

The mechanical advantage of the system may be found, using the lever principle as a reference. If two pistons are of the same area, the *force* applied to one piston will equal the *force* output of the other. However, if the output piston area is three times larger than the input piston area, the force at the output piston will be three times that applied to the

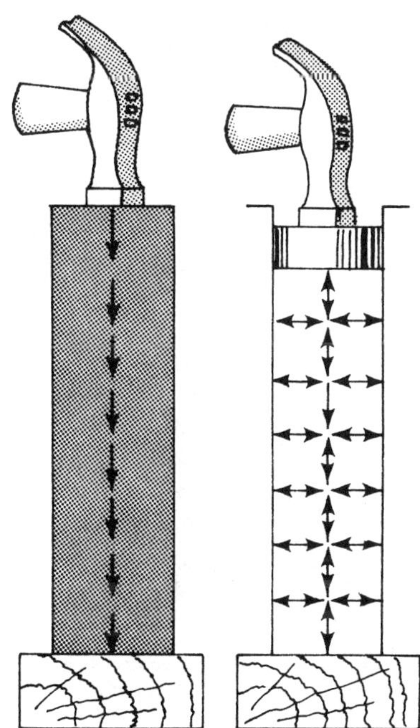

Fig. 21-5. Transmission of Force — Solid (Left); Column of Confined Liquid (Right)

input piston. See Fig. 21-6. The ratio of output force to input force is dependent upon the ratio of the input piston area to the output piston area. Since work input can never exceed work output, the increase in output force is always accomplished by a proportional decrease in the distance the force moves. In the example the force in the output piston was increased three times, but the distance the force moved was one-third that of the input piston. The volume of fluid moved by the input piston must equal the volume of fluid moving the output piston, since liquid is (practically) incompressible. In the case of a gas, the gas will compress momentarily but will eventually expand to its original volume.

A. Equal Area – Equal Pressure – Equal Force

B. Unequal Area – Equal Pressure – Unequal Force

Fig. 21-6. Applications of Pascal's Law

There are two basic rules regarding the application of Pascal's Law in a two-piston system. The first rule is: *If two pistons are used in a fluid system, the force acting on each is directly proportional to its area, and the magnitude of each force is the product of the pressure and the area.* The second rule is: *The distances moved by the pistons are inversely proportional to their areas.*

Fluids in Motion

The operation of fluid power systems involves such characteristics of fluids as: volume and velocity of flow, steady and unsteady flow, streamlined and turbulent flow, and the force and energy changes that occur in flow and the relations of different kinds of energy to each other in fluid power systems.

In a fluid power system the fluid is normally under pressure and completely fills the pipes of the system. This pressure is due in part to the force of gravity or the weight of the fluid and in part to externally applied forces such as those that might result from the action of a pump or compressor.

Volume and Velocity of Flow

The quantity of fluid that passes a given point in a fluid system in a unit of time is referred to as *volume of flow*. Gallons per minute (GPM) is the usual method of expressing volume of flow in hydraulic systems while cubic feet per minute (CFM) is common in pneumatic systems.

Velocity of flow is the rate or speed at which the fluid moves past a particular point in the system. It can be stated in a variety of ways, but usually in feet per second. Volume and velocity of flow are often considered together with other conditions unaltered; that is, with volume of input unchanged, the velocity of flow increases as the cross-sectional area or size of the pipe decreases, and the velocity of flow decreases as the cross-sectional area increases. In other words, velocity of flow is slow at wide parts and rapid in the narrow parts of the system.

Steady and Unsteady Flow

Fluids may flow in a single, continuous stream or fluctuate from moment to moment. When a valve is first opened in any system, the initial flow is unsteady during the short time that the rate of fluid flow is increasing from the initial zero rate to the full rate of flow of the system. The flow then becomes steady and is maintained if the pressure remains constant. If the pressure changes, the rate of flow changes.

Streamlined and Turbulent Flow

Streamlined flow is often referred to as *laminar flow*, defined as *a flow situation in which fluids move in parallel lamina or layers.* This condition exists usually where the fluids move straight and forward at a slow, uniform rate without obstruction. If, however, the path of fluid flow narrows and the volume of flow remains the same, the velocity of fluid flow must increase. If the velocity increases sufficiently, the fluid becomes turbulent: swirls, eddies, and cross-motions are set up within the fluid. Regardless of whether the fluid flow may be considered streamlined or turbulent, the fluid next to the wall of the pipe has little or no velocity because of friction. While a sufficient velocity of fluid flow will produce turbulence in any pipe, other factors also contribute to turbulence: roughness of pipe, obstruction, acuteness of bends, and number of bends. In designing a fluid power system, eliminate or minimize as many causes of turbulence as possible, since the energy consumed by turbulence is wasted. However, turbulence cannot be avoided completely. Losses due to friction increase directly with velocity in any system, but with turbulent flow these losses increase much more rapidly.

Factors Involved in Flow

There are five physical factors which act upon a fluid to affect its behavior. All of the physical actions of fluids in all possible systems are determined by the relationships of these five factors to each other:

1. Gravity – which acts at all times upon all bodies.
2. Atmospheric pressure – which acts upon any part of the system exposed to the open air.
3. Specific applied forces – which are independent of the presence or absence of motion.
4. Inertia – which is a consideration when fluids at rest must be made to move, or when fluids in motion must be brought to rest.
5. Friction—which is always present whenever there is motion.

Potential and Kinetic Energy

Energy has been defined as the capacity to do work. *Potential energy* is energy at rest and *kinetic energy* is energy in motion. A head of water or a coiled spring are examples of potential energy. When the water moves through a valve system that is opened, or the spring is allowed to uncoil and its energy drive some type of mechanism, the energy is in motion and is called kinetic energy.

Force must be applied to an object in order to give it velocity or to increase its velocity. The force must act over distance to perform work. Obviously then, energy is required to give an object velocity. The greater the energy used, the greater the velocity. Disregarding friction, a moving object to be brought to rest or have its motion slowed down requires a force opposite to its motion. This force also acts over distance. Energy is given up by the object and delivered in some form to whatever opposes its continued motion. Therefore, the moving object receives energy at one place where its motion is increased and delivers it to another where it is stopped or retarded.

An object in motion contains energy. Since energy can never be destroyed, it follows that if friction is disregarded, the energy delivered to stop the object will exactly equal the energy that was required to give it velocity. At all times the amount of kinetic energy possessed by an object depends upon its weight and the velocity at which it is moving.

Relationship of Force, Pressure, and Head

In dealing with fluids, pressure is considered to be a force applied over an area. Pressures may be stated in PSI or in terms of *head,* which is the vertical height of a column of fluid whose weight would produce that pressure. All five of the factors which control the actions of fluid can be expressed in terms of force or in terms of equivalent pressures or heads. In each situation, the factors are commonly referred to in the same terms since on this basis they can be added or subtracted to study the relationship to each other. *Gravity head,* when it is of sufficient importance to be considered, is sometimes referred to as *head. Inertia* effect is usually called *velocity head,* because it always is related to velocity, and *friction* is referred to as *friction head,* because it represents a loss of pressure or head.

Static and Dynamic Factors

Gravity, applied force, and atmospheric pressure apply to fluids at rest or in motion. Inertia and friction apply only to fluids in motion. The first three factors can be considered as static factors and the last two as dynamic factors. The mathematical sum of gravity, applied force, and atmospheric pressure is static pressure. Static pressure exists in addition to any dynamic factors which may also be present at the same point and time. Pascal's Law states that pressure set up in a confined fluid acts equally in all directions and at right angles to the container. This is sufficient for fluids at rest and practically at rest, but it is true only for the factors making static head. Obviously, when velocity becomes a factor, it must have direction. The force related to the velocity must also have direction, so that Pascal's Law is not sufficient for the dynamic factors of fluid power.

Inertia and friction, the dynamic factors, are related to the static factors. Velocity head and friction head are obtained at the expense of static head. However, a portion of velocity head can always be reconverted to static head. Force, which can be produced by pressure or head in a fluid, is necessary to start a body moving if it is at rest and is present in some form when the body is brought to rest. Therefore, whenever a fluid is given a velocity, some part of its original static head is used to impart this velocity which then exists as velocity head.

Characteristics of Hydraulic and Pneumatic Systems

The selection of a fluid power system, whether it be hydraulic, pneumatic, or a combination of the two, requires that many factors be considered:

1. type of action or operation required,
2. required speed and accuracy of operation,
3. surrounding atmospheric conditions,
4. heat,
5. availability of replacement fluid,
6. required pressure level,
7. temperature range,
8. contamination possibilities,
9. cost of transmission lines,
10. system cost,
11. limitations of the equipment,
12. lubricity,
13. operator safety, and
14. expected service life of the equipment.

Some general rules that may be followed in choosing a fluid system are: (1) if a great amount of force is required, use hydraulics; (2) if high speed and rapid response are required, use pneumatics; and (3) if fine feeds are required, and if force is not an important factor, a combination of pneumatics and hydraulics is desirable.

Pneumatic systems are suitable for operating die casting equipment, furnaces, and other systems where high ambient temperatures are present. In these applications, it is necessary that high temperature packings and seals be installed on the pneumatic components to insure longer life. Pneumatic systems are usually better in explosive environments. Pneumatic systems are often used if a portion of the system is to be submerged in some fluid such as water. In this application, piston rods and the cylinders are usually chrome-plated or made of stainless steel to resist corrosion. Pneumatic systems are preferred in extremely dusty operating conditions, but there are potential hazards from explosions in such locations as flour mills, coal mines, and grain elevators. When temperatures are below freezing, condensation may collect in low spots in the air lines, form ice and interrupt air flow. In situations where extremely low temperatures are encountered, an anti-freeze solution is sometimes used with the oil in the lubricator to prevent ice formation. This, however, is not entirely satisfactory. Control valves, especially those that are solenoid-operated, become sluggish because the lubrication congeals and forms a heavy film at low temperatures.

Hydraulic systems can function in adverse conditions, but it may be necessary to add extra equipment. For example, if a hydraulic system is used in an explosive atmosphere, the electric motor, switches, controls, and solenoids must be spark-protected. In some instances, most of the operating unit is placed in a separate enclosure which is isolated from the explosive area. If high ambient temperatures and fire hazards are involved, the hydraulic fluids selected must be fire resistant. These fluids usually require specially compounded seals and packings, which are more expensive than the standard materials and compounds. These fluids are often highly corrosive and require the use of special coatings on the interior surfaces of the operating units and/or special materials for the operating components. Hydraulic systems perform satisfactorily in extremely low temperatures but only after the hydraulic fluid is heated to working temperature. This may be accomplished by using a heater, by locating the reservoir near the operating motor, or by allowing the oil to flow through the pressure relief valve to increase turbulent flow and increase oil temperature.

When hydraulic systems are used in extremely dirty atmospheres, provision must be made for keeping the system as dirt-free as possible. Dirt may enter the system through the various openings in the power device, through the operating mechanisms on the control valve, and between the piston rod and the scraper or wiper seal on the cylinders. It may be necessary to install a large air cleaner on the power unit to assure full atmospheric pressure at all times on the surface of the reservoir fluid. The air within this system must be filtered. Scrapers, wipers, and boots are required on the control valves and cylinders to insure that contaminants will not get into the system.

The space requirement of the hydraulic system is comparable to that of a pneumatic system if the power unit and compressor are not considered. With the same power output, the overall size of the required hydraulic cylinder is somewhat smaller than the comparable pneumatic cylinder. In a pneumatic system the auxiliary equipment such as regulators, filters, and lubricators requires some additional space. Hydraulic systems today are quite compact, requiring only small quantities of operating fluid and demanding only a relatively small space for the force that they are capable of delivering. See Fig. 21-7.

In many industrial plants, a single compressor or central group of air compressors provides compressed air for all pneumatic circuits in the plant. Hydraulic systems typically contain their own hydraulic power unit for each circuit, or with each group of circuits. The grouping of circuits is often utilized in applications which have lengthy holding cycles, such as molding presses where no two presses need to be operational at the same time.

Regardless of the fluid system selected, internal leakage reduces efficiency and often leads to malfunction and breakage of controls and components. External leakage on hydraulic systems may become a fire hazard, cause slippery conditions that may be dangerous to

Fig. 21-7. Portable Hydraulic Hammer

workmen around the machinery, is very expensive, and often is detrimental to the material being processed, such as food, clothing, and synthetic products. Air leaks in pneumatic systems are sometimes overlooked and normally do not create any hazardous conditions. They are, however, costly in that they lower efficiency greatly.

The system designer may not be completely aware of the advantages of compounding both fluid and hydraulic control systems. Much research is being conducted to explore the many possibilities. Some of the apparent advantages follow:

1. Quickly responsive air controls can be used to operate large hydraulic control valves which contain air pilot operators.
2. Expensive hydraulic pilot valves can be replaced by inexpensive air valves.
3. Compounding permits air pressure to be used to operate the small devices such as clamping cylinders, pneumatic drills, pneumatic wrenches, etc., while hydraulic pressure performs the heavier tasks in an automated system.
4. Expensive piping from the control console to the pilot operated control valves can be eliminated, and inexpensive plastic tubing substituted. This not only eliminates initial assembly time, but also facilitates repairs and shortens down time. The two fluids should never be permitted to mix because it will invariably lead to a malfunction.

Hydraulic Fluids

Each hydraulic system designed to satisfy a specific need and operating environment requires that the operating fluid complement the system. Most often the term "fluid" means oil with additives. "Oil" is a misleading term as it gives no indication that anything has been added to it to improve it for hydraulic use.

Functions of Hydraulic Fluid

Hydraulic fluid must be capable of transmitting power. It must lubricate the moving parts and in many situations act as a sealing medium. Hydraulic fluid should maintain its viscosity over a wide spectrum of operating temperatures. It should resist oxidation, protect the machine parts against rust and corrosion, and resist emulsifying with air and water.

Viscosity

Viscosity is a most important property of any hydraulic fluid. Viscosity is the measurement of the resistance to flow of a fluid. Fluid of the correct viscosity has the ability to flow readily to the various parts of the system at the desired rate. Proper viscosity insures that the moving parts will be well lubricated. A good fluid has high enough viscosity to hold wear to a minimum and reduce internal leakage and low enough to permit the fluid to flow readily through the system.

Viscosity Index

The viscosity of a fluid changes with temperature, and is greater in some fluids than in others. The viscosity index is simply a measurement of the rate of change of viscosity over a certain range of temperature. If a fluid, for example, becomes thick at low temperatures and thin at high temperatures it has a low viscosity index (VI). However, if the viscosity remains relatively the same over a range of temperatures, it has a high VI. If a system is to operate over a wide temperature range, a fluid with a high VI is necessary. Of course, if a system operates within a narrow temperature range, then the fluid need not have a high VI. The proper selection of VI in the hydraulic fluid is a most important consideration in fluid choice.

Oxidation Resistance

Hydraulic fluids may combine with oxygen, leading to decomposition. This chemical combination forms organic acids which are harmful to metal parts and many types of seals and packings employed in the system, shortening the system's operational life.

Oxygen also combines with the hydraulic fluid to form sludge. Sometimes the natural environment of a hydraulic system hastens oxidation and sludge formation as a result of contact with air or water. Contaminants such as dust, dirt, and metallic particles also will speed up oxygen reaction, which is one reason filtering is so important.

To combat oxidation, hydraulic fluids should be refined carefully and chemical additives employed.

Rust and Corrosion Resistance

Rusting and corrosion affect the operating efficiency of the system. Rusting (the oxidation process) makes the parts larger, while corrosion (a chemical process) tends to eat the metal away. Corrosion, of course, affects the closeness of fits permitting excessive leakage and causing erratic action. Rusting affects the smoothness of operation with the loose particles causing undue wear. To resist rusting and corrosion, chemical additives are employed.

Oiliness

The very nature of the hydraulic system requires that precision-made system components be used. The operating tolerances are very close, and a very thin film of fluid must provide lubrication of these parts. The hydraulic fluid must possess a good *oiliness* characteristic. Oiliness, simply, is a term used to indicate the ability of the fluid to hold friction between parts to a minimum and may be further defined as the ability to stick to closely fitted, warm parts. The hydraulic fluid's lubricating characteristic becomes doubly important when it is expected to lubricate other parts in the machine, as when the rear frame of a tractor is a common sump for the hydraulic system transmission and final drive. Here the same fluid that operates the hydraulic system serves to lubricate the transmission and final drive.

Water Separation

In most hydraulic systems, it is almost impossible to keep water out of the system. Therefore, the hydraulic fluid must be able to rid itself of the water quickly. Contrary to popular opinion, oil and water will mix to form an emusient which leads to the formation of corrosive compounds. These emusients are often slimy, sticky, or of pasty consistency which interferes with the normal operation of system components. Hydraulic fluids vary in their ability to separate water.

Foaming Resistance

One difficulty often encountered in the operation of a hydraulic system is the formation of foam. Foam is caused by the constant pumping and churning action in the system, particularly when the fluid level gets too low. Sometimes turbulence which leads to the mixing of air with the fluid is hard to avoid and foaming becomes a serious problem. Fluids are basically incompressible; since foam is compressible, its formation is a serious detriment to proper action. The air that enters the hydraulic system is soluble in fluid to a certain extent. As pressure and temperature increase, the capability of fluid to absorb air increases. However, the air in solution does not affect compressibility. When pressure is relieved, the air will appear as bubbles or foam. If more air is trapped in the fluid than the fluid is able to absorb, foam will appear. Foaming is particularly detrimental in fluid couplings and torque convertors, as the foam will transmit less energy than fluid with no bubbles in it. Most recommended hydraulic fluids contain foam inhibitors.

Aniline Point

Aniline point is a numerical index. Aniline dyes will change color at certain temperatures in a given fluid. The temperature index is called the aniline point of the hydraulic fluid tested. This index indicates the effect of the fluid being tested upon the synthetic rubber used in seals. A high index indicates that the rubber will swell, a low index that the rubber will shrink. The aniline point, therefore, is a very important consideration in the selection of hydraulic fluid.

Other Properties

The factors previously described are considered the most important in the selection of hydraulic fluid. The following factors are of interest:

Pour point describes the fluid's ability to flow at low temperatures. Its only importance lies in the fact that hydraulic fluids also lubricate the components of a system, therefore, must have a pour point corresponding to the lowest starting temperature of the system.

The American Petroleum Institute gravity notation is a way of stating the specific gravity of fluid.

Color is used by refiners to maintain uniformity of product as well as to identify their product.

Flash point is the temperature at which the fluid vaporizes. It is of little significance except where the equipment is to be used in an environment of high temperature. Flash point is used by refiners as a means of product control.

Carbon residue is the quantity of carbon remaining when hydraulic fluid is subjected to destructive heating.

Acidity is a measurement of the amount of acid in a hydraulic fluid, used in laboratories to determine the degree of deterioration of fluids.

Toxicity of the hydraulic fluid is the quality, state, or degree of being toxic or poisonous. Present day hydraulic fluids are relatively free of harmful chemicals. All toxic fluids must be so labeled.

Types of Hydraulic Fluids

Hydraulic fluids are usually classified according to the type of base. The three most common types of hydraulic fluids are water base, petroleum base, and synthetic base. The most popular fluids include mineral oil, vegetable oil, water, phosphate esters, ethylene glycol compounds, and oil in water.

Water base fluids were used in the early hydraulic systems. Some large commercial installations that require high pressures and low operating speeds utilize them. However, they do not meet all the requirements for general hydraulic use. In fact, water may cause rust and corrosion. It is an ineffective lubricant, prone to extreme fluctuations with temperature variations. When water is used in a hydraulic installation it is usually combined with oil, ethylene glycol, and other substances. The combined fluid is usually fire resistant until the water evaporates, leaving the oil which may burn. Other combinations can eliminate ignition problems, but may have mechanical or economic limitations. Water-base hydraulic systems find their greatest application where there may be potential fire hazard in the event a hydraulic system may rupture. For example, the United States Navy employs water-base hydraulic fluids in the catapult systems on aircraft carriers.

Petroleum base automotive brake fluid was one of the first oils used by hydraulic systems designers. The fluid was incompatible with the rubber seals and packings that were in use. Oils containing 50% castor oil and 50% alcohol were substituted. However, this fluid eventually proved unsatisfactory because of the inclination of castor oil to oxidize readily.

Sometime in the middle 1930's a light petroleum base oil was developed, and when used with asbestos seals, proved quite successful. In the late 1930's new packing materials made of synthetic rubber permitted extensive use of the petroleum base fluids. As a result, a petroleum base oil was developed in the 1940's that proved quite satisfactory and, with certain refinements, it is popular today. The liquid was improved with additives such as oxidation and corrosion inhibitors, viscosity index improvers, and pour depressants. These additives produced a hydraulic fluid exhibiting a wide latitude of temperature stability with excellent lubricating characteristic and an extremely long life potential. Today petroleum base liquids are the most widely used for hydraulic systems.

Although petroleum base fluids contain most of the properties required of a hydraulic system, they are flammable under normal conditions and can be explosively dangerous when subjected to high pressures and high temperatures and particularly in the event of being exposed to an open flame.

Synthetic base fluids which are non-flammable have been developed for use in hydraulic systems where fire hazards may exist. A synthetic material is a chemical compound formed by man combining two or more compounds or elements. Some of the synthetics currently used are phosphate esters, chlorinated biphenyls or blends of each. Because these synthetic fluids have a tendency to attack conventional packings, special packings are normally required.

Contamination

Contamination may be abrasive including such particles as core sand, well spatter, machine chips, and rust; or non-abrasive including contaminants resulting from oil oxidation and worn or shredded soft particles from shields and other organic components.

The destructive action of abrasive contaminants is obvious. When particles are circulated within the system that are larger than the clearances between two moving parts, the clearance openings act as filters and retain these particles. Pressure of the hydraulic fluids then embeds these particles into the softer materials. The constant movement of these components results in premature wear, causing internal component leakage and decreased efficiency.

Non-abrasive contaminants called sludge are products of oil oxidation. These may prevent proper functioning of a hydraulic system by clogging valves, orifices, and filters.

Changing the hydraulic fluid is not a satisfactory solution. The lines and components should be completely flushed and cleaned of contamination. If the abrasive particles contained in the system are not flushed out, new particles are continually created as friction products. If the sludge is not completely cleaned from the system, the residue acts as a catalyst to speed up oxidation of fresh hydraulic fluid. Therefore, when the system is cleaned, all lines and components should be purged to remove any possible contamination that may remain. Care must be exercised in adding the new hydraulic fluid, making sure that all precautionary measures recommended by the manufacturer are taken.

Pneumatic Gases

Since gases serve the same purpose in pneumatic systems as liquids serve in hydraulic systems, many of the factors that are considered when a liquid is selected must be considered when a gas is selected.

Qualities

The ideal fluid medium for a pneumatic system must possess the following properties: non-poisonous; chemically stable; free from any acids that cause corrosion of system components; and non-flammable. It also should not support combustion of other elements.

The viscosity of gases is not important. Unlike liquids, however, the viscosity of gases increases as the temperature rises, and decreases as the temperature decreases. Most gases do not possess lubricating power and it is necessary to provide, as part of the pneumatic system, a means of lubrication. Most air compressors have their own internal lubricating system, others are lubricated externally, while still others require no lubrication because all bearings and seals are made of nylon or frictionless materials.

Typical Gases

Two of the most popular gases employed in pneumatic systems are compressed air and nitrogen.

Compressed air is the most popular pneumatic fluid because of the unlimited supply and the ease of compression. Most pneumatic systems are open systems; they constantly take in a fresh air supply, pressurize it, release the energy of compression in the form of work, and then exhaust the air to the atmosphere. Air exhibits non-poisonous and non-flammable characteristics that are most desirable. However, it contains oxygen which makes it capable of supporting combustion. One other fault is that changes in temperature cause condensation of moisture in the lines which can freeze if the ambient temperature is below freezing and make the system inoperative.

Nitrogen is slow to combine with other elements to form compounds, and for this reason, it is considered to be almost an inert gas. Nitrogen does not support fire nor life, nor cause rust nor decay. It is preferred to compressed air in many pneumatic systems, especially aircraft and rocket systems.

Nitrogen is acquired by fractional distillation of air. On some Navy installations, particularly aircraft carriers, nitrogen is obtained as a by-product of the oxygen plant. The acquired nitrogen is stored in cylinders and used to fill the pneumatic system.

Some systems use a mixture of air and nitrogen as a working gas. Compressed nitrogen is supplied from cylinders while a compressor provides compressed air to replenish any expended nitrogen and maintain the required pressure of the pneumatic system.

Potential Hazards

All compressed gases are hazardous. Although air and nitrogen are neither poisonous nor flammable, they should be handled carefully. Often pneumatic systems operate at pressures exceeding 3000 PSI. If lines and fittings rupture, they literally explode, injuring personnel and property. Carelessness has often

FLUID POWER SYMBOLS

WORKING LINE (MAIN)
PILOT LINE (CONTROL)
DRAIN LINE
LINES CROSSING
LINES CONNECTED
PNEUMATIC FLOW CONTROL
HYDRAULIC FLOW CONTROL
PLUGGED PORT
VENTED RESERVOIR
PRESSURIZED RESERVOIR
ACCUMULATOR
FLUID CONDITIONER
HEATER
COOLER
FILTER
SEPARATOR
HYDRAULIC OR PNEUMATIC CYLINDER

MANUAL CONTROL
HYDRAULIC MOTOR
HYDRAULIC PUMP
PNEUMATIC MOTOR
PNEUMATIC PUMP
ELECTRIC MOTOR
HEAT ENGINE
PRESSURE INSTRUMENT
TEMPERATURE INSTRUMENT
FLOW METER
PRESSURE SWITCH
FLOW SWITCH
VALVE ENVELOPE
VALVE PORTS
VALVE BLOCKED PORTS
VALVE OPEN
ON OFF VALVE (SIMPLIFIED)
COMPONENT ENCLOSURE

Fig. 21-8. Fluid Power Symbols

caused particle contaminants to be blown about creating a hazardous condition.

In systems employing nitrogen, care must be taken not to release this gas in a confined area. Since nitrogen does not support life, a concentration will cause asphyxia and sometimes death.

Contamination Control

Pneumatic systems should be purged periodically to remove contamination, moisture, and oil. Purging is accomplished by pressurizing the system and removing plumbing from the various components throughout the system. If an excessive amount of foreign matter, particularly oil, is exhausted from any one component, the entire system should be dismantled and cleaned and the cause of this condition corrected. Upon the completion of purging, all components must be reconnected with all drain valves closed. The system then should be serviced with the approved gas, under the proper pressure, and given a thorough operational check, including an inspection for leaks and security.

Future Systems

The development of fluid power and its mechanical equipment complements the development of specific fluids for specific applications. Recent breakthroughs in high temperature fluids indicate that satisfactory systems and fluids will be available when future equipment requires fluid power. Hot gas fluid power systems are now under study and being developed for use in our space program. These hot gases are obtained by bleeding off the main rocket engine or using a solid or liquid propellant gas generator.

Basic Systems and Circuit Diagrams

Components of the Basic Fluid System

The basic components of a fluid power system are essentially the same whether the system is hydraulic or pneumatic. These are: (1) reservoir; (2) pump or compressor; (3) tubing or piping; (4) control valve or selector valve; (5) actuating unit; and (6) pressure relieving device.

These basic components can be classified as: (1) a source of power, (2) a control device, (3) a load, and (4) conductor lines to allow the fluid to flow. Designers and draftsmen utilize symbols to represent components so that systems can be explained to installers, workmen and others. Figure 21-8 shows some typical fluid power symbols. The components represented by these symbols will be presented throughout this chapter. Often the symbol is expressive of the function of the component in the circuit. The schematic shown in Fig. 21-8A typifies the communication from design engineer to installer.

Reservoir

A very important requirement for the efficient operation of a hydraulic system is an adequate supply of fluid. Hydraulic fluid must be kept clean and free of air. The components used to provide for these requirements are the reservoir including the strainer and filter.

The primary function of the reservoir is to provide a storage space for the system's hy-

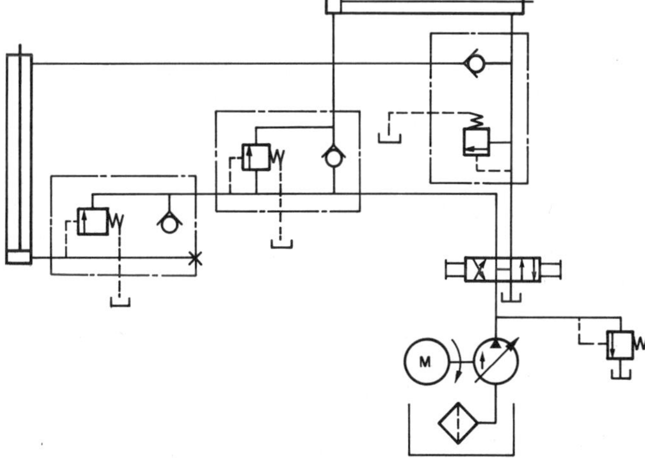

Fig. 21-8A. Schematic of Fluid Power Circuit

draulic liquid, Fig. 21-9. A well-constructed reservoir provides a means of keeping the oil at proper operating temperature. A hydraulic reservoir should be large enough to store two or three times the maximum rate of flow required by the system. Fixed installations may be provided a higher ratio while mobile installations may be provided a somewhat lower ratio. The oil in the reservoir serves to cool the oil as it returns from the system or as it is expelled by the relief valve. Space must be provided to allow for thermal expansion of the hydraulic liquid and for changes in liquid level due to the system operation. The design of the reservoir shell should allow heat to radiate from the oil. In operating environments of temperature extremes, it may be necessary to employ external radiating devices such as cooling coils or fins. The other extreme may require an immersion heater to warm the oil to proper operating temperature. The reservoir also may provide a base for holding the components of the hydraulic system.

Since the reservoir is usually the lowest component in the hydraulic system, all the dirt and foreign particles in the system tend to collect in it. Often the bottom of the reservoir is sloped so that the dirt will settle to one

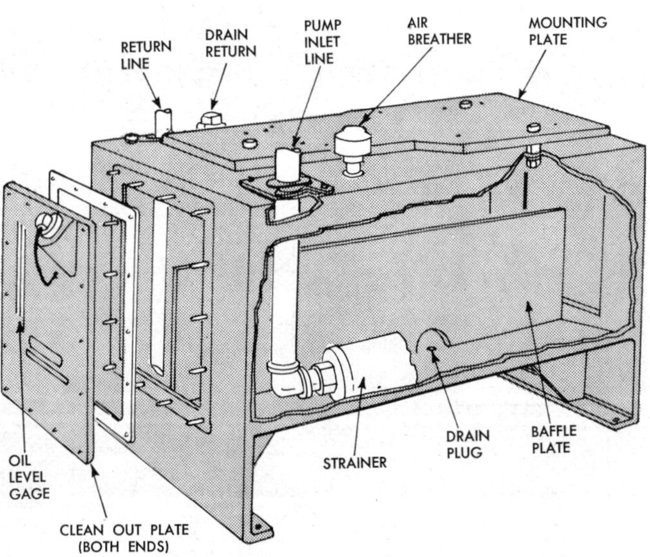

Fig. 21-9. Nonpressurized Hydraulic Reservoir (NAVPERS)

end and a drain plug is provided so that the reservoir can be emptied and easily cleaned. Sometimes this plug is magnetized to attract iron or steel particles. In order to provide for maximum cooling by air circulation, the unit is usually located off the floor.

Reservoirs are of two general types: pressurized and nonpressurized. Nonpressurized reservoirs are vented to the atmosphere to prevent a vacuum from being formed as the liquid level lowers. This vent also makes it possible for any trapped air to escape. Pressurized reservoirs are used to assure a positive flow of liquid throughout the system regardless of ambient pressure. Pressurized systems are used in aircraft and rocket installations where the operating environment is below atmospheric pressure.

Nonpressurized Reservoirs

In a typical nonpressurized reservoir, a baffle plate extends lengthwise through the center of the tank, separating the pump supply line from the system return line. The baffle usually extends from the bottom of the tank to two-thirds the normal liquid level. The purpose of the baffle is to reduce the turbulence created by return flow of fluid and prevent immediate recirculation of the fluid. It allows foreign matter to settle to the bottom of the compartment and air bubbles to escape through the surface of the slower moving fluid before it is recirculated. The air breather line maintains atmospheric pressure in the reservoir. To insure that the air which is drawn into the reservoir is clean, a filter is provided in this vent line. The pump inlet line enters the reservoir at the top and extends to within inches of the bottom. Sometimes a strainer is placed at the end of this line. Return lines are located well below the liquid surface to prevent foaming. The end of the return line is usually fashioned so that the flow is directed towards the walls of the tank and away from the pump inlet line. This permits maximum heat dissipation.

Pressurized Reservoirs

Aerospace vehicles are equipped with pressurized reservoirs assuring positive liquid flow in all operating environments. There are two basic types of pressurized reservoirs: air and liquid.

The *air pressurized reservoir* provides an air space in the top of the reservoir which is filled by tapping the air compressor section of the engine. The air is filtered and the pressure regulated to the desired PSI before it enters the reservoir. The regulator is designed to maintain constant pressure regardless of the fluid level within the reservoir – increasing the air flow when the liquid level is low or venting the excess pressure when the liquid rises in the reservoir. In the pressurized system, provision is made to fill the reservoir from a single point by forcing hydraulic fluid into the filler line.

The *liquid pressurized hydraulic system reservoir* is divided into two compartments by a floating piston, Fig. 21-10. The piston is forced downward in the reservoir by a spring and by a pressure probe which fits into the piston and is connected to the pump pressure line so that when the system is pressurized, pressure enters the probe and aides the springs in pressurizing the liquid in the lower compartment. This equalizes the pressure in the return and supply line, preventing pump starvation. This reservoir has five openings: pump supply, return; pump pressure; reser-

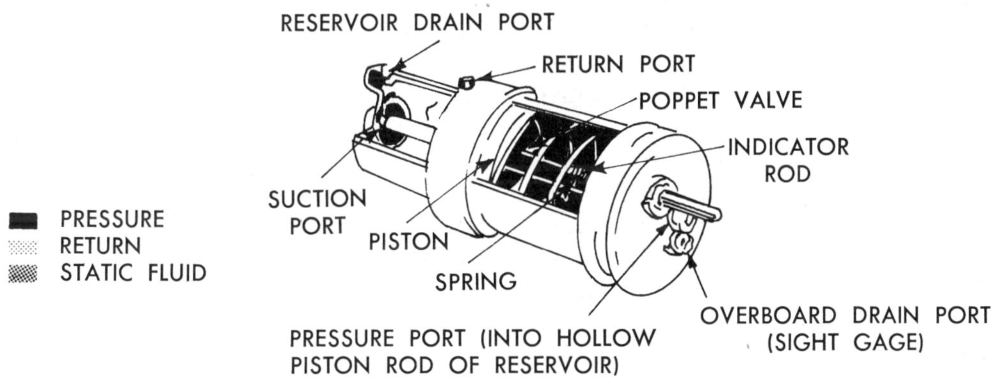

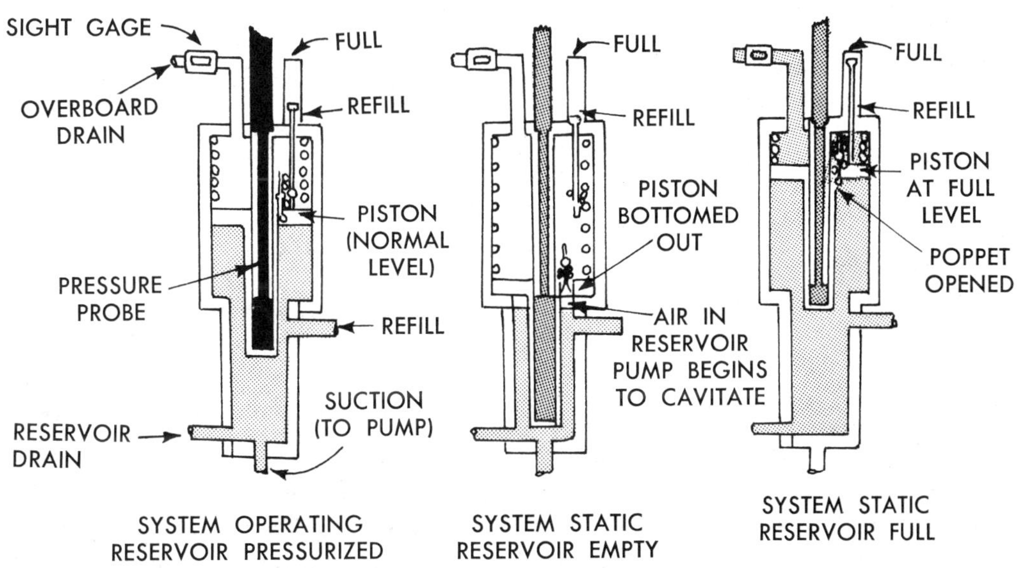

Fig. 21-10. Liquid Pressurized Reservoir (NAVPERS)

voir drain; and overboard drain. Liquid is supplied to the pump through the pump supply and returned to the reservoir from the system through the return line. Pressure from the system enters the pressure probe in the top of the reservoir through the pressure opening. The return drain is for the purpose of draining the reservoir when necessary. The overboard drain is equipped with a sight gauge which is used to determine reservoir fluid level and the condition of the fluid.

Regardless of the care taken in servicing, maintaining, and operating hydraulic systems, it is impossible to prevent contaminants from entering the system. In operation, the system itself deposits tiny particles of metal and requires a filtering device in the hydraulic system. Filtering devices used to remove large particles of foreign matter are normally called strainers, while those used to remove smaller particles are referred to as filters.

Strainers typically consist of a metal frame wrapped with a fine wire mesh screen or a screening element made of specially-processed wire. Strainers are usually placed in pump inlet lines because they offer little resistance to fluid flow. Strainers are also placed in filler necks and are often removable to facilitate cleaning. Those located in the reservoir below liquid level need only be hand-tightened, while those exposed to the air require wrench-tightening to be airtight.

The *filter* is the most common device used to remove contaminants from the system. These are usually located within the reservoir in the pressure line or return line. Filters are classified as full or proportional flow. Refer to Figs. 8-69 and 8-70. In full-flow filters, all the liquid enters the unit and passes through the filtering element, while in proportional flow only part of the liquid passes through the element. A full-flow filter offers resistance to fluid flow, especially when the element becomes dirty. For this reason, a by-pass valve is usually located within the filter to allow the fluid to by-pass the filter when the filter cannot handle all the fluid flowing through it. In normal operation, the hydraulic liquid enters the filter through the inlet in the body and flows around the element inside the filter bowl. Filtering takes place as the liquid passes through the element and into the hollow core, leaving the contaminant on the outside of the filter element. The filtered fluid then flows from the hollow core to the outlet and into the system. Filters not equipped with a by-pass port valve are equipped with a contamination indicator. The operation of this indicator depends on the pressure differential between the inlet and the outlet feeds. When the contamination clogs the element and the pressure increases to a specific value, an indicator pops out signifying that the element must be cleaned or replaced. The non by-passing filter eliminates the possibility of contaminated fluid — by-passing the filtering element and contaminating the entire system and minimizing the necessity for flushing the entire system and cleaning other components in the system that may be so affected.

The *proportional-flow filter* operates on the venturi principle. As the liquid passes through the venturi constriction, a drop in pressure is created, causing a siphoning action which draws a portion of the liquid down around the cartridge, through the filter element, and up into the venturi. Filtering is usually accomplished in either direction of fluid flow. This system depends on the constant recirculation of fluid, although only a portion of the fluid is filtered during any one cycle.

Filter elements are made of a variety of materials, such as cellulose paper (micronic), plastic, sintered metal, clay and Fuller's earth.

Accumulators

Most hydraulic systems require an accumulator to store a volume of liquid under pressure. Its function may be compared to that of a capacitor in an electronic circuit. The potential energy is provided by gravitation, spring tension, or the compressibility of gases.

Gravity Accumulator

The gravity or dead-weight accumulator is often used as a single unit to serve several hydraulic machines. It is the earliest form of accumulator. It consists of a vertical cylinder with a smoothly round bore into which a piston is fitted with suitable packing. The piston is weighted by a high density material, and the force of gravity provides the energy necessary to force the liquid from the cylinder throughout the systems that it services. An advantage of this accumulator is that the pressure is constant regardless of the amount of liquid that is in the cylinder, and its simplicity of operation permits a long life expectancy. Its main disadvantage is its cumbersome size and weight.

Spring-Operated Accumulators

The spring-operated accumulator is similar in principle and design to the gravity unit, except that spring compression supplies the pressure. The load characteristics of the spring depend upon the fluid level in the accumulator. At low level the spring affords low pressure. High liquid level compresses the spring further to afford greater pressure. These accumulators are usually smaller than the gravity accumulator.

Air-Operated Accumulators

The air-operated accumulator is commonly referred to as the pneumatic or hydro-pneumatic accumulator. This system utilizes compressed gas, usually air or nitrogen, to apply force to the stored liquid. Air-operated accumulators are classified as either separator or nonseparator types, depending on whether the air or gas is permitted to contact the hydraulic fluid. The separator type uses a bladder or bag diaphragm and piston to separate the air from the liquid.

Applications

Present-day hydraulic systems employ the accumulator as a leakage compensator, shock absorber, aid to the pump, and emergency power supply. Whether the system is open or closed, there is always some leakage. This leakage can decrease the desired pressure, and the proper use of an accumulator compensates for the leakage and pressure is maintained in the system. In the same manner, the accumulator compensates for thermal expansion and contraction of the hydraulic liquid.

Fluid flowing at a high velocity in a pipe creates a backwards surge when suddenly stopped by a valve and develops instantaneous pressures two or three times normal. This shock is objectionable because it can damage piping, fittings, and other components. The accumulator cushions this shock with the entrapped gas. Accumulators also dampen pressure surges caused by pulsating fluid delivery from the pump. During normal operation, some systems require large volumes of liquid for short periods of time. Because this need is sporadic, it is not necessary to use a large pump, especially if there is sufficient interval during the normal working cycle for an accumulator to store up a volume of hydraulic fluid to aid the pump during these peak demands. In the event the regular power system fails, or in an emergency, the accumulator should be able to operate the system through at least one complete cycle.

NOTE: An accumulator can be very dangerous in a system when the pump is shut down — the stored energy must be discharged or the system is still as active as when the pump was running.

Receivers, Filters and Condensers

Pnuematic systems require a supply of gas or air that is filtered and dry. The components that provide these functions are the receiver, filters, and condensers.

Receivers

Gas bottle, air cylinder and supply tank are terms used to describe that component of the pneumatic system that is similar to the reservoir of the hydraulic system. In the pneumatic system, the receiver stores the volume of gas at the pressure required by the system and supplies it as needed. In many systems, the air is supplied by an air compressor. In other systems, the receiver is a storage cylinder or bottle which is charged from an outside source. The receiver acts both as a storage tank and as a supply tank. When the demand for air pressure is in excess of the compressor capacity, some of the air from the receiver enters the system. When the demand is less than the compressor capacity, the excess air enters the receiver. The receiver, therefore, functions to maintain the system at constant pressure and, as a result, the start and stop cycle of the compressor is retarded.

The size and construction of the receiver depend on the maximum pressure and volume of air required to operate the pneumatic system. Usually the receiver is cylindrical in shape and mounted either horizontally or vertically, dependent upon the space available. Each receiver is fitted with an inlet connection which is located near the top of the receiver and an outlet connection which is located just above the bottom of the receiver. The line between the compressor and the receiver should be kept as short and as free from bends as possible to eliminate excessive vibration and pulsations and to reduce the loss of pressure due to friction.

Pneumatic systems in aircraft depend on a storage cylinder or bottle to provide compressed air or nitrogen as required. Some of these systems contain air compressors which replace the pressure and volume lost through leakage, thermal expansion, and system operation. Some require the system to be charged with an external compressor or pressure bottle. Of necessity these cylinders are made of nonshatterable material and are most often spherical or cylindrical in shape. Each is equipped with a manual moisture drain valve for periodic draining and bleeding of air from the cylinder. Their size depends on the operational requirements of the system. The cylinder size is determined by the volume in cubic inches, with pressures ranging up to 3,000 PSI.

Filtration of Pneumatic Gases

Clean dry gas is required for the efficient operation of a pneumatic system. Ambient air usually contains dust and impurities in varying amounts, with a substantial amount of moisture in vapor form. Solids such as dust, rust, or pipe scale ingested in pneumatic systems will lead to excessive wear, failure of components, and in some cases, prevent the pneumatic devices from operating. Moisture in the system is harmful because it leads to corrosion and washes lubrication away from the moving parts. In addition, if the system is operated in freezing temperatures, moisture collecting in the low spots in the system could freeze. Nitrogen minimizes these hazards; however, it is not economically feasible as a working medium except in small systems. Pneumatic systems typically require filters to remove dirt and moisture, if possible, without excessive pressure drop.

Air filters are similar in design and operation to hydraulic filters. The elements for some filters are woven screens, steel wool, glass fiber, and felt fabrics. Most often these filters are placed in the inlet pipe to the air compressor. They function in the same manner as the air filter located above the carburetor of an automobile engine. These filters must be checked periodically for an accumulation of foreign matter, with the elements cleaned and replaced as necessary. Filters of this type are usually designed to remove particles as small as 25 microns.

Filters made of porous metals and ceramic elements are installed in the compressed air supply line. Their internal design causes the air to flow in a centrifugal path within the filter bowl. Heavy particles and water droplets are spun out from the air stream, eventually to drop to the bottom of the bowl. The air then flows through the filter element which filters out most of the smaller contaminants. The filter is so designed that a drain valve at the bottom of the bowl may be opened to empty the accumulated solids and water. Some systems provide automatic drainage and some systems are made with transparent bowls so that the amount of accumulation can be observed. The removal of solids from a pneumatic system is generally accomplished by screening, centrifugal force, or a combination of the two.

Lubrication must be provided in a pneumatic system. Generally, it is added to the air supply with a *lubricator* which may be part of the filter unit. A drip-type lubricator operates in an air line much as a carburetor, atomizing the lubricant as it is drawn into the air stream. The filter, lubricator, and pressure regulator are often incorporated as a single unit, called the FLR unit.

Air Condensers: When air is drawn into the compressor, it contains a certain amount of moisture in vapor form. During compression, the temperature and pressure of the air are increased permitting the moisture to remain in vapor form. However, as the compressed air cools, moisture vapor condenses, creating a problem in the system. It is the cooling of the compressed air which causes the moisture to condense; therefore, all condensing devices are normally placed immediately after the compressor and before the air enters into the system. On the discharge side of the cooler, another condenser-separator is located. These separators are of a variety of designs. Most often, the removal of liquid is accomplished by centrifugal force, impact, or sudden change in velocity of the air stream.

Chemical dryers are incorporated in some pneumatic systems. These dryers contain a hydroscopic chemical such as silical gel to absorb moisture that may collect within the system. These dryers must be checked periodically to maintain their operational efficiency and to guard against contaminants and excessive moisture reducing their efficiency.

Pumps and Compressors

The heart of any fluid power system is the component which converts the *input mechanical energy* to *fluid energy*. The provider of mechanical power may be an electric motor, heat engine, a power take-off arrangement, or other mechanical device. It must input force and motion which can be converted to fluid power by the pump or compressor. *Pumps* provide this function in hydraulic systems, while *compressors* are used in pneumatic systems. Although these components serve a similar purpose, their principles of operation and their design differ to some degree.

Pumps

A hydraulic pump converts mechanical force and motion into fluid power. Pumps are used for a variety of purposes. In steam generating systems, pumps supply water to boilers, draw condensation from condensors, and circulate cooling water for coolers and condensors. In marine application, pumps clean out bilges, transfer fuel oil, and supply water to the distilling plants. Usually the pump is one of the most costly components used in the hydraulic power system. Many different power sources are used to provide mechanical energy to pumps.

Modern industrial plants use electric motors to drive hydraulic pumps. The motors are available in speeds which are compatible with most hydraulic pumps. The hydraulic power systems used in surface vehicles, marine vessels and aircraft typically depend on power take-off arrangements to operate hydraulic pumps. When power take-off arrangements cannot be made available on the basic prime mover, auxiliary prime movers are used, such as electric motors, air motors, and small internal combustion engines. The operating speed of these auxiliary engines must be compatible with the hydraulic pump. Those vehicles dependent upon turbine or turbine reaction engines require a specially-designed high speed pump or speed reduction devices. Some pumps and small pieces of equipment may be manually operated.

The hydraulic pump supplies a flow of liquid to the hydraulic system. A pump does not create pressure; it transmits a force to the liquid providing a flow. The force generated by the pump is not controlled by the pump. The force generated can build up a pressure if a constriction or load is imposed on the system. The operating pressure at any given moment in a hydraulic system depends primarily on the resistance due to the work load or the action of a pressure-regulating device. In order for a pump to supply a system with a flow of liquid, it must have a continuous supply available at the inlet opening. If the pump is located below the reservoir, the force of gravity supplements atmospheric pressure and insures a supply of liquid to the inlet port. If the pump is located, as in most systems, above the reservoir, a pressurized hydraulic reservoir is required to provide the necessary fluid for start. Aircraft and liquid rocket systems depend upon such pressurized hydraulic reservoirs.

As the pump forces the liquid through the outlet port, a partial vacuum is created in the inlet port; the pressure then acts on the supply liquid, forcing it into the pump.

Pump Performance

Normally pumps are rated in terms of *volumetric output and pressure.* The volumetric output is the amount of liquid the pump can deliver at its outlet port in a given period of time and at a given speed. Volumetric output in most pumps is expressed in gallons per minute (GPM). A change in operational speed affects volumetric output; therefore, most pumps are rated according to displacement at a certain pressure. The *displacement* is the amount of liquid a pump can deliver per revolution and is expressed in terms of cubic inches per revolution. While a pump does not create pressure, the pressure developed by a restriction in the pump system affects the volumetric output of the pump. As system pressure increases, the volumetric output decreases. This is the result of an increase in the internal leakage from the outlet side to the inlet side of the pump, and is usually referred to as *pump slippage.* This factor must be considered in all pumps. Therefore, pumps most often are rated in terms of volumetric output at given pressure. The internal slippage of a pump varies with the pump design. To indicate the efficiency of a pump, slippage is expressed in percentage.

Classes of Pumps

A fundamental classification of pumps is displacement method. Pumps which discharge liquid in a continuous flow are referred to as *nonpositive displacement pumps,* and those which discharge volumes noncontinuously are referred to as *positive displacement pumps.* Nonpositive displacement pumps are often referred to as variable displacement, and positive displacement pumps are referred to as constant displacement.

A *nonpositive displacement pump* delivers a volume of liquid for each cycle dependent upon the resistance offered to the flow. This pump produces a force on the liquid that is constant for each particular speed of the pump. The resistance in the discharge line produces a force in the opposite direction. When these forces are equal, the liquid is in a state of equilibrium and does not flow. If the outlet of the nonpositive displacement pump is closed, the discharge pressure will rise to maximum for that pump at that operating speed. Nothing more will happen except the pump will churn the liquid, resulting in the invested mechanical energy being converted to heat energy.

A *positive displacement pump* is one in which a definite volume of liquid is pumped for each cycle of operation, regardless of the resistance offered, provided the capacity of the power unit driving the pump is not exceeded. See Figs. 21-11 and 21-12. If the outlet of the positive displacement pump is completely closed, either the unit driving the pump will stall or something will break. Positive displacement systems require pressure regulators or pressure relief valves to control the amount of pressure in the system and to relieve the pump when the desired pressure is reached. The action of a pressure regulator keeps the pump from working against the load when the hydraulic system is at maximum pressure and not functioning, by-passing the liquid from the pump back to the reservoir.

Centrifugal Pumps

Centrifugal pumps utilize an impeller to impart velocity to the liquid, Fig. 21-13. The liquid is thrown off the impeller blades into a chamber called a *volute,* which continuously expands in a definite ratio. The size and shape of the volute are very important to the efficiency of the pump and must fit the exact shape, size, and speed of rotation of the impeller. In general, the impeller blade that curves backward with respect to the direction of rotation gives better results than straight blades or those that curve forward. The fluid flows from the center outward to the walls of the shroud. The fluid flows in a horizontal path tangent to the circular path of the impeller (the volute). As the fluid moves out, a partial vacuum is created within the center of the impeller, and it is at this point that the fluid supply is connected.

The two most common types of centrifugal pumps used in hydraulic systems are the *diffuser* and *volute* pumps. In both types, flow is provided by the action of centrifugal force.

In the *volute pump,* the impeller discharges the liquid at high velocity into a progressively expanding shroud. The contour of this shroud directs the movement of the liquid through the outlet port and into the system.

The *diffuser pump* is similar to the volute pump with a series of stationary blades incorporated around the outside circumference of the impeller blades. These diffuser blades are curved in the opposite direction from the rotating impeller blades. They serve to reduce the velocity of the liquid and decrease slippage, resulting in increased efficiency of the pump.

Centrifugal pumps are classified in several ways:

1. For example, centrifugal pumps may be *single- or multi-stage.* The single-stage has one impeller; the multi-stage has two or more impellers housed together in one casing, with

Fig. 21-11. Variable Volume, Axial Piston Pump with Handwheel Control and Pressure Compensator (Denison)

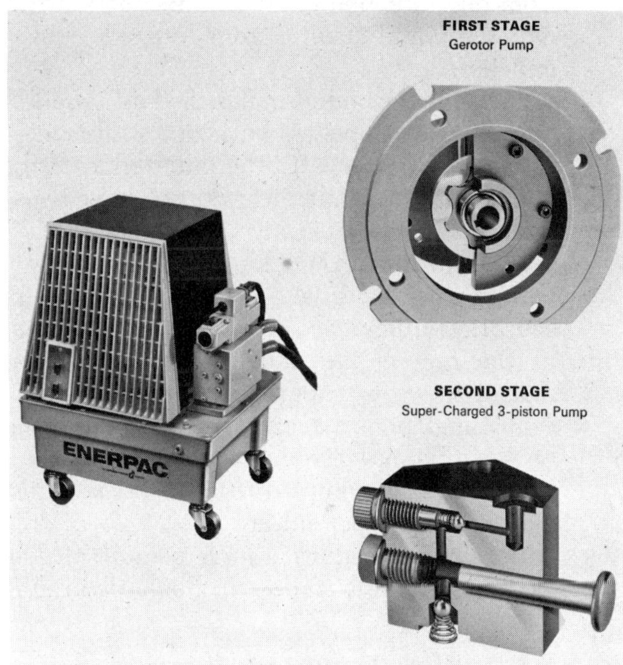

Fig. 21-12. Positive Displacement Pump with Electric Valve Control (Enerpac)

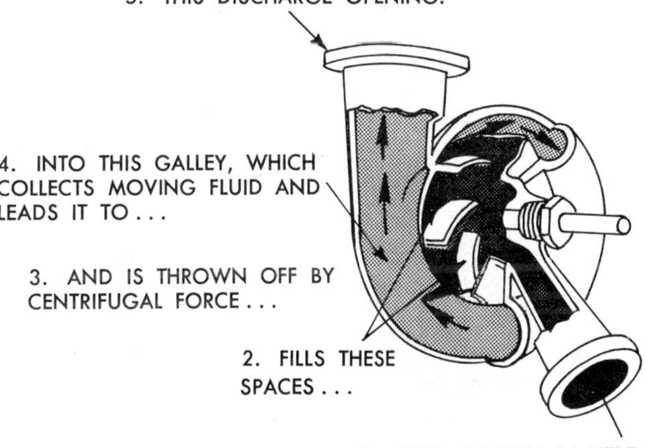

Fig. 21-13. Centrifugal Pump

each impeller acting separately and discharging to the eye of the next stage impeller. For compactness, the impellers of multi-stage pumps are often placed on one shaft.

2. Centrifugal pumps may also be classified as *horizontal or vertical,* depending upon the position of the pump shaft.

3. Another way of classifying the pumps is by *single- or double-suction.* The single-suction impeller allows liquid to enter its eye from one direction only; a double action permits the liquid to enter from both sides of the impeller.

4. Impellers are also classified as *closed or open.* Closed impellers have side walls which extend from the eye to the outer edge of the blade tip. Open impellers do not have these side walls.

5. Centrifugal pumps may be driven by a variety of sources. As a rule, high-pressure centrifugal pumps are direct drive pumps; that is, the rpm of the impeller is the same as that of the power source. Some low pressure centrifugal pumps require reduction gearing between the power source and the impeller.

Centrifugal pumps are nonpositive displacement pumps and are used in hydraulic systems which require a *large volume of flow at relatively low pressure.* Some hydraulic systems require variations of flow and pressures. In these systems, the centrifugal pump is usually used in combination with a positive displacement pump. The positive displacement pump maintains the system during periods requiring low volume and high pressure, and the centrifugal pump aids the positive displacement pump when the system requires large volumes and low pressure.

Fig. 21-14. Operating Principle of the External Gear Pump

Rotary Pumps

Rotary pumps utilize a rotating member, such as a gear, screw, lobe, or vane, or a cam and plunger arrangement to trap the fluid at the intake or suction side and force it through the discharge outlet. Rotary pumps are *positive displacement* units; each rotation delivers a definite quantity of fluid. In order to minimize slippage from the discharge side back to the suction side, rotary pumps have very small clearances between rotating and stationary parts. They are designed to operate at relatively moderate speeds. Operating these pumps at high speed causes erosion and excessive wear resulting in increased clearances and lower operating efficiency.

Classification of rotary pumps is usually made according to the *type of rotating element.*

External gear pumps provide constant delivery. As the gears revolve, fluid is trapped between the gear teeth and the housing and is carried from the suction inlet side to the discharge outlet side of the pump, Fig. 21-14. One gear is driven, the other follows. External timing is not required. The efficiency of the pump depends upon the close fit of the working parts. External gear pumps are used primarily where relatively low pressures, low volumes, economy, and restricted space are factors. Quieter and somewhat smoother operation, plus higher pressures, may be obtained by using helical or herringbone gears. Pressures in excess of 3,000 PSI are available by pressure-loading loose-fitting bearings so that a balance is set up between the pressure within the gear cavity and the thrust of the bearings against the gears. This enables the pump to be driven at very high speeds with increased efficiency. Gear pumps have a tendency to churn fluids which raises their temperature. This action hastens the mixing of any contaminants within the fluid.

Internal gear pumps are a modification of the external gear pump; pressure is developed by trapping the fluid between the meshing gears. Either the internal gear or the external ring may be the driven member, *A* in Fig. 21-15. A crescent-shaped divider separates the suction and discharge sides of the pump. In another design, the crescent is omitted, and the seal between discharge and suction is accomplished by the teeth being in constant sliding contact throughout the cycle. See *B* in Fig. 21-15. Also, there is one less tooth on the inside gear. Internal gear pumps have the same effect on fluids as the external gear pumps.

Lobe pumps are similar to gear pumps; they have rotating members with lobes or projections resembling teeth which intermesh, Fig. 21-16. In this pump, one rotor does not drive the other, so an external timed driving gear is required. These pumps are generally used for transferring fluids, not for providing pressure in the hydraulic systems. Two- or three-lobe cams are popular.

Screw pumps are simple, rugged and capable of working at very high speeds. They are useful in handling fluids with a great deal of entrapped air, Fig. 21-17. This pump is most often used to transfer fluids from one point to another and is not used to provide hydraulic power.

Vane pumps are a popular means of producing hydraulic power. They are constant-delivery pumps, unless special adaptors are made, Fig. 21-18. They produce a reasonably steady flow. Vane pumps are capable of handling large volumes of fluid at relatively high pressures. Wear does not greatly reduce efficiency because the vanes move out of their slots to maintain contact with the shroud. Sludge may, however, cause the vanes to stick in the slots and seriously affect the operation of the pump.

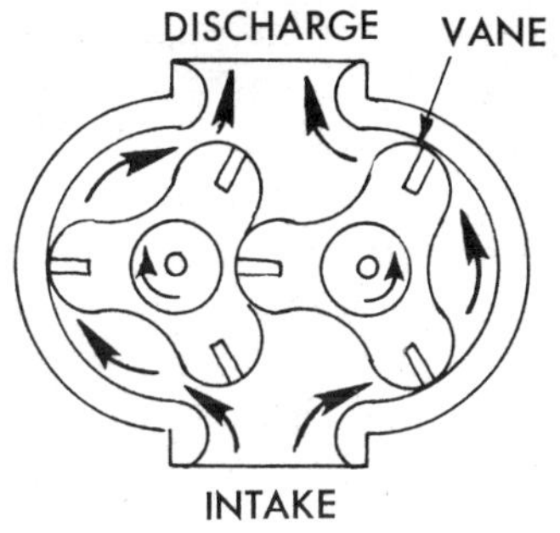

Fig. 21-16. Lobe Pump (NAVPERS)

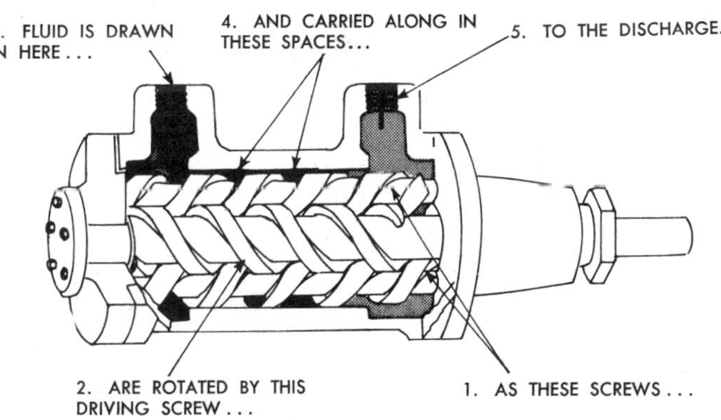

Fig. 21-17. Screw Pump (NAVPERS)

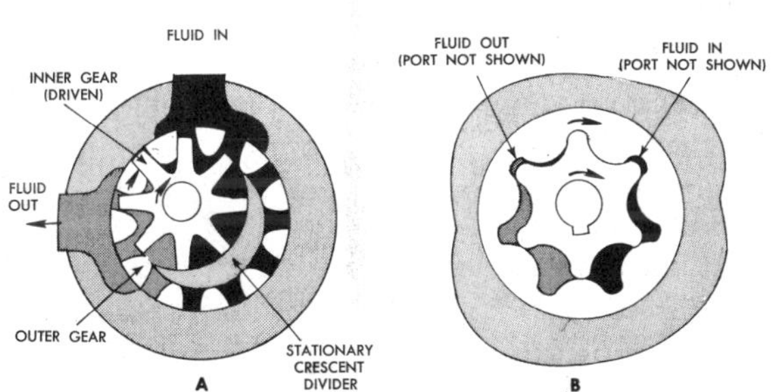

Fig. 21-15. Internal Gear Pump (NAVPERS)

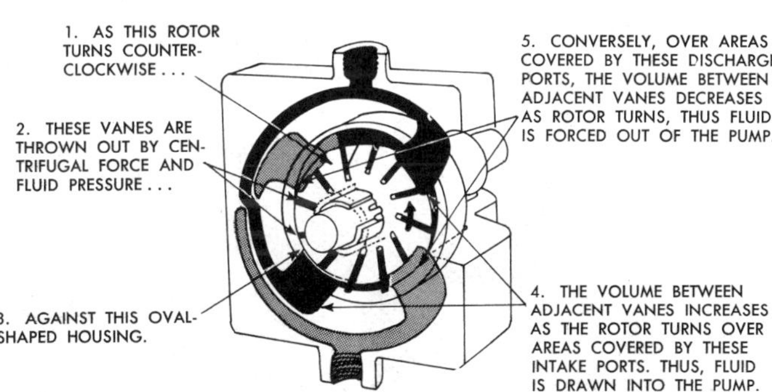

Fig. 21-18. Vane Pump (NAVPERS)

Vane pumps come in two basic designs. With inlet and outlet ports diametrically opposed, they are referred to as *hydraulically-balanced pumps.* In another design, the rotor is mounted eccentrically with respect to the circular housing. Adding a spring-loaded pressure plate and a movable inner housing provides a variable delivery feature, with delivery controlled manually or by a governor.

Although some rotary pumps are capable of operating in high pressure systems (above 1500 PSI), their normal operating limit is below this pressure. Compared with other hydraulic pumps, rotary pumps are less expensive, have fewer moving parts, and are simple in design and construction. Their efficiency depends on the close tolerances between the rotating elements and, in most pumps, between the rotors and the housing of the pump. This efficiency is quickly reduced bv excessive wear. For this reason, any dirt picked up by the fluid must be eliminated by suitable filters. Rotary pumps are often used in systems which do not require continuous or near-continuous operation, as in emergency hydraulic systems in aircraft. It is far less expensive than the type generally used in the main system and with only limited use it maintains efficiency.

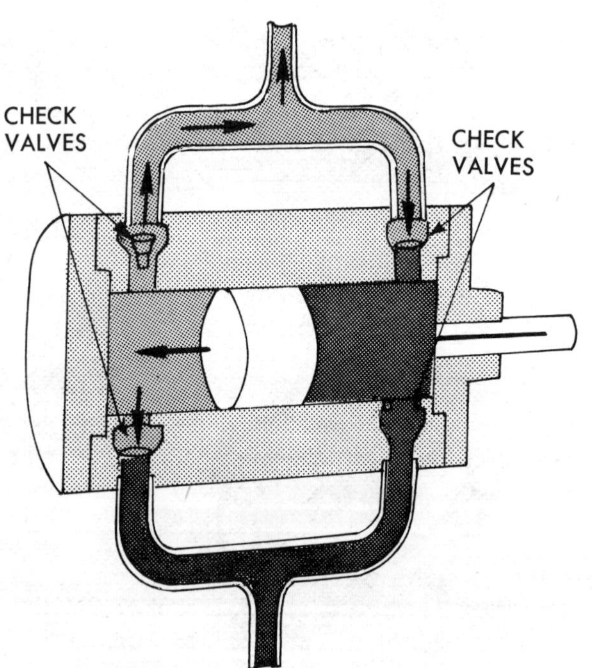

Fig. 21-19. Reciprocating Pump (NAVPERS)

Reciprocating Pumps

Reciprocating pumps use linear movement to transmit liquid from inlet to outlet port, Fig. 21-19. They are positive displacement; each stroke delivers a definite volume of liquid to the system. The hand water pump and the master cylinder of the automobile brake system are simple reciprocating pumps. Reciprocating pumps of this type are classified as direct- or indirect-acting, simple or duplex, single- or double-acting, vertical or horizontal. These classifications also describe the operation of the steam reciprocating engine.

Pumps with reciprocating piston action are useful in extremely high-pressure applications because of low-leakage losses, and also in applications where large volumes of fluids are required. The pulsating nature of the discharge from the reciprocating pumps may cause objectionable vibration in some installations, restricting their use. Pumps with three or more cylinders on the same shaft reduce this pulsation by overlapping the pumping strokes of each cylinder. Most of these pumps are of the fixed displacement type, although one variation is provided with a stroke transformer which permits variable delivery by varying the length of the piston strokes. Reciprocating pumps are capable of operating under adverse temperature conditions, are comparatively troublefree, and will handle high pressures.

Two other classes of reciprocating pumps are the radial piston and the axial piston pumps. Refer to Fig. 21-11. These pumps are classified as rotary piston pumps because a rotary motion is imparted to the pump by the source of power. However, the actual pumping action is performed by sets of reciprocating pistons.

Radial Piston Pumps

Radial piston pumps are rugged and compact. They are capable of delivering high pressure, high volume, can operate at high speed, and are very efficient. Because of the large number of closely fitted parts, wear is an extremely important consideration, and the fluid used must be kept clean and must have good lubricating properties. Generally, radial piston pumps have an odd number of pistons. They may be given a variable delivery feature by making it possible to adjust the eccentricity of the rotor to the circular housing, either manually or by using a governor. The movement of the pistons is driven by the rotating cylinder mounted eccentrically within the circular housing.

Axial Piston Pumps

Axial piston pumps, Fig. 21-20, exhibit the same characteristics as the radial piston pump. However, instead of the pistons being mounted at right angles to the driven shaft, they are parallel to it. Variable delivery is provided by making it possible to alter the angle of the cylinder block to the driving member during operation. Either manual or governor controls may be used.

Combination Pumps

Many hydraulic installations require two or more distinct functions of the hydraulic fluid. Multi-stage pumps provide fluid at more than one pressure. For example, a machine requires rapid movement to engage the work than a slow, high-pressure work force. It uses large-volume, low-pressure flow for rapid travel and low-volume, high-pressure flow for the work force. A combination pump can provide the two pressures required in this instance.

Combination pumps may also be used where pressure higher than that available from a single pump is required. Two single pumps operating in series will satisfy this requirement. This combination will also deliver a greater volume of fluid.

A duplex system consists of two pumps mounted on the same shaft with a common reservoir, Fig. 21-21. Each is provided separate delivery and input lines. Combination pumps are found in many hydraulic transmissions.

Two-stage pumps are similar to combination pumps: one stage provides high-volume, low-pressure fluid to a second stage which delivers a somewhat lower volume at higher pressure.

Rating Methods

Pumps are usually rated in terms of volumetric output and flow in gallons per minute at a designated driveshaft speed. Other terms may be used: delivery rate, capacity, or pump size. On industrial machinery where hydraulic pumps are usually direct-driven by electric motors, the designated pump speed is typically the same as the motor speed. SAE ratings used

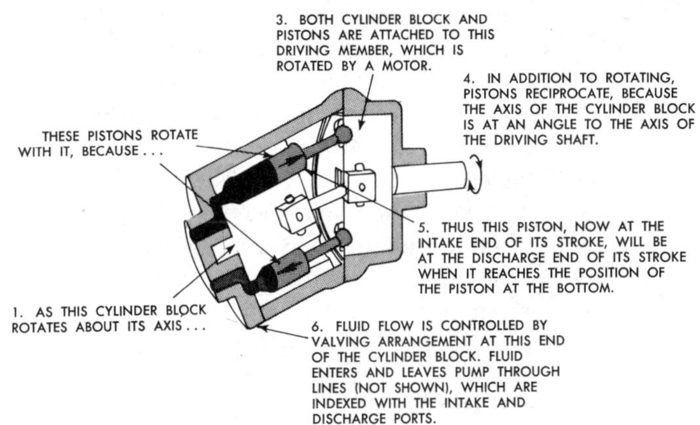

Fig. 21-20. Axial Piston Pump

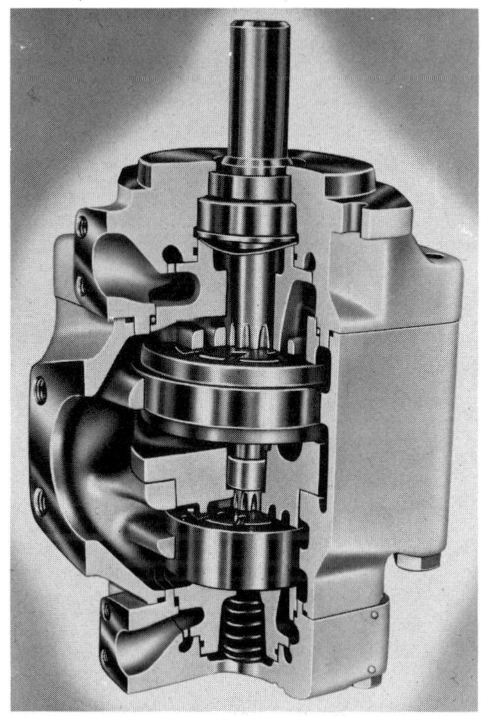

Fig. 21-21. Duplex Vane Pump (Denison)

in mobile applications are designated at 1200 rpm and 100 PSI.

Hydraulic pumps and other systems subject to varying drive speeds are sometimes rated in terms of displacement. Pump displacement is the amount of fluid delivered per stroke, revolution, or cycle. Rotary pump displacement is expressed in cubic inches per revolution. Due to the clearances necessary in all moving mechanisms, there is a certain amount of internal leakage. As the pressure differential from inlet to outlet increases, the volume decreases due to this internal leakage. A pump's volumetric efficiency, therefore, is expressed as a ratio of actual output to the theoretical output at rated speed and pressure. Most new pumps have volumetric efficiency exceeding 90%. Excessive speeds and pressures or fluid contaminants can greatly reduce this figure; however, if reasonably operated and properly maintained, these hydraulic systems can provide long and satisfactory service.

Air Compressors

Compressors are used in pneumatic systems as power sources and must satisfy requirements similar to those demanded of pumps in hydraulic systems.

Fig. 21-22. Single-Stage, Two-Cylinder Air Compressor (Zefex)

Compressor Classifications

Air compressors may be single-acting, double-acting, single-stage or multi-stage, horizontal or vertical. In general, compressors are described by the type of compressing element, the source of driving power, the method by which the driving unit is connected to the compressor, and by the pressure developed.

Compression Elements

Air compressing elements may be centrifugal, rotary, or reciprocating. In the reciprocating compressor, the air is compressed in one or more cylinders very much like the compression that takes place in the internal combustion engine, Fig. 21-22.

Compressors and hydraulic pumps are driven by electric motors, internal combustion engines, steam turbines, reciprocating steam engines, and hydraulic motors.

Drive Connections

The air compressor may be directly connected to the power source by a flexible coupling which joins the driven to the driving shaft. In a few installations, a rigid coupling is used between the two units. Obviously, the speed of the driven shaft and the speed of the driver are the same; therefore, the prime mover's speed must be compatible with the pump's operating speed.

Whenever it is necessary to adjust the speed of a pump in relation to the speed of the driver, a gear or belt transmission may be used that exhibits the proper speed ratio. Most often V-belting systems are preferred over gear reduction systems because they tend to minimize vibration. Vibration may be prohibitive if both the air compressor pump and the prime mover are of the reciprocating variety.

Sometimes, if the prime mover is a turbine, the compressor may be driven through the employment of a reduction gear system.

Pressure Classification

Low-pressure compressors produce 150 PSI or less, medium 151 to 1,000 PSI, and high-pressure systems provide 1,000 PSI or higher.

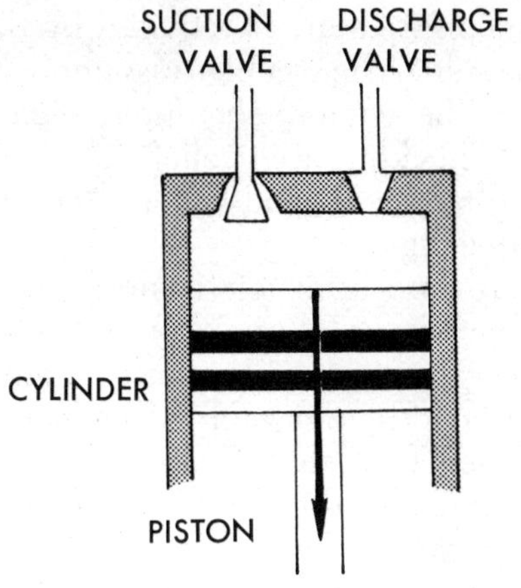

A. Vertical Compressor

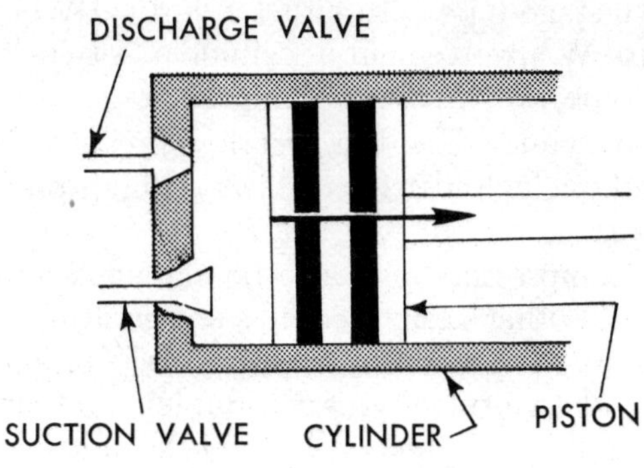

B. Horizontal Compressor

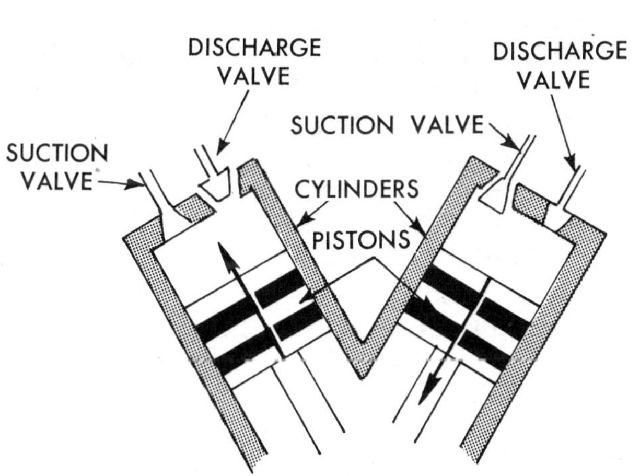

C. Angle Compressor

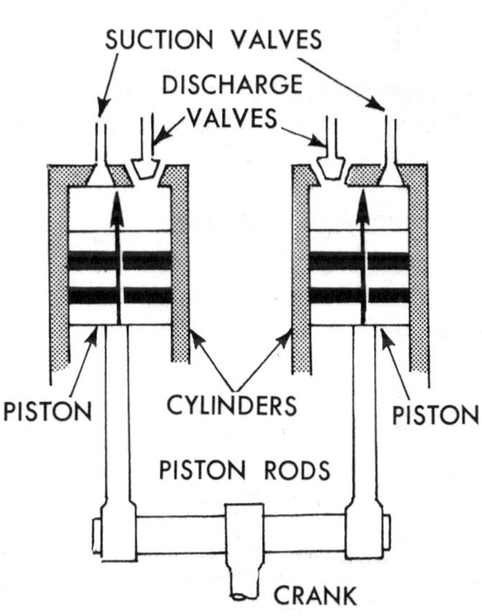

D. Duplex Compressor

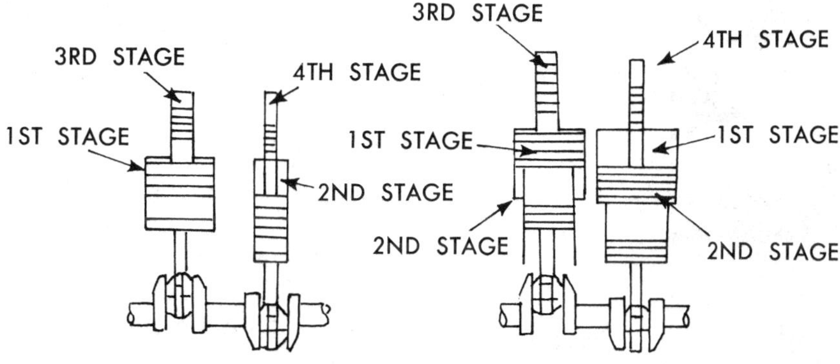

E. Multi-Stage Compressor

Fig. 21-23. Types of Air Compressors

Most low-pressure air compressors are of the two-stage type with either a vertical V or vertical W arrangement of cylinders. A two-stage, V-type, low-pressure compressor usually has one cylinder for the first low-pressure stage and one cylinder for the second high-pressure stage.

Compressors may also be classified according to other design features or operating characteristics. Medium-pressure air compressors are of two-stage, vertical, duplex, and single-acting types. See Figs. 21-23 and 21-24. Medium-pressure compressors often use a differential piston that has more than one stage of compression on each piston. Modern industrial air compressors are generally motor-driven, liquid-cooled, four-stage, single-acting units with vertical or horizontal cylinders. High-pressure air compressors range from three-stage compressors to six-stage compressors.

Reciprocating Air Compressor

Reciprocating air compressors are usually similar in design and operation. The assembly includes all the associated equipment necessary for delivering filtered, oil- and moisture-free compressed air, as required by the pneumatic system. The complete assembly normally includes the compressor, filter, separator assembly, an adjustable relief valve assembly, a control system, and an air receiver with pressure gauge.

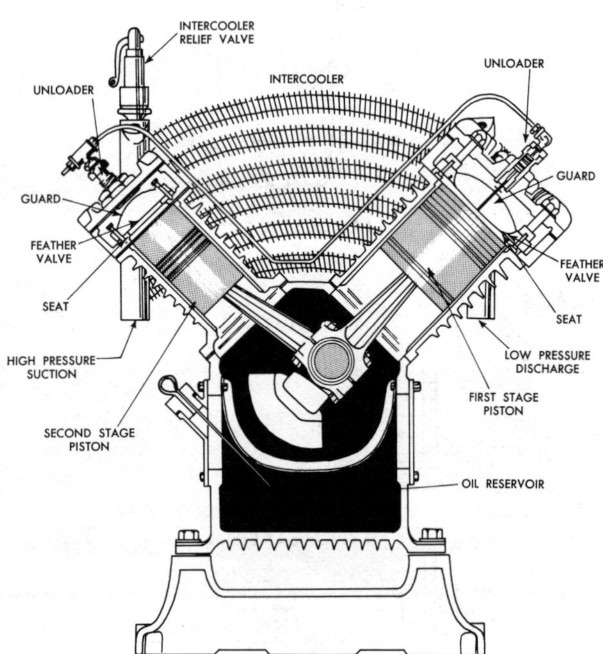

Fig. 21-24. A Simple Two-Stage Reciprocating Low-Pressure Air Compressor

The reciprocating air compressor is much the same as an internal combustion engine. The reciprocating pistons are connected to and actuated by a master rod assembly which is attached to a shaft coupled to the power source. Intake and exhaust valves are made of hardened steel, carefully ground and lapped to seat snugly against a shoulder at the end of the cylinder bore. These are held to the seat by tempered steel springs. At top dead center, both valves are seated and as the piston moves downward a partial vacuum is created within the chamber. The intake valve opens and atmospheric pressure forces the air into the cylinder chamber. As the piston travels upward, the intake valve closes. The air is then compressed until it overcomes the spring tension on the exhaust valve, which lifts and forces the compressed air into the delivery tubes, through the filter and separator, and out to the air receiver. In a multi-stage pump, air moves through the interstage tubing to the intake of the second piston where it is compressed, forced out into the interstage tubing to the third piston, and so on. In this instance, the air is raised to its ultimate delivery pressure in the last compression stage.

Compressor Lubrication

Unlike hydraulic pumps which are lubricated by the fluid of the system passing through the moving parts, the pneumatic compressor requires a lubrication system. Most compressors are lubricated by a simple but effective combination of pressure, splash, and mist. The lubrication is similar to the internal combustion engine. The only difference would be in the employment of an oil level gauge instead of a dip stick. This sight gauge may be mounted on the outside of the base.

Cooling

Low-pressure air compressors are cooled much the same way as air-cooled internal combustion engines. The compressed air is elevated in temperature because mechanical energy is invested in it and changed into heat energy. This heat energy must be dissipated before the temperature reaches a troublesome level. This is accomplished by using materials that radiate heat easily. In addition, integral cooling fins and a fan may be employed to move air past the cylinders and over the stage tubing. This type of cooling is usually sufficient for most low-pressure air compressors that are operated in well-ventilated spaces.

Most high-pressure and medium-pressure compressors are cooled by water much in the same way as the internal combustion engine is cooled in an automobile. The water is contained within a water jacket located around the cylinder and circulated to a radiator that is either exposed to the ambient air or located in cooling water. A water pump is required to circulate the water. In some systems an oil cooler is incorporated in the cooling system. Valves are usually provided so that the water to the oil cooler can be controlled independently of the rest of the system; thus oil as well as compressed gas temperature may be controlled efficiently. Compressors located outside larger machinery spaces are generally equipped with water-cooled systems. High-pressure air compressors require from six to 25 gallons of cooling water per minute while medium-pressure air compressors may require 10 to 20 gallons per minute.

In marine applications, sea water is used as the cooling agent, requiring that all parts of the circulating system be made of corrosion-resistant materials. The cylinder heads are made of gun metal or valve bronze composition, and water jackets are cast integrally with the cylinders. Each cylinder is then fitted with a liner of special cast iron or steel to withstand the wear of the piston. In these systems, intercoolers and aftercoolers remove the heat generated during compression.

Automatic temperature shutdown devices are fitted on all modern high-pressure air compressors. Thus, if the cooling water temperature rises above a safe limit, the compressor will stop and will not restart automatically. In addition, some compressors are fitted with a device that shuts down the compressor if the temperature of the air leaving the compressor exceeds a certain value.

Control Devices

The rate of energy transmission must be controlled in order to be most effective. Control devices in fluid power are called *valves*, and they provide both discontinuous and continuous control. Their principles of operation and design are similar for both hydraulic and pneumatic applications.

Introduction to Valves

A valve permits, stops, or regulates fluid flow by means of a movable part which opens or obstructs passage. Valves are used to control the flow of fluid, the pressure of the fluid, or the direction of fluid flow. They may be controlled manually, electrically, pneumatically, mechanically, hydraulically, or by a combination of two or more of these methods. Fluid pressure and flow must be controlled accurately. Usually no seals are used between the valving element and the valve seat since fluid leakage is negligible when precision-machined surfaces are mated. Seals are required, however, around valve stems, between lands of spool valves, etc. Oxidation particles or contaminants such as dust, dirt, and lint may raise havoc with precision valves, causing them to stick, plugging small orifices, or abrading valve surfaces which ultimately results in leakage or the valve sticking. Contamination of the fluid can result in inefficient operation or complete stoppage of equipment.

Classification of Valves

Most valves are variations of three fundamental classes: flow control, pressure control, and directional control.

Flow control valves are used in fluid power circuits to open or close a line to flow or to control the rate of flow. They are used sometimes to provide discontinuous control or to provide an on or off condition. Other times they are used to provide continuous control. They can provide control over a range or continuum – any degree of flow from zero to maximum.

Pressure control valves include safety valves. Their purpose is to limit the system pressure to protect the operator and the system components. At times they are used to control the sequence of operation of certain components within a system.

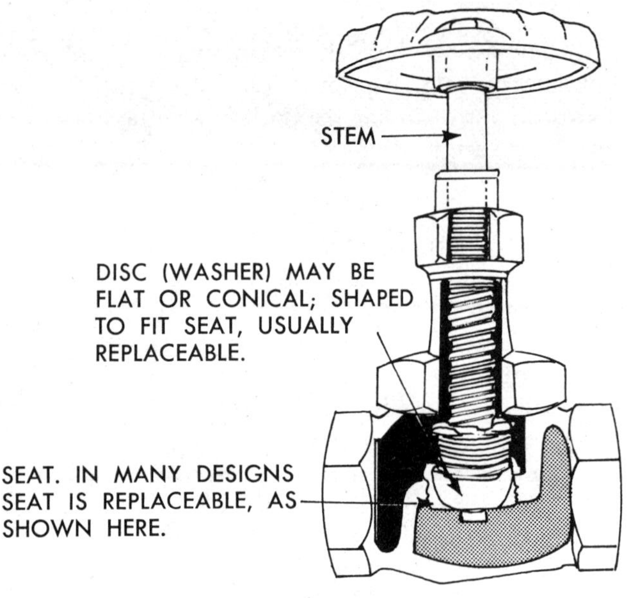

Fig. 21-25. Globe Valve in Closed Position

Directional control valves are used to control the paths of fluid to various components. They are primarily used to control direction of rotation of fluid motors and the direction of movement of actuators.

Flow Control Valves

Cock valves are simple valves, usually of small size. They are often used as bleed valves or small drain valves. Sometimes they are used to turn gauges on and off.

Globe valves are very simple in design and very reliable. They should be used fully open or fully closed, as leaks along the stem are more likely to occur in an intermediate position, Fig. 21-25. Particles of dirt on the seat or on the washer can cause leakage, but this will not seriously hamper the operation of the valve. Globe valves, because of their design, offer some resistance to fluid flow and may cause turbulence in the fluid.

Gate valves have several advantages over globe valves. At full open position, they offer no resistance to fluid flow. They are easily controlled with automatic mechanisms. See Fig. 21-26. Serious wear may occur when the valve is opened partially, as fluid flowing past the valve parts tends to erode them. Particles of dirt can interfere with the movement of the

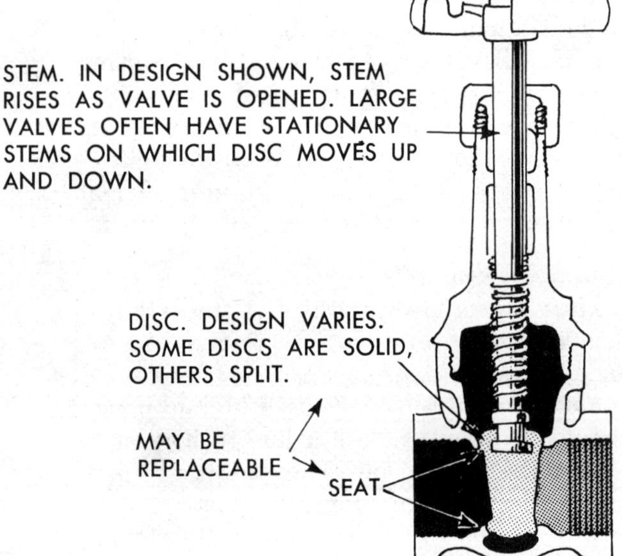

Fig. 21-26. Gate Valve in Closed Position

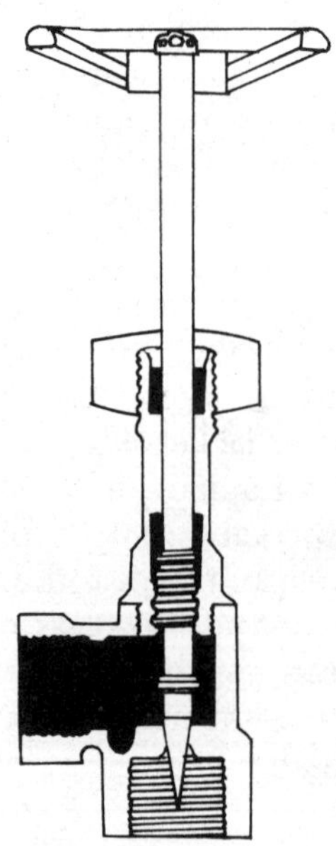

Fig. 21-27. Needle Valve in Closed Position

gate. The gate of the valve may be a solid wedge or a two-piece disk with an eccentric action, so that tightening the valve stem spreads the disks apart for a tighter fit on the seat.

Needle valves are mainly used to control fluid flow precisely. They can be used at any position from fully opened to fully closed, Fig. 21-27. They are usually manually operated. Their basic design makes it almost impossible to make an abrupt change in the rate of flow; therefore they are used in systems containing extremely sensitive components. As with other valves, dirt will easily interfere with the action.

Pressure Control Valves

Relief valves provide protection against overloading of circuit components or limit the force or torque which can be exerted by a hydraulic cylinder or motor. Relief valves are required in practically all power systems except where the compensator of a variable delivery pump is capable of providing the same function. Relief valves have been previously studied as a topic under steam boilers. Those relief valves were permitted to blow off to the atmosphere; however, hydraulic relief valves return the fluid to the reservoir.

The relief valve is installed with one port connected to the pressure line and the other to the reservoir, Fig. 21-28. Spring force is used to hold the ball on its seat, and the operating pressure can be changed by turning the adjusting screw which affects the tension on the ball. When the pressure at the inlet exceeds the spring force, the ball is forced off its seat and the fluid flows from the pressure line through the valve back to the reservoir. When the pressure drops below the valve setting, the ball reseats and closes the valve. The pressure at which the valve first begins to pass fluid is called the "cracking pressure." As the flow through the valve increases, the ball is pushed further and further off the seat. Full-flow pressure must be higher than cracking pressure because of this spring rate. The condition is referred to as *pressure override*. The relatively high override pressure of simple relief valves limits their use in many applications.

In a compound relief valve, line pressure and a relatively light spring combine to hold the piston in a closed position at pressure less than the valve setting. The setting of the poppet and adjustable spring limits the pressure acting to hold the valve closed. Pressure at the valve inlet under the piston can increase only slightly before overcoming spring tension, lifting the piston off its seat to permit flow to the reservoir and prevent further pressure increase. Increasing flow is permitted through this type of valve with only additional compression of the low-rate spring, and override is negligible. This method is usually used to unload the pump during periods of idleness.

Pressure-Reducing Valves

A pressure-reducing valve is used to limit the pressure in one part of the circuit to a value below the operating pressure required in the circuit. A relief valve used for this purpose would prevent further pressure buildup in the entire system. A pressure-reducing valve is normally open. Pressure vents from its outlet low-pressure port tends to close it as the valve setting is reached. Pressure above

Fig. 21-28. Relief Valve (Vickers)

and below a valve spool is equalized through a passage and the valve is held open by the force of a light spring. Pressure above the spool is limited by a poppet and spring. Pressure at the outlet port of the poppet setting forces the spool upwards, restricting flow through the valve to the extent necessary to prevent further buildup.

Unloading Valve

An unloading valve is designed for rapid discharge of fluid at near atmospheric pressure after permitting a buildup of pressure to a preset value. Generally it is used in high-volume or low-volume pump combinations where it is desirable to unload the delivery of the high-volume pump during the low-volume, high-pressure phase of a cycle. The unloading valve permits use of a small drive motor and prevents horsepower load by returning large volume pump delivery to tank at little or no pressure drop. Until pressure from a remote source acts on the bottom of the piston and overcomes the spring force (valve setting), flow from the primary port to the secondary port is blocked. When the spring force is overcome, the spool is then raised and the fluid passes freely through the secondary port to the tank, as long as the remote pressure is sufficient to fully open the valve. Often this type of valve is used to provide a second path for discharging from the large volume end of a double-acting cylinder on its return stroke. A balanced piston unloading valve is frequently used in circuits incorporating an accumulator. In this instance, the valve serves as a pressure regulator by automatically diverting pump flow to the reservoir at low pressure when the accumulator reaches its maximum pressure charge, and cutting it back into the system when the pressure drops to a predetermined minimum.

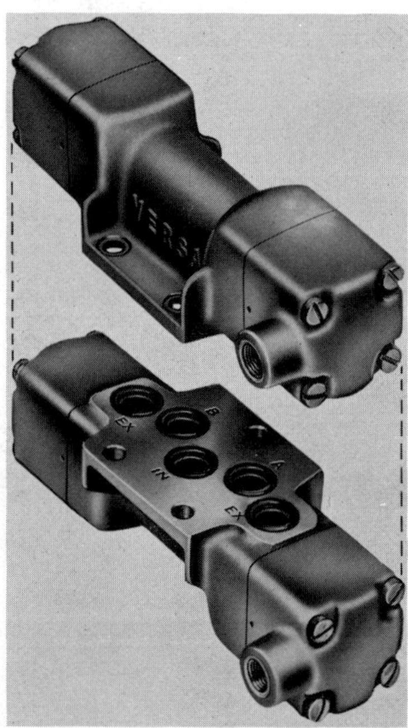

Fig. 21-29. Mirror Image of Four-Way, Pilot-Operated Valve (Versa)

If a valve is pilot-operated, bringing oil into the end will allow it to serve as a sequence valve.

Counterbalance Valve

The counterbalance valve is sometimes referred to as a "foot valve" and, as the name implies, it is used to support weight or prevent uncontrolled load drop. Installed in an outlet line, the counterbalance valve serves as a hydraulic resistance to a cylinder or motor. It is most often used in vertical applications where it is set to open at a pressure slightly higher than that generated by the load. Thus an additional force is required to cause the valve to open and permit the load to be lowered. Counterweights may be required where leakage of fluid past the cylinder seal, or valve spool would permit gradual settling over extended periods.

Sequence Valve

Where it is necessary to have one operation occur after another or to maintain a predetermined minimum pressure in a portion of a circuit, a sequence valve is often used. Similar to an unloading valve or a counterbalance valve in construction, a spring-loaded spool prevents flow to the secondary port until internal pressure opposing the spring setting causes it to open, Fig. 21-29. Where unintended pressure buildup might cause premature flow to the secondary operation, these valves can be controlled through a pilot, permitting sequence to be determined by the position of the primary cylinder, as well as the pressure.

Directional Control Valves

Directional control valves may be operated by employing differential pressure on the opposite sides of the valving element. They may also be operated manually, mechanically, or electrically. Often two or more methods of operating the same valve will be used in different phases of an operation.

Rotary Valves

Rotary valves are often operated by a lever or knob which is connected to the core which turns within a sleeve. The passages or recesses in the core connect or disconnect the passages in the sleeve, Fig. 21-30.

Although they are used by themselves, rotary valves are most often used as pilot valves to control the movement of spool valves. By adding extra ports and passages, it is possible to control the flow through several lines with one rotary valve. Rotary valves are capable of handling a wide range of pressures and will operate efficiently in the presence of relatively high amounts of dirt and sludge.

Poppet Valves

A poppet valve is usually spring-loaded. It is any valve which is opened either hydraulically or manually and in which flow of the fluid is past the sealing member through the seat of the valve. One type of poppet valve is used in the reciprocating internal combustion engine. Refer to Fig. 8-30. Another type of poppet valve is the spring-loaded ball valve. Poppet valves are becoming popular in farm and industrial equipment applications. They have an advantage over spool valves because they permit no leakage past their internal members and there is no consequent cylinder settling. A disadvantage of directional poppet valves is that it is difficult to obtain as fine a metering action as is possible with spool valves, and it is hard to obtain the shock-lessening, feathering action possible with spool valves.

The operating principle of a cone poppet valve is simple, Fig. 21-31. The cams, which are usually operated mechanically or manu-

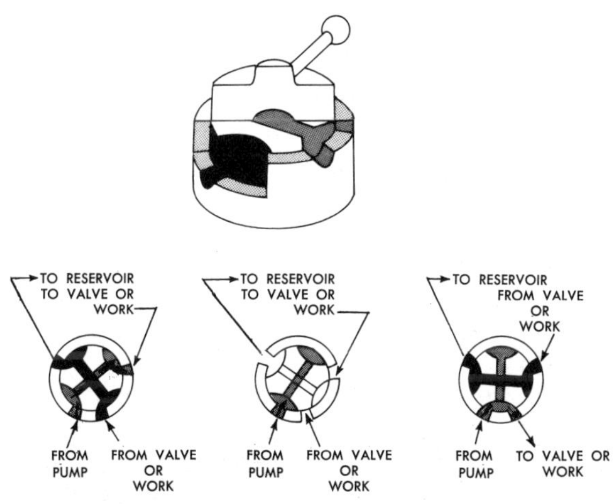

Fig. 21-30. Rotary Valve

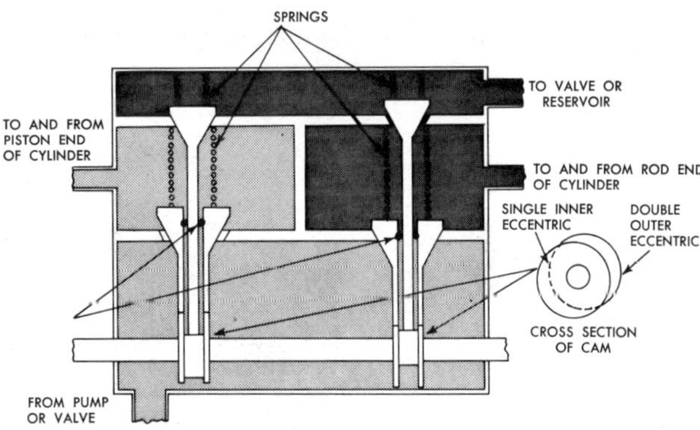

A. Cone Poppet Valve

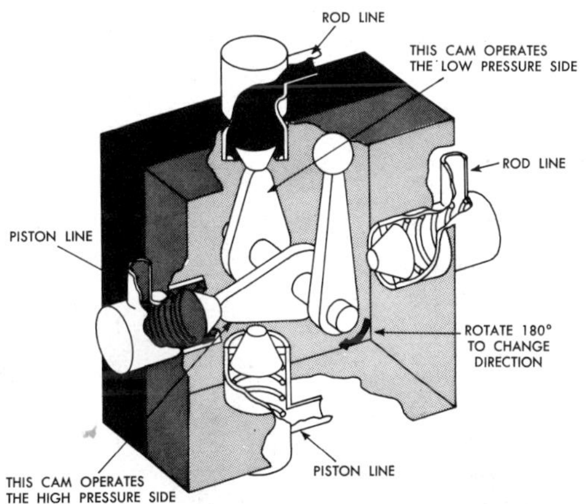

B. Mushroom Poppet Valve

Fig. 21-31. Poppet Valves

ally, are turned to open one high pressure valve and one return valve. When cylinder movement in the other direction is desired, the cam is turned so that the other two valves in the block are open. The operating principle of the mushroom poppet valve has been previously discussed, Fig. 21-31. It depends on the cam overcoming the spring pressure which holds the valve seated. This allows the fluid to flow as directed by the two open valves. To reverse the flow, the cam shaft is turned until the other two valves are opened.

Fig. 21-32. Flow Control and Check Valve (Vickers)

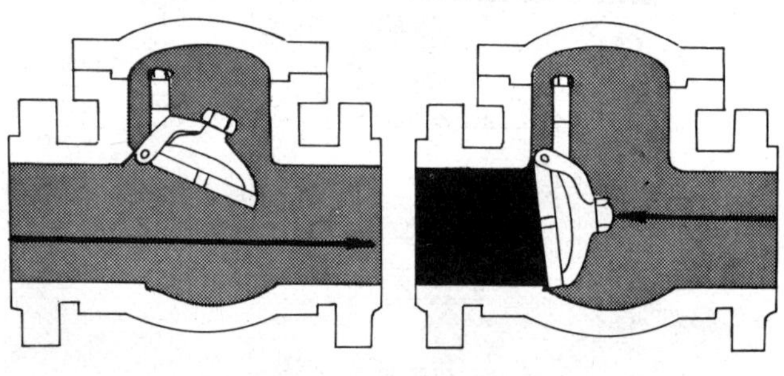

Fig. 21-33. Action of a Flapper Valve

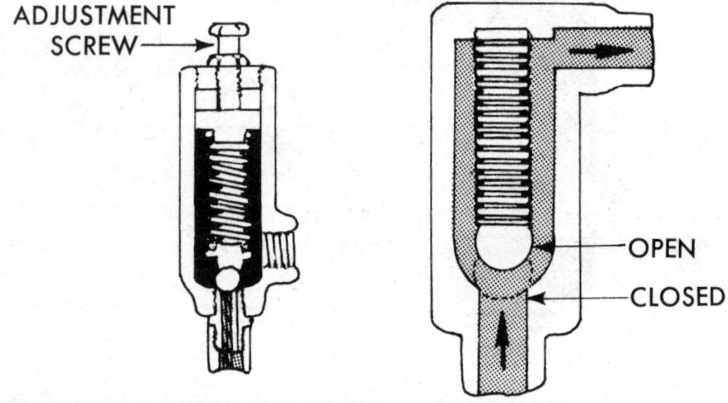

Fig. 21-34. Two Designs of the Ball Valve Principle

Check Valves

Check valves permit the flow of fluid in one direction while restricting it in the other, Fig. 21-32. Check valves serve the same function as rectifiers in electronics and a ratchet and pawl in mechanical transmission systems. They are the most widely used valve in fluid power systems. They may be installed independently in a line or incorporated as an integral part of some other valve, for example, a sequence or equalizing valve.

Flapper Valves

Flapper valves are essentially check valves, permitting flow in only one direction, Fig. 21-33. They are obtainable in all sizes. They offer very little resistance to fluid flow when fully opened. Most often they are installed so that gravity or reverse pressure closes them. They are sometimes equipped with a spring to start the flapper toward its closing position. Back pressure causes the flapper valve to seal tightly.

Ball Valves

Ball valves are often used as check valves. Their design and operation prevent their use in large sizes – anything above a one-inch ball is unusual, Fig. 21-34. They usually are spring loaded so that a certain predetermined pressure is required to open them. With an adaptation, the pressure range may be adjustable and the valve can be used as a pressure relief valve. Dirt can easily make the ball inefficient. Ball valves tend to chatter when operating, but this condition can be minimized by various modifications.

Shuttle Valves

Shuttle valves serve to isolate the main system from an alternate or emergency system. For example, in aircraft hydraulics the emergency source of pressure may be compressed air or nitrogen and usually this system is employed to get the vehicle on the ground safely.

The shuttle valve may be one of four types: sliding plunger, spring-loaded piston, spring-loaded poppet, and spring-loaded ball.

In normal operation the fluid has free flow from the normal system inlet port through the valve and out the outlet port to the actuating unit. The shuttle valve is held against the alternate system inlet port by a spring or the main system fluid pressure. When the alternate system is activated, fluid under pressure from the alternate system forces the shuttle to move away from the alternate inlet port to the main system inlet port. Fluid from the alternate system then has free flow to the unit outlet port, but is prevented from entering the main system by the shuttle.

Two- and Three-Way Valves

Two- and three-way valves control the functional flow of two or three ports, Fig. 21-35.

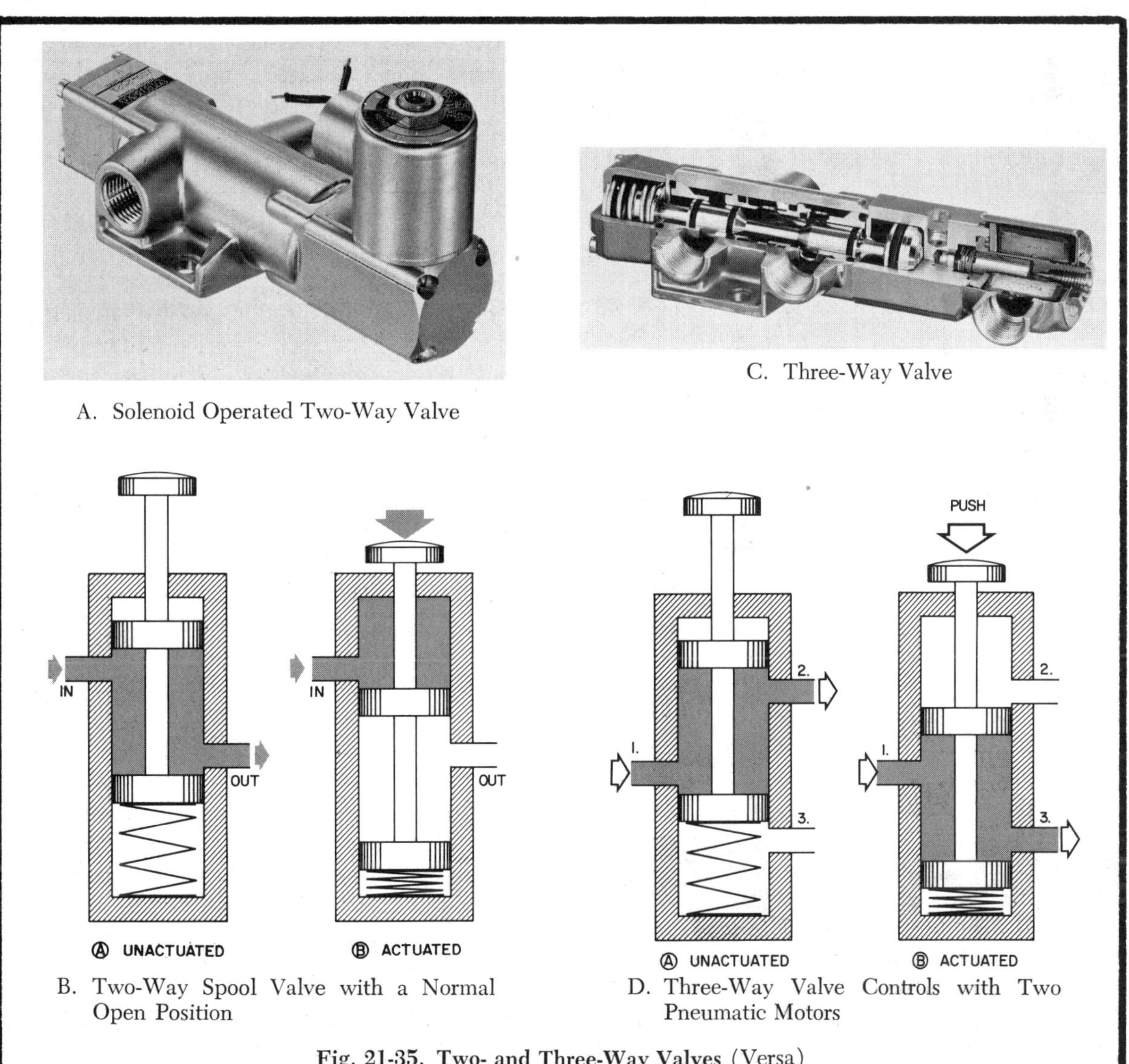

A. Solenoid Operated Two-Way Valve

C. Three-Way Valve

B. Two-Way Spool Valve with a Normal Open Position

D. Three-Way Valve Controls with Two Pneumatic Motors

Fig. 21-35. Two- and Three-Way Valves (Versa)

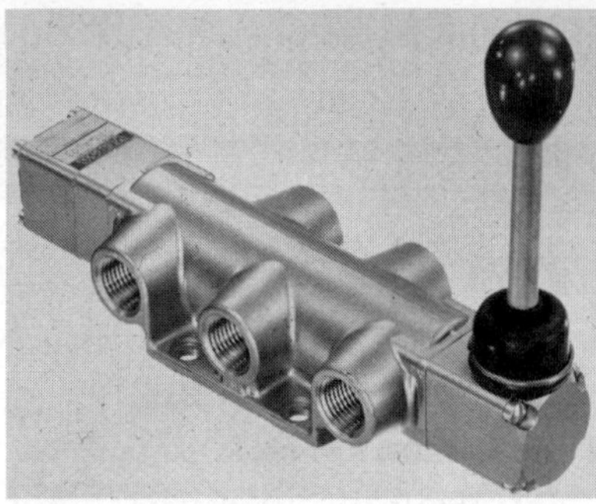

Fig. 21-36. Four-Way Valve (Versa)

These valves may use a poppet or spool as the controlling element. In the two-way sliding spool valve, the spool position allows or prevents fluid flow through the valve.

Three-way valves contain three ports: pressure, cylinder, and exhaust or return port. A pilot-operated, three-way poppet valve is often used in pneumatic systems. The valve is usually closed and is forced to open by fluid pressure entering the pilot chamber. The valve has two poppets connected by a common stem to each other. The movement of the poppet is controlled by differential pressure.

OPEN CENTER SPOOL VALVE
CLOSED CENTER SPOOL VALVE
FROM CYLINDER (CYLINDER FLOW SHUT OFF)
FROM PUMP
FROM PUMP
FROM CYLINDER
PUMP FLOW SHUT OFF
VALVED FLUID LINES CONNECTED HERE PROVIDE HYDRAULIC CONTROL OF VALVES
TO RESERVOIR
TO RESERVOIR
PUMP FLOW STRAIGHT THROUGH

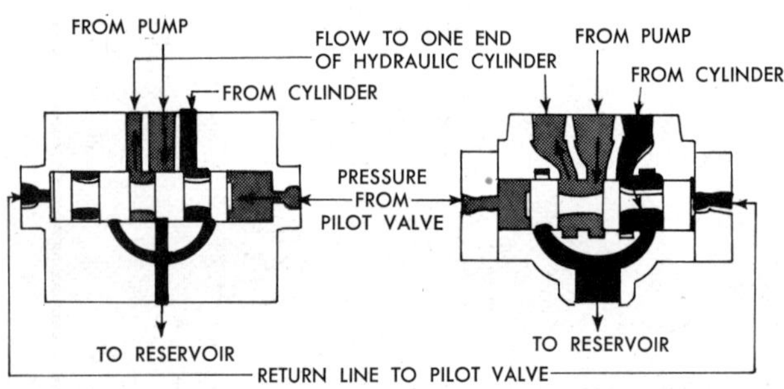

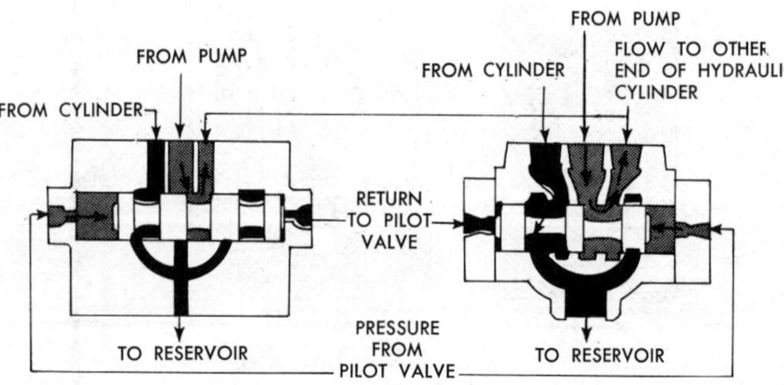

Fig. 21-37. Operating Principles of Center Spool Valves (International Harvester)

Four-Way Valves

Four-way valves usually contain four or five ports: one pressure, two cylinder and one or two ports to tank or reservoir. They are most common in hydraulic systems and can be pilot, mechanical, or solenoid operated, Fig. 21-36.

Spool Valves

Spool valves are used to control direction of flow, Fig. 21-37. They are popular in hydraulic equipment because of quick, positive action. They may be activated manually, electrically, or by using differential pressures. By an increase in the number of lands and additional appropriate ports, one spool valve can be made to handle flows in many directions. These valves can also be stacked so that supply ports of the added valves are in line with discharge ports of preceding valves. Grooves are often machined around the lands so that rings of fluid retained in the grooves will not only keep the spools centered, but will also provide lubrication.

All mating surfaces of spool valves must be accurately machined and fitted. Worn parts will cause leakage, and dirt within the fluid will cause erratic or sluggish action. If the valves are hydraulically or electrically operated, dirt and wear may upset delicate hydraulic balance and thus cause erratic action or perhaps render the system inoperative.

There are three basic types of spool valves: open center, tandem, and closed center. The difference in operation is simply that the fluid flow passes through the open center type in neutral position while the cylinder ports are blocked. In the closed center valve, the pump flow is blocked in the neutral position and the pump ports are open. In some designs, all three ports are blocked in neutral position.

Spool valves may have bored passages, slotted lands, or plain lands. The operating principles are basically the same, Figs. 21-38

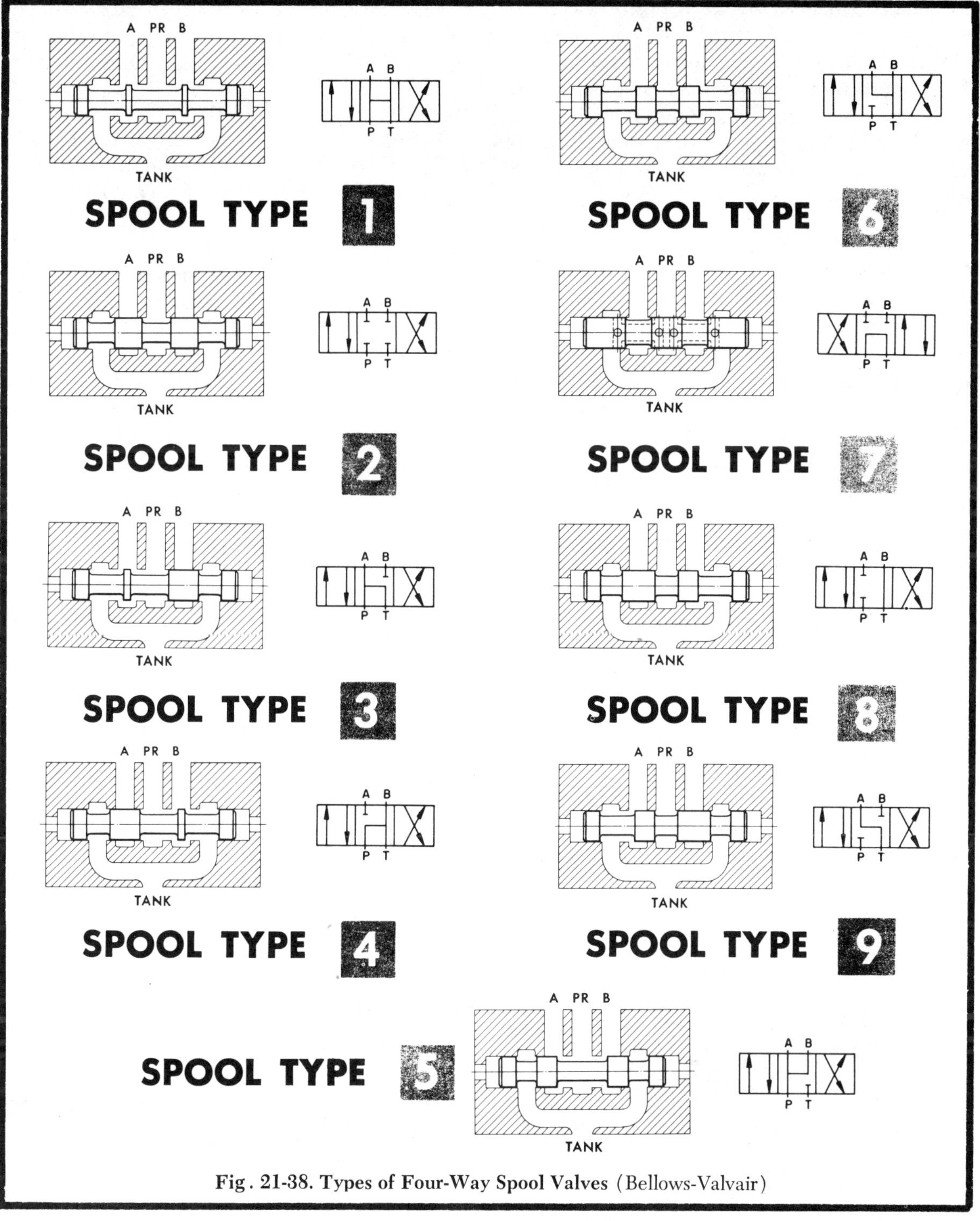

Fig. 21-38. Types of Four-Way Spool Valves (Bellows-Valvair)

and 21-39. Slotting or notching the lands in a spool valve is often used as a method of feathering the closing or opening of a valve to prevent fluid hammer and shock to the system.

Spool valves may be spring balanced or hydraulically balanced. Neutral position can be at either end or at center, and in some installations a detent mechanism is used to hold the spool in normal position. This mechanism holds the spool until its force is overcome, often by hydraulic pressure. The operator also can overcome this force by manipulating the controls manually.

Combination Valves

Spool valves may be stacked so that more than one operation is possible with one pump and reservoir. This configuration is especially suited to farm and industrial equipment. Other combinations are also common, such as a block with both pressure-regulating and check valves, or check valves and directional valves together. Valves often are incorporated into the body of a pump.

There are many combinations of valves, as many valve designs as there are manufacturers, and as many applications as there are fluid power devices. However, the operating principles of all of these valves are fundamentally the same.

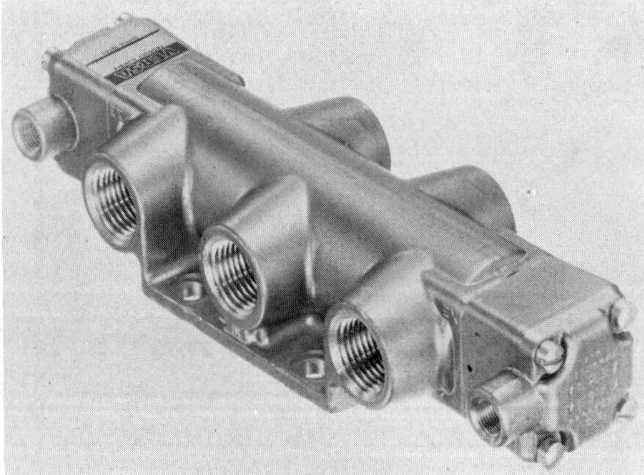

Fig. 21-39. Double-Pilot, Four-Way Valve

Restrictors

Restrictors, often called orifices, are placed in fluid lines to drop pressure and limit the flow of fluid. This slows the operation of actuating devices.

The similarity of a fixed restrictor (orifice) to that of a fixed resistor in electronics is apparent. Both devices serve the same function.

Measurement of Flow

In some fluid power systems it is necessary to know the rate of flow through the system in order to manage specific control devices properly and secure efficient operation of the system. Fluid components that measure rate of flow perform a function similar to ammeters in electronics.

Flowmeters are usually associated with systems in which fluids are consumed or delivered, such as gasoline, fuel oil, water, etc. They are sometimes required in fluid power systems. A fluid meter is made to measure a fluid of a particular specific gravity and characteristics, and must only be used for the purpose for which made. There are several types of popular flowmeters.

Piston Disk Flowmeters

In the piston disk flowmeter, the fluid passes through a volume-measuring chamber divided into upper and lower compartments by a disk, Fig. 21-40. During operation, one or the other compartment is being filled while the other is being emptied. As the fluid passes through these compartments, the disk rolls around in the chamber. This in turn revolves the indicating register of the meter by a shaft with suitable reduction gearing. Meters of this type are suitable for temperatures to 200°F and pressures to 150 PSI. Models are available for higher pressures and temperature; they are accurate to about 1% or less.

Propeller Flowmeters

The propeller flowmeter has a propeller located in the line of fluid flow, connected by suitable gearing to an indicator or counter, Fig. 21-41. The propeller rotates at a speed in proportion to the velocity of the fluid flowing through the line. The revolutions are registered through gearing to the counter and the rate of rotation can be interpreted into volume rate of flow. The accuracy of this meter depends on temperature and viscosity characteristics of the fluid.

Turbine Type Flowmeters

The turbine flowmeter is similar to the propeller flowmeter, Fig. 21-42. The fluid flows through a helical or spiral impeller causing the impeller to rotate proportionate to its rate of flow. The impeller is connected through suitable gearing to the counter. Like the propeller flowmeter the accuracy depends on temperature, pressure, and other characteristics of the fluid. Both the propeller and the turbine flowmeters are calibrated for a specific type of fluid by the manufacturer.

Rotameter

The rotameter is simply an upright glass tube through which the fluid flows. This tube is tapered, with the small end at the bottom. Inside a small metal rotor with vanes cut in its side and a central hole slides up and down on a guide rod. It is caused to spin as it slides up and down in the tube. Since the tube is tapered, the space between the rotor and the tube wall increases as the rotor rises, as it does when more fluid flows through the tube. Therefore, the rotor always rises to a height corresponding to a rate of flow. A scale on the tube is calibrated to indicate this rate of flow in a desired measurement – gallons per minute, gallons per hour, or pounds per hour.

Measurement of Pressure

In any fluid power system, a means must be provided for measuring the pressure within the system. In fluid power systems, the pressure is measured by various types of gauges.

Electrical circuitry is often introduced by using an analogy to a simple fluid system. The need to measure pressure is basic to both power systems to insure that the safe and proper investment of energy is efficiently being expended by the system to do work.

Pressure gauges are employed in fluid power systems so that the operator of the power equipment can maintain pressures at safe and efficient operating levels. Any excess or deficiency of pressure should be immediately investigated to correct the trouble. Pressure is generally measured in pounds per square inch and gauges are usually calibrated to register PSI. An absolute pressure gauge will show about 15 PSI when unconnected;

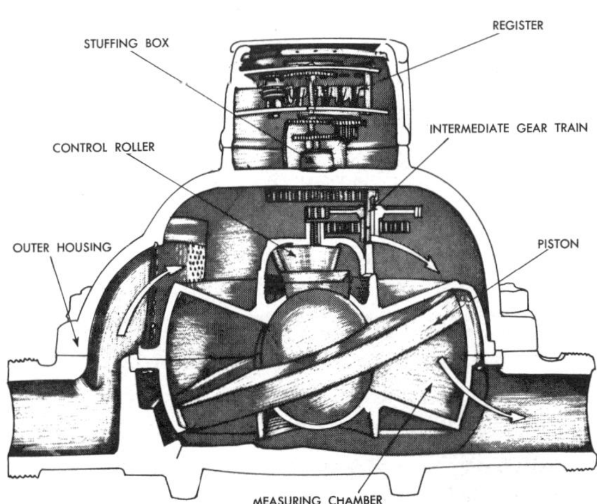

Fig. 21-40. Piston Disk Flowmeter

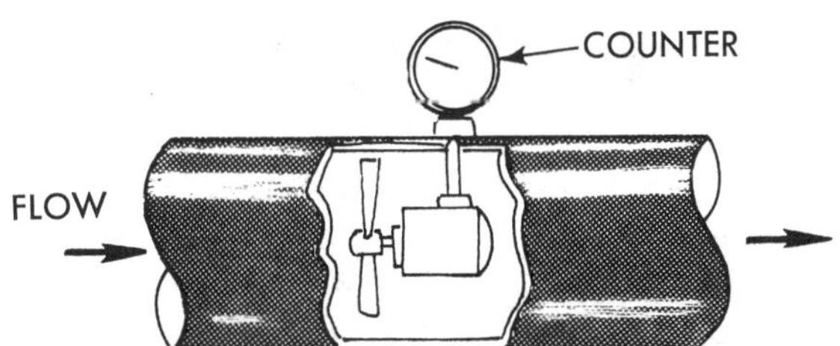

Fig. 21-41. Propeller Flowmeter

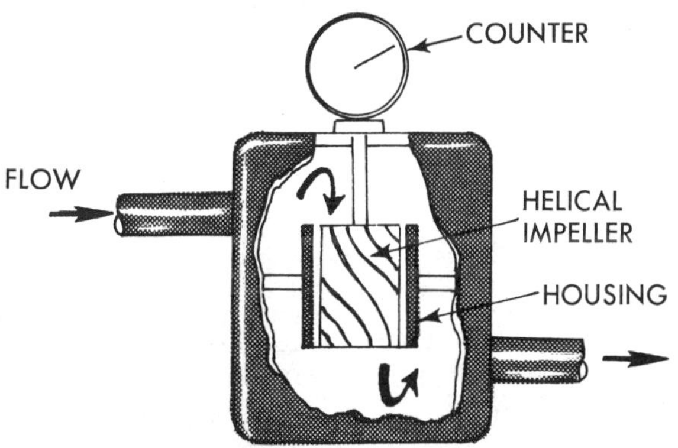

Fig. 21-42. Turbine Flowmeter

a regular gauge will indicate zero; and a compound gauge will indicate zero with scales in both directions.

Bourdon Tube Gauges

Bourdon tube gauges, Fig. 21-43, have been studied in the steam generating systems. Refer to Fig. 5-8. The indicating element of a Bourdon tube pressure gauge may be made in any one of a variety of shapes. The most common are the *C* tube, the spiral, and the helical. The movement of the pointer is directly proportionate to the distortion of the tube caused by the pressure of the fluid contained therein. As the pressure increases, the tube distorts, moving a rack and pinion and through mechanical leakage the pointer or recording device is moved proportionately.

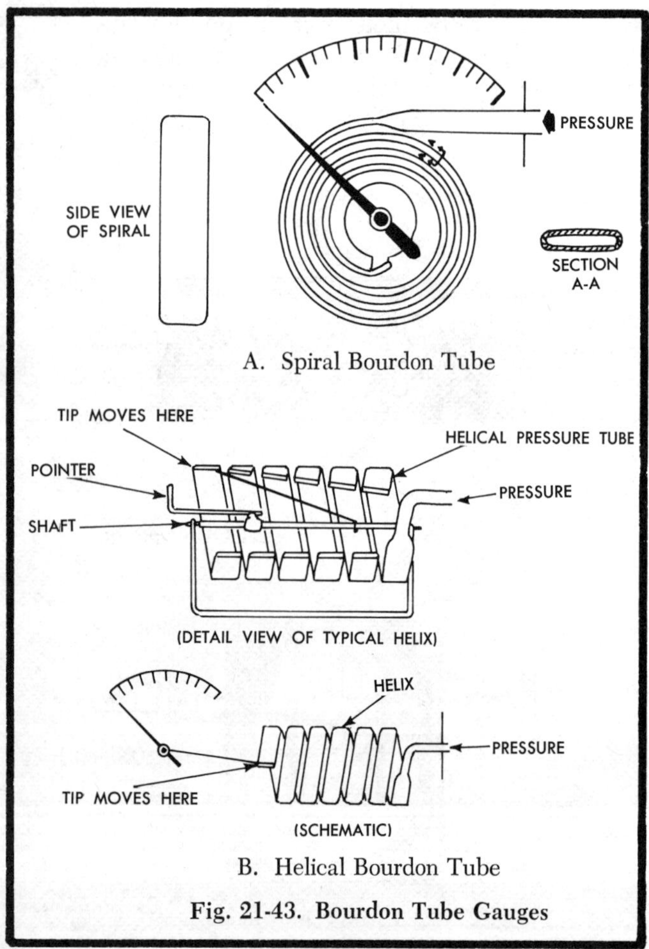

A. Spiral Bourdon Tube

B. Helical Bourdon Tube

Fig. 21-43. Bourdon Tube Gauges

Diaphragm Gauges

A diaphragm gauge gives sensitive and reliable indications of pressure, and it is often used to measure air pressure. This type of gauge is usually designed for a specific purpose and is calibrated accordingly. The mechanism of a diaphragm gauge consists of a tough, pliable leather or neophrene rubber membrane connected to a metal spring which is attached by a linkage to the gauge pointer. One side of the diaphragm is exposed to the pressure being measured; the other is exposed to the atmosphere. When no pressure is exerted against the diaphragm, both it and the metal spring attached are in neutral position and the gauge registers zero. When pressure is applied to the diaphragm, it moves the diaphragm upward and pushes this metal spring ahead. As the spring is pushed up, it moves the pointer proportionate to the pressure.

Spring-Loaded Pressure Gauges

Bourdon tube gauges are very delicate instruments; and in applications where pressure fluctuates rapidly, the gauge sometimes may cause trouble. For this reason, a spring-loaded direct-action gauge has become increasingly popular. In the spring-loaded gauge a piston is actuated by the pressure of the fluid. The piston moves up a cylinder against the resistance of a spring and carries a bar or indicator along a calibrated scale. In this manner gears, cams, and bearings are eliminated and a sturdy instrument is constructed.

Gauge Snubbers

The irregularity of impulses applied to a fluid power system by some pumps may cause the pressure gauge pointer to oscillate violently. This makes the gauge difficult to read, and also may affect the delicate internal mechanism. Therefore, a gauge snubber is usually installed in the fluid line to the pressure gauge. Its purpose is to dampen the oscillations and to provide a steady pressure for a steady gauge reading. The simple pressure gauge snubber consists of a two-port housing containing an orifice into which a floating plunger is inserted. The plunger tends to reduce the area of this orifice, thus increasing the dampening effect.

Actuators Convert Fluid Energy to Mechanical Energy

Hydraulic and pneumatic actuators convert fluid energy back to mechanical energy to perform work. One of the most outstanding features of a fluid power system is that force generated by the power supply, controlled and directed by suitable valving and transported by lines, can be converted to almost any kind of mechanical motion – easily and at the place it is needed. A linear actuator such as a ram or cylinder is used for such operations as clamping, pressing, traverse, and feed motions. Rotary actuators are usually used for chucking, indexing, and turning.

Cylinders

The cylinder and piston is the most popular method of turning fluid under pressure into a work force, Fig. 21-44. Cylinders may be classified into two general categories: single-acting, where the weight of the load returns the piston to its home position; and double-acting, where the piston moves under pressure in both directions.

The simple linear actuator, like the single-acting reciprocating steam engine, operates when a fluid under pressure is directed into the housing forcing the piston to move outward. Since there is no provision for retracting the rod hydraulically, the retracting force usually is gravity or some mechanical means such as a spring.

A double-acting cylinder is similar to the double-acting steam reciprocating engine. Fluids under pressure can be applied to both sides of the piston to control linear motion in two directions. This type is referred to as the "differential cylinder" because the piston area is larger opposite the connecting piston rod – providing a slower, more powerful work stroke when fluid is applied to that side. The return stroke is faster due to the smaller cross-sectional area resulting from the displacement of the piston rod. Reciprocating motions of this type are required on many machine tools such as the shaper.

Tandem Cylinders

Some fluid power systems require two or more independent systems such as the landing gear system on most airplanes and the brake system of most modern day automobiles. In these systems a tandem actuating cylinder and piston is used. A tandem piston and cylinder is defined as two or more, arranged one behind the other, but designed to function as a single unit. The pistons are connected to a single piston rod or shaft.

The fluid flow to and from the two chambers is provided by two independent fluid power systems and is controlled by two directional valves.

Piston Actuator Refinements

Reciprocating pistons and cylinders are available with a variety of refinements. Since pistons are often under heavy load and moving rapidly, a cushion for the end of the piston stroke is often provided by a boss on the piston which enters a bore in the end of the cylinder to shut off the normal discharge port. The remaining fluid is then forced through a smaller port which is often made adjustable by means of a ball or needle valve. The residual fluid serves to cushion the piston as it is compressed.

Another refinement includes a thermal safety valve (set far higher than the system pressure) to relieve any pressures caused by thermal expansion, while the system is at rest. A double wall cylinder can be used to provide fluid passages instead of using external

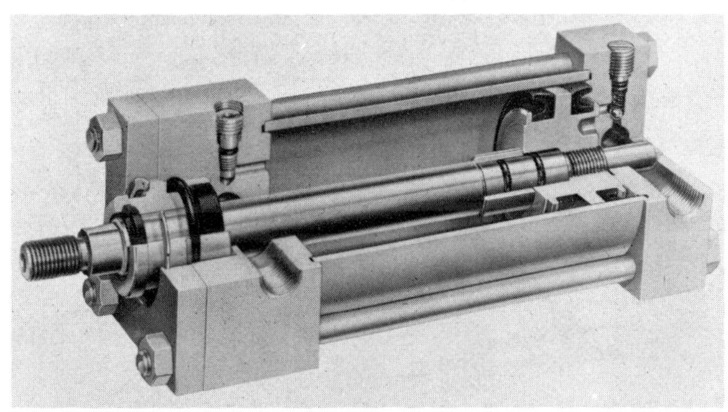

Fig. 21-44. Hydraulic Cylinder (Scovill)

hoses or tubings. This is found in many types of power steering applications such as trucks or marine installations. Still another refinement employs a stroke-control valve which is adjustable to stop the cylinder at any point in its travel by shutting off the flow of fluid to the cylinder or otherwise closing the valve.

A popular refinement is the telescopic piston. This piston acts as though it were one piece until the outer section reaches its stop, whereupon the inner section continues to the end of the stroke. It may be designed so that the inner section moves rapidly, followed by the outer section. The speeds of the various sections are dependent upon the square inches of pushing surface in each section.

Another feature is the variety of mounting styles which permits the actuators to be mounted close to the point of energy application. Other design features are possible: two pistons in one cylinder, internal stroke adjustments, speed variability, and many more.

Radial Piston Motor

The radial piston pump/motor is a popular multicylinder motor, Fig. 21-45. It provides increased and smoother power delivery by using the principles of power overlap: the very same principles that were employed in the design of multicylinder reciprocating engines.

The radial piston motor usually contains seven or nine pistons. In the radial piston pump the cylinder block is made to revolve and force the pistons in and out of the cylinders, causing each cylinder to take in fluid and force it out into the system. In the radial piston motor the reverse is true. Fluid under pressure forces the piston outward, and it pushes against the rotor causing the cylinder block to revolve. The rate at which the fluid flows into the cylinder determines the speed at which the cylinder block turns.

The radial piston unit is easy to transfer from motor to pump and vice versa.

Axial Piston Motor

The axial piston motor is identical to the constant displacement axial piston pump, and the principle of its operation is the reverse of the pump. See Fig. 21-11. Fluid from the system under pressure enters through one of the ports in the valve plate and then into the cylinder, forcing it to move outward, Fig. 21-46. Since the pistons are held by connecting rods at a fixed distance from the output shaft, they can move away from the valve plate only by moving in a rotary direction. The pistons move in this direction until they are completely extended. Therefore, driving the pis-

Fig. 21-45. Radial Piston Motor (Racine)

Fig. 21-46. Balanced Vane Motor (Racine)

tons axially causes them to rotate the shaft and cylinder block. While some are driving, the others are discharging flow from the outlet port.

This motor may be caused to rotate in either direction. Direction is controlled by the direction of fluid flow to the valve plate, and this flow may be instantly reversed, reversing the direction of the motor.

Gear Motors

In a gear motor, the fluid is forced against the gear with one gear connected to the output shaft. Operation is essentially the reverse of the gear pump. Fluid flows in both directions around the inside surface of the casing, forcing the gears to rotate. This rotary motion is made available to do work at the output shaft.

Balanced Vane Motors

The balanced vane motor employs fluid flow entering the inlet port to force the rotor and vane to rotate, leaving through the outlet port, Fig. 21-46. Reversing fluid flow reverses shaft rotation. Since no centrifugal force exists until the motor begins to rotate, some means must be provided to hold the vanes against the casing. Springs or rockets behind each vane are frequently used.

In a radial piston motor, fluid from the pump enters half of the cylinder block bores forcing the respective pistons radially from the cylinder block axis. These pistons move only by revolving the case; therefore driving the pistons radially causes the cylinder block and pistons to rotate. The cylinder block is connected to the output shaft. The same operating principle is used in the axial piston motor. Fluid enters half the cylinder bores and forces the pistons outward, causing them to rotate the cylinder block and output shaft. An axial piston motor is characterized by extremely low inertia, Fig. 21-47. It accelerates quickly and is well suited for quick reversal applications.

Modifications of the rotary motor are sometimes found in industrial machinery where special motions are required. One is the *limited rotation motor* which will not rotate continuously in either direction. The vane motor version has a movable vane which forms two chambers in an annulus. Pressure exerted against one side of the vane causes it to rotate and turn the motor and output shaft. Rotation is limited to less than full rotation by the width of the body segment containing inlet and outlet porting. Another version of the limited rotation motor is the piston type which converts the linear motion of the cylinder into semicircular motion through a crank arm.

Turbines

Another device for converting fluid power into rotary force and motion is the turbine. The turbine principles have been discussed previously under Steam and Air Stream Engines. Some of the most popular air turbines include the pinwheel turbine, the multi-stage turbine, and the single-stage turbine.

Pinwheel Turbines

The pinwheel turbine is a mechanical jet similar in principle to Hero's engine (aeolipile). Refer to Fig. 2-1. Compressed gas is led into a pinwheel hub through a hollow shaft, eventually passing through diametrically opposed nozzles where it is exhausted. The reaction to the exhaust causes rotation of the

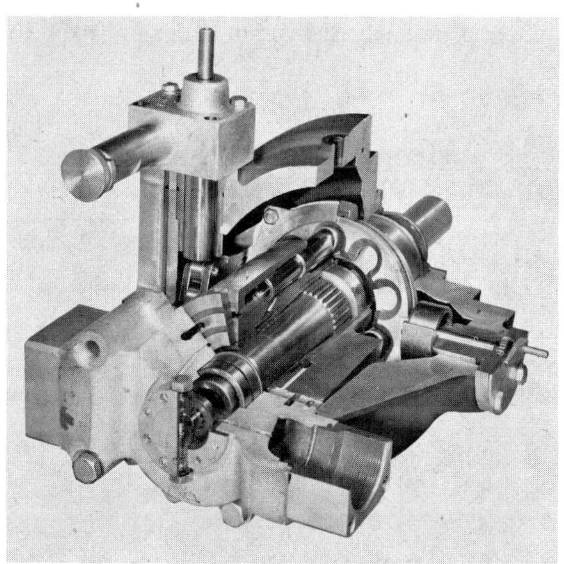

Fig. 21-47. Axial Piston Motor (Racine)

pinwheel. The amount of reaction is equal to the force of the escaping gas.

Multiple-Stage Turbines

In the multiple-stage turbine, the turbine wheel is a solid piece of steel having semicircular recesses or vanes in the surface of its circumference. Mounted on a casing around the wheel are four nozzles spaced 90° apart. Within the casing is a series of stationary semicircular reversing chambers. The pressurized gas is led through a manifold ring and passes through the nozzles, impinging at high velocity on the buckets. In passing through the buckets, the direction is reversed 180°. The gas is then caught by a semicircular reversing chamber in the casing where it is reversed again 180° and returned to another set of buckets on the wheel. The process is repeated five times through the 90° arc of the turbine housing, after which the gas is exhausted. Reversing the flow of gas several times gives a multiple-stage effect, thereby using more of the potential energy in the gas.

Single-Stage Turbines

In the single-stage turbine, the gas expelled through the nozzle is not reversed, but makes only one pass through the turbine. This is similar in operation to the Pelton or impulse wheel previously discussed. Refer to Fig. 1-16.

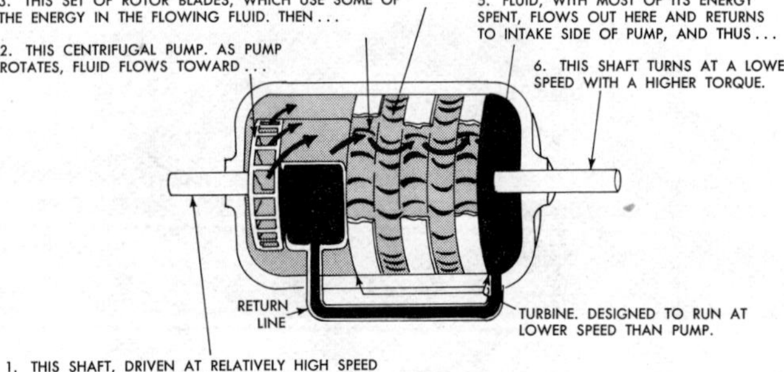

Fig. 21-48. Operating Principle of the Torque Converter

Movable Shutter Governor

The movable shutter governor is used to control the speed of the pinwheel turbine. It is mounted in the hub of the pinwheel, and the pressurized gas must pass through the jet of the governor before it passes through the jet nozzles. The governor consists of a shutter secured to a torsion bar. As the turbine rotates, centrifugal force causes the shutter to attempt to align itself to the plane of turbine rotation. The torsion bar restrains the shutter from blocking the outlet. As the turbine speed approaches the limit, the force on the shutter begins to overcome the resistance of the torsion bar, permitting the shutter to turn and partially block the outlet to maintain the speed by regulating the flow of gas to the turbine nozzles. If the speed decreases, the torsion bar overcomes the centrifugal force and the shutter moves counterclockwise to uncover the outlet. Thus the moving shutter governor continuously controls the turbine speed by monitoring the flow of gas to the nozzles.

Flyball Governor

The flyball governor has been previously discussed in the chapter on steam engines. Refer to Fig. 2-36. In both applications it monitors the amount of gas flowing through the inlet pipe to the engine or turbine.

Torque Converters

Steam and electric powered vehicles usually have the power plant either positively geared or direct connected to the driving wheels because these power plants are self-starting and are able to develop a starting torque several times their normal full load torque, Fig. 21-48. Internal combustion engines are not self-starting and their absolute maximum torque is not much greater than their normal full load torque. In addition, greater torque is required for rapid acceleration and to enable the vehicles to negotiate steep grades. To enable vehicles propelled by internal combustion engines to obtain this original torque, it is necessary to equip them with a drive of such design that the ratio between input torque, the engine, output torque, and the driving wheel can be changed while the vehicle is in motion. Presently, *transmission* is the term most commonly used to describe the system employed to convert the mechanical power generated by the prime mover and transmit it to the wheels. This power is made up of two factors – *torque and angular velocity.*

The chief function of the "transmission" device is to receive power at one torque and angular velocity and to deliver it at another torque and corresponding angular velocity. Early in the history of the automobile the term *change gear* was proposed, but it did not gain wide acceptance. In Europe the expression *gear set* was used. It, too, was not accepted by the industry. In England the term *torque converter* was first used after World War I to describe a mechanism for synchronizing machine guns firing through the propeller arcs of airplanes. This device permitted an infinite variation of torque and was based on the inertia principle. From this many people gained the impression that a torque converter must of necessity be complicated.

Any pair of gears with different numbers of teeth meshing together forms in essence a torque converter, for the output torque will be different from the input torque. The conventional automobile transmission consists of a number of gear trains, each capable of effecting a torque conversion and each able to be engaged at the will of the operator. In addition, one train of gears not only effects a quantitative change but also reverses direction. A truly descriptive term for what is called an automobile transmission would be a *variable ratio torque converter.* This term, however, is much too long and it is unlikely to find any degree of popularity.

From one point of view, the ideal transmission is the so-called infinitely variable gear in which the torque ratio can be varied continuously within wide limits because it permits operating the engine at all times under optimum conditions with respect to fuel consumption, wear and tear. In an ordinary gear transmission, only a small number of ratios or gear changes can be provided because it is necessary to avoid making the gear system too expensive and its operation too burdensome. The desirable number of gear changes depends upon the use to which the transmission system is to be put.

In the passenger cars of yesterday, transmission systems with two forward speeds were popular, but today this is inadequate for cars are expected to cover a speed range from 0 to over 100 miles per hour. Three is the minimum number acceptable in full size passenger cars with some cars today affording four-speed transmissions excluding reverse. The engine can be operated to better advantage with a four-speed transmission as then the overall reduction between engine and road wheels in high gear can be made smaller than with three-speed transmissions, with the result that the engine will make fewer revolutions per mile of travel, will consume less fuel, and be subject to less wear and tear. The three-forward-speed transmission systems have proven satisfactory to most American drivers, due to the fact that these cars are almost invariably powered by large engines. In European countries where cars for the general market must be powered conservatively because of high horsepower or engine displacement taxes, the lack of fuel and also its cost the great majority of automobiles are equipped with four-speed transmissions.

Variable Torque Load

In some applications of internal combustion engines, the torque load varies with the speed and is practically nothing when the engine starts from a standstill. This applies, for instance, when the engine is used to drive a propeller, either air or marine, a blower, or a centrifugal pump. No difficulty is experienced in starting an engine coupled directly to such a load, but in surface vehicles the torque load usually is quite high when the engine is started from rest. Some means must be provided to pick this load up gradually as otherwise the engine would stall. Usually the means employed is the friction clutch or the automatic hydraulic clutch, Fig. 21-49. The driver can increase the torque applied to the load gradually and keep it below the torque capacity of the engine so that the engine can continue to accelerate, or at least keep running.

With the friction clutch torque is applied to the load as soon as the friction surfaces of the clutch come in contact with each other. It increases with pressure between the friction surfaces, and when the applied torque becomes equal to the torque load, the vehicle starts to move. Slippage of the friction surfaces can continue for some time because the vehicle is just barely moving while the engine is turning over at a generally high rpm, sufficient to generate the necessary starting torque. As the vehicle accelerates, the slippage decreases with the final result of the clutch taking a firm hold with its driving and driven members rotating as a single unit. The manual clutch requires the operator to engage the clutch pedal. He determines the pressure between the friction surfaces. Clutches are needed in surface vehicles not only because the engine is unable to start satisfactorily under load, but also to provide a means to shift gears or engage jaw clutches while under load. Before a change in gear ratio can be undertaken, the friction clutch must be disengaged.

Modern automatic transmissi systems usually include a hydrodynamic torque converter or coupling which picks up the load gradually and does not require a friction clutch. These transmissions also include a

4. THIS DRIVEN MEMBER. HERE THE FLUID'S DIRECTION OF FLOW IS AGAIN CHANGED AND IT FLOWS BACK TO THE DRIVING MEMBER.

5. IN EFFECT, FLUID SWIRL THUS FORMED IS AN "ENDLESS CORKSCREW OF FLUID" THAT MOVES SIMULTANEOUSLY IN SEVERAL DIRECTIONS: IT SPINS AS SHOWN BY THE ARROWS AND ALSO ROTATES ABOUT THE AXIS OF THE COUPLING.

3. BUT THIS CURVATURE CAUSES FLUID TO MAKE A TURN AND FLOW TOWARD . . .

2. CENTRIFUGAL FORCE CAUSES FLUID TO FLOW TOWARD THE CIRCUMFERENCE AT RIGHT ANGLES TO THE AXIS OF ROTATION . . .

1. AS THIS DRIVING MEMBER ROTATES . . .

Fig. 21-49. Hydraulic Coupling

stepped gear transmission, and a friction clutch or its equivalent is required to make possible a smooth changeover from gear to gear. The planetary units usually employed in combination with hydrodynamic torque converters incorporate a friction clutch for the direct drive and friction bands for the other gears. Some of these automatic transmission systems have a main friction clutch to provide a direct drive and eliminate the slippage and power loss inherent in hydraulic couplings. Automatic transmission systems therefore may incorporate two, or even three, friction clutches.

Automatic Automobile Transmission

The high initial starting torque is provided by using the system's two gear trains for double-speed reduction, Fig. 21-50. As the vehicle accelerates, the system automatically shifts to second which puts the forward gear in direct drive while leaving the other gear in speed reduction. When the vehicle's speed permits, the transmission automatically shifts into third. This reverses the drives – the front gear is in speed reduction and the rear in direct drive. Because this ratio is lower than that of second gear, the output speed increases but with less torque. In overdrive or fourth gear, there is direct drive. The engine propeller shaft is directly connected to the pinion and ring gear in the rear axle. The ring and pinion is engaged at all times with a fixed speed ratio.

Fluid Lines and Fittings

A fluid power system depends on the various components being interconnected by lines to convey the fluid. Lines, pipes, tubings and hoses make up the circulatory system.

The proper selection and installation of these components is important in the operation of any fluid power system. Poorly selected components can result in a serious loss of power or harmful fluid contamination or loss. The lines and fittings of a fluid power system must meet several basic requirements:

1. The lines must be of sufficient strength to contain the fluid at the desired working pressure. This includes the surges of pressure

that may be expected to develop during normal operating cycles.

2. The lines must be of sufficient strength to support components mounted in or on them.

3. The lines must be capable of absorbing shock waves caused by surges of pressure and changes in the direction of fluid flow.

4. The lines should have a smooth interior surface to minimize fluid friction and turbulence.

5. The lines must be of correct length and size to insure optimum flow of fluid during the entire operation cycle.

6. Provision must be made to keep the lines clean by flushing or purging regularly to reduce any contamination.

7. Terminal fittings, flanges and unions must be provided at all junctions with parts or components that can be easily removed for repair or replacement.

8. Lines should be as short and have as few bends as possible, minimizing line loss due to fluid friction.

9. Lines and fittings should be properly installed and matched to provide leakproof connections.

The three most popular lines used in fluid power systems are pipes, tubings, and flexible hose. When the type of line for a particular power system is selected, the type of fluid medium, the required pressure of the system, and the location and operating environments must be considered. Heavy pipe is appropri-

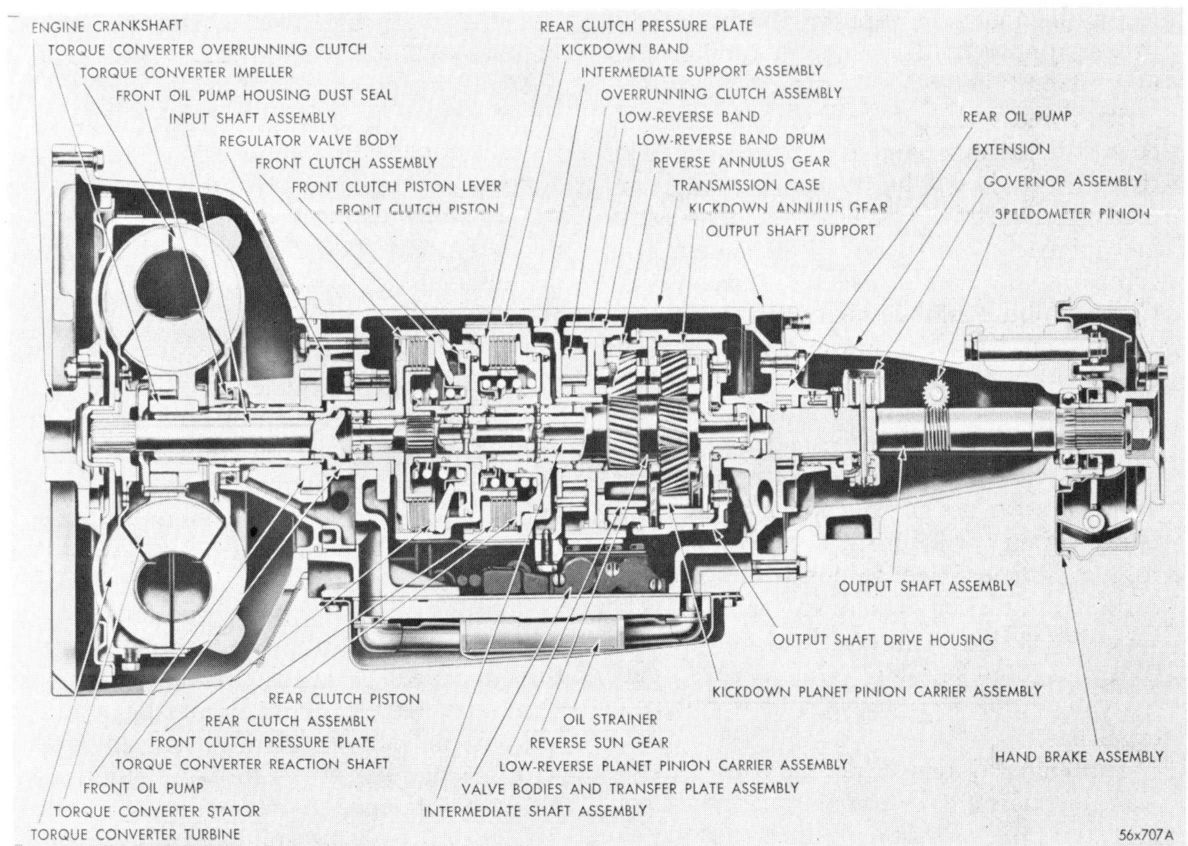

Fig. 21-50. Cutaway View of Torque Converter and Transmission (Chrysler)

ately used in a large stationary fluid power system, but comparatively lightweight tubing must be used in aircraft and missiles because of the limiting factors of weight and space.

Piping and Tubing

Piping is usually measured according to inside diameter and tubing by outside diameter and wall thickness. The choice between piping or tubing and associated fittings is a design decision. At no time should galvanized pipe be considered because of the possibility of flaking.

When piping or tubing is installed, the inside should be bright and clean. It is also desirable to have segments continuous and where bends are necessary they must not be too sharp. Ideally, the bending radius should be not less than three times the inside diameter of the tube or pipe. Compensation must be made for vibration which can set up stresses in the metal and eventually will cause the metal to rupture due to fatigue. Proper support of the piping or tubing minimizes vibration.

Steel and standard iron pipe is used for economic reasons. Steel is used because of its strength and suitability for bending and flanging, and its adaptability to high pressures and temperatures. Its one disadvantage is its comparatively low resistance to corrosion. Copper tubing exhibits high resistance to corrosion and is easily drawn and formed. It is, however, unsatisfactory for extremely high temperature or pressure conditions and has a tendency to work-harden and rupture at a point of vibration. Where weight is a factor, as in aircraft design, the majority of circulatory systems will consist of aluminum alloy tubing. Stainless steel tubing is also used for certain installations where the lines may be exposed to abrasion, intense heat, and extreme pressures. Stainless steel exhibits a resistance to being formed or drawn and is relatively expensive.

The material, the inside diameter, and the wall thickness are the three primary considerations in the selection of lines for a fluid power system. The inside diameter of a line is important since it determines the rate of flow without loss of power due to friction. A given flow velocity has less friction through a large opening than through a small opening. If the inside diameter of a line is too small for the amount of flow, line turbulence will result, increasing fluid temperature and creating unnecessary power loss.

The wall thickness and the material used, as well as the inside diameter, determine the bursting pressure of a line or fitting. The greater the wall thickness in relation to the inside diameter and the stronger the metal, the more able it is to withstand high pressures before bursting. However, the greater the inside diameter for a given wall thickness, the lower the bursting pressure because force is the product of area and pressure. The fluid power industry recommends that rigid lines should have a bursting pressure which provides a safety factor of at least eight; that is, the bursting pressure should be at least eight times greater than the maximum working pressure of the system.

Most manufacturers of pipe and tubing supply charts, graphs, or tables which aid in the selection of proper lines for fluid power systems. These define the strength of a line in terms of bursting pressure, give the inside diameter, and show flow capacity at recommended velocity.

Flexible Hose

Hose is selected where there is necessity for flexibility such as connections to units that move while in operation or units attached to a hinged portion of the equipment. Often flexible hose finds application where the line will be subjected to severe vibration such as on an operating pump. See Figs. 21-51 and 21-52.

The *size* of flexible hose is designated by a number on the side of the hose and refers to the equivalent tubing size. It does not denote inside or outside diameter of the hose. As long as the number of the hose corresponds with the number of the tubing, proper size is being maintained.

Rubber hose is a seamless, synthetic rubber tube covered with layers of cotton braid and wire braid and an outer layer of rubber-impregnated cotton braid, Fig. 21-51. The inner tube is designed to withstand chemical reaction from the materials which pass through it. The braid, which may consist of several layers, is the determining factor in the strength of the hose. The exterior cover is made to withstand external abuse.

Teflon® hose is designed for higher operating pressures and temperatures in a fluid power system. The teflon resin is extruded in the desired size and shape. It is covered with stainless steel wire, braided over the tube for extra strength and protection. Teflon exhibits excellent corrosion resistance, and its self-lubricity is conducive to laminar flow and smaller frictional losses. It will not absorb moisture and is inert to acids as well as all hydraulic fluids. Teflon is non-flammable and is capable of operating in a temperature range from 100°F to 500°F. Where the possibility of open flame exists, a special asbestos sleeve is usually used.

Flexible hose is provided in four pressure ranges. Low-pressure hose is used for systems below 150 PSI and for exhaust lines of high-pressure systems. Medium-pressure hose is used in systems ranging in pressure up to 1200 PSI. High pressure hose is used in systems with pressures in excess of 3,000 PSI, and extra-high-pressure hose in systems with up to 5,000 PSI. High-pressure and extra-high-pressure hose are available only in complete assemblies made at the factory. Medium- and low-pressure hose are available in bulk and are usually fabricated locally. Hose should be installed so that no twist of any kind or sharp bends are present. The bending radius should not be less than six times the inside diameter. Enough slack should be provided for changes in distance from one component to another and to allow for changes in relative motion.

Types of Connectors

Fittings are used to connect the units of a fluid power system. There are many different types of connectors available. The type required for a system depends on the type of pipe, tubing, or hose; the fluid medium; and the maximum operating pressure of the system.

Threaded connectors are used in low-pressure fluid systems. They are usually made of steel, copper, or brass and are available in a variety of designs. Threaded connectors are made with standard female threading cut on the inside surface. The end of the pipe is threaded with outside thread for connecting. Standard pipe threads are tapered approximately ¾″ per foot to insure tight connections. To prevent seizing, a suitable pipe thread compound or teflon tape is applied to the threads, with the two end threads kept free of the compound or tape so as not to contaminate the fluid.

Flanged connectors are suitable for most pressures now in use. The flanges are connected to pipes by welding or brazing, by tapered threads for low-pressure piping, or by rolling or bending into recesses. Standard fitting shapes — T's, cross, elbows, etc. — are manufactured for flange joints.

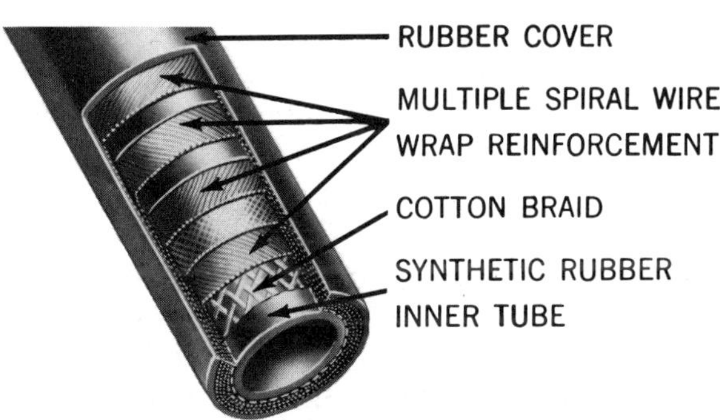

Fig. 21-51. Construction of Flexible Hose (Aeroquip)

Fig. 21-52. Variety of Industrial Hose (Gates)

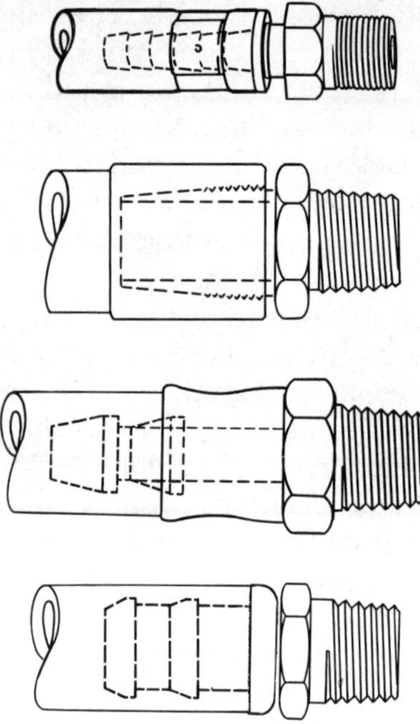

A. Flexible Hose Connectors

B. Quick Disconnect Fitting

C. Quick Disconnect Fitting

Fig. 21-53. Types of Connectors
(Aeroquip and Bruning)

Some circulatory lines are connected by *welded joint connectors,* especially in high-pressure systems.

Silver brazed connectors are commonly used for joining nonferrous piping. The operating conditions must not exceed 425°F and the pressures must not exceed 3,000 PSI. The brazing alloy is melted to form the joint. This alloy can be reheated and melted for disassembly and rebrazed easily when required.

Flared connectors are commonly used in circulatory systems consisting of lines made of tubing. These connectors provide safe, strong, dependable connections without necessity of threading, welding or brazing. The connector consists of a fitting, a sleeve, and a nut. Fittings should be made of a material similar to the tubing. There are a variety of fittings such as T's, crosses, elbows, etc., and also many different thread combinations. Unions have two connections on each end; elbows have two connections on one end, a pipe thread on the other, a female pipe thread on one end or a tube connection on the opposite end. Tubing used with this type of connector must be flared prior to assembly. The nut fits over the sleeve and, when tightened, draws the sleeve and tubing flare tightly against the male member to form a seal. The male fitting has a cone-shaped surface with the same angle as the inside of the flare. The sleeve supports the tube so that vibration does not concentrate at the end of the flare and distributes the shearing action over a wider area.

Bite connectors are often referred to as *flareless tube connectors.* This connector eliminates all tube flaring yet provides a safe, strong, and dependable tube connection. The connector consists of a fitting, a sleeve or ferrule, and a nut. These fittings are available in many shapes, sizes, and thread combinations. The nut presses on the bevel of the sleeve and causes it to clamp tightly on the tube. Resistance to vibration is concentrated at this point rather than at the sleeve cut. When fully tightened, the sleeve or ferrule is bowed slightly at the mid-section and acts as a spring, maintaining a constant tension between the body and the nut and thus preventing the nut from loosening. Prior to installation of a flareless tube connector, the tubing must be square, concentric, and free of burrs. For the connection to be effective, the cutting edge of the sleeve or ferrule must bite into the periphery of the tube. This is accomplished by presetting the sleeve or ferrule on the tube using a presetting tool which has the same dimensions as the fitting body and is usually distributed by the fitting manufacturer.

Connectors for Flexible Hose

Most of the flexible hose used in fluid power systems is equipped with end fittings. These end fittings most commonly used on flexible hose are adapted for either flared or flareless connectors as well as flanged connectors. See *A* in Fig. 21-53.

Quick Disconnect Couplings

Quick disconnect couplings of the self-sealing type are used at various points in many fluid power systems. These are installed in locations where frequent uncoupling is required for inspection, test, and maintenance of a line. These connectors can be separated or connected with very little effort on the part of the operator. Most consist of two parts held together by a union nut. Each part contains a valve which is held open when the coupling is connected, allowing fluid to flow in either direction through the coupling. When the coupling is disconnected, a spring closes the valve, preventing the loss of fluid and the entrance of contaminants. The union has a quick thread which permits connection or disconnection by turning the nut. Another typical disconnect coupling consists of two halves that are held together under spring tension. The male member fits within the female member and against an "O" ring to form a proper seal. See Fig. 21-53. Dust caps are provided for quick disconnect couplings to cover the ends of the couplings when separated.

Regardless of the type of connector, it should be the correct size and strength and perfectly clean on the inside. Open ends of pipes, tubing hose, and fittings should always be capped or plugged when they are stored for any considerable length of time. Rags or waste must not be used for this purpose because they deposit harmful lint which can cause severe damage to the fluid power system.

Terms to Understand

fluid power
hydraulics
pneumatics
density
buoyancy – Archimedes' Principle
pressure
compressibility
fluid flow – Bernoulli's Principle
fluid friction
kinetic molecular theory
compression of gases – Boyle's Law
temperature of gases – Charles' Law
fluid pressure – Pascal's Law
volume of flow
velocity of flow
laminar flow
potential energy
kinetic energy
head
viscosity
oxidation
corrosion
oiliness
foaming
aniline point
pour point
flash point
acidity
toxicity
sludge
reservoir
strainers
accumulator
pump
compressor
positive displacement pump
nonpositive displacement pump
centrifugal pump
rotary pump
gear pump
lobe pump
screw pump
vane pump
reciprocating pump
axial piston pump
air compressor
multi-stage compressor
flow control valves
pressure control valves
relief valve
directional control valves
four-way valves
restrictors
flowmeters
pressure gauges
Bourdon tube
fluid cylinders
piston actuators
fluid motors
turbines
governors
torque converter
automatic transmission
fluid lines
fittings
piping and tubing
flexible hose
connectors

Study Questions

1. Define and describe the scientific principles on which all fluid power systems are based.
2. List five advantages of fluid power systems over mechanical trans-actional systems.
3. In what ways are liquids and gases similar?

4. List and describe the function of the six major components of a fluid power transactional system.
5. Analyze how fluid power systems acquire tremendous force.
6. Compare pneumatic and hydraulic power systems.
7. List the advantages and disadvantages of pneumatic and hydraulic systems.
8. Describe five considerations in the selection of hydraulic oil.
9. Why is contamination the biggest problem in fluid power?
10. Control of fluid power may be continuous or discontinuous. List several components used in each type of control and describe the principle of operation.
11. The components that receive and provide mechanical energy are basically the same. Analyze this statement and cite illustrative examples.
12. What prime movers use fluid power principles in their operation?
13. List some applications of fluid power.

CHAPTER 22

Electrical Power and Fluidics

Electrical power systems were extensively discussed in Chapters 16, 17, 18, and 19. Those chapters considered the generation, power adaptations, and use of electricity as a prime mover. This chapter will briefly discuss electrical control. Electric motors have the ability to start under load, may be connected directly to the actuator or working component, and are utilized with both mechanical and fluid trans-actional systems.

The electrical *control system* regulates the electrical energy converted to mechanical energy. The system can provide for on-off control, directional control, control of rate, control of intensity, and/or control of time.

Fundamental Circuit

For electrical energy to be transmitted, a complete electron conducting circuit must be provided. Usually provided within this circuit are: (1) a power source consisting of magneto, cell, battery or power line; (2) a transmission component or electrical conductor; (3) one or more control components consisting of a switch, rheostat, relay, solenoid or such device; and (4) a load or working component that will convert the electrical energy into the required energy, such as a motor, heater, light, electromagnetic device, computer, etc. All components within an electrical circuit resist electron flow to some degree.

Sources of Electrical Energy

Electrical energy is made available to man in a variety of ways. Most common are the energy conversion devices (dynamos) that use magnetism as the working medium. Others include the use of chemical-electric, thermal-electric, photoelectric, and piezo-electric devices. Refer to Chapter 16 for information regarding the principles of how these energies are converted to electrical energy.

Electrical Transmission

The transmission of electrical energy may be accomplished through electric conduction or via electromagnetic radiation. Though the wireless transmission of energy is an intriguing aspect, especially with the advent of higher power transmitters and the Laser, the efficiency of these systems as yet makes their employment impractical for widespread energy distribution. Consequently, conduction is the chief means of electrical energy transmission and control.

The *wire conductor* (refer to Fig. 16-12) must provide a low resistance to electron flow in order to allow the greatest electron flow to the working component. The larger the conductor in cross-sectional area, the greater its capacity to pass electrons; large currents require larger conductors than small current circuits. If a small conductor is used as a conductor in a high amperage circuit, the internal resistance of the conductor will cause heat to be generated, resulting in a power loss by the working element. At times, such current will create excessive overheating of the circuit and prove dangerous since the heat further increases the conductor's resistance. Resistance is directly proportionate to the temperature of the conductor; that is the heating effect is proportional to the electric power used. Power is equal to the square of the current multiplied by the conductor's resistance.

The length of the conductor will also affect the total resistance of the circuit. Therefore, the resistance of an electrical conductor is directly proportional to the length of the conductor and inversely proportional to its cross-sectional area as previously noted. Two conductors of the same dimensions will have different resistances if made of different materials. Selecting the proper conductor for a given transmission junction is an economic consideration. Gold, silver, and platinum are all excellent conductors, but cost prohibits their use for general transmission. They are, however, used where cost is a secondary factor compared to conduction properties. For example, in some solid-state wafer systems, gold conductors are used because of their excellent current-carrying capability. Wires which are to transmit electricity from place to place are generally copper or aluminum because of their relative low resistivity and moderate cost.

In low-power-consuming indoor circuits where the transmission lines will be static and not subject to physical movement, single-strand wire is used. In high-power outdoor transmission circuits, multi-strand wire is employed because of its greater strength and ability to resist the fatigue caused by physical movement. In circuits where the incidence of vibration or movement of any kind is considerable multi-strand wire is preferred, as in an appliance cord.

To transmit electric power (the product of voltage and current) with as little heat or line loss as possible, the transmission should be at high voltage and low current values.

Transformers

A transformer serves as an inductive coupling device between two AC circuits and may be classified as a transmission device. As with gears, pulleys, levers, and fluid pistons, it is capable of altering the components of power in order to acquire a desired mechanical advantage. Refer to Figs. 18-25 through 18-29.

A step-up or step-down transformer is a transmission device that increases one component of power while decreasing the other proportionately. This principle, for example, is used to provide high *voltage* from low voltage in the automobile ignition circuit and high *current* in electric welding from a power source of moderately low current.

An *isolation transformer* is designed to couple two circuits in a 1:1 ratio while limiting the current component of power in the secondary circuit. In this application, the current in the secondary circuit is limited because the power output cannot exceed the rating of the transformer regardless of the power potential of the primary or feeder circuit. Isolation transformers are frequently used in conjunction with test equipment to protect the technician. Their operation may be compared to that of slip clutch, fluid regulator, or safety valve.

Resistors

Often times it is necessary to provide a partial, continual constriction to the normal flow of electricity in a circuit. This can be accomplished by using a resistor in the circuit, Fig. 22-1. A resistor transforms electrical energy to heat energy, reducing electron flow. The two most popular resistors are made of carbon or are wire-wound. Carbon resistors are used for low voltage applications; wire-wound resistors are preferred for high current reduction. Circuit designers sometimes use resistance wires to drop line voltage.

Control

Devices that provide noncontinual regulation of the flow of electrons are commonly classified as *control units.*

A simple on-off switch can be positioned to conduct or not conduct electron flow. A switch is then a control component, and because of its two-state function of providing circuit closure or nonclosure, it may be referred to as a *discontinuous* control device. A *continuous* control device is one which can exert control over a range or continuum providing any level of conduction from zero to maximum.

A single-pole, single-throw (SPST) switch is the simplest control device in electronics, Figs. 22-2 and 22-3. When one switch can affect two independent circuits with one movement, it is called a single-pole, double-throw switch (SPDT), Fig. 22-4.

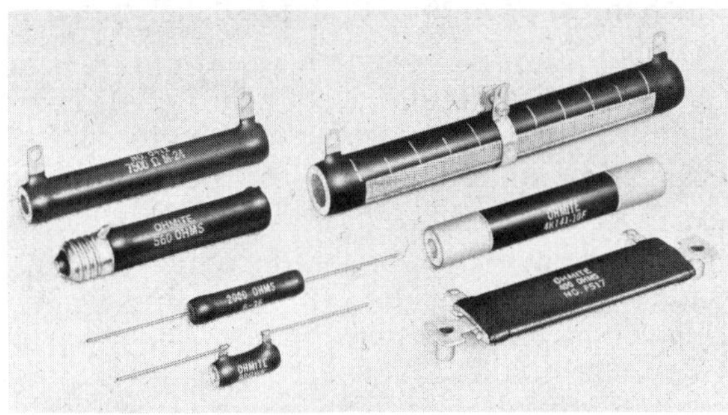

A. Common Resistors

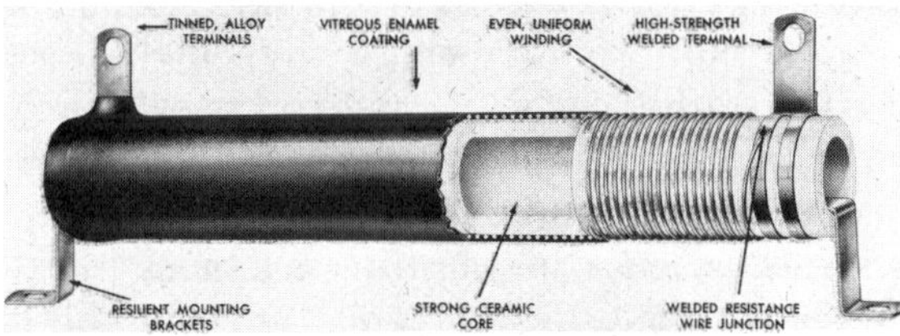

B. Resistor Construction

Fig. 22-1. Fixed and Variable Resistors in Common Use (Ohmite Manufacturing Co.)

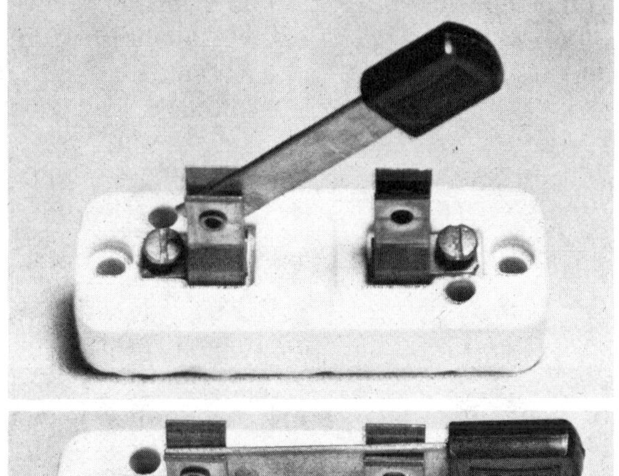

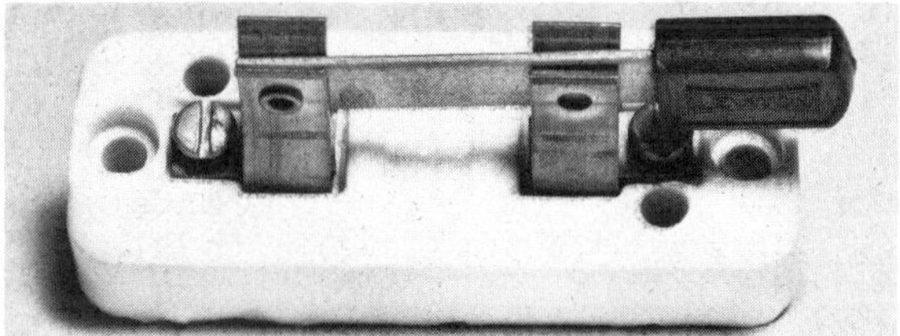

Fig. 22-3. Knife Switch — Open (Current Stopped) and Closed (Current Passing Through)

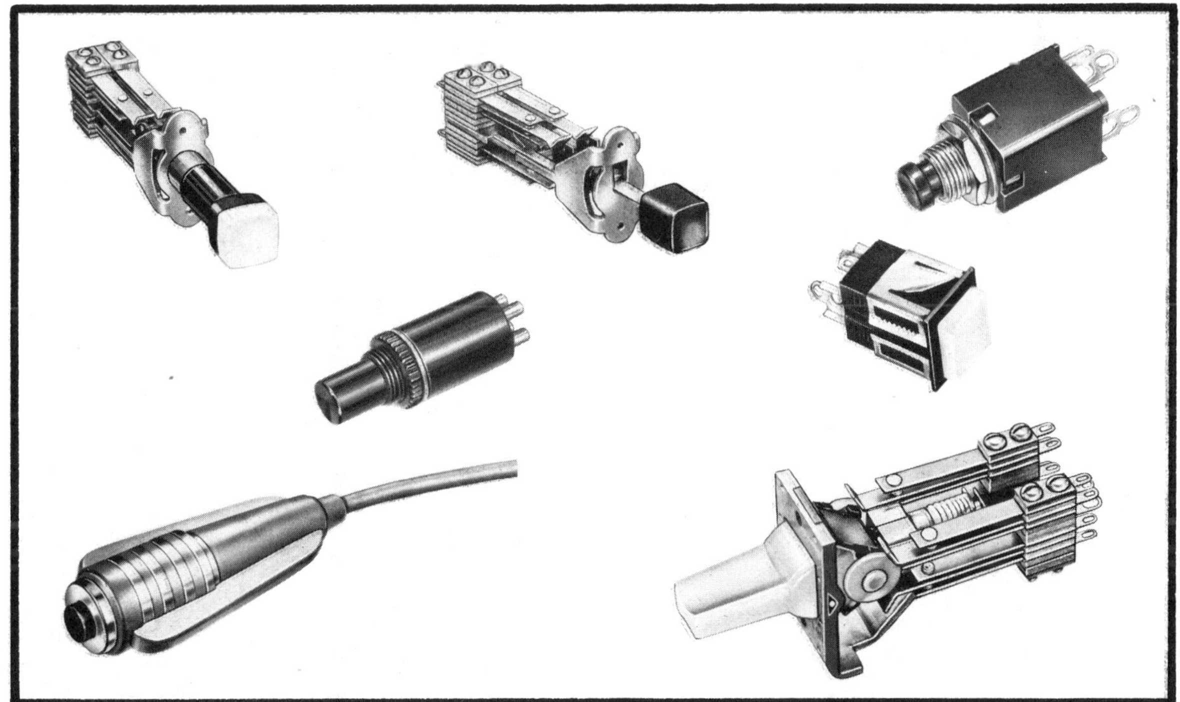

Fig. 22-2. Switches Commonly Used in Home and Industry (Switchcraft Inc.)

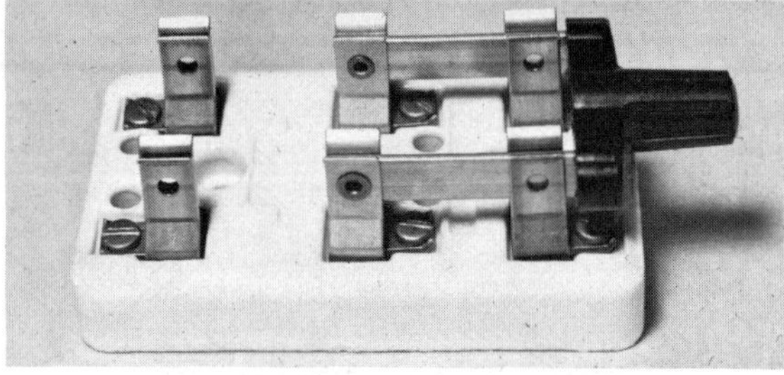

Fig. 22-4. Double-Pole, Double-Throw Knife Switch, Open Switch Above, Closed Switch Below

A. Plug Fuse

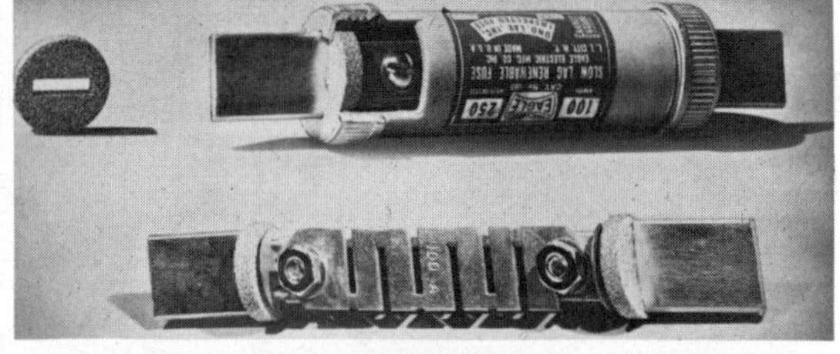

B. Cartridge Fuse

C. Slow-Blow Plug Fuse

Fig. 22-5. Various Fuse Designs (Eagle Electric Manufacturing Co.)

Three- and four-way switches are designed to permit two- or three-station control of a simple circuit.

Toggle switches vary in design from open, low-voltage knife switches to spring-loaded mechanical switches, and silent mercury switches.

When an operating device is located some distance from an operator, a remote control circuit is required. Most often this condition exists for the operator's safety or to provide an independent, efficient operating circuit of high power. In such a system of control, a simple switch is employed to operate a circuit that energizes an electromagnetic switch or relay to control the high power circuit. *Solenoids* and *relays* may be designed to operate one or more circuits simultaneously. When they are used in rather elaborate networks, extremely complex control functions may be undertaken; this includes most automatic telephone systems, electric accounting machines, automatic boiler controls, and printing press controls.

In a situation where a series of circuits must be controlled in sequence, a stepping switch may be used.

Automatic Control Using Discontinuous Devices

Sometimes it is necessary to use switches as a subsystem of a total system of control. Many of these systems employ energy-sensing devices such as light, heat, and stress sensors. These are connected to current amplifiers to provide enough power to the control circuit to operate a control device, such as a relay, solenoid, and transistor. Operation of the control device then brings about the desired result, such as the actuation of a motor or lamps.

Pressure-sensitive switches may be used to control movement. These limiting switches are placed strategically so that at the end of an operation sequence a switch is tripped and the circuit opens or reverses, or a feed or stepping switch circuit is energized to initiate a new operation. Many automatic doors are actuated by pressure-sensitive switches. These examples serve to indicate how switches, providing discontinuous control, may be used to provide automatic operation.

Unique Discontinuous Controlling Devices

A fuse or circuit breaker is a unique control device, designed to interrupt electron flow in its circuit when current exceeds a desired amount. These devices, of necessity, are placed in series within the circuit, Fig. 22-5.

Fuses are made with a low-melting-point alloy serving as the current controlling conductor. This element is designed to carry or conduct a certain current or line load without undue increase in temperature. When this level is exceeded, the fusible element's operating temperature causes it to melt and open the circuit. The fusible link's melting point is designed to be well below the safe operating temperature of the circuit.

In some high-voltage fuses, the fusible element can be replaced but in most household uses, the entire fuse must be changed. Some fuses are designed to withstand high initial loads; for example overcoming the initial starting torque of a motor. They are called "slow-blow" fuses.

The *circuit breaker* provides the same control function as the fuse, but need not be replaced if it opens a circuit because of an overload. Circuit breakers are usually designed to use an electromagnetic or a bimetallic element. The electromagnetic circuit breaker operates similarly to the cutout relay shown in Figs. 10-20 and 10-21 (Chapter 10). The electromagnetic element is placed in series with the switching armature. When the current is of sufficient magnitude, the electromagnetic force attracts the armature and opens the circuit.

The bimetallic circuit breaker usually is affixed to a motor and is sometimes called a *thermal overload protector*. The switching element is cup-shaped and bimetallic. When this element overheats, the two metals expand in different amounts causing the element to spring outward away from a micro-switch and open the circuit. A micro-switch acquires its name from the fact that a small movement activates it.

Circuit breakers are usually manually reset. Fuses and circuit breakers control or limit current flow, Fig. 22-6.

Continuous Control Devices

Electrical devices that provide a range of conduction from zero to maximum resistance include potentiometers, rheostats, and variable transformers.

Potentiometers

A potentiometer is a variable resistor. It is classed as a voltage-affecting device. It is usually made of a doughnut shaped nonconductor

A. Typical home circuit breaker having thermal magnetic operation.

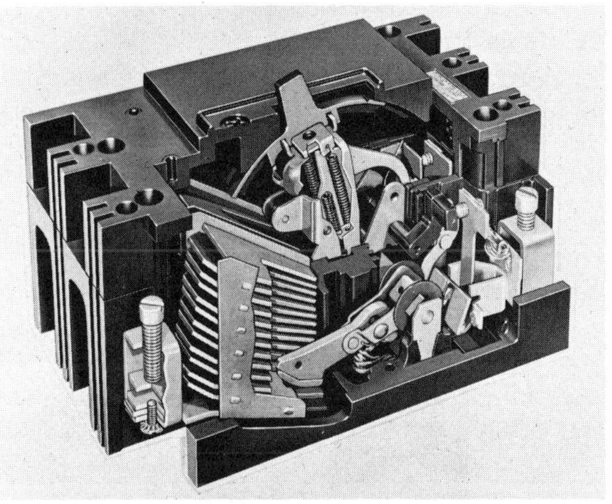

B. Cutaway view of a thermal magnetic circuit breaker.

Fig. 22-6. Thermal Magnetic Circuit Breaker
(Standard Control Div., Westinghouse Electric Corp.)
This type of breaker provides protection against short circuits, while providing for sudden power surges when the motor is first turned on.

with a high resistance wire wound around it to form the resistor element. A centrally located, rotating or sliding contact can be manually moved along the resistor element, Fig. 22-7.

The potentiometer is connected so that the electron flow must go through the resistor element to the sliding contact to complete the circuit. The distance the sliding contact causes the electron flow to travel through the resistance element determines its resistance in the circuit; zero distance provides least resistance; maximum distance provides maximum resistance.

Potentiometers are designed in a variety of ranges and for specific voltages and currents.

Rheostats

Rheostats are continuous control devices that are connected and function in much the same way as potentiometers. They are, however, designed to regular current and for this reason they are made to dissipate heat quickly. They usually employ as a resistance element a helix of relatively heavy resistance wire wound around an insulative material. This element may be made straight or circular with a sliding contact designed to move along its entire length.

Variable Transformer

A variable transformer uses a movable slide to change the turns ratio between the primary and secondary windings. This will provide continuous control over the transformer output.

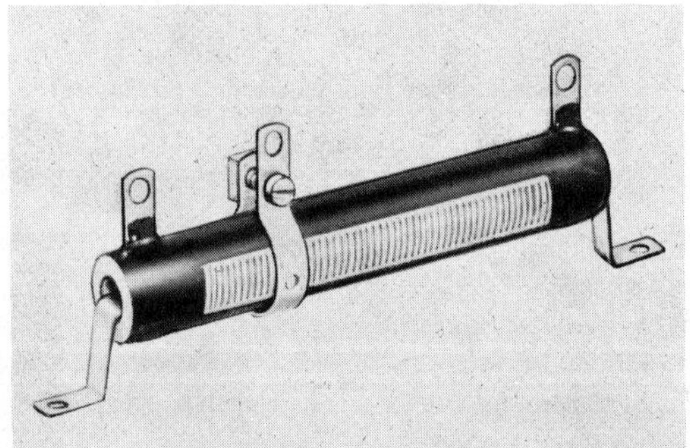

Fig. 22-7. Adjustable (Variable) Resistor
(Ohmite Manufacturing Co.)
The output connection is made to the movable center terminal. The resistance is changed by sliding the center unit back and forth.

Rectifiers

Rectifiers convert AC to DC. Today the most popular rectifiers may be classified as electronic. They include tube diodes and solid-state rectifiers such as selenium, germanium, and silicon diodes and copper oxide rectifiers.

The tube diode has two components – the plate and cathode – located in a partial vacuum within a glass envelope. The tube may possess a heater filament, but this is not considered an operating component. In an AC circuit, the electrons flow on to the cathode during one-half the cycle. At this time, the electrons move off the cathode through the vacuum to the plate and complete the circuit. During the other half cycle the electrons move on to the plate, but they cannot move to the cathode because the relative heat of the cathode does not accept current flow readily. Therefore, the circuit is complete only half the time, and the current flows only in one direction. This is called a half-wave rectifier. Two diodes may be employed, each conducting current flow during opposite halves of the cycle, and the circuit is then referred to as a full-wave rectifier. If these two diodes are located in one tube it is called a dual diode.

Solid-state rectifiers, including copper oxide rectifiers, conduct electrons during half the AC cycle. These rectifiers require no heating filament. The natural property of the material used conducts electricity in one direction and not in the other. These rectifier components may also be connected to provide full-wave rectification.

Triodes and Transistors as Power Amplifiers

Triode tubes and transistors are very similar in their operating principles. They both permit a very small current to control a much larger current. In the triode tube, a third element, the control grid, is added between the cathode and plate.

A small current on this grid causes it to permit or repel electron flow from the cathode to the plate. In the triode, the cathode is negative and the plate is always relatively positive. The filament is made more or less negative and this controls the electron flow. A small change in the value of the voltage applied to the control grid can control a large amount of plate current. This action permits the tube to act as an amplifier, a device that is capable of increasing the value of current or voltage.

A transistor provides the same operational function. The components are called *emitter, base,* and *collector.* The emitter is like the cathode, the base like the grid, and the collector like that of the plate of a triode. Since the collector current may be many times larger than the emitter current, the transistor acts as an amplifier.

Electrical power systems are applied in a myriad of ways. Their popularity is due in major degree to their flexibility. Huge motors are called upon to provide the required mechanical energy to operate hydropumps, locomotives, cranes, ships, etc. Smaller motors provide the mechanical energy required to operate a watch.

In today's automated technology electrical subsystems, as part of larger subsystems, control the mechanical, fluid, and electric power contrivances of society.

Servomechanisms and Feedback Control

A relatively new word in our technological vocabulary is "servo." It is the abbreviated form of the word *servomechanism.* In some foreign countries cars are said to be fitted with servo-assisted brakes and servo-assisted steering. In this country the corresponding terms are *power brakes* and *power steering.* Actually the term "servo" is derived from a Greek word which means slave. A servomechanism behaves much like a mechanical slave where the output is regulated to repeat the input conditions but at an increased power level.

A servomechanism is an automatic feedback control system frequently referred to as a *closed-loop system.* In general terms, *feedback* describes a system that takes action at its control *input* based on information derived at its own *output* and communicated to input. There are basically two different feedback systems: those that use a servomechanism and those that use a regulator. Both of these may exhibit continuous or discontinuous control of the input.

Servo-Control

The servo-control feedback system employs an element called a *comparator.* This device compares the actual output against the desired output, Fig. 22-8. If they are the same, a zero error is detected and a zero corrective signal is sent to the control input. If an error or difference is detected, this condition will have sign (direction) and magnitude (degree). This error measurement provides the correction signal that is sent to the control input. The machine responds by bringing its output state in line with the desired state. The control input is continuously energized by the output from the comparator which continually compares the actual output condition against the desired output. In this system, any change of actual output caused by a disturbance to the system is compensated for because the actual and desired outputs are under constant comparison.

The continuously-controlled servomechanism is usually applied in *position control systems.* These, for example, permit remote control of the linear or angular displacement of an output shaft that is connected to a ship's

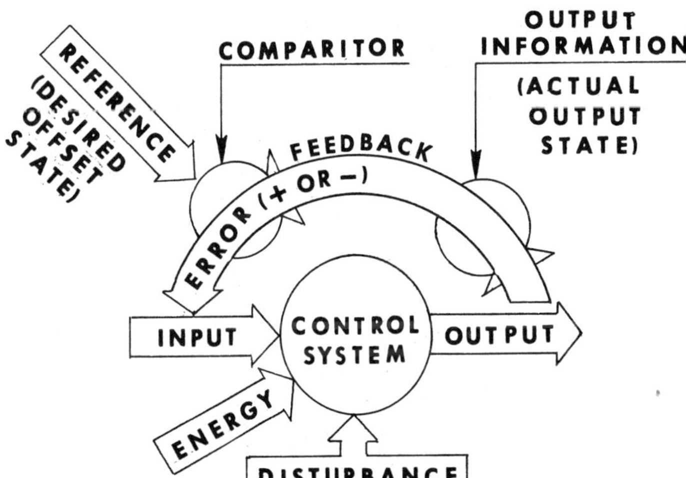

Fig. 22-8. Comparator Feedback System

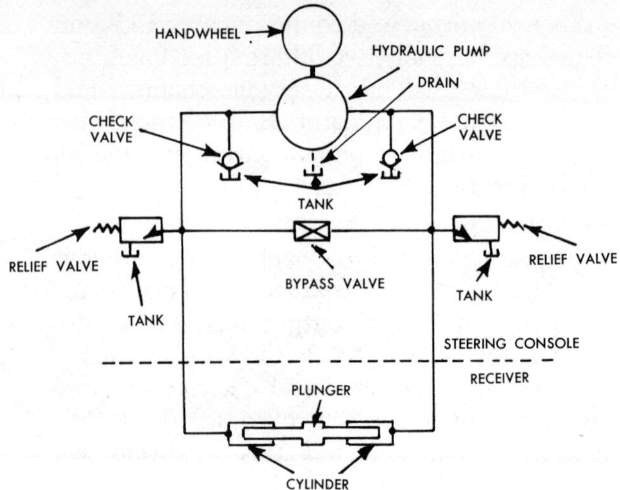

A. Hydraulic Circuit Diagram

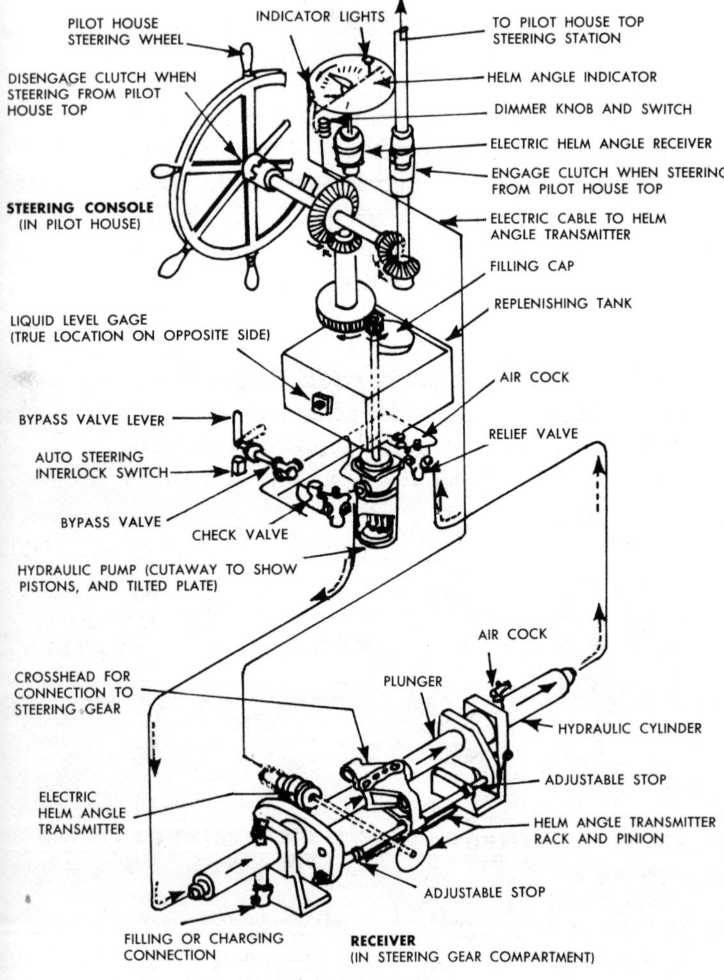

B. Schematic

Fig. 22-9. Hydraulic Telemotor Control of Ship

rudder, a control surface of an aircraft, a gimballing device of a rocket engine, or a cutting head of a machine tool, Fig. 22-9. In these instances the direction and the degree of operator movement establish the reference or desired conditions to which the system automatically regulates its output. Ambient disturbances such as current, wind, temperature, sharpness of cutting tool may affect the actual output condition. These interferences, however, are continually compensated for by the comparator. In these examples the output condition is frequently changed by the establishment of a new reference condition by the operator.

Regulator Control

The distinction between servomechanism and *regulator feedback control* is difficult to make. Essentially the regulator compares output against a fixed reference, whereas the servomechanism compares output against a changing reference. Both of these control systems may provide continuous or discontinuous (on/off) control.

The on/off control system is by far the most common because it is usually simple and less costly to build and maintain. One of the most widely used examples is the domestic thermostatically controlled furnace system. In this system the furnace is either *on* or *off*. It is switched *on* when the temperature of the house is below the desired setting and it is switched *off* when the temperature reaches that desired setting. The ratio of the on and off cycles depends on how much heat is lost through conduction, convection, and radiation. These losses are determined by factors outside such as temperature, wind velocity and direction, and the effectiveness of thermo-insulation. These factors are referred to as *ambient conditions* and they constitute the extraneous disturbances mentioned previously. The on and off control has the thermostat (regulator) regulating the furnace. The thermostat (regulator) turns the furnace either on or off, and for this reason the behavior of the system is inherently oscillatory.

The discontinuous system just described could be converted to a continuously controlled system by adding to the regulator a variable resistor that would provide an infinite control to the burner, thereby regulating the heat output over a continuum from minimum to maximum.

Open Loop Control

In the study of control systems, mention must be made of the *open loop system.* In this system no feedback or input control is expressed as a direct result of comparing the desired output with the actual output, Fig. 22-10. Open loop systems are popular in industry and around the modern home. Any device that operates on a timed cycle or time line is an open loop system, such as the toaster, dishwasher and clothes washer. So are machines that are controlled by mechanical cams or pressure-sensitive switches. In all of these machines the actual output does not control the input. The input control is external and independent of the output condition or state, but the cycle can be varied. These devices cannot compensate for disturbances or interferences, but can be programed for different brownness of toast or length of washing cycle.

Automation

Open and closed loop control systems describe the two different classes of automated machines. The control systems can be designed as mechanical, electrical, hydraulic, or pneumatic systems. Frequently these systems may employ two or more systems in combination and are referred to as hybrid systems.

Since the control systems are independent of the working system, little power is required to effect control. For instance, in electrically-controlled feedback systems very small amounts of current are necessary to operate the logic or comparator or feedback circuits. Through the employment of amplifiers or relays, the resultant electrical signal can be made to operate valves, solenoids, and motors to actuate the control elements of the hydraulic, pneumatic, electrical, or mechanical working system.

The advent of miniaturization and wafer technology in electronics and the employment of solid-state components have made electronic control devices very popular. They also exhibit high reliability, are fast acting, have long life, have no moving parts, and express a high tolerance to vibration. Electronic control is a major thrust of our technology; detailed consideration of systems and devices is beyond the scope of this book.

Fluidics

Electronic control systems cannot be operated in environments that present extreme temperature, nuclear, and electrical radiation conditions. These limitations prompted research and development of a new system of automatic control called *fluidics* in the late 1950's and early 1960's. The progress made since then assures fluidics a permanent place in the science of control. Fluidic components are small, reliable, and extremely long-lived. They have no moving parts, require low maintenance, show high tolerance to vibration and temperature, are not affected by electromagnetic radiation, and their operating characteristics are ideal for hazardous applications.

The term *fluidics* has been derived from the two words, *fluid* and *logic.* Both liquids and gases are used as fluid media in fluidics, although gases are most popular. *Logic* deals with the criteria, or formal principles, of reasoning and thought. Logic, as applied to control systems, is a means of making decisions concerning what operation to perform and

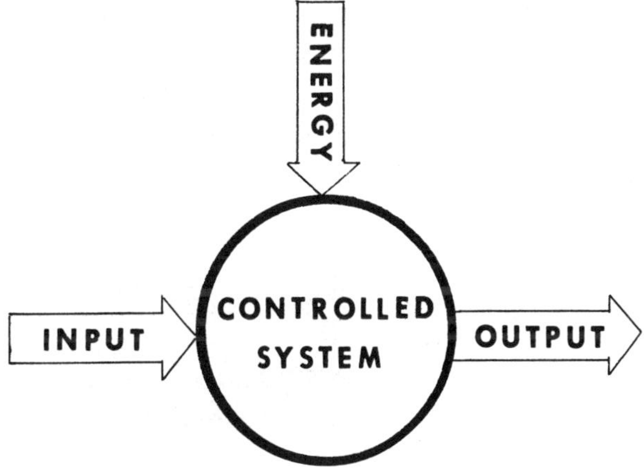

Fig. 22-10. Open Loop Control System Principle

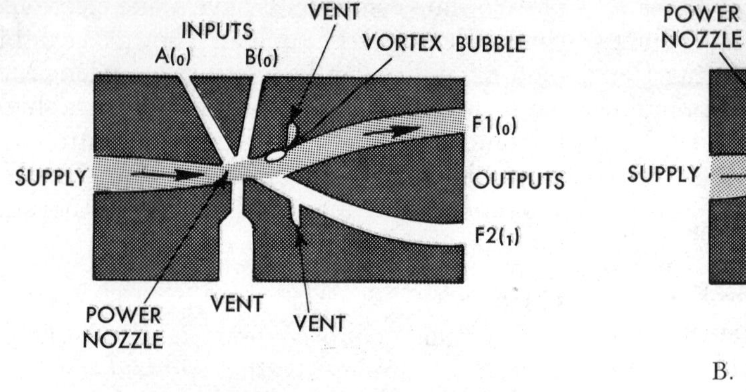

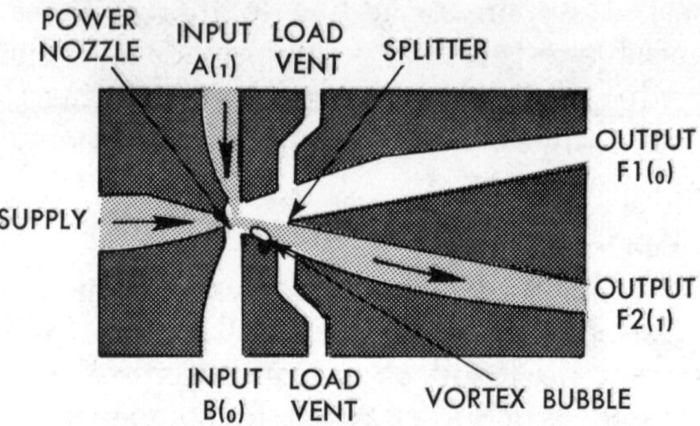

B. Bistable Wall Attachment Device

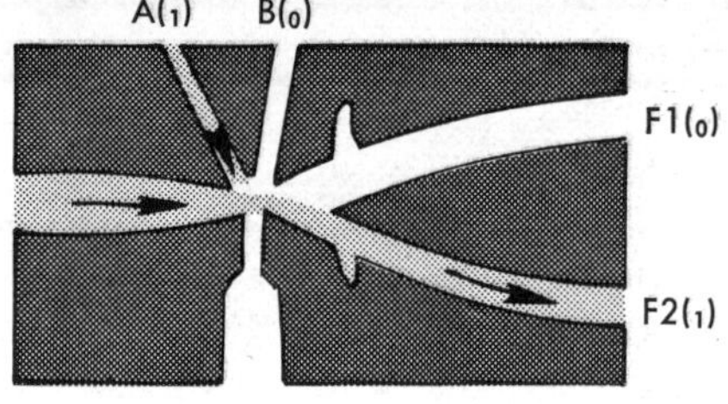

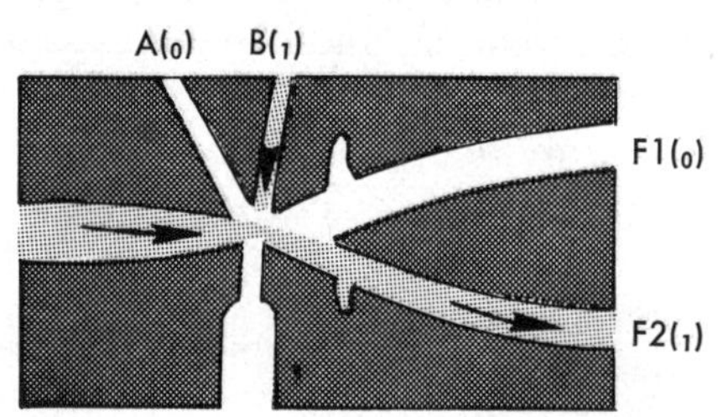

A. Monostable Wall Attachment Devices

C. Wall Attachment OR/NOR Device to Perform Flip-Flop Operation

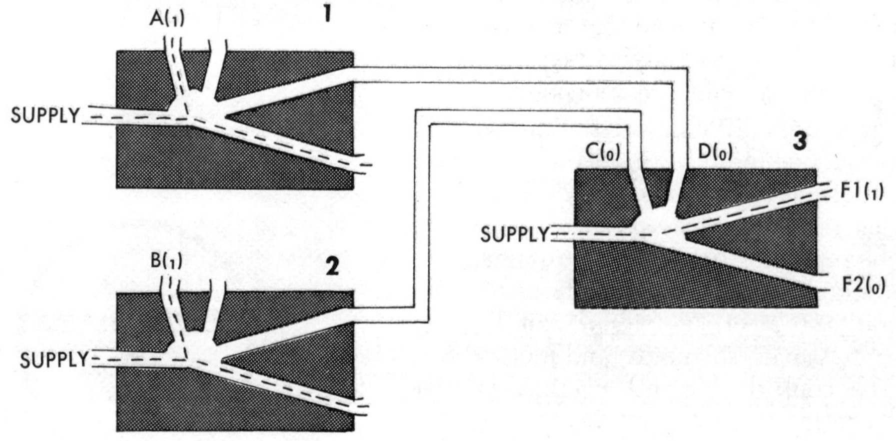

D. Wall Attachment OR/NOR Device to Perform AND/NAND Operations

Fig. 22-11. Wall Attachment Devices

when, how, and where to perform it. Fluidics, therefore, is a technology concerned with control as applied to switching, sensing, and performing logic functions. Fluidics and electronics may be used for computerized control; they are complementary. Fluidic devices are not as fast in reaction as electronic devices.

Terminology

Since fluidics serves as an alternate for electronic devices for computerized control, many of the terms used in the study of fluidics were adopted from computer and electronic terminology.

Computers never reason why or think out an answer; they only operate on instructions prepared by man. Man must apply the thought process to a problem to the degree that logic decisions can provide the correct answer.

The symbolic logic symbols used in digital computers are based on the investigations of George Boole, and the algebraic system referred to as Boolean algebra. It is a method of dealing with logic problems in a mathematical way. Boolean algebra is based on a two-state condition: Yes or no, on or off. Its application to electronics is logical: a switch can be on or off, a signal present or not. These two states can represent *1* or *0*. Binary number systems consist of only two symbols *1* or *0* – the symbols of Boolean algebra.

Fluidic Methods

There are several ways to classify fluidic logic devices. Sometimes they are classified as two general types: pure fluidic and moving part devices. Another method of classifying is by the basic principles of operation: wall attachment, jet interaction, turbulence amplification, vortex valve amplification, and moving parts.

Wall Attachment

A jet fluid under pressure directed toward a wall of a channel attaches itself to the wall, Fig. 22-11. This is known as the *Coanda effect*, after Henri Coanda who explained the phenomenon in 1932.

As fluid touches the surface, the fluid nearest the surface is slowed down by friction, while the fluid furthest from the surface flows with the greatest velocity. Eventually the fluid at the surface stops flowing, and there is a void in the fluid. The fluid flowing above this void moves downward to fill the space, causing a whirlpool or circular motion called a *vortex bubble*, or "Coanda bubble." By controlling the vortex bubble, the wall attachment principle may be used to perform logic functions. The bubble may be caused to shift direction to another wall by means of a signal (a smaller jet of fluid) which directs the main stream of fluid toward another channel wall. Variation on where the fluid stream output goes in response to a *signal condition* or *no signal condition* is determined by the construction of the fluidic element and is very critical.

Regardless of the type of device, all logic functions cannot be performed by a single element. However, several elements of the same type can be used to build circuits and changed to suit different logic requirements. Several elements are usually manufactured in one unit; much the same as the printed and integrated circuits used in electronics. Such blocks are referred to as integrated or printed circuits.

Jet Interaction

The flow of fluid from supply is in the form of a power jet which moves in a straight line across a gap to one of two receiving passages, Fig. 22-12. The design of the component is

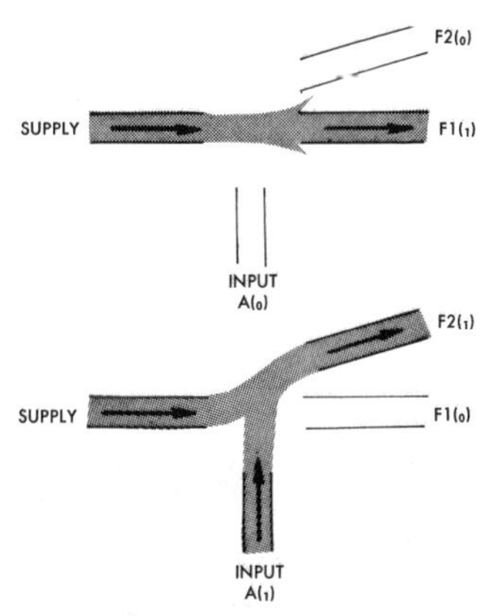

Fig. 22-12. Principles of Operation of Jet Interaction

such that little fluid is lost as it crosses the gap. At right angles to the gap is a smaller fluid passage. When fluid is emitted from the smaller passage, it is able to divert the main jet stream into the second receiving passage. This type of jet interaction device is very similar to the wall attachment device. The main difference is the method used to control the fluid flow. The same combinations of inputs provide the same outputs, and make

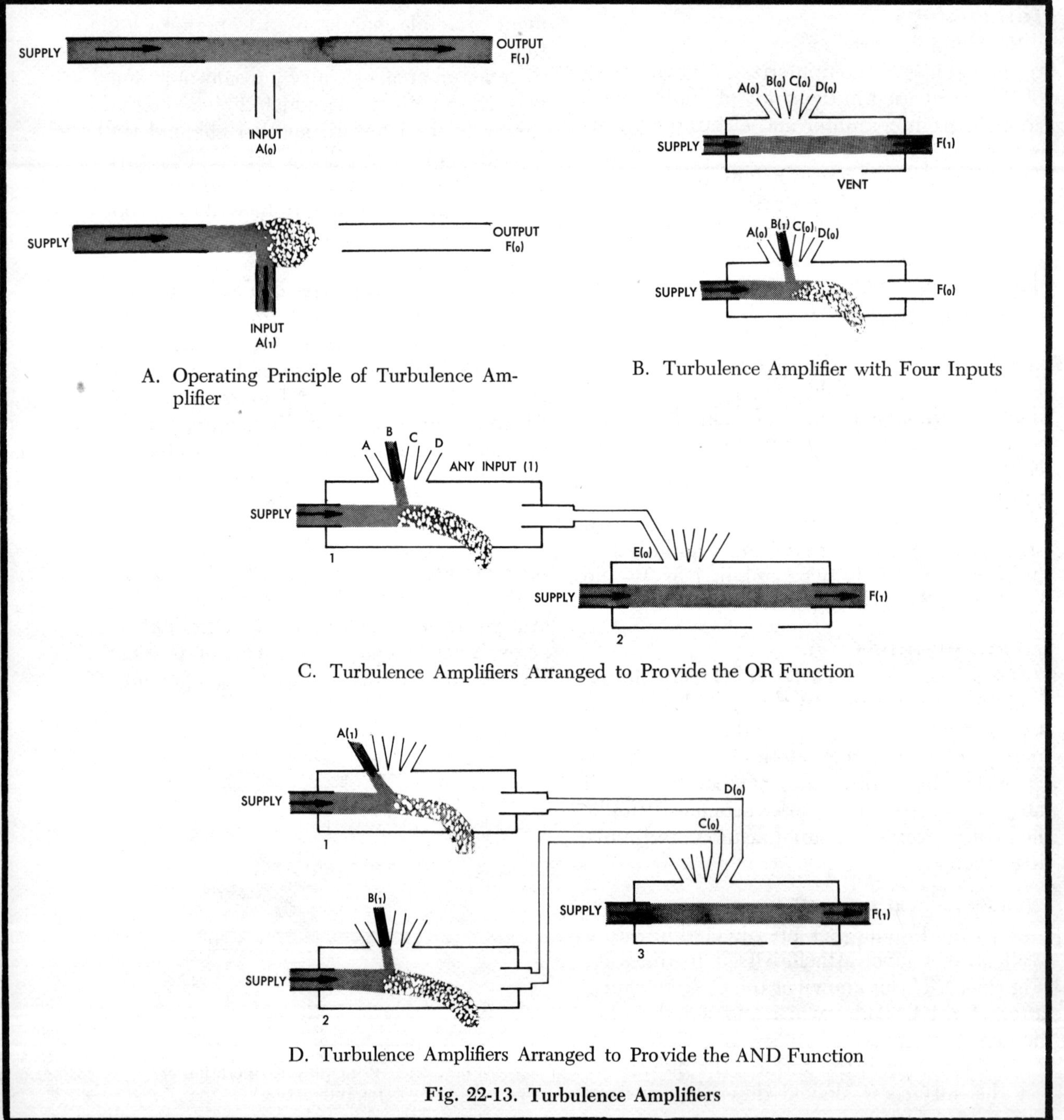

A. Operating Principle of Turbulence Amplifier

B. Turbulence Amplifier with Four Inputs

C. Turbulence Amplifiers Arranged to Provide the OR Function

D. Turbulence Amplifiers Arranged to Provide the AND Function

Fig. 22-13. Turbulence Amplifiers

available all the necessary logic operations by combining units.

Turbulence Amplifier

The operating principles of the turbulence amplifier are similar to the jet interaction device, Fig. 22-13. In both of these devices the output is determined by the interaction of the supply jet with that of a smaller input jet. However, the input jet does not divert the supply jet to another passage or output, but changes the flow conditions to prevent an output. This system is a true amplifier because the supply jet may be controlled by a much smaller input jet. Turbulence amplifiers may be compounded or ganged to provide the necessary logic functions.

Vortex Amplifier

The velocity of a fluid increases if the fluid is moved by centrifugal force outward from the center of a container. The reverse is true also: the velocity of a fluid decreases as it moves from the outer wall to the center of a container. This is the basic principle of operation of the vortex amplifier, Fig. 22-14. With no flow at the input port, supply fluid flows directly. The action of the fluid entering from input causes supply fluid to flow in a circular or swirling motion, consuming the energy imparted to the fluid as it moves to the center of the cylinder and the outlet passage. No swirling takes place when there is no flow from input, and the supply fluid flows out the passage with no appreciable velocity loss. Therefore, the fluid flow is impeded in one direction, and not in the other. This is the behavior of a diode in an electrical circuit.

The vortex device may be made in several configurations and provide a variety of logic functions, Fig. 22-15.

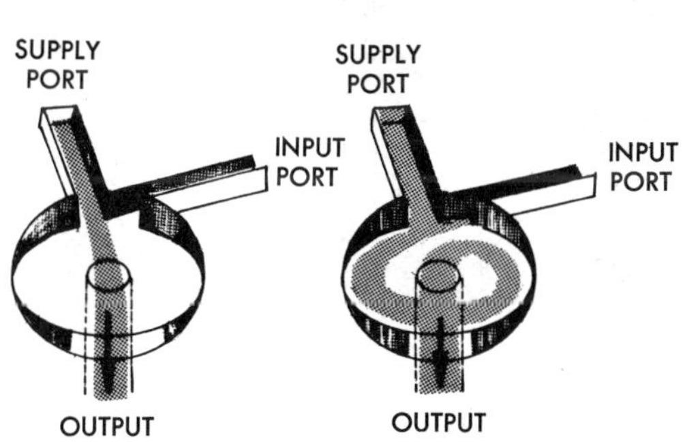

A. Vortex Amplifier with One Control Input

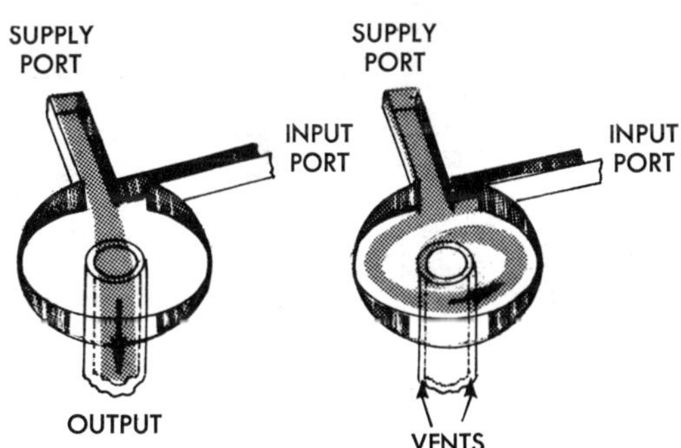

B. Vented Vortex Amplifier

Fig. 22-14. Vortex Amplifiers

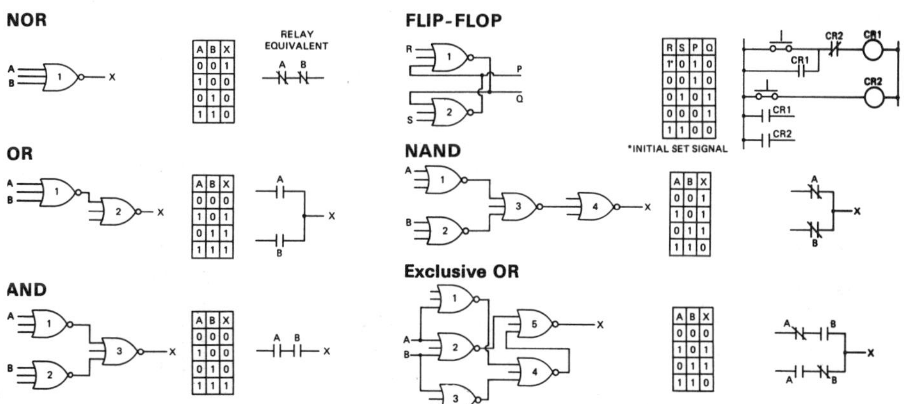

Fig. 22-15. Logic Functions (Double A Products Co.)

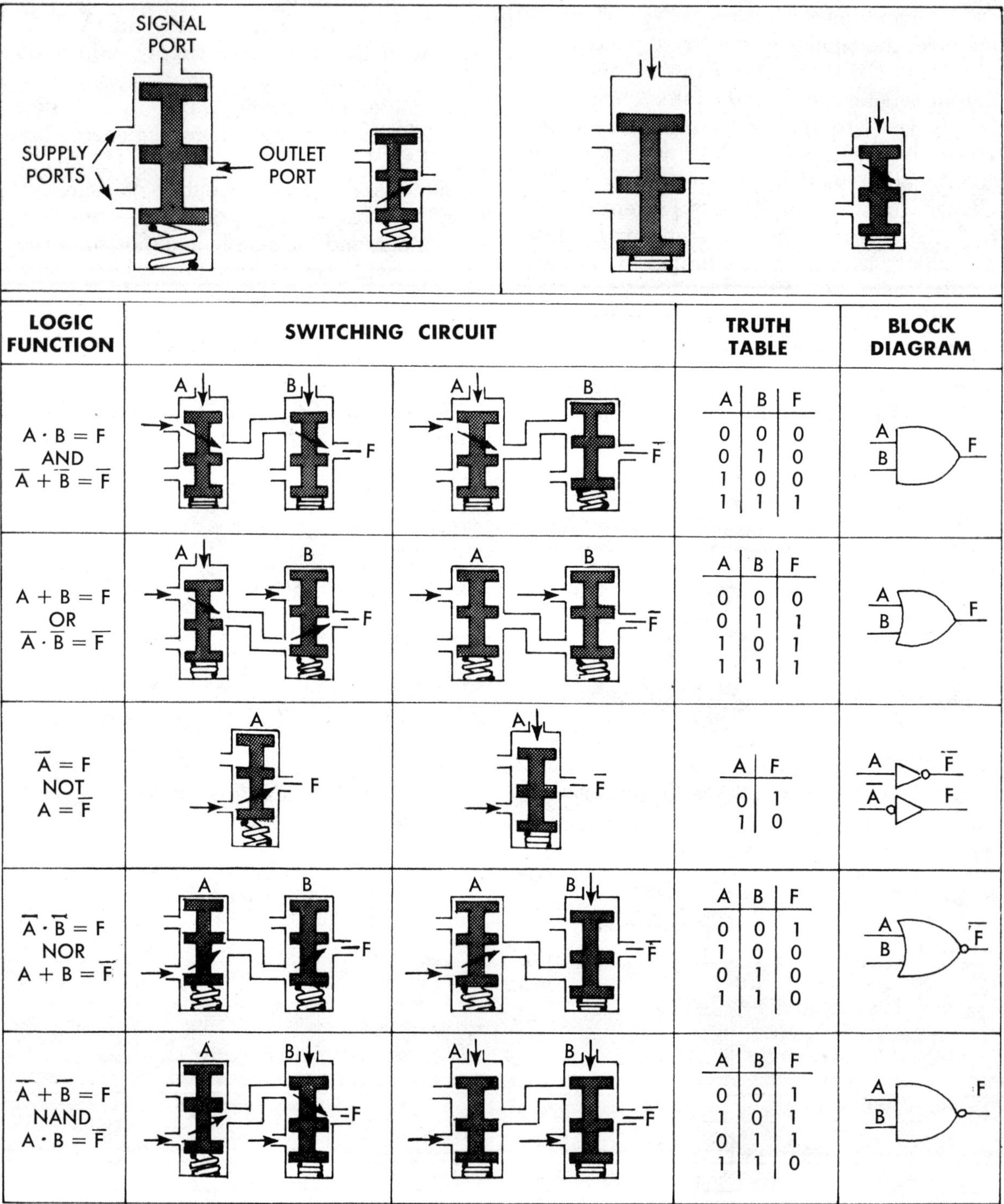

Fig. 22-16. Spool Type Control Device and Logic Functions

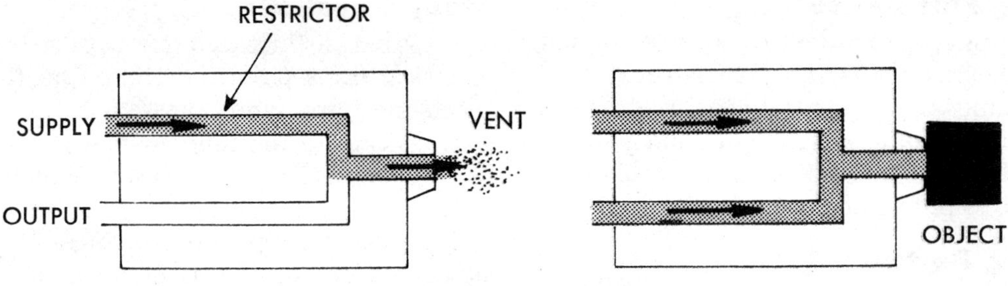

A. Back Pressure Sensing Device

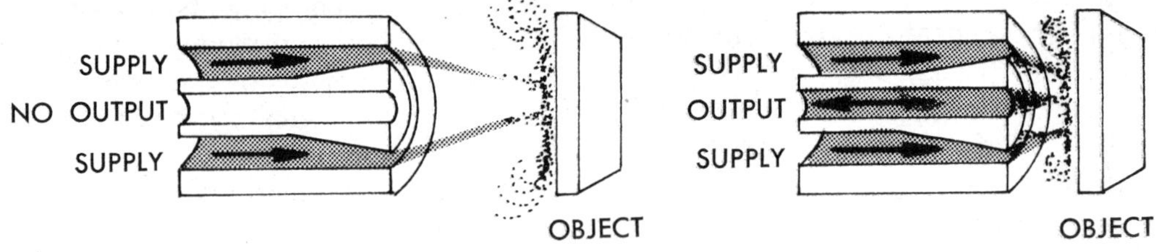

B. Diverging Cone Sensor

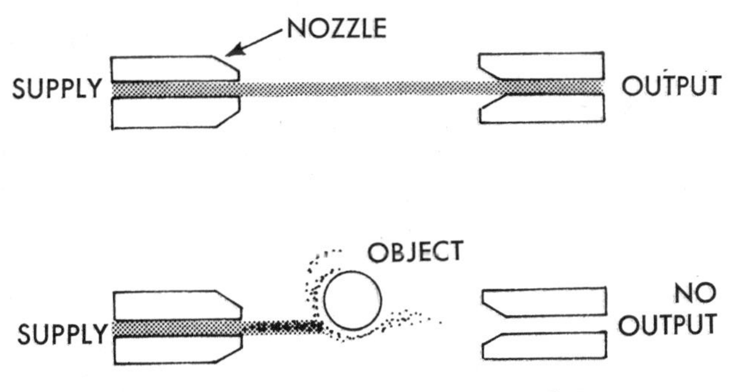

C. Interrupted Jet Sensor – Single Jet

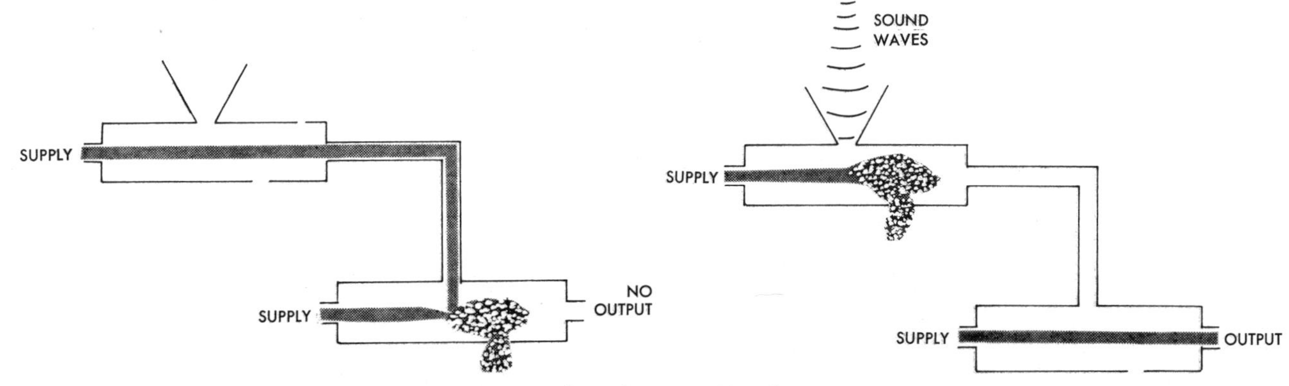

D. Interrupted Jet Sensor – Two Jets

Fig. 22-17. Fluidic Sensing Devices

Moving Part Devices

Some moving part devices are very similar to the two- and three-way spool valves studied under fluid power control. See Fig. 22-16. Diaphragms, springs, steel balls, and poppets are some of the other moving parts that may be used to provide fluid control.

Sensing Devices

Most control systems require sensors to provide initial inputs to the logic or comparator device. Sensors are devices that measure change in distance, heat, temperature, speed, sound, etc. As a result of a change in the factor under measurement, the sensor either does or does not send an input signal to the control system. Some principles of fluidic sensors are shown in Fig. 22-17.

Terms to Understand

electrical circuit
wire conductor
resistance
isolation transformer
resistor
wire-wound resistor
carbon resistor
switch
solenoid
relay
fuse
circuit breaker
potentiometer
rheostat
variable transformer
rectifier
diode
triode
transistor
servomechanism
closed loop system
open loop system
comparator
regulator feedback control
automation
fluidics
logic
Boolean algebra
wall attachment
jet interaction
turbulence amplifier
vortex amplifier
sensing devices

Study Questions

1. What distinct differences exist between electrical trans-actional systems and those of mechanical and fluid power?
2. What are the fundamental components of an electrical circuit? Describe their functions.
3. What principles of electrical transmission must be considered in designing a particular system?
4. In what way is a transformer like a lever?
5. List five components that provide discontinuous and continuous control, and describe the principles of their operation.
6. How do triodes and transistors function as power amplifiers?
7. What is a servomechanism?
8. Describe the operation of a servomechanism.
9. How does a regulator feedback system differ from a servomechanism?
10. Describe the operating principles of an open loop control system. Cite examples.
11. What are the advantages of a hybrid system?
12. Electrical control systems exhibit several limitations as compared to fluidic systems. Explain.
13. What are the fundamental operating principles of fluidic control systems?
14. Compare fluidic and electronic control systems; note particularly their advantages and limitations.

Selected Readings for Part VI
Trans-Actional Systems

Amber, G. H., and Amber, P. S., *Anatomy of Automation,* (Englewood Cliffs, New Jersey: Prentice-Hall, Inc., 1962)

Automatic Control, (New York: Simon & Schuster, 1955)

Chute, George M., *Electronics in Industry,* (New York: McGraw-Hill Book Co., 1965)

deLatil, Pierre, and Asimov, Isaac, *Thinking by Machine, A Study of Cybernetics,* (Boston: Houghton Mifflin Co., 1957)

Donachie, Ray J., *Power Transmission Design:* Lesson 1, Fundamentals of Power Transmission; Lesson 2, Joining and Coupling Devices; Lesson 3, Chain Drives; Lesson 4, Belt Drives; Lesson 5, Gears. (Cleveland, Ohio: Industrial Publishing Co., 1970)

Fink, Donald G., *Computers and the Human Mind,* (New York: Doubleday and Company, Inc., 1966)

Fundamentals of Service – Hydraulics, (Moline, Illinois: John Deere Service Publications, 1971)

Fundamentals of Service – Power Trains, (Moline, Illinois: John Deere Service Publications, 1971)

Herkimer, Herbert, *Engineers' Illustrated Thesaurus,* (New York: Chemical Publishing Co., Inc., 1952)

Hunter, Bob R., and Allen, Henry, *Unified Physics – Fluids,* Electromechanical Technology Series TERC EMT STAFF, (Albany, New York: Delmar Publishers, 1971)

Industrial Fluid Power, Vol. I and II, (Dallas: Womack Machine Supply Co.)

Industrial Hydraulics Manual 935100, *Practical Hydraulics,* (Troy, Michigan: Vickers, Inc., Sperry Rand Corp.)

Koff, Richard, *How Does It Work?* (Manhasset, New York: Popular Science Book Club)

Lent, Deane, *Analysis and Design of Mechanisms,* (Englewood Cliffs, New Jersey: Prentice-Hall)

Lister, Eugene C., *Electric Circuits and Machines,* (New York: McGraw-Hill Book Co., 1960)

"Low Cost N/C for Small Shops," *Machine and Tool Blue Book,* Vol. 60, May, 1965, p. 127.

McDonald, William C., Chairman – PTDA Technical Training Committee, *The Official Power Transmission Handbook,* Power Transmission Distributors Association, (Julian J. Jackson Publications, Inc., 1969)

McNickle, L. S., Jr., *Simplified Hydraulics,* (New York: McGraw-Hill Book Co., 1966)

Miller, Rex, and Culpepper, Fred W., Jr., *Energy, Electricity and Electronics,* (Bloomington, Illinois: McKnight & McKnight Publishing Co., 1964)

Morris, N. M., *Control Engineering,* (New York: McGraw-Hill Book Co.)

Morse, H. C., and Cox, D. M., *Numerically Controlled Machine Tools,* (Detroit, Michigan: America Data Processing, Inc., 1965)

NAVPERS 10624-A, *Basic Machines,* (Washington, D. C.: Superintendent of Documents, U. S. Government Printing Office, 1965)

NAVPERS 16193, *Basic Hydraulics,* (Washington, D. C.: Superintendent of Documents, U. S. Government Printing Office, 1945)

NAVPERS 16193-B, *Fluid Power,* (Washington, D. C.: Superintendent of Documents, U. S. Government Printing Office, 1966, Reprinted 1969)

Newell, John, and Horton, Holbrook L., *Ingenious Mechanisms,* Vols. 1, 2, 3, 4, (New York: Industrial Press, Inc., 1969)

Packaged Starts and Stops, A Programmed Learning Series. Book 1, Basics; Book 2, Hardware; Book 3, Controls; Book 4, Automatic Control; Book 5, Automatic Control Systems; (Beloit, Wisconsin: Warner Electric and Clutch Co., 1967)

Pease, D., *Basic Fluid Power,* (New York: Prentice-Hall, 1967)

Pippenger, John P., and Hicks, Tyler G., *Industrial Hydraulics,* (New York: McGraw-Hill Book Co., 1962)

Porter, Arthur, *Cybernetics Simplified,* (New York: Barnes & Noble, Inc., 1969)

Powell, Ralph W., *An Elementary Text in Hydraulics and Fluid Mechanics,* (New York: The Macmillan Co., 1958)

Robertson, L. Paul; Hunter, Bob R.; Allan, Richard L., *Electro Mechanisms – Devices.* Electromechanical Technology Series TERC EMT STAFF, (Albany, New York: Delmar Publishers, 1971)

Stewart, Harry, *Audels Practical Guide to Fluid Power,* (Indianapolis: Howard W. Sams Co., Inc., 1968)

Stewart, H. L., *Practical Guide to Fluid Power,* (Indianapolis: Theodore Audel & Co., Div. of Howard W. Sams and Co., Inc., 1966)

Svoboda, Antonin, and James, Hubent M., *Computing Mechanisms and Linkages,* (New York: McGraw-Hill Book Co.)

Tinnell, Richard W., *Mechanisms – Drives.* Electromechanical Technology Series TERC EMT STAFF, (Albany, New York: Delmar Publishers, 1971)

Walton, Harry, *The How and Why of Mechanical Movements,* (New York: Popular Science Publishing Company, E. P. Dutton & Co., Inc., 1968)

Weinstein, Seymour M., and Keim, A., *Fundamentals of Digital Computers,* (New York: Holt, Rinehart and Winston, Inc., 1965)

Wilson, Frank W. (Editor-in-Chief), *Numerical Control in Manufacturing,* National Technical Publications Committee, American Society of Tool & Manufacturing Engineers, (New York: McGraw-Hill Book Co., 1963)

Epilogue

There is no doubt that the more advanced cultures, those that exhibit a higher standard of living, depend on greater motive power. Where there are depressed living conditions, there is little resourcefulness or use of prime movers. Such backwardness is at least partially caused by men feeling no demand to satisfy their basic needs by utilizing more complex power multipliers, machines, and raw materials.

Power is Basic

A major reason for the strength and prosperity of this country is the increasing effort spent in technological research to improve and acquire new prime movers. Other reasons for the strength of this country would include such developments as systems of duplicate parts, mass production, distribution of goods, advertising, finance and banking, and insurance. The total effect of all of these has brought about an elevated standard of living undreamed of a century ago. Only 100 years ago, 15 percent of the energy sources were mechanical while muscle power (human and animal) produced the balance. Today, it is estimated that over 96 percent of all energy is derived from mechanical power.

This is the outgrowth of constantly improving our means of converting the form of our natural resources—resources which many other countries have in more abundance. Fundamentally, this is achieved by employing mechanical power for a number of purposes: to extract minerals, to fashion patterns for duplicate parts, to operate forges, presses, and machine tools for the mass production of goods, and to power means of mass communication and distribution which make goods available to everyone at a price he can afford.

It is safe to conclude that mechanical power, raw materials, production tools, and industrial and technological research are the basis upon which today's society is built. But *power* is more a controlling factor in industrial production than the availability of raw materials or production tools.

Power in the Future

Because of the voluminous appetites of these prime movers, scientists and research laboratories must be expected to design newer and more efficient energy converters. There now appears to be no definite limit to the fossil fuels which can be obtained economically from the ground, but there will come a day when such a concern will be paramount. Much apprehension has been expressed concerning the possibility of exhausting the world's oil supply. However, new findings of oil have exceeded the present-day consumption so that we are adding to, rather than subtracting from our known oil supply. Many years will pass before this supply is exhausted, but that day might eventually arrive.

The solution to the problem of acquiring an unlimited reservoir of power may be found in the use of atomic fuels and solar energy.

The use of the sun's energy offers quite a challenge because it is estimated that for the next 10 to 50 billion years, the earth will be basking in its heat and light. Actually already we are getting all power through the sun, since the fuel used by us to obtain power derives its energy from the sun. Water power is dependent on sun-induced precipitation. The fossil fuels are a result of the vegetation grown by the rays of the sun millions of years ago. It is interesting to note that the human race could not possibly use in one year, the entire energy imparted by the sun in one minute. It is no wonder that with all of the energy being emitted by the sun—and the fact that most of it is wasted—man has been striving to find ways to make better use of its myriad of forms.

Evolution of Prime Movers

The conclusions just made can be easily substantiated by the study we have just undertaken. It should be apparent that technological advance is forged by a definite progression of events. First, a *need* must be established, followed in time by a *solution*, and then further *refinement* until the solution's potential is fully realized. When this point is reached, a total departure from what has been previously done provides *additional solutions* to be experimented with until their potential is realized.

For instance, man has always wished to light the darkness that shrouded him as the sun went below the horizon. He first used fire and pitch torches. Then to provide more light, he employed animal fats contained in specially designed lamps, first with one wick and then with multiple wicks. The fatty fuel had limitations, so other fuels were found that gave more light per station. Petroleum products and then natural gases were substituted. The limits of wick or mantel type lamps was about reached. Man had to wait for the availability of a new energy source and for Edison to make a complete departure from what had been done by inventing the incadescent lamp. Improvement on this invention had provided us with the electric light that is presently used. However, newer and more efficient means of lighting are being developed, such as the fluorescent and cold lights. These reflect a complete departure from the incadescent type lamp.

Many examples have already been cited as the evolution of prime movers was undertaken. It is interesting to note that sometimes a discovery or an invention may come before there is a need for it. For instance, the discovery of steam power and the invention of the solid-fuel rocket provide us with classic examples. These discoveries had to be rediscovered as the progress of man evolved their need.

Power and Man

Today, we have inherited a vast accumulation of inventions, both basic discoveries and refinements. These provide us with a standard of living that yesterday was considered unattainable. Yet the end is not in sight. Man is interested in going to the moon, increasing his life's span, seriously considering living in harmony, shortening his work week, and elevating his position in life. His progress toward these lofty ambitions will undoubtedly evolve from constantly finding and refining solutions to problems which once appeared to be insurmountable. His pace to improve in the field of science and technology must be matched with equal strides in fields of economics, production, and distribution.

For most, the *simple life* is the thing of the past. Today's din and pace can be met only by competent, educated minds, oriented to the problems resulting from this highly mechanized world. The burden of mans' progress lies on the shoulders of youth who must be trained to accept, improve, and pioneer as generations have done in the past. This burden must also be borne by those individuals who have been displaced by technological changes and who must be rehabilitated since this change has and will direct the nature of occupations.

In the United States, manufacturing provides employment for a wide variety of people beyond those who are traditionally thought of as factory workers. Between 1952 and 1957, the number of professional workers increased by 45 percent. Proportionately, fewer individuals work at a bench or tend machines, while more are concerned with the managerial, technical, or sales aspects of manufacturing. These phenomena are paralleled by a general expansion of the service industries. In 1960, 44 percent were gainfully employed in the production industries and 56 percent were employed in the service industries. This is contrasted to 54 percent in production and 46 percent in service industries in 1940.

Power and Its Transmission

These industries involve not only the prime mover, but the methods of transmitting power whether it be by mechanical transmissions (belts or gears), fluid-power transmissions (pneumatic or hydraulic) or those using electricity.

Reversibility of converters: It should be noted that the physical principles involved in energy conversion and transmission have converse applications. Many illustrations could be named. A refrigerator may be considered a heat engine operated in reverse. A heat engine takes heat (the input) from a high temperature source, converts part of the heat energy into mechanical energy (the output) and exhausts the difference. A refrigerator takes in heat at a low temperature; the compressor supplies mechanical energy (the input), and the total (the output) is exhausted as heat at higher temperature.

An electric motor converts electrical energy into mechanical energy. It may, if mechanical energy is introduced into it, convert mechanical to electrical energy.

A piston within a cylinder works as a compressor or an extractor depending upon the pressure differential. The pressure differential determines whether the rotor of a turbine will eject fluids (as in a centrifugal pump or air compressor) or extract the energy from fluids as done in a steam turbine.

The transmission of power from the engine to its point of use is in reality a separate study involving advanced principles of mechanics, fluid power, electromagnetics, and thermodynamics. Trans-actional systems include a coupling system such as mechanical or friction clutches, torque converters, fluid drives, and other components designed for a particular need so as to yield the proper mechanical advantage as well as the proper form and direction of motion. Related to this are various control and braking systems, vehicular steering mechanisms, and power-assist devices. The combined study of prime movers and trans-actional systems can be effectively utilized to explain the operation of self-contained systems such as automobiles, airplanes, locomotives, earth movers, marine craft, and submarines as well as subsystems such as engines, motors, and machines.

Power and Your Education

Further studies growing out of this introduction to power include such work in fluid power and control systems, in the specifics of automotive and power mechanics, in training for aircraft, rocketry, or military specialities, in related fields of manufacturing, construction, transportation, mass communication, or electronics (all which depend upon prime movers for power), and in mechanical, electrical, or power plant engineering. Further study can be pursued in high schools, on-the-job training programs, vocational and technical institutes, manufacturers' training schools and seminars, schools of the armed services, as well as numerous college programs.

Education for tomorrow, whether it be on-the-job training or of a formal academic origin must be extensive and varied providing the individual with concepts that can form the basis upon which specifics can be taught. Man himself must not, in his vast technology be obscured or frustrated. The potential of each individual must be nurtured and developed. General education and industry must unite in planning systematic educational programs which may be broad or specific to suit individual needs, but all with the common purpose of personal development, a continuous life process.

Index